The
National Electrical Code®
Handbook

The
National Electrical Code® Handbook

Based on the 1987 Edition of the *National Electrical Code*

PETER J. SCHRAM, Editor

RICHARD H. MURRAY, Associate Editor

Fourth Edition

**National Fire Protection Association
Quincy, Massachusetts**

This is the fourth edition of *The National Electrical Code® Handbook* published by the National Fire Protection Association. The National Fire Protection Association formerly sponsored a handbook which was published by the McGraw-Hill Book Company and based on the *National Electrical Code.®* This publication, *The National Electrical Code® Handbook,* does not emanate from and is not in any way connected with or associated with the McGraw-Hill Book Company.

®Registered trademarks of the National Fire Protection Association
Life Safety Code® is a registered trademark of the National Fire Protection Association.

NFPA No. 70-87 -H B
ISBN 0-87765-326-7
Library of Congress No. 85-63883
Printed in the United States of America
Third Printing, May 1988

Contents

Chapter 1. General

Chapter 2. Wiring Design and Protection

CONTENTS

CONTENTS

CONTENTS

CONTENTS

Chapter 6.   Special Equipment

CONTENTS

Chapter 8. Communication System

Chapter 9. Tables and Examples

Preface

The *National Electrical Code* is the most widely adopted code in the world. Sales of the 1984 edition totaled over 800,000 copies. The *National Electrical Code* is a nationally accepted guide for the safe installation of electrical conductors and equipment and is, in fact, the basis for all electrical codes used in the United States. It is also used extensively outside of the United States, particularly where American-made equipment is installed.

The *National Electrical Code Handbook* is published by the National Fire Protection Association in order to assist those concerned with electrical safety in understanding the intent of the 1987 edition of the *Code*. A verbatim reproduction of the 1987 *National Electrical Code* is included, and added where necessary are comments, diagrams, and illustrations that are intended to clarify further some of the intricate requirements of the *National Electrical Code*.

The editor has worked very closely with members of the National Electrical Code Committee in discussions that have led to the various revisions that have been incorporated in the 1987 edition of the *Code*. The assistance and cooperation of the Code-Making Panel Chairmen and various Committee members are herein gratefully acknowledged.

This edition of the *Handbook* would not have been possible without the invaluable technical assistance of Mark W. Earley, NFPA Senior Electrical Field Service Engineer, and John M. Caloggero, NFPA Electrical Field Service Specialist. Their contributions are appreciated.

The editor acknowledges with thanks the manufacturers and their representatives who generously supplied photographs, drawings, and data upon request. Special thanks, too, go to the editors and contributors to past editions.

Appreciation is expressed to the NFPA staff members who attended to the countless details that went into the preparation of this *Handbook*, and especially to Hilary Davis, project editor; Elizabeth Carmichael, Louise Grant, and Peggy Travers, composition; Jim L. Linville, project manager; Amato Prudente, illustrator; Gloria Levine, typing; and Donald McGonagle, production.

Finally, the editor wishes to express his sincere appreciation to Paul Duks of UL and Jay A. Stewart of FMC Corp. for their special help on specific articles.

Peter J. Schram, *Editor*

Concise History of the
National Electrical Code

In 1881, the National Association of Fire Engineers met in Richmond, Virginia. From this meeting came a proposal that served as a basis for the first *National Electrical Code*, covering items such as the use of insulated conduit, the use of single disconnect devices, and the identification of the white wire. The first nationally recommended electrical code was published by the National Board of Fire Underwriters (now the American Insurance Association) in 1895. (The National Board of Fire Underwriters continued to publish the *National Electrical Code* until 1962, thus contributing greatly to its current universality.) With this 1895 code as a basis, in 1897 the *National Electrical Code* was drafted, the product of the combined labors of architectural, electrical, insurance, and allied interests which, through the National Conference on Standard Electrical Rules, composed of delegates from various national associations, unanimously voted to recommend it to their respective associations for approval or adoption.

In 1911, the National Fire Protection Association (NFPA) assumed sponsorship and control of the *National Electrical Code*, the National Conference on Standard Electrical Rules having disbanded in that very same year. Since 1920, the *National Electrical Code* has also been officially endorsed by the American National Standards Institute (formerly the United States of America Standards Institute and the American Standards Association), and the NFPA has maintained its capacity as Administrative Sponsor. Since that date, the Committee has been identified as "ANSI Standards Committee C1" (formerly "USAS C1" or "ASA C1").

In 1923, the *National Electrical Code* was rearranged and rewritten; in 1937 it was editorially revised so that all of the general rules would appear in the first chapters followed by supplementary rules in the following chapters; and, in 1959, it was editorially revised again, this time in order to incorporate a new numbering system under which each section of each article is identified by the article number preceding the section number. The National Fire Protection Association has been publishing and distributing the *National Electrical Code* since 1951. It does so through its own office and through the American National Standards Institute. In addition, the *National Electrical Code* is found in Volume Three of the NFPA's annual *National Fire Codes®*. The *National Electrical Code* is acknowledged to be the most widely adopted code of standard practices in the U.S.A.

1987 Edition of the *National Electrical Code*

This 1987 edition of the *National Electrical Code* (NFPA 70-1987) was adopted by the National Fire Protection Association on May 21, at its 1986 Annual Meeting held in Atlanta, Georgia. It was approved by the American National Standards Institute on July 30, 1986 and is known as ANSI/NFPA 70-1987. It supersedes all previous editions of the *National Electrical Code*, the most recent previous edition being 1984.

This *Code* is purely advisory as far as the NFPA and ANSI are concerned but is offered for use in law and for regulatory purposes in the interest of life and property protection. Anyone noticing any errors should please notify the NFPA Executive Office, the Chairman and the Secretary of the Committee.

Development of the *National Electrical Code*

In accordance with the provisions of the NFPA Regulations Governing Committee Projects, a National Electrical Code Technical Committee Report containing proposed amendments to the 1984 *National Electrical Code* was published by the NFPA in June 1985. This report recorded the actions of the various Code-Making Panels and the Correlating Committee of the National Electrical Code Committee on each proposal that had been made to revise the 1984 *Code*. The report was circulated to all members of the National Electrical Code Committee, and was made available to other interested NFPA members and to the public for review and comment. Following the close of the public comment period, the Code-Making Panels met, acted on each comment, and reported their action to the Correlating Committee. The NFPA published the National Electrical Code Technical Committee Documentation in April 1986, which recorded the actions of the Code-Making Panels and the Correlating Committee on each public comment to the National Electrical Code Technical Committee Report. The NFPA also published the Advanced Printing of the Proposed 1987 *National Electrical Code* in April 1986, to permit the study and evaluation by those interested, prior to formal action on the Committee Report by the 1986 NFPA Annual Meeting. The National Electrical Code Technical Committee Report and National Electrical Code Technical Committee Documentation were presented to the 1986 NFPA Annual Meeting for adoption. The proceedings of that adoption are published in the September 1986 issue of the NFPA *Fire Journal*®

Coincident with the above processing procedures, each of the Code-Making Panels and the Chairman of the Correlating Committee reported their recommendations to meetings of the Electrical Section at the 1986 NFPA Annual Meeting. The Electrical Section thus had opportunity to discuss and review the report of the National Electrical Code Committee prior to the adoption of this edition of the *Code* by the Association.

The *Electrical Code for One- and Two-Family Dwellings*, NFPA 70A-1987, is an abridged version of the 1987 text, edited only as dictated to eliminate extraneous material not of concern to this type of occupancy, and to place in the text only the more popular types of wiring methods, not to exclude any other type authorized by the complete *Code*.

1987 *National Electrical Code* Changes

Note: Does not include editorial-type changes.

ARTICLE 90 - Introduction

Sections 90-2(a)(1) and 90-2(b)(1): The term "floating dwelling units" was changed to "floating buildings" to correlate with title of new Article 553. In addition, a new fine print note has been added following Section 90-2(a)(1) to reference the National Electrical Safety Code, ANSI C2-1984 for additional information pertaining to an industrial or multibuilding complex.

Section 90-3: A new fourth paragraph has been added to indicate that text identified by the superscript letter "x" includes text extracted from other NFPA documents listed in Appendix A.

ARTICLE 100 - Definitions

Scope: The first sentence has been revised to clarify that Article 100 is not intended to include commonly defined general terms nor commonly defined technical terms from related Codes and Standards.

Branch Circuit (FPN): Revised to include reference to Section 240-10, to clarify that supplementary overcurrent devices are not included in this definition.

Enclosure (FPN): A new fine print note was added to reference ANSI/NEMA 250.

Feeder: Definition was revised to include all types of separately derived systems.

Interrupting Rating: Revised by deleting "overcurrent protective."

Low-Energy Power Circuit: This definition has been deleted.

Separately Derived System: A new definition was added which references Section 250-5(d).

Setting (of Circuit Breaker): The previous definition was deleted and replaced with a reference to the definition of "Circuit Breaker."

Watertight (FPN): Reference to the NEMA standard for "enclosure for electrical equipment" hose-down test was revised.

Controlled Vented Power Fuse (FPN): Second sentence changed to fine print note.

ARTICLE 110 - Requirements for Electrical Installations

Section 110-12(b): A new section was added on subsurface enclosures (manholes, etc.)

Section 110-16(a): A new sentence was added at the end of the second paragraph to require that in all cases the work space must allow at least a 90-degree opening of equipment doors or hinged panels.

Section 110-16(c), Exception No. 2: This paragraph has been expanded to make it clear that where the work space required by Section 110-16(a) is doubled, only one entrance to the work space is required. In addition, a second paragraph was added to clarify that when one entrance is provided, it must be located so that the edge of the entrance nearest the switchboard or panelboard is the minimum clear distance given in Table 110-16(a) away from the equipment.

Section 110-33(a), Exception No. 2: A new second paragraph was added to clarify the intent in the same manner as Section 110-16(c).

ARTICLE 200 - Use and Identification of Grounded Conductors

Section 200-2, Exception: References to Sections 668-11 and 668-21 pertaining to electrolytic cell dc power supplies have been added to exempt the grounded conductor from being identified in accordance with Section 200-6.

Section 200-6(a): Three new exceptions have been added (Exceptions Nos. 1, 2, and 3), which exempt multiconductor varnished-insulated cables, fixture wires (as outlined in Article 402), and conductors identified in accordance with Section 210-5(a) for branch circuits.

Section 200-6(a), Exception No. 1: Renumbered to be Exception No. 5 with a new paragraph added to allow a colored tracer thread in the insulation, identifying the source of manufacture. Also, a new paragraph was added to permit a ridge for identification of aerial cable.

Section 200-6(b): This section has been expanded to include multiconductor flat cable No. 4 or larger to be identified by an external ridge on the grounded conductor.

Section 200-6(d): A new section was added to cover color coding of grounded conductors of different systems, essentially the same as Section 210-5(a) but applying to feeder as well as branch circuit conductors.

Section 200-7, Exception No. 1: The word "outlet" was replaced with "location."

ARTICLE 210 - Branch Circuits

Section 210-1 and Exception: The scope has been revised to clarify that Article 210 applies to branch circuits supplying all loads, except for branch circuits which supply only motor loads, which are covered in Article 430.

SUMMARY OF CODE CHANGES

Section 210-2. Other Articles for Specific-Purpose Branch Circuits: This list has been expanded to include new Article 780, "Closed-Loop and Programmed Power Distribution Systems."

Section 210-4(b): This section has been divided into paragraphs (a), (b), and (c) with no significant changes except to revise the second paragraph by adding "or equipment" between "device" and "on."

Section 210-4: A new fine print note has been added to reference Section 300-13(b) for continuity of the grounded conductor on multiwire circuits.

Section 210-5(a): This section has been revised by changing the word "neutral" in two locations to "grounded conductor."

Section 210-6: This section has been completely rewritten to more accurately reflect intent. Branch circuit voltage limitations have been divided into three categories. (a) The branch circuit voltage limitation of 150 volts between conductors has been reduced to 120 volts nominal where the circuit supplies certain devices and utilization equipment in specific type occupancies. (b) The voltage limitation to ground has been changed from 150 volts to ground to 277 volts to ground when supplying specific types of equipment. (c) Clarification is provided for circuits exceeding 277 volts to ground and not exceeding 600 volts between conductors are permitted to supply specific types of equipment with specific height limitations pertaining to that application.

Section 210-7(a), Exception No. 1: This exception has been deleted.

Section 210-7(d), Exception: The exception has been revised to permit the connection of receptacle outlets on the load side of the GFCI, but prohibits the use of an equipment grounding conductor installed between the GFCI and the receptacles on the load side of the GFCI.

Section 210-8(a): This section has been revised by the addition of four new paragraphs. (3) The second paragraph has been deleted and "direct grade level access" is defined as being located not more than 6 feet 6 inches above grade level and being readily accessible without entering or passing through a dwelling unit. (4) At least one 125-volt, single-phase, 15- or 20-ampere receptacle is required to be installed in the basement with GFCI protection and be so identified. (5) All 125-volt, single-phase, 15- and 20-ampere receptacles installed within six feet of the kitchen sink above countertops are required to be GFCI protected. (6) All 125-volt, single-phase, 15- or 20-ampere receptacles installed in boathouses are required to have GFCI protection for personnel. In addition, a new fine print note has been added to (5) to clarify that receptacles which are located specifically for appliances such as refrigerators and freezers are exempt from the GFCI requirement.

Section 210-8(b): The definition of a bathroom following Section 210-8(b) has been revised to make it clear that the definition applies to both Sections 210-8(a) and (b).

Section 210-19(b), Exception No. 1: This exception has been revised so that the 70% applies to the branch-circuit rating rather than the ampacity of the ungrounded conductors.

Section 210-24, Exception: A new exception has been added to allow branch circuits in two-family or multifamily dwellings to serve more than one dwelling unit for the purpose of central alarm, signal, communications, or similar functions.

Section 210-52(a): A new fine print note has been added to alert installers that listed baseboard heaters may include instructions which may not permit their installation below receptacle outlets.

Section 210-52(f): This section has been expanded to require at least one receptacle outlet to be installed in each detached garage where electric power is supplied to the garage.

Section 210-60, Exception: The exception has been revised to make it clear that the number of receptacles determined in accordance with Section 210-52(a) must still be installed in rooms of hotels and motels, but their location will be permitted to be changed to suit the permanent furniture layout.

Section 210-63: A new section has been added to require a 125-volt, single-phase, 15- or 20-ampere receptacle outlet be installed in an accessible location for the servicing of rooftop-mounted heating, air-conditioning and refrigeration equipment. The receptacle outlet must be located on the same roof level and within 75 feet of the equipment.

Section 210-70(a) and Exception No. 1: This section has been expanded to require detached garages with electric power to have at least one wall switch-controlled lighting outlet installed in them, and to add "or exits" after "entrances." Exception No. 1 has been expanded by adding bathrooms as one of the rooms where a wall switch-controlled receptacle is not permitted in place of a lighting outlet.

ARTICLE 215 - Feeders

Section 215-1: The last sentence has been deleted.

ARTICLE 220 - Branch Circuit and Feeder Calculations

Section 220-1: The second paragraph has been moved to new Section 220-2, "Voltages."

Section 220-3: A new fine print note has been added referencing Section 600-6(c) for exterior signs and outline lighting.

Section 220-3(a): This section has been revised to clarify that the branch-circuit rating is not to be less than the noncontinuous load plus 125% of the continuous load.

Table 220-3(b): This single asterisk (*) note was revised to make it clear that the note is applicable only to general use receptacle outlets, and to include a reference to Section 220-4(c) in addition to 220-4(b).

Section 220-3(c)(5): The asterisk (*) note has been revised to eliminate the exception for outlets provided per Section 400-7.

Section 220-3(c), Exception No. 1: The last sentence was revised to reference "this exception" instead of "this section."

Section 220-3(c), Exception No. 5: This is a new exception added to permit the use of the demand factors in Table 220-18 for household electric clothes dryers.

Section 220-4(b), Exception No. 3: This new exception has been added to permit the installation of switched receptacles supplied from a general-purpose branch circuit in those rooms in which small appliance circuits are required in accordance with Section 220-3(b).

Section 220-10(b): This section has been revised to require that only the rating of the overcurrent device must be not less than the noncontinuous load plus 125% of the continuous load. A new paragraph has been added to clarify that it is the ampacity of the ungrounded service conductor which must not be less than the continuous load plus 125% of the continuous load.

Section 220-22: The last sentence has been expanded to prohibit the reduction of the neutral capacity for that portion of the load which consists of data processing or similar equipment, when supplied from a 4-wire, wye-connected, 3-phase system.

ARTICLE 225 - Outside Branch Circuits and Feeders

Section 225-1 and Exception: The scope has been revised to make it clear that this article covers electric equipment and wiring located on or attached to, or run between buildings, or other structures, rather than the electrical equipment wiring for the supply of utilization equipment. The exception has been expanded to be more specific.

Section 225-2. Other Articles: This list has been expanded by the addition of Article 553 - Floating Buildings, and Article 320 - Open Wiring on Insulators.

Section 225-4, Exception: A new exception has been added which allows the equipment grounding conductor to be uninsulated.

Section 225-7(a): The heading of Section 225-7 and the first paragraph have been revised to clarify that this section applies to branch circuits supplying lighting equipment installed outdoors.

Section 225-7(c) and (d): The exception to paragraph (c) has been deleted and the voltage limitations have been raised from 150 volts to 277 volts to ground. (d) Has been expanded to specify the voltage permitted between conductors on branch circuits supplying auxiliary equipment of electric-discharge lamps and limits the voltage between conductors to 600 volts and not more than 277 volts to ground, with a reference to Section 210-6(d)(1).

Section 225-10: This section has been expanded to include messenger supported wiring, cable trays, cablebus, wireways, auxiliary gutters, flexible metal conduit, liquidtight flexible metal conduit, and busways as wiring methods permitted to be installed on the outside surfaces of buildings.

Section 225-18: The "12-foot" rule has been clarified to apply to over residential driveways, and those commercial areas not subject to truck traffic where the voltage is limited to 300 volts to ground. The "15-foot rule" has been clarified to apply to those areas listed in the 12-foot classification where the voltage exceeds 300 volts to ground.

Section 225-21: This section has been revised to clarify the intent pertaining to supporting of multiconductor cables.

Section 225-22: Revised to clarify intent that raceways must be raintight. A new exception has been added referencing Section 350-2.

Section 225-25: The word "utilization" has been added between "electric" and "equipment."

Section 225-26: A new section has been added to prohibit live vegetation, such as trees, for support of overhead conductor spans or other electric equipment, with an exception for temporary wiring in accordance with Article 305.

ARTICLE 230 - Services

Section 230-1: The scope has been revised as follows: "This article covers service conductors and equipment for control and protection of services and their installation requirements." A new Diagram 230-1, similar to Diagram 430-1, has been added and a fine print note referencing this diagram has been added to Section 230-1.

Section 230-3: The exception to this section has been deleted.

Section 230-4: This section has been deleted.

Section 230-5: This section has been deleted.

Section 230-6: Section 230-44 has been relocated to become the new Section 230-6. It has been expanded to include the following: "or (3) installed in a transformer vault conforming to the requirements of Article 450, Part C."

Section 230-7: Section 230-47 has been relocated and is now Section 230-7. Exception No. 2 to this section has been revised by deleting "time switch" and replacing it with "load management control."

Section 230-8: Section 230-48 has been relocated and is now Section 230-8.

Section 230-9 and Exception: The material in Section 230-24(c) has been relocated to this section and expanded to more clearly define the type of wiring method that pertains to the clearance from building openings. An additional paragraph was added to address service conductors installed beneath openings, through which materials may be moved, such as openings in farm and commercial buildings.

Section 230-21: The phrase "from another building or other structure" has been deleted.

Section 230-22: This section has been rewritten to incorporate the pertinent requirements which existed in Section 230-4 and to consolidate and clarify the requirements pertaining to insulation or covering of service conductors.

Section 230-23: This section has been rewritten to incorporate the pertinent requirements of Section 230-5 and to consolidate related requirements pertaining to the current-carrying requirements of service conductors.

Section 230-24(a), Exception No. 3: This new exception has been added to require roof space, subject to vehicular traffic, to have a vertical clearance for service drops in accordance with Section 230-24(b).

Section 230-24(b): The "10-foot rule" in this section has been revised to indicate that the 10-foot clearance requirement pertains to areas or sidewalks accessible only to pedestrians.

Section 230-24(c): This section has been moved to Section 230-9. A reference to Section 230-9 remains.

Section 230-26: This section has been revised to make it clear that the point of attachment pertains to the service-drop conductors.

Section 230-30: This section has been revised to include the information previously contained in Section 230-4 pertaining to insulation of service-lateral conductors.

Section 230-31: This section has been expanded to include three paragraphs and a fine print note. Paragraph (a) requires that the service-lateral conductors must have sufficient ampacity to carry the current for the load computed in accordance with Article 220. Paragraph (c) requires that the grounded conductor be not less than the minimum size required by Section 250-23(b). A fine print note alerts the readers that the voltage drop should be taken into consideration for more efficient operation.

Section 230-32: This new section has been added to require that underground service-lateral conductors be protected against damage in accordance with Section 300-5. In addition, service-lateral conductors entering a building must be installed in accordance with Section 230-6, or protected by a raceway wiring method identified in Section 230-43.

Section 230-41: Section 230-41 has been expanded to include requirements from Section 230-4 of the 1984 *NEC*.

Section 230-43: This section has been revised to add item (13), flexible metal conduit, with restrictions.

Section 230-44: This section has been relocated to Section 230-6.

Section 230-45: This section has been deleted with the requirements moved to Section 230-40, Exception No. 2.

Section 230-47 and the Exceptions: This section has been relocated to Section 230-7.

Section 230-48: This section has been relocated to Section 230-8.

Section 230-49: This section has been revised by the addition of the word "physical" and replacing the words "service conductors" with "service-entrance conductors," to make it clear that underground service-entrance conductors must be protected against physical damage.

Section 230-50(a): This section has been revised by deleting item (5), Type MC cable.

Section 230-51(a): The support requirements for Type SE cable have been changed from 4½ feet to 30 inches.

Section 230-54(a): This section has been expanded by adding the following to the end of the sentence: "at the point of connection to service-drop conductors" to make it clear that all service raceways do not require a raintight service head (underground service raceway).

Section 230-64: This text was previously located in Section 230-73 and has been revised by changing "disconnecting means" to "equipment." This makes it clear that all service equipment requires the working space specified by Section 110-16.

Section 230-65: This text was previously located in Section 230-98.

Section 230-70(b): This section has been revised so that it provides marking requirements rather than suitability.

Section 230-71(a): The reference to Section 230-40 was changed to "Section 230-40, Exception No. 1." Also, a new exception has been added indicating that for the purpose of this section, the disconnecting means for ground-fault protection systems installed as part of listed equipment is not considered a service disconnecting means.

Section 230-72(c): A new exception has been added to indicate that in multiple occupancy buildings where electric service and electrical maintenance are provided by the building management and where these are under continuous building management supervision, the service disconnecting means supplying more than one occupancy is permitted to be accessible to authorized management only.

Section 230-73: This section has been revised and moved to Section 230-64.

Section 230-82, Exceptions No. 4 and 5: "Time switches" was changed to "load management devices."

Section 230-82, Exception No. 7: A new exception has been added permitting the control circuit to be ahead of the service disconnecting means where the disconnecting means is power operable, if suitable overcurrent protection and disconnecting means are provided.

Section 230-82, Exception No. 8: A new exception has been added permitting ground-fault protection systems to be ahead of the disconnecting means if installed as part of listed equipment, and if suitable overcurrent protection and disconnecting means are provided.

Section 230-90: The word "overcurrent" has been replaced with "overload" to more accurately describe the type of protection required for service conductors.

Section 230-90(a), Exception No. 4: Exception No. 4 in the 1984 edition was deleted and the remaining exceptions renumbered.

Section 230-90(a), Exception No. 4: The parenthetical reference to NFPA 20 has been changed to a fine print note.

Section 230-90(c): This section has been deleted and the requirement incorporated into Section 230-91(b).

Section 230-91: The title has been expanded to read as follows: "Location of Overcurrent Protection." This section has been revised to include Sections 230-90(a), Exception No. 4, and 230-90(c) of the 1984 *NEC* requirements to consolidate and clarify the requirements.

Section 230-92: The title of this section has been revised to read as follows: "Locked Service Overcurrent Devices."

Section 230-94, Exception No. 3: The term "time switches" has been changed to "load management devices."

Section 230-95(b), (FPN): The word "wye" has been inserted between the words "grounded" and "systems" in the second fine print note, to more accurately describe the type of system.

Section 230-98: This section has been relocated and renumbered Section 230-65.

Section 230-201: This section has been clarified and specifies that the service conductors can be either on the primary or secondary side of a transformer.

Sections 230-202(a) and (d): Revised by changing "service" to "service-entrance."

Section 230-202(i): This section has been deleted.

Section 230-203: This section has been revised by deleting the words "High voltage" at the beginning of the sentence and the sign requirement expanded to read "Danger High Voltage Keep Out."

ARTICLE 240 - Overcurrent Protection

Section 240-2: This list of articles has been revised by adding Article 780, "Closed-Loop and Programmed Power Distribution Systems," deleting "Electrical Floor Assemblies," and revising the title of Article 670 to "Industrial Machinery."

Section 240-3: A new paragraph has been added after Exception No. 1 to clarify that the Code does not prohibit the use of an overcurrent device rated less than the ampacity of the conductor and that it need not be of standard rating.

Section 240-3, Exception No. 3: This exception has been revised to delete the 25 foot length restriction.

Section 240-6: A new paragraph has been added indicating that for the purposes of Article 240, the rating of an adjustable trip circuit breaker having a readily accessible external means for adjusting the trip setting is the maximum permissible rating or setting.

Section 240-12: The words "in industrial locations" were deleted in the first sentence.

Section 240-20(c): A new paragraph has been added to permit listed devices providing equivalent overcurrent protection in closed-loop power distribution systems in place of fuses or circuit breakers.

Section 240-21, Excpetion No. 11: A new exception has been added to address transformer secondary conductors of separately derived systems for industrial installations whose length does not exceed 25 feet.

Section 240-24(a), Exception No. 3: A new exception has been added to allow the accessibility of service overcurrent devices to be as described in Section 230-92.

Section 240-51(a): Revised to add "and below" after "30 amperes."

Section 240-80, Exception: A new exception was added referencing Section 230-76(2) for circuit breakers used as service disconnecting means.

Section 240-83(a): The second sentence was revised to clarify the Panel's intent.

ARTICLE 250 - Grounding

Section 250-2: This list has been revised by adding Agricultural Buildings, Closed-Loop and Programmed Power Distribution, Floating Buildings, Over 600 Volts, deleting Electrical Floor Assemblies, and changing Metal Working Machine Tools and Plastics Machinery to Industrial Machinery.

Section 250-5(b), Exception No. 5: A new exception added to cover high-impedance grounded-neutral systems for three-phase ac systems of 480 volts to 1000 volts under certain conditions.

Section 250-5(d), (FPN): A new fine print note has been added stating that an ac on-site generator is not a separately derived system if the neutral is solidly interconnected to the service-supplied system neutral.

A second fine print note has been added for systems that are not separately derived and not required to be grounded, referencing Section 445-5 for the minimum size of conductors which must carry fault current.

Section 250-22, Exception: A new exception was added to cover the location of a dc system source grounding connection on the premises.

Section 250-23(a), Exception No. 6: A new exception was added referencing Section 250-27 for high-impedance grounded-neutral systems grounding connection requirements.

Section 250-23(b): A third sentence has been added requiring that where the service phase conductors are paralleled, the size of the grounded conductor is to be based on the equivalent area for parallel conductors.

Section 250-23(b), Exception No. 1: This exception has been expanded by adding the phrase "or equivalent area for paralleled conductors."

Section 250-23(b), Exception No. 2: This new exception was added referencing Section 250-27 for high-impedance grounded-neutral systems.

Section 250-24(a), Exception No. 2: A sentence has been added requiring a grounding electrode to be installed where there are no existing electrodes and the structure supplies more than one branch circuit.

Section 250-24(b), Exception No. 2: A new exception was added to permit deletion of the grounding electrode and grounding electrode conductor connection to the metal enclosure of a building under certain specified conditions.

Section 250-27: A new section was added to cover the requirements of high-impedance grounded-neutral systems.

Section 250-33, Exception No. 1: Revised to add "which do not provide an equipment ground" between "nonmetallic-sheathed cable" and "if."

Section 250-33, Exception No. 2: Revised to include "Short sections of" at beginning of the sentence.

SUMMARY OF CODE CHANGES

Section 250-42(e): Revised by deleting "metallic" from title, by adding "or other wiring method which provides an equipment ground" after "raceway," and by changing "raceways" to "enclosures" at the end of the sentence.

Section 250-42(f), Exception No. 4: A new exception has been added which exempts listed information processing and listed office equipment protected by a system of double insulation, or its equivalent, from grounding requirements where the equipment operates with any terminal at over 150 volts to ground. Where such a system is used, the equipment must be distinctively marked.

Section 250-43(a), Exception: Revised by changing the words "single-polarity" to "two-wire."

Section 250-45(b), Exception No. 3: A new exception was added to cover cord- and plug-connected equipment operating at over 150 volts to ground. Listed information processing and listed office equipment protected by a system of double insulation, or its equivalent, are exempted from grounding requirements. Where such a system is used, the equipment must be distinctively marked.

Section 250-45(d)(2): Revised by adding "electronic computer/data processing equipment."

Section 250-50, (FPN): A new fine print note added to Section 250-50(b) to reference Section 210-7(d), Exception.

Section 250-51: A new paragraph added to clarify that the earth shall not be used as the sole equipment grounding conductor.

Section 250-53(b): The last sentence in this section has been relocated to become the ending of the second sentence in Section 250-79(a).

Section 250-54: A new sentence has been added to this paragraph to require separate services supplying a building be connected to the same grounding electrode. In addition, the word "grounding" has been inserted ahead of "electrode" in the last paragraph.

Section 250-61(b), Exception No. 4: A new exception has been added to reference Sections 710-72(e)(1) and 710-74.

Section 250-71(a)(2): The phrase "service-entrance conductors" was replaced with "service conductors."

Section 250-71(b), (FPN): A new fine print note has been added to provide an example of an approved means of meeting the requirements of Section 250-71(b)(3).

Section 250-72(a): The title of this section has been changed from "Pressure Connectors, Clamps, etc." to "Grounded Service Conductor."

Section 250-72(c): A new sentence has been added to this section to indicate that standard locknuts or bushings are not to be used for the bonding required by this section.

Section 250-75: This section has been revised to require the metal noncurrent-carrying parts of electrical equipment to be effectively bonded to assure electrical continuity regardless of whether or not a supplementary equipment grounding conductor is installed.

Section 250-79(a): The last sentence of Section 250-53(b) of the 1984 Code has been relocated to become the last sentence of this section.

Section 250-79(c): The last sentence has been revised by adding a phrase after "cables" as follows: "the equipment bonding jumper, where routed with the raceways or cables, shall be run in parallel."

Section 250-79(e): A new sentence was added to require the equipment bonding jumper to comply with the requirements of Section 310-12(b) where installed in a raceway.

Section 250-80(a): The last sentence was revised to clarify that it is the point of attachment of the bonding jumper that must be accessible.

Section 250-80(a), Exception: The first sentence has been revised by inserting the phrase "(other than service equipment)" after the word "enclosure."

Section 250-81: Revised to add a phrase "shall be installed in accordance with Section 250-92(a)" in the second sentence.

Section 250-83: The last sentence has been rearranged to clarify the intent of this section.

Section 250-86, 2nd, (FPN): Revised to change "grounding electrode systems" to "grounding electrodes."

Section 250-91(b): The word "approved" was replaced by "listed" in (5) and (10), and also in Exceptions No. 1c. and No. 2.

Section 250-92: Revised by adding reference to "(c)" as part of the installation requirements for grounding conductors.

Section 250-92(a): The third sentence was revised by replacing the words "rigidly stapled" with "securely fastened."

The second paragraph of Section 250-92(a) has been relocated as Section 250-92(b) and the previous (b) relocated to become (c) of this section.

Section 250-92(c)(2): The word "equipment" was inserted between "separate" and "grounding."

Section 250-94, Exceptions No. 1 and No. 2: Revised to change the wording in each part from "the sole connection between the grounding electrode and the grounded system conductor shall" to "the sole connection to the grounding electrode shall."

Section 250-113: Revised to delete the word "required" and add "exothermic welding" and to require that connectors, clamps, etc. be listed. The word "solely" added between "depending" and "on."

Section 250-114: The word "solely" inserted between "depending" and "on". A new third sentence has been inserted as follows: "Splices shall be made in accordance with Section 110-14(b) except that insulation shall not be required."

Section 250-114(a): The word "approved" was replaced with "listed."

Section 250-115: Revised to include exothermic welding and to require lugs, connectors and other devices for connection of the grounding conductor to the grounding electrode to be listed.

Section 250-152(a), Exception No. 2, (FPN): A new fine print note added to reference Section

225-4 for conductor covering where within ten feet of any building or other structure.

ARTICLE 280 - Surge Arresters

Section 280-4(b): Revised to recognize the rating systems for both silicon carbon and metal oxide types of surge arresters.

Section 280-4(b), (FPN): A new fine print note added providing information on how metal oxide surge arresters are rated.

Section 280-24: The word "permitted to be" has been deleted to clarify that the grounding conductor of a surge arrester protecting a transformer supplying a secondary distribution system must be interconnected as specified in (a) or (b) of this section.

A similar revision has been made to paragraph (a) of this Section.

Section 280-24(b): This section has been rewritten and subdivided into three paragraphs to address the spark gap device breakdown voltage for ungrounded or unigrounded, or multigrounded neutral primary systems.

ARTICLE 300 - Wiring Methods

Section 300-1(a): Reworded for clarity.

Section 300-1(c): This section has been relocated and renumbered as Section 300-3(a).

Section 300-2(b): A new section was added to require that the temperature limitations of conductors must be in accordance with the requirements in Section 310-10.

Section 300-3(a): This section was previously identified as Section 300-1(c).

Section 300-3(b): This is a new paragraph to require all conductors of the same circuit including the neutral and equipment grounding conductors to be contained within the same raceway, cable tray, trench, cable, or cord.

Section 300-3(b), Exception: This is a new exception exempting certain conductors from the requirements of paragraphs (a) and (b).

Section 300-3(c), Exception, (FPN): A new fine print note was added after the exception to reference Section 725-38(a)(2) for Class 2 and Class 3 circuit conductors.

Section 300-4(b): Revised to include electrical nonmetallic tubing installed through metal framing members. (1) of this section was revised to require bushings or grommets to be installed in the metal framing member openings prior to installation of the cable.

Section 300-4(b), Exception: The exception has been deleted.

Section 300-5(a): In the note to Table 300-5, the definition of "cover" has been relocated to the second paragraph of Section 300-5(a).

Section 300-5(a), Exception No. 3: The word "thoroughfares" was deleted and replaced with "streets, highways, roads, alleys, driveways and parking lots."

Section 300-5(a), Exception No. 8: The word "approved" was deleted and replaced with "identified."

Section 300-5(d): This section has been revised to clarify that direct buried conductors and cables emerging from the ground are required to be protected in accordance with Section 300-5(a)

and in no case is the protection required to exceed 18 inches below finished grade.

Section 300-5(g), (FPN): A new fine print note has been added as follows: "Presence of hazardous gases or vapors may also necessitate sealing of underground conduit or raceways entering buildings."

Section 300-5(h): A terminal fitting with a integral bushed opening has been added as a means of achieving protection of conductors or cable and emerging as a direct burial wiring method.

Section 300-5(i): Revised to also include the neutral conductor to be installed in the raceway or enclosed proximity when in the same trench.

Section 300-6(a), Exception: A new exception was added as follows: "Threads at joint shall be permitted to be coated with an identified electrically conductive compound."

Section 300-8: This new section was added to prohibit installation of electric conductors in any raceway, cable, or cable tray that contains a pipe, tube, or equal for steam, water, air, gas, drainage, or any service other than electrical. An exception to this section allows cables approved for the purpose.

Section 300-11: This section has been revised by changing the title to "Securing and Supporting," separating the section into two sections (a) and (b). The first paragraph has been revised by the addition of a new sentence as follows: "Support wires that do not provide rigid support shall not be permitted as the sole support."

The previous second paragraph has been revised to become (b) and reads as follows: "Raceways shall not be used as a means of support for other raceways, cables, or nonelectric equipment. Three new exceptions were added to Section 300-11(b) as follows:

Exception No. 1: "Where the raceways or means of support are identified for the purpose."

Exception No. 2: "Raceways containing power supply conductors for electrically controlled equipment shall be permitted to support Class 2 circuit conductors or cables that are solely for the purpose of connection to the equipment controls circuits."

Exception No. 3: "As permitted in Sections 370-13 for boxes or conduit bodies, or for 410-16(f) for fixtures."

Section 300-14: The title was revised to read "Length of Free Conductors at Outlets, Junctions, and Switch Points." This section, including the exception, has been revised to include "junction points."

Section 300-15(b), Exception No. 8: A new exception was added to permit a device identified and listed for installation without a box when used with a closed-loop power distribution system.

Section 300-15, Exception No. 9: A new exception was added permitting a fitting identified for the use in lieu of a box where accessible after installation and where the conductors are not spliced or terminated.

SUMMARY OF CODE CHANGES

Section 300-17, (FPN): A reference to Article 770 added.

Table 300-19(a): The format was revised to make it easier to read.

Section 300-21, (FPN): The fine print note was deleted.

Section 300-22(c): This section has been divided into two separate paragraphs. The first paragraph was revised for clarification purposes, and where accessible, solid bottom metal cable tray with solid metal covers has been added as another wiring method.

A new third paragraph has been added to permit electric equipment with a metal enclosure or with a nonmetallic enclosure listed for the use, and having adequate fire-resistant and low-smoke producing characteristics, suitable for the ambient temperature, to be installed in other spaces used for environmental air.

Section 300-22(c), Exception No. 6: A new exception has been added to this section to exclude the underfloor area specified in Section 645-2(c)(3).

ARTICLE 305 - Temporary Wiring

Section 305-1: The first paragraph has been subdivided into two separate paragraphs. The second paragraph has been identified as Section 305-2 and titled "Other Articles," with the section's numbers revised sequentially. Paragraphs (a), (b), (c), and (d) transferred to a new Section 305-3 titled "Time Constraints."

Section 305-4(b): This section has been revised to permit flexible multiconductor cord or cable assemblies to be used as feeders, provided they are the type identified in Table 400-4 for hard usage or extra hard usage, where the voltage does not exceed 150 volts to ground and where they are not subject to physical damage.

A new exception was added as follows: "Where installed for the purposes specified in Section 305-3(c)."

Section 305-4(c): The same revisions were made to this section "Branch Circuits" as for Section 304-5(b).

Section 305-4(d): The second sentence was revised as follows: "Unless installed in a continuous grounded metal raceway or metal-covered cable all branch circuits shall contain a separate equipment grounding conductor and all receptacles shall be electrically connected to the equipment grounding conductors."

Section 305-4(e): A new second sentence was added requiring multiwire branch circuits to be provided with a means to disconnect simutaneously all ungrounded conductors at the power outlet or panelboard. Single pole breakers with approved handle ties are permitted.

Section 305-4(f): This section has been revised to eliminate the seven feet of elevation as a means of protection for general illumination, and requires the lamp to be protected from accidental contact or breakage by a suitable fixture or lampholder with a guard.

ARTICLE 310 - Conductors for General Wiring

Section 310-4, Exceptions No. 1 and No. 2: Relocated to follow the first paragraph of this section.

Section 310-4, Exception No. 3: A new exception was added as follows: "Conductors in sizes smaller than 1/0 shall be permitted to be run in parallel for frequencies of 360 hertz and higher when all of the conditions of Exceptions No. 2(a), (b), and (c) are met."

Section 310-8(a): Type RUW has been deleted.

Section 310-10, (FPN): The full size text following the fine print note has been changed to fine print to identify it as part of the fine print note.

Section 310-14: Revised to limit solid aluminum conductors No. 8, 10, and 12 AWG to AA-8000 series electrical grade aluminum alloy. Stranded aluminum conductors No. 8 AWG through 1,000 MCM marked as Type XHHW, THW, THWN, THHN, service entrance Type SE Style U and SE Style R are required to be of an AA-8000 series electrical grade aluminum alloy conductor material.

Section 310-15: A new first paragraph was added to this section to define the term "electrical duct."

Section 310-15(a): The January 1, 1987 effective date for the ampacity of conductors rated 0-2,000 volts has been deleted.

Section 310-15(b): The first sentence of this section has been revised to permit conductor ampacities not covered by the tables to be calculated under engineering supervision, by means of the general formula provided.

Section 310-15(c): This new section was added to indicate that when more than one calculated or tabulated ampacity could apply for a given circuit length, the lowest value must be used.

Table 310-13: Insulation Types RUH, RUW, and T have been deleted. The description of materials used for Types FEPP, AA, AIA, and AVA have been revised to include "other suitable grade material."

Under the Column titled "Application Provisions" "Dry Locations" has been changed to "Dry and Damp Locations" for the following types of cable: FEP, FEPB, PFA, RH, RHH, SA, THHN, XHHW, Z, and ZW.

Table 310-16: This table has been revised as follows: (1) to limit the table to Types AC, NM, NMC, SE, and raceway in free air; (2) to expand the ampacity correction factor range down to 21°C and also subdivide the temperature ranges into smaller increments; (3) to include damp locations in a single asterisk note to the table; (4) to delete Type RUW, RUH, and T; (5) to delete Type MI from the 85°C columns; (6) the obelisk note at the bottom of the table was revised by adding the phrase "unless otherwise specifically permitted elsewhere in this Code."

Table 310-17: Table 310-17 has been revised;

(1) format of the title was changed for clarity;

(2) ampacity correction factors were expanded and subdivided as in Table 310-16.

XXVI

Table 310-18: This table is similar to Table 310-18 in the 1984 *NEC* except the ampacities have changed and it is now based on a 40°C (104°F) ambient. Also, it does not include underground wiring.

Table 310-19: This table is similar to Table 310-19 in the 1984 *NEC* except the ampacities have changed and it is now based on a 40°C (104°F) ambient. Also, it does not include bare or covered conductors.

Table 310-22: This new table is based on proposed Table 310-24 in the 1984 *NEC*. It covers three conductor cable installed in a raceway where the raceway is located in free air. This was previously covered in Table 310-16 of the 1984 *NEC*.

Table 310-23: This table is based on proposed Table 310-22 in the 1984 *NEC*. It covers messenger supported wiring.

Table 310-24: This new table is based on proposed Table 310-20 in the 1984 *NEC*. It includes bare or covered conductors previously covered in Table 310-19 of the 1984 *NEC*.

Table 310-25: This new table is based on proposed Table 310-25 in the 1984 *NEC*. It covers single conductors installed in nonmagnetic underground electrical ducts. This was previously covered in Table 310-16 in the 1984 *NEC*.

Table 310-26: This new table is based on proposed Table 310-26 in the 1984 *NEC*. It covers three conductor cable, installed in underground electrical ducts, where one cable is installed in each duct. This was previously covered in Table 310-16 in the 1984 *NEC*.

Table 310-27: This new table is based on proposed Table 310-27 in the 1984 *NEC*. It covers three single insulated conductors in underground electrical ducts where three conductors are installed in each duct. This was previously covered in Table 310-16 in the 1984 *NEC*.

Table 310-28: This new table is based on proposed Table 310-28 in the 1984 *NEC*. It covers two- or three-conductor cable directly buried in earth, such as Type UF cable. This was previously covered in Table 310-16 in the 1984 *NEC*.

Table 310-29: This new table is based on proposed Table 310-29 in the 1984 *NEC*. It covers three triplexed single insulated conductors, directly buried in earth, Types UF and USE. This was previously covered in Table 310-16 in the 1984 *NEC*.

Table 310-30: This new table is based on proposed Table 310-30 in the 1984 *NEC*. It covers three single insulated conductors directly buried in earth, Types UF and USE. This was previously covered in Table 310-16 in the 1984 *NEC*.

Table 310-31: This new table is based proposed Table 310-20A in the 1984 *NEC*. It covers multiconductor cables with not more than three insulated conductors, Types MC, MI, SNM, and TC, in free air, previously covered in Table 310-16 in the 1984 *NEC*.

Tables 310-16 through 310-31, Notes:
Note 3: Revised to permit grounded service-entrance conductors to be 2 AWG sizes smaller

than the ungrounded conductors provided the neutral is suitably sized for the calculated load.
Note 4: Deleted.
Note 5: Revised by inserting "adjacent" after "the" and before "insulated." The phrase "of the same size" was deleted at the end of the sentence.
Note 6: Revised by changing "85°C" to "90°C" in last line.
Note 7: This note has been changed to a fine print note referencing NFPA 79-1985.
Note 8: Note 8 was renumbered 8(a).
Note 8 (a) Table: An asterisk (*) note was added to indicate that where more than 9 conductors are in the same raceway, the derating factors are based on a load diversity of 50 percent.
Note 8(a), Exception No. 2: Deleted and other exceptions renumbered.
Note 8(a), Exceptions No. 3 and 4: The previous Exception No. 4 is now Exception No. 3. A new Exception No. 4 was added to indicate the derating factors do not apply to underground conductors entering or leaving an outdoor trench if those conductors have physical protection in the form of rigid metal conduit, intermediate metal conduit, or rigid nonmetallic conduit Schedule 80, having a length not exceeding 8 feet and the number of conductors in a conduit does not exceed 4.
Note 8(b): A new part (b) was added to require the spacing to be maintained between conduits, tubing, or raceways where more than one conduit, tube, or raceway is installed.
Note 11: Revised to exclude a bonding conductor when applying the ampacity adjustment factors in Note 8.
Figure 310-1: This figure has been revised by changing "raceway bank" to "electrical duct bank." Details 2 and 3 have an additional figure added. Detail 4 has been revised to show a different configuration. The burial depth in Details 5 through 10 were revised to show that it is the depth to the top of the electrical ducts or cables. New Notes and a legend have been added for all details.
Table 310-64: Revised to add "215" for conductor size 2 AWG in the 8001-15000 volt, 133 percent insulation level column.
Tables 310-77 through 310-84: Headings of Tables 310-77 through 310-84 revised to clarify application and to refer to Figure 310-1.

ARTICLE 318 - Cable Trays
Section 318-1: Revised to include only the last sentence of the first paragraph. New Section 318-2 includes the first sentence of existing Section 318-1. The rest of the sections were renumbered sequentially.
Section 318-3(b): This section was expanded by adding 6-inch ventilated channel-type cable trays.
Section 318-3(b)(1): Revised to insert "identified as being" after "cables shall," at the end of the sentence. Also, a new exception was added for welding cables as permitted in Article 630, new Part E.
Section 318-3(b)(2): Revised to insert "identified as being" after "shall be."

SUMMARY OF CODE CHANGES

Section 318-3(d), (FPN): A new fine print note was added to indicate that it is not the intent of this article to limit the use of cable trays to industrial establishments only.

Section 318-3(e): A new section was added to allow nonmetallic cable tray in corrosive areas and in areas requiring voltage isolation. This was originally located in Section 318-1.

Section 318-5: Revised to insert the words "cable trays" at the beginning of each paragraph (b) through (e).

Section 318-5(f): A new paragraph was added to require nonmetallic cable trays to be made of flame-retardent material.

Section 318-6(c): Revised to change "raceway or enclosure" to "raceways or other enclosures."

Section 318-6(f), Exception No. 2: Revised to exempt Type MC cables over 600 volts.

Section 318-6(i), (FPN): A new fine print note added to reference Section 301-10 for temperature limitation of conductors.

Section 318-7(b): This section has been revised to permit steel or aluminum cable tray systems to be used as equipment grounding conductors provided that they satisfy the requirements in the rest of Section 318-7(b).

Table 318-7(b)(2): The heading of the first column of the table and double asterisk (**) note revised to make it clear that the overcurrent protection specified is for ground-fault protection.

Section 318-9(e): This section has been expanded to include 3.8 square inches in 6-inch wide channel trays.

Section 318-9(e), Exception: This has been expanded to include 7-square inches in a 6-inch wide channel tray.

Section 318-10(b): This section has been expanded to include 6-inch wide ventilated channel-type cable tray.

Section 318-11(a), Exception No. 2: A new exception has been added for multiconductor cables installed in a single layer in uncovered trays, with a maintained spacing of not less than one cable diameter between cables.

Section 318-11(b)(4): A new section was added to cover single conductors installed in a triangular configuration in uncovered cable trays, with a maintained spacing of not less than 2.15 times one conductor diameter between circuits.

Section 318-13(b)(3): A new section was added to cover single conductors installed in a triangular configuration in uncovered cable trays, with a maintained space of not less than 2.15 times one conductor diameter between circuits.

ARTICLE 320 - Open Wiring on Insulators

Section 320-11, (FPN): A new fine print note added to reference Section 310-15 for temperature limitation of conductors.

ARTICLE 321 - Messenger Supported Wiring

Section 321-3(a)(6): This section has been expanded by adding power-limited tray cable (Section 725-40).

Section 321-3(b)(1): Revised to add Table 310-62.

ARTICLE 324 - Concealed Knob-and-Tube Wiring

Section 324-4: Revised by adding: "or in the hollow spaces of walls, ceilings and attics when such spaces are insulated by loose or rolled insulating material."

Section 324-11, (FPN): A new fine print note added to reference Section 310-10 for temperature limitation of conductors.

ARTICLE 325 - Integrated Gas Spacer Cable

No changes.

ARTICLE 326 - Medium Voltage Cable

No changes.

ARTICLE 328 - Flat Conductor Cable Type FCC

Section 328-2, Definitions: The definition of "Bottom Shield" was revised to make it clear that this shield may or may not be incorporated as an integral part of the cable assembly.

Section 328-10: Revised to allow carpet squares no larger than 36 inches square.

ARTICLE 330 Mineral-Insulated Metal-Sheathed Cable

No changes.

ARTICLE 331 - Electrical Nonmetallic Tubing

Sections 331-3 and 331-4: These sections have been reformatted and renumbered. They have been revised to eliminate the three floor restriction, to require the tubing to be installed within walls, floors, and ceilings behind a thermal barrier with at least a 15-minute finish rating, and to permit the tubing to be embedded in poured concrete, provided fittings identified for this purpose are used for connections.

A new fine print has been added warning that extreme cold may cause some types of nonmetallic conduit to become brittle and, therefore, more susceptible to damage from physical contact.

Section 331-14, (FPN): The last sentence of Section 331-14 has been moved and revised to become a fine print note.

ARTICLE 333 - Armored Cable

Section 333-5: The first sentence has been expanded to include other insulated conductors identified for use in this cable. A new sentence was added as follows: "The ampacity shall be determined by Section 310-15."

Section 333-5, Exception: A new exception was added to require that when armored cable is installed in thermal insulation, the conductors must have a rating of at least 90°C. The ampacity of cables installed under those conditions shall be that of 60°C conductors.

Section 333-6(a): In the last sentence of this section the word "and" was changed to "where."

Section 333-7: Revised to add "junction box, cabinet" after "outlet box."

Section 333-7, Exception No. 3: A new exception was added permitting unsupported lengths of Type AC cable of not more than 6 feet from a outlet for connections within an accessible ceiling to lighting fixtures or equipment.

Section 333-9: In the last sentence "fitting or conduit body" added after "box."

ARTICLE 334 - Metal-Clad Cable

Section 334-3: Revised to clarify the intent that Type MC cables can be directly buried only when identified for such use.

Section 334-10(e): Revised to add a reference to Article 321.

Section 334-13, (FPN): A new fine print note has been added to this section referencing Section 310-10 for temperature limitations.

ARTICLE 336 - Nonmetallic-Sheathed Cable

General: Article 336 has been reorganized and renumbered.

Section 336-3, (FPN): A new fine print note has been added to this section referencing Section 310-10 for temperature limitation of conductors.

Section 336-16, Exception: Revised to change "approved" to "identified for use with."

Section 336-25: This section (relocated from Section 336-2) was revised by changing "an approved" to "in conformity with Section 336-26." In the last sentence, "may" was changed to "shall be permitted to." A new sentence was added as follows: "When provided, the grounding conductor shall be sized in accordance with Article 250."

Section 336-26: This section (relocated from the second paragraph of Section 336-2) was revised by inserting "insulated" ahead of "conductors." The second paragraph was revised by adding "and shall comply with Section 310-15" following "conductors" at the end of the sentence.

ARTICLE 337 - Shielded Nonmetallic-Sheathed Cable

Section 337-3, (FPN): A new fine print note was added referencing Section 310-10 for temperature limitation of conductors.

ARTICLE 338 - Service-Entrance Cable

Section 338-4(c), (FPN): A new fine print note was added referencing Section 310-10 for temperature limitation of conductors.

ARTICLE 339 - Underground Feeder and Branch-Circuit Cable

Section 339-1(a): The third sentence of this section was deleted.

Section 339-3(a)(4): Revised by inserting "and conductor" following "installation." A new fine print note was added to this section referencing Section 310-10 for temperature limitation of conductors.

Section 339-5: Revised to require the ampacity of Type UF cable to be that of 60 degree C conductors in accordance with Section 310-15.

ARTICLE 340 - Power and Control Tray Cable

Section 340-4, (FPN): A new fine print note was added referencing Section 310-10 for temperature limitation of conductors.

ARTICLE 342 - Nonmetallic Extensions

Section 342-3(c1),(FPN): A new fine print note was added referencing Section 310-10 for temperature limitation of conductors.

ARTICLE 344 - Under Plaster Extensions

Section 344-2: Revised for clarification, and to add "metal conduit" after "rigid." Also electrical nonmetallic tubing and Type MC cable were added to the list of wiring methods.

ARTICLE 345 - Intermediate Metal Conduit

Section 345-3(a), (FPN): Revised to reference Section 250-91(b) for types of equipment grounding conductors.

Sections 345-3(b) and (c), (FPN): The fine print notes were expanded to indicate that the reference is for protection against corrosion.

Section 345-8: The last sentence was revised to limit a thread cutting die to one with a ¾-inch taper per foot. A new fine print note was added to reference ANSI/ASME B.1.20.1-1983.

Section 345-15: Revised by adding "fitting, or other enclosure" after "box" in two places. The last sentence of this section was relocated to become a new fine print note referencing Section 373-6(c) for the protection of conductors No. 4 AWG and larger at bushings.

ARTICLE 346 - Rigid Metal Conduit

Section 346-1(c), (FPN): The fine print note was expanded by adding "for protection against corrosion."

Section 346-7(b)(FPN): A new fine print note was added referencing the ANSI standard for pipe thread.

Section 346-8: Revised to include other enclosures where a bushing must be provided to protect the wire from abrasion.

ARTICLE 347 - Rigid Nonmetallic Conduit

Section 347-2, (FPN): A new fine print note was added alerting installers that extreme cold may cause some types of nonmetallic conduit to become brittle and therefore more susceptible to damage from physical contact.

Section 347-8: Revised by changing "supported" to "secured." The second sentence revised by inserting "shall be securely fastened" in place of "there shall be a support."

Section 347-12, (FPN): The fine print note expanded to indicate that it is referencing conductors No. 4 AWG and larger.

Section 347-13: The word "intended" was changed to "identified."

ARTICLE 348 - Electrical Metallic Tubing

Section 348-1, (FPN): The fine print note has been revised by the addition of "for protection against corrosion."

Section 348-4, (FPN): The fine print note has been expanded by the addition of "for protection against corrosion."

ARTICLE 349 - Flexible Metallic Tubing

Section 349-1: Revised to delete use requirements.

Section 349-3(2): The phrase "such as above suspended ceilings" was added after "concealed."

SUMMARY OF CODE CHANGES

Section 349-18, (FPN): The following was added to the end of the sentence: "for use in ducts, plenums, and other spaces used for environmental air."

ARTICLE 350 - Flexible Metal Conduit

Section 350-3, Exception No. 4: A new exception was added permitting ⅜-inch trade size flexible metal conduit for manufactured wiring systems as permitted in Section 604-6(a).

Section 350-3, Exception No. 5: A new exception was added referencing Section 620-21, Exception No. 5.

Table 350-3: The asterisk (*) note was revised to add "equipment" before "grounding."

Section 350-4: Revised to include junction boxes and cabinets.

Section 350-5: Revised to reference Section 250-91(b).

Section 350-5, Exception No. 2: A new exception was added as follows: "where used to connect equipment where flexibility is required, a grounding conductor shall be installed."

ARTICLE 351 - Liquidtight Flexible Metal Conduit and Liquidtight Flexible Nonmetallic Conduit

Section 351-1: Title of Article 351 and Section 351-1 revised to include liquidtight flexible nonmetallic conduit, previously located in Section 351-21.

Section 351-3: Article 553 has been included in the list of referenced articles.

Section 351-4(a)(2): Revised to include Section 553-7(b).

Section 351-8: Revised to include junction boxes and cabinets.

Section 351-9, Exception No. 2: Revised to clarify that the grounding conductor is an equipment grounding conductor

Section 351-9, (FPN): Revised by adding "for types of equipment grounding conductors."

Section 351-21: Deleted.

Section 351-23(a), (FPN): A new fine print note was added alerting installers that extreme cold may cause some types of nonmetallic conduit to become brittle and therefore more susceptible to damage from physical contact.

Section 351-23(a)(3): A new section was added permitting liquidtight flexible nonmetallic conduit in outdoor locations where it is listed and marked as suitable for the purpose.

Section 351-27: Revised to permit the equipment grounding conductor to be installed on the outside or inside of the conduit. Where it is installed on the outside, the length of the equipment grounding conductor must not exceed six feet and must be routed with the raceway or enclosure.

ARTICLE 352 - Surface Metal Raceways and Surface Nonmetallic Raceways

General: "Metal surface" raceway was changed to "Surface metal" raceway throughout Article 355.

Title, Article 352: Revised by adding "and Surface Nonmetallic Raceways."

Part A, Article 352: Change heading to "A. Surface Metal Raceways."

Part B, Article 352: The heading changed to read: "B. Surface Nonmetallic Raceway." The words "nonmetallic" and "surface" transposed in all sections of Part B except in the third sentence of Section 352-27.

ARTICLE 353 - Multioutlet Assembly

Editorial changes only.

ARTICLE 354 - Underfloor Raceways

Section 354-6, Exception: A new exception has been added permitting splices and taps in trench-type flush raceway having a removable cover that is accessible after installation. The conductors, including splices and taps, shall not fill the raceway more than 75% of its area at that point.

Section 354-15: Revised to add electrical nonmetallic tubing.

ARTICLE 356 - Cellular Metal Floor Raceways

Section 356-2: The last sentence of this section was deleted and a new fine print note added referencing Section 300-8 for installation of conductors with other systems.

Section 356-11: Revised to add electrical nonmetallic tubing.

ARTICLE 358 - Cellular Concrete Floor Raceways

Section 358-1: Revised to delete requirements and definitions.

Section 358-2: A new section was added to include definitions previously located in Section 358-1.

Section 358-3: A new section was added to separate information previously located in the first sentence of Section 358-1.

Section 358-4: The last sentence of this section has been deleted, and a new fine print note added referencing Section 300-8 for installation of conductors with other systems.

ARTICLE 362 - Wireways

Section 362-2, Exception: A new exception was added permitting wireways in concealed spaces in accordance with Section 640-4, Exception c.

Section 362-10: Revised to include electrical nonmetallic tubing.

Section 362-12: A new section was added to require grounding to be according to the provisions of Article 250.

ARTICLE 363 - Flat Cable Assemblies

Section 363-19: Revised to change "neutral" to "grounded."

ARTICLE 364 - Busways

Section 364-4(a): Revised by inserting "they are" following "where."

Section 364-8: The first sentence was revised to include electrical nonmetallic tubing. The last sentence was revised to substitute "a nonmetallic raceway" for "rigid nonmetallic conduit" in the first phrase and "nonmetallic raceway" for "rigid nonmetallic conduit" in the second phrase.

Section 364-21, (FPN): The second paragraph of Section 364-21 of the 1984 *NEC* was revised to become a fine print note.

Section 364-25: A new second paragraph was added as follows: "Fire barriers shall be provided where fire walls, floors, or ceilings are penetrated." This terminology was originally found in the exception to this section and has been deleted from the exception.

ARTICLE 365 - Cablebus

Section 365-1: The last sentence has been deleted from this section and relocated in the first paragraph, last sentence, of Section 365-2.

Section 365-2: Revised to become Section 365-2(a), limited to cables rated 600 volts or less.

Section 365-2(b): A new section added permitting cablebus rated over 600 volts per Section 710-3(a).

ARTICLE 366 - Electrical Floor Assemblies

This article has been deleted.

ARTICLE 370 - Outlet, Device, Pull and Junction Boxes, Conduit Bodies and Fittings

Section 370-1: Revised to delete those parts of this section that include requirements which have been transferred to other sections.

Section 370-3: Revised by adding "electrical nonmetallic tubing" in the first paragraph. The second paragraph has been revised by deleting the requirement that nonmetallic boxes over 100 cubic inches must be manufactured with a bonding means between all raceway and cable entries. Integral bonding means must be provided between all threaded entries for metal raceways or metal-sheathed cables at the time of their installation.

Section 370-5: The heading has been expanded to include hazardous (classified) locations.

Section 370-5(b): A new section was added requiring installations in hazardous (classified) locations to conform to Articles 500 through 517.

Section 370-6(a): Revised by deleting "conductors, not counting fixture wires smaller than No. 14."

Section 370-6(a)(1): In the second sentence, "devices" was changed to "fittings." Revised to require an additional deduction of one conductor where a second set of grounding conductors, as permitted by Section 250-74, Exception No. 4, are present in the box.

Section 370-6(a)(2): Revised to require that the maximum number of conductors permitted be computed using the volume per conductor listed in Table 370-6(b), with the deductions provided for, and that these volume deductions be based on the largest conductor entering the box.

Section 370-6(b): Revised to require that the maximum number of conductors permitted be computed using the volume per conductor listed in Table 370-6(b), with the deductions provided for, and that these volume deductions be based on the largest conductor entering the box. Also, the last paragraph in this section was deleted.

Tables 370-6(a) and 370-6(b): These two tables have been expanded by including Nos. 18 and 16 AWG conductor sizes.

Section 370-7(b): A new sentence was added at the end of this section which was previously located in the first paragraph of Section 370-1.

Section 370-11: Revised to limit the gaps or open spaces to not more than ⅛ inch at the edge of the box or fitting. The exception to this section has been deleted.

Section 370-12: Revised by adding the following: "Extensions shall not be made from the cover. Where required, equipment grounding shall be in accordance with Article 250."

Section 370-13: Revised by replacing "in all cases boxes" with "enclosures within the scope of Article 370."

Section 370-13(a): Revised by replacing "by some structural member" with "in accordance with (b)."

Section 370-13(b): Revised to require enclosures to be rigidly supported from a structural member of the building either directly or by using a metal or wood brace. Support wires that do not provide rigid support are not to be permitted as the sole support of an enclosure.

Section 370-13(b)(1): This section has been relocated from Section 370-13(c) and revised for clarity.

Section 370-13(b)(2): This section was relocated from the last two sentences of Section 370-13(d) and revised for clarity.

Section 370-13(c): This section has been relocated from Section 370-13(e) and revised for clarity and to reflect concerns for adequate support of enclosures.

Section 370-13(d): This section has been relocated from Section 370-13(f) and revised with a new heading to address raceway supported enclosures.

Section 370-13(d), Exception: A new exception was added to permit conduit or electrical metallic tubing to support conduit bodies not larger than the largest trade size of the conduit or EMT.

Section 370-13(e): This section has been relocated from Section 370-13(g). The heading has been changed to "Raceway Supported Enclosures, With Devices" and revised for clarity.

Section 370-13(e), Exception: A new exception has been added to permit conduit to support conduit bodies provided the conduit bodies are not larger than the largest trade size of the conduit.

Section 370-13(f): This section was relocated from Section 370-13(b) and revised for clarity.

Section 370-13(g): This is a new section permitting nonthreaded nonmetallic conduit to support nonmetallic enclosures provided it is installed in accordance with the listing or labeling instructions provided, and the two or more conduit support distances comply with Sections 370-13(d) or (e).

Section 370-13(h): This is a new section added to allow boxes to be supported from a multiconductor cable in some satisfactory manner that protects the conductors against strain, such as a strain relief connector threaded into a box with a hub.

Section 370-16: This section has been deleted.

SUMMARY OF CODE CHANGES

Section 370-17(c): A new section has been added prohibiting outlet boxes as the sole support for ceiling (paddle) fans, with an exception for boxes listed for the application.

Section 370-18(a)(2): Revised to make it clear that the distance is to be increased by the amount of the sum of the diameters of the maximum number of all other raceway entries in one row on the same wall of the box.

Section 370-51(a): Revised to permit the length to be 32 times the outside diameter for unshielded conductor or cable.

Section 370-51(b), Exception No. 1: Revised to permit nonshielded and non-lead-covered cables to be installed with a box length of 24 times the outside diameter.

ARTICLE 373 - Cabinets and Cutout Boxes

Section 373-1: The scope has been revised to make it clear that Article 373 covers meter socket enclosures. The reference to installations in hazardous (classified) locations has been deleted and transferred to new Section 373-2(b).

Section 373-2(a): The title of this section has been revised to include hazardous (classified) locations.

Section 373-6(b)(1), Exception No. 1: Revised to clarify that a conductor is permitted to enter or leave an enclosure through the wall opposite its terminal provided the conductor enters or leaves the enclosure where the gutter joins an adjacent gutter that has a width that conforms to Table 373-6(b) for that conductor.

Section 373-6(b), Exception No. 2: A new exception has been added permitting a conductor not larger than 350 MCM to enter or leave an enclosure containing only a meter socket (or sockets) through the wall opposite its terminal provided its terminal is a lay-in type where either: (a) the terminal is directly facing the enclosure wall and offset is not greater than 50% of the bending space specified in Table 373-6(a), or (b) the terminal is directed toward the opening in the enclosure and is within a 45 degree angle or directly facing the enclosure wall. A new fine print note has been added defining offset.

Table 373-6(b): The last paragraph of the note to the table has been revised to add lay-in wire terminals.

Section 373-6(c): "Bushings" changed to "fittings" throughout this section.

ARTICLE 374 - Auxiliary Gutters

Editorial changes only.

ARTICLE 380 - Switches

Section 380-2(a): The second sentence was revised to reference Section 300-20(a).

Section 380-2(a), Exception: A new exception was added to indicate that switch loops do not require a grounded conductor.

Section 380-6(c): This is a new section relocated from Section 380-7.

Section 380-6(c), Exception: A new exception was added to require single-throw knife switches, which may provide a backfeed source of power, to have a permanent sign installed on a switch enclosure or adjacent to open switches.

Section 380-7: A new section was added to require general-use and motor-circuit switches and circuit breakers, where mounted in an enclosure described in Section 380-3, to clearly indicate whether they are in the "off" or "on" position. Where the switch or circuit breaker handles are operated vertically, the up position of the handle shall be the "on" position. An exception is included for double-throw switches.

Section 380-12: Revised by deleting the words "on circuits of over 150 volts to ground."

Section 380-14: Revised to indicate that snap switches are to be used within their ratings as indicated in (a) through (c) of this section.

ARTICLE 384 - Switchboards and Panelboards

Section 384-1(a): This section has been relocated to Section 384-2 and revised to clarify that switches and overcurrent devices used on switchboards, panelboards, and distribution boards are required to comply with Article 384 as well as the other listed articles in this section.

Section 384-2, Exceptions No. 1, 2, 3, & 4 : These have been relocated and follow Section 384-4.

Section 384-3(f), Exception: Revised to indicate that the exception applies to equipment within the same multisection switchboard or panelboard.

Section 384-4: This section has been relocated from Section 384-2 and revised to clarify that the exclusively dedicated space extends from the floor to the structural ceiling.

Section 384-4, (FPN): Two new fine print notes have been added to make it clear Section 384-4 is not intended to mandate a dedicated room and is not intended to prohibit sprinkler protection for the electrical installation.

Section 384-8: This section has been relocated from Section 384-7 and identified as "Clearances."

Section 384-27: Revised by adding the following sentence to the end of the paragraph: "The terminal bar shall be bonded to the cabinet or panelboard frame, or at the first system disconnecting means or overcurrent device for a separately derived system, and shall not be connected to the neutral bar in other than service equipment."

Section 384-27, Exception No. 1: Revised to make it clear that the exception applies to an equipment grounding conductor.

ARTICLE 400 - Flexible Cords and Cables

Table 400-4: This table was revised as follows:

(1) Under Asbestos-Covered Heat-Resistant Cord AFPO was added.

(2) Under Type C Nos. 14-10 AWG insulation thickness was added.

(3) Portable power cable Type G was added.

(4) Types HS, the descriptions of HSJ, HSJO, and HSO were revised.

(5) Type SEO was added.

(6) There were revisions under junior hard service cord.

(7) Under Types SO, SOO, ST, STO and STOO references were added to Note 5.

(8) Type TP was deleted.

(9) Portable power cable, Type W was added.

Notes to Tables 400-4

Note 1: This note was revised to add reference to Types SPE-1, SPE-2, AFPO, SPE-3, SRDE, and SRDT, and to delete the reference to Type TP.

Note 5: This note was revised to add Types SE, SEO, SOO, STOO, G, and W.

Note 8: This note was revised to add Type AFPO and delete Type CFTD. Also the last sentence was revised to delete Types HS and HSO and to limit Type HPD to sizes 18 and 16 AWG.

Note 9: This note was revised to add Types SE, SEO, SOO, and STOO.

Section 400-5: This section was revised by adding the words "from the three conductor rating" between the words "reduced" and "as." A new second paragraph was added which explains the use of subheading C of Table 400-5 for Type W cable. A new third paragraph was added which addresses neutral conductors which carry only unbalanced current from other conductors. A new fourth paragraph was added which addresses 3-wire circuits consisting of two-phase wires and the neutral of a 4-wire three-phase wye connected system. A new fifth paragraph was added which addresses 4-wire, 3-phase wye circuits where the major portion of the load consists of electric-discharge lighting, data processing, or similar equipment where harmonic currents are present. A new sixth paragraph was added which indicates that equipment grounding conductors are not considered current-carrying conductors.

Table 400-5: This table was revised to extend the first column to include up to 500 MCM, to add Types G and W cable to the heading of third column, and to extend the ampacities in the third column under A, B and C to 500 MCM. Type TP and Types SOO, SGOO, SVOO, SP1, SP2, SP3, STOO, SJTOO, SVTOO, SPT-1, SPT-2, SPT-3, SE, SEO, SJE, SJEO, SVE, SVEO, SRDE, SPE-1, SPE-2, SPE-3, and AFPO were added. Type CFPD was deleted.

Section 400-6: The second paragraph was revised to add Types SJE, SJEO, SJTOO, SE, SEO, SOO, and STOO cords and G and W cables.

Section 400-11: This section was revised to add Types SE, SEO, SOO, SJE, SJEO, SJOO, STOO and SJTOO.

ARTICLE 402 - Fixture Wires

Table 402-3: Types FFH-1 and CF were deleted from the table.

Section 402-5, (FPN): This new fine print note references Section 310-10 for temperature limitation of conductors.

ARTICLE 410 - Lighting Fixtures, Lampholders, Lamps, Receptacles, and Rosettes

Section 410-1 and Exception: A period was added after "lighting installation" in Section

410-1 and the rest of the sentence was deleted. The exception was also deleted.

Section 410-4(a): The word "wireways" in the first sentence was changed to "wiring compartments."

Section 410-4(c)(3): The word "noncorrosive" was changed to "corrosion resistant."

Section 410-4(d): This section was revised by including cord-connected fixtures in the list of those fixtures that are prohibited from being installed within the bathtub zone.

Section 410-15(b): This section was added to provide requirements for metal poles supporting lighting fixtures.

Section 410-16(c): This section was revised to require fixtures to be securely fastened to the ceiling framing members, whether or not they are supported independently.

Section 410-21: This section was revised to clarify that all metal raceways are not suitable as an unrestricted equipment grounding conductor. The change references the appropriate section which describes acceptable equipment grounding conductors.

Section 410-27, Exception: This exception was revised to change "approved" to "listed."

Section 410-36: This section was revised to change "wireways" to "wiring compartments."

Section 410-37: This section was revised to change "wireways" to "wiring compartments."

Section 410-48: This section was revised to require the switching device of switched lampholders to simultaneously disconnect both ungrounded conductors from the circuit.

Section 410-54: The title to this section was changed to "Electric-Discharge Lamp Auxiliary Equipment." The existing rule was changed to paragraph (a) Enclosures. A new paragraph (b) Switching was added which requires all ungrounded conductors of a circuit to auxiliary equipment to be simultaneously disconnected by the switching device.

Section 410-56(d): This section was revised to require the mounting yoke or strap of the receptacle to be seated against the box, raised cover, or wall surface.

Section 410-65(b): This section was revised to indicate that it applies only to listed fixtures.

Section 410-65(c), Exception No. 2: The existing Exception No. 2 was deleted in its entirety. A new exception was added which recognizes fixtures that, by their construction design, are not subject to exceeding presently established operating temperature limits.

Section 410-66(a): This section was revised by deleting the word "Incandescent."

Section 410-66(a) Exception No. 2: This is a new exception which excludes recessed fluorescent fixtures.

Section 410-66(b), Exception No. 2: This is a new exception which excludes recessed fluorescent fixtures.

Section 410-67(c): This section was revised by deleting "metal" from the last sentence.

Section 410-73(f): This section was revised to require thermal protection for an HID fixture ballast when the ballast is located remote from the fixture.

Section 410-76(b): This section was revised to require fixtures mounted on combustible low-density cellulose fiberboard to be listed for this condition or spaced more than ½ inch from the surface of the fiberboard.

Section 410-101(a): This section was revised to prohibit general purpose receptacles in lighting track fittings.

Section 410-102: This section was revised to require that where multicircuit track is installed, the load requirement of this section shall be considered to be divided equally between the circuits.

Section 410-104: This section was revised to allow lighting track to be fastened to other than the ceiling or wall.

Section 410-105: This section was revised to better define "accidental contact." In addition, the last sentence from 410-105(b) was relocated to this section.

ARTICLE 422 - Appliances

Section 422-8(d)(3): This is a new section which requires the supply cord conductors and internal wiring of portable high-pressure spray washing machines to be provided with GFCI protection for personnel. The GFCI is required to be identified for use with portable equipment and permitted as an integral part of the attachment plug.

Section 422-9: The last sentence of this section was deleted.

Section 422-13: This section was revised to require an identified temperature limiting means.

Section 422-14(b): This section was revised to make it clearer and more grammatically correct.

Section 422-17(a): This section was revised to clarify intent that these are permanently connected appliances where cord-plug-connection is permitted for ease in installation or servicing.

Section 422-18: This section was added to indicate that ceiling fans not exceeding 35 pounds in weight, with or without accessories, may be supported by outlet boxes identified for such use and supported in accordance with Sections 370-13 and 370-17.

Section 422-22(a): This section was revised to make it clear that a cord- and plug-connection as the disconnecting means is acceptable only where the receptacle and plug are accessible.

Section 422-22(d)(4) and (FPN): This section and the fine print note were added to require the plugs and connectors to be polarized or of the grounding type, and to reference Section 410-42.

Section 422-24(a): This section was revised to correlate with the wording in Section 424-19(a)(3).

Section 422-24(c): This section was revised to correlate with the wording in Section 424-19(b)(3)c.

Section 422-24(d): This section was revised to correlate with the wording in Section 424-19(b)(3)d.

Section 422-27(a): This section was revised to clarify the intent.

Section 422-27(e): This section was revised to provide requirements for nonmotor-operated appliances rated less than 16.7 amperes. An appliance rating not exceeding 13.3 amperes can be protected by an overcurrent device rated at not more than 20 amperes. An appliance rating greater than 13.3 amperes can be protected by a device rated at not more than 150% of the appliance rating.

ARTICLE 424 - Fixed Electric Space Heating Equipment

Section 424-3(b): The second paragraph of this section was revised to add the word "hermetic" before the words "refrigerant motor-compressor."

Section 424-19(c): This section was formerly 424-19(b)(3).

Section 424-19(c)(1): This section was revised to correlate with Section 424-24(a).

Section 424-19(c)(2): This section was revised to add a new second sentence to indicate that in this case, an individual switch or circuit breaker for the dwelling unit shall be permitted and shall also be permitted to control lamps and appliances.

Section 424-19(c)(3): This section was revised to delete the word "units" after the word "dwelling."

Section 424-20(b): This section was revised to clearly permit the commonly used thermostats that do not directly interrupt all ungrounded conductors.

Section 424-37: This section was expanded to apply also to feeder wiring, and revised to reference Article 300 and Section 310-10.

Section 424-41(i): The second sentence and the fine print note were deleted.

Section 424-41(j): This section was added to indicate that cables shall cross joists only at the ends of the rooms. An exception was added to provide for installations where the cable is required to cross joists elsewhere in order to satisfy the manufacturer's instructions that the installer avoid placing the cable too close to ceiling penetrations and light fixtures.

Section 424-92(4): This section was revised to clarify the intent.

Section 424-92(4), Exception: This new exception was added for heating panels and heating panel set installations that are visible and distinguishable after installation.

Section 424-95: The title of this section was revised to apply to feeder wiring in addition to branch-circuit wiring.

Section 424-95(a): The wiring methods in exterior walls now refer to requirements in Article 300 and Section 310-10.

Section 424-99: This is a new section which provides installation requirements for conductive film-type heating panels installed under floor coverings.

ARTICLE 426 - Fixed Outdoor Electric De-Icing and Snow-Melting Equipment

Section 426-50: This section was revised to add "to ground" after "150 volts or less."

ARTICLE 427 - Fixed Electric Heating Equipment for Pipelines and Vessels

Section 427-22: This section was added to require ground fault protection (GFP) for electric heating equipment not having a metal covering.

ARTICLE 430 - Motors, Motor Circuits, and Controllers

Section 430-1, (FPN): The second fine print note to this section was deleted.

Diagram 430-1: This diagram was revised by identifying it as a fine print note and by including the section numbers for each part number in the material preceding the diagram.

Section 430-6: This section was revised to reference Tables 310-16 through 310-31.

Section 430-9: The title of this section was changed to "Terminals." The requirements for old Section 430-9 are now located in Section 430-9(a) Markings.

Section 430-9(b): A new section was added to require motor controllers and terminals of control circuit devices to be connected with copper conductors unless otherwise identified.

Section 430-9(c): This is a new section which adds minimum torque requirements for screw-type pressure terminals used with No. 14 AWG or smaller copper conductors.

Section 430-12(a), Exception: This exception was revised to delete reference to motors larger than 34 inches in diameter.

Section 430-12(a), (FPN): This fine print note was deleted.

Section 430-21, (FPN): The second fine print note is new. It refers to Section 430-9(b) for device terminal requirements.

Section 430-22: The fine print note after Table 430-22(a) Exception was moved to between Section 430-22(a) and Exception No. 1 of this section.

Section 430-42(a): A reference to Section 430-32(b) was added.

Section 430-52: The last sentence of this section was changed from the permissive "shall be permitted" to the mandatory requirement "shall be used."

Section 430-52, Exception No. 1: This exception was revised to clarify the intent.

Section 430-53(c)(5), (FPN): This fine print note was added to reference Section 110-10.

Section 430-62(a): This section was revised to reference Section 440-22(a) for hermetic refrigerant motor-compressors, in addition to Table 430-152.

Section 430-71(a), (FPN): This fine print note was added to reference Section 430-9(b).

Section 430-81(a): This section was revised to clarify the intent.

Section 430-86: This section was deleted. These requirements now appear in Section 430-102.

Section 430-90: This section was revised to change "motor-running overload" to "motor overload."

Table 430-91: An asterisk (*) was inserted next to the word "sleet" and a footnote added after the Table for Outdoor Use to indicate that the mechanism must be operable when ice covered.

Section 430-102: The title of this section was changed to "Location." The wording from the existing 1984 Section 430-102 is now titled "430-102(a) Controller."

Section 430-102(b): This is a new section which requires the disconnecting means to be located in sight from the motor location and the driven machinery location. An exception was added for locations where the disconnecting means provided in accordance with Section 430-102(a) is capable of being locked in the open position.

Section 430-109, Exception No. 5: This exception was revised to require the plug and receptacle to be horsepower rated.

Part L: The title of this part was changed to "Grounding All Voltages."

Section 430-144: This section was revised to require controller enclosures to have a means for attachment of an equipment grounding conductor termination.

Part M: Tables 430-147 through 430-152 are now in Part M titled "TABLES."

ARTICLE 440 - Air-Conditioning and Refrigerating Equipment

Section 440-2: The second paragraph of Section 440-1 was revised to become new Section 440-2 "Definitions." The remainder of the article was renumbered in sequence.

Section 440-4(c), (FPN): This fine print note was revised to make it clear that the value of branch circuit selection current may be equal to, as well as greater than, the marked rated-load current.

Section 440-6: This section was revised to reference Tables 310-16 through 310-31.

Section 440-14: This section was revised to make it clear a single disconnect is not required, and to permit the disconnecting means to be installed on or within the air-conditioning or refrigerating equipment.

ARTICLE 445 - Generators

Section 445-4(a): "Current-limiting means" was changed to "overcurrent protective means."

ARTICLE 450 - Transformers and Transformer Vaults

Section 450-2: This new section was added to indicate that the word "transformer" is intended to mean an individual transformer, single or polyphase, identified by a single nameplate. Existing Section 450-2 was renumbered to Section 450-13.

Section 450-3(a): This section was extensively revised. Transformers over 600 volts in unsupervised locations are required to have protection in accordance with Table 450-3(a)(1) unless the required fuse rating or circuit breaker setting does not correspond to a standard rating or setting. Higher fuse or circuit breaker settings in accordance with 450-3(a)(2) are permitted for locations where maintenance and supervision assure that only qualified persons will monitor and service the transformer installation.

Section 450-4(b), (FPN): This is a new fine print note which references Section 210-9 for information on the permitted uses of autotransformers.

SUMMARY OF CODE CHANGES

Section 450-6: The fine print note to this section was changed to full text.

Section 450-8(c): This section was revised to include a reference to Section 110-34.

Section 450-21(a): The first sentence of this section was changed from "transformers" to "dry-type transformers."

Section 450-21(b): The first sentence of this section was changed from "individual transformers" to "individual dry-type transformers."

Section 450-21(b), Exceptions No. 1 and 2: These exceptions were revised to change "higher insulation" to "higher ratings."

Section 450-21(c): This section was revised to change "transformers" to "dry-type transformers."

Section 450-27: The last sentence of this section was changed to a fine print note.

Section 450-42: This section was revised to change the references to a fine print note.

Section 450-43(a): This section was revised to change the reference to NFPA 80 to a fine print note.

ARTICLE 460 - Capacitors
Section 460-25(d): The reference to ANSI C55.1 was changed to a fine print note.

ARTICLE 470 - Resistors and Reactors
No changes.

ARTICLE 480 - Storage Batteries
Section 480-7(a)(2): This section was changed from "suitable nonmetallic materials" to "suitable nonconductive materials."

ARTICLE 500 - Hazardous (Classified) Locations
Section 500-1: This section was shortened to include only the first paragraph. The remainder of Article 500 was renumbered in sequence.

Section 500-2: The second paragraph of former Section 500-1 has now been titled: Location and General Requirements. A new sentence was added to the end of this paragraph to address locations in which pyrophoric materials are the only materials used or handled. These locations would not be classified under Article 500.

Section 500-2: A new sentence was added to the third paragraph to require wiring of intrinsically safe circuits to be physically separated from wiring of all other circuits that are not intrinsically safe.

Section 500-3, (FPN No.2): Class II, Group F was added back into this section. (See changes for Section 300-3, FPN No. 14).

Section 500-3, (FPN No. 12): A reference to NFPA 325M-1986, Fire Hazard Properties of Flammable Liquids, Gases, and Volatile Solids was added to this FPN.

Section 500-3, (FPN No. 14): This is a new fine print note which reintroduces Group F into the Code. Group F has a resistivity greater than 10^2 ohm-centimeter but equal to or less than 10^8 ohm-centimeter.

Two fine print notes from the 1984 Code which reference requirements for Group F locations from the 1981 and previous editions of the Code, have been deleted.

Section 500-3(d), Exception: A new exception was added for Class II, Group F equipment to require equipment subject to overloads to have a maximum temperature of 150°C in normal operation and a maximum temperature which does not exceed the ignition temperature of the specific dust or 200°C, whichever is lower, when installed in Group F locations.

ARTICLE 501 - Class I Locations
Section 501-3(a), (FPN): The second sentence of the last paragraph of Section 501-3(a), which references NFPA 496 has been changed to a fine print note.

Section 501-3(b)(3): A new sentence has been added to this section to permit general-purpose type enclosures for meters, instruments and relays without make-or-break contacts in Class I, Division 2 locations.

Section 501-5(e)(1) and (4): These sections were revised to recognize that conduit seals minimize the passage of gases or vapors; they do not prevent passage of gases or vapors.

Section 501-6(b)(5): This section was revised to permit approved cartridge fuses internal to lighting fixtures as supplementary protection.

Section 501-10(b)(1)a, Exception: An exception was added to exclude motor-mounted anti-condensation space heaters from the rule which requires that they not exceed 80% of the ignition temperature in degrees Celsius at 120% of rated voltage.

Section 501-16(a): Revised to require bonding of all intervening raceways, fittings, boxes, enclosures, etc. between Class I locations and the point of grounding for service equipment.

Section 501-16(b): This section was revised to require internal or external bonding jumpers in parallel with each conduit, and complying with Section 250-79, where flexible metal conduit is used as permitted in Section 501-4(b), and is to be relied upon to complete a sole equipment grounding path. Revision makes it clear this particular requiremnt does not apply to liquidtight flexible metal conduit.

ARTICLE 502 - Class II Locations
Section 502-1: In last paragraph Group F was added since some carbonacious dusts have resisitivities less than 10^5 ohm-centimeter.

Section 502-4(b): This section is revised to permit Types PLTC and TC cables installed in ventilated channel-type cable trays in a single layer with a space of not less than the larger diameter between the two adjacent cables in Class II, Division 2 locations and to provide installation requirements.

Section 502-4(b), Exception: A new exception was added to this section which permits any wiring method suitable for ordinary locations to be used in Class II, Division 2 locations where the wiring cannot, under normal conditions, release sufficient energy to ignite a specific combustible dust mixture by opening, shorting, or grounding.

Section 502-8(b): This section was revised to reference Section 500-3(d) rather than provide a specific temperature.

Section 502-10(b), Exception: This is a new exception which requires metal-enclosed radiant heating panels to be dusttight and marked with a maximum surface temperature in accordance with Section 500-3(d).

Section 502-11(b)(2): Revised to reference Section 500-3(d) rather than provide a specific temperature.

Section 502-14(b)(5): A new section added to require the wiring methods for Class II, Division 2 locations in Section 502-4(b).

Section 502-16(a): Same as change for Section 501-16(a).

Section 502-16(b): Same as change for Section 501-16(b).

Section 502-16(b), Exception: A new exception was added which permits the bonding jumper to be omitted where approved liquidtight flexible metal conduit six feet or less in length and fittings are utilized on nonpower instrumentation-type loads of 10 amperes or less.

ARTICLE 503 - Class III Locations

Section 503-3(a)(1): This section was revised to require dusttight enclosures for all boxes and fittings in Class III, Division 1 locations.

Section 503-3(a)(2): This section was revised to require that where necessary to employ flexible connections, dusttight flexible connectors, liquidtight flexible conduit with approved fittings, or flexible cord approved for extra-hard usage and provided with bushed fittings be used. An additional conductor for grounding is required to be provided in the flexible cord unless other acceptable means of grounding is provided.

Section 503-4: This section was revised to require dusttight enclosures for switches, circuit breakers, motor controllers and fuses rather than the tight metal enclosures formerly required.

Section 503-5: This section was revised to require dusttight enclosures complying with the temperature limitations in Section 503-1 for control transformers and resistors. The exception to this section was deleted.

Section 503-12: The last sentence was editorially revised to change: "lights" to "lighting fixtures."

Section 503-16(a): Same as change for Section 501-16(b).

Section 503-16(a): Last sentence added to the requirements for bonding which had been inadvertently deleted in the 1984 Code and was subsequently added as a TIA.

ARTICLE 510 - Hazardous (Classified) Locations—Specific

No changes.

ARTICLE 511 - Commercial Garages, Repair and Storage

Sections 511-1 and 511-2: Section 511-1 was split into two sections. Section 511-1 consists only of the first sentence of the former scope statement. The remainder of this paragraph is now Section 511-2 with the title: "Locations." The remainder of this article was renumbered in sequence.

Section 511-6: This section was revised to permit the use of electrical nonmetallic tubing in spaces above the Class I locations. The last sentence of this section, which prohibited installation of conductors in any cell, header, or duct which contains a pipe for any service except electrical or compressed air, was deleted. The installation of conductors with any pipe, tube, or equal for steam, water, air, gas, drainage, or any other service other than electrical is now prohibited in Section 300-8.

Section 511-10: A new section was been added to require ground-fault circuit-interrupter protection for personnel for all 125-volt, single-phase, 15- and 20-ampere receptacles for electrical automotive diagnostic equipment, electric hand tools and portable lighting equipment.

ARTICLE 513 - Aircraft Hangers

Section 513-11(b): The word "equipment" was inserted before "grounding conductor" to clarify the Panel's intent.

Section 513-11(c): This section revised to clarify the intent that the requirements apply to equipment that is not identified as suitable for Class I, Division 2 locations.

ARTICLE 514 - Gasoline Dispensing and Service Stations

Section 514-1, (FPN): Revised to identify a new standard for safeguards for gasoline dispensing and service stations. This new Standard is NFPA 30A-1984, Automotive and Marine Service Station Code

Table 514-2: Revised to recognize that NFPA 30A now contains the requirements for automotive and marine service stations.

Section 514-8: The word "threaded" was inserted before "rigid metal conduit" to indicate that threaded connections are warranted for rigid metal conduit as well as intermediate metal conduit. An additional revision extends the Class I, Division 1 location to at least the point of emergence or the conduit or MI cable above grade. This revision restored wording that was inadvertently omitted in the 1981 Code.

ARTICLE 515 - Bulk Storage Plants

Section 515-5: The word "threaded" was added before "rigid metal conduit" to require rigid metal conduit to be threaded.

ARTICLE 516 - Spray Coating, Dipping and Coating Processes

Section 516-1, Title: Changed from Definition to Scope because the present definition is actually a scope statement.

Section 516-4(b): The fine print note in the 1984 NEC was changed to a second paragraph as it contains requirements.

Section 516-7(a): Electrical nonmetallic tubing was added to the wiring methods permitted above the Class I and Class II locations. The last sentence was deleted as similar requirements are now contained in Section 300-8.

ARTICLE 517 - Health Care Facilities

Section 517-1, (FPN's): A new fine print note was added to this section to indicate that this article does not apply to veterinary facilities. The second fine print note was revised to indicate that performance, maintenance and testing criteria can be found in the appropriate health care facilities documents. The last paragraph of Section 517-1 was relocated to Section 517-3.

Section 517-2, Definitions: Several definitions were changed or added to coordinate with changes in NFPA 99-1984.

Anesthetizing Location: The phrase "including the use of such agents for relative analgesia" was added.

Electrical Life Support Equipment: This is a new definition for electrically powered equipment whose continuous operation is necessary to maintain a patient's life.

Flammable Anesthetizing Location: This is a complete revision of the definition.

Health Care Facilities: This definition was revised to include supervisory care facilities and ambulatory health care facilities.

Life Safety Branch: This definition was revised to indicate that the transformer switch or switches are automatically connected to the alternate power sources during interruption of normal power.

Patient Equipment Grounding Point: The phrase "or for grounding other items in order to eliminate electromagnetic interference problems" was added to this definition.

Patient Vicinity: The phrase "Typically in a patient room," was added to the beginning of the second sentence.

Reference Grounding Point: This definition was simplified to indicate that the reference grounding point is an equipment grounding bus and is a convenient collection point for grounding wires and bonding wires where used.

Selected Receptacles: The phrase "minimal electrical receptacles" was revised to "a minimum number of electrical."

Section 517-11: Revised to reflect the Panel's desire for redundant grounding with an insulated copper conductor.

Section 517-11, Exception No. 1: This exception recognizes cable types that meet the preferred redundant grounding. The existing Exception No. 1 becomes Exception No. 2, the existing Exception No. 2 becomes Exception No. 3.

Section 517-13: This section was editorially revised to change "receptacles with insulated grounds" to "receptacles with insulated grounding terminals" to comply with the description in Section 250-74.

Sections 517-30, 517-31 and 517-32: These sections were revised in accordance with TIA 70-84-2. These sections are intended to eliminate conflicts with Chapter 8, Essential Electrical Systems for Health Care Facilities in NFPA 99-1984.

Section 517-40, Exception a: This exception was changed to apply to electrical life support equipment only, not electrical and mechanical life support devices as covered in the 1984 Code.

Section 517-40, Exception c: "Four or more hours" changed to "or at least 1½ hours."

Section 517-43: This is a new section with an exception titled Wiring, Grounding, and Receptacles. This section was added to clarify the intent of the Panel which is to require an assured ground by using an insulated grounding conductor in the areas specified. The exception applies to patient sleeping areas wired in accordance with the requirements of Chapters 1 through 4.

Section 517-44(a): The last sentence of this section was deleted.

Section 517-44(b): This section was revised to define a small facility as one with a maximum demand on the essential electrical system of 150 kVA. The diagrams were revised to change "minimum" to "small."

Section 517-45, (FPN): This is a new fine print note which indicates that the Life Safety Branch is called the emergency system in NFPA 99-1984.

Section 517-45(g): This section was added to indicate that elevator cab lighting control and communication systems shall be connected to the life safety branch.

Section 517-46(a)(3): This section in the 1984 *NEC* has been deleted.

Section 517-46(b)(2): A new sentence was added to the end of this section to indicate that elevator cab lighting control and signaling systems are required to be connected to the life safety branch.

Section 517-60(a)(4): This section was revised to add a definition for small facilities as those in which the maximum demand on the essential electrical system is 150 kVA. The titles of the diagrams were revised to change "Minimum" to "Small."

Section 517-60(b), Exception No. 3: This is a new exception to mechanical protection of the emergency system for branch circuit wiring as permitted in Sections 517-101(b)(1) and (c)(1).

Section 517-62(f): This section was added to indicate that the life safety branch shall provide power for elevator cab lighting control and signaling systems.

Section 517-63(a): This section was revised to include fixed equipment and special power circuits to the list of items to be connected to the critical branch circuit.

Section 517-63(a)(1): Receptacles and fixed equipment were added to the items in anesthetizing locations to be connected to the critical branch circuit.

Section 517-63(a)(2): This section was revised to delete the words "required in anesthetizing locations."

Section 517-63(a)(9): A new sentence was added which permits single-phase fractional horsepower exhaust fan motors which interlock with 3-phase motors on the equipment to be connected to the critical branch.

Section 517-63(b), (FPN): A new fine print note was added which recommends an analysis of the consequences of a failure between the area being supplied by a transfer switch and the transfer switch when the area is supplied with only critical branch circuit power.

Section 517-64(a)(1): This section was revised to indicate that central suction systems are permitted to be connected to critical branch circuits.

Section 517-64(b)(1), Exception: This exception was revised to include infection isolation rooms in the areas not requiring heating under specified conditions.

Section 517-64(b)(2): The second sentence of this section was deleted as the requirements for cab lighting control and signaling systems are now required to be connected to the life safety branch.

Section 517-64(b)(3): This section was revised as follows: infant nurseries was deleted "special and intensive care units" was added. "Isolation rooms" was expanded to "isolation rooms constructed specifically for infection control."

Section 517-64(b)(7): Other loads deemed necessary by the hospital was deleted and (b)(8) and (b)(9) renumbered.

Part F, (FPN): A new fine print note was added which refers to NFPA 99-1984.

Section 517-80(b): This section was editorially revised to conform to with NFPA 99-1984.

Section 517-81: The title of this section was changed to "Grounding."

Section 517-81(a): This is a new section which requires, in addition to Section 517-11, that all branch circuits supplying patient care areas be provided with a path for ground-fault current by installation of rigid metal conduit, intermediate metal conduit, electrical metallic tubing, Type MI cable, Type MC cable, or Type AC cable where the outer metal jacket is an approved grounding means. It also requires that the integrity of the ground path be verified.

Section 517-83(a), Exception No. 2: Psychiatric, substance abuse, and rehabilitation hospitals were added to this exception.

Section 517-83(b), Exceptions No. 1 and No. 2: Exception No. 1 is a new exception to the requirements for the minimum number of receptacles located in patient bed located in general care areas. The exceptions to the rule apply to psychiatric, substance abuse, and rehabilitation hospitals meeting the requirements of the exception in Section 517-40. The existing exception was deleted and a new Exception No. 2 for psychiatric security rooms was added. This new exception states that psychiatric security rooms shall not be required to have receptacle outlets installed in the room.

Section 517-84(a): This section was revised to require at least one of the branch circuits to be supplied from the normal system and to require at least one branch circuit from the emergency system to supply an outlet or outlets only at that bed location.

Section 517-84(b): This section was revised to require receptacles to be listed "Hospital Grade" and so identified.

Section 517-84(e), (FPN): This fine print note indicates that that although it is permitted to run the grounding conductor outside of conduits, it is safer to run them within the power

conductors to provide better protection in case of a second ground fault.

Section 517-84(f): This section was revised to clarify that the reference grounding points are for branch circuits.

Section 517-100(b): The last sentence of this section was deleted.

Section 517-101(a)(1): "8 volts" was changed to "10 volts" to correlate with NFPA 99-1984.

Section 517-101(c)(1): This section was expanded to permit the use of Type AC cable with an insulated equipment grounding conductor in other-than-hazardous anesthetizing locations.

Section 517-103: This section was revised to add "metal-sheathed cables" to the list of items to be grounded in any anesthetizing area.

Section 517-103, Exception: "8 volts" was changed to "10 volts" to correlate with NFPA 99-1984.

Section 517-104(a)(1): Revised to change "an anesthetizing" to "a flammable anesthetizing" in line 2 and to change "other-than-anesthetizing" to "other-than-flammable anesthetizing" in line 4 to correlate with NFPA 99-1984.

Section 517-104(b)(1): The minimum fault hazard current for alarm has been changed from 0.7 milliamperes to 3.7 milliamperes. The minimum current at which the line isolation monitor is to alarm was changed from 1.7 milliamperes to 5.0 milliamperes.

Section 517-104(b)(2), Exception: A new exception was added to permit a line isolation monitor of the low impedance type.

Section 517-104(c)(2), Exception: A new exception was added which indicates that Parts c. and d. shall not apply in other-than-hazardous (classified) locations.

Section 517-105(a)(1): "8 volts" was changed to "10 volts" to correlate with NFPA 99-1984.

ARTICLE 518 - Places of Assembly

Section 518-1: This section was revised to include only the first paragraph. The last three paragraphs become new Section 518-2 and Sections 518-2 and 518-3 were renumbered.

Section 518-2: The last paragraph of this section was expanded to explain which equipment and wiring shall be installed in accordance with Article 520.

ARTICLE 520 - Theaters and Similar Locations

Section 520-4, Exception No. 2: This exception was revised to clarify the intent and to prohibit fastening of flexible cables and cords by uninsulated staples or nailing.

Section 520-26(c): This new section was added to provide requirements for intermediate (patch panel) stage switchboards provided for the interconnection of stage lighting circuits.

Section 520-27(b): This section was revised to better define multiple feeders. In addition a new requirement was added to require the neutral of multiple feeders supplying solid state dimmer equipment, where combined, to have an ampacity sufficient to carry the maximum unbalanced current supplied by multiple feeder conductors in the same raceway (but not greater than the ampacity of the neutral supplying the primary state switchboard). This section was also revised to make it clear that only paralleled neutral conductors are required to be the same length.

Section 520-27(c): This section was added to provide requirements for separate feeders to a single primary stage switchboard (dimmer bank).

Section 520-44(b): This section was revised to add Types G and W flexible cables.

Section 520-46: Title was revised to "Connector Strips, Drop Boxes, and Stage Pockets." The text was revised to permit pendant receptacles.

Section 520-50: This new section was added to provide requirements for road show connection panels.

Section 520-51: A new sentence was added to the end of this section to indicate that the neutral of feeders supplying solid-state, 3-phase, 4-wire dimmer systems are considered current-carrying conductors.

Section 520-52: There are two changes in this section. The first change was adding the word "protective" between "overcurrent" and "devices." The second change was deleting the last sentence.

Section 520-53: The title of this section was changed to "Construction and Feeders" and the word "feeders" was included in the first sentence.

Section 520-53(g): The phrase "independent circuit" was changed to "individual branch circuit."

Section 520-53(h): This section was revised to include Types G and W cables and to permit the supply cable to terminate in a connector assembly identified for the purpose. A new second paragraph was added to require that single conductor cables be a minimum No. 1 AWG in size, that single conductor cables for supply be of the same length, type, size, and be grouped together, but not bundled. The equipment grounding conductor is permitted to be of a different type provided it meets the other requirements of this section and Section 250-95. Neutral and grounding conductors are required to be identified per Section 310-12.

Section 520-53(i): A new sentence was added to reemphasize the requirements of Section 300-20(b).

Section 520-53(n): A new sentence was added which requires the neutral to be sized as a current-carrying conductor.

Section 520-53(n), Exception: This exception was revised to delete the rule which required the neutral conductor to have an ampacity 100 per cent larger than the required size of the ungrounded conductors.

Section 520-62(b): This section was completely revised to reflect current practice. In addition, requirements for cords or cables supplying pendant receptacles were added.

Section 520-62(c): This section was revised to replace the word "receptacles" with "circuits connected to the busbar."

Section 520-62(e): This new section provides requirements for installation of cables in plugging boxes.

Section 520-64, (FPN): A new fine print note was added to refer to Section 520-68, Exception No. 2 for insulation types required on single conductors.

Section 520-67: This section was revised to require ac multipole connectors to be polarized and comply with Sections 410-56(e) and 410-58.

Section 520-68: This section was revised to add Types G and W cables. New exceptions were added to permit single conductors under specified conditions.

Section 520-69: This is a new section to provide requirements for the use of adaptors, two-fers and other single and multiple circuit outlet devices. Each receptacle and its corresponding cable are required to have the same current and voltage rating as the plug supplying it. In addition the section was revised to add "exposed" between "all" and "incandescent."

Section 520-72: This section was revised to make it clear it applies only to exposed lamps.

Section 520-81: This section was revised to insert "and metal sheathed cable" after "raceway."

ARTICLE 530 - Motion Picture and Television Studios and Similar Locations

Section 530-14: This section was revised to limit the requirement to dc plugging boxes.

Section 530-18, (FPN): This fine print note was revised to indicate that the short duration of filming periods is 20 minutes.

Section 530-18(b): A new sentence was added to the end of this section to indicate that the short term ratings are not permitted for equipment operated in excess of 20 minutes.

Section 530-18(d): This section was revised to indicate that plugging boxes are not permitted on ac systems.

Section 530-20: This section was revised to include Type MI cable. In addition, the last sentence was revised to indicate that this section applies to 150 volts dc to ground.

Section 530-21: A new sentence was added to indicate that all ac plugs and receptacles shall be grounded and polarized.

Part E: The title of this part has been changed to "Celluose Nitrate Film Storage Vaults" as the requirements of this part now pertain only to celluose nitrate film storage.

Section 530-51: This section was editorially revised to indicate that the lamps shall be installed in rigid fixtures.

Section 530-52: This section was revised to indicate that the requirements apply only to celluose nitrate film storage.

Section 530-66: This section was revised to add a reference to Article 250.

ARTICLE 540 - Motion Picture Projectors
Editorial changes only.

ARTICLE 545 - Manufactured Building

Section 545-4(a): This section was revised to indicate that raceway and cable wiring methods and other such systems and fittings used in manufactured buildings shall be listed.

Section 545-5: A new fine print note was added which references Section 310-10 for temperature limitation of conductors.

Section 545-9: The title of this section was revised to delete the word "outlet."

Section 545-9(a): This section was revised to indicate that boxes shall be tested, identified, and listed to applicable standards.

Section 545-9(b): The words "outlet" and "approved" were deleted from this section.

Section 545-10: This section was revised to replace "and approved" with "identified and listed."

Section 545-13: This section was revised to replace "tested and approved" with "tested, identified and listed."

ARTICLE 547 - Agricultural Buildings

Section 547-2: Former Section 547-1(c) was revised to become Section 547-2, and subsequent sections were renumbered.

Section 547-4: Copper SE was added to the list of approved wiring methods for agricultural buildings.

Section 547-4, (FPN): A new fine print note was added referencing Sections 300-7 and 347-9, which provide requirements for raceways exposed to widely different temperatures.

Section 547-4(a): This section was revised to indicate that all boxes and fittings are required to comply with Section 547-5.

Section 547-4(b): This section was revised to indicate that flexible connections, dusttight flexible connectors, liquidtight flexible metal conduit, or flexible cord shall be listed and identified for hard usage.

Section 547-5: The title of this section was revised to delete the word "motor."

Section 547-8: This section was completely revised and greatly expanded to provide requirements for bonding and equipotential planes. A new fine print note was added to reference Section 250-21 for objectional current over grounding conductors.

Section 547-8, Exception: An exception was added which permits installations without a main bonding jumper under specified conditions.

Section 547-8(b): This is a new section which provides installation requirements for equipotential planes which consist of wire mesh or other concrete embedded elements.

Section 547-8(b), (FPN): A new fine print note was added which explains the advantages of the equipotential plane.

Section 547-8(c): This is a new section which provides requirements for separate equipment grounding conductors.

Section 547-8, (FPN): This is a new fine print note which advises that ground resistances lower than required by Article 250 Part H may reduce potential differences in livestock facilites.

ARTICLE 550 - Mobile Homes and Mobile Home Parks

General: Article 550 was revised in all sections to change "115-volt" to "120-volt," "115/230-volt" to "120/240-volt" and "230-volt" to "240-volt," with appropriate changes in the calculations.

Section 550-1: This section was revised to make the first paragraph (550-1(a)) the scope of Article 550. The second sentence is now Section 550-3. Section 550-1(b) became new Section 550-4, "General Requirements" was added to the subheadings and present text of Sections 550-1(b),(c),(d) and (e).

Section 550-2 Definitions Feeder Assembly: This definition was revised to indicate that the power-supply cord shall be listed for mobile home use.

Section 550-5(a): This section was revised to indicate that a power-supply cord shall be a listed 50-ampere mobile home power-supply cord.

Section 550-5, Exception: This exception was revised to indicate that the 40-ampere cord referenced in the exception shall be a listed mobile home power-supply cord. Former paragraphs (c), (b), and (e) were changed from subsections to paragraphs which are part of Section 550-5(b). Paragraph (f) was changed to (c) accordingly.

Section 550-5(i): This section was revised to delete the word "metal" between "or" and "raceway."

Section 550-5(i)(2): The words "rigid nonmetallic conduit" were added to this section.

Section 550-6(a): This section was revised to add to the end of the fourth sentence: "in accordance with Section 550-9(a)."

Section 550-8(a): This section was revised to include 20-ampere receptacles.

Section 550-8(c): This section was revised to require a grounding-type receptacle outlet to be provided for each cord-connected fixed appliance installed.

Section 550-9(a)(1): This section was revised to require that pendant-type fixtures or pendant cords be listed and identified for the interconnection of building components.

Section 550-9(a)(2): This section was revised to require lighting fixtures installed over a bathtub or in a shower stall to be listed for wet locations.

Section 550-10(a): This is a new section which provides requirements for nonmetallic boxes.

Section 550-10(b): This section was revised to change "conduit" to "raceways."

Sections 550-10(c) and (e): These sections were revised to change "metal-clad" to "metal-covered."

Section 550-10(f): This section was revised to change the title from "Metal Conduit" to "Conduit" and the requirements revised to provide requirements for metal conduit and nonmetallic conduit.

Section 550-10(h): This section was revised to include pull and junction boxes.

Section 550-10(i)(1), Exception: This exception was revised to include rigid nonmetallic conduit.

Section 550-10(k)(1): This section was revised to indicate that the fittings and connectors intended to be concealed at the time of assembly shall be listed and identified for the interconnection.

SUMMARY OF CODE CHANGES

Section 550-11(a)(2): This section was formerly Section 550-9. It was revised to include Type MC cable. The last paragraph was deleted.

Section 550-11(c)(2): This section was revised to require the grounding terminals to be listed as pressure-terminal connectors recognized for the wire size used.

Section 550-12(a), Exception: This exception was revised to indicate that it applies only to listed fixtures or appliances.

Section 550-15(a): This section was revised to indicate that it applies to devices listed for outdoor use.

Section 550-22(a): This section was revised to clarify that when mobile homes having a calculated load greater than 16,000 VA are to be served, the greater load is to be used for applying demand factors.

Table 550-22: This table was revised to delete the Column "Volt-Amperes for Mobile Home Site (Min)."

Section 550-23(c): This section was revised to require a listed GFCI.

Section 550-23(e): This is a new section which was added to require that mobile home disconnecting means be located not less than 2 feet nor more than 6½ feet above the ground or working platform. Other sections following were renumbered.

Section 550-24: This section was revised to clarify the intent that coloring or painting be done during manufacturing so the coloring or painting would be a part of the manufacturing process for durability, and would not cover or conceal the labeling and identification of the product.

ARTICLE 551 - Recreational Vehicles and Recreational Vehicle Parks

General: Article 551 was revised in all sections to change "115-volt" to "120-volt," "115/230-volt" to "120/240-volt," and 230-volt" to "240-volt" with appropriate changes in calculations where necessary.

Section 551-1: This section was revised to make Section 551-1 the scope with remaining material in Sections 551-1(b) and (c) becoming new Sections 551-4(a) and (b) respectively. The last sentence of Section 551-1(a) has been relocated to become Section 551-3. The remainder of the article was renumbered.

Section 551-2 Definitions: A new definition was added for "Frame."

Part A: Relocated so that it no longer includes the scope statement or definitions. Part A now begins with Section 551-3.

Section 551-5(a): A new sentence was added to this section which requires circuits supplying lights subject to federal or state regulations to comply with the applicable government regulations as well as the *NEC*.

Section 551-5(b)(1) Exceptions: This section was revised to clarify the intent and to require that the connections be made in an accessible location with copper conductors and copper or copper alloy terminals.

Section 551-5(b)(2): This section was revised to require listed conductors No. 6 through 18 AWG meeting the stated conditions if Types HDT, SGT, SGR, or SXL meeting SAE requirements are not used.

Section 551-5(c)(2): The word "approved" was deleted from this section.

Section 551-5(c)(4): This section was revised to change "external toothed lock washer" to "internal-external toothed lock washer."

Section 551-5(c)(5): This section was revised to require a larger bonding conductor from the battery than No. 8 AWG if the power lead from the battery exceeds No. 8 AWG.

Section 551-5(g): This section was revised to require that the lighting fixtures be listed.

Section 551-5(h): This section was revised to permit 12-volt receptacles that will accept and energize cigarette lighters to be installed in assemblies which are identified by the manufacturer of the product as thermally protected.

Section 551-6(b): This exception was revised so that it applies only to converters supplied as an integral part of a listed appliance.

Section 551-6(d): This section was revised to indicate that the dual voltage fixtures or appliances shall be listed for dual voltage.

Section 551-7(b): The word "approved" was deleted from this section. In addition, the last sentence was deleted.

Section 551-7(d): The word "approved" was deleted from this section.

Section 551-7(e): This section was revised to update requirements to current installation practices.

Section 551-8(a): This section was revised to require listed equipment.

Sections 551-8(c) and (d): These sections were added to cover other sources of ac power such as inverters or motor generators, and to require that equipment, if not integral with the listed power source, be installed to insure that current-carrying conductors from the other sources of ac power and from an outside square are not connected to the vehicle circuit at the same time.

Section 551-8(e): This section was added to require vehicles with only one 15- or 20-ampere branch circuit as permitted in Sections 351-10(a) and (b) to be equipped with ground-fault circuit-interrupter protection for personnel.

Section 551-9(c), Exception: A new exception was added after the last paragraph to exempt recreational vehicles with one 15- or 20-ampere circuit which is provided with GFCI protection for personnel at the point where the power supply assembly terminates, from the requirements of this section.

Sections 551-12(a),(b),(c) and (d): These sections were revised to require listed power-supply assemblies.

Section 551-13(a): This section was revised to clarify the intent.

Section 551-14(a): This section was revised to change "Dual-Supply" to "Multiple Supply," and "generator" to "alternate power source."

Section 551-12(c): This section was revised to change "two" to "multiple."

Section 551-14(d): This section was revised to include alternate power-supply sources exceeding 30 amperes.

Section 551-15(a)(1): This section was revised to require that the attachment plug cap be a listed type.

Section 551-15(a)(2): This section was revised to delete the word "approved."

Section 551-15(d): This section was revised to change "approved material" to "suitable material."

Section 551-16(a): This section was revised to read as follows: "Rigid metal conduit, intermediate metal conduit, electrical metallic tubing, flexible metal conduit, metal-clad cable, Type AC cable, and nonmetallic-sheathed cable shall be permitted. An equipment grounding conductor shall be provided in accordance with Section 250-91."

Section 551-14(b): This section was revised to clarify the intent.

Section 551-16(c): This section was revised to add "rigid and nonmetallic conduit."

Section 551-16(d): This section was revised to delete the word "outlet."

Section 551-16(e): This section was revised to clarify the intent.

Section 551-16(f): This section was revised to clarify the intent.

Section 551-16(g): This section was revised to add Type AC cable.

Section 551-16(j), Exception: This exception was revised to indicate that the exception applies to wiring devices.

Section 551-16(k): This section was revised to change "conduit" to "raceways."

Section 551-16(l): This section was revised to require nonmetallic faceplates to be listed.

Section 551-16(n): This section was revised to add rigid nonmetallic conduit.

Section 551-16(o): This section was revised to indicate that fittings and connectors for the interconnection of building components shall be listed and identified for the use.

Section 551-16(p)(1), Exception: This new exception was added to cover installations where the attachment plug and cord are located within the vehicle's interior.

Section 551-17: This section was revised to delete the word "outlet."

Section 551-19: The second sentence of this section was revised to clarify the intent and to include boxes containing devices other than receptacles.

Section 551-22(b): This section was revised to require ground-fault circuit-interupter protection for 120-volt shower fixtures.

Section 551-22(c): This section was revised to require outdoor outlets, fixtures, air-cooling equipment etc. be listed for outdoor use.

Section 551-24(c)(1): This section was revised to add Type AC cable.

Section 551-24(c)(2): This section was revised to identify the grounding conductor as an equipment grounding conductor,

Section 551-24(c)(3): This section was revised to change "grounding wire" to "equipment grounding conductor." In addition, the section

was revised to require that the grounding means (plate) be listed.

Section 551-24(f): The word "equipment" was added before the words "grounding conductor."

Section 551-25(c): This section was revised to require listed pressure terminal connectors for grounding terminals.

Section 551-40: This section in the 1984 NEC, which contained an application and scope statement was deleted.

Section 551-42: This section was revised to require every recreational vehicle site with electrical supply to be equipped with at least one 15- or 20-ampere, 125-volt receptacle. The second paragraph was revised to require listed GFCI protection for personnel.

Section 551-44(d), (FPN): A new fine print note was added to indicate that because of the long circuit lengths typical in most recreational vehicle parks, feeder conductor sizes found in the ampacity tables may be inadequate to maintain voltage regulation. The note also indicates that the total circuit voltage drop is a summation of the voltage drops for each serial circuit segment, where the load for each segment is calculated using the load that segment sees and the demand factors of Section 551-44(a).

Section 551-48(a): This section was revised to change "grounding conductor" to "equipment grounding conductor."

Section 551-50: The title to this section was changed to "Clearance for Overhead Conductors." Subsections (a) and (b) were combined into one section for vertical and horizontal clearances.

Section 551-50, (FPN): A new fine print note was added which references the National Electrical Safety Code, ANSI C2-1984.

Section 551-51(a): This section was revised to require all splices and taps be made in approved junction boxes or by use of material listed and identified for the purpose.

Article 553 - Floating Buildings

This is a new article which replaces former Article 555, Part B, Floating Dwelling Units. It applies these and new requirements to all floating buildings, not just floating dwelling units.

Article 555 - Marinas and Boatyards

Section 555-1, (FPN): The fine print note to this section was deleted.

Section 555-2, (FPN): The second sentence of Section 555-2 was changed to a fine print note.

Section 555-3: The first sentence of this section was deleted and new paragraphs were added requiring that where shore power is provided, 20-ampere receptacles be provided for accomodations for boats 20 feet or less in length and 30-ampere receptacles be provided for accomodations for boats longer than 20 feet.

Section 555-5: The demand factors in this section were revised to provide a more uniform gradient of demand factor.

Section 555-5, (FPN): This is a new fine print note which cautions that the demand factors in

Section 555-5 may be inadequate in areas of extreme hot or cold temperatures.

Section 555-6(6): The words "this Code" were changed to "Chapter 3 of this Code."

Part B: Part B of this article was deleted.

ARTICLE 600 - Electric Signs and Outline Lighting

Section 600-5, Exception No. 1 The words "they need not be grounded" have been deleted.

Section 600-6(b): The last sentence has been revised to clarify that the required 20-ampere circuit is not permitted to supply other loads.

Section 600-8(g): Revised by deleting the last sentence.

Section 600-21(a): Revised to add liquidtight flexible nonmetallic conduit and metal poles complying with all requirements of new Section 410-15(b).

Section 600-21(c): Revised to change "approved" to "listed."

Section 600-21(c), Exception: Revised to include rigid nonmetallic conduit.

ARTICLE 604 - Manufactured Wiring Systems

Section 604-3, Exception: Revised to delete "in an approved manner."

Section 604-6(a): Revised to subdivide the section into paragraphs (1), (2) and (3). The word "equipment" added before the word "grounding" in paragraphs (1) and (2), and the words "or bare" were added after "insulated" in paragraph (2), and "or conduit" added in paragraph (3).

ARTICLE 605 - Office Furnishings

Section 605-5: The words "listed and" have been added after "equipment," requiring lighting accesories to be listed as well as identified for the use.

Section 605-5(b): The maximum cord length was changed from 8 to 9 feet.

ARTICLE 610- Cranes and Hoists

Section 610-12(a): Nonmetallic-sheathed cable was deleted from this section.

Section 610-14(e)(2): Revised by deleting the phrase "on a crane or hoist" between "conductors" and "shall."

Section 610-61: A comma was placed after "attachments" and the comma after "surfaces" was deleted to clarify that "having metal-to-metal bearing surfaces" modifies "moving parts" and not "other than removable accessories."

ARTICLE 620 - Elevators, Dumbwaiters, Escalators, and Moving Walks

Section 620-11: Section 610-11(a) of the 1984 Code was deleted, and remaining sections were renumbered.

Section 620-11(a). The term "moisture resistant" has been deleted, and a requirement that conductors be Type SF or equivalent added.

Section 620-11(c): The term "moisture resistant" has been deleted.

Section 620-11(d): The words "Thickness of" have been deleted from the title and a new

second paragraph has been added listing required insulation types.

Section 620-21: First paragraph was revised to include rigid nonmetallic conduit. Second paragraph was revised to include pumping unit motors and valves.

Section 620-21, Exception No. 1: Second sentence was revised to include escalators and moving walks when the low voltage cable (24 volts or less) is supported and protected from physical abuse.

Section 620-21, Exception No. 3: Revised to refer to hard service and junior hard service cords listed in Table 400-4 for the flexible connections between the fixed car wiring and devices on the car doors or gates, and to permit other than those types if listed for this use.

Section 620-21, Exception No. 4: Revised to permit flexible metal conduit or Type AC cable up to six feet in length between control panels and machine motors, machine brakes, motor-generator sets and pumping unit motors and valves.

Section 620-21, Exception No. 6: A new exception was added permitting hard service cords as flexible connections on escalators or moving walk control panels and disconnecting means where the entire control panel and disconnecting means are arranged for removal from machine spaces as permitted in Section 620-72, Exception.

Section 620-22: Revised to delete "on multicar installations."

Section 620-31: The word "conduits" was deleted and replaced with the word "raceways."

Section 620-36: Last sentence was revised to permit shielded conductors and coaxial cables for telephone, audio, video, or higher frequency communication circuits.

Section 620-37: The second sentence was revised by replacing "conduit" with "raceways" and to include wiring for heating and air conditioning, and pit sump pumps.

Section 620-37, Exception: Revised by deleting "or other purposes."

Section 620-41: A change was made in No. (1) to replace "fillers" with "members."

Part F: This title was changed to read: "Disconnecting Means and Control."

Section 620-51(b)(1): First sentence was revised to cover both ac and dc direct drive controlled elevators.

Section 620-81: The word "conduit" was changed to "raceways."

Sections 620-82 and 620-83: The phrase "in accordance with Article 250" was added to the end of both sections.

Section 620-85: Section 680-25 in the 1984 NEC was deleted.

Section 620-101, Exception: The word "power" between "the" and "side" was changed to "line."

ARTICLE 630 - Electric Welders

Sections 630-12, 630-22, and 630-32: These sections have been revised by inserting "standard" following "higher" in the last phrase of each section.

Part E, Sections 630-41 and 630-42: A new Part E has been added to provide requirements for welding cables and for the safe use of cabletrays to route welding cables.

ARTICLE 640 - Sound-Recording and Similar Equipment

Section 640-3: The heading revised by replacing "Raceway" with "Conduit or Tubing." This same change incorporated in the main rule and the two exceptions.

Section 640-4, Exception c: Revised to delete the last sentence.

Section 640-4, Exception d: Revised by inserting "and bonded" following "grounded" in the first sentence. The word "equipment" was inserted ahead of "grounding conductor" in the second and last sentences.

Section 640-6: Revised by replacing "conduit" with "raceway" and deleting "metal" before "enclosure."

ARTICLE 645 - Electronic Computer/Data Processing Equipment

Section 645-1: The title and scope of this article have been revised to correlate with NFPA 75, by including electronic computers.

Section 645-3: Revised by adding a new sentence to permit a single means to control both the electronic equipment and air-conditioning system disconnecting means.

ARTICLE 650 - Organs

Section 650-1: Revised by transferring the second sentence to a new Section 650-2 and renumbering the article sequentially.

ARTICLE 660 - X-ray Equipment

Section 660-4(b): In the first sentence "medical" was deleted following "transportable."

ARTICLE 665 - Induction and Dielectric Heating Equipment

No changes.

ARTICLE 668 - Electrolytic Cells

Section 668-3(b), (FPN): The word "shall" was deleted.

ARTICLE 669 - Electroplating

No changes.

ARTICLE 670 - Industrial Machinery

Section 670-1: The title, scope and fine print note have been revised to correlate with NFPA 79.

Section 670-2: A new second paragraph added to define mass production industrial equipment.

Section 670-4(a): The 25 percent changed to 125 percent.

Section 670-4(a), (FPN): A new fine print note was added to reference Tables 310-16 through 310-31 for ampacity ratings of conductors rated 600 volts and below.

Section 670-4(b): Reference to NFPA 79 was deleted.

ARTICLE 675 - Electrically Driven or Controlled Irrigation Machines

Section 675-4(c): This section has been revised by replacing "approved" with "identified."

ARTICLE 680 - Swimming Pools, Fountains, and Similar Installations

Section 680-1: Revised by adding hydromassage bathtubs.

Section 680-1, (FPN): Revised by deleting "shall" in two places.

Section 680-4: The definition of hydromassage bathtubs has been revised by inserting "permanently installed" ahead of "bathtub."

The definition of spa or hot tub has been revised to include a tub for recreational or therapeutic use, not located in health care facilities.

Section 680-6(a)(1), Exception: Revised to clarify that receptacles that provide power for water-pump motors for permanently installed pools are permitted to be installed between 5 and 10 feet from the inside walls of the pool, provided they are of the single and locking and grounding type, and protected by a GFCI.

Section 680-6(a)(3), (FPN): Revised to make it clear that hinged or sliding doors, and windows, are considered effective permanent barriers.

Section 680-9: A new second paragraph added to require that the ampacity of the branch-circuit conductors, and the rating or setting of overcurrent protective devices, be not less than 125% of the total load of the nameplate rating of pool water heaters.

Section 680-20(a): The second sentence of this section deleted.

Section 680-20(b)(1): This section has been split into four paragraphs and editorially revised.

Section 680-20(c), Exception: A new exception has been added permitting electrical metallic tubing to be used to protect conductors where installed on or within buildings.

Section 680-21(a)(1): Revised to require the junction box to be equipped with threaded hubs or bosses for conduit entries.

Section 680-21(b)(1): Revised to require enclosures to be equipped with threaded hubs or bosses.

Section 680-23(b): In the second sentence, "solid" was deleted.

Section 680-25(b)(2), Exception No. 2: Revised to include a snap switch and the outlet box for a snap switch.

Section 680-25(c), Exception No. 2: The liquidtight flexible conduit has been identified as metal.

Section 680-25(c), Exception No. 3: A new exception was added to permit any of the wiring methods recognized in Chapter 3 in the interior of a one-family dwelling unit.

Section 680-25(c), Exception No. 4: A new exception was added to permit flexible cord in accordance with Section 680-7.

Part D: Title was changed by deleting "Hydromassage Bathtubs."

Section 680-41, Exception: Revised by changing "connected with a flexible" to "cord-and plug-connected."

Section 680-41(a), Exception: This exception has been deleted.

Section 680-41(a)(2): Revised by changing the 20 feet to 10 feet.

Section 680-41(b)(1), Exception No. 2: A new exception was added permitting a lighting fixture to be installed less than 7½ feet over a spa or hot tub if it is a recessed fixture with a glass or plastic lens and nonmetallic trim suitable for use in wet locations, or surface-mounted fixture with a glass or plastic globe and nonmetallic body suitable for use in wet locations. In either case, the fixture is required to be protected by a GFCI.

Section 680-41(c), Exception: This exception has been deleted.

Section 680-41(h): A new section has been added to require electric spa or hot tub water heaters to be listed and have the heating elments to be subdivided into loads not exceeding 48 amperes and protected at not more than 60 amperes. The ampacity of the branch-circuit conductors and the rating or setting of overcurrent protected devices shall be not less than 125% of the total load of the nameplate rating.

Section 680-51(d): Phrase "if the water level drops below normal" replaced with "when not submerged."

Section 680-52(b): In the first sentence "watertight" change to "submersible."

Section 680-52, (FPN): A new fine print note was added referencing Section 370-13 for support of enclosures.

Section 680-54(1): Revised to include electric equipment located within the fountain.

Part G: This is a new part added to cover hydromassage bathtubs and their associated electric components, which are required to have GFCI protection. Other electric equipment such as lighting fixtures, receptacles, and switches located in the same room, and not directly associated with a hydromassage bathtub are permitted to be installed in accordance with the requirements of Chapters 1-4 covering the installation of that equipment in bathrooms.

ARTICLE 685 - Integrated Electrical Systems

Section 685-2: Revised by adding a reference to more than one building or other structure, Section 230-84(a), Exception No. 2; and a reference to the point of connection of interconnected power production sources Section 705-12, Exception No. 1.

ARTICLE 690 - Solar Photovoltaic Systems

Section 690-7(d), (FPN): A new fine print note was added referencing Sections 110-17 for guarding of live parts, and 210-6 for voltage to ground and between conductors.

Section 690-14, Exception No. 2: Revised to clarify intent.

Section 690-41: Revised to require system grounding for two-wire systems only if rated over 50 volts.

Section 690-41, (FPN): Revised to reference the first fine print note under Section 250-1.

Section 690-61: Revised to clarify that the other sources to which the photovoltaic system may be connected to may be a stand-alone system, not a electric utility system. A new paragraph has been added to permit interactive systems to operate as a stand-alone system to supply premises loads.

Section 690-61, (FPN): A new fine print note was added to reference Article 705.

Section 690-64: This new section was added to cover how and where the connection of the power production source is to be made when it is not a stand-alone system.

Part H, Sections 690-71, 690-72, 690-73: This is a new part added to provide the installation requirements for storage batteries used in conjunction with solar photovoltaic systems.

ARTICLE 700 - Emergency Systems

Section 700-1, (FPN): A new fine print note has been added to this section to reference NFPA 110.

Section 700-5(b): The title of this section has been revised to: "Selective Load Pickup, Load Shedding and Peak Load Shaving." A new sentence has been added to permit the alternate power source to be used for peak load shaving providing the conditions of Section 700-5(b) are met.

Section 700-5(b), (FPN): A new fine print note was added to indicate peak load shaving operation may be acceptable for satisfying the test requirements of Section 700-4(b) when all conditions of Section 700-4 are met.

Section 700-7(b): Revised by deleting "or generator set."

Section 700-7(d): This section has been deleted.

Section 700-7(d), (FPN): A new fine print note was added to reference NFPA 110.

Section 700-9(a): A new section added, requiring all boxes and enclosures for emergency circuits to be marked so they will be readily identified as a component of an emergency circuit.

Section 700-12: Revised for clarity and expanded to require consideration be given to the type of occupancy as well as the type of service rendered.

Section 700-12(a): The first paragraph has been revised to make it clear that the 87½% applies to the voltage applied to the load.

Section 700-12(b)(4): Revised to make the requirements applicable to control or signal power related to the generator, as well as to cranking power for the prime mover, and to require that battery charging means shall be independent of the generator set.

Section 700-12(b)(5), (FPN): The fine print note was deleted.

Section 700-12(f), Exception: A new exception was added to permit a separate branch circuit for unit equipment in a separate and uninterrupted area supplied by a minimum of three normal lighting circuits, if the separate branch circuit originates from the same panelboard as that of the normal lighting circuits and is provided with a lock-on feature.

Section 700-16: Revised by replacing the words "required exit lights" with "means of egress lighting." A new third paragraph was added requiring the emergency lighting system to operate until normal illumination has been restored where high-intensity discharge lighting such as high- and low-pressure sodium, mercury vapor, and metal halide is used as a sole source of normal illumination.

Section 700-16, Exception: A new exception has been added as follows: "Where alternative means have been taken to insure that the emergency lighting illumination level is maintained."

Section 700-25, (FPN): A new fine print note was added as follows: "Fuses and circuits breakers for emergency circuit overcurrent protection, where coordinated to insure selective clearing of fault currents, increase overall reliability of the system."

ARTICLE 701 - Legally Required Standby Systems

Section 701-1: The second paragraph revised to exclude mandatory requirements in the scope.

Section 701-1, (FPN): A new second fine print note added to reference NFPA 110.

Section 701-8(d): Deleted.

Section 701-8, (FPN): A new fine print note added to reference NFPA 110.

Section 701-11(b)(4): This section has been revised to make the requirements applicable to control or signal power related to the generator as well as to cranking power for the prime mover, and to require the battery charging means to be independent of the generator set. The fine print note following this section has been deleted.

ARTICLE 702 - Optional Standby Systems
No changes.

ARTICLE 705 - Interconnected Electric Power Production Sources

General: This is a new article which covers the installation of one or more electric power production sources operating in parallel with a prime source(s) of electricity. The primary source may be a utility supply, on-site electric power source(s), or other sources.

ARTICLE 710 - Over 600 Volts, Nominal, General

Section 710-3(b)(3): A new paragraph was added to require that where necessary to prevent physical damage to the raceway or cable, protection must be provided in the form of granular or selected material, or suitable sleeves.

Section 710-21(b)(7), Exception: A new exception has been added permitting more than one switch as the disconnecting means for one set of fuses where the switches are installed to provide connection to more than one set of supply conductors. The switches must be mechanically or electrically interlocked to permit access to the fuses only when all switches are open. A conspicuous sign must be placed at the fuses.

Section 710-21(e): A new paragraph added to require that where more than one switch is installed with interconnected load terminals to provide for alternate connection to different supply conductors, each switch must be provided with a warning sign.

Section 710-42: Revised to clarify intent.

ARTICLE 720 - Circuits and Equipment Operating at Less Than 50 Volts
No changes.

ARTICLE 725 - Class 1, Class 2, and Class 3 Remote-Control, Signaling and Power-Limited Circuits

Section 725-1, (FPN): This fine print note was revised to change "special consideration is given" to "alternative requirements to those of Chapters 1 through 4 are given," and "conductor insulation requirements" was changed to "insulation requirements, and wiring methods and materials."

Section 725-2(b): The exception and the second fine print note were deleted. A new exception was added: "As permitted in Section 725-38(b)(3)."

Section 725-11(a): The second sentence was revised by changing "The source" to "Power sources other than transformers."

Section 725-12, Exception No. 1, (FPN): This section was revised to add as examples Section 610-53 for cranes and hoists, and Section 660-9 for x-ray equipment.

Section 725-13, Exception No. 2: This new exception was added covering circuits where overcurrent protection is provided in accordance with Section 725-12, Exception No. 2.

Section 725-15, Exception No. 2: This new exception was added covering underground conductors in a manhole where certain specified conditions are met.

Section 725-16(a): This section was revised to add "an approved enclosure" in the first sentence.

Section 725-36: This section was editorially revised to insert "where required" between "overcurrent devices" and "shall be located."

Section 725-38: The title of this section was revised to "Wiring Methods and Materials on Load Side."

Section 725-38(a)(1), Exception No. 1: The exception was revised to indicate that not all conductors of the specified systems are required to be installed by the wiring methods indicated.

Section 725-38(a)(2), Exception No. 3: This new exception was added to permit underground conductors in a manhole where specified conditions are met.

Section 725-38(a)(3): This section was deleted. The requirements for shafts now appear in Section 725-38(b)(2).

Section 725-38(a)(3): This section [old 725-38(a)(4)] was revised to insert the words "metal" between "rigid" and "conduit."

Section 725-38(b): This section was completely rewritten to: (1) require cables in Class 2 and 3 circuits installed as wiring within buildings, except spaces used for air handling, to be listed as being resistant to the spread of fire (with three exceptions); (2) require cables in Class 2 and 3 circuits in vertical runs and shafts to be listed as having fire-resistant characteristics capable of preventing the carrying of fire from floor to floor (with one exception); and (3) to require cables in Class 2 and 3 circuits in ducts, plenums, and other spaces used for environmental air to comply with Section 300-22 with one exception. Fine print notes to this section reference test methods for cables to be used in various installations. This section creates several new designations for cables having fire-resistant characteristics for the applicable installation. See Table 725-41 for a chart of the cable designations.

Section 725-40(a): This section was revised by adding to the first sentence "and shall meet the requirements of Section 725-38(b)." The fine print note to this section was deleted.

Section 725-40(b)(2): This section was revised to require cables used for Class 3 circuits to be listed as suitable for Class 3 power-limited fire protective signaling or communication circuits.

Section 725-40(b)(3): Reference to Section 725-41 was added, in addition to Section 310-11.

Section 725-40(b)(4): This section was deleted.

Section 725-41 and Table 725-41: This new section includes a new table which lists cable markings and cable types for the new fire resistant cables required in this article. A third column lists references to particular sections of the article to which the cable type applies.

ARTICLE 760 - Fire Protective Signaling Systems

Section 760-2: This section was formerly Section 760-4. The paragraphs were rearranged.

Section 760-2(b), Exception: This is a revised exception [formerly the exception to Section 760-4(d)] which references Section 760-28(c)(3), instead of giving the requirements. The fine print note has been deleted.

Section 760-3: This is old Section 760-2. The fine print note has been included in the section as a requirement.

Section 760-13, Exception No. 2: This is a new exception which covers those circuits where overcurrent protection is provided in accordance with Section 725-12, Exception No. 2.

Section 760-23: The title of this section was changed to "Circuit Marking."

Section 760-26: The words "where required" were inserted between the words "devices" and "shall."

Section 760-28(a): This section was revised to add: "and, in addition conductors shall be copper, either solid, bunch-tinned, or stranded with a maximum of 19 strands."

Section 760-28(a), (FPN): This is a new fine print note which indicates power-limited circuits can be reclassified and installed as nonpower-limited circuits if the markings required by Section 760-23 are eliminated and the entire circuit is installed using the wiring methods and materials in accordance with Part B.

Section 760-28(b)(1): This section was revised for clarification and to delete the phrase "such as insulated stapling" in the last sentence.

Section 760-28(b)(3): This section was revised to prohibit rigid nonmetallic conduit.

Section 760-28(b)(4): This section has been deleted.

Section 760-28(c): This section was extensively revised to provide new requirements for fire resistance of cables. The changes in this section are similar to those in Section 725-38(b).

Section 760-29(a)(1): This section was revised to delete the word "open."

Section 760-30(b): This section was revised to permit No. 24 AWG conductors for six or more conductor multiconductor cables.

Section 760-30(c): This section was added to require cables be listed as being suitable for Class 3, power-limited fire-protective signaling, or communication circuits. Existing Sections 760-30(c) and (d) were deleted and the remaining sections renumbered.

Section 760-30(f): This section was added to permit optical fiber cables.

Section 760-31: This is a new section which contains a table to identify and require markings on all listed power-limited fire-protective signaling cables, similar to new Section 725-41.

Section 760-32(b): This section was revised to require that insulated continuous line-type fire detectors be listed as being resistant to the spread of fire in accordance with the requirements of Section 760-28(c), have a voltage rating not less than 300 volts, and to have a jacket compound with a high degree of abrasion resistance.

ARTICLE 770 - Optical Fiber Cables

Section 770-2: This is a new section which requires optical fiber cables to comply with the spread of fire or products of combustion requirements of Section 300-21, and where installed in ducts, plenums, and other air-handling spaces, the requirements of Section 300-22. An exception is permitted where the cables comply with Section 770-6(c).

Section 770-5(a), and Exceptions No. 1, 2, and 3: This section [old Section 770-4(a)] and its exceptions were revised to make it clear that conductive and hybrid optical fiber cables are not permitted to occupy the same raceway or cable tray with conductors for electric light, power, or Class 1 circuits. In addition, nonconductive optical fiber cables are not permitted to occupy the same cabinet, panel, outlet box or similar enclosure housing the electrical termination of an electric light, power, or Class 1 circuit. The two exceptions have been revised and a new exception added.

Section 770-5(b)(4): This section [old Section 770-4(b)(4)] related to radio and television circuits was deleted and the following section renumbered.

Section 770-6: This section was revised in a manner similar to Section 725-38(b).

Section 770-7: Existing section deleted. This section (formerly Section 770-8) was revised to delete the reference to aerial cable and to clarify the point of entrance to the building.

Section 770-8: This new section provides the cable marking requirements for the new cables required under this article. It is similar to Section 725-41.

ARTICLE 780 - Closed-Loop and Programmed Power Distribution

This is a new article which applies to premise power distribution systems jointly controlled by a signaling between the energy controlling equipment and utilization equipment. This is a new concept in which the key defining features are: 1. Programmed power to branch circuits. 2. Continuous monitoring of branch circuits. 3. Availability of low voltage dc power. 4. Integrated wiring. 5. Integrated receptacles. 6. Flexible switching.

ARTICLE 800 - Communication Circuits

Section 800-1: The last sentence of this paragraph has been relocated to become a fine print note referencing Article 770. A new fine print note has been added to reference Section 725-5 for the classification of Class 2 and 3 circuits as communication circuits.

Section 800-2(FPN): A new third fine print note has been added to indicate that on a circuit not exposed to accidental contact with power conductors, providing a listed protector will help protect against other hazards, such as lightning and above-normal voltages induced by fault currents on paralleling power circuits. When protecting a circuit run within the block between two buildings on the same premises, providing a listed protector on each end of the circuit affords protection for both buildings.

Section 800-2(a): A new second paragraph added to this section defining the point at which the exposed conductors enter.

Section 800-2(a), (FPN): A new fine print note was added to warn installers to locate the protector so that the grounding conductor will be short as possible and thereby help limit potential differences between communication circuits and other metallic systems.

Section 800-2(b), Exception: A new exception added referencing the permission in Sections 501-14, 502-14, and 503-12.

Section 800-2(c)(1): Paragraphs a, b, c, and e, have been revised by deleting the reference to "ampacity."

Section 800-2(d): A new section has been added to cover the situation where a secondary protector is installed in series with the indoor communication wire and cable between the protector and the equipment. The secondary protector must include overcurrent protection which will fuse at currents less than the current-carrying capacity of listed indoor communication wire and cable, listed telephone set line cords, and listed communication terminal equipment having ports for external wire line communication circuits. Any overvoltage protection, arresters, or grounding connection must be connected on the equipment terminals side of the secondary protector overcurrent protection.

Section 800-3(a)(1), Exception No. 1: Revised to include communication circuit conductors and Type AC cable.

Section 800-3(a)(3), Exception No. 2: Revised to limit the raceways to metal raceways.

Section 800-3(b): This section has undergone extensive revision, requiring fire resistance for wires and cables installed in a building.

Section 800-3(d): This section has been revised to address the installation of communication conductors with conductors of other circuits.

Section 800-3(e): This is a new section permitting communication wires and cables, listed as being suitable for the purpose, to be installed under carpets.

Section 800-4: This is a new section requiring communication wires and cables in a building to be listed as being suitable for the purpose.

Section 800-4, Exception No. 1: This is a new exception exempting cable lengths being listed for the purpose if the cable length within the building does not exceed 50 feet and the cable enters the building from the outside and terminates in an enclosure or on a listed protector. A new fine print note has been added indicating that both metallic and plastic-type split cases or terminal boxes are typically used as enclosures for splicing or terminating telephone cables.

Section 800-4, Exception No. 2: This is a new exception exempting cables from being listed for the purpose where the cable enters the building from the outside and is run in rigid metal conduit or IMC and the conduits are grounded in accordance with Section 800-31(b)(5).

Section 800-5: This is a new section providing a new table describing how listed communication cables are to be identified.

Section 800-11(c)(1): The existing paragraph has been deleted and replaced with a requirement that wires and cables without a metallic shield, running from the outdoor support to the protector, be listed as being suitable for the purpose, and have a current-carrying capacity as specified in Sections 800-2(c)(1)b or c.

Section 800-11(c)(2): In the first sentence "conduit" was changed to "raceway."

Section 800-21(a): The word "duct" was changed to "raceway."

Section 800-31(a): Revised to delete the reference to aerial cable and to clarify the point of entrance to the building.

Section 800-31(b)(4): A new sentence added to require that where the grounding conductors run in a metal raceway, both ends of the raceway must be bonded to the grounding conductor or the same terminal or electrode to which the grounding conductor is connected.

Section 800-31(b)(5)a: Revised to add a new item (7), the grounding conductor or the grounding electrode of a building or structure disconnecting means which is grounded to an electrode as covered in Section 250-24.

Section 800-31(b)(5)c(2): The word "metal" was added ahead of "gas piping."

Section 800-31(b)(6): The first sentence was revised to require connections to grounding electrodes to comply with Section 250-115.

ARTICLE 810 - Radio and Television Equipment

Section 810-12: The word "open" was added in the third sentence before "electric light."

XLIX

SUMMARY OF CODE CHANGES

Section 810-13: Revised to make it clear that the electric light and power conductors are "open" conductors.

Section 810-18(c): A new section was added permitting indoor antennas and indoor lead-ins to occupy the same box or enclosure with conductors of other wiring systems were separated from other conductors by an effective permanently installed barrier.

Section 810-21(f)(3): Item (2) has been revised to reference any of the individual electrodes described in Section 250-83.

Section 810-70: Revised to change "lighting" to "electric light, power."

Section 810-70, Exception No. 2: "Conduit" has been changed to "Raceway."

Section 810-71(d): Deleted.

ARTICLE 820 - Community Antenna Television and Radio Distribution Systems

Section 820-1: Paragraph one was revised to change the second sentence to a fine print note. The second paragraph of this section has been renumbered to become Section 820-2 "Energy Limitations."

Section 820-1,(FPN): A new fine print note has been added referencing Articles 770 and 800 where the installation is other than coaxial.

Section 820-2: Renumbered in sequence.

Section 820-4: This is a new section added to provide a new table describing cable marking for listed community antenna television and radio distribution cables.

Section 820-7: Revised by adding a new sentence to define the point of emergence of cables entering buildings.

Section 820-7, (FPN): A new fine print note has been added alerting installers that selecting a grounding location to achieve the shortest practicable grounding conductor will help to limit potential difference between CATV and other metallic systems.

Section 820-13(a): The phrase "or coaxial cable circuits" was added to the end of the sentence.

Section 820-13(a), Exception No. 3: A new exception was added to permit coaxial cable to occupy the same box or enclosure with conductors of other wiring systems where they are separated from the other conductors by an effective permanently installed barrier.

Section 820-13(c): The existing section was deleted and replaced with requirements to permit coaxial cables to be installed in the same raceway or enclosure with jacketed cables of Class 2 and 3 circuits in compliance with Article 725, power-limited fire protective signaling systems in compliance with Article 760, communications circuits in compliance with

Article 800, and optical fiber cables in compliance with Article 770.

Section 820-15: This is a new section providing the requirements for the fire resistance of coaxial cables installed within buildings. The requirements of this section are similar in concept to those required in Section 725-38(b).

Section 820-22(c): Revised to require the grounding conductor to be not smaller than No. 14 AWG.

Section 820-22(f)(1): Revised by adding a new item (7): "to the grounding conductor or to the grounding electrode of a building or structure disconnecting means which is grounded to an electrode as covered in Section 250-24."

Section 820-22(f)(3): Item (2) deleted and Item (3) revised to reference any electrode covered in Section 250-83.

CHAPTER 9 Tables and Examples

Part A. Tables, Notes to Tables: The first paragraph was revised to delete "short." The second paragraph was revised to include bonding conductors. In the third paragraph "tubing nipples" was added.

Table 1: "(new or rewiring)" was deleted. In Note 1 to Table 1, "tubing" was added.

Table 2: Wire Types FFH-1 and CF deleted to correlate with changes in Table 402-3.

Table 3A: This table has been revised to correlate with changes to Table 310-13. A new note added to specify that this table is for concentric stranded conductors only and Table 5A shall be used for cables with compact conductors.

Tables 3B and 3C: A new note added to specify that the tables are for concentric stranded conductors only and Table 5A shall be used for cables with compact conductors. Also revised to correlate with changes in Table 310-13.

Table 5A: This is a new table added for use with compact aluminum conductors.

Table 6: Revised to correlate with changes in Table 310-13.

Table 8: The formula in second note has been corrected. Reference to new Table 5A was added in third note. The reference to NEMA WC8-1976 was changed from a note to the table to a fine print note.

Table 9: The table and notes have been extensively revised and reformatted to provide additional information.

Part B. Examples: The examples have been revised to correlate with changes in the preceding chapters.

Appendix A: A new appendix has been added to the *NEC* to identify the source of text extracted from other NFPA documents in accordance with Section 90-3.

L

The
National Electrical Code®
Handbook

National Electrical Code

NFPA 70

ARTICLE 90 — INTRODUCTION

Contents

90-1. Purpose.

(a) Practical Safeguarding. The purpose of this Code is the practical safeguarding of persons and property from hazards arising from the use of electricity.

The *National Electrical Code (NEC)* is prepared by the NFPA National Electrical Code Committee. The scope of this Committee is as follows:
Scope: This Committee shall consist of a Correlating Committee and Code-Making Panels. It shall have primary responsibility for preparing documents on minimizing the risk of electricity as a source of electric shock and as a potential ignition source of fires and explosions. It shall also be responsible for text to minimize the propagation of fire and explosions due to electrical installations.
The *National Electrical Code* is the most widely adopted set of electrical safety requirements in the world and is offered for use in law and for regulatory purposes in the interest of life and property protection. NFPA has available a model state law on inspection of electrical installations (formerly NFPA 70L) which provides information on adopting the *NEC*.

(b) Adequacy. This Code contains provisions considered necessary for safety. Compliance therewith and proper maintenance will result in an installation essentially free from hazard, but not necessarily efficient, convenient, or adequate for good service or future expansion of electrical use.

(FPN): Hazards often occur because of overloading of wiring systems by methods or usage not in conformity with this Code. This occurs because initial wiring did not provide for increases in the use of electricity. An initial adequate installation and reasonable provisions for system changes will provide for future increases in the use of electricity.

Consideration should always be given to future expansion of electrical uses. Future expansion may not be likely in some occupancies, but in others it is wise to plan an initial installation comprising service-entrance conductors and equipment, feeder conductors, and panelboards that will allow for future additions, alterations, designs, etc.

(c) Intention. This Code is not intended as a design specification nor an instruction manual for untrained persons.

The *National Electrical Code* is intended for use by capable engineers and electrical contractors for the basic design and/or installation of electrical equipment; by inspection authorities exercising legal jurisdiction over electrical installations; by property insurance inspectors; by qualified industrial, commercial, and residential electricians; and by instructors teaching electrical apprentices or students.

90-2. Scope.

(a) Covered. This Code covers:

(1) Installations of electric conductors and equipment within or on public and private buildings or other structures, including mobile homes, recreational vehicles, and floating buildings; and other premises such as yards, carnival, parking and other lots, and industrial substations.

(FPN): For additional information concerning such installations in an industrial or multibuilding complex, see the National Electrical Safety Code, ANSI C2-1984.

Industrial and multibuilding complexes (such as some universities) often include substations and other installations employing construction and wiring similar to electric utility installations. Although such nonutility installations are within the scope of the *National Electrical Code*, the *NEC* requirements may not always be sufficient or complete. In such cases, the user can find additional information in the *National Electrical Safety Code*, published by the Institute of Electrical and Electronics Engineers, Inc., 345 East 47th St., New York, NY 10017.

(2) Installations of conductors that connect to the supply of electricity.

(3) Installations of other outside conductors on the premises.

(4) Installations of optical fiber cable.

See Article 770 for the installation requirements for optical fiber cable and Article 690 regarding solar photovoltaic systems.

(b) Not Covered. This Code does not cover:

(1) Installations in ships, watercraft other than floating buildings, railway rolling stock, aircraft, or automotive vehicles other than mobile homes and recreational vehicles.

Requirements for floating buildings will be found in Article 553.

(2) Installations underground in mines.

(3) Installations of railways for generation, transformation, transmission, or distribution of power used exclusively for operation of rolling stock or installations used exclusively for signaling and communication purposes.

(4) Installations of communication equipment under the exclusive control of communication utilities, located outdoors or in building spaces used exclusively for such installations.

(5) Installations under the exclusive control of electric utilities for the purpose of communication, or metering; or for the generation, control, transformation, transmission, and distribution of electric energy located in buildings used exclusively by utilities for such purposes or located outdoors on property owned or leased by the utility or on public highways, streets, roads, etc., or outdoors by established rights on private property.

(FPN): It is the intent of this section that this Code covers all premises' wiring or wiring other than utility owned metering equipment, on the load side of the service point of buildings, structures, or any other premises not owned or leased by the utility. Also, it is the intent that this Code cover installations in buildings used by the utility for purposes other than listed in (b)(5) above, such as office buildings, warehouses, garages, machine shops, and recreational buildings which are not an integral part of a generating plant, substation, or control center.

See Figure 90-1.

Figure 90-1. A typical electric utility complex indicating those facilities subject to the provisions of the *NEC*.

(c) Special Permission. The authority having jurisdiction for enforcing this Code may grant exception for the installation of conductors and equipment, not under the exclusive control of the electric utilities and used to connect the electric utility supply system to the service-entrance conductors of the premises served, provided such installations are outside a building or terminate immediately inside a building wall.

90-3. Code Arrangement. This Code is divided into the Introduction and nine chapters. Chapters 1, 2, 3, and 4 apply generally; Chapters 5, 6, and 7 apply to special occupancies, special equipment, or other special conditions. These latter chapters supplement or modify the general rules. Chapters 1 through 4 apply except as amended by Chapters 5, 6, and 7 for the particular conditions.

Chapter 8 covers communications systems and is independent of the other chapters except where they are specifically referenced therein.

Chapter 9 consists of tables and examples.

Material identified by the superscript letter "x" includes text extracted from other NFPA documents as identified in Appendix A.

> The reference to the Introduction and Tables and Examples is made with the intention that Article 90 and Chapter 9 be included in the application of this *Code*.
>
> Chapters 1 through 4 apply generally, except as amended or specifically referenced in Chapters 5, 6, and 7 (Articles 500 through 780). For example, Section 300-22 (Chapter 3) is modified by Sections 725-2(b), 760-2(b), and 770-2(b) (Chapter 7) and specifically referenced in Sections 800-3(b)(3) and 820-15(c) (Chapter 8). See commentary following Section 300-1, also.

90-4. Enforcement. This Code is intended to be suitable for mandatory application by governmental bodies exercising legal jurisdiction over electrical installations and for use by insurance inspectors. The authority having jurisdiction of enforcement of the Code will have the responsibility for making interpretations of the rules, for deciding upon the approval of equipment and materials, and for granting the special permission contemplated in a number of the rules.

> Section 90-4 advises that an authority must grant approval for all materials and equipment used under the requirements of the *Code* in its area of jurisdiction. The texts of Sections 90-6, 110-2, and 110-3, along with the definitions of "approved," "identified," "listed," and "labeled," are intended to provide a basis for the authority having jurisdiction to make necessary judgments that are its responsibility.

The authority having jurisdiction may waive specific requirements in this Code or permit alternate methods, where it is assured that equivalent objectives can be achieved by establishing and maintaining effective safety.

> It is the responsibility of the local authority enforcing the *Code* to make interpretations of the specific rules of the *Code*.
>
> The second paragraph to Section 90-4 is included to allow the authority having jurisdiction the option of making an individual judgment to permit alternative methods where specific rules are not established in the *Code*. This also, for example, allows the local authority to waive specific requirements in industrial occupancies, research and testing laboratories, and other occupancies where the specific type of installation was not contemplated in the *Code* rules.
>
> Some localities do not adopt the *National Electrical Code* but, even in those localities, installations meeting the current *Code* are prima facie evidence that the electrical installation is safe.

This Code may require new products, constructions, or materials which may not yet be available at the time the Code is adopted. In such event, the authority having jurisdiction may permit the use of the products, constructions, or materials which comply with the most recent previous edition of this Code adopted by the jurisdiction.

The second paragraph permits the authority having jurisdiction to waive specific requirements on the basis of equivalent safety. The third paragraph of Section 90-4 permits the authority to waive a new *Code* requirement during the interim period between the acceptance of a new edition of the *NEC* and the availability of the new product, construction, or material redesigned to comply with the increased safety required by the new *Code* edition. It is difficult to establish a viable future effective date in the *NEC* because the time needed to change existing products and standards, and to develop new materials and test methods, is not usually known at the time of adoption of the new requirement in the *NEC*.

90-5. Formal Interpretations. To promote uniformity of interpretation and application of the provisions of this Code, Formal Interpretation procedures have been established.

(FPN): These procedures may be found in the "NFPA Regulations Governing Committee Projects."

The procedures for formal interpretations of the provisions of the *National Electrical Code* are outlined in the Regulations Governing Committee Projects that may be obtained from the Secretary of the Standards Council of the National Fire Protection Association. These regulations are included in the NFPA *Directory*. The formal interpretations procedure can be found in Section 16 of the *Directory* and has been reprinted in its entirety in the appendix to this Handbook. Additional information on interpretations from the NEC Operating Procedures is included.

The National Electrical Code Committee has established a policy of not processing formal interpretations that do not involve a question of national significance, as evidenced by essentially the same question submitted to NFPA by a number of different interests from various parts of the country.

When a formal interpretation is processed, a special Interpretations Subcommittee is established. This subcommittee is made up of five or more members or alternates of the Code Panel(s) having primary jurisdiction over the part(s) of the *Code* covering the subject under consideration. The members are selected by the Chairman of the Correlating Committee or the Secretary of the Standards Council, if the Chairman is not available. No member or alternate is eligible for appointment to an Interpretations Subcommittee if he or she is directly involved in the particular case prompting the request for the Interpretation. The personnel of NEC Interpretations Subcommittees are varied for each request.

The National Electrical Code Committee cannot be responsible for subsequent actions by authorities enforcing the *NEC* as to whether they accept or reject the findings. The authority having jurisdiction has the responsibility of interpreting the *Code* rules and should attempt to resolve all disagreements at the local level.

Two general forms of Formal Interpretations are recognized: (1) those making an interpretation of the literal text and (2) those making an interpretation of the intent of the Committee when the particular text was adopted.

Interpretations of the *NEC* not subject to processing are those that (1) involve a determination of compliance of a design, installation, or product or equivalency of protection, including the suitability of isolation or guarding; (2) involve a review of plans or specifications or require judgment or knowledge that can only be acquired as a result of on-site inspection, including the degree and extent of a hazardous (classified) location; and (3) involve text that clearly and decisively provides the requested information.

Formal Interpretations of *Code* rules are published in the NFPA *Fire News* or the NFPA *Fire Journal*, and the NFPA Electrical Section News Bulletin, and are sent to interested trade publications.

Most interpretations of the *NEC* are rendered as the personal opinion of NFPA Electrical Department staff, or of the involved member of the National Electrical

Code Committee, because the request does not qualify for processing as a Formal Interpretation in accordance with the Regulations Governing Committee Projects or the NEC Committee policy. Such opinions are rendered in writing only in response to written requests. They are identified as personal opinions, and the response indicates that the opinion shall not be considered the official position of the NFPA or of the National Electrical Code Committee, and shall not be considered to be, nor be relied upon as, a Formal Interpretation.

90-6. Examination of Equipment for Safety. For specific items of equipment and materials referred to in this Code, examinations for safety made under standard conditions will provide a basis for approval where the record is made generally available through promulgation by organizations properly equipped and qualified for experimental testing, inspections of the run of goods at factories, and service-value determination through field inspections. This avoids the necessity for repetition of examinations by different examiners, frequently with inadequate facilities for such work, and the confusion that would result from conflicting reports as to the suitability of devices and materials examined for a given purpose.

It is the intent of this Code that factory-installed internal wiring or the construction of equipment need not be inspected at the time of installation of the equipment, except to detect alterations or damage, if the equipment has been listed by a qualified electrical testing laboratory which is recognized as having the facilities described above and which requires suitability for installation in accordance with this Code.

(FPN): See Examination of Equipment, Section 110-3.

(FPN): See definition of "Listed," Article 100.

Qualified testing laboratories, inspection agencies, or other organizations concerned with product evaluation publish lists of equipment or materials that have been tested and meet nationally recognized standards or that have been found suitable for use in a specified manner. The *Code* does not contain detailed information on equipment or materials, but refers to the products as "listed," "labeled," or "identified." See Article 100, "Definitions," for explanation of these terms.

The National Fire Protection Association does not approve, inspect or certify any installations, procedures, equipment, or materials nor does it approve or evaluate testing laboratories. In determining the acceptability of installations or procedures, equipment or materials, the authority having jurisdiction may base acceptance on compliance with NFPA or other appropriate standards. In the absence of such standards, the authority may require evidence of proper installation, procedure, or use. The authority having jurisdiction may also refer to the listings or labeling practices of an organization concerned with product evaluations which is in a position to determine compliance with appropriate standards for the current production of listed items.

It is not the intent of the *Code* to apply to the internal factory-installed wiring, or to the construction of listed equipment at the time of installation, unless damage or alterations are detected.

90-7. Wiring Planning.

(a) Future Expansion and Convenience. Plans and specifications that provide ample space in raceways, spare raceways, and additional spaces will allow for future increases in the use of electricity. Distribution centers located in readily accessible locations will provide convenience and safety of operation. See Sections 110-16 and 240-24 for clearances and accessibility.

Providing the exclusively dedicated space required by Section 384-4 supports the intent of Section 90-7 regarding future increases.

6

(b) Number of Circuits in Enclosures. It is elsewhere provided in this Code that the number of wires and circuits confined in a single enclosure be varyingly restricted. Limiting the number of circuits in a single enclosure will minimize the effects from a short-circuit or ground fault in one circuit.

Distribution centers should contain additional spaces and capacity for future additions and should be conveniently located for accessibility.

Where easy access is not achieved, a spare raceway(s) or "pull line(s)" should be run to specific areas. See Figure 90-2.

Figure 90-2. Spare raceways or "pull lines" provide additional capacity for future additions to the distribution system.

90-8. Metric Units of Measurement. For the purpose of this Code metric units of measurement are in accordance with the modernized metric system known as the International System of Units (SI).

Values of measurement in the Code text will be followed by an approximate equivalent value in SI units. Tables will have a footnote for SI conversion units used in the table.

Conduit size, wire size, horsepower designation for motors, and trade sizes that do not reflect actual measurements, e.g., box sizes, will not be assigned dual designation SI units.

(FPN): For metric conversion practices, see ANSI/ASTM E380-1984, Standard for Metric Practice.

In addition, warning signs stating specific clearances, such as in Section 513-11(a), do not include metric equivalents.

An example of an application of SI conversion units as used in Table 110-16(a) is as follows:

$$3 \text{ ft} = 36 \text{ in.} \times 25.4 \text{ mm} = 914 \text{ mm}$$
$$3\frac{1}{2} \text{ ft} \times 0.3048 \text{ m} \quad\quad = 1.07 \text{ m}$$
$$4 \text{ ft} \times 0.3048 \text{ m} \quad\quad = 1.22 \text{ m}$$

Generally, dimensions up to 36 inches are expressed in millimeters, and those over 36 inches are expressed in meters. Footnotes to tables involving dimensions in feet are expressed as "one foot = 0.3048 meter." However, throughout the *Code* text the metric equivalent has been converted to millimeters and rounded off to 305 millimeters.

1 General

ARTICLE 100 — DEFINITIONS

Contents
A. General
B. Over 600 Volts, Nominal

Scope. This article contains only those definitions essential to the proper application of this Code. It is not intended to include commonly defined general terms nor commonly defined technical terms from related codes and standards. In general, only those terms used in two or more articles are defined in Article 100. Other definitions are included in the article in which they are used but may be referenced in Article 100.

Commonly defined general terms include those terms defined in general English-language dictionaries that are not used in some unique or restricted manner in the *NEC*. Commonly defined technical terms such as "volt" and "ampere" will be found in the IEEE dictionary.

Other definitions are included in the following sections:

ARTICLE 100—DEFINITIONS

Part A of this article contains definitions intended to apply wherever the terms are used throughout this Code. Part B contains definitions applicable only to the parts of articles covering specifically installations and equipment operating at over 600 volts, nominal.

A. General

AC General-Use Snap Switch: See under "Switches."

AC-DC General-Use Snap Switch: See under "Switches."

Accessible: (As applied to wiring methods.) Capable of being removed or exposed without damaging the building structure or finish, or not permanently closed in by the structure or finish of the building. (See "Concealed" and "Exposed.")

Wiring methods located behind removable panels designed to allow access are not considered permanently enclosed. See Figure 100-1. See also Section 300-4(c).

Busways installed according to the provisions of Section 364–4

Suspended ceiling

Junction box

AC cable installed as permitted by Section 333–7, Exception No. 3

Figure 100-1. Busways and junction boxes are considered accessible when located above hung ceilings having lift-out panels.

Accessible: (As applied to Equipment.) Admitting close approach: not guarded by locked doors, elevation, or other effective means. (See "Accessible, Readily.")

Accessible, Readily: (Readily Accessible.) Capable of being reached quickly for operation, renewal, or inspections, without requiring those to whom ready access is requisite to climb over or remove obstacles or to resort to portable ladders, chairs, etc. (See "Accessible.")

General rule

6 ft 6 in.

Busway

Chain

Portable means

Isolating switch

Hook stick

Figure 100-2. This figure illustrates some exceptions to the provisions of Section 380-8. See also Section 364-12 which permits ropes, chains, or hook sticks as suitable for operating disconnecting means mounted on busways.

Ampacity: The current in amperes a conductor can carry continuously under the conditions of use without exceeding its temperature rating.

The definition of "ampacity" recognizes that the maximum current a conductor can carry continuously varies with the conditions of use as well as with the temperature rating of the conductor insulation. For example, ambient temperature is a condition of use. A conductor with 60°C insulation installed near a furnace so that the ambient temperature is 60°C continuously has no current-carrying capacity. Any current flowing through the conductor will raise its temperature beyond the 60°C insulation rating. The ampacity of this conductor, regardless of its

11

size, is therefore zero. See the ampacity correction factors following Tables 310-16 through 310-31.

Another condition of use is the number of conductors in a raceway or cable. See Note 8(a) to Tables 310-16 through 310-31.

Anesthetizing Location: See Section 517-2.

Appliance: Utilization equipment, generally other than industrial, normally built in standardized sizes or types, which is installed or connected as a unit to perform one or more functions such as clothes washing, air conditioning, food mixing, deep frying, etc.

Appliance Branch Circuit: See "Branch Circuit, Appliance."

Approved: Acceptable to the authority having jurisdiction.

The phrase "authority having jurisdiction" is used in NFPA documents in a broad manner since jurisdictions and "approval" agencies vary as do their responsibilities. Where public safety is primary, the "authority having jurisdiction" may be a federal, state, local, or other regional department or individual such as a fire chief, fire marshal, chief of a fire prevention bureau, labor department, health department, building official, electrical inspector, or others having statutory authority. For insurance purposes, an insurance inspection department, rating bureau, or other insurance company representative may be the "authority having jurisdiction." In many circumstances the property owner or his designated agent assumes the role of the "authority having jurisdiction"; at government installations, the commanding officer or departmental official may be the "authority having jurisdiction."

Askarel: A generic term for a group of nonflammable synthetic chlorinated hydrocarbons used as electrical insulating media. Askarels of various compositional types are used. Under arcing conditions the gases produced, while consisting predominantly of noncombustible hydrogen chloride, can include varying amounts of combustible gases depending upon the askarel type.

Attachment Plug (Plug Cap) (Cap): A device which, by insertion in a receptacle, establishes connection between the conductors of the attached flexible cord and the conductors connected permanently to the receptacle.

Attachment plugs are available fuseless, with a switch, and with overload protection. Attachment plugs with built-in ground-fault circuit-interrupters are also available.

Automatic: Self-acting, operating by its own mechanism when actuated by some impersonal influence, as for example, a change in current strength, pressure, temperature, or mechanical configuration. (See "Nonautomatic.")

Bare Conductor: See under "Conductor."

Block (City, Town, or Village): See Section 800-2.

Bonding: The permanent joining of metallic parts to form an electrically conductive path which will assure electrical continuity and the capacity to conduct safely any current likely to be imposed.

Bonding Jumper: A reliable conductor to assure the required electrical conductivity between metal parts required to be electrically connected.

See Figure 100-3.

Figure 100-3. A bonding jumper around a concentric or eccentric knockout is required by Section 250-76 for circuits over 250 volts to ground.

Bonding Jumper, Circuit: The connection between portions of a conductor in a circuit to maintain required ampacity of the circuit.

Bonding Jumper, Equipment: The connection between two or more portions of the equipment grounding conductor.

Bonding Jumper, Main: The connection between the grounded circuit conductor and the equipment grounding conductor at the service.

See Figure 100-4.

Figure 100-4. The equipment grounding terminal bar is required to be bonded to the panelboard (or cabinet) frame and is not permitted to be connected to the neutral bar in other than service equipment. See Section 384-27. The bonding method may be by bonding screws, bonding bus, bonding jumpers, or other suitable conductor. See Section 250-79(b).

Branch Circuit: The circuit conductors between the final overcurrent device protecting the circuit and the outlet(s).

(FPN): See Section 240-9 and Section 240-10 for thermal cutouts, thermal relays, supplementary overcurrent protection, and other devices.

See Figure 100-5.

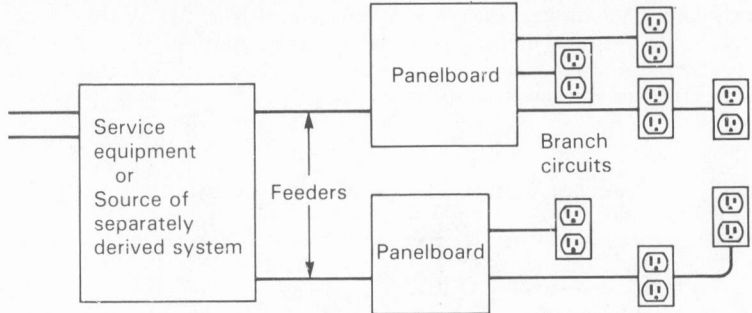

Figure 100-5. Conductors between the overcurrent device in the panelboards and the duplex receptacles are branch-circuit conductors. Conductors between the service equipment, or source of separately derived systems, and the panelboards are feeders.

Branch Circuit, Appliance: A branch circuit supplying energy to one or more outlets to which appliances are to be connected; such circuits to have no permanently connected lighting fixtures not a part of an appliance.

Receptacle outlets as required in Section 220-4(b) for the kitchen, pantry, etc. and Section 220-4(c) for laundry areas are not to have any other outlets or permanently connected lighting fixtures connected to them.

Branch Circuit, General Purpose: A branch circuit that supplies a number of outlets for lighting and appliances.

Branch Circuit, Individual: A branch circuit that supplies only one utilization equipment.

An individual branch circuit is a circuit that supplies "only" one utilization equipment, that is, one range, or one space heater, or one motor. See Section 210-23.

It may supply "only" one single receptacle for the connection of a single attachment plug. See Section 210-21(b).

A branch circuit may be installed to supply one duplex receptacle which can accommodate two cord- and plug-connected appliances or similar equipment. This circuit would not be considered an individual branch circuit. See Figure 100-6.

Figure 100-6. Illustrated is a single receptacle, which is intended for the connection of one utilization equipment. This single receptacle is required to have an ampere rating not less than the branch circuit. See Section 210-21(b)(1).

Branch Circuit, Multiwire: A branch circuit consisting of two or more ungrounded conductors having a potential difference between them, and a grounded conductor having equal potential difference between it and each ungrounded conductor of the circuit and which is connected to the neutral conductor of the system.

See Sections 210-4, 210-6(c), and 240-20(b).

Branch-Circuit Selection Current: See Section 440-4(c), Definition.

Building: A structure which stands alone or which is cut off from adjoining structures by fire walls with all openings therein protected by approved fire doors.

A building is a structure that may be used or intended for supporting or sheltering any use or occupancy. It may also be a separate structure such as a pole or water tower. Definitions of the terms "fire walls" and "fire doors" are the responsibility of the municipal and/or state building codes and interpretations of building terms have been avoided by *NEC* committees. "Fire-resistance rating" is defined as the time, in minutes or hours, that materials or assemblies have withstood a fire exposure.

Cabinet: An enclosure designed either for surface or flush mounting and provided with a frame, mat, or trim in which a swinging door or doors are or may be hung.

Both cabinets and cutout boxes are covered in Article 373. Cabinets are designed for surface or flush mounting with a trim to which a swinging door(s) is hung. Cutout boxes are designed for surface mounting with a swinging door(s) secured directly to the box. Panelboards are electrical assemblies designed to be placed in a cabinet or cutout box. See definitions of "cutout box" and "panelboard."

Cell (As applied to Raceways): See Sections 356-1 and 358-2.

Circuit Breaker: A device designed to open and close a circuit by nonautomatic means and to open the circuit automatically on a predetermined overcurrent without injury to itself when properly applied within its rating.

(FPN): The automatic opening means can be integral, direct acting with the circuit breaker or remote from the circuit breaker. See definition of "Switching Devices" in Part B of this article for definition applying to circuits and equipment over 600 volts, nominal.

Adjustable: (As applied to Circuit Breakers.) A qualifying term indicating that the circuit breaker can be set to trip at various values of current and/or time within a predetermined range.

Instantaneous Trip: (As applied to Circuit Breakers.) A qualifying term indicating that no delay is purposely introduced in the tripping action of the circuit breaker.

Inverse Time: (As applied to Circuit Breakers.) A qualifying term indicating there is purposely introduced a delay in the tripping action of the circuit breaker, which delay decreases as the magnitude of the current increases.

Nonadjustable: (As applied to Circuit Breakers.) A qualifying term indicating that the circuit breaker does not have any adjustment to alter the value of current at which it will trip or the time required for its operation.

Setting: (of Circuit Breaker.) The value of current and/or time at which an adjustable circuit breaker is set to trip.

Concealed: Rendered inaccessible by the structure or finish of the building. Wires in concealed raceways are considered concealed, even though they may become accessible by withdrawing them. [See "Accessible — (As applied to wiring methods)."]

Raceways and cables supported or located within the hollow frames or permanently closed in by the finish of buildings are considered "concealed." Open-type work, such as raceways and cables in exposed areas, in unfinished basements, in accessible underfloor areas or attics, attached to the surface of finished areas, or behind panels designed to allow access and which may be removed without damage to the building structure or finish, are not considered "concealed." See definition of "Exposed (as applied to wiring methods)."

Conductor:

Bare: A conductor having no covering or electrical insulation whatsoever. (See "Conductor, Covered.")

Covered: A conductor encased within material of composition or thickness that is not recognized by this Code as electrical insulation. (See "Conductor, Bare.")

A typical covered conductor is the green-colored covered equipment grounding conductor in nonmetallic-sheathed cable. A covered conductor should be treated as a bare conductor for working clearances, etc.

Insulated: A conductor encased within material of composition and thickness that is recognized by this Code as electrical insulation.

Conduit Body: A separate portion of a conduit or tubing system that provides access through a removable cover(s) to the interior of the system at a junction of two or more sections of the system or at a terminal point of the system.
Boxes such as FS and FD or larger cast or sheet metal boxes are not classified as conduit bodies. See Table 370-6(a).

Conduit bodies are a portion of a raceway system with removable covers to allow access to the interior of the system.
Conduit bodies are referred to in the trade as "condulets" and include the LB, LL, LR, C, T, and X designs. Sections 300-15, 331-13, 345-14, 346-14, 347-16, and 348-14, and Article 370 may be referred to for the rules on the usage of conduit bodies.
Fittings, such as capped elbows and service-entrance elbows, are not classified as conduit bodies.
Type FS or FD boxes are not classified as conduit bodies; they are listed with boxes in Table 370-6(a).

Connector, Pressure (Solderless): A device that establishes a connection between two or more conductors or between one or more conductors and a terminal by means of mechanical pressure and without the use of solder.

Continuous Duty: See under "Duty."

Continuous Load: A load where the maximum current is expected to continue for three hours or more.

Control Circuit: See Section 430-71.

Controller: A device or group of devices that serves to govern, in some predetermined manner, the electric power delivered to the apparatus to which it is connected. See also Section 430-81(a).

A "controller" may be a switch, circuit breaker, or device normally used to start and stop motors and other apparatus and, in the case of motors, is to be capable of interrupting the stalled-rotor current of the motor. Stop and start stations and similar control circuit components are not considered controllers.

Cooking Unit, Counter-Mounted: A cooking appliance designed for mounting in or on a counter and consisting of one or more heating elements, internal wiring, and built-in or separately mountable controls. (See "Oven, Wall-Mounted.")

Copper-Clad Aluminum Conductors: Conductors drawn from a copper-clad aluminum rod with the copper metallurgically bonded to an aluminum core. The copper forms a minimum of 10 percent of the cross-sectional area of a solid conductor or each strand of a stranded conductor.

Covered Conductor: See under "Conductor."

Current-Limiting Overcurrent Protective Device: See Section 240-11.

Cutout Box: An enclosure designed for surface mounting and having swinging doors or covers secured directly to and telescoping with the walls of the box proper. (See "Cabinet.")

Damp Location: See under "Location."

Dead Front: Without live parts exposed to a person on the operating side of the equipment.

Demand Factor: The ratio of the maximum demand of a system, or part of a system, to the total connected load of a system or the part of the system under consideration.

Device: A unit of an electrical system which is intended to carry but not utilize electric energy.

Units, such as switches, circuit breakers, fuseholders, receptacles, attachment plugs, and lampholders, that distribute or control, but do not consume electricity, are termed "devices."

Disconnecting Means: A device, or group of devices, or other means by which the conductors of a circuit can be disconnected from their source of supply.

For disconnecting means for service equipment, see Part F of Article 230; for fuses and thermal cutouts, see Part D of Article 240; for circuit breakers, see Part G of Article 240; for appliances, see Part D of Article 422; for space heating equipment, see Part C of Article 424; for motors and controllers, see Part H of Article 430; and for air-conditioning and refrigerating equipment, see Part B of Article 440. See also references for "disconnecting means" in Index.

(FPN): See definition in Part B of this article for definition applying to circuits and equipment over 600 volts, nominal.

Dry Location: See under "Location."

Dust-Ignitionproof: See Section 502-1.

Dustproof: So constructed or protected that dust will not interfere with its successful operation.

Dusttight: So constructed that dust will not enter the enclosing case under specified test conditions.

(FPN): For test conditions other than for rotating equipment, see ANSI/NEMA 250-1979, Enclosures for Electrical Equipment, Paragraph 250.5.05.

Reference to the ANSI/NEMA Standard will permit the user to evaluate the enclosure with regard to actual conditions of use. See Section 430-91 for motor controller enclosure types.

See paragraph following Table 430-22(a), Exception.

Duty:

Continuous Duty: Operation at a substantially constant load for an indefinitely long time.

Intermittent Duty: Operation for alternate intervals of (1) load and no load; or (2) load and rest; or (3) load, no load, and rest.

Periodic Duty: Intermittent operation in which the load conditions are regularly recurrent.

Short-Time Duty: Operation at a substantially constant load for a short and definitely specified time.

Varying Duty: Operation at loads, and for intervals of time, both of which may be subject to wide variation.

(FPN): See Table 430-22(a), Exception for illustration of various types of duty.

For the protection of intermittent, periodic, short-time, and varying-duty motors against overload, see Section 430-33.

Duty Cycle (Welding): See Section 630-31(b), Fine Print Note.

Dwelling:

Dwelling Unit: One or more rooms for the use of one or more persons as a housekeeping unit with space for eating, living, and sleeping, and permanent provisions for cooking and sanitation.

Where dwelling units are referenced throughout the *Code*, it is important to note that rooms of motels, hotels, and similar occupancies may be classified as dwelling units. See Figure 100-7.

Multifamily Dwelling: A building containing three or more dwelling units.

One-Family Dwelling: A building consisting solely of one dwelling unit.

Two-Family Dwelling: A building consisting solely of two dwelling units.

Electric Sign: A fixed, stationary, or portable self-contained, electrically illuminated utilization equipment with words or symbols designed to convey information or attract attention.

Enclosed: Surrounded by a case, housing, fence, or walls which will prevent persons from accidentally contacting energized parts.

Enclosure: The case or housing of apparatus, or the fence or walls surrounding an installation to prevent personnel from accidentally contacting energized parts, or to protect the equipment from physical damage.

Figure 100-7. A motel or hotel room with eating, living, and sleeping areas and areas having permanent provisions for cooking and sanitation meets the definition of a "dwelling unit."

(FPN): For enclosure types, see ANSI/NEMA 250-1979, Enclosures for Electrical Equipment (1000 Volts Maximum).

Equipment: A general term including material, fittings, devices, appliances, fixtures, apparatus, and the like used as a part of, or in connection with, an electrical installation.

Equipment Grounding Conductor: See "Grounding Conductor, Equipment."

See Section 250-91(b) for types of equipment grounding conductors.

Explosionproof Apparatus: Apparatus enclosed in a case that is capable of withstanding an explosion of a specified gas or vapor which may occur within it and of preventing the ignition of a specified gas or vapor surrounding the enclosure by sparks, flashes, or explosion of the gas or vapor within, and which operates at such an external temperature that a surrounding flammable atmosphere will not be ignited thereby.

Exposed: (As applied to live parts.) Capable of being inadvertently touched or approached nearer than a safe distance by a person. It is applied to parts not suitably guarded, isolated, or insulated. (See "Accessible" and "Concealed.")

See Section 110-17.

Exposed: (As applied to wiring methods.) On or attached to the surface or behind panels designed to allow access. [See "Accessible — (As applied to wiring methods)."]

See Figure 100-1.

Externally Operable: Capable of being operated without exposing the operator to contact with live parts.

Feeder: All circuit conductors between the service equipment or the source of a separately derived system and the final branch-circuit overcurrent device.

See Figure 100-5.

Festoon Lighting: See Section 225-6(b).

Fitting: An accessory such as a locknut, bushing, or other part of a wiring system that is intended primarily to perform a mechanical rather than an electrical function.

Garage: A building or portion of a building in which one or more self-propelled vehicles carrying volatile flammable liquid for fuel or power are kept for use, sale, storage, rental, repair, exhibition, or demonstrating purposes, and all that portion of a building which is on or below the floor or floors in which such vehicles are kept and which is not separated therefrom by suitable cutoffs.

(FPN): See Section 511-1.

General-Purpose Branch Circuit: See "Branch Circuit, General Purpose."

General-Use Snap Switch: See under "Switches."

General-Use Switch: See under "Switches."

Ground: A conducting connection, whether intentional or accidental, between an electrical circuit or equipment and the earth, or to some conducting body that serves in place of the earth.

Grounded: Connected to earth or to some conducting body that serves in place of the earth.

Grounded (Effectively Grounded Communication System): See Section 800-2(c)(1).

Grounded Conductor: A system or circuit conductor that is intentionally grounded.

Grounding Conductor: A conductor used to connect equipment or the grounded circuit of a wiring system to a grounding electrode or electrodes.

Grounding Conductor, Equipment: The conductor used to connect the noncurrent-carrying metal parts of equipment, raceways, and other enclosures to the system grounded conductor and/or the grounding electrode conductor at the service equipment or at the source of a separately derived system.

Grounding Electrode Conductor: The conductor used to connect the grounding electrode to the equipment grounding conductor and/or to the grounded conductor of the circuit at the service equipment or at the source of a separately derived system.

The grounding electrode conductor is required to be copper, aluminum, or copper-clad aluminum and is used to connect the equipment grounding conductor or the grounded conductor (at the service equipment or at the separately derived system) to the grounding electrode for either grounded or ungrounded systems. It is sized by using Table 250-94. See also Article 250, Parts H and J.

Ground-Fault Circuit-Interrupter: A device intended for the protection of personnel that functions to de-energize a circuit or portion thereof within an established period of time when a current to ground exceeds some predetermined value that is less than that required to operate the overcurrent protective device of the supply circuit.

See Figures 210-11, 210-12, and 210-13. See also references for "ground-fault circuit-interrupters" in Index.

Ground-Fault Protection of Equipment: A system intended to provide protection of equipment from damaging line-to-ground fault currents by operating to cause a disconnecting means to open all ungrounded conductors of the faulted circuit. This protection is provided at current levels less than those required to protect conductors from damage through the operation of a supply circuit overcurrent device.

See commentary on Section 230-95.

Guarded: Covered, shielded, fenced, enclosed, or otherwise protected by means of suitable covers, casings, barriers, rails, screens, mats, or platforms to remove the likelihood of approach or contact by persons or objects to a point of danger.

Hazardous (Classified) Locations: See Article 500.

Header: See Sections 356-1 and 358-2.

Hermetic Refrigerant Motor-Compressor: See Section 440-2.

Hoistway: Any shaftway, hatchway, well hole, or other vertical opening or space in which an elevator or dumbwaiter is designed to operate.

See Article 620 for the installation of electric equipment and wiring methods in hoistways.

Identified: (As applied to Equipment.) Recognizable as suitable for the specific purpose, function, use, environment, application, etc., where described in a particular Code requirement. (See "Equipment.")

(FPN): Suitability of equipment for a specific purpose, environment, or application may be determined by a qualified testing laboratory, inspection agency, or other organization concerned with product evaluation. Such identification may include labeling or listing: see "Labeled," "Listed," and Section 90-6.

Individual Branch Circuit: See "Branch Circuit, Individual."

In Sight From (Within Sight From, Within Sight): Where this Code specifies that one equipment shall be "in sight from," "within sight from," or "within sight," etc., of another equipment, one of the equipments specified is to be visible and not more than 50 feet (15.24 m) distant from the other.

See Figures 430-18, 430-19, and 430-20, and Figure 600-1.

Insulated Conductor: See under "Conductor."

Intermittent Duty: See under "Duty."

Interrupting Rating: The highest current at rated voltage that a device is intended to interrupt under standard test conditions.

(FPN): Equipment intended to break current at other than fault levels may have its interrupting rating implied in other ratings, such as horsepower or locked rotor current.

Interrupting ratings are essential to coordinating electrical systems so that available fault currents can be properly controlled.

Isolated: Not readily accessible to persons unless special means for access are used.

See definition of "isolating switch" under "Switches" in Article 100.

Labeled: Equipment or materials to which has been attached a label, symbol, or other identifying mark of an organization acceptable to the authority having jurisdiction and concerned with product evaluation, that maintains periodic inspection of production of labeled equipment or materials and by whose labeling the manufacturer indicates compliance with appropriate standards or performance in a specified manner.

Equipment and conductors required or permitted by this *Code* are acceptable only when approved for a specific environment or application by the authority having jurisdiction. See Section 110-2.

"Listing" or "labeling" by a qualified testing laboratory will provide a basis for approval. See Section 90-6.

Lighting Outlet: An outlet intended for the direct connection of a lampholder, a lighting fixture, or a pendant cord terminating in a lampholder.

Listed: Equipment or materials included in a list published by an organization acceptable to the authority having jurisdiction and concerned with product evaluation, that maintains periodic inspection of production of listed equipment or materials, and whose listing states either that the equipment or material meets appropriate standards or has been tested and found suitable for use in a specified manner.

(FPN): The means for identifying listed equipment may vary for each organization concerned with product evaluation, some of which do not recognize equipment as listed unless it is also labeled. The authority having jurisdiction should utilize the system employed by the listing organization to identify a listed product.

See comments that follow the definition of "labeled."

Location:

Damp Location: Partially protected locations under canopies, marquees, roofed open porches, and like locations, and interior locations subject to moderate degrees of moisture, such as some basements, some barns, and some cold-storage warehouses.

Dry Location: A location not normally subject to dampness or wetness. A location classified as dry may be temporarily subject to dampness or wetness, as in the case of a building under construction.

Wet Location: Installations underground or in concrete slabs or masonry in direct contact with the earth, and locations subject to saturation with water or other liquids, such as vehicle washing areas, and locations exposed to weather and unprotected.

See Sections 300-6(c) and 410-4.

Multioutlet Assembly: A type of surface or flush raceway designed to hold conductors and receptacles, assembled in the field or at the factory.

In dry locations, metallic and nonmetallic multioutlet assemblies are permitted; however, they are not permitted to be installed where concealed. See Article 353 for details on recessing these assemblies.

Multiwire Branch Circuit: See "Branch Circuit, Multiwire."

Neutral Conductor: See Note 10 to Tables 310-16 through 310-31.

Nonautomatic: Action requiring personal intervention for its control. (See "Automatic.")

(FPN): As applied to an electric controller, nonautomatic control does not necessarily imply a manual controller, but only that personal intervention is necessary.

Outlet: A point on the wiring system at which current is taken to supply utilization equipment.

For example, a lighting outlet or a receptacle outlet.

Outline Lighting: An arrangement of incandescent lamps or electric discharge tubing to outline or call attention to certain features such as the shape of a building or the decoration of a window.

See Article 600, Part B (600 Volts, Nominal, or Less) and Part C (Over 600 Volts, Nominal).

Oven, Wall-Mounted: An oven for cooking purposes designed for mounting in or on a wall or other surface and consisting of one or more heating elements, internal wiring, and built-in or separately mountable controls. (See "Cooking Unit, Counter-Mounted.")

Overcurrent: Any current in excess of the rated current of equipment or the ampacity of a conductor. It may result from overload (see definition), short circuit, or ground fault.

(FPN): A current in excess of rating may be accommodated by certain equipment and conductors for a given set of conditions. Hence the rules for overcurrent protection are specific for particular situations.

Overload: Operation of equipment in excess of normal, full-load rating, or of a conductor in excess of rated ampacity which, when it persists for a sufficient length of time, would cause damage or dangerous overheating. A fault, such as a short circuit or ground fault, is not an overload. (See "Overcurrent.")

(FPN): For motor apparatus applications, see Section 430-31.

Panelboard: A single panel or group of panel units designed for assembly in the form of a single panel; including buses, automatic overcurrent devices, and with or without switches for the control of light, heat, or power circuits; designed to be placed in a cabinet or cutout box placed in or against a wall or partition and accessible only from the front. (See "Switchboard.")

See Article 384.

Periodic Duty: See under "Duty."

Power Outlet: An enclosed assembly which may include receptacles, circuit breakers, fuseholders, fused switches, buses, and watt-hour meter mounting means; intended to supply and control power to mobile homes, recreational vehicles, or boats; or to serve as a means for distributing power required to operate mobile or temporarily installed equipment.

See Figures 305-1 and 550-1.

Premises Wiring (System):   That interior and exterior wiring, including power, lighting, control, and signal circuit wiring together with all of its associated hardware, fittings, and wiring devices, both permanently and temporarily installed, which extends from the load end of the service drop, or load end of the service lateral conductors to the outlet(s). Such wiring does not include wiring internal to appliances, fixtures, motors, controllers, motor control centers, and similar equipment.

Premises wiring also includes interior and exterior wiring that extends from the source of a separately derived system, as defined in Section 250-5(d), to the outlet(s). In many cases, most of a building wiring system is supplied by a separately derived system. An example would be an on-premises privately owned transformer supplying all building loads. The transformer is part of the premises wiring system.
On the other hand, a premises wiring system does not include the internal wiring that is part of electrical equipment that includes a transformer as part of the equipment.

23

ARTICLE 100—DEFINITIONS

Projector, Nonprofessional: See Section 540-3.

Projector, Professional: See Section 540-2.

Qualified Person: One familiar with the construction and operation of the equipment and the hazards involved.

Raceway: An enclosed channel designed expressly for holding wires, cables, or busbars, with additional functions as permitted in this Code.

(FPN): Raceways may be of metal or insulating material, and the term includes rigid metal conduit, rigid nonmetallic conduit, intermediate metal conduit, liquidtight flexible metal conduit, flexible metallic tubing, flexible metal conduit, electrical nonmetallic tubing, electrical metallic tubing, underfloor raceways, cellular concrete floor raceways, cellular metal floor raceways, surface raceways, wireways, and busways.

Cable trays (see Article 318) are not considered raceways in the *NEC*.

Rainproof: So constructed, protected, or treated as to prevent rain from interfering with the successful operation of the apparatus under specified test conditions.

Testing laboratories perform tests which are used to evaluate equipment under specified test conditions. These tests are well known to manufacturers of electrical products as well as to users of this type of equipment. Descriptions of the tests are available from the testing laboratories. Users of the *NEC* should be alerted to the existence of these tests.

Raintight: So constructed or protected that exposure to a beating rain will not result in the entrance of water under specified test conditions.

Raceways on exterior surfaces of buildings are required to be made raintight. See Sections 225-22 and 230-53.
For boxes and cabinets, see Section 300-6.
See comments following definition of "Rainproof."

Rated-Load Current: See Section 440-4(a), Definition.

Readily Accessible: (See "Accessible, Readily.")

Overcurrent devices are required to be readily accessible. See Section 240-24(a). There is considered to be a high degree of safety when switches or circuit breakers can be disconnected quickly without being hindered by obstacles. See Section 230-72(c) for services. See also the exceptions to this rule for busways, Section 364-12; and for supplementary overcurrent protection, Section 240-10.

Receptacle: A receptacle is a contact device installed at the outlet for the connection of a single attachment plug.

(FPN): A single receptacle is a single contact device with no other contact device on the same yoke. A multiple receptacle is a single device containing two or more receptacles.

The basic receptacle is a single contact device for the connection of a single attachment plug. A multiple receptacle is a contact device containing two or more receptacles for the connection of two or more attachment plugs. A duplex receptacle is a multiple receptacle. See Figure 100-8.

Receptacle Outlet: An outlet where one or more receptacles are installed.

See Figure 100-8.

One
receptacle

Multiple receptacles

Figure 100-8. When calculating other loads — all occupancies [Section 220-3(c)], loads for additions to existing dwelling units [Section 220-3(d)(1)], and other than dwelling units [Section 220-3(d)(2)] each single or multiple receptacle is to be considered at not less than 180 VA.

Remote-Control Circuit: Any electric circuit that controls any other circuit through a relay or an equivalent device.

See Figure 100-9.

Stop

Start

Remote control
circuit

Motor

Figure 100-9. A remote-control circuit for starting and stopping an electric motor.

ARTICLE 100—DEFINITIONS

Sealable Equipment: Equipment enclosed in a case or cabinet that is provided with a means of sealing or locking so that live parts cannot be made accessible without opening the enclosure. The equipment may or may not be operable without opening the enclosure.

Separately Derived System: See Section 250-5(d).

Service: The conductors and equipment for delivering energy from the electricity supply system to the wiring system of the premises served.

Service Cable: Service conductors made up in the form of a cable.

Service Conductors: The supply conductors that extend from the street main or from transformers to the service equipment of the premises supplied.

Service conductors from an overhead distribution system originate at the utility pole, or wires attached to it, and terminate at the service equipment.

Service conductors from an underground distribution system originate at the utility manhole and terminate at the service equipment. When primary conductors are extended to outdoor pad-mounted or underground transformers on private property, the service conductors originate at the secondary connections of the transformers.

See Figure 100-10.

See Article 230, Part H for service conductors exceeding 600 V, nominal.

Service Drop: The overhead service conductors from the last pole or other aerial support to and including the splices, if any, connecting to the service-entrance conductors at the building or other structure.

See Figure 100-11.

Service-Entrance Conductors, Overhead System: The service conductors between the terminals of the service equipment and a point usually outside the building, clear of building walls, where joined by tap or splice to the service drop.

See Figure 100-11.

Service-Entrance Conductors, Underground System: The service conductors between the terminals of the service equipment and the point of connection to the service lateral.

See Figure 100-12.

(FPN): Where service equipment is located outside the building walls, there may be no service-entrance conductors, or they may be entirely outside the building.

Service Equipment: The necessary equipment, usually consisting of a circuit breaker or switch and fuses, and their accessories, located near the point of entrance of supply conductors to a building or other structure, or an otherwise defined area, and intended to constitute the main control and means of cutoff of the supply.

Service equipment consists of a circuit breaker or a fused switch provided to disconnect all ungrounded conductors in a building or other structure from the service-entrance conductors.

The disconnecting means at any one location is to consist of not more than six circuit breakers or six switches and is required to be readily accessible, either inside or outside the building or structure, nearest the point of entrance of the service-entrance conductors. See Section 230-6.

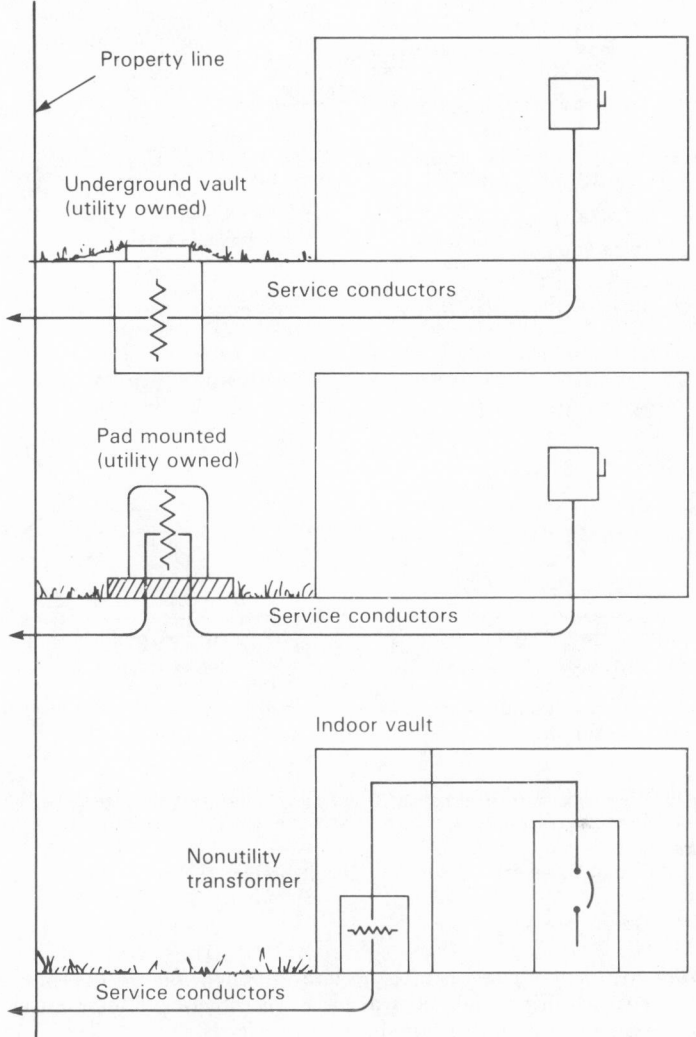

Figure 100-10. This illustrates a situation where the service conductors may be located on the primary side of a transformer.

See Article 230, Part F.

Service Lateral: The underground service conductors between the street main, including any risers at a pole or other structure or from transformers, and the first point of connection to the service-entrance conductors in a terminal box or meter or other enclosure with adequate space, inside or outside the building wall. Where there is no terminal box, meter, or other enclosure with adequate space, the point of connection shall be considered to be the point of entrance of the service conductors into the building.

See Figure 100-12.

Service Raceway: The raceway that encloses the service-entrance conductors.

Figure 100-11. Illustration of an overhead system showing a service drop from a utility pole to attachment on the house and service-entrance conductors from point of attachment (spliced to service-drop conductors), down the side of the house, through the meter socket, and terminating within the service equipment.

Figure 100-12. Service laterals (underground systems) may be run from poles or from transformers and with or without terminal boxes.

Setting (of Circuit Breaker): See under "Circuit Breaker."

Short-Time Duty: See under "Duty."

Show Window: Any window used or designed to be used for the display of goods or advertising material, whether it is fully or partly enclosed or entirely open at the rear and whether or not it has a platform raised higher than the street floor level.

See Figure 220-5.

Sign: See "Electric Sign."

Signaling Circuit: Any electric circuit that energizes signaling equipment.

Solar Photovoltaic System: The total components and subsystems which in combination convert solar energy into electrical energy suitable for connection to a utilization load.

See Article 690 for requirements for solar photovoltaic systems.

Special Permission: The written consent of the authority having jurisdiction.

The authority having jurisdiction for enforcement of the *Code* has responsibility for making interpretations and granting special permission contemplated in a number of the rules. Examples: see Section 110-16(a), Exception No. 2; Section 230-2, Exception Nos. 3, 4c., and 5; and Section 426-14.

Switchboard: A large single panel, frame, or assembly of panels on which are mounted, on the face or back or both, switches, overcurrent and other protective devices, buses, and usually instruments. Switchboards are generally accessible from the rear as well as from the front and are not intended to be installed in cabinets. (See "Panelboard.")

Busbars are to be arranged to avoid inductive overheating.

Service busbars are required to be isolated by barriers from the remainder of the switchboard.

Most modern switchboards are totally enclosed to reduce to a minimum the probability of communicating fire to adjacent combustible materials and to guard live parts.

Switches:

General-Use Switch: A switch intended for use in general distribution and branch circuits. It is rated in amperes, and it is capable of interrupting its rated current at its rated voltage.

General-Use Snap Switch: A form of general-use switch so constructed that it can be installed in flush device boxes or on outlet box covers, or otherwise used in conjunction with wiring systems recognized by this Code.

AC General-Use Snap Switch: See Section 380-14(a).

AC-DC General-Use Snap Switch: See Section 380-14(b).

Isolating Switch: A switch intended for isolating an electric circuit from the source of power. It has no interrupting rating, and it is intended to be operated only after the circuit has been opened by some other means.

Motor-Circuit Switch: A switch, rated in horsepower, capable of interrupting the maximum operating overload current of a motor of the same horsepower rating as the switch at the rated voltage.

Thermal Cutout: An overcurrent protective device that contains a heater element in addition to and affecting a renewable fusible member which opens the circuit. It is not designed to interrupt short-circuit currents.

Thermally Protected: (As applied to motors.) The words "Thermally Protected" appearing on the nameplate of a motor or motor-compressor indicate that the motor is provided with a thermal protector.

Thermal Protector: (As applied to motors.) A protective device for assembly as an integral part of a motor or motor-compressor and which, when properly applied, protects the motor against dangerous overheating due to overload and failure to start.

(FPN): The thermal protector may consist of one or more sensing elements integral with the motor or motor-compressor and an external control device.

Utilization Equipment: Equipment which utilizes electric energy for mechanical, chemical, heating, lighting, or similar purposes.

Varying Duty: See under "Duty."

Ventilated: Provided with a means to permit circulation of air sufficient to remove an excess of heat, fumes, or vapors.

See commentary following Section 110-13(b).

Volatile Flammable Liquid: A flammable liquid having a flash point below 38°C (100°F), or a flammable liquid whose temperature is above its flash point, or a Class II combustible liquid having a vapor pressure not exceeding 40 psia (276 kPa) at 38°C (100°F) whose temperature is above its flash point.

The flash point of a liquid is the minimum temperature at which it gives off sufficient vapor to form an ignitible mixture with the air near the surface of the liquid or within the vessel used. An "ignitible mixture" is a mixture within the explosive or flammable range (between upper and lower limits) that is capable of the propagation of flame away from the source of ignition when ignited. Some emission of vapors takes place below the flash point but not in sufficient quantities to form an ignitible mixture.

Voltage (of a Circuit): The greatest root-mean-square (effective) difference of potential between any two conductors of the circuit concerned.

(FPN): Some systems, such as 3-phase 4-wire, single-phase 3-wire, and 3-wire direct-current may have various circuits of various voltages.

A 3-phase, 4-wire wye system has two voltages (for example, 277/480 or 120/208). The "voltage of the circuit" is the highest voltage between any two conductors, that is, 480 V and 208 V. The "voltage of the circuit" of a 2-wire feeder or branch circuit (one phase and the grounded conductor) derived from the above systems would be the voltage between the two conductors at the lower voltage, that is, 277 V and 120 V.
The same applies to dc or single-phase, 3-wire systems where there are two voltages.

Voltage, Nominal: A nominal value assigned to a circuit or system for the purpose of conveniently designating its voltage class (as 120/240, 480Y/277, 600, etc.).

See Section 220-2.

The actual voltage at which a circuit operates can vary from the nominal within a range that permits satisfactory operation of equipment.

(FPN): See "Voltage Ratings for Electric Power Systems and Equipment (60 Hz)," ANSI C84.1-1982.

Voltage to Ground: For grounded circuits, the voltage between the given conductor and that point or conductor of the circuit that is grounded; for ungrounded circuits, the greatest voltage between the given conductor and any other conductor of the circuit.

The "voltage to ground" of a 277/480 V wye system would be 277 V; of a 120/208 V wye system, 120 V; and of a 3-phase, 3-wire ungrounded 480 V system, 480 V.
For a 3-phase, 4-wire delta system with the center of one leg grounded, there are two voltages to ground. For example, on a 240-volt system, two legs would have 120 V to ground and the third or "high" leg would have 208 volts to ground. See Sections 215-8, 230-56, and 384-3(e) for special marking on such circuits.

Watertight: So constructed that moisture will not enter the enclosure under specified test conditions.

(FPN): For test conditions other than for rotating equipment, see NEMA standards Publication No. 250-1979 - Enclosure for Electrical Equipment (1000 Volts Maximum) Section 250-5.07, Hosedown Test.

Unless the enclosure is hermetically sealed, it is possible for moisture to enter the enclosure. The ANSI/NEMA Standard alerts the user to the possibility of condensation in the enclosure and contains widely used testing procedures for enclosures for electrical equipment.

Weatherproof: So constructed or protected that exposure to the weather will not interfere with successful operation.

(FPN): Rainproof, raintight, or watertight equipment can fulfill the requirements for weatherproof where varying weather conditions other than wetness, such as snow, ice, dust, or temperature extremes, are not a factor.

Welder, Electric:

Actual Primary Current: See Section 630-31(b).

Rated Primary Current: See Section 630-31(b).

Wet Location: See under "Location."

X-ray:

Long-Time Rating: See Sections 517-140 and 660-2.

Momentary Rating: See Sections 517-140 and 660-2.

B. Over 600 Volts, Nominal

Whereas the preceding definitions are intended to apply wherever the terms are used throughout this Code, the following ones are applicable only to the parts of articles specifically covering installations and equipment operating at over 600 volts, nominal.

Circuit Breaker: See under "Switching Devices."

Cutout: See under "Switching Devices."

Disconnect (Isolator):   See under "Switching Devices."

Disconnecting Means: See under "Switching Devices."

Fuse: An overcurrent protective device with a circuit opening fusible part that is heated and severed by the passage of overcurrent through it.

(FPN): A fuse comprises all the parts that form a unit capable of performing the prescribed functions. It may or may not be the complete device necessary to connect it into an electrical circuit.

Expulsion Fuse Unit (Expulsion Fuse):   A vented fuse unit in which the expulsion effect of gases produced by the arc and lining of the fuseholder, either alone or aided by a spring, extinguishes the arc.

Power Fuse Unit: A vented, nonvented or controlled vented fuse unit in which the arc is extinguished by being drawn through solid material, granular material, or liquid, either alone or aided by a spring.

Vented Power Fuse: A fuse with provision for the escape of arc gases, liquids, or solid particles to the surrounding atmosphere during circuit interruption.

Nonvented Power Fuse: A fuse without intentional provision for the escape of arc gases, liquids, or solid particles to the atmosphere during circuit interruption.

Controlled Vented Power Fuse: A fuse with provision for controlling discharge circuit interruption such that no solid material may be exhausted into the surrounding atmosphere.

(FPN): The fuse is designed so that discharged gases will not ignite or damage insulation in the path of the discharge or propagate a flashover to or between grounded members or conduction members in the path of the discharge when the distance between the vent and such insulation or conduction members conforms to manufacturer's recommendations.

Grounded, Effectively: Permanently connected to earth through a ground connection of sufficiently low impedance and having sufficient ampacity that ground-fault current which may occur cannot build up to voltages dangerous to personnel.

Interrupter Switch: See under "Switching Devices."

Multiple Fuse: An assembly of two or more single-pole fuses.

Oil (Filled) Cutout: See under "Switching Devices."

Power Fuse: See under "Fuse."

Regulator Bypass Switch: See under "Switching Devices."

Switching Device: A device designed to close and/or open one or more electric circuits.

Switching Devices:

Circuit Breaker: A switching device capable of making, carrying, and breaking currents under normal circuit conditions, and also making, carrying for a specified time, and breaking currents under specified abnormal circuit conditions, such as those of short circuit.

Cutout: An assembly of a fuse support with either a fuseholder, fuse carrier, or disconnecting blade. The fuseholder or fuse carrier may include a conducting element (fuse link), or may act as the disconnecting blade by the inclusion of a nonfusible member.

Disconnecting (or Isolating) Switch (Disconnector, Isolator): A mechanical switching device used for isolating a circuit or equipment from a source of power.

Disconnecting Means: A device, group of devices, or other means whereby the conductors of a circuit can be disconnected from their source of supply.

Interrupter Switch: A switch capable of making, carrying, and interrupting specified currents.

Oil Cutout (Oil-Filled Cutout): A cutout in which all or part of the fuse support and its fuse link or disconnecting blade are mounted in oil with complete immersion of the contacts and the fusible portion of the conducting element (fuse link), so that arc interruption by severing of the fuse link or by opening of the contacts will occur under oil.

Oil Switch: An oil switch is a switch having contacts which operate under oil (or askarel or other suitable liquid).

Regulator Bypass Switch: A specific device or combination of devices designed to bypass a regulator.

ARTICLE 110 — REQUIREMENTS FOR
ELECTRICAL INSTALLATIONS

Contents

A. General

110-1. Mandatory Rules and Explanatory Material. Mandatory rules of this Code are characterized by the use of the word "shall." Explanatory material is in the form of Fine Print Notes (FPN).

In addition to printing explanatory material in fine print (small type), the material is further identified in the *Code* by the term "(FPN)" preceding the paragraph. Footnotes to tables, although also in fine print, are not explanatory material unless identified by the term "(FPN)"; the footnotes are part of the tables and are necessary for the proper use of the tables. For example, see the footnotes to Table 310-16.

110-2. Approval. The conductors and equipment required or permitted by this Code shall be acceptable only if approved.

(FPN): See Examination of Equipment for Safety, Section 90-6 and Examination, Identification, Installation, and Use of Equipment, Section 110-3. See definitions of "Approved," "Identified," "Labeled," and "Listed."

Section 110-2 of the *Code* requires that all equipment be approved as defined in Article 100 and, as such, be acceptable to the authority having jurisdiction. Section 110-3 provides guidance for the judging of equipment and recognizes listing or labeling as a means of establishing suitability.

Approval of equipment is the responsibility of the electrical inspection authority, and many such "approvals" are based on tests and listings of testing laboratories such as Underwriters Laboratories Inc. (UL), Factory Mutual Engineering and Research Corp. (FM), ETL Testing Laboratories, Inc. (ETL), etc.

110-3. Examination, Identification, Installation, and Use of Equipment.

(a) Examination. In judging equipment, considerations such as the following shall be evaluated:

(1) Suitability for installation and use in conformity with the provisions of this Code. Suitability of equipment use may be identified by a description marked on or provided with a product to identify the suitability of the product for a specific purpose, environment, or application. Suitability of equipment may be evidenced by listing or labeling.

(2) Mechanical strength and durability, including, for parts designed to enclose and protect other equipment, the adequacy of the protection thus provided.

(3) Wire-bending and connection space.

(4) Electrical insulation.

(5) Heating effects under normal conditions of use and also under abnormal conditions likely to arise in service.

(6) Arcing effects.

(7) Classification by type, size, voltage, current capacity, specific use.

(8) Other factors which contribute to the practical safeguarding of persons using or likely to come in contact with the equipment.

For wire-bending and connection space in cabinets and cutout boxes, see Section 373-6, Tables 373-6(a) and 373-6(b), and Sections 373-7, 373-9, and 373-11. For wire-bending and connection space in other equipment, see the appropriate *NEC* article and section. For example, see Section 370-18 for outlet, device, pull and junction boxes, and conduit bodies; Sections 380-3 and 380-18 for switches; Section 384-3(g) for switchboards and panelboards; and Section 430-10 for motors and motor controllers.

(b) Installation and Use. Listed or labeled equipment shall be used or installed in accordance with any instructions included in the listing or labeling.

Installation instructions are usually supplied with equipment by the manufacturer for use by the general contractor, erector, electrical contractor, electrical inspector, and others concerned with the installation. It is very important to consider the listing or labeling installation instructions. For example, Section 210-52(a), Exception, permits permanently installed electric baseboard heaters to be equipped with receptacle outlets that are the required receptacle outlets for the wall space utilized by such heaters. Installation instructions for such permanent baseboard heaters indicate that these heaters should not be mounted beneath a receptacle. In dwelling units, it is very common to use low-density heat units which may measure in excess of 12 ft in length. Therefore, to meet the provisions of Section 210-52(a), first paragraph, and also the installation instructions, a receptacle must either be part of the heating unit or be installed in the floor close to the wall but not above the heating unit. See Section 210-52(a), Exception, FPN, and Figures 210-26 and 210-27.

110-4. Voltages. Throughout this Code the voltage considered shall be that at which the circuit operates.

See definitions of "voltage (of a circuit)," "voltage, nominal," and "voltage to ground" in Article 100.
See also Sections 300-2 and 300-3.

110-5. Conductors. Conductors normally used to carry current shall be of copper unless otherwise provided in this Code. Where the conductor material is not specified, the sizes given in this Code shall apply to copper conductors. Where other materials are used, the size shall be changed accordingly.

(FPN): For aluminum and copper-clad aluminum conductors, see Tables 310-16 through 310-31.

See Section 310-14 for aluminum conductor material.

110-6. Conductor Sizes. Conductor sizes are expressed in American Wire Gage (AWG) or in circular mils.

For copper, aluminum, or copper-clad aluminum conductors up to size No. 4/0, this *Code* uses the American Wire Gage (AWG) for size identification, which is the same as the Brown and Sharpe Gage (BS).
Conductors larger than 4/0 are sized in circular mils, beginning with 250,000 circular mils (or 250 MCM). See Tables 310-16 through 310-31.
The circular mil (CM) area of a conductor is equal to its diameter, in mils, squared (1 in. equals 1,000 mils).
Example: The diameter of a No. 8 solid conductor is 0.1285 in.

$$0.1285 \text{ in.} \times 1,000 = 128.5 \text{ mils}$$
$$128.5 \times 128.5 \qquad = 16512.25 \text{ CM}$$

or 16510 CM, as rounded off by Table 8 of Chapter 9.
This represents the circular mil area for one conductor. Where stranded conductors are used, the resulting figure must be multiplied by the number of strands (see Table 8 of Chapter 9).

110-7. Insulation Integrity. All wiring shall be so installed that when completed the system will be free from short circuits and from grounds other than as permitted in Article 250.

Insulation is the material between points of different potential in an electrical system preventing the flow of electricity between those points. Failure of the insulation system is one of the most common causes of problems in electrical installations. This is true on both high-voltage and low-voltage systems.

Insulation tests are performed on new or existing installations to determine the quality or condition of the insulation of conductors and equipment.

The principal causes of insulation failures are heat, moisture, and dirt. Insulation can also fail due to chemical attack, mechanical damage, sunlight, and excessive voltage stresses.

In an insulation resistance test, an applied voltage from 100 to 5,000 V (usually 500 to 1,000 V for systems of 600 V or less), supplied from a source of constant potential, is applied across the insulation. A hand-generated megohmmeter is the usual potential source, and it indicates the insulation resistance directly on a scale calibrated in megohms. The quality of the insulation is evaluated based on the level of the insulation resistance.

The insulation resistance of many types of insulation is quite variable with temperature, so the data obtained should be corrected to the standard temperature for the class of equipment under test.

The megohm value of insulation resistance obtained will be inversely proportional to the volume of insulation being tested. As an example, a cable 1,000 ft long would be expected to have one-tenth the insulation resistance of a cable 100 ft long, if all other conditions were identical.

The insulation resistance test is relatively easy to perform and is useful on all types and classes of electrical equipment. Its main value lies in the charting of data from periodic tests, corrected for temperature, over a long period so that deteriorative trends can be detected.

Excellent manuals on this subject are available from instrument manufacturers. Thorough knowledge in the use of insulation testers is essential, if the test results are to be meaningful.

See Figure 110-1 for a typical megohmmeter insulation tester.

110-8. Wiring Methods. Only wiring methods recognized as suitable are included in this Code. The recognized methods of wiring shall be permitted to be installed in any type of building or occupancy, except as otherwise provided in this Code.

The scope of Article 300 applies generally to all wiring methods, except as amended, modified, or supplemented by Chapter 5 (Special Occupancies), Chapter 6 (Special Equipment), and Chapter 7 (Special Conditions).

Chapter 8 (Communication Systems) is independent of the other chapters, except where some other section is specifically referenced in Chapter 8 of the *Code*. For example, see Section 800-3(b)(3).

110-9. Interrupting Rating. Equipment intended to break current at fault levels shall have an interrupting rating sufficient for the system voltage and the current which is available at the line terminals of the equipment.

Equipment intended to break current at other than fault levels shall have an interrupting rating at system voltage sufficient for the current that must be interrupted.

Section 110-9 states that all fuses and circuit breakers intended to break the circuit at fault levels must have an adequate interrupting rating wherever they are used in the electrical system. Fuses or circuit breakers that do not have adequate interrupting ratings could rupture while attempting to clear a short circuit.

Instructions for calculating available short-circuit currents are provided in ANSI/IEEE Std. C37.010b-1984 Supplement, Application Guide for AC High-Voltage Circuit Breakers Rated on a Symmetrical Current Basis. Additional details are provided in IEEE Std. 141-1976, Recommended Practice for Electric Power Distribution for Industrial Plants, Chapter 4; and ANSI/IEEE Std. 241-1983, Recommended Practice for Electric Power Systems in Commercial Buildings, Chapter 9.

Figure 110-1. Multivoltage multirange insulation tester. (*James G. Biddle Co.*)

110-10. Circuit Impedance and Other Characteristics. The overcurrent protective devices, the total impedance, the component short-circuit withstand ratings, and other characteristics of the circuit to be protected shall be so selected and coordinated as to permit the circuit protective devices used to clear a fault without the occurrence of extensive damage to the electrical components of the circuit. This fault shall be assumed to be either between two or more of the circuit conductors, or between any circuit conductor and the grounding conductor or enclosing metal raceway.

The basic purpose of overcurrent protection is to open the circuit before conductors or conductor insulation are damaged when an overcurrent condition occurs. An overcurrent condition can be the result of an overload, a ground fault, or a short circuit, and must be removed before the conductor insulation damage point is reached.

Overcurrent protective devices (such as fuses and circuit breakers) should be selected in a manner that the short-circuit withstand rating of the system components will not be exceeded should a short circuit or high-level ground fault occur.

System components include wire, bus structures, switching, protection and disconnect devices, distribution equipment, etc., all of which have limited short-circuit ratings and would be damaged or destroyed if these short-circuit ratings are exceeded. Merely providing overcurrent protective devices with sufficient inter-rupting capacity will not assure adequate short-circuit protection for the system components to be protected. When the available short-circuit current exceeds the withstand rating of an electrical component, the overcurrent protective device must limit the let-through energy to within the rating of that electrical component.

Utility companies usually determine and provide information on available short-circuit current levels at the service equipment. Literature on how to calculate short-circuit currents at each point in any distribution can generally be obtained by contacting manufacturers of overcurrent protective devices or by referring to the IEEE "Redbook" (IEEE Standard 141-1976).

For a typical one-family dwelling with a 100-ampere service using No. 2 aluminum supplied by a 1.72 percent, 37 ½ kVA transformer at a distance of 25 ft the available short-circuit current would be approximately 6000 amperes.

Adequate short-circuit protection can be provided by fuses, molded case circuit breakers, and low-voltage power circuit breakers depending upon the specific circuit and installation requirements.

Fuses

The following information on fuses is based on the UL "Guide Card" information on fuses Guide No. CQR, in the UL Electrical Construction Material Directory.

Cartridge-enclosed are fuses of the nonrenewable type, rated 0-600 A, 250 V; 0-1200 A, 300 V; and 0-6000 A, 600 V. Fuses are intended for use on ac circuits only, unless also marked with a dc voltage rating.

Nonrenewable fuses of a given voltage rating or current rating range are not interchangeable in the same fuseholders with fuses of a different voltage or current rating range.

Fuses designated as Class K1, K5, K9 (0-600 A, 250 V, ac, or 600 V, ac) are classified as to interrupting capacity and in terms of maximum clearing ampere squared seconds and maximum peak let-through current. They incorporate dimensional features equivalent to, and are interchangeable with, other nonrenewable cartridge fuses intended for installation in conventional designs of equipment recognized by the *NEC* for branch circuit, service, and motor-overload use. They are not marked "Current Limiting."

Fuses designated as Class RK1 and RK5 (0-600 A, 250 V, ac, or 600 V, ac) are high-interrupting capacity types and are marked "Current Limiting." They are classified in terms of maximum clearing ampere squared seconds and maximum peak let-through current at 50,000, 100,000, and 200,000 rms symmetrical amperes. They incorporate features which permit their insertion into holders for other nonrenewable cartridge fuses intended for installation in conventional designs of equipment recognized by the *NEC* for branch circuit, service, and motor-overload use. They are provided with a feature which allows their insertion into rejection-type fuseholders designed to accept only Class RK1 or RK5 fuses.

The rejection-type fuseholders are used in equipment as covered in the *NEC*.

Fuses designated as Class CC (0-30 A, 600 V, ac) are high-interrupting capacity types and are marked "Current Limiting." They are not interchangeable with fuses of higher voltage or interrupting rating or lower current rating.

Fuses designated as Class G (0-60 A, 300 V, ac) are high-interrupting capacity types and are marked "Current Limiting." They are not interchangeable with other fuses mentioned above and below.

Fuses designated as Class J (0-600 A, 600 V, ac) or Class L (601-6000 A, 600 V, ac) are high-interrupting capacity types and are marked "Current Limiting." They are not interchangeable with other fuses such as those mentioned above and below.

Fuses designated as Class T (0-1200 A, 300 V, and 0-800 A, 600 V, ac) are high-interrupting capacity types and are marked "Current-Limiting." They are not interchangeable with other fuses mentioned above.

The term "Current Limiting" indicates that a fuse, when tested on a circuit capable of delivering a specific short-circuit current (rms amperes symmetrical) at rated voltage, will start to melt within 90 electrical degrees and will clear the circuit within 180 electrical degrees (½ cycle).

Because the time required for a fuse to melt is dependent on the available current of the circuit, a fuse which may be "Current Limiting" when subjected to a specific short-circuit current (rms amperes symmetrical) may not be current limiting on a circuit of lower maximum available current.

The performance of a fuse as it is determined by the ability of the fuse to open and clear a circuit is indicated by the following maximum permissible let-through values which are obtained when fuses of the Class K designs are connected to circuits having an available current of up to 100,000 A maximum (rms symmetrical), but not greater than the marked interrupting rating of the fuse if it is less than 100,000 A, when fuses of the Class G design are connected to circuits having an available current of 100,000 A maximum (rms symmetrical), and when fuses of the Class CC, J, L, RK and T designs are connected to circuits having available currents of 50,000, 100,000 and 200,000 A maximum (rms symmetrical).

NONRENEWABLE CARTRIDGE FUSES

Class CC Fuses
MAXIMUM PEAK LET-THROUGH CURRENT (Ip amperes) AND CLEARING
I^2t (ampere squared seconds)

Rating Amps	Between Threshold and 50KA		100KA		200KA	
	I^2tx10^3	$Ipx10^3$	I^2tx10^3	$Ipx10^3$	I^2tx10^3	$Ipx10^3$
0-15	2	3	2	3	3	4
16-20	2	3	3	4	3	5
21-30	7	6	7	7.5	7	12

Class G Fuses

Cartridge Size Amp	Maximum Peak Let-Through Current Ampere X 10^3	Maximum Clearing I^2T (Amp-Squared Seconds X 10^3)
0-15	3	2
16-20	4	3
21-30	6	5
31-60	10	25

Class J and 600 Volt T Fuses
MAXIMUM PEAK LET-THROUGH CURRENT (Ip-amperes) AND CLEARING
I^2t (amperes squared seconds)

Cartridge Size Amperes	Between Threshold and 50KA		100KA		200KA	
	I^2tx10^3	$Ipx10^3$	I^2tx10^3	$Ipx10^3$	I^2tx10^3	$Ipx10^3$
0-30	7	6	7	7.5	7	12
31-60	30	8	30	10	30	16
61-100	60	12	80	14	80	20
101-200	200	16	300	20	300	30
201-400	1000	25	1100	30	1100	45
401-600	2500	35	2500	45	2500	70
601-800	4000	50	4000	55	4000	75

300 Volt T Fuses
MAXIMUM PEAK LET-THROUGH CURRENT (Ip-amperes) AND CLEARING
I^2t (amperes squared seconds)

Cartridge Size Amperes	Between Threshold and 50KA		100KA		200KA	
	I^2tx10^3	$Ipx10^3$	I^2tx10^3	$Ipx10^3$	I^2tx10^3	$Ipx10^3$
0-30	3.5	5	3.5	7	3.5	9
31-60	15	7	15	9	15	12
61-100	40	9	40	12	40	15
101-200	150	13	150	16	150	20
201-400	550	22	550	28	550	35
401-600	1000	29	1000	37	1000	46
601-800	1500	37	1500	50	1500	65
801-1200	3500	50	3500	65	4000	80

Class K Fuses

Cartridge Size Amp	Maximum Peak Let-Through Current Ampere X 10^3			Maximum Clearing I^2T (Amp-Squared Seconds X 10^3)		
	K1	K5	K9	K1	K5	K9
30	10	11	14	10	50	50
60	12	21	28	40	200	250
100	16	25	35	100	500	650
200	22	40	60	400	1,600	3,500
400	35	60	80	1,200	5,000	15,000
600	50	80	130	3,000	10,000	

Class L Fuses
MAXIMUM PEAK LET-THROUGH CURRENT (Ip amperes) AND CLEARING
I^2t (ampere squared seconds)

Cartridge Size Amps	50KA or Threshold Current-Whichever is Greater		100KA		200KA	
	I^2tx10^6	$IPx10^3$	I^2tx10^6	$Ipx10^3$	I^2tx10^6	$Ipx10^3$
601-800	10	80	10	80	10	80
801-1200	12	80	12	80	15	120
1201-1600	22	100	22	100	30	150
1601-2000	35	110	35	120	40	165
2001-2500	—	—	75	165	75	180
2501-3000	—	—	100	175	100	200
3001-4000	—	—	150	220	150	250
4001-5000	—	—	350	—	350	300
5001-6000	—	—	350	—	500	350

NONRENEWABLE CARTRIDGE FUSES—CONTINUED

Cartridge Nonrenewable
Class RK1 Fuses
MAXIMUM PEAK LET-THROUGH CURRENT (Ip amperes) AND CLEARING
I²t (ampere squared seconds)

Cartridge Size	Between Threshold and 50KA		100KA		200KA	
Amps	I²tx10³	Ipx10³	I²tx10³	Ipx10³	I²tx10³	Ipx10³
0-30	10	6	10	10	11	12
31-60	40	10	40	12	50	16
61-100	100	14	100	16	100	20
101-200	400	18	400	22	400	30
201-400	1200	33	1200	35	1600	50
401-600	3000	43	3000	50	4000	70

Class RK5 Fuses
MAXIMUM PEAK LET-THROUGH CURRENT (Ip amperes) AND CLEARING
I²t (ampere squared seconds)

Cartridge Size	Between Threshold and 50KA		100KA		200KA	
Amps	I²tx10³	Ipx10³	I²tx10³	Ipx10³	I²tx10³	Ipx10³
0-30	50	11	50	11	50	14
31-60	200	20	200	21	200	26
61-100	500	22	500	25	500	32
101-200	1600	32	1600	40	2000	50
201-400	5000	50	5000	60	6000	75
401-600	10000	65	10000	80	12000	100

(Underwriters Laboratories Inc.)

Class K-1, K-5, and K-9 fuses are marked, in addition to their regular voltage and current ratings, with an interrupting rating of 200,000, 100,000, or 50,000 A (rms symmetrical).

Class CC, RK1, RK5, J, L, and T fuses are marked, in addition to their regular voltage and current ratings, with an interrupting rating of 200,000 A (rms symmetrical).

Class G fuses are marked, in addition to their regular voltage and current ratings, with an interrupting rating of 100,000 A (rms symmetrical).

A Class H fuse has an interrupting rating of 10,000 A, dc.

A Class CC, G, J, K, RK, or T fuse may have an interrupting rating of 10,000, 20,000, 50,000, or 100,000 amp, dc.

When a fuse has a dc rating, it is marked with the dc voltage and interrupting rating.

Equipment (switches, motor starters, panelboards, etc.) that has been investigated and found suitable for use with these fuses is marked with the class of fuse intended to be used in the equipment, and available current rating applicable to that piece of equipment.

The equipment, when so marked, with these fuses installed, is considered to be suitable for use on circuits that can deliver currents under short-circuit conditions up to the available current rating of the equipment, or the interrupting rating of the fuse, whichever is lower.

An interrupting rating on a fuse included in a piece of equipment does not automatically qualify the equipment in which the fuses are installed for use on circuits with higher available currents than the rating of the equipment itself.

Class L fuses are designed for use in equipment to which line and load connections are made by means of solid bus bars. For this reason, temperature rises on Class L fuse blades may exceed those observed in connection with other cartridge fuse designs. Terminal connections for wires in such equipment must be designed to avoid excessive temperatures on the wire insulation.

Class CC, G, H, J, K, L, and RK fuses may be marked as having a time delay characteristic. For Class CC, G, H, J, K, and RK fuses, this characteristic (a minimum clearing time under a particular overcurrent condition) has been investigated. Class G or CC fuses, which can carry 200 percent of rated current for

40

12 seconds or more, and Class H, J, K, or RK fuses, which can carry 500 percent of rated current for 10 seconds or more, may be marked with "D", "Time Delay," "Dual Element," or some equivalent designation. Class L fuses are permitted to be marked "Time Delay," but have not been evaluated for such performance. Class T fuses are not permitted to be marked "Time Delay."

Circuit Breakers

When using circuit breakers, current limiting can be accomplished by using a "current limiting" molded-case circuit breaker, a fused circuit breaker having integrally mounted current-limiting fuses, or by current limiters designed to be used in conjunction with specific circuit breakers.

The following information on circuit breakers is based on the UL "Guide Card" information on molded-case circuit breakers, Guide No. DIVQ, in the UL Electrical Construction Materials Directory.

A current-limiting circuit breaker is one that does not employ a fusible element and that, when operating within its current-limiting range, limits the let-through I^2t to a value less that the I^2t of a ½-cycle wave of the symmetrical prospective current.

Current-limiting circuit breakers are marked "Current Limiting" and are marked either to indicate the let-through characteristics or to indicate where such information may be obtained.

The following information on fused circuit breakers is based on the UL "Guide Card" information on fused circuit breakers, Guide No. DIYV, in the UL Electrical Construction Materials Directory.

Fused circuit breakers include all the mechanical features of molded-case circuit breakers and, in addition, have one or more replaceable current limiters or fuses which function to increase the fault current interrupting ability.

Fused circuit breakers are indentified with respect to their performance characteristics as either Type 1 or Type 2. They are rated at 600 volts or less.

Type 1 fused circuit breakers meet all performance requirements of molded-case circuit breakers. The fuse, fuses, or replaceable current limiters function only to extend the fault-current interrupting rating beyond the short circuit test requirement applicable. Type 1 devices are limited to constructions which are designed to accommodate and coordinate with fuses or replaceable current limiters having high interrupting capacity ratings.

Type 2 fused circuit breakers use a fuse, fuses, or current limiters so coordinated that they function at currents below those specified in short-circuit test requirements. Except for this feature of short-circuit operation, Type 2 fused circuit breakers meet all requirements applicable to molded-case circuit breakers and, in addition, are required to clear circuits up to and including 25 times their ampere rating, and circuits of 1000 amperes or less regardless of ampere rating, without causing operation of the fuse, fuses, or current limiters which are a part of the device. Type 2 devices are limited to constructions which are designed to accommodate and coordinate with fuses having high interrupting capacity ratings.

The following information on circuit breaker current limiters is based on the UL "Guide Card" information on circuit breaker current limiters, Guide No. DIRW, in the UL Electrical Construction Materials Directory.

Circuit breaker current limiters are designed to be used in conjunction with specific circuit breakers and to be directly connected to the load terminals of the circuit breakers. They contain fusible elements which function only to increase the fault-current interrupting ability of the combination. The limiters are rated 600 volts or less.

The fusible elements in circuit breaker current limiters are so coordinated that they function at currents below those specified in short-circuit test requirements for circuit breakers. Except for this feature of short-circuit operation, combinations of circuit breakers and circuit breaker current limiters meet all requirements applicable to branch-circuit and service circuit breakers and, in addition, are required to clear circuits up to and including 25 times their ampere rating, and circuits of 1000 amperes or less regardless of ampere rating, without causing operation of the fusible elements in the current limiter.

Circuit breaker current limiters are marked to indicate the breakers with which they are intended to be used.

110-11. Deteriorating Agents. Unless identified for use in the operating environment, no conductors or equipment shall be located in damp or wet locations; where exposed to gases, fumes, vapors, liquids, or other agents having a deteriorating effect on the conductors or equipment; nor where exposed to excessive temperatures.

(FPN): See Section 300-6 for protection against corrosion.

Control equipment, utilization equipment, and busways approved for use in dry locations only shall be protected against permanent damage from the weather during building construction.

110-12. Mechanical Execution of Work. Electric equipment shall be installed in a neat and workmanlike manner.

(a) Unused Openings. Unused openings in boxes, raceways, auxiliary gutters, cabinets, equipment cases or housings shall be effectively closed to afford protection substantially equivalent to the wall of the equipment.

(b) Subsurface Enclosures. Conductors shall be racked to provide ready and safe access in underground and subsurface enclosures, into which persons enter for installation and maintenance.

This regulation calling for "neat and workmanlike" installations has appeared in the *NEC* as worded for over a half a century. It stands as a basis for pride in one's work and has been pointed out effectively by persons involved in the training of apprentice electricians for many years.

Many *Code* conflicts or violations have been cited by the authority having jurisdiction based on the authority's interpretation of "neat and workmanlike manner."

Many electrical inspection authorities use their own experience, or precedents in their local areas, as the basis for their judgments. Any ruling, however, should be based on uniformity as intended by the National Electrical Code Committee.

Examples of installations that are considered not to be "in a neat and workmanlike manner" are exposed runs of cables or raceways that are improperly supported, that is, sagging between supports or using improper methods for supports; field-bent and kinked, flattened, or poorly measured raceways; or cabinets, cutout boxes, and enclosures that are not plumb or that are not properly secured.

110-13. Mounting and Cooling of Equipment.

(a) Mounting. Electric equipment shall be firmly secured to the surface on which it is mounted. Wooden plugs driven into holes in masonry, concrete, plaster, or similar materials shall not be used.

(b) Cooling. Electrical equipment which depends upon the natural circulation of air and convection principles for cooling of exposed surfaces shall be installed so that room air flow over such surfaces is not prevented by walls or by adjacent installed equipment. For equipment designed for floor mounting, clearance between top surfaces and adjacent surfaces shall be provided to dissipate rising warm air.

See Sections 430-14(a) and 430-16 for motor locations, and Sections 450-9 and 450-45 for transformer locations.

Electrical equipment provided with ventilating openings shall be installed so that walls or other obstructions do not prevent the free circulation of air through the equipment.

For example, a ventilated busway must be located where there are no walls or other objects that might interfere with the natural circulation of air and convection principles for cooling. See definition of "ventilated" in Article 100.

Some types of equipment, such as panelboards and transformers, are adversely affected if enclosure surfaces normally exposed to room air are covered or tightly enclosed. Ventilating openings in equipment are provided to allow the circulation of room air around internal components of the equipment, and the blocking of such openings can cause dangerous overheating.

110-14. Electrical Connections. Because of different characteristics of copper and aluminum, devices such as pressure terminal or pressure splicing connectors and soldering lugs shall be suitable for the material of the conductor and shall be properly installed and used. Conductors of dissimilar metals shall not be intermixed in a terminal or splicing connector where physical contact occurs between dissimilar conductors (such as copper and aluminum, copper and copper-clad aluminum, or aluminum and copper-clad aluminum), unless the device is suitable for the purpose and conditions of use. Materials such as solder, fluxes, inhibitors, and compounds, where employed, shall be suitable for the use and shall be of a type which will not adversely affect the conductors, installation, or equipment.

(FPN): Many terminations and equipment are marked with a tightening torque.

Section 110-3(b) applies when terminations and equipment are marked with tightening torques.

Tightening Torques

Figures 110-2, 110-3, 110-4, and 110-5 provide information on the tightening torques used by Underwriters Laboratories Inc. when testing wire connectors unless the manufacturer assigns another value appropriate for the design. This information should be used for guidance only where no tightening information on the specific wire connector is available. It should not be used to replace manufacturer's instructions, which should always be followed. This information was taken from the edition of UL Standard 486B that was in effect at the time of the printing of this Handbook. Similar information can be found in UL 486A and UL 486C.

(a) Terminals. Connection of conductors to terminal parts shall ensure a thoroughly good connection without damaging the conductors and shall be made by means of pressure connectors (including set-screw type), solder lugs, or splices to flexible leads.

Exception: Connection by means of wire binding screws or studs and nuts having upturned lugs or equivalent shall be permitted for No. 10 or smaller conductors.

Terminals for more than one conductor and terminals used to connect aluminum shall be so identified.

(b) Splices. Conductors shall be spliced or joined with splicing devices suitable for the use or by brazing, welding, or soldering with a fusible metal or alloy. Soldered splices shall first be so spliced or joined as to be mechanically and electrically secure without solder and then soldered. All splices and joints and the free ends of conductors shall be covered with an insulation equivalent to that of the conductors or with an insulating device suitable for the purpose.

Field observations and trade magazine articles indicate that failures of electrical connections have been determined as the cause of many equipment burnouts and

43

Tightening Torques for Screws—Pound Inches[a]

| Wire Size | Slotted Head No. 10 and Larger | | | | Hexagonal Head—External Drive Socket Wrench | |
| | Slot Width—Inches[b] | | Slot Length—Inches[b] | | | |
	to $3/64$	over $3/64$	to $1/4$	over $1/4$	Split-Bolt Connectors	Other Connectors
18-10 AWG	20	35	20	35	80	75
8	25	40	25	40	80	75
6	35	45	35	45	165	110
4	35	45	35	45	165	110
3	35	50	35	50	275	150
2	40	50	40	50	275	150
1	—	50	—	50	275	150
1/0	—	50	—	50	385	180
2/0	—	50	—	50	385	180
3/0	—	50	—	50	500	250
4/0	—	50	—	50	500	250
250 MCM	—	50	—	50	650	325
300	—	50	—	50	650	325
350	—	50	—	50	650	325
400	—	50	—	50	825	325
500	—	50	—	50	825	375
600	—	50	—	50	1000	375
700	—	50	—	50	1000	375
750	—	50	—	50	1000	375
800	—	50	—	50	1100	500
900	—	50	—	50	1100	500
1000	—	50	—	50	1100	500
1250	—	—	—	—	1100	600
1500	—	—	—	—	1100	600
1750	—	—	—	—	1100	600
2000	—	—	—	—	1100	600

a. Clamping screws with multiple tightening means: for example, for a slotted hexagonal head screw, use the torque value associated with the tool used in the installation. UL uses both values when testing.

b. For values of slot width or length other than those specified, select the largest torque value associated with conductor size.

Figure 110-2. Tightening torques for screws in pound-inches. (*Underwriters Laboratories Inc.*)

Torques in Pound-Inches for Slotted Head Screws[a]
Smaller than No. 10, for Use with No. 8 AWG or Smaller Conductors

Screw-Slot Length in Inches[b]	Screw-Slot Width Less than $3/64$ in.	Screw-Slot Width $3/64$ in. and Larger
to $5/32$	7	9
$5/32$	7	12
$3/16$	7	12
$7/32$	7	12
$1/4$	9	12
$9/32$	—	15
above $9/32$	—	20

a. Clamping screws with multiple tightening means: for example, for a slotted hexagonal head screw, use the torque value associated with the tool used in the installation. UL uses both values when testing.

b. For slot lengths of intermediate values, select torques pertaining to next shorter slot length.

Figure 110-3. Tightening torques for slotted head screws in pound-inches. (*Underwriters Laboratories Inc.*)

Torques for Socket Head Screws[a]

Socket Size Across Flats—Inches	Torque, Pound-Inches
⅛	45
5⁄32	100
3⁄16	120
7⁄32	150
¼	200
5⁄16	275
⅜	375
½	500
9⁄16	600

a. Clamping screws with multiple tightening means: for example, for a slotted hexagonal head screw, use the torque value associated with the tool used in the installation. UL uses both values when testing.

Figure 110-4. Tightening torques for socket head screws in pound-inches. (*Underwriters Laboratories Inc.*)

Lug Bolting Torques for Connection of Wire Connectors to Busbars, etc.

Bolt Diameter— Inches	Tightening Torque Pound-Feet
No. 8	1.5
No. 10	2.0
¼ or less	6
5⁄16	11
⅜	19
7⁄16	30
½	40
⅝ or more	55

Figure 110-5. Lug bolting torques in pound-feet for connection of wire connectors to busbars, etc. (*Underwriters Laboratories Inc.*)

fires. Many of these failures are attributable to improper terminations, poor workmanship, the differing characteristics of dissimilar metals, and improper binding screws or splicing devices.

Underwriters Laboratories Inc. requirements for listing solid aluminum conductors in sizes No. 12 and No. 10 AWG and for listing snap switches and receptacles for use on 15- and 20-A branch circuits incorporate stringent tests which take the factors listed in the previous paragraph into account. See Sections 380-14(c) and 410-56(b).

Screwless pressure terminal connectors of the conductor push-in type are for use with copper and copper-clad aluminum conductors only.

Instructions describing proper installation techniques and emphasizing the need to follow these techniques and practice good workmanship are required to be included with each coil of No. 12 and No. 10 AWG insulated aluminum wire or cable. Also, see commentary on tightening torque under Section 110-14, FPN.

New product and material designs which provide for increased levels of safety of aluminum wire terminations have been developed by the electrical industry.

To assist all concerned parties in the proper and safe use of solid aluminum wire in making connections to wiring devices used on 15- and 20-A branch circuits, the following information is presented. Understanding and utilizing this information is essential to proper application of materials and devices now available.

For New Installations

The following was prepared by the Ad Hoc Committee on Aluminum Terminations: Comply with Section 110-14(a) of the 1987 *NEC* when aluminum wire is used in new installations.

New Materials and Devices

a. For direct connection use only 15- and 20-A receptacles and switches marked "CO/ALR" and connected as described under "Installation Method."

The "CO/ALR" marking is on the device mounting strap. The "CO/ALR" marking means the devices have been tested to stringent heat cycling requirements to determine their suitability for use with UL-labeled aluminum, copper, or copper-clad aluminum wire.

Note: Detailed installation instructions provided with pressure wire connectors must be followed

To branch-circuit wiring

6 in.

Short insulated copper lead (pigtail) No. 14-12 AWG connected to wiring device

From branch-circuit wiring   Aluminum wire No. 12-10 AWG

U.L. listed AL/CU insulated wire connector provided in carton marked "FOR DRY LOCATIONS ONLY" and for the aluminum-to-copper combinations for which it is suitable

Figure 110-6. Pigtailing copper to aluminum conductor. Tool-applied crimp-type connectors suitable for connection of copper and aluminum wire are also available (*Underwriters Laboratories Inc.*).

Note. Pigtailing, either field- or factory-wired, as illustrated in Figure 110-6, is recognized by the *NEC*.

b. Use solid aluminum wire, No. 12 or No. 10 AWG, marked with the UL aluminum insulated wire label, as shown in Figure 110-7. Follow the installation instructions packaged with the wire.

Installation Method

1. Wrap the freshly stripped end of the wire two-thirds to three-quarters of the distance around the wire-binding screw post, as shown in Step A of Figure 110-7.

The loop is made so that rotation of the screw in tightening will tend to wrap the wire around the post rather than unwrap it.

2. Tighten the screw until the wire is snugly in contact with the underside of the screw head and with the contact plate on the wiring device, as shown in Step B of Figure 110-7.

3. Tighten the screw an additional one-half turn, thereby providing a firm connection. Where torque screwdrivers are used, tighten to 12 pound-inches. See Step C of Figure 110-7.

4. Position the wires behind the wiring device so as to decrease the likelihood of the terminal screws loosening when the device is positioned into the outlet box.

Figure 110-8 illustrates incorrect methods for connection and should not be used.

Existing Inventory

When UL-labeled solid aluminum wire No. 12 and No. 10 AWG not bearing the new aluminum wire label is used, it should be used with wiring devices marked "CO/ALR" and connected as described in "Installation Method." This is the preferred and recommended method for using such wire.

Note. Pigtailing, either field- or factory-wired, as illustrated in Figure 110-6, is recognized by the *NEC*.

In the following types of devices, the terminals shall not be directly connected

Correct method of terminating aluminum wire at wire-binding-screw terminals of receptacles and snap switches

Two-thirds

Three-quarters

Screw post

Step A: Strip and wrap wire

Snug contact

Contact plate on wiring device marked "CO/ALR"

Step B: Tighten screw to full contact

Screw tightened an additional half-turn, or to 12 lb-in.

Wire firmly in contact

Step C: Complete connection

Figure 110-7. Correct method of terminating aluminum wire at wire-binding screw terminals of receptacles and snap switches. (*Underwriters Laboratories Inc.*)

Overlap

Straight in

Wrong direction

Incorrect tightening torque

Incorrect wire wrap

One-half wrap

Less than two-thirds wrap

Figure 110-8. Incorrect methods of terminating aluminum wire at wire-binding screw terminals of receptacles and snap switches. (*Underwriters Laboratories Inc.*)

to aluminum conductors but may be used with UL-labeled copper or copper-clad conductors:

Receptacles and snap switches marked "AL-CU";

Receptacles and snap switches having no conductor marking;

Receptacles and snap switches having backwired terminals or screwless terminals of the push-in type.

For Existing Installations

If examination discloses overheating or loose connections the recommendations described under "For New Installations Existing Inventory" should be followed.

110-16. Working Space About Electric Equipment (600 Volts, Nominal, or Less). Sufficient access and working space shall be provided and maintained about all electric equipment to permit ready and safe operation and maintenance of such equipment.

(a) Working Clearances. Except as elsewhere required or permitted in this Code, the dimension of the working space in the direction of access to live parts operating at 600 volts, nominal, or less and likely to require examination, adjustment, servicing, or maintenance while energized shall not be less than indicated in Table 110-16(a). Distances shall be measured from the live parts if such are exposed or from the enclosure front or opening if such are enclosed. Concrete, brick, or tile walls shall be considered as grounded.

In addition to the dimensions shown in Table 110-16(a), the work space shall not be less than 30 inches (762 mm) wide in front of the electric equipment. In all cases the work space shall permit at least a 90-degree opening of equipment doors or hinged panels.

> Note that the 30-in. wide dimension is intended to be clear all the way to the floor. See Figures 110-9 and 110-10.
>
> The equipment must not be installed so close to walls, etc., that the equipment door or hinged panel cannot open at least 90 degrees. Where the doors or hinged panels are wider than 36 in., more than a 36-in. wide space will be needed.
>
> The minimum working clearances of Section 110-16(a) are not required if the equipment is such that it is not likely to require examination, adjustment, servicing, or maintenance while energized. However "sufficient" access and working space is still required by the first paragraph of Section 110-16. Also, see commentary following Section 384-4.

Table 110-16(a). Working Clearances

Voltage to Ground, Nominal	Minimum Clear Distance (feet)		
Condition:	1	2	3
0–150	3	3	3
151–600	3	3½	4

For SI units: one inch = 25.4 millimeters; one foot = 0.3048 meter.

Where the "Conditions" are as follows:

1. Exposed live parts on one side and no live or grounded parts on the other side of the working space, or exposed live parts on both sides effectively guarded by suitable wood or other insulating materials. Insulated wire or insulated busbars operating at not over 300 volts shall not be considered live parts.

2. Exposed live parts on one side and grounded parts on the other side.

3. Exposed live parts on both sides of the work space (not guarded as provided in Condition 1) with the operator between.

Exception No. 1: Working space shall not be required in back of assemblies such as dead-front switchboards, or motor control centers where there are no renewable or adjustable parts such as fuses or switches on the back and where all connections are accessible from locations other than the back.

Exception No. 2: By special permission smaller spaces may be permitted (1) where it is judged that the particular arrangement of the installation will provide adequate accessibility, or (2) where all uninsulated parts are at a voltage no greater than 30 volts RMS or 42V dc.

(b) Clear Spaces. Working space required by this section shall not be used for storage. When normally enclosed live parts are exposed for inspection or servicing, the working space, if in a passageway or general open space, shall be suitably guarded.

(c) Access and Entrance to Working Space. At least one entrance of sufficient area shall be provided to give access to the working space about electric equipment.

Figure 110-9. The 30-in. wide front working space is not required to be directly centered on the electrical equipment where it can be assured that the space is sufficient for safe operation and maintenance of such equipment.

Figure 110-10. Distances are measured from the live parts if such are exposed or from the enclosure front if live parts are enclosed. If any assemblies, such as switchboards or motor-control centers, are accessible from the back and expose live parts, the working clearance dimensions would be required at the rear of the equipment as illustrated above.

For switchboards and control panels rated 1200 amperes or more and over 6 feet (1.83 m) wide, there shall be one entrance not less than 24 inches (610 mm) wide and 6½ feet (1.98 m) high at each end.

See Figures 110-11, 110-12, and 110-13.

Figure 110-11. Section 110-16(c), Basic Rule, first paragraph. At least one entrance is required to provide access to the working space around electric equipment. The installation shown in the sketch on the right would not be acceptable if the electric equipment was a switchboard or panelboard over 6 ft wide and rated 1200 A or more.

Figure 110-12. Section 110-16(c), Basic Rule, second paragraph. For switchboards and control panels rated 1200 A or more, and over 6 ft wide, there shall be one entrance not less than 24 in. wide and 6 ½ ft high at each end.

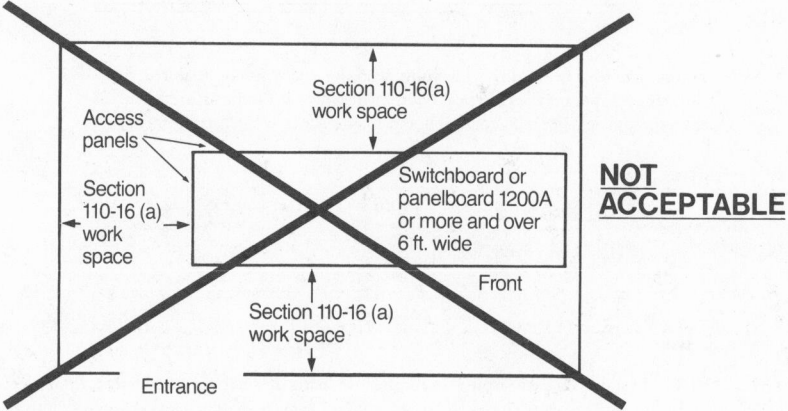

Figure 110-13. Unacceptable arrangement of large switchboard or panelboard. A person could be trapped behind arcing electric equipment.

Exception No. 1: Where the switchboards and panelboards location permits a continuous and unobstructed way of exit travel.

See Figure 110-14.

Exception No. 2: Where the work space required by Section 110-16(a) is doubled, only one entrance to the working space is required.

Working space with one entrance provided shall be so located that the edge of the entrance nearest the switchboards and panelboards is the minimum clear distance given in Table 110-16(a) away from such equipment.

See Figure 110-15.

(d) Front Working Space. In all cases where there are live parts normally exposed on the front of switchboards or motor control centers, the working space in front of such equipment shall not be less than 3 feet (914 mm).

(e) Illumination. Illumination shall be provided for all working spaces about service equipment, switchboards, panelboards, or motor control centers installed indoors.

Exception: Service equipment or panelboards, in dwelling units, that do not exceed 200 amperes.

Figure 110-14. Section 110-16(c), Exception No. 1. Where the equipment location permits a continuous and unobstructed way of exit travel.

Figure 110-15. Section 110-16(c), Exception No. 2. Where the work space required by Section 110-16(a) is doubled, only one entrance to the working space is required.

(f) Headroom. The minimum headroom of working spaces about service equipment, switchboards, panelboards, or motor control centers shall be 6¼ feet (1.91 m).

See commentary on Section 384-4.

Exception: Service equipment or panelboards, in dwelling units, that do not exceed 200 amperes.

(FPN): For higher voltages, see Article 710.

(FPN): As used in this section, a motor control center is an assembly of one or more enclosed sections having a common power bus and principally containing motor control units.

110-17. Guarding of Live Parts (600 Volts, Nominal, or Less).

(a) Live Parts Guarded Against Accidental Contact. Except as elsewhere required or permitted by this Code, live parts of electric equipment operating at 50 volts or more shall be guarded against accidental contact by approved enclosures or by any of the following:

(1) By location in a room, vault, or similar enclosure that is accessible only to qualified persons.

(2) By suitable permanent, substantial partitions or screens so arranged that only qualified persons will have access to the space within reach of the live parts. Any openings in such partitions or screens shall be so sized and located that persons are not likely to come into accidental contact with the live parts or to bring conducting objects into contact with them.

(3) By location on a suitable balcony, gallery, or platform so elevated and arranged as to exclude unqualified persons.

(4) By elevation of 8 feet (2.44 m) or more above the floor or other working surface.

For example, see the requirements of Sections 610-13, Exception No. 2 and 610-21(a). Although contact conductors obviously have to be bare in order for contact shoes on the moving member to make contact with the conductor, it is also possible to place guards near the conductor to prevent accidental contact with it by persons and yet have slots or spaces through which the moving contacts can operate. Note that the *Code* also recognizes the guarding of live parts by elevation.

(b) Prevent Physical Damage. In locations where electric equipment would be exposed to physical damage, enclosures or guards shall be so arranged and of such strength as to prevent such damage.

(c) Warning Signs. Entrances to rooms and other guarded locations containing exposed live parts shall be marked with conspicuous warning signs forbidding unqualified persons to enter.

(FPN): For motors, see Sections 430-132 and 430-133. For over 600 volts, see Section 110-34.

Live parts of electric equipment should be covered, shielded, enclosed, or otherwise protected by covers, barriers, mats, or platforms to remove the likelihood of contact by persons or objects. See definitions for "dead front," "guarded," and "isolated" in Article 100.

110-18. Arcing Parts. Parts of electric equipment which in ordinary operation produce arcs, sparks, flames, or molten metal shall be enclosed or separated and isolated from all combustible material.

(FPN): For hazardous (classified) locations, see Articles 500 through 517. For motors, see Section 430-14.

An example of electric equipment that in "ordinary" operation produces sparks is an open motor having commutators or collector rings. Adequate separation from combustible material is necessary where open motors are used.

110-19. Light and Power from Railway Conductors. Circuits for lighting and power shall not be connected to any system containing trolley wires with a ground return.

Exception: Car houses, power houses, or passenger and freight stations operated in connection with electric railways.

110-21. Marking. The manufacturer's name, trademark, or other descriptive marking by which the organization responsible for the product may be identified shall be placed on all electric equipment. Other markings shall be provided giving voltage, current, wattage, or other ratings as are specified elsewhere in this Code. The marking shall be of sufficient durability to withstand the environment involved.

The *Code* requires that the rating of equipment be marked on the equipment and that such markings be located so as to be visible or easily accessible, during or after installation.

110-22. Identification of Disconnecting Means. Each disconnecting means required by this Code for motors and appliances, and each service, feeder, or branch circuit at the point where it originates shall be legibly marked to indicate its purpose unless located and arranged so the purpose is evident. The marking shall be of sufficient durability to withstand the environment involved.

> Note that proper identification is to be specific. For example, the marking is not merely to indicate "motor," but rather "motor, water pump"; not merely "lights," but rather "lights, front lobby." Consideration should also be given to the form of identification. Marking often fades or is painted over after installation.

B. Over 600 Volts, Nominal

110-30. General. Conductors and equipment used on circuits over 600 volts, nominal, shall comply with all applicable provisions of the preceding sections of this article and with the following sections, which supplement or modify the preceding sections. In no case shall the provisions of this part apply to equipment on the supply side of the service conductors.

> See "Over 600 Volts" in the Index for various articles, sections, and parts that include requirements for installations over 600 volts.

110-31. Enclosure for Electrical Installations. Electrical installations in a vault, room, or closet or in an area surrounded by a wall, screen, or fence, access to which is controlled by lock and key or other approved means, shall be considered to be accessible to qualified persons only. The type of enclosure used in a given case shall be designed and constructed according to the nature and degree of the hazard(s) associated with the installation.

A wall, screen, or fence less than 8 feet (2.44 m) in height shall not be considered as preventing access unless it has other features that provide a degree of isolation equivalent to an 8-foot (2.44-m) fence.

(FPN): Article 450 covers minimum construction requirements for transformer vaults.

(FPN): Isolation by elevation is covered in paragraph (b) of this section and in Section 110-34.

(a) Indoor Installations.

(1) In Places Accessible to Unqualified Persons. Indoor electrical installations that are open to unqualified persons shall be made with metal-enclosed equipment or shall be enclosed in a vault or in an area access to which is controlled by a lock. Metal-enclosed switchgear, unit substations, transformers, pull boxes, connection boxes, and other similar associated equipment shall be marked with appropriate caution signs. Openings in ventilated dry-type transformers or similar openings in other equipment shall be designed so that foreign objects inserted through these openings will be deflected from energized parts.

(2) In Places Accessible to Qualified Persons Only. Indoor electrical installations considered accessible to qualified persons only in accordance with this section shall comply with Sections 110-34, 710-32, and 710-33.

(b) Outdoor Installations.

(1) In Places Accessible to Unqualified Persons. Outdoor electrical installations that are open to unqualified persons shall comply with Article 225.

(FPN): For clearances of conductors for system voltages over 600 volts, nominal, see National Electrical Safety Code (ANSI C2-1984).

(2) In Places Accessible to Qualified Persons Only. Outdoor electrical installations having exposed live parts shall be accessible to qualified persons only in accordance with the first paragraph of this section and shall comply with Sections 110-34, 710-32, and 710-33.

(c) Metal-Enclosed Equipment Accessible to Unqualified Persons. Ventilating or similar openings in equipment shall be so designed that foreign objects inserted through these openings will be deflected from energized parts. When exposed to physical damage from vehicular traffic suitable guards shall be provided. Metal-enclosed equipment located outdoors accessible to the general public shall be designed so that exposed nuts or bolts cannot be readily removed, permitting access to live parts. Where metal-enclosed equipment is accessible to the general public and the bottom of the enclosure is less than 8 feet (2.44 m) above the floor or grade level, the enclosure door or hinged cover shall be kept locked.

110-32. Work Space about Equipment. Sufficient space shall be provided and maintained about electric equipment to permit ready and safe operation and maintenance of such equipment. Where energized parts are exposed, the minimum clear work space shall not be less than 6 ½ feet (1.98 m) high (measured vertically from the floor or platform), or less than 3 feet (914 mm) wide (measured parallel to the equipment). The depth shall be as required in Section 110-34(a). In all cases, the work space shall be adequate to permit at least a 90-degree opening of doors or hinged panels.

110-33. Entrance and Access to Work Space.

(a) Entrance. At least one entrance not less than 24 inches (610 mm) wide and 6½ feet (1.98 m) high shall be provided to give access to the working space about electric equipment. On switchboard and control panels exceeding 6 feet (1.83 m) in width, there shall be one entrance at each end of such board.

Section 110-33(a) coordinates with Section 110-16(c). See commentary following Section 110-16(c). However, because of the high voltages involved, Section 110-33(a) includes minimum work space entrance dimensions, even for switchboards 6 ft or less in width.

Exception No. 1: Where the switchboards and panelboards location permits a continuous and unobstructed way of exit travel.

See commentary following Section 110-16(c), Exception No. 1.

Exception No. 2: Where the work space required in Section 110-34(a) is doubled.

See commentary following Section 110-16(c), Exception No. 2.

Working space with one entrance provided shall be so located that the edge of the entrance nearest the switchboards and panelboards is the minimum clear distance given in Table 110-34(a) away from such equipment.
Where bare energized parts at any voltage or insulated energized parts above 600 volts, nominal, are located adjacent to such entrance, they shall be suitably guarded.

(b) Access. Permanent ladders or stairways shall be provided to give safe access to the working space around electric equipment installed on platforms, balconies, mezzanine floors, or in attic or roof rooms or spaces.

110-34. Work Space and Guarding.

(a) Working Space. The minimum clear working space in front of electric equipment such as switchboards, control panels, switches, circuit breakers, motor controllers, relays, and similar equipment shall not be less than specified in Table 110-34(a) unless otherwise specified in this Code. Distances shall be measured from the live parts if such are exposed, or from the enclosure front or opening if such are enclosed.

Table 110-34(a)
Minimum Depth of Clear Working Space in Front of Electric Equipment

Nominal Voltage to Ground	Conditions		
	1	2	3
	(Feet)	(Feet)	(Feet)
601–2500	3	4	5
2501–9000	4	5	6
9001–25,000	5	6	9
25,001–75 kV	6	8	10
Above 75 kV	8	10	12

For SI units: one foot = 0.3048 meter.

Where the "Conditions" are as follows:

1. Exposed live parts on one side and no live or grounded parts on the other side of the working space or exposed live parts on both sides effectively guarded by suitable wood or other insulating materials. Insulated wire or insulated busbars operating at not over 300 volts shall not be considered live parts.

2. Exposed live parts on one side and grounded parts on the other side. Concrete, brick, or tile walls will be considered as grounded surfaces.

3. Exposed live parts on both sides of the work space (not guarded as provided in Condition 1) with the operator between.

Exception: Working space is not required in back of equipment such as dead-front switchboards or control assemblies where there are no renewable or adjustable parts (such as fuses or switches) on the back and where all connections are accessible from locations other than the back. Where rear access is required to work on de-energized parts on the back of enclosed equipment, a minimum working space of 30 inches (762 mm) horizontally shall be provided.

(b) Separation from Low-Voltage Equipment. Where switches, cutouts, or other equipment operating at 600 volts, nominal, or less, are installed in a room or enclosure where there are exposed live parts or exposed wiring operating at over 600 volts, nominal, the high-voltage equipment shall be effectively separated from the space occupied by the low-voltage equipment by a suitable partition, fence, or screen.

Exception: Switches or other equipment operating at 600 volts, nominal, or less, and serving only equipment within the high-voltage vault, room, or enclosure shall be permitted to be installed in the high-voltage enclosure, room, or vault if accessible to qualified persons only.

(c) Locked Rooms or Enclosures. The entrances to all buildings, rooms, or enclosures containing exposed live parts or exposed conductors operating at over 600 volts, nominal, shall be kept locked.

Exception: Where such entrances are under the observation of a qualified person at all times.

Equipment used on circuits over 600 volts, nominal, containing exposed live parts or exposed conductors is required to be located in a locked room or enclosure. The provisions for locking are not required where the location is under observation at all times such as some engine rooms.

Where the voltage exceeds 600 volts, nominal, permanent and conspicuous warning signs shall be provided, reading substantially as follows: "Warning—High Voltage—Keep Out."

(d) Illumination. Adequate illumination shall be provided for all working spaces about electrical equipment. The lighting outlets shall be so arranged that persons changing lamps or making repairs on the lighting system will not be endangered by live parts or other equipment.

The points of control shall be so located that persons are not likely to come in contact with any live part or moving part of the equipment while turning on the lights.

(e) Elevation of Unguarded Live Parts. Unguarded live parts above working space shall be maintained at elevations not less than required by Table 110-34(e).

Table 110-34(e)
Elevation of Unguarded Live Parts above Working Space

Nominal Voltage Between Phases	Elevation
601–7500	8′6″
7501–35000	9′
Over 35 kV	9′ + 0.37″ per kV above 35

For SI units: one inch = 25.4 millimeters; one foot = 0.3048 meter.

2 Wiring Design and Protection

ARTICLE 200 — USE AND IDENTIFICATION
OF GROUNDED CONDUCTORS

Contents

200-1. Scope. This article provides requirements for: (1) identification of terminals; (2) grounded conductors in premises wiring systems; and (3) identification of grounded conductors.

(FPN): See Article 100 for definitions of "Grounded Conductor" and "Grounding Conductor."

200-2. General. All premises wiring systems shall have a grounded conductor that is identified in accordance with Section 200-6.

Exception: Circuits and systems exempted or prohibited by Sections 210-10, 215-7, 250-3, 250-5, 250-7, 503-13, 517-104, 668-11, 668-21, and 690-41 Exception.

Isolated circuits are required in flammable anesthetizing locations. The ungrounded conductors of these circuits are colored orange and brown (for 3-phase systems, the third conductor is yellow) and are provided with a continually operating "line isolation monitor." See Section 517-104 and NFPA 99, Standard for Health Care Facilities. Isolated circuits are also required in wet locations in patient care areas on circuits supplying 125V single-phase 15 and 20 A receptacles, if interruption of power cannot be tolerated. See Section 517-90(c).

The grounded conductor, when insulated, shall have insulation: (1) which is suitable, other than color, for any ungrounded conductor of the same circuit on circuits of less than 1000 volts, or (2) rated not less than 600 volts for solidly grounded neutral systems of 1 kV and over as described in Section 250-152(a).

200-3. Connection to Grounded System. Premises wiring shall not be electrically connected to a supply system unless the latter contains, for any grounded conductor of the interior system, a corresponding conductor which is grounded.

For the purpose of this section, "electrically connected" shall mean connection capable of carrying current as distinguished from connection through electromagnetic induction.

ARTICLE 200—USE AND IDENTIFICATION OF GROUNDED CONDUCTORS

Grounded conductors of premises wiring are required to be connected to the supply system grounded conductor to assure a common, continuous grounded system.

200-6. Means of Identifying Grounded Conductors.

(a) Sizes No. 6 or Smaller. An insulated grounded conductor of No. 6 or smaller shall be identified by a continuous white or natural gray outer finish along its entire length.

Exception No. 1: Multiconductor varnished-cloth-insulated cables.

Exception No. 2: Fixture wires as outlined in Article 402.

Exception No. 3: A conductor identified as required by Section 210-5(a) for branch circuits.

Exception No. 4: Where the conditions of maintenance and supervision assure that only qualified persons will service the installation, grounded conductors in multiconductor cables shall be permitted to be permanently identified at their terminations at the time of installation by a distinctive white marking or other equally effective means.

See Figure 200-1.

Multiconductor
cable

Grounded conductor,
(Generally, white tape or paint)

Figure 200-1. The grounded conductor of multiconductor cable is identified at the time of installation by qualified persons, generally in commercial or industrial locations, where supervision and maintenance are assured. This method is permitted for all sizes of conductors of multiconductor cables.

Exception No. 5: The grounded conductor of a mineral-insulated, metal-sheathed cable shall be identified at the time of installation by distinctive marking at its terminations.

See Figure 330-1.

For aerial cable, the identification shall be as above, or by means of a ridge so located on the exterior of the cable as to identify it.

Wires having their outer covering finished to show a white or natural gray color but having colored tracer threads in the braid, identifying the source of manufacture, shall be considered as meeting the provisions of this section.

(b) Sizes Larger than No. 6. An insulated grounded conductor larger than No. 6 shall be identified either by a continuous white or natural gray outer finish along its entire length or at the time of installation by a distinctive white marking at its terminations. Multiconductor flat cable No. 4 or larger shall be permitted to employ an external ridge on the grounded conductor.

See Figure 200-2.

Grounded conductor,
(Generally white tape or paint)

Figure 200-2. The "larger than No. 6" in Section 200-6(b) applies to all conductor materials including multiconductor flat cable No. 4 or larger which is permitted to employ an external ridge to identify the grounded conductor.

Exception: Where the conditions of maintenance and supervision assure that only qualified persons will service the installation, grounded conductors in multiconductor cables shall be permitted to be permanently identified at their terminations at the time of installation by a distinctive white marking or other equally effective means.

(c) Flexible Cords. An insulated conductor intended for use as a grounded conductor, where contained within a flexible cord, shall be identified by a white or natural gray outer finish or by methods permitted by Section 400-22.

(d) Grounded Conductors of Different Systems. Where conductors of different systems are installed in the same raceway, box, auxiliary gutter, or other types of enclosures, one system grounded conductor, if required, shall have an outer covering conforming to (a) or (b) above. Each other system grounded conductor, if required, shall have an outer covering of white with an identifiable colored stripe (not green) running along the insulation, or other and different means of identification as allowed by (a) or (b).

This section corresponds to Section 210-5(a) and applies in general to all grounded conductors including feeder conductors. See Figure 210-3.

Article 200 contains the grounded circuit identification requirements. The grounded circuit conductor is referred to throughout the *Code* as the grounded conductor. It is often, but not always (as in corner-grounded delta systems), also referred to as the neutral conductor.

Section 215-8, covering 3-phase, 4-wire delta-connected systems with the midpoint of one phase grounded, requires that the conductor with the higher phase-to-ground voltage be identified by the color orange, by tagging, or by some other effective means at every point of connection where the grounded conductor is also present. The high leg of 120/240 V 4-wire, 3-phase delta systems is 208 V to ground (120 V x 1.73).

Both Sections 200-6(a) and (b) contain exceptions introducing a concept for identifying grounded conductors of multiconductor cables. These exceptions allow the identification of conductors at the time of installation by a distinctive white marking or other equally effective means. A variety of other schemes, equally effective, include numbering, lettering, or tagging. These exceptions are intended to apply in locations where a regulated system of maintenance and supervision assures that only qualified persons will service the installation.

For the identification of branch-circuit conductors, see Section 210-5. For the identification of the high leg (delta-system) conductor, see Sections 215-8 and 230-56. See Section 384-3(f) for the phase arrangement of 3-phase buses on switchboards and panelboards.

200-7. Use of White or Natural Gray Color.   A continuous white or natural gray covering on a conductor or a termination marking of white or natural gray color shall be used only for the grounded conductor.

Exception No. 1: An insulated conductor with a white or natural gray finish shall be permitted as an ungrounded conductor where permanently reidentified to indicate its use, by painting or other effective means at its termination, and at each location where the conductor is visible and accessible.

Exception No. 2: A cable containing an insulated conductor with a white or natural gray outer finish shall be permitted for single-pole, 3-way, or 4-way switch loops where the white or natural gray conductor is used for the supply to the switch, but not as a return conductor from the switch to the switched outlet. In these applications, reidentification of the white or natural gray conductor shall not be required.

Exception No. 3: A flexible cord for connecting an appliance having one conductor identified with a white or natural gray outer finish, or by any other means permitted by Section 400-22, shall be permitted whether or not the outlet to which it is connected is supplied by a circuit having a grounded conductor.

Exception No. 4: A white or natural gray conductor of circuits of less than 50 volts shall be required to be grounded only as required by Section 250-5(a).

200-9. Means of Identification of Terminals.   The identification of terminals to which a grounded conductor is to be connected shall be substantially white in color. The identification of other terminals shall be of a readily distinguishable different color.

Exception: Where the conditions of maintenance and supervision assure that only qualified persons will service the installations, terminals for grounded conductors shall be permitted to be permanently identified at the time of installation by a distinctive white marking or other equally effective means.

See the comments following Section 200-6.

200-10. Identification of Terminals.

(a) Device Terminals.   All devices provided with terminals for the attachment of conductors and intended for connection to more than one side of the circuit shall have terminals properly marked for identification.

Exception No. 1: Where the electrical connection of a terminal intended to be connected to the grounded conductor is clearly evident.

Exception No. 2: Single-pole devices to which only one side of the line is connected.

Exception No. 3: The terminals of lighting and appliance branch-circuit panelboards.

Exception No. 4: Devices having a normal current rating of over 30 amperes other than polarized attachment plugs and polarized receptacles for attachment plugs as required in (b) below.

(b) Receptacles, Plugs, and Connectors.   Receptacles, polarized attachment plugs and cord connectors for plugs and polarized plugs shall have the terminal intended for connection to the grounded (white) conductor identified.

Identification shall be by a metal or metal coating substantially white in color or the word "white" located adjacent to the identified terminal.

This paragraph permits the identification of the terminal for the grounded conductor to be accomplished by the use of the word "white." It also permits the terminal to be otherwise identified by a distinctive white color on all devices, including those with binding head screws. These permitted methods would allow

60

plating of all screws and terminals to meet requirements of specific applications, such as corrosion-resistant devices.

If the terminal is not visible, the conductor entrance hole for the connection shall be colored white or marked with the word "white."

The terminal for the connection of the equipment grounding conductor shall be identified by: (1) a green-colored, not readily removable terminal screw with a hexagonal head; (2) a green-colored, hexagonal, not readily removable terminal nut; or (3) a green-colored pressure wire connector. If the terminal for the grounding conductor is not visible, the conductor entrance hole shall be marked with the word "green" or otherwise identified by a distinctive green color.

Exception: Terminal identification shall not be required for 2-wire nonpolarized attachment plugs.

This exception coordinates with Section 410-42(a) and makes it clear that two-wire polarized attachment plugs are required to have the grounded terminal identified.

(c) Screw Shells. For devices with screw shells, the terminal for the grounded conductor shall be the one connected to the screw shell.

(d) Screw-Shell Devices with Leads. For screw-shell devices with attached leads, the conductor attached to the screw shell shall have a white or natural gray finish. The outer finish of the other conductor shall be of a solid color that will not be confused with the white or natural gray finish used to identify the grounded conductor.

(e) Appliances. Appliances that have a single-pole switch or a single-pole overcurrent device in the line or any line-connected screw-shell lampholders, and that are to be connected: (1) by permanent wiring methods; or (2) by field-installed attachment plugs and cords with three or more wires (including the equipment grounding conductor) shall have means to identify the terminal for the grounded circuit conductor (if any).

The "means" for identifying the terminal for the grounded conductor may be by metal, or metal coating, substantially white in color or by the word "white" located adjacent to the terminal to be so identified. It may also be by marking on a wiring diagram.

200-11. Polarity of Connections. No grounded conductor shall be attached to any terminal or lead so as to reverse designated polarity.

ARTICLE 210 — BRANCH CIRCUITS

Contents

A. General Provisions

210-1. Scope. This article covers branch circuits except for branch circuits which supply only motor loads, which are covered in Article 430. Provisions of this article and Article 430 apply to branch circuits with combination loads.

Exception: Branch circuits for electrolytic cells as covered in Section 668-3(c), Exceptions No. 1 and 4.

Section 668-3(c), Exception Nos. 1 and 4 indicate that electrolytic cell line conductors, cells, cell line attachments, and the wiring of auxiliary equipment and devices within the cell line working zone are not required to comply with the provisions of Article 210.

210-2. Other Articles for Specific-Purpose Branch Circuits. Branch circuits shall comply with this article and also with the applicable provisions of other articles of this Code. The provisions for branch circuits supplying equipment in the following list amend or supplement the provisions in this article and shall apply to branch circuits referred to therein:

210-3. Classifications. Branch circuits recognized by this article shall be classified in accordance with the maximum permitted ampere rating or setting of the overcurrent device. The classification for other than individual branch circuits shall be: 15, 20, 30, 40, and 50 amperes. Where conductors of higher ampacity are used for any reason, the ampere rating or setting of the specified overcurrent device shall determine the circuit classification.

Conductors of higher ampacity may be necessary to compensate for voltage drop. For example, a branch circuit of No. 10 AWG Type TW copper conductors with a 30-ampere ampacity protected by a 20-ampere overcurrent device is classified as a 20-ampere branch circuit.

Exception: Multioutlet branch circuits greater than 50 amperes shall be permitted on industrial premises where maintenance and supervision indicate that qualified persons will service equipment.

It is common in industrial establishments to provide several single receptacles of 50-ampere or higher rating on a single branch circuit to allow quick relocation of equipment for production and/or maintenance use, such as electric welders. Generally, only one piece of equipment is operated at a time. The type of receptacles used are generally of the non-ANSI-type configuration, known as a pin-and-sleeve receptacle, although the *Code* does not so limit the design. These may or may not be horsepower rated.

210-4. Multiwire Branch Circuits.

(a) General. Branch circuits recognized by this article shall be permitted as multiwire circuits. A multiwire branch circuit shall be permitted to be considered as multiple circuits. All conductors shall originate from the same panelboard.

(b) Dwelling Units. In dwelling units a multiwire branch circuit supplying more than one device or equipment on the same yoke shall be provided with a means to disconnect simultaneously all ungrounded conductors at the panelboard where the branch circuit originated.

A "device" is defined in Article 100 as "a unit of an electrical system which is intended to carry but not utilize electric energy." The term "device" includes receptacles, switches, and lampholders, — the three types of "devices" normally used on dwelling unit switch and receptacle yokes. The term "or equipment" includes such items as pilot lights which do utilize electric energy.

Many 125-volt, 15- and 20-ampere duplex receptacles have a break-off tab (Section 210-4) that permits each of the two receptacles to be supplied from a different polarity and the single grounded conductor of a three-wire (multiwire) branch circuit. This is commonly called a "split-wired" receptacle, i.e., one-half of the duplex receptacle on one circuit and the other half on another circuit. The simultaneous opening of both "hot" conductors at the panelboard will effectively protect personnel from inadvertent contact with an energized conductor or device terminal. The simultaneous disconnection can be secured by a 2-pole circuit breaker or by two single-pole circuit breakers with a handle tie. Where fuses are used, a 2-pole disconnect switch is required. See Figure 210-1.

Figure 210-1. These multiwire branch circuits supply more than one device or equipment on the same yoke. For dwelling units, Section 210-4(b) requires simultaneous disconnection of all ungrounded conductors at the panelboard where the branch circuits originate.

(c) Line to Neutral Load. Multiwire branch circuits shall supply only line to neutral load.

Exception No. 1: A multiwire branch circuit that supplies only one utilization equipment.

Exception No. 2: Where all ungrounded conductors of the multiwire branch circuit are opened simultaneously by the branch-circuit overcurrent device.

(FPN): See Section 300-13(b) for continuity of grounded conductor on multiwire circuits.

Figure 210-2. Section 210-4(c) does not permit a multiwire branch circuit (See Article 100, Definitions) to supply other than line-to-neutral loads. However, Exception No. 2 permits line-to-line loads if the ungrounded conductors are opened simultaneously by the branch-circuit overcurrent device.

Article 100 defines "branch circuit, multiwire" as "two or more ungrounded conductors having a potential difference between them, and a grounded conductor having equal potential difference between it and each ungrounded conductor of the circuit and which is connected to the neutral conductor of the system."

The circuit most commonly used as a multiwire branch circuit consists of two ungrounded conductors and one grounded conductor supplied from a single-phase, 3-wire system. Multiwire branch circuits have many advantages, such as three wires doing the work of four (in place of two 2-wire circuits), less raceway fill, easier balancing and phasing of a system, and less voltage drop (see comments following Section 215-2, FPN).

Other multiwire branch circuits are 3-phase, 4-wire; 2-phase, 3-wire; and 2-phase, 5-wire. It is always advisable to properly balance all multiwire branch circuits. See Section 220-4(d). In a 3-phase, 4-wire circuit the neutral could be called upon to carry a current equal to that carried by each of the three phase conductors and should, therefore, be sized the same. The neutral for a 2-phase, 3-wire or 2-phase, 5-wire circuit must be sized to carry 140 percent of the ampere rating of the circuit. See Section 220-22.

Where loads are connected "line-to-line" (utilization equipment connected between two or three phases), 2-pole or 3-pole circuit breakers or switches are required to disconnect all ungrounded conductors simultaneously. There have been cases of multiwire branch circuits supplying a "line-to-line" load (240 V) and a "line-to-neutral" load (120 V) causing a hazard where two single-pole circuit breakers are used and the opening of one could cause the two loads (240 V and 120 V) to create a 120-V series circuit. In testing 240-V equipment, it is quite possible not to realize that the circuit is still energized with 120 V if one overcurrent device is open. See Sections 210-10 and 240-20(b).

210-5. Color Code for Branch Circuits.

(a) Grounded Conductor. The grounded conductor of a branch circuit shall be identified by a continuous white or natural gray color. Where conductors of different systems are installed in the same raceway, box, auxiliary gutter, or other types of enclosures, one system grounded conductor, if required, shall have an outer covering of white or natural gray. Each other system grounded conductor, if required, shall have an outer covering of white with an identifiable colored stripe (not green) running along the insulation or other and different means of identification.

See Figure 210-3.

Figure 210-3. Illustrated are conductors of different systems in the same enclosure. Phase conductors may be any color other than white, gray, or green.

Exception No. 1: The grounded conductors of mineral-insulated, metal-sheathed cable shall be identified by distinctive marking at the terminals during the process of installation.

See Figure 330-1.

Exception No. 2: As permitted in Exception No. 4 of Section 200-6(a) and the Exception to Section 200-6(b).

See Figure 200-1.

(b) Equipment Grounding Conductor. The equipment grounding conductor of a branch circuit shall be identified by a continuous green color or a continuous green color with one or more yellow stripes unless it is bare.

Exception No. 1: As permitted in Section 250-57(b), Exceptions No. 1 and 3 and Section 310-12(b), Exceptions No. 1 and 2.

Exception No. 2: The use of conductor insulation having a continuous green color or a continuous green color with one or more yellow stripes shall be permitted for internal wiring of equipment if such wiring does not serve as the lead wires for connection to branch-circuit conductors.

The color-coding requirements for grounded and grounding conductors are given in Section 210-5. Section 210-5(a) covers installations where more than one grounded branch circuit conductor is carried in a raceway, box, or other enclosure. It requires that one grounded conductor have an outer covering of white or natural gray, and each other system neutral in the raceway, etc., where required, have an outer coloring of white with an identifiable colored stripe (not green) to provide a means of identifying the grounded conductors of each different system. See Section 200-6(d) for the equivalent requirement for other than branch-circuit conductors.

Although the *Code* does not recommend the use of specific colors for phase (ungrounded) conductors of a circuit, it is extremely important that multiwire branch circuits and their grounded circuit conductors (neutral conductors) be identified in the course of installation to assure that the phase conductors are connected to the proper circuit breakers so that the grounded circuit conductors will not be overloaded.

210-6. Branch Circuit Voltage Limitations.

Section 210-6 was completely rewritten for the 1987 edition of the *Code* to clarify the requirements and more accurately reflect the intent. Also see Sections 225-7(c) and (d) for voltages on outside branch circuits and feeders.

(a) Occupancy Limitation.   In dwelling units and guest rooms of hotels, motels, and similar occupancies, the voltage shall not exceed 120 volts, nominal, between conductors that supply the terminals of:

"Similar occupancies" include sleeping rooms in dormitories, nursing homes, etc.

(1) Lighting fixtures;

(2) Cord- and plug-connected loads of less than 1380 volt-amperes, nominal.

The 1380 volt-ampere limit permits high-wattage cord- and plug-connected loads, such as electric ranges, clothes dryers, and some window air conditioners, to be connected to a 240-volt circuit.

(b) 120 Volts Between Conductors.   Circuits not exceeding 120 volts, nominal, between conductors shall be permitted to supply:

(1) The terminals of medium-base screw-shell lampholders or lampholders of other types applied within their voltage ratings.

"Lampholders of other types" include fluorescent lampholders, screw-shell lampholders of the admedium- and mogul-base type, and special lampholders such as those intended for pin-type and blade-type lamp bases, and those intended for tubular-type quartz-iodine (incandescent) lamps. See Figure 210-4.

(2) Auxiliary equipment of electric discharge lamps.

This includes ballasts for fluorescent and high-intensity-discharge (mercury vapor, etc.) lamps.

(3) Cord- and plug-connected or permanently connected utilization equipment.

(c) 277 Volts to Ground.   Circuits exceeding 120 volts, nominal, between conductors and not exceeding 277 volts, nominal, to ground shall be permitted to supply:

(1) Lighting fixtures equipped with mogul-base screw-shell lampholders or with lampholders other than the screw-shell type applied within their voltage ratings.

Lighting fixtures equipped with medium-base and smaller (intermediate-base, candelabra-base, etc.) screw-shell lampholders are not permitted to be connected to circuits exceeding 120 volts, nominal, to ground (480-volt and 277-volt circuits, for example). See Section 225-7(c) and (d) for additional restrictions for installation of outdoor lighting fixtures on 277-volt and 480-volt circuits.

(2) Auxiliary equipment of electric discharge lamps.

The auxiliary equipment (ballast) supplied with many HID (high-intensity-discharge) fixtures consists of an autotransformer, with one conductor of the branch circuit supplying the fixture connected to both the ballast and one terminal

Figure 210-4. Some examples of lighting units permitted to be connected to branch circuits. Note that a mogul-base screw-shell lampholder is required on a circuit operating at 277 volts to ground.

of the lampholder. In such a construction, Section 210-6(c)(1) prohibits use of a medium-base screw-shell lampholder if the branch circuit exceeds 120 volts, nominal, to ground.

(3) Cord- and plug-connected or permanently connected utilization equipment.

(d) 600 Volts Between Conductors. Circuits exceeding 277 volts, nominal, to ground and not exceeding 600 volts, nominal, between conductors shall be permitted to supply:

(1) The auxiliary equipment of electric discharge lamps mounted in permanently installed fixtures where the fixtures are mounted in accordance with one of the following:

a. Not less than a height of 22 feet (6.71 m) on poles or similar structures for the illumination of outdoor areas, such as highways, roads, bridges, athletic fields, or parking lots.

b. Not less than a height of 18 feet (5.49 m) on other structures, such as tunnels.

See Figure 210-5.

Figure 210-5. Minimum mounting heights are required to be maintained for circuits exceeding 277 volts to ground and not exceeding 600 volts between conductors when supplying auxiliary equipment of electric discharge lampholders.

(2) Cord- and plug-connected or permanently connected utilization equipment.

(FPN): See Section 410-78 for auxiliary equipment limitations.

Exception No. 1 to (b), (c) and (d) above: For lampholders of infrared industrial heating appliances as provided in Section 422-15(c).

Exception No. 2 to (b), (c) and (d) above: For railway properties as described in Section 110-19.

210-7. Receptacles and Cord Connectors.

(a) Grounding Type. Receptacles installed on 15- and 20-ampere branch circuits shall be of the grounding type. Grounding-type receptacles shall be installed only on circuits of the voltage class and current for which they are rated, except as provided in Tables 210-21(b)(2) and (b)(3).

A single receptacle installed on an individual branch circuit is required to have an ampere rating of not less than that of the branch circuit. That is, a single receptacle on a 20-ampere circuit must be rated at 20 amperes; however, two or more 15-ampere receptacles would be permitted on a 20-ampere general-purpose branch circuit.

Exception: Nongrounding-type receptacles installed in accordance with Section 210-7(d), Exception.

(b) To Be Grounded. Receptacles and cord connectors having grounding contacts shall have those contacts effectively grounded.

Grounding is not required on all cord- and plug-connected equipment such as toasters and other types of heating appliances having exposed or nonsheathed elements. These appliances are subject to physical contact of the heating elements by insertion of knives, forks, or other objects. It is a common occurrence for a householder to insert a utensil in a toaster to remove a slice of toast, and additional hazards are thereby introduced by grounding such appliances.

Exception No. 1: Receptacles mounted on portable and vehicle-mounted generators in accordance with Section 250-6.

Exception No. 2: Ground-fault circuit-interrupter replacement receptacles as permitted by Section 210-7(d), Exception.

See commentary following Section 210-7(d), Exception.

(c) Methods of Grounding. The grounding contacts of receptacles and cord connectors shall be grounded by connection to the equipment grounding conductor of the circuit supplying the receptacle or cord connector.

(FPN): For installation requirements for the reduction of electrical noise, see Section 250-74, Exception No. 4.

The branch circuit or branch-circuit raceway shall include or provide a grounding conductor to which the grounding contacts of the receptacle or cord connector shall be connected.

(FPN): Section 250-91(b) describes acceptable grounding means.

(FPN): For extensions of existing branch circuits, see Section 250-50.

(d) Replacements. Grounding-type receptacles shall be used as replacements for existing nongrounding types and shall be connected to a grounding conductor installed in accordance with (c) above.

Exception: Where a grounding means does not exist in the receptacle enclosure either a nongrounding or a ground-fault circuit-interrupter type of receptacle shall be used. A grounding conductor shall not be connected from the ground-fault circuit-interrupter-type receptacle to any outlet supplied from the ground-fault circuit-interrupter-type receptacle.

When existing nongrounding-type receptacles are replaced, only grounding-type receptacles are permitted where a grounding means exists in the receptacle enclosure. Where a grounding means does not exist in the receptacle enclosure, there are three choices: (1) a nongrounding-type receptacle can be used, thereby indicating to the user that a grounding means for an appliance is not available; (2) a grounding-type receptacle can be used; or (3) a ground-fault circuit-interrupter type of receptacle can be used. If the ground-fault circuit-interrupter type of receptacle is used, it can either be the nonfeed-through type, or a feed-through type wired so that a grounding conductor is not connected to any outlet supplied by this receptacle.

The ability of the GFCI to provide shock hazard protection is independent of whether or not the tool, appliance, etc., connected to it is grounded. A nongrounding type of receptacle provides no shock hazard protection.

If the ungrounded GFCI type of receptacle is used, care should be exercised in the installation to be sure the grounding lead of the receptacle is insulated or otherwise kept from contacting uninsulated live parts in the box. Since the box is not grounded in this type of installation, Section 250-74 does not require bonding the grounding lead to the box.

See also Section 250-50, Exception.

(e) Cord- and Plug-Connected Equipment. The installation of grounding-type receptacles shall not be used as a requirement that all cord- and plug-connected equipment be of the grounded type.

(FPN): See Section 250-45 for type of cord- and plug-connected equipment to be grounded.

Over the years there has been a requirement that grounding-type receptacles be used as replacements for nongrounding types. See Section 210-7(d). It is intended that grounding-type receptacles be conveniently located for use with utilization equipment that is required to be grounded. For cord- and plug-connected equipment that is required to be grounded, see Section 250-45.

Many appliances are not required to be grounded, for example, toasters, flat irons, and some heating equipment [see commentary following Section 210-7(b)], and there are still many nongrounding-type receptacles in use. The use of an adapter or other approved means is necessary where grounding is required. Distinctively marked, listed, double-insulated tools and appliances are not required to be grounded.

(f) Noninterchangeable Types. Receptacles connected to circuits having different voltages, frequencies, or types of current (ac or dc) on the same premises shall be of such design that the attachment plugs used on these circuits are not interchangeable.

See Figures 210-6 and 210-7.

210-8. Ground-Fault Circuit-Interrupter Protection for Personnel.

(a) Dwelling Units.

(1) All 125-volt, single-phase, 15- and 20-ampere receptacles installed in bathrooms shall have ground-fault circuit-interrupter protection for personnel.

The requirement for ground-fault circuit-interrupters for receptacles in bathrooms was originally inserted in the *Code* because data supplied with the *Code* proposal for GFCIs indicated that a number of accidents occurring in bathrooms could be prevented by GFCIs. See Figure 210-8.

(2) All 125-volt, single-phase, 15- or 20-ampere receptacles installed in garages shall have ground-fault circuit-interrupter protection for personnel.

Exception No. 1 to (a)(2): Receptacles which are not readily accessible.

This would include a ceiling-mounted receptacle installed for connection of a garage door opener.

Exception No. 2 to (a)(2): Receptacles for appliances occupying dedicated space which are cord- and plug-connected in accordance with Section 400-7(a)(6), (a)(7), or (a)(8).

This means that the appliance must physically be in place at the time of inspection.

Receptacles installed under Exceptions to Section 210-8(a)(2) shall not be considered as meeting the requirements of Section 210-52(f).

The purpose of GFCIs in garages is to provide a degree of safety for persons using portable hand-held tools, gardening appliances, and snow blowers, which might be connected in the garage because it is the closest receptacle. Also, auto repair work and general workshop electrical tool usage are protected. GFCIs are not required for appliances such as freezers or refrigerators. See Figure 210-10.

(3) All 125-volt, single-phase, 15- and 20-ampere receptacles installed outdoors where there is direct grade level access to the dwelling unit and to the receptacles shall have ground-fault circuit-interrupter protection for personnel.

(FPN): See Section 215-9 for feeder protection.

For the purposes of this section, "direct grade level access" is defined as being located not more than 6 feet, 6 inches (1.98 m) above grade level and being readily accessible without entering or passing through a dwelling unit.

71

ARTICLE 210—BRANCH CIRCUITS

See commentary following Section 210-52(d) and Section 410-57. See also Figure 210-11.

		15 AMPERE		20 AMPERE		30 AMPERE		50 AMPERE		60 AMPERE	
		RECEPTACLE	PLUG	RECEPTACLE	PLUG	RECEPTACLE	PLUG	RECEPTACLE	PLUG	RECEPTACLE	PLUG
2-POLE 2-WIRE	1 · 125 V	1-15R	1-15P								
	2 · 250 V		2-15P	2-20R	2-20P	2-30R	2-30P				
	3 · 277 V				(RESERVED FOR FUTURE CONFIGURATIONS)						
	4 · 600 V				(RESERVED FOR FUTURE CONFIGURATIONS)						
2-POLE 3-WIRE GROUNDING	5 · 125 V	5-15R	5-15P	5-20R	5-20P	5-30R	5-30P	5-50R	5-50P		
	6 · 250 V	6-15R	6-15P	6-20R	6-20P	6-30R	6-30P	6-50R	6-50P		
	7 · 277 V AC	7-15R	7-15P	7-20R	7-20P	7-30R	7-30P	7-50R	7-50P		
	24 · 347 V AC	24-15R	24-15P	24-20R	24-20P	24-30R	24-30P	24-50R	24-50P		
	8 · 480 V AC				(RESERVED FOR FUTURE CONFIGURATIONS)						
	9 · 600 V AC				(RESERVED FOR FUTURE CONFIGURATIONS)						
3-POLE 3-WIRE	10 · 125/250 V			10-20R	10-20P	10-30R	10-30P	10-50R	10-50P		
	11 · 3 ∅ 250 V	11-15R	11-15P	11-20R	11-20P	11-30R	11-30P	11-50R	11-50P		
	12 · 3 ∅ 480 V				(RESERVED FOR FUTURE CONFIGURATIONS)						
	13 · 3 ∅ 600 V				(RESERVED FOR FUTURE CONFIGURATIONS)						
3-POLE 4-WIRE GROUNDING	14 · 125/250 V	14-15R	14-15P	14-20R	14-20P	14-30R	14-30P	14-50R	14-50P	14-60R	14-60P
	15 · 3 ∅ 250 V	15-15R	15-15P	15-20R	15-20P	15-30R	15-30P	15-50R	15-50P	15-60R	15-60P
	16 · 3 ∅ 480 V				(RESERVED FOR FUTURE CONFIGURATIONS)						
	17 · 3 ∅ 600 V				(RESERVED FOR FUTURE CONFIGURATIONS)						
4-POLE 4-WIRE	18 · 3 ∅ 208Y/120 V	18-15R	18-15P	18-20R	18-20P	18-30R	18-30P	18-50R	18-50P	18-60R	18-60P
	19 · 3 ∅ 480Y/277 V				(RESERVED FOR FUTURE CONFIGURATIONS)						
	20 · 3 ∅ 600Y/347 V				(RESERVED FOR FUTURE CONFIGURATIONS)						
4-POLE 5-WIRE GROUNDING	21 · 3 ∅ 208Y/120 V				(RESERVED FOR FUTURE CONFIGURATIONS)						
	22 · 3 ∅ 480Y/277 V				(RESERVED FOR FUTURE CONFIGURATIONS)						
	23 · 3 ∅ 600Y/347 V				(RESERVED FOR FUTURE CONFIGURATIONS)						

Figure 210-6. Configuration chart for general-purpose nonlocking plugs and receptacles; taken from ANSI C73 Standard.

			15 AMPERE		20 AMPERE		30 AMPERE	
			RECEPTACLE	PLUG	RECEPTACLE	PLUG	RECEPTACLE	PLUG
2-pole 2-wire	125 V	L1						
	250 V	L2						
	277 V AC	L3						
	600 V	L4						
2-pole 3-wire grounding	125 V	L5						
	250 V	L6						
	277 V AC	L7						
	480 V AC	L8						
	600 V AC	L9						
3-pole 3-wire	125/250 V	L10						
	3 phase 250 V	L11						
	3 phase 480 V	L12						
	3 phase 600 V	L13						
3-pole 4-wire grounding	125/250 V	L14						
	3 phase 250 V	L15						
	3 phase 480 V	L16						
	3 phase 600 V	L17						
4-pole 4-wire	3 phase 208Y/120 V	L18						
	3 phase 480Y/277 V	L19						
	3 phase 600Y/347 V	L20						
4-pole 5-wire grounding	3 phase 208Y/120V	L21						
	3 phase 480Y/277 V	L22						
	3 phase 600Y/347 V	L23						

Figure 210-7. Configuration chart for specific-purpose locking plugs and receptacles; taken from ANSI C73 Standard.

ARTICLE 210—BRANCH CIRCUITS

Figure 210-8. Section 210-8(a)(1) indicates that all 125-V, single-phase, 15 and 20 A receptacles in bathrooms are to have GFCI protection for personnel. This includes any such receptacles located for a clothes washer, clothes dryer (gas), or integral with the lighting fixture, and, of course, the one wall-mounted adjacent to the basin. The definition of bathroom refers to an area that includes the entire area shown above, whether a separating door (as illustrated) is present or not. Where receptacles are provided in bathroom areas of hotels and motels ground-fault circuit-interrupter protection for the receptacles is required. See Figure 210-9.

Figure 210-9. Typical motel "bathroom" as defined at the end of Section 210-8 includes the wash basin outside the door for the room containing the tub, toilet, and (other) wash basin.

(4) At least one 125-volt, single-phase, 15- or 20-ampere receptacle installed in a basement shall have ground-fault circuit-interrupter protection for personnel and it shall be so identified.

This requirement is new in the 1987 *NEC*. The intent is to enhance safety where portable tools, etc., are used.

(5) All 125-volt, single-phase, 15- and 20-ampere receptacles required by Section 210-52(b) installed within 6 feet (1.83 m) of the kitchen sink above counter top surfaces shall have ground-fault circuit-interrupter protection for personnel.

Most kitchen appliances are ungrounded, and the presence of water and grounded surfaces leads to a hazardous environment, leading to this new requirement for GFCI protection around the kitchen sink.

(FPN): The intent of this section is to permit the exemption of receptacles which are located specifically for appliances such as refrigerators and freezers from ground-fault circuit-interrupter protection for personnel.

74

Figure 210-10. Receptacles that are not readily accessible (e.g., door opener) or are located for appliances occupying dedicated space (e.g., food freezer) are not required to have GFCI protection for personnel.

Figure 210-11. The three receptacles located outdoors at a dwelling unit are considered to be at direct grade level access and must have GFCI protection for personnel.

(6) All 125-volt, single-phase, 15- or 20-ampere receptacles installed in boathouses shall have ground-fault circuit-interrupter protection for personnel.

The requirements of Sections 210-8(a)(5) and (a)(6) are new in the 1987 *NEC*. The intent is to increase safety in these higher risk areas. A boathouse, as contemplated by the National Electrical Code Committee, is a structure, either floating or built on piles, and intended to house boats or marine equipment. The requirement covers only boathouses associated with dwelling units.

(b) Hotels and Motels. All 125-volt, single-phase, 15- and 20-ampere receptacles installed in bathrooms of guest rooms in hotels and motels shall have ground-fault circuit-interrupter protection for personnel.

See commentary following Section 210-8(a)(1) and Figure 210-9.

The requirement for ground-fault circuit-interrupter protection for receptacles on construction sites is covered under Section 305-6.

Bathroom: As used in Section 210-8, a bathroom is an area including a basin with one or more of the following: a toilet, a tub, or a shower.

Figure 210-12 shows a typical circuit arrangement of a GFCI for personnel protection. The line conductors are passed through a toroidal coil and connected to a shunt-trip device.

Figure 210-12. The circuitry and components for a typical ground-fault circuit-interrupter.

As long as the current in each conductor remains equal, the device remains in a closed position. If one of the conductors comes in contact with a grounded object, either directly or through a person's body, some of the current returns by an alternative path and an unbalanced current results. The unbalanced current is sensed by the toroidal coil, and a circuit is established to the shunt-trip which opens the circuit. Note that the design technology does not require the presence of an equipment grounding conductor. Ground-fault circuit-interrupters operate on currents of 5 mA with a plus or minus (±) value of 1 mA. Evaluation standards permit a differential of 4 to 6 mA. At trip levels of 5 mA (the instantaneous current could be much higher), a shock can be felt during the time of the fault, leading to involuntary reactions that may cause secondary accidents, such as falls. GFCIs will not sense phase-to-phase faults.

A variety of GFCIs are available, including portable types, plug-in circuit-breaker types, types built into attachment plug caps, and receptacle types. Each has a test switch so that the unit can be checked periodically to ensure proper operation. See Figures 210-12 and 210-13.

210-9. Circuits Derived from Autotransformers. Branch circuits shall not be supplied by autotransformers.

Exception No. 1: Where the system supplied has a grounded conductor that is electrically connected to a grounded conductor of the system supplying the autotransformer.

Exception No. 2: An autotransformer used to extend or add an individual branch circuit in an existing installation for an equipment load without the connection to a similar grounded conductor when transforming from a nominal 208 volts to a nominal 240-volt supply or similarly from 240 volts to 208 volts.

(FPN): An autotransformer is a transformer in which a part of the winding is common to both primary and secondary circuits.

Figures 210-16 and 210-17 illustrate autotransformers used to derive 120-V and 240-V systems from 240-V and 208-V systems. In Figure 210-16 the grounded conductor of the primary system is electrically connected to the grounded conductor of the secondary system.

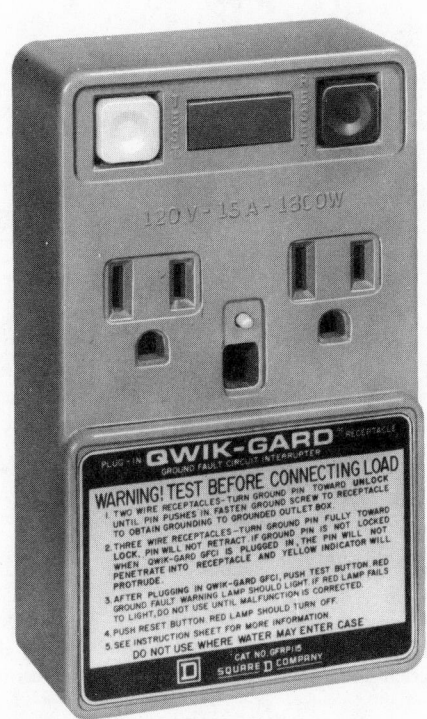

Figure 210-13. A portable plug-in-type ground-fault circuit-interrupter. (*Square D Co.*)

Exception No. 2 allows an autotransformer (without an electrical connection to a grounded conductor) to extend or add an individual branch circuit in an existing installation when, for example, transforming (boosting) 208 V to 240 V as shown in Figure 210-17, or transforming (bucking) 240 V to 208 V for use with appliances, for example, ranges, air conditioners, heating elements, and motors. It is also possible to increase 240 V to 277 V for lighting systems, and 440 V to 550 V for power equipment. A single unit is used to boost or buck single-phase voltage, but two or three units are used to boost or buck 3-phase voltage. An autotransformer requires little physical space, is economical, and, above all, efficient.

A buck-boost transformer is a means of raising or lowering (boosting or bucking) a supply line voltage by a small amount—usually no more than ± 20 percent. It is an insulating transformer with two primary (input) windings, both rated at 120 V or 240 V and two secondary (output) windings, both rated at either 12 V, 16 V, or 24 V. Its primary and secondary windings can be connected together so that the electrical characteristics are changed from an insulating transformer to those of a "boosting" or "bucking" autotransformer correcting voltage up to ± 20 percent.

Literature is available from manufacturers containing diagrams for connection and application of autotransformers.

210-10. Ungrounded Conductors Tapped from Grounded Systems. Two-wire dc circuits and ac circuits of two or more ungrounded conductors shall be permitted to be tapped from the ungrounded conductors of circuits having a grounded neutral conductor. Switching devices in

Figure 210-14. A 15-A duplex receptacle with integral ground-fault circuit-interrupter, which also protects downstream loads. (*Pass & Seymour, Inc.*)

each tapped circuit shall have a pole in each ungrounded conductor. All poles of multipole switching devices shall manually switch together where such switching devices also serve as a disconnecting means as required by Section 422-21(b) for an appliance; Section 424-20 for a fixed electric space heating unit; Section 426-51 for electric de-icing and snow-melting equipment; Section 430-85 for a motor controller; and Section 430-103 for a motor.

Two-wire ungrounded branch circuits may be tapped from ac or dc circuits of two or more ungrounded conductors having a grounded neutral conductor. Figure 210-20 (on the left) illustrates ungrounded 2-wire branch circuits tapped from the ungrounded conductors of a dc or single-phase system to supply a small motor. Figure 210-21 illustrates a 3-phase, 4-wire wye system.

Circuit breakers or switches used as the disconnecting means for a branch circuit are required to open all poles simultaneously. This requirement involves only the manual operation of the disconnecting means; thus, where switches and fuses are used and one fuse blows, or where circuit breakers (two single-pole circuit breakers with a "handle-tie") are used and one breaker trips, one pole could remain closed. The intention is not to provide a common trip of fuses or circuit breakers, but to disconnect "manually" the ungrounded conductors of the branch circuit with one manual operation.

B. Branch-Circuit Ratings

210-19. Conductors — Minimum Ampacity and Size.

(a) **General.** Branch-circuit conductors shall have an ampacity not less than the maximum load to be served. In addition, conductors of multioutlet branch circuits supplying receptacles for cord- and plug-connected portable loads shall have an ampacity of not less than the rating of the branch circuit. Cable assemblies with the neutral conductor smaller than the ungrounded conductors shall be so marked.

Only multioutlet branch circuit conductors supplying receptacles for cord- and plug-connected portable loads are required to have an ampacity not less than the

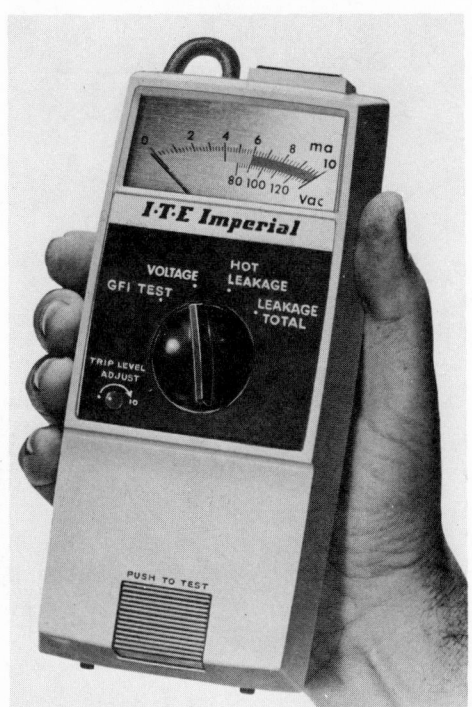

Figure 210-15. Leakage of the neutral conductor to ground and ground-fault leakage current from the hot conductor can be measured by this GFI tester. (*Gould Inc.*)

Figure 210-16. The circuitry for an autotransformer used to derive a 2-wire, 120-V system for lighting from a 240-V corner-grounded delta power system.

rating of the circuit (the rating of the overcurrent device per Section 210-3), because the loading of such circuits is unpredictable.

(FPN): See Tables 310-16 through 310-31 for ampacity ratings of conductors.

(FPN): See Part B of Article 430 for minimum rating of motor branch-circuit conductors.

(FPN): See Section 310-10 for temperature limitation of conductors.

(FPN): Conductors for branch circuits as defined in Article 100, sized to prevent a voltage drop exceeding 3 percent at the farthest outlet of power, heating, and lighting loads, or combinations of such loads and where

Figure 210-17. The circuitry for an autotransformer used to derive a 240-V system from a 208-V supply.

Figure 210-18. Typical hookups for buck or boost transformers connected as autotransformers to change 240 V single-phase to 208 V or vice versa.

Figure 210-19. Typical hookups for buck or boost transformers connected in 3-phase open delta as autotransformers to change 240 V to 208 V or vice versa.

the maximum total voltage drop on both feeders and branch circuits to the farthest outlet does not exceed 5 percent, will provide reasonable efficiency of operation. See Section 215-2 for voltage drop on feeder conductors.

(b) Household Ranges and Cooking Appliances. Branch-circuit conductors supplying household ranges, wall-mounted ovens, counter-mounted cooking units, and other household cooking appliances shall have an ampacity not less than the rating of the branch circuit and not

80

Figures 210-20 and 210-21. Branch circuits tapped from ungrounded conductors of multiwire systems.

less than the maximum load to be served. For ranges of 8 ¾ kW or more rating, the minimum branch-circuit rating shall be 40 amperes.

For a minimum 40-A branch-circuit rating, for example:

> No. 8 AWG copper, Type TW = 40 A.
> No. 6 AWG aluminum, Type TW = 40 A.

See Table 310-16 for other applications.

Exception No. 1: The neutral conductor of a 3-wire branch circuit supplying a household electric range, a wall-mounted oven, or a counter-mounted cooking unit shall be permitted to be smaller than the ungrounded conductors where the maximum demand of a range of 8 ¾ kW or more rating has been computed according to Column A of Table 220-19, but shall have an ampacity of not less than 70 percent of the branch-circuit rating and shall not be smaller than No. 10.

Column A of Table 220-19 and Section 220-19 indicate that the maximum demand for one range (not over 12 kW rating) is 8 kW (8 kW = 8000 volt-amperes; 8000 volt-amperes divided by 240 V = 33.3 A). The allowable ampacity of a No. 8 TW copper conductor is 40 A (see Table 310-16) and may be used for the range branch circuit. According to this computation, the neutral of this 3-wire circuit can be smaller than No. 8 but not smaller than No. 10 which has an allowable ampacity of 30 A (30 A is more than 70 percent of 40 A, as per the exception). The maximum demand for a neutral of an 8 kW range circuit seldom exceeds 25 A since current is drawn from the neutral only for lights, clocks, timers, and heating elements when in the low-heating position.

Exception No. 2: Tap conductors supplying electric ranges, wall-mounted electric ovens, and counter-mounted electric cooking units from a 50-ampere branch circuit shall have an ampacity of not less than 20 and shall be sufficient for the load to be served. The taps shall not be longer than necessary for servicing the appliance.

This exception permits a 20-A tap conductor from a range, oven, or cooking unit to be connected to a 50-A branch circuit provided: the taps are no longer than necessary for servicing or to allow accessibility to the junction box; the taps to each unit are properly spliced; the junction box is adjacent to each unit; and the taps are of sufficient size for the load to be served. See Figure 210-22.

counter top unit

oven

Tap conductors rated
not less than 20 A.

50 ampere branch circuit

Figure 210-22. Tap conductors are permitted to be sized smaller than the branch-circuit conductors, but they are to be no longer than necessary for servicing.

(c) Other Loads. Branch-circuit conductors supplying loads other than cooking appliances as covered in (b) above and as listed in Section 210-2 shall have an ampacity sufficient for the loads served and shall not be smaller than No. 14.

Exception No. 1: Tap conductors for such loads shall have an ampacity not less than 15 for circuits rated less than 40 amperes and not less than 20 for circuits rated at 40 or 50 amperes and only where these tap conductors supply any of the following loads:

a. Individual lampholders or fixtures with taps extending not longer than 18 inches (457 mm) beyond any portion of the lampholder or fixture.

b. A fixture having tap conductors as provided in Section 410-67.

c. Individual outlets with taps not over 18 inches (457 mm) long.

d. Infrared lamp industrial heating appliances.

e. Nonheating leads of de-icing and snow-melting cables and mats.

Exception No. 2: Fixture wires and cords as permitted in Section 240-4.

Tap conductors are required to be suitable for the temperature encountered and, where the conductors supply loads as specified in subparts a. through e. of Exception No. 1, are required to have an ampacity of 15 A or more (No. 14 AWG copper conductors) for circuits rated less than 40 A, and an ampacity of 20 A or more (No. 12 AWG copper conductors) for circuits rated 40 or 50 A.

210-20. Overcurrent Protection. Branch-circuit conductors and equipment shall be protected by overcurrent protective devices having a rating or setting (1) not exceeding that specified in Section 240-3 for conductors; (2) not exceeding that specified in the applicable articles referenced in Section 240-2 for equipment; and (3) as provided for outlet devices in Section 210-21.

Exception No. 1: Tap conductors as permitted in Section 210-19(c) shall be permitted to be protected by the branch-circuit overcurrent device.

Exception No. 2: Fixture wires and cords as permitted in Section 240-4.

(FPN): See Section 240-1 for the purpose of overcurrent protection and Sections 210-22 and 220-3 for continuous loads.

210-21. Outlet Devices. Outlet devices shall have an ampere rating not less than the load to be served and shall comply with (a) and (b) below.

(a) Lampholders. Where connected to a branch circuit having a rating in excess of 20 amperes, lampholders shall be of the heavy-duty type. A heavy-duty lampholder shall have a rating of not less than 660 watts if of the admedium type and not less than 750 watts if of any other type.

The intent is to restrict a fluorescent lighting branch-circuit rating to not more than 20 A, because most lampholders manufactured for use with fluorescent lights are not of the heavy-duty type and are rated at 660 W or 250 W.

Branch-circuit conductors for fluorescent electric-discharge lighting are usually connected to a ballast rather than to lampholders, and, by specifying a wattage rating for these lampholders, a limit of 20 A is applied to ballast circuits.

It is only the admedium-base lampholder that is recognized as heavy duty at the rating of 660 W. Other lampholders are required to have a rating of not less than 750 watts to be recognized as heavy duty. The requirement stated in Section 210-21(a) prohibits the use of medium-base screw-shell lampholders on branch circuits in excess of 20 amperes.

(b) Receptacles.

(1) A single receptacle installed on an individual branch circuit shall have an ampere rating of not less than that of the branch circuit.

See comment following Section 210-7(a).

(FPN): See definition of Receptacle in Article 100.

(2) Where connected to a branch circuit supplying two or more receptacles or outlets, a receptacle shall not supply a total cord- and plug-connected load in excess of the maximum specified in Table 210-21(b)(2).

(3) Where connected to a branch circuit supplying two or more receptacles or outlets, receptacle ratings shall conform to the values listed in Table 210-21(b)(3) or where larger than 50 amperes, the receptacle rating shall not be less than the branch-circuit rating.

A single receptacle installed on an individual branch circuit is required to have an ampere rating of not less than that of the branch circuit. For example, a single receptacle on a 20-A branch circuit must be rated at 20 A; however, two or more 15-A receptacles are permitted on a 20-A general-purpose branch circuit.

(4) It shall be acceptable to base the ampere rating of a range receptacle on a single range demand load specified in Table 220-19.

210-22. Maximum Loads. The total load shall not exceed the rating of the branch circuit, and it shall not exceed the maximum loads specified in (a) through (c) below under the conditions specified therein.

(a) Motor-Operated and Combination Loads. Where a circuit supplies only motor-operated loads, Article 430 shall apply. Where a circuit supplies only air-conditioning and/or refrigerating equipment, Article 440 shall apply. For circuits supplying loads consisting of motor-operated utilization equipment that is fastened in place and that has a motor larger than 1/8 horsepower in combination with other loads, the total computed load shall be based on 125 percent of the largest motor load plus the sum of the other loads.

Table 210-21(b)(2)
Maximum Cord- and Plug-Connected Load to Receptacle

Circuit Rating Amperes	Receptacle Rating Amperes	Maximum Load Amperes
15 or 20	15	12
20	20	16
30	30	24

Table 210-21(b)(3)
Receptacle Ratings for Various Size Circuits

Circuit Rating Amperes	Receptacle Rating Amperes
15	Not over 15
20	15 or 20
30	30
40	40 or 50
50	50

(b) Inductive Lighting Loads. For circuits supplying lighting units having ballasts, transformers, or autotransformers, the computed load shall be based on the total ampere ratings of such units and not on the total watts of the lamps.

(c) Other Loads. Continuous loads, such as store lighting and similar loads, shall not exceed 80 percent of the rating of the branch circuit.

Exception No. 1: Motor loads having demand factors computed in accordance with Article 430.

Exception No. 2: Circuits supplied by an assembly together with its overcurrent devices that is listed for continuous operation at 100 percent of its rating.

It shall be acceptable to apply demand factors for range loads in accordance with Table 220-19, including Note 4.

Article 100 defines a "continuous load" as "a load where the maximum current is expected to continue for three hours or more." Continuous loads, such as lighting in mercantile occupancies, restaurants, etc., must not exceed 80 percent of the branch-circuit rating. Exception No. 1 prevents a "double" derating of circuits. Exception No. 2 provides for a 100 percent rating of a circuit if supplied by an overcurrent device and the assembly is listed by a qualified testing laboratory for continuous operation.

210-23. Permissible Loads. In no case shall the load exceed the branch-circuit ampere rating. It shall be acceptable for an individual branch circuit to supply any load for which it is rated. A branch circuit supplying two or more outlets shall supply only the loads specified according to its size in (a) through (c) below and summarized in Section 210-24 and Table 210-24.

(a) 15- and 20-Ampere Branch Circuits. A 15- or 20-ampere branch circuit shall be permitted to supply lighting units, other utilization equipment, or a combination of both. The rating of any one cord- and plug-connected utilization equipment shall not exceed 80 percent of the branch-circuit ampere rating. The total rating of utilization equipment fastened in place shall not exceed 50 percent of the branch-circuit ampere rating where lighting units, cord- and plug-connected utilization equipment not fastened in place, or both, are also supplied.

Exception: The small appliance branch circuits required in a dwelling unit(s) by Section 220-4(b) shall supply only the receptacle outlets specified in that section.

This permits a 15- or 20-A branch circuit for lighting to also supply utilization equipment fastened in place, such as an air conditioner rated not to exceed 50

84

percent of the branch-circuit ampere rating (7.5 A on a 15-A circuit and 10 A on a 20-A circuit). Such equipment, fastened in place, is not permitted to be installed on the small-appliance branch circuits required in the kitchen, dining room, etc., by Section 220-4(b).

(b) 30-Ampere Branch Circuits.   A 30-ampere branch circuit shall be permitted to supply fixed lighting units with heavy-duty lampholders in other than dwelling unit(s) or utilization equipment in any occupancy. A rating of any one cord- and plug-connected utilization equipment shall not exceed 80 percent of the branch-circuit ampere rating.

(c) 40- and 50-Ampere Branch Circuits.   A 40- or 50-ampere branch circuit shall be permitted to supply cooking appliances that are fastened in place in any occupancy. In other than dwelling units, such circuits shall be permitted to supply fixed lighting units with heavy-duty lampholders, infrared heating units or other utilization equipment.

A branch circuit supplying two or more outlets is to supply only the loads specified according to its size in accordance with Sections 210-23(a) through (c) and summarized in Section 210-24 and Table 210-24. Other circuits are not permitted to have more than one outlet and are considered individual branch circuits. However, individual branch circuits are not required for portable, mobile, and transportable medical X-ray equipment requiring a capacity of not over 60 A [see Sections 517-141(b) and 660-4(b).]

(d) Branch Circuits Larger than 50 Amperes.   Branch circuits larger than 50 amperes shall supply only nonlighting outlet loads.

See commentary following the exception to Section 210-3.

210-24. Branch-Circuit Requirements — Summary.   The requirements for circuits having two or more outlets, other than the receptacle circuits of Section 220-4(b) as specifically provided for above, are summarized in Table 210-24. Branch circuits in dwelling units shall not be connected to serve more than one dwelling unit.

Exception: Branch circuits in two-family or multifamily dwellings, with dwelling units under single management, shall be permitted to be connected to serve more than one dwelling unit for the purpose of central alarm, signal, communications, or similar functions.

The last sentence of Section 210-24 is intended to prevent overloading of branch circuits.

Table 210-24 summarizes branch-circuit requirements of conductors, overcurrent protection, outlet devices, maximum load, and permissible loads where two or more outlets are supplied.

Where the branch circuit serves a fixture load and supplies two or more fixture outlets, Section 210-23 requires the branch circuit to have a specific ampere rating which is also the rating of the overcurrent device as stated in Section 210-3. Thus, if the circuit breaker protecting the branch circuit is rated 20 A, the conductors supplying this circuit must have a 20-A ampacity. Note that in accordance with the definition of ampacity, the ampacity is determined after applying all derating factors, such as those in Note 8(a) to Tables 310-16 through 310-31. Where 7 to 24 such conductors are in one conduit, a No. 12 AWG THHN copper conductor (30 A per Table 310-16) derated to 70 percent per Note 8(a) would have an ampacity of 21 A and would be suitable for a load of 20 A. It would thus be acceptable for use on the 20-A multioutlet branch circuit.

C. Required Outlets

210-50. General.   Receptacle outlets shall be installed as specified in Sections 210-52 through 210-63.

ARTICLE 210—BRANCH CIRCUITS

Table 210-24
Summary of Branch-Circuit Requirements
(Type FEP, FEPB, SA, TW, RH, RHW, RHH, THHN, THW, THWN, and XHHW
conductors in raceway or cable.)

CIRCUIT RATING	15 Amp	20 Amp	30 Amp	40 Amp	50 Amp
CONDUCTORS (Min. Size)					
Circuit Wires*	14	12	10	8	6
Taps	14	14	14	12	12
Fixture Wires and Cords			Refer to Section 240-4		
OVERCURRENT PROTECTION	15 Amp	20 Amp	30 Amp	40 Amp	50 Amp
OUTLET DEVICES:					
Lampholders Permitted	Any Type	Any Type	Heavy Duty	Heavy Duty	Heavy Duty
Receptacle Rating**	15 Max. Amp	15 or 20 Amp	30 Amp	40 or 50 Amp	50 Amp
MAXIMUM LOAD	15 Amp	20 Amp	30 Amp	40 Amp	50 Amp
PERMISSIBLE LOAD	Refer to Section 210-23(a)	Refer to Section 210-23(a)	Refer to Section 210-23(b)	Refer to Section 210-23(c)	Refer to Section 210-23(c)

*These gages are for copper conductors.
**For receptacle rating of cord-connected electric-discharge lighting fixtures, see Section 410-30(c).

(a) Cord Pendants. A cord connector that is supported by a permanently installed cord pendant shall be considered a receptacle outlet.

(b) Cord Connections. A receptacle outlet shall be installed wherever flexible cords with attachment plugs are used. Where flexible cords are permitted to be permanently connected, it shall be permitted to omit receptacles for such cords.

Flexible cords are permitted to be permanently connected to boxes or fittings where specifically permitted by the *Code*. However, plugging a cord into a lampholder by inserting a screw-plug adapter is not permissible (see Section 410-47).

(c) Laundry Outlet. Appliance outlets installed in a dwelling unit for specific appliances, such as laundry equipment, shall be installed within 6 feet (1.83 m) of the intended location of the appliance.

See Sections 210-52(e) and (f) and 220-4(c).

210-52. Dwelling Unit Receptacle Outlets.

(a) General Provisions. In every kitchen, family room, dining room, living room, parlor, library, den, sun room, bedroom, recreation room, or similar rooms of dwelling units, receptacle outlets shall be installed so that no point along the floor line in any wall space is more than 6 feet (1.83 m), measured horizontally, from an outlet in that space, including any wall space 2 feet (610 mm) or more in width and the wall space occupied by sliding panels in exterior walls. The wall space afforded by fixed room dividers, such as free-standing bar-type counters, shall be included in the 6-foot (1.83-m) measurement.

See Figures 210-23 and 210-24.

Figure 210-23. Section 210-52(a) requires the wall space afforded by fixed room dividers, such as bar-type counters, to be included in the 6-ft measurement. Section 210-52(b) requires a receptacle at each counter space wider than 12 in.

Figure 210-24. Railings (or lattice-work) are not considered equivalent to free-standing bar-type counters, and need not be counted as wall space.

As used in this section a "wall space" shall be considered a wall unbroken along the floor line by doorways, fireplaces, and similar openings. Each wall space 2 or more feet (610 mm or more) wide shall be treated individually and separately from other wall spaces within the room. A wall space shall be permitted to include two or more walls of a room (around corners) where unbroken at the floor line.

(FPN): The purpose of this requirement is to minimize the use of cords across doorways, fireplaces, and similar openings.

Receptacle outlets shall, insofar as practicable, be spaced equal distances apart. Receptacle outlets in floors shall not be counted as part of the required number of receptacle outlets unless located close to the wall.

Receptacles are required to be located so that no "point" in any wall space is more than 6 ft from a receptacle. This rule intends that an appliance or lamp with a flexible cord attached may be placed anywhere in the room and be within 6 ft of a receptacle, thus eliminating the need for extension cords.

A "wallspace" is a wall unbroken along the floor line by doorways, fireplaces, archways and similar openings, and may include two or more walls of a room (around corners, as illustrated in Figure 210-25).

Fixed room dividers, such as bar-type counters, are to be included in the 6-ft measurement; however, see Figure 210-24. Isolated, individual wall spaces 2 ft or more in width are considered usable for the location of a lamp or appliance, and a receptacle outlet must be provided. This also applies to counter spaces wider than 12 in. in kitchen or dining areas. Receptacles are required to be located at these spaces, thereby eliminating probable hazards caused by running cords across doorways or passageways or across sinks or range tops, etc. Sliding panels in exterior walls are counted as regular wall space, and a floor-type receptacle can be used to meet the required spacing.

Figure 210-25. Plan view of the location of receptacles in a typical room. Receptacles are spaced to permit a lamp or appliance equipped with 6-ft cords to be located anywhere in the room.

The receptacle outlets required by this section shall be in addition to any receptacle that is part of any lighting fixture or appliance, located within cabinets or cupboards, or located over 5 ½ feet (1.68 m) above the floor.

Exception: Permanently installed electric baseboard heaters equipped with factory-installed receptacle outlets or outlets provided as a separate assembly by the manufacturer shall be permitted as the required outlet or outlets for the wall space utilized by such permanently installed heaters. Such receptacle outlets shall not be connected to the heater circuits.

(FPN): Listed baseboard heaters include instructions which may not permit their installation below dwelling unit receptacle outlets.

According to listing instructions [see Section 110-3(b)], permanent electric baseboard heaters are not permitted to be located beneath wall receptacles. Where the receptacle is a part of the heater, cords of appliances or lamps are less apt to be exposed to the heating elements, such as falling into convector slots. See Figures 210-26 and 210-27.

Figure 210-26. An electric baseboard heater with a receptacle outlet provided as the required receptacle outlet for the wall space.

Figure 210-27. Many electrical baseboard heaters are of the low-density type and are designed to be longer than 12 ft. To meet the spacing requirements of Section 210-52(a), it is necessary that the required receptacle be located as a part of the heater unit.

(b) Counter Tops. In kitchen and dining areas of dwelling units a receptacle outlet shall be installed at each counter space wider than 12 inches (305 mm). Counter top spaces separated by range tops, refrigerators, or sinks shall be considered as separate counter top spaces. Receptacles rendered inaccessible by appliances fastened in place or appliances occupying dedicated space shall not be considered as these required outlets.

ARTICLE 210—BRANCH CIRCUITS

Receptacles rendered inaccessible by appliances fastened in place or installed for appliances occupying dedicated space, such as dishwashers, garbage disposal units, built-in gas ovens, waste compactors, etc., are not considered as the required receptacles.

(c) Bathrooms. In dwelling units at least one wall receptacle outlet shall be installed in the bathroom adjacent to the basin location. See Section 210-8(a)(1).

In bathrooms of a dwelling unit, one wall receptacle is required to be installed adjacent to the wash basin and is required in addition to any receptacle that may be part of any lighting fixture or medicine cabinet. All 125-V single-phase, 15- and 20-A receptacles installed in bathroom areas are required to have ground-fault circuit-interrupter protection for personnel including the optional receptacle that may be part of a lighting fixture.

(d) Outdoor Outlets. For a one-family dwelling at least one receptacle outlet accessible at grade level shall be installed outdoors. For a two-family dwelling at least one receptacle outlet accessible at grade level shall be installed outdoors for each dwelling unit which is at grade level. See Section 210-8(a)(3).

Section 210-52(d) requires two receptacle outlets, one for each dwelling unit, for a two-family dwelling such as shown in Figure 210-28. If the two dwelling units were one over the other rather than side by side, only one receptacle outlet would be required.

Installation of outdoor receptacles requires that care be taken to assure that the receptacle faceplate rests securely on the supporting surface to prevent moisture from entering the enclosure. Where uneven surfaces such as brick, stone, or stucco are encountered, it may be necessary to close openings with caulking compound or mastic. See, also, Section 410-57.

Figure 210-28. Illustration of the intended number of outdoor receptacles for a two-family dwelling with dwelling units at grade level.

(e) Laundry Areas. In dwelling units at least one receptacle outlet shall be installed for the laundry.

Exception No. 1: In a dwelling unit that is an apartment or living area in a multifamily building where laundry facilities are provided on the premises that are available to all building occupants, a laundry receptacle shall not be required.

Exception No. 2: In other than one-family dwellings where laundry facilities are not to be installed or permitted, a laundry receptacle shall not be required.

(f) Basements and Garages. For a one-family dwelling, at least one receptacle outlet in addition to any provided for laundry equipment shall be installed in each basement and in each attached garage, and in each detached garage with electric power. See Sections 210-8(a)(2) and (a)(4).

It is mandatory in a one-family dwelling to install a receptacle in the basement (in addition to the laundry receptacle, which is also mandatory), in each attached garage, and in each detached garage with electric power. The *Code* intends that it is not mandatory to install a receptacle in detached garages, if no electric power is provided in the detached garage. GFCIs must be provided in accordance with Section 210-8(a)(2).

210-60. Guest Rooms. Guest rooms in hotels, motels, and similar occupancies shall have receptacle outlets installed in accordance with Section 210-52. See Section 210-8(b).

Exception: In rooms of hotels and motels, the required number of receptacle outlets determined by Section 210-52(a) shall be permitted to be located convenient for permanent furniture layout.

This exception to Section 210-60 permits receptacles in guest rooms of hotels and motels to be placed in locations convenient for use with permanent furniture. However, the minimum number of receptacles that would ordinarily be required in accordance with Section 210-52 must not be reduced. The minimum number of receptacle outlets should be determined by assuming there is no furniture in the room. The location of this minimum number is then determined based on the permanent furniture layout.

Bathroom areas for guest rooms of hotels and motels are required to be provided with a receptacle outlet adjacent to the basin location in accordance with Section 210-8(b).

See Figure 210-29. There are no receptacle outlets in some small (but 2-ft or more) spaces because the exception permits the required number of outlets to be located convenient for the permanent furniture layout.

210-62. Show Windows. At least one receptacle outlet shall be installed directly above a show window for each 12 linear feet (3.66 m) or major fraction thereof of show window area measured horizontally at its maximum width.

Show windows are usually designed from floor to ceiling for maximum display. To discourage floor receptacles and unsightly extension cords likely to cause physical injury, receptacles must be installed "directly above" a show window, and one receptacle is required for every 12 linear feet or "major (6 ft or more) fraction" thereof.

210-63. Rooftop Heating, Air-Conditioning, and Refrigeration Equipment Outlet. A 125-volt, single-phase, 15- or 20-ampere rated receptacle outlet shall be installed at an accessible location for the servicing of rooftop-mounted heating, air-conditioning, and refrigeration equipment. The receptacle outlet shall be located on the same roof level and within 75 feet (22.82 m) of the heating, air-conditioning, and refrigeration equipment. The receptacle outlet shall not be connected to the load side of the equipment disconnecting means.

Exception: One- and two-family dwellings.

This requirement, new in the 1987 *NEC*, is intended to help prevent makeshift methods of obtaining power for servicing and troubleshooting rooftop equipment.

Some mechanical codes may require receptacle outlets within 25 (instead of 75) feet of the equipment.

210-70. Lighting Outlets Required. Lighting outlets shall be installed where specified in (a) and (b) below.

Figure 210-29. Receptacle outlets in guest rooms of hotels may be located convenient for the permanent furniture layout. The receptacle outlet adjacent to the permanent dresser is needed because the exception applies only to the location of receptacle outlets, not the minimum number.

(a) Dwelling Unit(s). At least one wall switch-controlled lighting outlet shall be installed in every habitable room; in bathrooms, hallways, stairways, attached garages, and detached garages with electric power; and at outdoor entrances or exits.

It is not permitted to switch a receptacle as a lighting outlet on a small-appliance branch circuit. It is permitted to switch a receptacle as a lighting outlet, in the dining room for example, supplied by a branch circuit other than a small-appliance branch circuit.

(FPN): A vehicle door in an attached garage is not considered as an outdoor entrance.

At least one lighting outlet shall be installed in an attic, underfloor space, utility room and basement only where these spaces are used for storage or contain equipment requiring servicing.

Exception No. 1: In habitable rooms, other than kitchens and bathrooms, one or more receptacles controlled by a wall switch shall be permitted in lieu of lighting outlets.

Exception No. 2: In hallways, stairways, and at outdoor entrances remote, central, or automatic control of lighting shall be permitted.

(b) Guest Rooms. At least one wall switch-controlled lighting outlet or wall switch-controlled receptacle shall be installed in guest rooms in hotels, motels, or similar occupancies.

This section points out that adequate lighting and proper control and location of switching is as essential to the safety of occupants of dwelling units(s), hotels, motels, etc., as are proper wiring requirements. Proper illumination assures safe movement for persons of all ages and many accidents are avoided.

Installation of lighting outlets in attics, under floor space or crawl areas, utility rooms or basements are required "only" where these spaces are used for storage (e.g., Christmas decorations, luggage, etc.) or where such spaces contain equipment requiring servicing (e.g., air-handling units, cooling and heating equipment, water pumps, sump pumps, etc.).

Remote, central, or automatic control of lighting for hallways, stairways, and outdoor entrances is practical in multifamily dwellings where it is desirable to use time clocks or to locate switches where they may not be intentionally or inadvertently turned "off."

Although the requirement calls for a switched lighting outlet at outdoor entrances and exits, it does not prohibit a single lighting outlet, if suitably located, from serving more than one door.

A wall switch-controlled lighting outlet is required in the kitchen and bathroom. A receptacle outlet controlled by a wall switch is not permitted to serve as a lighting outlet in these rooms.

ARTICLE 215 — FEEDERS

Contents

215-1. Scope. This article covers the installation requirements and minimum size and ampacity of conductors for feeders supplying branch-circuit loads as computed in accordance with Article 220.

Exception: Feeders for electrolytic cells as covered in Section 668-3(c), Exceptions No. 1 and 4.

A thorough calculation of the total connected load to be supplied by the feeder is required to determine accurately feeder conductor ampacity. The sum of the computed and connected loads supplied by a feeder is multiplied by the "demand factor" to determine the load that the feeder conductors must be sized to serve. (See Article 100 for definition of "demand factor.")

When the total connected load is operated simultaneously, the demand factor is 100 percent; that is, the maximum demand is equal to the total connected load. Due to diversity, the maximum operating load ever carried may be only ¾ of the total connected load; the demand factor is thus 75 percent.

On a new installation, a minimum value for the demand factor can be determined by applying the requirements and tables of Article 220, Branch Circuit and Feeder Calculations.

Feeder conductor sizes are determined by calculating the total volt-amperes of the feeder load at the nominal voltage of the feeder circuit:

Single Phase

$$I = \frac{\text{volt-amperes load}}{E}$$

Three Phase

$$I = \frac{\text{volt-amperes load}}{E \times 1.73}$$

where I = current in amperes
E = volts

See Tables of Article 310 for allowable ampacities and sizes of insulated conductors.

Feeder circuits are required to have sufficient ampacity for safety. Overloading of a wiring system that does not provide for increases in the use of electricity often creates hazards. It is good practice to allow for future expansion and convenience increases. See Section 90-7.

215-2. Minimum Rating and Size. Feeder conductors shall have an ampacity not lower than required to supply the load as computed in Parts B, C, and D of Article 220. The minimum sizes shall be as specified in (a) and (b) below under the conditions stipulated. Feeder conductors for a dwelling unit or a mobile home need not be larger than service-entrance conductors. Note 3 of Table 310-16 shall be permitted to be used for conductor size.

This section correlates with Note 3 of Notes to Tables 310-16 through 310-31. For example, Table 310-16 allows 200 amperes for a No. 3/0 THW copper wire. However, for a 3-wire, single-phase dwelling service, Note 3 permits 200 amperes for a 2/0 AWG copper THW conductor or 200 amperes for a 4/0 AWG aluminum THW conductor. It stands to reason that feeder conductors carrying the total load supplied by the service should not be required to be sized larger than the service-entrance conductors. See Figure 215-1.

Service—entrance and feeder conductors are the same size.

200

Main Disconnect   Panelboard

Figure 215-1. For a 3-wire, single-phase dwelling service, Note 3 permits an ampacity of 200 A for 2/0 copper conductors for use as service-entrance conductors and for feeder conductors.

(a) For Specified Circuits. The ampacity of feeder conductors shall not be less than 30 where the load supplied consists of the following number and types of circuits: (1) two or more 2-wire branch circuits supplied by a 2-wire feeder; (2) more than two 2-wire branch circuits supplied by a 3-wire feeder; and (3) two or more 3-wire branch circuits supplied by a 3-wire feeder.

(b) Ampacity Relative to Service-Entrance Conductors. The feeder conductor ampacity shall not be lower than that of the service-entrance conductors where the feeder conductors carry the total load supplied by service-entrance conductors with an ampacity of 55 or less.

(FPN): See Examples 1 through 8 in Chapter 9.

(FPN): Conductors for feeders as defined in Article 100, sized to prevent a voltage drop exceeding 3 percent at the farthest outlet of power, heating, and lighting loads, or combinations of such loads and where the maximum total voltage drop on both feeders and branch circuits to the farthest outlet does not exceed 5 percent, will provide reasonable efficiency of operation.

(FPN): See Section 210-19(a) for voltage drop for branch circuits.

Reasonable operating efficiency will be achieved if the voltage drop of a feeder or the voltage drop of a branch circuit is limited to 3 percent. However, the total voltage drop of a branch circuit plus a feeder can reach 5 percent and still allow for reasonable operating efficiency. See Article 100 for definition of "feeder" and "branch circuit."

The 5 percent voltage drop value is explanatory material, and, as such, it appears as a Fine Print Note. Fine Print Notes are not mandatory (see Section 110-1). See Section 250-95 which requires adjustment, according to circular mil area, for equipment grounding conductors when voltage drop is considered.

The resistance or impedance of conductors may cause a substantial difference between voltage values at service equipment and voltage values at the point of utilization equipment. Excessive voltage drop impairs the starting and operation of electrical equipment. In addition to resistance or impedance, the type of raceway or cable enclosure, type of circuit (ac, dc, single-phase, 3-phase), and power factor should be considered to determine voltage drop.

The basic formula for determining voltage drop in a 2-wire dc circuit, a 2-wire ac circuit, or a 3-wire ac single-phase circuit with a balanced load at 100 percent power factor and where reactance can be neglected is:

$$VD = \frac{2 \times L \times R \times I}{1000}$$

where VD = voltage drop (based on conductor temperature of 75°F)
L = One-way length of circuit (feet)
R = Conductor resistance in ohms per thousand feet (from Chapter 9, Table 8)
I = Load current (amperes)

For 3-phase circuits (at 100 percent power factor) the voltage drop between any two phase conductors is 0.866 times the voltage drop calculated by this formula.

Example: 240-V 2-wire heating circuit. Load is 50 A. Circuit size is No. 6 AWG THHN copper and the one-way circuit length is 100 ft.

$$VD = \frac{2 \times L \times R \times I}{1000} = \frac{2 \times 100 \times 0.491 \times 50}{1000}$$

$$VD = \frac{4910}{1000} = 4.91\text{-V drop}$$

A 12-V drop on a 240-V circuit is a 5 percent drop; therefore, a 4.91-V drop falls within this percentage.

Should the voltage drop exceed 5 percent, a larger size conductor should be used, the circuit length shortened, or the circuit load reduced.

Voltage drop tables and calculations are available from various manufacturers.

215-3. Overcurrent Protection. Feeders shall be protected against overcurrent in accordance with the provisions of Part A of Article 240.

215-4. Feeders with Common Neutral.

(a) Feeders with Common Neutral. Feeders containing a common neutral shall be permitted to supply two or three sets of 3-wire feeders, or two sets of 4-wire or 5-wire feeders.

(b) In Metal Raceway or Enclosure. Where installed in a metal raceway or other metal enclosure, all conductors of all feeders using a common neutral shall be enclosed within the same raceway or other enclosure as required in Section 300-20.

> Where feeder conductors carrying ac current, including the neutral, are installed in metal raceways, they are required to be grouped together to avoid induction heating of the surrounding metal.
>
> A 3-phase, 4-wire (208 wye/120-V, 480 wye/277-V) system is often used to supply both lighting and motor loads. The 3-phase motor loads will not cause current to flow in the neutral conductor. Therefore, the maximum current on the neutral is due to lighting loads, or circuits where the neutral is used. On this type of system (3-phase, 4-wire), a demand factor of 70 percent is permitted for that portion of the neutral load in excess of 200 A. See Section 220-22. Thus, if the maximum possible load is 500 A, the neutral would have to be large enough to carry 200 A plus 70 percent of 300 A, or 410 A. No reduction of the neutral capacity for that portion of the load consisting of electric-discharge lighting is permitted. See Note 10(c) to Tables 310-16 through 310-31. See Section 220-22 for other systems to which the 70 percent demand factor may be applied. The maximum unbalanced load for feeders supplying clothes dryers, household ranges, wall-mounted ovens, and counter-mounted cooking units is required to be considered as 70 percent of the load of the ungrounded conductors. See Example Nos. 1 through 5(b) of Chapter 9.
>
> See Examples 5(a) and 5(b) of Chapter 9 for a multifamily dwelling served at 208Y/120 volts, three phase.

215-5. Diagrams of Feeders. If required by the authority having jurisdiction, a diagram showing feeder details shall be provided prior to the installation of the feeders. Such a diagram shall show the area in square feet of the building or other structure supplied by each feeder, the total connected load before applying demand factors, the demand factors used, the computed load after applying demand factors, and the size and type of conductors to be used.

215-6. Feeder Conductor Grounding Means. Where a feeder supplies branch circuits in which equipment grounding conductors are required, the feeder shall include or provide a grounding means in accordance with the provisions of Section 250-57 to which the equipment grounding conductors of the branch circuits shall be connected.

215-7. Ungrounded Conductors Tapped from Grounded Systems. Two-wire dc circuits and ac circuits of two or more ungrounded conductors shall be permitted to be tapped from the ungrounded conductors of circuits having a grounded neutral conductor. Switching devices in each tapped circuit shall have a pole in each ungrounded conductor.

> It is not intended by Section 215-7 to require a common trip or simultaneous opening of circuit breaker fuses but to provide a switching device to disconnect "manually" the ungrounded conductors of the feeder. See Section 210-10.

215-8. Means of Identifying Conductor with the Higher Voltage to Ground. On a 4-wire, delta-connected secondary where the midpoint of one phase is grounded to supply lighting and similar loads, the phase conductor having the higher voltage to ground shall be identified by an outer finish that is orange in color or by tagging or other effective means. Such identification shall be placed at each point where a connection is made if the neutral conductor is also present.

It is permitted to ground the midpoint of one phase to supply 120-V lighting and similar loads from a delta-connected secondary. This results in one phase conductor having a higher voltage to ground, and it is identified by an orange finish at any point, such as junction or pull boxes, panelboards, etc., where connections may be made and the neutral is also present. The orange high-leg of a 3-phase, 4-wire (120/240-V) delta system is 208 V to ground (120 V × 1.73 = 208 V) and should obviously not be used for 120-V circuits. See Sections 230-56, and 384-3(e) and (f). See Figure 215-2.

Figure 215-2. With a 4-wire, delta-connected secondary in which the midpoint of one phase is grounded, one phase conductor has a higher voltage to ground than the other two. It is identified in this illustration as having an "orange" finish. The identification must be visible at every point where a connection is made, if a neutral is present.

215-9. Ground-Fault Protection for Personnel. Feeders supplying 15- and 20-ampere receptacle branch circuits shall be permitted to be protected by a ground-fault circuit-interrupter in lieu of the provisions for such interrupters as specified in Section 210-8 and Article 305.

Several manufacturers offer double-pole 120/240-V circuit breaker-type ground-fault circuit-interrupters for application to a feeder, thereby protecting all branch circuits supplied by that feeder. This installation is in lieu of provisions of Section 210-8 for outdoor, bathroom, garage, kitchen, basement, and boathouse receptacles. They can also be used to protect construction-site receptacles as covered in Section 305-6(a).

It may be more economical or convenient to install ground-fault circuit-interrupters for feeders. However, it will be monitoring several branch circuits and, in response to a line-to-ground fault from one branch circuit, it will de-energize all of the branch circuits.

ARTICLE 220 — BRANCH-CIRCUIT AND FEEDER CALCULATIONS

Contents

A. General

220-1. Scope. This article provides requirements for determining the number of branch circuits required and for computing branch-circuit and feeder loads.

For uniform application of the provisions of Articles 210, 215, and 220, nominal voltages as listed in Section 220-2 are required to be used in computing the ampere load on the conductors.

See Chapter 9, Examples 1 through 5(b). The results of these examples are generally expressed in amperes. Except where the computations result in a major fraction of an ampere (0.5 or larger), such fractions may be dropped.

To select conductor sizes, refer to Tables 310-16 through 310-31 and the notes that pertain to these tables.

Loads are computed on the basis of volt-amperes (VA) or kVA rather than watts or kW. However, the rating of equipment is given in watts or kW. Such ratings are considered the equivalent of the same rating in volt-amperes or kVA. See, for example, Section 220-19. This recognizes that load calculations are to determine conductor and circuit sizes, that the power-factor of the load is often unknown, and that the conductor "sees" the circuit volt-amperes only, not the circuit power (watts).

Exception: Branch-circuit and feeder calculations for electrolytic cells as covered in Section 668-3(c), Exceptions No. 1 and 4.

This exception also appears after Sections 210-1, 215-1, and 225-1.

220-2. Voltages. Unless other voltages are specified, for purposes of computing branch-circuit and feeder loads, nominal system voltages of 120, 120/240, 208Y/120, 240, 480Y/277, 480, and 600 volts shall be used.

220-3. Computation of Branch Circuits. Branch-circuit loads shall be computed as shown in (a) through (d) below.

(FPN): See Section 600-6(c) for exterior signs and outline lighting.

(a) Continuous and Noncontinuous Loads. The branch-circuit rating shall not be less than the noncontinuous load plus 125 percent of the continuous load.

See Figure 220-1.

Total load = 16 amperes

20 A branch circuit OC device

Figure 220-1. Continuous loads, such as store lighting, must not exceed 80 percent of the branch-circuit rating.

Exception: Where the assembly, including overcurrent devices, is listed for continuous operation of 100 percent of its rating.

The load determines the branch-circuit rating, which in turn is determined by the selection of the overcurrent device (See Section 210-3). The overcurrent device

ARTICLE 220—BRANCH-CIRCUIT AND FEEDER CALCULATIONS

must be no larger than the ampacity of the conductors after any applicable derating factors have been calculated (See Section 240-3). Section 220-3 then limits any continuous load to 80 percent of the branch circuit so determined.

(b) Lighting Load for Listed Occupancies. A unit load of not less than that specified in Table 220-3(b) for occupancies listed therein shall constitute the minimum lighting load for each square foot (0.093 sq m) of floor area. The floor area for each floor shall be computed from the outside dimensions of the building, apartment, or other area involved. For dwelling unit(s), the computed floor area shall not include open porches, garages, or unused or unfinished spaces not adaptable for future use.

Examples of "unused or unfinished" spaces are some attics or some crawl spaces.

(FPN): The unit values herein are based on minimum load conditions and 100 percent power factor, and may not provide sufficient capacity for the installation contemplated.

Table 220-3(b). General Lighting Loads by Occupancies

Type of Occupancy	Unit Load per Sq. Ft. (Volt-Amperes)
Armories and Auditoriums	1
Banks	3½**
Barber Shops and Beauty Parlors	3
Churches	1
Clubs	2
Court Rooms	2
*Dwelling Units	3
Garages—Commercial (storage)	½
Hospitals	2
*Hotels and Motels, including apartment houses without provisions for cooking by tenants	2
Industrial Commercial (Loft) Buildings	2
Lodge Rooms	1½
Office Buildings	3½**
Restaurants	2
Schools	3
Stores	3
Warehouses (storage)	¼
In any of the above occupancies except one-family dwellings and individual dwelling units of two-family and multifamily dwellings: Assembly Halls and Auditoriums	1
Halls, Corridors, Closets, Stairways	½
Storage Spaces	¼

For SI units: one square foot = 0.093 square meter.
*All general use receptacle outlets of 20-ampere or less rating in one-family, two-family and multifamily dwellings and in guest rooms of hotels and motels [except those connected to the receptacle circuits specified in Sections 220-4(b) and (c)] shall be considered as outlets for general illumination, and no additional load calculations shall be required for such outlets.
**In addition a unit load of 1 volt-ampere per square foot shall be included for general purpose receptacle outlets when the actual number of general purpose receptacle outlets is unknown.

(c) Other Loads — All Occupancies. In all occupancies the minimum load for each outlet for general-use receptacles and outlets not used for general illumination shall be not less than the following, the loads shown being based on nominal branch-circuit voltages.

(1) Outlet for a specific appliance or other load except for a motor load .... ampere rating of appliance or load served.

(2) Outlet for motor load .... See Sections 430-22 and 430-24 and Article 440.

(3) An outlet supplying recessed lighting fixture(s) shall be the maximum volt-ampere rating of the equipment and lamps for which the fixture(s) is rated.

(4) Outlet for heavy-duty lampholder .... 600 volt-amperes.

(5) *Other outlets .... 180 volt-amperes per outlet.

For receptacle outlets, each single or multiple receptacle shall be considered at not less than 180 volt-amperes.

*This provision shall not be applicable to receptacle outlets connected to the circuit specified in Section 220-4(b).

A load of 180 volt-amperes is not required to be considered for outlets supplying recessed lighting fixtures, outlets for general illumination, and small appliance branch circuits. To apply the 180-VA requirement, in this case, would be unrealistic as it would restrict the number of lighting or receptacle outlets on a branch circuit unnecessarily. See the single asterisk note below Table 220-3(b) and the asterisk note below Section 220-3(c)(5). These indicate the 180-VA requirement is not applicable to most receptacle outlets in dwellings.

180 VA outlet   180 VA outlet   180 VA outlet   180 VA outlet

Figure 220-2. The 180-VA rating is applied to the receptacle outlet, regardless of whether a single, duplex, or any number of receptacles are connected to that outlet.

Exception No. 1: Where fixed multioutlet assemblies are employed, each 5 feet (1.52 m) or fraction thereof of each separate and continuous length shall be considered as one outlet of not less than 180 volt-amperes capacity, except in locations where a number of appliances are likely to be used simultaneously, when each 1 foot (305 mm) or fraction thereof shall be considered as an outlet of not less than 180 volt-amperes. The requirements of this exception shall not apply to dwelling unit(s) or the guest rooms of hotels or motels.

See Figure 220-4.

Exception No. 2: Table 220-19 shall be considered as an acceptable method of computing the load for a household electric range.

Exception No. 3: A load of not less than 200 volt-amperes per linear foot (305 mm) of show window, measured horizontally along its base, shall be permitted instead of the specified unit load per outlet.

See Figure 220-5.

$$15 \text{ amperes} \times 120 \text{ volts} = 1800 \text{ VA} \div 180 \text{ VA} = 10 \text{ receptacle outlets}$$
$$20 \text{ amperes} \times 120 \text{ volts} = 2400 \text{ VA} \div 180 \text{ VA} = 13 \text{ receptacle outlets}$$

Figure 220-3. Computation of the maximum number of outlets permitted on 15- and 20-A branch circuits. This is not applicable to outlets connected to a general lighting or small appliance branch circuit.

Figure 220-4. Fixed multioutlet assemblies are commonly used in commercial or industrial locations and may have been selected for a number of receptacles along a given work area (light use) or for the simultaneous connection and use of a number of appliances (heavy use).

200 volt-amperes per linear foot
$$200 \text{ VA} \times 10 \text{ ft} = 2000 \text{ volt-amperes}$$

Figure 220-5. The linear foot calculation method is permitted in lieu of the specified unit load per outlet.

Exception No. 4: The loads of outlets serving switchboards and switching frames in telephone exchanges shall be waived from the computations.

Exception No. 5: Section 220-18 shall be considered as an acceptable method of computing the load for a household electric clothes dryer.

(d) Loads for Additions to Existing Installations.

(1) Dwelling Units. Loads for structural additions to an existing dwelling unit or to a previously unwired portion of an existing dwelling unit, either of which exceeds 500 square feet (46.5 sq m), shall be computed in accordance with (b) above. Loads for new circuits or extended circuits in previously wired dwelling units shall be computed in accordance with either (b) or (c) above.

(2) Other than Dwelling Units. Loads for new circuits or extended circuits in other than dwelling units shall be computed in accordance with either (b) or (c) above.

220-4. Branch Circuits Required. Branch circuits for lighting and for appliances, including motor-operated appliances, shall be provided to supply the loads computed in accordance with Section 220-3. In addition, branch circuits shall be provided for specific loads not covered by Section 220-3 where required elsewhere in this Code; for small appliance loads as specified in (b) below; and for laundry loads as specified in (c) below.

(a) Number of Branch Circuits. The minimum number of branch circuits shall be determined from the total computed load and the size or rating of the circuits used. In all installations the number of circuits shall be sufficient to supply the load served. In no case shall the load on any circuit exceed the maximum specified by Section 210-22.

(b) Small Appliance Branch Circuits — Dwelling Unit.

(1) In addition to the number of branch circuits determined in accordance with (a) above, two or more 20-ampere small appliance branch circuits shall be provided for all receptacle outlets specified by Section 210-52 for the small appliance loads, including refrigeration equipment, in the kitchen, pantry, breakfast room, and dining room of a dwelling unit. Such circuits, whether two or more are used, shall have no other outlets.

See Figure 220-6.

Exception No. 1: A receptacle installed solely for the electric supply to and support of an electric clock in any of the rooms specified above.

Exception No. 2: Outdoor receptacles.

Exception No. 3: In addition to the required receptacles specified by Section 210-52, switched receptacles supplied from a general-purpose branch circuit as defined in Section 210-70(a), Exception No. 1 shall be permitted.

(2) Countertop receptacle outlets installed in the kitchen shall be supplied by not less than two small appliance branch circuits, either or both of which shall also be permitted to supply receptacle outlets in kitchen and other rooms specified in (b)(1) above. Additional small appliance branch circuits shall be permitted to supply receptacle outlets in kitchen and other rooms specified in (b)(1) above.

> Two or more 20-A circuits are required to be provided for all receptacle outlets for the small appliance loads, including refrigeration equipment [see FPN following Section 210-8(a)(5)], in the kitchen, dining room, pantry, and breakfast room of a dwelling unit. Countertop receptacle outlets in kitchens are required to be supplied by no fewer than two small appliance branch circuits. These circuits may also supply receptacle outlets in the pantry, dining room, and breakfast room as well as an electric clock receptacle or outdoor receptacles, but are to have no other outlets. See Sections 210-8(a)(3) and (a)(5).
>
> At least one additional 20-A branch circuit is required to be provided for the supply to the laundry receptacle outlet(s). This circuit is to have no other outlets. See Figure 220-7.

Figure 220-6. This figure illustrates the requirements of Section 220-4(b)(1) and (2). Though these small appliance branch circuits may serve certain outlets in other specified areas, they are not permitted to serve any other outlets such as might be connected to exhaust hoods or fans, disposal units, or dishwashers. The countertop receptacles within 6 ft of the kitchen sink are required to be GFCI protected in accordance with Section 210-8(a)(5).

There is no restriction placed on the number of outlets connected to a general lighting or small appliance branch circuit. The number of receptacle outlets in a room is determined by Section 210-52(a). It is desirable to provide more than the minimum number of receptacle outlets required, thereby further reducing the need for use of extension cords.

(c) Laundry Branch Circuits — Dwelling Unit. In addition to the number of branch circuits determined in accordance with (a) and (b) above, at least one additional 20-ampere branch circuit shall be provided to supply the laundry receptacle outlet(s) required by Section 210-52(e). This circuit shall have no other outlets.

See Figure 220-7.

(d) Load Evenly Proportioned Among Branch Circuits. Where the load is computed on a volt-amperes-per-square-foot (0.093 sq m) basis, the wiring system up to and including the branch-circuit panelboard(s) shall be provided to serve not less than the calculated load. This load shall be evenly proportioned among multioutlet branch circuits within the panelboard(s). Branch-circuit overcurrent devices and circuits need only be installed to serve the connected load.

(FPN): See Examples 1(a), 1(b), 2(b) and 4(a), Chapter 9.

Consideration must be given to balancing the loads when terminating circuits in panelboards.

B. Feeders

220-10. General.

(a) Ampacity and Computed Loads. Feeder conductors shall have sufficient ampacity to supply the load served. In no case shall the computed load of a feeder be less than the sum of the

Figure 220-7. At least one 20-A branch circuit is required to supply the laundry receptacle outlet(s). Lighting outlets in laundry areas must not be connected to the laundry branch circuit. If the laundry area is in a basement or garage, this receptacle outlet is not considered as that required by Section 210-52(f).

loads on the branch circuits supplied as determined by Part A of this article after any applicable demand factors permitted by Parts B, C, or D have been applied.

See Figure 220-8.

(FPN): See Examples 1 through 8, Chapter 9. See Section 210-22(b) for maximum load in amperes permitted for lighting units operating at less than 100 percent power factor.

Figure 220-8. Each panel serves an 80-A load. The feeder size is based on the sum of the computed and connected loads served by each panel not on the sum of the panel or overcurrent device rating.

(b) Continuous and Noncontinuous Loads. Where a feeder supplies continuous loads or

105

any combination of continuous and noncontinuous loads, the rating of the overcurrent device shall not be less than the noncontinuous load plus 125 percent of the continuous load.

The ampacity of the ungrounded service conductor shall not be less than the noncontinuous load plus 125 percent of the continuous load.

Exception: Where the assembly including the overcurrent devices protecting the feeder(s) are listed for operation at 100 percent of their rating, neither the ampere rating of the overcurrent device nor the ampacity of the feeder conductors shall be less than the sum of the continuous load plus the noncontinuous load.

Sections 220-10 through 220-22, which are included in Part B, give the requirements for calculating feeder loads. Sections 220-30 and 220-32 give optional methods for calculating feeder loads in dwelling units and multifamily dwellings.

220-11. General Lighting. The demand factors listed in Table 220-11 shall apply to that portion of the total branch-circuit load computed for general illumination. They shall not be applied in determining the number of branch circuits for general illumination.

(FPN): See Section 220-16 for application of demand factors to small appliance and laundry loads in dwellings.

Table 220-11.   Lighting Load Feeder Demand Factors

Type of Occupancy	Portion of Lighting Load to Which Demand Factor Applies (volt-amperes)	Demand Factor Percent
Dwelling Units	First 3000 or less at	100
	From 3001 to 120,000 at	35
	Remainder over 120,000 at. . . .	25
*Hospitals	First 50,000 or less at	40
	Remainder over 50,000 at.	20
*Hotels and Motels—Including	First 20,000 or less at	50
Apartment Houses without	From 20,001 to 100,000 at . . .	40
Provision for Cooking by	Remainder over 100,000 at. . . .	30
Tenants		
Warehouses	First 12,500 or less at	100
(Storage)	Remainder over 12,500 at.	50
All Others	Total Volt-amperes.	100

*The demand factors of this table shall not apply to the computed load of feeders to areas in hospitals, hotels, and motels where the entire lighting is likely to be used at one time, as in operating rooms, ballrooms, or dining rooms.

220-12. Show-Window Lighting.   For show-window lighting, a load of not less than 200 volt-amperes shall be included for each linear foot (305 mm) of show window, measured horizontally along its base.

(FPN): See Section 220-3(c), Exception No. 3, for branch circuits supplying show windows.

See Figure 220-5.

220-13. Receptacle Loads — Nondwelling Units.   In other than dwelling units, the use of the demand factors for lighting loads in Table 220-11 or those shown in Table 220-13 shall be permitted for receptacle loads computed at not more than 180 volt-amperes per outlet in accordance with Section 220-3(c)(5).

220-14. Motors.   Motor loads shall be computed in accordance with Sections 430-24, 430-25, and 430-26.

220-15. Fixed Electric Space Heating.   Fixed electric space heating loads shall be computed at 100 percent of the total connected load; however in no case shall a feeder load current rating be less than the rating of the largest branch circuit supplied.

Exception No. 1: Where reduced loading of the conductors results from units operating on duty-cycle, intermittently, or from all units not operating at one time, the authority having jurisdiction may grant permission for feeder conductors to have an ampacity less than 100 percent, provided the conductors have an ampacity for the load so determined.

Exception No. 2: The use of the optional calculations in Sections 220-30 and 220-31 shall be permitted for fixed electric space heating loads in a dwelling unit. In a multifamily dwelling the use of the optional calculation in Section 220-32 shall be permitted.

Table 220-13
Demand Factors for Nondwelling Receptacle Loads

Portion of Receptacle Load to which demand factor applies (volt-amperes)	Demand Factor Percent
First 10 kVA or less	100
Remainder over 10 kVA at	50

220-16. Small Appliance and Laundry Loads — Dwelling Unit.

(a) Small Appliance Circuit Load. In each dwelling unit the feeder load shall be computed at 1500 volt-amperes for each 2-wire small appliance branch circuit required by Section 220-4(b) for small appliances supplied by 15- or 20-ampere receptacles on 20-ampere branch circuits in the kitchen, pantry, dining room, and breakfast room. Where the load is subdivided through two or more feeders, the computed load for each shall include not less than 1500 volt-amperes for each 2-wire branch circuit for small appliances. These loads shall be permitted to be included with the general lighting load and subjected to the demand factors permitted in Table 220-11 for the general lighting load.

(b) Laundry Circuit Load. A feeder load of not less than 1500 volt-amperes shall be included for each 2-wire laundry branch circuit installed as required by Section 220-4(c). It shall be permissible to include this load with the general lighting load and subject it to the demand factors provided in Section 220-11.

In each dwelling unit, the feeder load is required to be calculated at 1500 VA for each of the two or more (2-wire) small appliance branch circuits and 1500 VA for each (2-wire) laundry branch circuit. It is permissible to total these loads and add them to the general lighting load and subject the total load (small appliance, laundry, plus general lighting) to the demand factors provided in Table 220-11.

220-17. Appliance Load — Dwelling Unit(s). It shall be permissible to apply a demand factor of 75 percent to the nameplate-rating load of four or more appliances fastened in place served by the same feeder in a one-family, two-family, or multifamily dwelling.

Exception: This demand factor shall not be applied to electric ranges, clothes dryers, space heating equipment, or air-conditioning equipment.

Example: 120/240 V fastened in place appliance load — dwelling unit(s)

water heater	4,000 W	240 V		4000 VA
kitchen disposal	½ hp	120 V		1176 VA
dishwasher	1,200 W	120 V		1200 VA
furnace motor	¼ hp	120 V		696 VA
attic fan	¼ hp	120 V		696 VA
water pump	½ hp	240 V		1176 VA
			Total	8944 VA

For appliances fastened in place (other than ranges, clothes dryers, space heating equipment, and air-conditioning equipment), feeder capacity must be provided for the sum of these loads, and the total load of four or more such appliances may be reduced by a demand factor of 75 percent.

Seventy-five percent of 8944 VA = 6708 VA, which is the load to be added to the other determined loads for calculating the size of service and/or feeder conductors.

See Table 430-148 for the full-load current in amperes of single-phase ac motors. Note the information above the table allows for voltage ranges when applying the table as per Section 430-6.

220-18. Electric Clothes Dryers — Dwelling Unit(s). The load for household electric clothes dryers in a dwelling unit(s) shall be 5000 watts (volt-amperes) or the nameplate rating, whichever is larger, for each dryer served. The use of the demand factors in Table 220-18 shall be permitted.

This requirement provides a minimum demand of 5 kVA for the calculation of feeder conductors to compute the load of household electric dryers. Where the nameplate rating is known and exceeds 5 kW, the larger rating is to be applied.

Table 220-18
Demand Factors for Household Electric Clothes Dryers

Number of Dryers	Demand Factor Percent
1	100
2	100
3	100
4	100
5	80
6	70
7	65
8	60
9	55
10	50
11–13	45
14–19	40
20–24	35
25–29	32.5
30–34	30
35–39	27.5
40 & over	25

220-19. Electric Ranges and Other Cooking Appliances — Dwelling Unit(s). The feeder demand load for household electric ranges, wall-mounted ovens, counter-mounted cooking units, and other household cooking appliances individually rated in excess of 1 ¾ kW shall be permitted to be computed in accordance with Table 220-19. Where two or more single-phase ranges are supplied by a 3-phase, 4-wire feeder, the total load shall be computed on the basis of twice the maximum number connected between any two phases. kVA shall be considered equivalent to kW for loads computed under this section.

(FPN): See Example 5(a), Chapter 9.

It is permissible to add the nameplate ratings of all household cooking appliances rated more than 1¾ kW, but not more than 8¾ kW, and multiply the sum by the demand factors specified in Column B or C of Table 220-19 for the given number of appliances.

For feeder demand factors other than for dwelling unit(s), that is, commercial electric cooking equipment, dishwasher booster heaters, water heaters, etc., see Table 220-20.

Demand factors of this *Code* are based on the diversified use of appliances since it is unlikely that all appliances will be utilized simultaneously or that all cooking units and the oven of a range will be at maximum heat for any length of time.

Table 220-19. Demand Loads for Household Electric Ranges, Wall-Mounted Ovens, Counter-Mounted Cooking Units, and Other Household Cooking Appliances over 1¾ kW Rating. Column A to be used in all cases except as otherwise permitted in Note 3 below.

Number of Appliances	Maximum Demand (See Notes) Column A (Not over 12 kW Rating)	Demand Factors Percent (See Note 3) Column B (Less than 3½ kW Rating)	Column C (3½ kW to 8¾ kW Rating)
1	8 kW	80%	80%
2	11 kW	75%	65%
3	14 kW	70%	55%
4	17 kW	66%	50%
5	20 kW	62%	45%
6	21 kW	59%	43%
7	22 kW	56%	40%
8	23 kW	53%	36%
9	24 kW	51%	35%
10	25 kW	49%	34%
11	26 kW	47%	32%
12	27 kW	45%	32%
13	28 kW	43%	32%
14	29 kW	41%	32%
15	30 kW	40%	32%
16	31 kW	39%	28%
17	32 kW	38%	28%
18	33 kW	37%	28%
19	34 kW	36%	28%
20	35 kW	35%	28%
21	36 kW	34%	26%
22	37 kW	33%	26%
23	38 kW	32%	26%
24	39 kW	31%	26%
25	40 kW	30%	26%
26–30	15 kW plus 1 kW	30%	24%
31–40	for each range	30%	22%
41–50	25 kW plus ¾	30%	20%
51–60	kW for each	30%	18%
61 & over	range	30%	16%

Note 1.   Over 12 kW through 27 kW ranges all of same rating. For ranges individually rated more than 12 kW but not more than 27 kW, the maximum demand in Column A shall be increased 5 percent for each additional kW of rating or major fraction thereof by which the rating of individual ranges exceeds 12 kW.

The size of the conductors is required to be determined by the rating of the range. By referring to Table 220-19, it can be seen that for a range not over 12 kW the demand load is 8 kW (8 kVA per Section 220-19), and a No. 8 AWG copper conductor, with 60°C insulation, would suffice. Note: Section 210-19(b) does not permit the branch-circuit rating of a circuit supplying household ranges of 8 ¾ kW nameplate rating to be less than 40 amperes.

Note 2.   Over 12 kW through 27 kW ranges of unequal ratings. For ranges individually rated more than 12 kW and of different ratings but none exceeding 27 kW, an average value of rating shall be computed by adding together the ratings of all ranges to obtain the total connected load (using 12 kW for any range rated less than 12 kW) and dividing by the total number of ranges; and then the maximum demand in Column A shall be increased 5 percent for each kW or major fraction thereof by which this average value exceeds 12 kW.

Note 2 provides for ranges larger than 12 kW, and Note 4 covers situations in which the range consists of several components.

Note 3.   Over 1 ¾ kW through 8 ¾ kW. In lieu of the method provided in Column A, it shall be permissible to add the nameplate ratings of all ranges rated more than 1 ¾ kW but not more than 8 ¾ kW and multiply the sum by the demand factors specified in Column B or C for the given number of appliances.

Note 4.   Branch-Circuit Load. It shall be permissible to compute the branch-circuit load for one range in accordance with Table 220-19. The branch-circuit load for one wall-mounted oven or one counter-mounted cooking unit shall be the nameplate rating of the appliance. The branch-circuit load for a counter-mounted cooking unit and not more than two wall-mounted ovens, all supplied from a single branch circuit and located in the same room, shall be computed by adding the nameplate rating of the individual appliances and treating this total as equivalent to one range.

It is permissible to compute the branch-circuit load for one range by the nameplate rating of the appliance or in accordance with Table 220-19. Where a single branch circuit supplies a counter-mounted cooking unit and not more than two wall-mounted ovens, all of which are located in the same room, it is permissible to add the nameplate ratings of these appliances and treat this total as equivalent to one range.

Example: a single branch circuit for

one counter-mounted cooking unit	8 kW
one wall-mounted oven	7 kW
one wall-mounted oven	6 kW
Total	21 kW

The maximum demand from Column A of Table 220-19 for one range not over 12 kW is 8 kW.

21 kW is less than 27 kW and exceeds 12 kW by 9 kW (see Note 1). The maximum demand in Column A (8 kW) is to be increased 5 percent for each additional kW exceeding 12 kW (9 kW).

$$5 \text{ percent} \times 8 \text{ kW} = 0.40 \text{ kW}$$
$$0.40 \text{ kW} \times 9 \text{ percent} = 3.6 \text{ kW increase}$$
$$8 \text{ kW} + 3.6 \text{ kW} = 11.6 \text{ kW load}$$
$$11,600 \text{ watts} = 11,600 \text{ volt-amperes} \div 240 \text{ V} = 48.3 \text{ A}$$

Note 5.   This table also applies to household cooking appliances rated over 1 ¾ kW and used in instructional programs.

(FPN): See Table 220-20 for commercial cooking equipment.

(FPN): See Examples, Chapter 9.

220-20. Kitchen Equipment — Other than Dwelling Unit(s).   It shall be permissible to compute the load for commercial electric cooking equipment, dishwasher booster heaters, water heaters, and other kitchen equipment in accordance with Table 220-20. These demand factors shall be applied to all equipment which has either thermostatic control or intermittent use as kitchen equipment. They shall not apply to space heating, ventilating or air-conditioning equipment.

However, in no case shall the feeder demand be less than the sum of the largest two kitchen equipment loads.

Table 220-20
Feeder Demand Factors for Kitchen Equipment—Other than Dwelling Unit(s)

Number of Units of Equipment	Demand Factors Percent
1	100
2	100
3	90
4	80
5	70
6 & over	65

220-21. Noncoincident Loads. Where it is unlikely that two dissimilar loads will be in use simultaneously, it shall be permissible to omit the smaller of the two in computing the total load of a feeder.

220-22. Feeder Neutral Load. The feeder neutral load shall be the maximum unbalance of the load determined by this article. The maximum unbalanced load shall be the maximum net computed load between the neutral and any one ungrounded conductor, except that the load thus obtained shall be multiplied by 140 percent for 5-wire, 2-phase systems. For a feeder supplying household electric ranges, wall-mounted ovens, counter-mounted cooking units, and electric dryers the maximum unbalanced load shall be considered as 70 percent of the load on the ungrounded conductors, as determined in accordance with Table 220-19 for ranges and Table 220-18 for dryers. For 3-wire dc or single-phase ac, 4-wire, 3-phase, and 5-wire, 2-phase systems, a further demand factor of 70 percent shall be permitted for that portion of the unbalanced load in excess of 200 amperes. There shall be no reduction of the neutral capacity for that portion of the load which consists of electric-discharge lighting, data processing, or similar equipment, and supplied from a 4-wire, wye-connected 3-phase system.

(FPN): See Examples 1(a), 1(b), 2(b), 4, and 5(a), Chapter 9.

Section 220-22 of the *Code* describes the basis for calculating the neutral load as the maximum unbalanced load that can occur between the neutral and any other ungrounded conductor.

For a household electric range or clothes dryer, the maximum unbalanced load may be assumed at 70 percent, so the neutral may be sized on this basis. Section 250-60 of the *Code* permits use of the grounded circuit conductor, where sized at not less than No. 10 AWG, to ground the frame of a range, except for ranges in mobile homes and travel trailers. The supply cable to the range or electric clothes dryer may be service-entrance cable with an uninsulated grounded conductor, if the branch circuit originates at the service equipment. If the range or dryer is supplied with a three-conductor branch circuit, a receptacle and attachment plug, if used, may be of the three-pole type without an equipment ground. If nonmetallic-sheathed cable is used to supply the range, the conductor provided for equipment grounding purposes cannot be used for the grounded circuit conductor, as stated in Section 336-25.

Where the system supplies electric discharge lighting, such as fluorescent or HID, or data processing or similar equipment, the neutral is considered to be a current-carrying conductor if the electric discharge lighting, data processing, etc., load on the feeder neutral consists of more than half of the total load. Electric discharge lighting and data processing equipment will have harmonic current in the neutral which may approximate the load current, and it would be appropriate to require a full-size feeder neutral conductor.

ARTICLE 220—BRANCH-CIRCUIT AND FEEDER CALCULATIONS

C. Optional Calculations for Computing Feeder and Service Loads

220-30. Optional Calculation — Dwelling Unit.

(a) Feeder and Service Load. For a dwelling unit having the total connected load served by a single 3-wire, 120/240-volt or 208Y/120-volt set of service-entrance or feeder conductors with an ampacity of 100 or greater, it shall be permissible to compute the feeder and service loads in accordance with Table 220-30 instead of the method specified in Part B of this article. Feeder and service-entrance conductors whose demand load is determined by this optional calculation shall be permitted to have the neutral load determined by Section 220-22.

The optional method given in Section 220-30 is applicable to a single-dwelling unit, whether it is a separate building or located in a multifamily dwelling. The optional calculation permitted by Section 220-30 may be used only where the service-entrance or feeder conductors have an ampacity of at least 100 amperes.

Examples of the optional calculation for a dwelling unit are given in Chapter 9, Example Nos. 2(a), 2(b), and 4(b).

See Article 100 for definition of "dwelling unit."

(b) Loads. The loads identified in Table 220-30 as "other load" and as "remainder of other load" shall include the following:

(1) 1500 volt-amperes for each 2-wire, 20-ampere small appliance branch circuit and each laundry branch circuit specified in Section 220-16.

(2) 3 volt-amperes per square foot (0.093 sq m) for general lighting and general-use receptacles.

(3) The nameplate rating of all fastened in place appliances, ranges, wall-mounted ovens, and counter-top cooking units.

(4) The nameplate ampere or kVA rating of all motors and of all low-power-factor loads.

Table 220-30
Optional Calculation for Dwelling Unit Load in kVA

Largest of the following four selections.

(1) 100 percent of the nameplate rating(s) of the air conditioning and cooling, including heat pump compressors.

(2) 65 percent of the nameplate rating(s) of the central electric space heating including integral supplemental heating in heat pumps.

(3) 65 percent of the nameplate rating(s) of electric space heating if less than four separately controlled units.

(4) 40 percent of the nameplate rating(s) of electric space heating of four or more separately controlled units.

Plus: 100 percent of the first 10 kVA of all other load. 40 percent of the remainder of all other load.

Section 220-21 states that when considering noncoincident loads the largest of those being considered is to be used. While the air-conditioning load is considered at 100 percent, the central electric space heating load is considered at 65 percent including supplemental heaters. If the air-conditioning equipment is also a heat pump, it is added to the heating load at 100 percent.

220-31. Optional Calculation for Additional Loads in Existing Dwelling Unit. For an existing dwelling unit presently being served by an existing 120/240 volt or 208Y/120, 3-wire service, it shall be permissible to compute load calculations as follows:

Load (in kVA)	Percent of Load
First 8 kVA of load at	100%
Remainder of load at	40%

Load calculation shall include lighting at 3 volt-amperes per square foot (0.093 sq m); 1500 volt-amperes for each 20-ampere appliance circuit; range or wall-mounted oven and counter-mounted cooking unit, and other appliances that are permanently connected or fastened in place, at nameplate rating.

If air-conditioning equipment or electric space heating equipment is to be installed the following formula shall be applied to determine if the existing service is of sufficient size.

Air-conditioning equipment* 100%
Central electric space heating* 100%
Less than four separately controlled space heating units* 100%
First 8 kVA of all other load 100%
Remainder of all other load 40%
    Other loads shall include:
    1500 volt-amperes for each 20-ampere appliance circuit.
    Lighting and portable appliances at 3 volt-amperes per square foot (0.093 sq m)
    Household range or wall-mounted oven and counter-mounted cooking unit.
    All other appliances fastened in place, including four or more separately controlled space heating units, at nameplate rating.

*Use larger connected load of air conditioning and space heating, but not both.

This optional method allows an additional load to be supplied by an existing service.

Example: An existing dwelling unit is served by a 100-A service. An additional load of 5 kVA, 240-V air conditioning is to be installed. The existing load consists of the following:

general lighting 24 ft × 40 ft = 960 sq ft × 3 VA/sq ft	=	2880 VA
small appliance circuits 3 × 1500 VA	=	4500 VA
laundry circuit at 1500 VA	=	1500 VA
electric range rated 10.5 kW	=	10,500 VA
electric water heater rated 3.0 kW	=	3000 VA
existing other load		
Total		22,380

Computation of existing load plus additional load

air conditioning 5 kVA at 100%	=	5000 VA
first 8 kVA of all other load at 100%	=	8000 VA
remainder of other load at 40%		
22,380 − 8000 = 14,380 × 0.40	=	5752 VA
Total		18,752 VA

18,752 ÷ 240 = 78.1 amperes

The additional load contributed by the 5 kVA air conditioning does not exceed the allowable load permitted on a 100-A service.

113

220-32. Optional Calculation — Multifamily Dwelling.

(a) Feeder or Service Load. It shall be permissible to compute the feeder or service load of a multifamily dwelling in accordance with Table 220-32 instead of Part B of this article where all the following conditions are met:

(1) No dwelling unit is supplied by more than one feeder.

(2) Each dwelling unit is equipped with electric cooking equipment.

It should be recognized that the method of calculation of load under Section 220-32 is optional and only applies where one feeder supplies all of the load of a dwelling unit and has the other limitations that are intended to provide appropriate diversity. It should also be understood that where all of the stated conditions prevail, it is intended that the optional calculations in Section 220-32 may be used instead of those in Part B of Article 220, and this is stated in paragraph (a).

Exception: When the computed load for multifamily dwellings without electric cooking in Part B of this article exceeds that computed under Part C for the identical load plus electric cooking (based on 8 kW per unit), the lesser of the two loads shall be permitted to be used.

Section 220-32(a)(2) requires each dwelling unit to be equipped with electric cooking in order to use this method of calculation. This exception permits calculation under this section for dwelling units which do not have electric cooking by calculating a simulated electric cooking load of 8 kW per unit, and selecting the lesser of the two loads.

(3) Each dwelling unit is equipped with either electric space heating or air conditioning or both.

Feeders and service-entrance conductors whose demand load is determined by this optional calculation shall be permitted to have the neutral load determined by Section 220-22.

(b) House Loads. House loads shall be computed in accordance with Part B of this article and shall be in addition to the dwelling unit loads computed in accordance with Table 220-32.

(c) Connected Loads. The connected load to which the demand factors of Table 220-32 apply shall include the following:

(1) 1500 volt-amperes for each 2-wire, 20-ampere small appliance branch circuit and each laundry branch circuit specified in Section 220-16.

(2) 3 volt-amperes per square foot (0.093 sq m) for general lighting and general-use receptacles.

(3) The nameplate rating of all appliances that are fastened in place, permanently connected or located to be on a specific circuit, ranges, wall-mounted ovens, counter-mounted cooking units, clothes dryers, water heaters, and space heaters.

If water heater elements are so interlocked that all elements cannot be used at the same time, the maximum possible load shall be considered the nameplate load.

(4) The nameplate ampere or kVA rating of all motors and of all low-power-factor loads.

(5) The larger of the air-conditioning load or the space heating load.

Table 220-32
Optional Calculation—Demand Factors for Three or More
Multifamily Dwelling Units

Number of Dwelling Units	Demand Factor Percent
3–5	45
6–7	44
8–10	43
11	42
12–13	41
14–15	40
16–17	39
18–20	38
21	37
22–23	36
24–25	35
26–27	34
28–30	33
31	32
32–33	31
34–36	30
37–38	29
39–42	28
43–45	27
46–50	26
51–55	25
56–61	24
62 & over	23

220-33. Optional Calculation — Two Dwelling Units. Where two dwelling units are supplied by a single feeder and the computed load under Part B of this article exceeds that for three identical units computed under Section 220-32, the lesser of the two loads shall be permitted to be used.

220-34. Optional Method — Schools. The calculation of a feeder or service load for schools shall be permitted in accordance with Table 220-34 in lieu of Part B of this article where equipped with electric space heating, or air conditioning, or both. The connected load to which the demand factors of Table 220-34 apply shall include all of the interior and exterior lighting, power, water heating, cooking, other loads, and the larger of the air-conditioning load or space heating load within the building or structure.

Feeders and service-entrance conductors whose demand load is determined by this optional calculation shall be permitted to have the neutral load determined by Section 220-22. Where the building or structure load is calculated by this optional method, feeders within the building or structure shall have ampacity as permitted in Part B of this article; however, the ampacity of an individual feeder need not be larger than the ampacity for the entire building.

This section shall not apply to portable classroom buildings.

Many schools add small portable classroom buildings. The air-conditioning load is to comply with Article 440, and the lighting load is to be considered as continuous. To allow the demand factors of Table 220-34 to be applied to a portable classroom would decrease the feeder or service size to below that required for the connected continuous load.

220-35. Optional Calculations for Additional Loads to Existing Installations. For the purpose of allowing additional loads to be connected to existing feeders and services, it shall be permitted to use actual maximum kVA demand figures to determine the existing load on a service or feeder when all the following conditions are met:

(1) The maximum demand data is available in kVA for a minimum of a one-year period.

(2) The existing demand at 125 percent plus the new load does not exceed the ampacity of the feeder or rating of the service.

(3) The feeder or service has overcurrent protection in accordance with Sections 230-90 and 240-3.

Where existing installations have been checked and the maximum demand kVA data for a minimum of a one-year period is available and the installation complies with (2) and (3), connection of additional loads to existing services and feeders is permitted.

Table 220-34
Optional Method—Demand Factors for Feeders
and Service-Entrance Conductors for Schools

Connected Load Volt-Amperes per Square Foot	Demand Factors Percent
Connected load up to and including 3, plus	100
Connected load over 3 and including 20, plus	75
Connected load over 20 at	25

For SI units: one square foot = 0.093 square meter.

D. Method for Computing Farm Loads

220-40. Farm Loads — Buildings and Other Loads.

(a) Dwelling Unit. The feeder or service load of a farm dwelling unit shall be computed in accordance with the provisions for dwellings in Part B or C of this article.

(b) Other than Dwelling Unit. For each farm building or load supplied by two or more branch circuits the load for feeders, service-entrance conductors, and service equipment shall be computed in accordance with demand factors not less than indicated in Table 220-40.

(FPN): See Section 230-21 for overhead conductors from a pole to a building or other structure.

Section 230-21 requires such overhead conductors to be considered as a service drop and installed accordingly.

Table 220-40
Method for Computing Farm Loads for Other Than Dwelling Unit

Ampere Load at 240 Volts	Demand Factor Percent
Loads expected to operate without diversity, but not less than 125 percent full-load current of the largest motor and not less than the first 60 amperes of load	100
Next 60 amperes of all other loads	50
Remainder of other load..	25

220-41. Farm Loads — Total. The total load of the farm for service-entrance conductors and service equipment shall be computed in accordance with the farm dwelling unit load and demand factors specified in Table 220-41. Where there is equipment in two or more farm equipment buildings or for loads having the same function, such loads shall be computed in accordance with

116

Table 220-40 and shall be permitted to be combined as a single load in Table 220-41 for computing the total load.

(FPN): See Section 230-21 for overhead conductors from a pole to a building or other structure.

Table 220-41
Method for Computing Total Farm Load

Individual Loads Computed in Accordance with Table 220-40	Demand Factor Percent
Largest load	100
Second largest load	75
Third largest load	65
Remaining loads	50

To this total load, add the load of the farm dwelling unit computed in accordance with Part B or C of this article.

ARTICLE 225 — OUTSIDE BRANCH CIRCUITS AND FEEDERS

Contents

117

ARTICLE 225—OUTSIDE BRANCH CIRCUITS AND FEEDERS

225-1. Scope. This article covers electric equipment and wiring located on or attached to the outside of public or private buildings, or run between buildings, other structures, or poles on the premises served.

Exception: Outside branch circuits and feeders for electrolytic cells as covered in Section 668-3(c), Exceptions No. 1 and 4.

(FPN): For additional information on wiring over 600 volts, see the *National Electrical Safety Code* (ANSI C2-1984).

225-2. Other Articles. Application of other articles, including additional requirements to specific cases of equipment and conductors, is as follows:

	Article
Branch Circuits	210
Class 1, Class 2, and Class 3 Remote Control, Signaling, and Power-Limited Circuits	725
Communications Circuits	800
Community Antenna Television and Radio Distribution Systems	820
Conductors	310
Electrically Driven or Controlled Irrigation Machines	675
Electric Signs and Outline Lighting	600
Feeders	215
Fire Protective Signaling Systems	760
Fixed Outdoor Electric De-icing and Snow-Melting Equipment	426
Fixtures	410
Floating Buildings	553
Grounding	250
Hazardous (Classified) Locations	500
Hazardous (Classified) Locations, Specific	510
Marinas and Boatyards	555
Messenger Supported Wiring	321
Open Wiring on Insulators	320
Over 600 Volts, General	710
Overcurrent Protection	240
Radio and Television Equipment	810
Services	230
Solar Photovoltaic Systems	690
Swimming Pools, Fountains and Similar Installations	680
Use and Identification of Grounded Conductors	200

225-3. Calculation of Load.

(a) Branch Circuits. The load on outdoor branch circuits shall be as determined by Section 220-3.

(b) Feeders. The load on outdoor feeders shall be as determined by Part B of Article 220.

225-4. Conductor Covering. Where within 10 feet (3.05 m) of any building or other structure, open wiring on insulators shall be insulated or covered. Conductors in cables or raceways, except Type MI cable, shall be of the rubber-covered type or thermoplastic type and in wet locations shall comply with Section 310-8. Conductors for festoon lighting shall be of the rubber-covered or thermoplastic type.

Exception: Equipment grounding conductors.

225-5. Size of Conductors. The ampacity of outdoor branch-circuit and feeder conductors shall be in accordance with Tables 310-16 through 310-31 based on loads as determined under Section 220-3 and Part B of Article 220.

225-6. Minimum Size of Conductor.

(a) Overhead Spans. Overhead conductors shall not be smaller than the following:

(1) For 600 volts, nominal, or less, No. 10 copper or No. 8 aluminum for spans up to 50 feet (15.2 m) in length and No. 8 copper or No. 6 aluminum for a longer span.

(2) For over 600 volts, nominal, No. 6 copper or No. 4 aluminum where open individual conductors and No. 8 copper or No. 6 aluminum where in cable.

The size limitation of copper or aluminum conductors is based upon an adequate mechanical strength. See Figure 225-1.

No. 8 copper
No. 6 aluminum

No. 10 copper
No. 8 aluminum

Longer than 50 ft   Up to 50 ft

Figure 225-1. Overhead spans run between buildings, structures, or poles for 600 V or less.

(b) Festoon Lighting. Overhead conductors for festoon lighting shall not be smaller than No. 12.

Exception: Where supported by messenger wires.

(FPN): See Section 225-24 for outdoor lampholders.

Definition: Festoon lighting is a string of outdoor lights suspended between two points more than 15 feet (4.57 m) apart.

See Figure 225-5.

225-7. Lighting Equipment Installed Outdoors.

(a) General. For the supply of lighting equipment installed outdoors, the branch circuits shall comply with Article 210 and (b) through (d) below.

(b) Common Neutral. It shall be permissible to use a multiwire branch circuit consisting of the neutral and not more than eight ungrounded conductors. The ampacity of the neutral conductor shall not be less than the calculated sum of the currents in all ungrounded conductors connected to any one phase of the circuit.

See Figures 225-2 and 225-3.

(c) 277 Volts to Ground. Circuits exceeding 120 volts, nominal, between conductors and not exceeding 277 volts, nominal, to ground shall be permitted to supply lighting fixtures for illumination of outdoor areas of industrial establishments, office buildings, schools, stores, and other commercial or public buildings where the fixtures are not less than 3 feet (914 mm) from windows, platforms, fire escapes, and the like.

Multiwire branch circuits consisting of a neutral and not more than eight ungrounded conductors are permissible, provided the neutral capacity is not less than the total load of all ungrounded conductors connected to any one phase of the circuit.

Figure 225-2. The maximum unbalanced current that can occur will be four times 20 A which is 80 A.

Figure 225-3. The maximum unbalanced current that can occur on a 3-phase system with the load connected as shown will be 80 A due to the load on phase C.

Branch circuits for outdoor illumination of industrial establishments, office buildings, schools, stores, and other commercial or public buildings are permitted to operate with a voltage to ground of 277 volts.

Many designers of outdoor lighting installations on poles prefer a nominal 10 percent under voltage (130-V rated lamps on nominal 120-V circuits). Although this decreases the light intensity somewhat, it prolongs the life of the lamps, minimizing pole lamp maintenance, which can be difficult.

The restrictions in Section 225-7(c) are in addition to those in Section 210-6.

(d) 600 Volts Between Conductors. Circuits exceeding 277 volts, nominal, to ground and not exceeding 600 volts, nominal, between conductors shall be permitted to supply the auxiliary equipment of electric-discharge lamps in accordance with Section 210-6(d)(1).

Section 210-6(d)(1)a. and b. list the height requirements for circuits exceeding 277 volts, nominal, to ground but not exceeding 600 volts, nominal, between conductors and supplying the auxiliary equipment of electric-discharge lamps.

225-8. Disconnection. The disconnecting means for branch-circuit and feeder fuses shall be in accordance with Section 240-40.

225-9. Overcurrent Protection. Overcurrent protection shall be in accordance with Section 210-20 for branch circuits and Part A of Article 240 for feeders.

225-10. Wiring on Buildings. The installation of outside wiring on surfaces of buildings shall be permitted for circuits of not over 600 volts, nominal, as open wiring on insulators, as multiconductor cable, as Type MC cable, as Type MI cable, as messenger supported wiring, in rigid metal conduit, in intermediate metal conduit, in rigid nonmetallic conduit, in cable trays, as cablebus, in wireways, in auxiliary gutters, in electrical metallic tubing, in flexible metal conduit, in liquidtight flexible metal conduit, and in busways. Circuits of over 600 volts, nominal, shall be installed as provided in Section 710-3. Circuits for signs and outline lighting shall be installed in accordance with Article 600.

225-11. Circuit Exits and Entrances. Where outside branch and feeder circuits leave or enter a building, the requirements of Sections 230-43, 230-52, and 230-54 shall apply.

See Figure 225-4.

225-12. Open-Conductor Supports. Open conductors shall be supported on glass or porcelain-knobs, racks, brackets, or strain insulators.

225-13. Festoon Supports. In spans exceeding 40 feet (12.2 m), the conductors shall be supported by a messenger wire; and the messenger wire shall be supported by strain insulators. Conductors or messenger wires shall not be attached to any fire escape, downspout, or plumbing equipment.

Section 225-6 defines "festoon lighting" as "a string of outdoor lights suspended between two points more than 15 ft apart." The conductors are not permitted to be smaller than No. 12, unless they are supported by a messenger wire. On all spans of festoon lighting exceeding 40 ft, messenger wire is required and is to be supported by strain insulators. Where no messenger wire is required, the No. 12 or larger conductors are required to be supported by strain insulators. See Figure 225-5.

Attachment to fire escapes, plumbing equipment, or drainspouts is prohibited since they could provide a path to ground. Moreover, such methods of attachment could not be relied upon for a permanent or secure means of support.

225-14. Open-Conductor Spacings.

(a) 600 Volts, Nominal, or Less. Conductors of 600 volts, nominal, or less, shall comply with the spacings provided in Table 230-51(c).

(b) Over 600 Volts, Nominal. Conductors of over 600 volts, nominal, shall comply with the spacings provided in Part D of Article 710.

(c) Separation from Other Circuits. Open conductors shall be separated from open conductors of other circuits or systems by not less than 4 inches (102 mm).

Figure 225-4. Section 225-11 references Sections 230-43 (Wiring Methods for 600 Volts, Nominal, or Less), 230-52 (Individual Conductors Entering Buildings or Other Structures), and 230-54 (Connections at Service Head). Section 225-18 covers the requirements for clearances from ground (not over 600 V), and Section 225-19 covers the requirements for clearances from buildings (not over 600 V). See Section 225-19(d) for clearances from windows, doors, fire escapes, etc.

Figure 225-5. Messenger wires are required for festoon lighting conductors smaller than No. 12 or for spans exceeding 40 ft.

(d) Conductors on Poles. Conductors on poles shall have a separation of not less than 1 foot (305 mm) where not placed on racks or brackets. Conductors supported on poles shall provide a horizontal climbing space not less than the following:

Power conductors, below communication conductors .... 30 inches (762 mm)
Power conductors alone or above communication conductors:
  300 volts or less .... 24 inches (610 mm)
  Over 300 volts .... 30 inches (762 mm)
Communication conductors below power conductors................................ same as power conductors
Communication conductors alone... no requirement

122

Ample space is required to enable linemen to climb over or through conductors to safely service conductors on the pole.

225-15. Supports Over Buildings.   Supports over a building shall be in accordance with Section 230-29.

225-16. Point of Attachment to Buildings.   The point of attachment to a building shall be in accordance with Section 230-26.

225-17. Means of Attachment to Buildings.   The means of attachment to a building shall be in accordance with Section 230-27.

225-18. Clearance from Ground.   Open conductors of not over 600 volts, nominal, shall conform to the following:

10 feet (3.05 m) — above finished grade, sidewalks, or from any platform or projection from which they might be reached where the supply conductors are limited to 150 volts to ground and accessible to pedestrians only.

12 feet (3.66 m) — over residential driveways, and those commercial areas not subject to truck traffic where the voltage is limited to 300 volts to ground.

15 feet (4.57 m) — for those areas listed in the 12-foot (3.66-m) classification where the voltage exceeds 300 volts to ground.

18 feet (5.49 m) — over public streets, alleys, roads, parking areas subject to truck traffic, driveways on other than residential property, and other land traversed by vehicles such as cultivated, grazing, forest, and orchard.

The clearances from ground, as given, coordinate with the *National Electrical Safety Code*. See Section 230-24 and Figure 225-4.

(FPN): Note: For clearances of conductors of over 600 volts, see National Electrical Safety Code (ANSI C2-1984).

225-19. Clearances from Buildings for Conductors of Not Over 600 Volts, Nominal.

(a) Above Roofs.   Conductors not fully insulated for the operating voltage shall have a vertical or diagonal clearance of not less than 10 feet (3.05 m) from the roof surface.

Exception No. 1: Fully insulated conductors shall be permitted to have vertical or diagonal clearance of 3 feet (914 mm) or more.

Exception No. 2: Above roof space accessible to pedestrians. Vertical clearance shall not be less than 15 feet (4.57 m) for uninsulated, 8 feet (2.44 m) for insulated conductors.

Exception No. 3: Above roof space accessible to vehicular traffic, vertical clearance shall not be less than 18 feet (5.49 m).

Exception No. 4: Where the voltage between conductors does not exceed 300 and the roof has a slope of not less than 4 inches (102 mm) in 12 inches (305 mm), a reduction in clearance to 3 feet (914 mm) shall be permitted.

Exception No. 5: Where the voltage between conductors does not exceed 300, a reduction in clearance above only the overhanging portion of the roof to not less than 18 inches (457 mm) shall be permitted if (1) not more than 4 feet (1.22 m) of the conductors pass above the roof overhang, and (2) they are terminated at a through-the-roof raceway or approved support.

(b) From Nonbuilding or Nonbridge Structures.   From signs, chimneys, radio and television antennas, tanks, other nonbuilding or nonbridge structures, clearances, vertical, diagonal and horizontal, shall not be less than 5 feet (1.52 m) for uninsulated conductors, 3 feet (914 mm) for insulated conductors.

(c) Horizontal Clearances. Clearances shall not be less than 5 feet (1.52 m) for uninsulated conductors, 3 feet (914 mm) for insulated conductors.

(d) Final Spans. Final spans of feeders or branch circuits to a building they supply or from which they are fed shall be permitted to be attached to the building, but they shall be kept 3 feet (914 mm) from windows, doors, porches, fire escapes, or similar locations.

Exception: Conductors run above the top level of a window shall be permitted to be less than the 3 feet (914 mm) requirement above.

See Figure 225-4.

(e) Zone for Fire Ladders. Where buildings exceed three stories or 50 feet (15.2 m) in height, overhead lines shall be arranged, where practicable, so that a clear space (or zone) at least 6 feet (1.83 m) wide will be left either adjacent to the buildings or beginning not over 8 feet (2.44 m) from them to facilitate the raising of ladders when necessary for fire fighting.

(FPN): Note: For clearance of conductors over 600 volts, see National Electrical Safety Code (ANSI C2-1984).

225-20. Mechanical Protection of Conductors. Mechanical protection of conductors on buildings, structures, or poles shall be as provided for services in Section 230-50.

225-21. Multiconductor Cables on Exterior Surfaces of Buildings. Supports for multiconductor cables on exterior surfaces of buildings shall be as provided in Section 230-51.

225-22. Raceways on Exterior Surfaces of Buildings. Raceways on exterior surfaces of buildings shall be raintight and arranged to drain.

Exception: As permitted in Section 350-2.

"Raintight" is defined as "so constructed or protected that exposure to a beating rain will not result in the entrance of water." To assure this, all conduit bodies, fittings, and boxes used in wet locations are required to be provided with threaded hubs or other approved means. Threadless couplings and connectors used with metal conduit or electrical metallic tubing are required to be of the raintight type (see Sections 345-9, 346-9, and 348-8).

Where exposed to weather or rain through weatherhead openings, condensation is likely to occur, causing moisture to accumulate within raceways at low points of the installation and in junction boxes. Raceways should thus be installed to permit drainage through drain holes at appropriate locations.

225-23. Underground Circuits. Underground circuits shall meet the requirements of Section 300-5.

225-24. Outdoor Lampholders. Where outdoor lampholders are attached as pendants, the connections to the circuit wires shall be staggered. Where such lampholders have terminals of a type that puncture the insulation and make contact with the conductors, they shall be attached only to conductors of the stranded type.

Splices to branch-circuit conductors for outdoor lampholders of the Edison-base type or "pig-tail sockets" are required to be staggered so as not to place splices in close proximity to each other.

"Pin-type" terminal sockets are required to be attached to stranded conductors only and are intended for installations for temporary lighting or decorations, signs, or specifically approved applications.

225-25. Location of Outdoor Lamps. Locations of lamps for outdoor lighting shall be below all live conductors, transformers, or other electric utilization equipment.

Exception No. 1: Where clearances or other safeguards are provided for relamping operations.

Exception No. 2: Where equipment is controlled by a disconnecting means that can be locked in the open position.

Since Section 225-18 requires a minimum clearance for open conductors of 10 ft above grade or platforms, it would be difficult to keep all electrical equipment above the lamps. Exception No. 1, therefore, allows other clearances or safeguards to permit safe relamping, and Exception No. 2 permits the use of a disconnecting means to de-energize the circuit.

225-26. Live Vegetation. Live vegetation such as trees shall not be used for support of overhead conductor spans or other electric equipment.

Exception: For temporary wiring in accordance with Article 305.

When overhead conductor spans are attached to a tree, the tree will grow around the attachment device, often causing the mounting insulators to break and degrading conductor insulation. This requirement also reduces the likelihood of chafing of the conductor insulation and the danger of shock to tree trimmers and tree climbers.

ARTICLE 230 — SERVICES

Contents

(c) Access to Occupants.

230-92. Locked Service Overcurrent
Devices.

230-93. Protection of Specific
Circuits.

230-94. Relative Location of
Overcurrent Device and
Other Service Equipment.

230-95. Ground-Fault Protection of
Equipment.

(a) Setting.

(b) Fuses.

(c) Performance Testing.

**H. Services Exceeding 600 Volts,
Nominal**

230-200. General.

230-201. Service Conductors.

230-202. Service-Entrance Conductors.

(a) Conductor Size.

(b) Wiring Methods.

(c) Open Work.

(d) Supports.

(e) Guarding.

(f) Service Cable.

(g) Draining Raceways.

(h) Over 15,000 Volts.

230-203. Warning Signs.

230-204. Isolating Switches.

(a) Where Required.

(b) Fuses as Isolating Switch.

(c) Accessible to Qualified Persons Only.

(d) Grounding Connection.

230-205. Disconnecting Means.

(a) Location.

(b) Type.

230-206. Overcurrent Devices as Disconnecting Means.

230-207. Equipment in Secondaries.

230-208. Overcurrent Protection
Requirements.

(a) In Vault or Consisting of
Metal-Enclosed Switchgear.

(b) Not in Vault or Not Consisting of Metal-Enclosed
Switchgear.

(c) Fuses.

(d) Circuit Breakers.

(e) Enclosed Overcurrent
Devices.

230-209. Surge Arresters (Lightning
Arresters).

230-210. Service Equipment — General Provisions.

230-211. Metal-Enclosed Switchgear.

Article 230 has been rearranged, in part, for the 1987 *NEC*. The following identifies those sections and parts that have been reidentified.

1984 NEC	*1987 NEC*
230-3, Exception	deleted
230-4	230-22, -30, -41
230-5	230-23, -31, -42(a)
230-24(c)	230-9
Part C	Part B
Part D	Part C
Part E	Part D
Part F	deleted
230-40, Exception No. 2	deleted
230-44	230-6
230-45	230-40, Exception No. 2
230-47	230-7
230-48	230-8
230-49	230-32
230-50(a)(5)	deleted
Part G	Part E
Part H	Part F
230-73	230-64
Part J	Part G
230-90(a), Exception No. 4	deleted
230-90(c)	230-91(b)

ARTICLE 230—SERVICES

1984 NEC	*1987 NEC*
230-98	230-65
Part K	Part H
230-202(i)	deleted

230-1. Scope. This article covers service conductors and equipment for control and protection of services and their installation requirements.

(FPN): See Diagram 230-1.

Diagram 230-1 Services

General... Part A
Overhead Service Drop Conductors................................ Part B
Underground Service-Lateral Conductors...................... Part C
Service-Entrance Conductors... Part D
Service Equipment — General.. Part E
Service Equipment — Disconnecting Means................... Part F
Service Equipment — Overcurrent Protection................ Part G
Services over 600 Volts, Nominal................................... Part H

SOURCE

	OVERHEAD		UNDERGROUND	
	Last Pole		Street Main	
Part B	Service Drop		Service Lateral	Part C
230-24	Clearances		Depth of burial and protection	230-49
	Service Head		Terminal box, meter, or other enclosure	

SERVICE—ENTRANCE CONDUCTORS	Part D

SERVICE EQUIPMENT	
General	Part E
Grounding	230-63
Disconnecting means	Part F
Overcurrent protection	Part G

BRANCH CIRCUITS FEEDERS	Articles 210, 225 Articles 215, 225

The part numbers are divided into sections as follows:

Subject	Part	Sections
General	A	230-2 — 230-9
Overhead Service-Drop Conductors	B	230-21 — 230-29
Underground Service-Lateral Conductor	C	230-30 — 230-32
Service-Entrance Conductors	D	230-40 — 230-56
Service-Equipment—General	E	230-62 — 230-65
Service-Equipment—Disconnecting Means	F	230-70 — 230-84
Service Equipment—Overcurrent Protection	G	230-90 — 230-95
Services Exceeding 600 Volts, Nominal	H	230-200 — 230-211

A. General

230-2. Number of Services.   A building or other structure served shall be supplied by only one service.

Where more than one service is permitted by any of the following exceptions, a permanent plaque or directory shall be installed at each service drop or lateral or at each service-equipment location denoting all other services on or in that building or structure and the area served by each.

The basic requirement of this section is that a building or other structure can be supplied by only one service. A permanent plaque or directory is required to be installed at each service drop or lateral or at each service-equipment location denoting all of the other services on or in that building or structure and the area served by each. This plaque or directory should be constructed of sufficient durability to withstand the ambient environment. See Figure 230-1.

The service disconnecting means for each service or for each set of service-entrance conductors permitted by Section 230-2, Exception No. 3 shall consist of not more than six switches or six circuit breakers, at any one location, mounted in a single enclosure, in a group of separate enclosures, or in or on a switchboard. See Sections 230-71 and 230-72.

The *Code* permits a separate service for each occupancy in multiple-occupancy buildings, provided the service-entrance conductors are installed outside of the building, or installed so that they can be considered outside the building in accordance with Section 230-6, to a point where the conductors enter the individual occupancy. See Figure 230-4.

Exception No. 1: For fire pumps where a separate service is required.

Exception No. 2: For emergency, legally required standby, optional standby, or parallel power production systems where a separate service is required.

Service No.1 of 2 services. Service No. 2 is located on the North corner of the building supplying the North Wing.

Figure 230-1. Where more than one service is installed, a permanent plaque or directory is required denoting all other services and the area served by each.

Exception No. 3: Multiple-Occupancy Buildings. By special permission, in multiple-occupancy buildings where there is no available space for service equipment accessible to all the occupants.

Exception No. 4: Capacity Requirements. Two or more services shall be permitted:

a. Where the capacity requirements are in excess of 3000 amperes at a supply voltage of 600 volts or less; or

b. Where the load requirements of a single-phase installation are greater than the serving agency normally supplies through one service; or

c. By special permission.

Exception No. 5: Buildings of Large Area. By special permission, for a single building or other structure sufficiently large to make two or more services necessary.

Exception No. 6: For different characteristics, such as for different voltages, frequencies, or phases, or for different uses, such as for different rate schedules.

Exception No. 7: For the purpose of Section 230-40, Exception No. 2, underground sets of conductors, size 1/0 and larger, running to the same location and connected together at their supply end but not connected together at their load end shall be considered to be one service lateral.

The basic rule is that a building or other structure is to be supplied by only one service. There are, however, several exceptions.

Exception Nos. 1 and 2 permit separate services where necessary for fire pumps (with one to six switches or circuit breakers) or emergency, legally required standby, optional standby electrical systems, or parallel power production systems in accordance with Article 705 (with one to six switches or circuit breakers) in addition to the regular building service (with one to six switches or circuit breakers). The intent here is that a disruption of the main building service should not disconnect fire pump equipment or emergency, legally required standby, optional standby, or parallel power production systems. Exception No. 2 permits a solar photovoltaic system as covered in Article 690. See Section 230-72(b).

Exception No. 3 permits a separate service in multiple-occupancy buildings by special permission {the written consent of the authority having jurisdiction (see Definitions, Article 100)}, where there is no space available for service equipment accessible to all occupants as permitted by the exception to Section 240-24(b).

Exception No. 4 permits two or more services where capacity requirements are in excess of 3,000 A, where supplied by 600 V or less, or for lesser loads by special permission.

Many electric power companies have specifications and have adopted special regulations covering certain types of electrical loads and service equipment that may be energized from their lines. It is advisable to consult with the serving utility to determine line capacities before designing electrical services for large buildings.

Exception No. 5 requires special permission for the installation of more than one service to a sufficiently large building. Expansion of buildings, shopping centers, or industrial plants often necessitates the addition of two or more services. It would, for example, be impractical or impossible to install one service for an industrial plant with capacity requirements to compensate for any and all future load requirements. It is also impractical to run feeders extremely long distances due to high costs and voltage drop problems. Again, it is advisable to consult with the serving utility and the authority having jurisdiction before contemplating use of this exception.

Exception No. 6 permits the installation of more than one service for different characteristics, such as different voltages, frequencies, single-phase and 3-phase, or different utility rate schedules for different uses. For example, different service characteristics exist between a 3-wire, 120/240-V single-phase service and a 3-phase, 4-wire, 480Y/277-V service. For different uses, such as different rate schedules, it is intended to allow a second service for supplying a second meter for equipment such as an electric water heater on a different rate.

Exception No. 7 permits from two to six sets of service lateral conductors to serve up to six service disconnecting means, provided the service lateral conductors are 1/0 AWG or larger and are connected together at their supply end, which is normally at the transformer secondary terminals. This exception is included in the *Code* to increase the cable impedance by not paralleling the conductors, thereby lowering the available short-circuit current at the building. See Sections 110-9 and 110-10. Also, Exception No. 7 does not require that each set of service lateral conductors be of the same size, provided that each set of service lateral conductors is 1/0 AWG or larger. Note that this lateral arrangement is considered to be one service lateral. Therefore, the total number of disconnects cannot exceed six in accordance with Section 230-71(a). See Figure 230-2.

Figure 230-2. Illustrated are two sets of underground conductors, size 1/0 and larger (4/0), connected at their supply and running to the same location, not connected together at their load end, and not more than six disconnects. It is permissible to run six such sets of conductors to six individual service disconnects.

230-3. One Building or Other Structure Not to Be Supplied Through Another. Service conductors supplying a building or other structure shall not pass through the interior of another building or other structure.

(FPN): See Section 230-6 for masonry-encased conductors considered outside of a building.

It is permissible for service conductors to be installed along the "exterior" of one building to supply another building. However, service conductors supplying a building are not permitted to pass through the "interior" of a building. Each building served in this manner is required to be provided with a disconnecting means for all ungrounded conductors as required by Section 230-84(a). See Figure 230-3.

Service-entrance conductors are considered to be outside of a building where they are installed beneath the building under not less than 2 in. of concrete or concealed in a raceway within the building and enclosed by not less than 2 in. of concrete or brick, or installed in a transformer vault. See Section 230-6 and Figure 230-4.

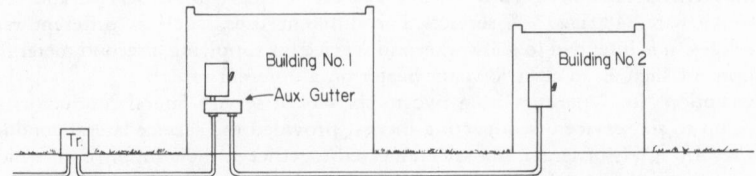

Figure 230-3. Service conductors are not permitted to pass through the interior of Building No. 1 to supply Building No. 2. The disconnecting means shown for building No. 1 is located on the exterior wall. A disconnecting means suitable for use as service equipment is required to be provided for each building.

230-6. Conductors Considered Outside of Building. Conductors shall be considered outside of a building or other structure under any of the following conditions: (1) where installed under not less than 2 inches (50.8 mm) of concrete beneath a building or other structure; (2) where installed within a building or other structure in a raceway that is enclosed by concrete or brick not less than 2 inches (50.8 mm) thick; or (3) installed in a transformer vault conforming to the requirements of Article 450, Part C.

See Figure 230-4.

Figure 230-4. Conductors are considered outside of a building where installed under not less than 2 in. of concrete beneath a building or in a raceway enclosed by 2 in. of concrete or brick within a building. They are also considered outside the building when installed in a transformer vault. See Sections 450-41 through 450-48.

230-7. Other Conductors in Raceway or Cable. Conductors other than service conductors shall not be installed in the same service raceway or service-entrance cable.

Exception No. 1: Grounding conductors.

Exception No. 2: Load management control conductors having overcurrent protection.

Load management control conductors are control circuit or switch leg conductors for use with special rate meters, usually for water heater circuits. Electric utility companies usually refer to these special-rate meters as "off peak." See Figure 230-11.

230-8. Raceway Seal. Where a service raceway enters from an underground distribution system, it shall be sealed in accordance with Section 300-5. Spare or unused raceways shall also be sealed. Sealants shall be identified for use with the cable insulation, shield, or other components.

Sealing, such as duct seal or a bushing incorporating the physical characteristics of a seal, is required to be used to seal the ends of service raceways. The intent of this requirement is to prevent water, usually the result of condensation, from entering the service equipment via the raceway. See Figure 300-5. Some sealants are known to have deleterious effects on insulations, extruded semiconducting layers, etc.

230-9. Clearance from Building Openings. Service conductors installed as open conductors or multiconductor cable without an overall outer jacket shall have a clearance of not less than 3 feet (914 mm) from windows, doors, porches, fire escapes, or similar locations.

Exception: Conductors run above the top level of a window shall be permitted to be less than the 3 feet (914 mm) requirement above.

The clearance of 3 ft is applicable to the conductors and not to a raceway or cable assembly approved for use as service conductors. The intent is to protect the conductors from physical damage and/or accidental contact. The exception permits service conductors, including drip loops and service-drop conductors, to be located just above window openings, because they are considered to be "out of reach." See Figure 230-5.

Figure 230-5. Illustration showing service conductors spaced 3 ft from a window and service conductors above the top level of a window.

ARTICLE 230—SERVICES

Service conductors shall not be installed beneath openings through which materials may be moved, such as openings in farm and commercial buildings. Overhead wires shall not be run such that they obstruct entrance to these building openings.

The second paragraph of Section 230-9 is new for the 1987 edition. Building openings through which materials may be moved are often high enough for the service conductors to be installed below the opening and still meet the height requirement of Section 230-24. This new requirement is intended to reduce the likelihood of damage to the service conductors and the potential for electric shock to persons using these high building openings.

B. Overhead Service-Drop Conductors

230-21. Overhead Supply. Overhead conductors to a building or other structure (such as a pole) on which a meter or disconnecting means is installed shall be considered as a service drop and installed accordingly.

(FPN): Example: Farm loads in Part D of Article 220.

230-22. Insulation or Covering. Service conductors shall normally withstand exposure to atmospheric and other conditions of use without detrimental leakage of current. Individual conductors shall be insulated or covered with an extruded thermoplastic or thermosetting insulating material.

The intent of this section is to prevent problems that are created by covered cable or covered open wiring, which over a period of years is subjected to weather, abrasion, and other deleterious effects that reduce the nonconductive properties of the covering.

Exception: The grounded conductor of a multiconductor cable shall be permitted to be bare.

230-23. Size and Rating.

(a) General. Conductors shall have sufficient ampacity to carry the load without a temperature rise detrimental to the covering or insulation of the conductors and shall have adequate mechanical strength.

When adding load to any service it is the installer's responsibility to be aware of all existing loads. The potential for overloading the service conductors must be governed by installer responsibility and inspector awareness, not by the usual method of overcurrent protection. Load diversity makes this a reasonable approach.

(b) Minimum Size. The conductors shall not be smaller than No. 8 copper, No. 6 aluminum or copper-clad aluminum.

Exception: For installations to supply only limited loads of a single branch circuit such as small polyphase power, controlled water heaters and the like, they shall not be smaller than No. 12 hard-drawn copper or equivalent.

(c) Grounded Conductors. The grounded (neutral) conductor shall not be less than the minimum size as required by Section 250-23(b).

230-24. Clearances. The vertical clearances of all service-drop conductors shall be based on conductor temperature of 60°F (15°C), no wind, with final unloaded sag in the wire, conductor, or cable.

Service-drop conductors shall not be readily accessible and shall comply with (a) through (d) below for services not over 600 volts, nominal.

(a) Above Roofs. Conductors shall have a vertical clearance of not less than 8 feet (2.44 m) from all points of roofs above which they pass.

Exception No. 1: Where the voltage between conductors does not exceed 300 and the roof has a slope of not less than 4 inches (102 mm) in 12 inches (305 mm), a reduction in clearance to 3 feet (914 mm) shall be permitted.

Service-drop conductors are not permitted to be readily accessible and, where passing over roofs and not over 600 V, are required to have a clearance of 8 ft. Exception No. 1 permits a clearance of 3 ft where the voltage between conductors does not exceed 300 and the roof is sloped at not less than 4 in. in 12 in. It is difficult to walk upon a sloped roof of this angle or pitch. See Figure 230-6.

Exception No. 2: Where the voltage between conductors does not exceed 300, a reduction in clearance above only the overhanging portion of the roof to not less than 18 inches (457 mm) shall be permitted if (1) not more than 4 feet (1.22 m) of service-drop conductors pass above the roof overhang, and (2) they are terminated at a through-the-roof raceway or approved support.

(FPN): See Section 230-28 for mast supports.

| More than 300 volts between conductors, 8 ft clearance is required by Section 230–24(a) | 300 volts or less between conductors, 3 ft minimum clearance is permitted by Section 230–24(a), Exception No. 1 if roof slope is standard 4 × 12 | 300 volts or less between conductors, 18 in. clearance is permitted by Section 230–24(a), Exception No. 2 if conductors pass over not more than 48 in. of roof overhang |

Figure 230-6. Clearances for service-drop conductors passing over the overhanging portion of a roof and minimum angle of roof slope permitting a 3-ft clearance for service-drop conductors.

A further reduction of service-drop conductor clearances to 18 in. is permitted by Exception No. 2 for service-mast (through-the-roof) installations where the voltage between conductors does not exceed 300 and the mast is located within 4 ft of the edge of the roof. See Figure 230-6. This exception applies to either sloped or flat roofs. Many electric utility companies will not permit a coupling between the service head and the point where a service raceway extends through the roof.

Exception No. 3: The area above a roof surface subject to vehicular traffic shall have a vertical clearance from the roof surface in accordance with the clearance requirements of Section 230-24(b).

ARTICLE 230—SERVICES

See Figure 230-7.

Clearance per Section 230–24(b) required (12 ft, 15 ft, or 18 ft)

Service drop

Figure 230-7. Section 230-24(a), Exception No. 3 requires clearance above a roof surface subject to vehicular traffic, such as rooftop parking areas, to meet the 12-, 15-, or 18-ft clearance requirements of Section 230-24(b). See Figure 230-8.

(b) Vertical Clearance from Ground. Service-drop conductors where not in excess of 600 volts, nominal, shall have the following minimum clearance from final grade.

10 feet (3.05 m) — at the electric service entrance to buildings, or at the drip loop of the building electric entrance, or above areas or sidewalks accessible only to pedestrians, measured from final grade or other accessible surface only for service-drop cables supported on and cabled together with a grounded bare messenger and limited to 150 volts to ground.

12 feet (3.66 m) — for those areas listed in the 15 foot (4.57 m) classification when the voltage is limited to 300 volts to ground.

15 feet (4.57 m) — over residential property and driveways, and those commercial areas not subject to truck traffic.

18 feet (5.49 m) — over public streets, alleys, roads, parking areas subject to truck traffic, driveways on other than residential property, and other land traversed by vehicles such as cultivated, grazing, forest, and orchard.

See Figure 230-8.

12 ft
(300 V or less to ground)

10 ft
(150 V to ground)

18 ft

PETE'S

15 ft

This area accessible to pedestrians only

Figure 230-8. Illustrated clearances are coordinated with the National Electrical Safety Code (ANSI C2).

136

(c) Clearance from Building Openings. See Section 230-9.

Minimum service-drop, drip loop, or service-entrance conductor clearances of 8 ft over flat or easily walked-upon roofs, and 10 ft above grade or any platform, and 3 ft from any window, porch or fire escape are considered to be out of the normal reach of people. See Figures 230-5, 230-6, and 230-8. See also Section 230-9, second paragraph.

(d) Clearance from Swimming Pools. See Section 680-8.

230-26. Point of Attachment. The point of attachment of the service-drop conductors to a building or other structure shall provide the minimum clearances as specified in Section 230-24. In no case shall this point of attachment be less than 10 feet (3.05 m) above finished grade.

230-27. Means of Attachment. Multiconductor cables used for service drops shall be attached to buildings or other structures by fittings identified for use with service conductors. Open conductors shall be attached to fittings identified for use with service conductors or to noncombustible, nonabsorbent insulators securely attached to the building or other structure.

See Section 230-51 for mounting and supporting of service cables or individual open service conductors and Section 230-54 for connections at service heads.

230-28. Service Masts as Supports. Where a service mast is used for the support of service-drop conductors, it shall be of adequate strength or be supported by braces or guys to withstand safely the strain imposed by the service drop. Where raceway-type service masts are used, all raceway fittings shall be identified for use with service masts.

See Figure 230-6.

230-29. Supports Over Buildings. Service-drop conductors passing over a roof shall be securely supported by substantial structures. Where practicable, such supports shall be independent of the building.

C. Underground Service-Lateral Conductors

230-30. Insulation. Service-lateral conductors shall withstand exposure to atmospheric and other conditions of use without detrimental leakage of current. Service-lateral conductors shall be insulated for the applied voltage.

Exception: A grounded conductor shall be permitted to be uninsulated as follows:

a. Bare copper used in a raceway.

b. Bare copper for direct burial where bare copper is judged to be suitable for the soil conditions.

c. Bare copper for direct burial without regard to soil conditions where part of a cable assembly identified for underground use.

d. Aluminum or copper-clad aluminum without individual insulation or covering where part of a cable assembly identified for underground use in a raceway or for direct burial.

See Figure 230-9.

a.Bare copper,raceway

b.Bare copper direct
buried, suitable for
soil conditions.

c. and d. Bare copper or
aluminum,part of an identified
cable assembly.

Figure 230-9. Various applications of bare grounded service-lateral and service-entrance conductors for underground locations. Aluminum or copper-clad aluminum conductors must be insulated where run in a raceway or direct-buried, unless they are part of a cable assembly identified for the use. (See Notes 3 and 5 to Tables 310-16 through 310-31, also.)

230-31. Size and Rating.

(a) General. Service-lateral conductors shall have sufficient ampacity to carry the current for the load as computed in accordance with Article 220 and shall have adequate mechanical strength.

(b) Minimum Size. The conductors shall not be smaller than No. 8 copper or No. 6 aluminum or copper-clad aluminum.

Exception: For installations to supply only limited loads of a single branch circuit such as small polyphase power, controlled water heaters and the like, they shall not be smaller than No. 12 copper or No. 10 aluminum or copper-clad aluminum.

(c) Grounded Conductors. The grounded (neutral) conductor shall not be less than the minimum size required by Section 250-23(b).

(FPN): Reasonable efficiency of operation can be provided when voltage drop is taken into consideration in sizing the service-lateral conductors.

See Section 215-2(b), second fine print note and commentary.

230-32. Protection Against Damage.
Underground service-lateral conductors shall be protected against damage in accordance with Section 300-5. Service-lateral conductors entering a building shall be installed in accordance with Section 230-6 or protected by a raceway wiring method identified in Section 230-43.

D. Service-Entrance Conductors

230-40. Number of Service-Entrance Conductor Sets.
Each service drop or lateral shall supply only one set of service-entrance conductors.

Exception No. 1: Buildings with more than one occupancy shall be permitted to have one set of service-entrance conductors run to each occupancy or to a group of occupancies.

Exception No. 2: Where two to six service disconnecting means in separate enclosures are grouped at one location and supply separate loads from one service drop or lateral, one set of service-entrance conductors shall be permitted to supply each or several such service equipment enclosures.

See Figures 230-2 and 230-14.

230-41. Insulation of Service-Entrance Conductors.
Service-entrance conductors shall normally withstand exposure to atmospheric and other conditions of use without detrimental leakage

of current. Service-entrance conductors entering or on the exterior of buildings or other structures shall be insulated.

Exception: A grounded conductor shall be permitted to be uninsulated as follows:

a. Bare copper used in a raceway or part of a service cable assembly.

b. Bare copper for direct burial where bare copper is judged to be suitable for the soil conditions.

c. Bare copper for direct burial without regard to soil conditions when part of a cable assembly identified for underground use.

d. Aluminum or copper-clad aluminum without individual insulation or covering when part of a cable assembly or identified for underground use in a raceway or for direct burial.

See Figure 230-9. For service-entrance conductors a grounded bare copper conductor is also permitted in a service cable assembly.

230-42. Size and Rating.

(a) General. Service-entrance conductors shall be of sufficient size to carry the loads as computed in Article 220. Ampacity shall be determined from Tables 310-16 through 310-31 and all applicable notes to these tables.

(b) Ungrounded Conductors. Ungrounded conductors shall have an ampacity of not less than:

(1) 100 ampere for a 3-wire service to a one-family dwelling with six or more 2-wire branch circuits.

(2) 100 ampere for a 3-wire service to a one-family dwelling with an initial net computed load of 10 kVA or more.

This section requires that only the ungrounded (hot) conductors be sized to conform with Sections 230-42(b)(1) and 230-42(b)(2), and permits, in most cases, a smaller neutral conductor in accordance with Section 220-22.

Section 220-22 requires that the feeder neutral load be the maximum unbalance of the load determined by Article 220. If the service to a building is a single-phase, three-wire, 120/240-volt circuit, and there are no 240-volt loads, the maximum current in the neutral would be the same as the maximum current in the ungrounded conductor when all loads on one leg are "on" and all on the other are "off." Therefore, the service neutral would be sized the same as the ungrounded conductors. See Note 3 to Tables 310-16 through 310-31.

(3) 60 amperes for other loads.

See Figure 230-10.

Exception No. 1: For loads consisting of not more than two 2-wire branch circuits, No. 8 copper or No. 6 aluminum or copper-clad aluminum.

Exception No. 2: By special permission, for loads limited by demand or by the source of supply, No. 8 copper or No. 6 aluminum or copper-clad aluminum.

Exception No. 3: For limited loads of a single branch circuit, No. 12 copper or No. 10 aluminum or copper-clad aluminum, but in no case smaller than the branch-circuit conductors.

(c) Grounded Conductors. The grounded (neutral) conductor shall not be less than the minimum size as required by Section 250-23(b).

6 or more 2-wire branch circuits   10 kVA load   other loads

Figure 230-10. Ungrounded service-entrance conductors are required to have an ampacity of at least 100 A for a 3-wire service to a one-family dwelling if it has six or more 2-wire branch circuits or a computed load of 10 kVA or more. Sixty (60) A would be permissible for a one-family dwelling or other occupancy with four branch circuits and a computed load of less than 10 kVA.

230-43. Wiring Methods for 600 Volts, Nominal, or Less. Service-entrance conductors shall be installed in accordance with the applicable requirements of this Code covering the type of wiring method used and limited to the following methods: (1) open wiring on insulators; (2) rigid metal conduit; (3) intermediate metal conduit; (4) electrical metallic tubing; (5) service-entrance cables; (6) wireways; (7) busways; (8) auxiliary gutters; (9) rigid nonmetallic conduit; (10) cablebus; (11) Type MC cable; (12) mineral-insulated, metal-sheathed cable; or (13) flexible metal conduit not over 6 feet (1.83 m) long between raceways, or between raceway and service equipment, with equipment bonding jumper installed around the flexible metal conduit according to provisions of Section 250-79(a), (b), (c), and (e). Also see Section 350-2.

Section 350-2(1) prohibits flexible metal conduit (Item 13 above) in wet locations unless the conditions itemized in Section 350-2(1) are met.

Approved cable tray systems shall be permitted to support cables approved for use as service-entrance conductors. See Article 318.

230-46. Unspliced Conductors. Service-entrance conductors shall not be spliced.

Exception No. 1: Clamped or bolted connections in metering equipment enclosures shall be permitted.

Exception No. 2: Where service-entrance conductors are tapped to supply two to six disconnecting means grouped at a common location.

Exception No. 3: At a properly enclosed junction point where an underground wiring method is changed to another type of wiring method.

Where a building has a basement, an underground service raceway usually terminates at a terminal box. At this point, service conductors may be spliced or run directly to the service equipment. Splices are permitted where, for example, conduit enters a terminal box and a different wiring method, such as service cable, continues to the service equipment. See Section 230-43 for wiring methods for service conductors for 600 V, nominal, or less.

Exception No. 4: A connection shall be permitted where service conductors are extended from a service drop to an outside meter location and returned to connect to the service-entrance conductors of an existing installation.

Splices may be necessary where metering equipment is located on the line side of service equipment. See Figure 230-11.

Figure 230-11. Time clock and control switch integral to a meter for use, generally, with water heaters.

Exception No. 5: When the service-entrance conductors consist of busway, connections shall be permitted as required to assemble the various sections and fittings.

Exception No. 5 permits splicing (connecting) busway to facilitate the necessary splices required to connect the various components of a busway service-entrance system together.

230-49. Protection Against Physical Damage — Underground. Underground service-entrance conductors shall be protected against physical damage in accordance with Section 300-5.

230-50. Protection of Open Conductors and Cables Against Damage — Aboveground. Service-entrance conductors installed aboveground shall be protected against physical damage as specified in (a) or (b) below.

(a) Service-Entrance Cables. Service-entrance cables, where subject to physical damage, such as where installed in exposed places near driveways or coal chutes, or where subject to contact with awnings, shutters, swinging signs, or similar objects, shall be protected in any of the following ways: (1) by rigid metal conduit; (2) by intermediate metal conduit; (3) by rigid nonmetallic conduit suitable for the location; (4) by electrical metallic tubing; or (5) by other approved means.

(b) Other than Service-Entrance Cable. Individual open conductors and cables other than service-entrance cables shall not be installed within 10 feet (3.05 m) of grade level or where exposed to physical damage.

230-51. Mounting Supports. Cables or individual open service conductors shall be supported as specified in (a), (b), or (c) below.

(a) Service-Entrance Cables. Service-entrance cables shall be supported by straps or other approved means within 12 inches (305 mm) of every service head, gooseneck, or connection to a raceway or enclosure and at intervals not exceeding 30 inches (762 mm).

141

ARTICLE 230—SERVICES

The 30-in. spacing requirement represents a considerable change from the 4 ½-ft rule in the 1984 *NEC*.

(b) Other Cables. Cables that are not approved for mounting in contact with a building or other structure shall be mounted on insulating supports installed at intervals not exceeding 15 feet (4.57 m) and in a manner that will maintain a clearance of not less than 2 inches (50.8 mm) from the surface over which they pass.

(c) Individual Open Conductors. Individual open conductors shall be installed in accordance with Table 230-51(c). Where exposed to the weather, the conductors shall be mounted on insulators or on insulating supports attached to racks, brackets, or other approved means. Where not exposed to the weather, the conductors shall be mounted on glass or porcelain knobs.

Table 230-51(c). Supports and Clearances for Individual Open Service Conductors

Maximum Volts	Maximum Distance In Feet Between Supports	Minimum Clearances In Inches	
		Between Conductors	From Surface
600	9	6	2
600	15	12	2
300	4½	3	2
600*	4½*	2½*	1*

For SI units: one inch = 25.4 millimeters; one foot = 0.3048 meter.
*Where not exposed to weather.

230-52. Individual Conductors Entering Buildings or Other Structures. Where individual open conductors enter a building or other structure, they shall enter through roof bushings or through the wall in an upward slant through individual, noncombustible, nonabsorbent insulating tubes. Drip loops shall be formed on the conductors before they enter the tubes.

230-53. Raceways to Drain. Where exposed to the weather, raceways enclosing service-entrance conductors shall be raintight and arranged to drain. Where embedded in masonry, raceways shall be arranged to drain.

Service raceways exposed to the weather are required to have raintight fittings and drainholes. During installation of raceways in masonry, it is nearly impossible to prevent the entrance of surface water, rain, or water from poured concrete.

230-54. Connections at Service Head.

(a) Raintight Service Head. Service raceways shall be equipped with a raintight service head at the point of connection to service-drop conductors.

(b) Service Cable Equipped with Raintight Service Head or Gooseneck. Service cables, either (1) unless continuous from pole to service equipment or meter, shall be equipped with a raintight service head, or (2) formed in a gooseneck and taped and painted or taped with a self-sealing, weather-resistant thermoplastic.

(c) Service Heads Above Service-Drop Attachment. Service heads and goosenecks in service-entrance cables shall be located above the point of attachment of the service-drop conductors to the building or other structure.

Exception: Where it is impracticable to locate the service head above the point of attachment, the service head location shall be permitted not farther than 24 inches (610 mm) from the point of attachment.

(d) Secured. Service cables shall be held securely in place.

(e) Opposite Polarity Through Separately Bushed Holes. Service heads shall have conductors of opposite polarity brought out through separately bushed holes.

(f) Drip Loops. Drip loops shall be formed on individual conductors. To prevent the entrance of moisture, service-entrance conductors shall be connected to the service-drop conductors either (1) below the level of the service head, or (2) below the level of the termination of the service-entrance cable sheath.

(g) Arranged that Water Will Not Enter Service Raceway or Equipment. Service-drop conductors and service-entrance conductors shall be arranged so that water will not enter service raceway or equipment.

Many areas throughout the country require that service raceways and service cables be equipped with a raintight service (weather) head. Type SE service-entrance cables, however, may be run continuous from a utility pole to metering or service equipment or, where shaped in a downward direction or "gooseneck" and sealed by taping and painting, may be installed without a service head. See Figure 230-12.

Wherever practical, service heads and goosenecks are required to be located above the service-drop attachment. Individual conductors should extend in a downward direction, as shown in Figure 230-12, or drip loops are required to be formed.

Figure 230-12. A service-entrance cable that terminates in a "gooseneck" without a raintight service weather head.

230-55. Termination at Service Equipment. Any service raceway or cable shall terminate at the inner end in a box, cabinet, or equivalent fitting that effectively encloses all live metal parts.

Exception: Where the service disconnecting means is mounted on a switchboard having exposed busbars on the back, a raceway shall be permitted to terminate at a bushing.

230-56. Service-Entrance Conductor with the Higher Voltage-to-Ground. On a 4-wire delta-connected service where the midpoint of one phase is grounded, the service-entrance conductor having the higher phase voltage-to-ground shall be durably and permanently marked by an outer finish that is orange in color or by other effective means.

Proper service connections cannot be made without durably marking the service conductor having the higher voltage-to-ground by an outer finish of orange, by tagging, etc. Marking should be both at the point of connection to the service-entrance conductors and the point of connection to the service disconnect. See Figure 215-2. See Sections 215-8 and 384-3(e) and (f).

E. Service Equipment — General

230-62. Service Equipment — Enclosed or Guarded. Live parts of service equipment shall be enclosed as specified in (a) below, or guarded as specified in (b) below.

(a) Enclosed. Live parts shall be enclosed so that they will not be exposed to accidental contact or guarded as in (b) below.

(b) Guarded. Live parts that are not enclosed shall be installed on a switchboard, panelboard, or control board and guarded in accordance with Sections 110-17 and 110-18. Such an enclosure shall be provided with means for locking or sealing doors giving access to live parts.

230-63. Grounding and Bonding. Service equipment, raceways, cable armor, cable sheaths, etc., and any service conductor that is to be grounded shall be grounded in accordance with the following parts of Article 250.

Part B.   Circuit and System Grounding.
Part C.   Location of System Grounding Connections.
Part D.   Enclosure Grounding.
Part F.   Methods of Grounding.
Part G.   Bonding.
Part H.   Grounding Electrode Systems.
Part J.   Grounding Conductors.

230-64. Working Space. Sufficient working space shall be provided in the vicinity of the service equipment to permit safe operation, inspection, and repairs. In no case shall this be less than that specified by Section 110-16.

230-65. Available Short-Circuit Current. Service equipment shall be suitable for the short-circuit current available at its supply terminals.

See commentary, Section 110-9.

F. Service Equipment — Disconnecting Means

230-70. General. Means shall be provided to disconnect all conductors in a building or other structure from the service-entrance conductors.

(a) Location. The service disconnecting means shall be installed either inside or outside of a building or other structure at a readily accessible location nearest the point of entrance of the service conductors.

No maximum distance or footage is specified from the point of entrance of service conductors to a readily accessible location for the installation of a service disconnecting means. The authority enforcing this *Code* has the responsibility and is charged with making interpretations related to specific individual installations. The length of service-entrance conductors should be kept to a minimum inside buildings since power utilities provide limited overcurrent protection and, in the event of a "fault," the service conductors could ignite nearby combustible materials.

Some local jurisdictions have written rules giving details on distances the service-entrance conductors can be run inside a building. The authority having jurisdiction may permit service conductors to bypass coal bins, oil barrels, or gas meters, etc., permitting the service disconnecting means to be located in a readily accessible location. However, if the authority judges the distance as being excessive, the disconnecting means may be required to be located outside, according to this section. See also Section 230-6 and Figure 230-4 for conductors considered to be outside of a building.

See Section 380-8(a) for mounting height restrictions for switches and circuit breakers used as switches.

(b) Marking. Each service disconnecting means shall be permanently marked to identify it as a service disconnecting means.

(c) Suitable For Use. Each service disconnecting means shall be suitable for the prevailing conditions. Service equipment installed in hazardous (classified) locations shall comply with the requirements of Articles 500 through 517.

230-71. Maximum Number of Disconnects.

(a) General. The service disconnecting means for each service permitted by Section 230-2, or for each set of service-entrance conductors permitted by Section 230-40, Exception No. 1, shall consist of not more than six switches or six circuit breakers mounted in a single enclosure, in a group of separate enclosures, or in or on a switchboard. There shall be no more than six disconnects per service grouped in any one location.

One set of service-entrance conductors, either overhead or underground, is permitted to supply two to six service disconnecting means in lieu of a single main disconnect. A single-occupancy or multiple-occupancy building (either residential or other than residential) may have one main service disconnect or up to six main disconnects supplying separate loads.

An installation where the main service disconnecting means is rated 1200 A, 480 Y/277-V (see Section 230-95) would require ground-fault protection of equipment. However, this same installation with two service disconnects rated at 600 A each, three service disconnects rated at 400 A each, or six rated at 200 A each would not require ground-fault protection.

Where two to six sets of fuses or circuit breakers are used, the total rating of the multiple overcurrent devices is not required to match the ampacities of the service-entrance conductors. The combined ratings of all switches or circuit breakers are required to be not less than the rating required for a single overcurrent device and may exceed the ampacity of the service-entrance conductors. See Figure 230-13.

See Section 230-2, Exception No. 7 for (underground) sets of service lateral conductors.

Exception: For the purpose of this section, disconnecting means used solely for the control circuit of the ground-fault protection system, installed as part of the listed equipment, shall not be considered a service disconnecting means.

This exception makes it clear that the disconnect for the control circuit of a ground-fault protector is not one of the one to six service disconnects.

(b) Single-Pole Units. Two or three single-pole switches or breakers, capable of individual operation, shall be permitted on multiwire circuits, one pole for each ungrounded conductor, as one multipole disconnect provided they are equipped with "handle ties" or a "master handle" to disconnect all conductors of the service with no more than six operations of the hand.

(FPN): See Section 384-16(a) for service equipment in panelboards.

230-72. Grouping of Disconnects.

(a) General. The two to six disconnects as permitted in Section 230-71 shall be grouped. Each disconnect shall be marked to indicate the load served.

Exception: One of the two to six service disconnecting means permitted in Section 230-71, when used only for a water pump also intended to provide fire protection, shall be permitted to be located remote from the other disconnecting means.

145

Figure 230-13. An enclosure for grouping service equipment, consisting of six circuit breakers or six fused-switches. This arrangement does not require a main switch. Six separate enclosures would also be permitted as the service equipment. (*Anchor Electric*)

(b) Additional Service Disconnecting Means. The one or more additional service disconnecting means for fire pumps or for emergency, legally required standby, or optional standby services permitted by Section 230-2 shall be installed sufficiently remote from the one to six service disconnecting means for normal service to minimize the possibility of simultaneous interruption of supply.

The intent of Section 230-2, Exception Nos. 1 and 2, is to permit separate services where necessary for fire pumps (with one to six disconnects) or emergency, legally required standby, or optional standby systems (with one to six disconnects) in addition to the one to six disconnects for the normal building service. Article 230 recognizes that a disruption of the normal building service should not disconnect the fire pump, emergency, or other systems exempted.

(FPN): See Section 700-12(d) and (e) for emergency system services.

(c) Access to Occupants. In a multiple-occupancy building, each occupant shall have access to the occupant's service disconnecting means.

Exception: In a multiple-occupancy building where electric service and electrical maintenance are provided by the building management and where these are under continuous building management supervision, the

Figure 230-14. Either of the above arrangements is permitted by Section 230-71(a) and Section 230-40, Exception No. 2. Meters are usually required by the serving utility to be on the line side of the disconnects; however the *NEC* does not require that meters be provided.

service disconnecting means supplying more than one occupancy shall be permitted to be accessible to authorized management personnel only.

A multiple-occupancy building is a building that may have any number of dwelling units, offices, and the like, that are independent of each other. Unless electric service and maintenance are provided by and under continuous supervision of the building management, each occupant is to have access to his or her disconnecting means. See Section 240-24(b).

Multiple-occupancy buildings may have service-entrance conductors run to each occupancy and each such set of service-entrance conductors may have from one to six disconnects. See Section 230-40, Exception No. 1 and Section 230-71(a).

Where service-entrance conductors are run to each occupancy or to a location where they will serve several occupancies, the service-entrance conductors are required to be installed outside of the building or are required to be encased in at least 2 in. of concrete or equal (see Section 230-6 and Figure 230-4). See also Figure 310-4.

230-74. Simultaneous Opening of Poles. Each service disconnecting means shall simultaneously disconnect all ungrounded service conductors from the premises wiring system.

230-75. Disconnection of Grounded Conductor. Where the service disconnecting means does not disconnect the grounded conductor from the premises wiring, other means shall be provided for this purpose in the service equipment. A terminal or bus to which all grounded conductors can be attached by means of pressure connectors shall be permitted for this purpose.

Provisions are required to be provided at the service equipment for disconnecting the grounded conductor from the premises wiring. This disconnection need

147

not be by operation of the service disconnecting means. Disconnection can be, and most commonly is, accomplished by "manually" removing it from the bus or terminal bar to which it is lugged or bolted. This is often referred to as the "neutral disconnect link."

Manufacturers design neutral terminal bars for service equipment so that grounded conductors must be cut to be attached, that is, the grounded conductor cannot be run straight through the service equipment without means of disconnection from the premises wiring.

230-76. Manually or Power Operable. The service disconnecting means for ungrounded service conductors shall consist of either (1) a manually operable switch or circuit breaker equipped with a handle or other suitable operating means, or (2) a power-operated switch or circuit breaker provided the switch or circuit breaker can be opened by hand in the event of a power supply failure.

230-77. Indicating. The service disconnecting means shall plainly indicate whether it is in the open or closed position.

230-78. Externally Operable. An enclosed service disconnecting means shall be externally operable without exposing the operator to contact with live parts.

Exception: A power-operated switch or circuit breaker shall not be required to be externally operable by hand to a closed position.

A service disconnecting means must be capable of being operated to the "on" or "off" position without exposing unqualified persons to live parts. See Article 100 for definition of "dead front."

230-79. Rating of Disconnect. The service disconnecting means shall have a rating not less than the load to be carried, determined in accordance with Article 220. In no case shall the rating be lower than specified in (a), (b), (c), or (d) below.

(a) One-Circuit Installation. For installations to supply only limited loads of a single branch circuit, the service disconnecting means shall have a rating of not less than 15 amperes.

(b) Two-Circuit Installations. For installations consisting of not more than two 2-wire branch circuits, the service disconnecting means shall have a rating of not less than 30 amperes.

(c) One-Family Dwelling. For a one-family dwelling, the service disconnecting means shall have a rating of not less than 100 amperes, 3-wire under either of the following conditions: (1) where the initial computed load is 10 kVA or more, or (2) where the initial installation consists of six or more 2-wire branch circuits.

A service disconnecting means is required to have a rating of not less than the load to be carried. See Example 2(a) in Chapter 9 and Figure 230-10.

(d) All Others. For all other installations the service disconnecting means shall have a rating of not less than 60 amperes.

230-80. Combined Rating of Disconnects. Where the service disconnecting means consists of more than one switch or circuit breaker, as permitted by Section 230-71, the combined ratings of all the switches or circuit breakers used shall not be less than the rating required for a single switch or circuit breaker.

Section 230-71(a) permits up to six individual switches or circuit breakers, mounted in a single enclosure or in a group of separate enclosures or in or on a switchboard, to serve as the required service disconnecting means at any one location. Section 230-80 refers to where more than one switch or circuit breaker is used and indicates that the combined rating of all the switches or circuit breakers used shall not be less than the rating required for a single switch or circuit breaker. Section 230-90 requires that overcurrent protection be provided in each ungrounded service conductor. This overcurrent protection must have a rating or setting not higher than the allowable ampacity of the service conductors. Exception No. 3 to Section 230-90(a) allows not more than six circuit breakers or six sets of fuses to be considered as the overcurrent device. None of these individual overcurrent devices can have a rating or setting higher than the ampacity of the service conductors.

In complying with these rules, it is possible for the total of the six overcurrent devices to be larger than the rating of the service-entrance conductors. However, the size of the service-entrance conductors is required to be adequate for the connected load and each individual service disconnecting means is required to be large enough for the individual loads supplied. See Figure 230-17 and commentary following Section 230-90(a), Exception No. 3.

230-81. Connection to Terminals. The service conductors shall be connected to the service disconnecting means by pressure connectors, clamps, or other approved means. Connections that depend upon solder shall not be used.

230-82. Equipment Connected to the Supply Side of Service Disconnect. Equipment shall not be connected to the supply side of the service disconnecting means.

Exception No. 1: Cable limiters or other current-limiting devices.

Section 230-91 does not permit service overcurrent devices to be located at the point of connection to the service drop or service lateral where joined to the service-entrance conductors. The requirement is that the overcurrent device be an integral part of the service disconnecting means. See Figures 230-13 and 230-14. The safest practice is to disconnect the service before replacing an overcurrent device.

Exception No. 2: Fuses and disconnecting means or circuit breakers suitable for use as service equipment, in meter pedestals or otherwise provided and connected in series with the ungrounded service conductors and located away from the building supplied.

Exception No. 3: Meters nominally rated not in excess of 600 volts, provided all metal housings and service enclosures are grounded in accordance with Article 250.

Exception No. 4: Instrument transformers (current and voltage), high-impedance shunts, surge-protective devices identified for use on the supply side of the service disconnect, load management devices, and surge arresters.

Exception No. 5: Taps used only to supply load management devices, circuits for emergency systems, stand-by power systems, fire pump equipment, and fire and sprinkler alarms if provided with service equipment and installed in accordance with requirements for service-entrance conductors.

Systems such as emergency lighting, fire alarms, fire pumps, stand-by power, and sprinkler alarms are permitted to be connected ahead of the normal service disconnecting means only where such systems are provided with a separate disconnecting means and overcurrent protection. See Section 700-12(e).

Exception No. 6: Interconnected electric power production sources. See Article 690.

See also Article 705.

149

Exception No. 7: Where the service disconnecting means is power operable, the control circuit shall be permitted to be connected ahead of the service disconnecting means if suitable overcurrent protection and disconnecting means are provided.

Exception No. 8: Ground-fault protection systems where installed as part of listed equipment, if suitable overcurrent protection and disconnecting means are provided.

230-83. Transfer Equipment. Transfer equipment shall operate such that all ungrounded conductors of one source of supply are disconnected before any ungrounded conductors of the second source are connected.

Exception No. 1: Where manual equipment identified for the purpose, or suitable automatic equipment is utilized, two or more sources shall be permitted to be connected in parallel through transfer equipment.

Suitable transfer equipment is required to assure that successful shifting of loads from normal power to emergency power will occur without back-feeding into utility power lines.

Exception No. 2: Where parallel operation is used and suitable automatic or manual control equipment is provided.

See Article 705.

230-84. More than One Building or Other Structure.

(a) Disconnect Required for Each. Where more than one building or other structure is on the same property and under single management, each building or other structure served shall be provided with means for disconnecting all ungrounded conductors.
Location shall be in accordance with Section 230-70.

Exception No. 1: For large capacity multibuilding industrial installations under single management, where it is assured that the disconnecting can be accomplished by establishing and maintaining safe switching procedures, the disconnecting means shall be permitted to be located elsewhere on the premises. See Section 230-91(b).

Exception No. 2: Buildings or other structures qualifying under the provisions of Article 685.

(b) Suitable for Service Equipment. The disconnecting means specified in (a) above shall be suitable for use as service equipment.

Exception: For garages and outbuildings on residential property, a snap switch or a set of 3-way or 4-way snap switches suitable for use on branch circuits shall be permitted as the disconnecting means.

Section 230-70 provides for the service equipment disconnecting means, specifying its location, marking, and suitability for use under the prevailing conditions.
Exception No. 1 is applicable to industrial installations. The reference to Section 230-91(b) clarifies that ungrounded conductors, where run to each building, are required to be provided with overcurrent protection.
Exception No. 2 correlates with Article 685, allowing for a safe and orderly shutdown.
The requirements for applying the rule of a disconnect for each building, for two buildings under single management, and for three buildings under single management are shown in Figures 230-15 and 230-16. The garage circuits for a detached garage supplied from a dwelling unit are required to be controlled by a switch. This is normally done by either single-pole or 3-way snap switches. All farm

buildings are required to be provided with a disconnecting means to disconnect the wiring in each building.

Figure 230-15. A switch (S) is required in Building No. 2.

Figure 230-16. Switches are required in Buildings Nos. 2 and 3.

Figures 230-15 and 230-16 show permissible arrangements. Other arrangements are also permitted if disconnecting means are provided where required. For example, separate sets of service-entrance conductors may be run from the meter in Building No. 1 to the other building(s), or the service-entrance conductors may be run from the service drop or lateral directly to the other building, with separate metering. Local serving utility rules should be followed with regard to number and location of meters.

G. Service Equipment — Overcurrent Protection

230-90. Where Required. Each ungrounded service conductor shall have overload protection.

Service-entrance conductors, overhead or underground, are the supply conductors from the point of connection of service drop or service lateral conductors to the service equipment. Service equipment is intended to constitute the main control and means of cutoff of the supply to the premises wiring system. At this point an overcurrent device, which usually consists of circuit breakers or a set of fuses, is required to be installed in series with each ungrounded service conductor. This will protect "loadside" conductors and will open under an overload condition on service-entrance conductors, thus protecting the conductors against overload conditions.

The service overcurrent device will not protect the service conductors under conditions of short circuit or ground fault on the line side of the disconnect. A degree of protection under these overcurrent conditions is provided by the special requirements for service conductor physical protection and location.

151

(a) Ungrounded Conductor. Such protection shall be provided by an overcurrent device in series with each ungrounded service conductor having a rating or setting not higher than the allowable ampacity of the conductor.

Exception No. 1: For motor-starting currents, ratings in conformity with Sections 430-52, 430-62, and 430-63 shall be permitted.

Where a service supplies a motor load as well as lighting or a lighting and appliance load, the overcurrent protective device is required to have a rating sufficient for the lighting and/or appliance load as determined in accordance with Articles 210 and 220 plus, for an individual motor, the rating permitted by Section 430-52 and, for two or more motors, the rating permitted by Section 430-62.

Example: A service consisting of a 100-A, lighting and appliance load, one 25-hp squirrel cage induction motor (full-voltage starting, service factor 1.15, Code letter F), and two 30-hp wound rotor induction motors (40°C rise) on a 240-V, 3-phase system is to have the service conductors and service disconnecting means calculated as follows:

Conductor Loads

The full-load current of the 25-hp motor is 68 A (Table 430-150). The full-load current of the 30-hp motor is 80 A (Table 430-150). The service-entrance conductors are calculated at 125 percent of 80 A (100 A), plus 80 A, plus 68 A, for a total of 248 A (Section 430-24).

248-A motors
100-A lighting and appliance
Total   348 A

Therefore, the service-entrance conductors would have to be, for example, 500 MCM Type THW copper or 700 MCM Type THW aluminum or copper-clad aluminum conductors (Table 310-16).

Overcurrent Protection

The maximum rating of the service overcurrent protective device is based on the sum of the largest branch-circuit overcurrent device [300 percent for the 25-hp motor using a nontime delay fuse (Table 430-152) = 68 × 3 = 204 A, therefore the next larger size 225 A] plus the sum of the full-load currents of the other motors plus the lighting and appliance load (see Section 430-63).

225-A 25-hp motor
80-A 30-hp motor
80-A 30-hp motor
100-A lighting and appliance load
Total   485 A

The nearest standard fuse that does not exceed this total value is 450 A. See Section 240-6.

Exception No. 2: Fuses and circuit breakers with a rating or setting in conformity with Section 240-3, Exception No. 1, and Section 240-6.

Exception No. 3: Not more than six circuit breakers or six sets of fuses shall be considered as the overcurrent device.

Circuit-breaker or fuse-ampere ratings are not permitted to be greater than the ampacity of the service conductor (except for motor-starting currents), unless such conductor rating does not correspond to the standard ampere rating of a circuit breaker or fuse, whereupon the next larger size circuit breaker or fuse may be used, provided its rating does not exceed 800 A as permitted in Section 240-3, Exception No. 1. See Section 240-6 for standard ampere ratings of fuses and circuit breakers.

Example: The ampacity of a 500 MCM THW copper conductor is 380 A (Table 310-16) and may be protected by a 400-A fuse or circuit breaker. The rating of the fuse or circuit breaker is based on the ampacity of the service conductor and not the rating of the service disconnect switch.

As shown in the example, a 400-A fuse or circuit breaker may be considered as properly sized for the protection of 500 MCM THW copper service conductors. If the service disconnecting means (see Exception No. 3) consists of six circuit breakers or six sets of fuses, the combined ratings must not be less than the rating required for a single switch or circuit breaker in accordance with Section 230-80. See commentary following Section 230-80. Also see Figure 230-17.

In the example shown in Figure 230-17 the combined ratings of the overcurrent devices equals the size of the overcurrent device required by Section 240-3 and Exception No. 1 to this section. However, the combined ratings of the overcurrent devices are not required to be equal to or less than this value. For example, all disconnects could have been rated 100 amperes. See commentary following Section 230-23(a).

Figure 230-17. The combined ratings of the overcurrent devices are permitted to exceed the ampacity of the service conductors.

Exception No. 4: Fire Pumps. Where the service to the fire pump room is judged to be outside of buildings, these provisions shall not apply. Overcurrent protection for fire pump services shall be selected or set to carry locked-rotor current of the motor(s) indefinitely.

(FPN): See NFPA 20-1983 (ANSI), Standard for Centrifugal Fire Pumps.

Section 230-90(a), Exception No. 4, permits service-entrance conductors connected ahead of the main service disconnect for a service to a fire pump room and one permitted to be installed without overload protection for the conductors. Two methods of installation are considered as meeting the intent of this section. They are (1) where the service conductors to the pump room are installed outside the building; or (2) where the conductors are installed under not less than 2 in. of concrete or concealed in a raceway enclosed by concrete or brick not less than 2 in. thick (see Section 230-6 and Figure 230-4) that terminates in a fire-resistant pump room.

Section 430-31 of the *Code* indicates that provisions for motor and branch circuit running overload protection are not to be interpreted as requiring overload protection in cases where it might introduce additional or increased hazards. Fire pump motors are a case in point; they are permitted much larger overcurrent protection than other motors, recognizing that fire pumps should be allowed to operate to failure rather than be removed from the line in order to prolong their usefulness under adverse fire conditions. See Section 230-95(a), Exception No. 2.

Figure 230-18. A typical fire pump installation.

Figure 230-18 is a diagram of the wiring and components of a fire pump circuit designed to comply with requirements of the *NEC* and NFPA 20, Standard for the Installation of Centrifugal Fire Pumps. The pump motor represented is a 100-hp, 460-V, 3-phase, squirrel-cage induction type, and its full-load current, taken from Table 430-150, is 124 A.

The service conductors, feeder conductors, and branch-circuit conductors are sized at 125 percent of the motor full-load current rating (124 A × 125 percent = 155 A). According to Table 310-16, the next closest copper wire size for 155 A is a 2/0 AWG THW conductor with an allowable ampacity of 175 A; therefore, all the conductors would be sized at 2/0 AWG THW copper. (See Sections 430-22 and 430-23 for sizing of conductors.) Other conductors with an ampacity of 155 A or more would also be permitted in this instance.

The locked-rotor current of the motor in the installation illustrated is 744 A, as derived from Table 430-151, and the power supply protection may consist of either fuses or circuit breakers sized so that they will not open at locked-rotor current. In either case, the next standard ampere rating for fuses or circuit breakers is 800 A. (See Section 240-6.) This protection complies with the intent of the requirements of Section 6-3.4 of NFPA 20 and also of Section 430-31 of the *NEC*.

The isolating means in the illustrated pump's controller could be a motor circuit switch rated in horsepower (see Section 430-109) or a suitable nonautomatic circuit interrupter (molded case switch), as required by Section 7-4.1 of NFPA 20.

If a motor circuit switch were used for the isolating means, it would be horsepower rated at 100 hp and have an ampere rating of at least 115 percent of the full-load current rating of the motor, that is, 124 A × 115 percent = 142.6 A, to meet requirements of Section 430-110(a) of the *NEC* and Subsection 7-4.1.2 of NFPA 20.

The circuit breaker used to protect the branch circuit to the squirrel-cage induction motor would be a magnetic trip type having a time delay of not over 20 seconds at locked-rotor current, and it would be calibrated up to and set at 300 percent of the motor's full-load current (see Section 7-4.3 of NFPA 20). In this particular instance it would be calibrated at 372 A (124 A × 300 percent).

Circuit breakers for dc and wound-rotor ac motors for fire pumps are of the instantaneous type, calibrated up to and set at 400 percent of the motor's full-load current. See Section 7-4.3 of NFPA 20.

UL-listed pump controllers are investigated for their ability to meet the requirements of the *NEC* and NFPA 20 for the time-current characteristics of the magnetic circuit breakers to assure the 20-second delay at locked-rotor current and 300 percent or 400 percent trip setting, depending on the type of motor used.

The motor starter (without overload relays) is of a magnetic type with a contact in each ungrounded conductor, in accordance with Section 7-4.4 of NFPA 20.

A set of fuses shall be considered all the fuses required to protect all the ungrounded conductors of a circuit. Single-pole circuit breakers, grouped in accordance with Section 230-71(b), shall be considered as one protective device.

Two or three single-pole switches or circuit breakers on multiwire circuits and capable of individual operation are permitted as one protective device, provided they are equipped with "handle ties" or a "master handle" so that all ungrounded conductors of a service can be disconnected with not more than six operations of the hand. See Section 230-71(b).

(b) Not in Grounded Conductor.   No overcurrent device shall be inserted in a grounded service conductor except a circuit breaker which simultaneously opens all conductors of the circuit.

230-91. Location of Overcurrent Protection.

(a) General.   The service overcurrent device shall be an integral part of the service disconnecting means or shall be located immediately adjacent thereto.

Service overcurrent protective devices (fuses or circuit breakers), where within a building, are required to be located at a readily accessible location nearest to the point of entrance of the service conductors. If there is no readily accessible area, or if the available readily accessible area is not near the point of entrance of the service conductors, and the distance is judged by the authority having jurisdiction to be a potential hazard, the overcurrent devices are permitted to be located outside of the building. See Section 230-70(a) and its following commentary.

(b) More than One Building.   In a property comprising more than one building under single management, the ungrounded conductors supplying each building served shall be protected by overcurrent devices, which may be located in the building served or in another building on the same property, provided they are accessible to the occupants of the building served.

(c) Access to Occupants.   In a multiple-occupancy building each occupant shall have access to the overcurrent protective devices.

Exception: As permitted in Section 240-24(b), Exception.

230-92. Locked Service Overcurrent Devices.   Where the service overcurrent devices are locked or sealed, or otherwise not readily accessible, branch-circuit overcurrent devices shall be installed on the load side, shall be mounted in an accessible location, and shall be of lower rating than the service overcurrent device.

230-93. Protection of Specific Circuits. Where necessary to prevent tampering, an automatic overcurrent device protecting service conductors supplying only a specific load, such as a water heater, shall be permitted to be locked or sealed where located so as to be accessible.

230-94. Relative Location of Overcurrent Device and Other Service Equipment. The overcurrent device shall protect all circuits and devices.

Exception No. 1: The service switch shall be permitted on the supply side.

Exception No. 2: High-impedance shunt circuits, lightning arresters, surge protective capacitors, and instrument transformers (current and voltage) shall be permitted to be connected and installed on the supply side of the service disconnecting means as permitted in Section 230-82.

Exception No. 3: Circuits for emergency supply and load management devices shall be permitted to be connected on the supply side of the service overcurrent device where separately provided with overcurrent protection.

Exception No. 4: Circuits used only for the operation of fire alarm, other protective signaling systems, or the supply to fire pump equipment shall be permitted to be connected on the supply side of the service overcurrent device where separately provided with overcurrent protection.

Exception No. 5: Meters nominally rated not in excess of 600 volts, provided all metal housings and service enclosures are grounded in accordance with Article 250.

Exception No. 6: Where service equipment is power operable, the control circuit shall be permitted to be connected ahead of the service equipment if suitable overcurrent protection and disconnecting means are provided.

230-95. Ground-Fault Protection of Equipment. Ground-fault protection of equipment shall be provided for solidly grounded wye electrical services of more than 150 volts to ground, but not exceeding 600 volts phase-to-phase for each service disconnecting means rated 1000 amperes or more.

See definition of "ground-fault protection of equipment" in Article 100.

The reason for requiring ground-fault protection of equipment on services rated 480Y/277 V was the unusually high number of burndowns that were reported on this type of service. Ground-fault protection of services will not protect the conductors on the supply side of the service disconnecting means but is designed to provide protection from line-to-ground faults that occur on the load side of the service disconnecting means rated 1,000 A or more. An alternative to installing ground-fault protection may be to provide multiple disconnects rated less than 1,000 A. For instance, six 800-A disconnecting means may be used and, in this case, ground-fault protection would not be necessary. The second Fine Print Note in Section 230-95(b) recognizes that ground-fault protection may be desirable at lesser amperages on solidly grounded systems for voltages exceeding 150 V to ground, but not exceeding 600 V phase-to-phase.

In addition to providing ground-fault protection, engineering studies should be made to determine the circuit impedance and the short-circuit currents that would be available at the supply terminals so that equipment and overcurrent protection of the proper interrupting rating is used. See Sections 110-9 and 110-10.

There are two basic types of ground-fault equipment protectors. They are illustrated in Figures 230-19 and 230-20. In Figure 230-19, the ground-fault sensor is installed around all the circuit conductors, and a stray current on a line-to-ground fault will set up an unbalance of the currents flowing in individual conductors installed through the ground-fault sensor. When this current exceeds

Transformer secondary
(480 Y/277 V)

Solidly
grounded

Service equipment
(1000 A or more)

Circuit breaker
with shunt trip

Relay

Insulated
neutral bar

Ground-fault
sensor

Grounding
conductor

Load

Figure 230-19. Ground-fault sensor encircling all circuit conductors, including the neutral.

the setting of the ground-fault sensor, the shunt trip will operate and open the circuit breakers.

The ground-fault sensor illustrated in Figure 230-20 is installed around the bonding jumper only, and when an unbalanced current from a line-to-ground fault occurs, the current will flow through the bonding jumper and the shunt trip will cause the circuit breaker to operate and remove the load from the line. See also Section 250-23(a), Exception No. 5.

The maximum setting is 1,200 A; however, there is no minimum, and it should be noted that setting at lower levels increases the likelihood of unwanted shutdowns. The requirements provide a maximum time delay of 1 second for ground-fault currents equal to or greater than 3,000 A in order to minimize the amount of damage done by an arcing fault, which is directly proportional to the time it is allowed to burn.

Where interconnection is made between multiple supply systems, care should be taken to assure proper ground-fault sensing by the ground-fault protection equipment and, in most cases, a careful engineering study must be made to assure that fault currents do not take parallel paths to ground, causing no trip or unwanted trips (the ground-fault protected system. See Section 705-32.

(a) Setting. The ground-fault protection system shall operate to cause the service disconnecting means to open all ungrounded conductors of the faulted circuit. The maximum setting of the ground-fault protection shall be 1200 amperes and the maximum time delay shall be one second for ground-fault currents equal to or greater than 3000 amperes.

Exception No. 1: The provisions of this section shall not apply to a service disconnecting means for a continuous industrial process where a nonorderly shutdown will introduce additional or increased hazards.

Exception No. 2: The provisions of this section shall not apply to fire pumps.

157

Figure 230-20. Ground-fault sensor encircling the bonding jumper conductor only.

Most fire pumps rated 100 hp and over would require a disconnecting means rated at 1000 A or more. However, due to the emergency nature of their use, fire pumps are exempt from the provisions of Section 230-95.

(b) Fuses. If a switch and fuse combination is used, the fuses employed shall be capable of interrupting any current higher than the interrupting capacity of the switch during a time when the ground-fault protective system will not cause the switch to open.

(FPN): As used in this section, the rating of the Service Disconnecting Means is considered to be the rating of the largest fuse that can be installed or the highest trip setting for which the actual overcurrent device installed in a circuit breaker is rated or can be adjusted.

(FPN): It is recognized that ground-fault protection may be desirable for service disconnecting means rated less than 1000 amperes on solidly grounded wye systems having more than 150 volts to ground, not exceeding 600 volts phase-to-phase.

(FPN): As used in this section, solidly grounded means that the grounded conductor (neutral) is grounded without inserting any resistor or impedance device.

(FPN): Ground-fault protection that functions to open the service disconnecting means will afford no protection from faults on the line side of the protective element. It serves only to limit damage to conductors and equipment on the load side in the event of an arcing ground fault on the load side of the protective element.

(FPN): This added protective equipment at the service equipment will make it necessary to review the overall wiring system for proper selective overcurrent protection coordination. Additional installations of ground-fault protective equipment will be needed on feeders and branch circuits where maximum continuity of electrical service is necessary.

(FPN): Where ground-fault protection is provided for the service disconnecting means and interconnection is made with another supply system by a transfer device, means or devices may be needed to assure proper ground-fault sensing by the ground-fault protection equipment.

(c) Performance Testing. The ground-fault protection system shall be performance tested when first installed on site. The test shall be conducted in accordance with instructions which shall be provided with the equipment. A written record of this test shall be made and shall be available to the authority having jurisdiction.

The requirement for ground-fault protection system "performance testing" is a result of numerous reports of ground-fault protection systems that were improperly wired and that could not or did not perform the function for which they were intended. The *Code* and qualified testing laboratories require a set of performance testing instructions to be supplied with the equipment. Evaluation and listing of the instructions falls under the jurisdiction of those best qualified to make such judgments, the "Qualified Electrical Testing Laboratory." See Section 90-6. If listed equipment is not installed in accordance with the instructions provided, the installation does not comply with Section 110-3(b).

Figure 230-21. Ground-fault protection system. (*Square D Co.*)

H. Services Exceeding 600 Volts, Nominal

230-200. General. Service conductors and equipment used on circuits exceeding 600 volts, nominal, shall comply with all applicable provisions of the preceding sections of this article and with the following sections, which supplement or modify the preceding sections. In no case shall the provisions of this article apply to equipment on the supply side of the service-point.

Service-Point. Service-point is the point of connection between the facilities of the serving utility and the premises' wiring.

(FPN): For clearances of conductors of over 600 volts, nominal, see National Electrical Safety Code (ANSI C2-1984).

230-201. Service Conductors. The conductors from the service-point to the service disconnecting means shall be considered service conductors regardless of whether they are on the primary or secondary side of a step-down transformer.

Section 230-201 has been revised for the 1987 edition of the *Code* to permit the primary (over 600-volt) conductors to be the service conductors, regardless of the location of the step-down transformer. Where the service disconnecting means is in the secondary circuit of the transformer, both the primary conductors (from the service point to the transformer) and the secondary conductors (from the transformer to the service disconnect) would be service conductors, subject to all the requirements for service conductors. See Figure 230-22. Also see Section 450-3 for transformer overcurrent protection requirements.

Where the service disconnect is in the primary circuit, and the secondary is 480Y/277-volt, 3-phase, 4-wire, Section 230-95 is no longer applicable as the 480-volt circuit is not the service (see definition of "Service" in Article 100), and ground-fault protection would not be required. However, the need for ground-fault protection would be the same as it was before Section 230-201 was revised. See Figure 230-23. Also see Section 450-3 for transformer overcurrent protection requirements.

Figure 230-22. Service disconnect in secondary circuit of transformer. Transformer overcurrent protection, if required, not shown.

Figure 230-23. Service disconnect in primary circuit of transformer. Transformer overcurrent protection, if required, not shown.

230-202. Service-Entrance Conductors. Service-entrance conductors to buildings or enclosures shall be installed to conform to the following:

(a) Conductor Size. Service-entrance conductors shall not be smaller than No. 6 unless in cable. Conductors in cable shall not be smaller than No. 8.

(b) Wiring Methods. Service-entrance conductors shall be installed by means of one of the following wiring methods: (1) in rigid metal conduit; (2) in intermediate metal conduit; (3) in rigid nonmetallic conduit; (4) as multiconductor cable identified as service cable; (5) as open conductors where supported on insulators and where either accessible only to qualified persons or where effectively guarded against accidental contact; (6) in cablebus; or (7) in busways.

Underground service-entrance conductors shall conform to Section 710-3(b).

Cable tray systems shall be permitted to support cables identified as service-entrance conductors. See Article 318.

(FPN): See Section 310-6 for shielding of solid dielectric insulated conductors.

(c) Open Work. Open wire services over 600 volts, nominal, shall be installed in accordance with the provisions of Article 710, Part D.

(d) Supports. Service-entrance conductors and their supports, including insulators, shall have strength and stability sufficient to ensure maintenance of adequate clearance with abnormal currents in case of short circuits.

(e) Guarding. Open wires shall be guarded to make them accessible only to qualified persons.

(f) Service Cable. Where cable conductors emerge from a metal sheath or raceway, the insulation of the conductors shall be protected from moisture and physical damage by a pothead or other approved means.

(g) Draining Raceways. Unless conductors identified for use in wet locations are used, raceways embedded in masonry or exposed to the weather shall be arranged to drain.

(h) Over 15,000 Volts. Where the voltage exceeds 15,000 volts between conductors they shall enter either metal-enclosed switchgear or a transformer vault conforming to the requirements of Sections 450-41 through 450-48.

230-203. Warning Signs. Signs with the words "Danger High Voltage Keep Out" shall be posted in plain view where unauthorized persons might come in contact with live parts.

230-204. Isolating Switches.

(a) Where Required. Where oil switches or air or oil circuit breakers constitute the service disconnecting means, an air-break isolating switch shall be installed on the supply side of the disconnecting means and all associated service equipment.

Exception: Where such equipment is mounted on removable truck panels or metal-enclosed switchgear units, which cannot be opened unless the circuit is disconnected, and which, when removed from the normal operating position, automatically disconnect the circuit breaker or switch from all live parts.

(b) Fuses as Isolating Switch. Where fuses are of the type that can be operated as a disconnecting switch, a set of such fuses shall be permitted as the isolating switch where: (1) the oil disconnecting means is a nonautomatic switch, and (2) the set of fuses disconnect the oil switch and all associated service equipment from the service-entrance conductors.

(c) Accessible to Qualified Persons Only. The isolating switch shall be accessible to qualified persons only.

(d) Grounding Connection. Isolating switches shall be provided with a means for readily connecting the load side conductors to ground when disconnected from the source of supply.

A means for grounding the load side conductors need not be provided for any duplicate isolating switch installed and maintained by the electric supply company.

Figure 230-24. A two-position switch grounds load-side conductors when disconnected from high-voltage line buses.

230-205. Disconnecting Means.

(a) Location. The service disconnecting means shall be located in accordance with Section 230-70 or Section 230-208(b).

Exception: Where under single management, the service disconnecting means shall be permitted to be located in a separate building or structure on the same premises. In such case the service disconnecting means shall be capable of being electrically opened by a readily accessible control device located as near as practicable to where the service conductors enter the building served. The control device shall be permanently marked to identify its function and shall provide visual indication of the On or Off status of the remote service disconnect.

(FPN): See Sections 230-3, 230-6, 230-70, 230-71(a) and 230-200.

(b) Type. The service disconnecting means shall simultaneously disconnect all ungrounded conductors and shall be capable of being closed on a fault equal to or greater than the maximum available short-circuit current in the circuit at its supply terminals.

Where fused switches or separately mounted fuses are installed, the fuse characteristics shall be permitted to contribute to the fault-closing rating of the disconnecting means.

230-206. Overcurrent Devices as Disconnecting Means.
Where the circuit breaker or alternative for it specified in Section 230-208 for service overcurrent devices meets the requirements specified in Section 230-205, they shall constitute the service disconnecting means.

230-207. Equipment in Secondaries.
Where the primary service equipment supplies one or more transformers whose secondary windings connect to a common bus of bars or wires, and the primary load-interrupter switch or circuit breaker is capable of being opened and closed from a point outside the transformer vault, the disconnecting means and overcurrent protection shall not be required in the secondary circuit if the primary fuse or circuit breaker is rated or set to protect the secondary circuit.

230-208. Overcurrent Protection Requirements.
Service-entrance conductors shall have a short-circuit protective device in each ungrounded conductor, on the load side of, or as an integral part of, the service-entrance switch. The protective device shall be capable of detecting and interrupting all values of current in excess of its trip setting or melting point, which can occur at its location. A fuse rated in continuous amperes not to exceed three times the ampacity of the conductor, or a circuit breaker with a trip setting of not more than six times the ampacity of the conductors shall be considered as providing the required short-circuit protection.

(FPN): See Tables 310-69 through 310-84 for ampacity of high-voltage conductors.

Figure 230-25. In installations where a transformer supplies a single set of secondary mains, the mains may be connected directly to the buses at the distribution center without a switch or overload protection; however, the primary breaker must be set to protect the secondary circuit.

Overcurrent devices shall conform to the following:

(a) In Vault or Consisting of Metal-Enclosed Switchgear. Where the service equipment is installed in a transformer vault meeting the provisions of Sections 450-41 through 450-48, or consists of metal-enclosed switchgear, the overcurrent protection and disconnecting means shall be one of the following:

(1) A nonautomatic oil switch, oil fuse cutout, or air load-interrupter switch shall be permitted with fuses. The interrupting rating of this switch shall equal or exceed the continuous current rating of the fuse.

(2) An automatic trip circuit breaker of suitable current-carrying and interrupting capacity.

(3) A switch capable of interrupting the no-load current of the transformer supplied through the switch and suitable fuses shall be permitted provided the switch is interlocked with a single switch or circuit breaker on the secondary circuit of the transformer so that the primary switch cannot be opened when the secondary circuit is closed.

(b) Not in Vault or Not Consisting of Metal-Enclosed Switchgear. Where the service equipment is not in a vault or metal-enclosed switchgear, the overcurrent protection and disconnecting means shall be either of the following:

(1) An air load-interrupter switch or other switch capable of interrupting the rated circuit load shall be permitted with fuses on a pole or elevated structure outside the building provided the switch is operable by persons using the building.

(2) An automatic-trip circuit breaker of suitable ampacity and interrupting capacity. The circuit breaker shall be located outside the building as near as practicable to where the service conductors enter the building. The location shall be permitted on a pole, roof, foundation, or other structure.

(c) Fuses. Fuses shall have an interrupting rating no less than the maximum available short-circuit current in the circuit at their supply terminals.

(d) Circuit Breakers. Circuit breakers shall be free to open in case the circuit is closed on an overload. This can be accomplished by means such as trip-free circuit breakers. A service circuit breaker shall indicate clearly whether it is open or closed, and shall have an interrupting rating no less than the maximum available short-circuit current at its supply terminals.

Overcurrent relays shall be furnished in connection with current transformers in one of the following combinations:

(1) Three overcurrent relays operated from current transformers in each phase.

(2) Two overcurrent relays operated by current from current transformers in any two phases and one overcurrent relay sensitive to ground-fault current that is operated by the sum of the currents from current transformers in each phase.

(3) Two overcurrent relays operated by current from current transformers in any two phases and one overcurrent relay sensitive to ground-fault current that is operated from a current transformer which links all three phase conductors and the grounded circuit conductor (neutral), if provided.

(e) Enclosed Overcurrent Devices. The restriction to 80 percent of rating for an enclosed overcurrent device on continuous loads shall not apply to overcurrent devices installed in services operating at over 600 volts.

230-209. Surge Arresters (Lightning Arresters). Surge arresters installed in accordance with the requirements of Article 280 shall be placed on each ungrounded overhead service conductor on the supply side of the service equipment, when called for by the authority having jurisdiction.

230-210. Service Equipment-General Provisions. Service equipment including instrument transformers shall conform to Article 710, Part B.

230-211. Metal-Enclosed Switchgear. Metal-enclosed switchgear shall consist of a substantial metal structure and a sheet metal enclosure. Where installed over a wood floor, suitable protection thereto shall be provided.

Figure 230-26. An assembly of metal-enclosed switchgear. (*Federal Pacific Electric Co.*)

ARTICLE 240 — OVERCURRENT PROTECTION

Contents

ARTICLE 240—OVERCURRENT PROTECTION

240-1. Scope. Parts A through G of this article provide the general requirements for overcurrent protection and overcurrent protective devices not more than 600 volts, nominal. Part H covers overcurrent protection over 600 volts, nominal.

(FPN): Overcurrent protection for conductors and equipment is provided to open the circuit if the current reaches a value that will cause an excessive or dangerous temperature in conductors or conductor insulation. See also Sections 110-9 and 110-10 for requirements for interrupting capacity and protection against fault currents.

A. General

240-2. Protection of Equipment. Equipment shall be protected against overcurrent in accordance with the article in this Code covering the type of equipment as specified in the following list.

	Article
Air-Conditioning and Refrigerating Equipment	440
Appliances	422
Branch Circuits	210
Capacitors	460
Class 1, Class 2, and Class 3 Remote Control, Signaling, and Power-Limited Circuits	725
Closed-Loop and Programmed Power Distribution Systems	780
Cranes and Hoists	610
Electric Signs and Outline Lighting	600
Electric Welders	630
Electrolytic Cells	668
Elevators, Dumbwaiters, Escalators, and Moving Walks	620
Emergency Systems	700
Fire Protective Signaling Systems	760
Fixed Electric Heating Equipment for Pipelines and Vessels	427
Fixed Electric Space Heating Equipment	424
Fixed Outdoor Electric De-icing and Snow-Melting Equipment	426
Generators	445
Induction and Dielectric Heating Equipment	665
Industrial Machinery	670
Motion Picture and Television Studios and Similar Locations	530
Motors, Motor Circuits, and Controllers	430
Organs	650
Over 600 Volts, Nominal—General	710
Places of Assembly	518
Services	230
Solar Photovoltaic Systems	690
Sound-Recording and Similar Equipment	640
Switchboards and Panelboards	384
Theaters and Similar Locations	520
Transformers and Transformer Vaults	450
X-ray Equipment	517
	660

240-3. Protection of Conductors — Other than Flexible Cords and Fixture Wires. Conductors, other than flexible cords and fixture wires, shall be protected against overcurrent in accordance with their ampacities as specified in Tables 310-16 through 310-31 and all applicable notes to these tables.

Exception No. 1: Next Higher Overcurrent Protective Device Rating. Where the ampacity of the conductor does not correspond with the standard ampere rating of a fuse or a circuit breaker without overload trip adjustment above its rating (but which may have other trip or rating adjustments), the next higher standard device rating shall be permitted only if this rating does not exceed 800 amperes and the conductor is not part of a multioutlet branch circuit supplying receptacles for cord- and plug-connected portable loads.

Where the rating exceeds 800 amperes, a lower than standard rated and listed fuse or a circuit breaker without overload trip adjustment above its rating shall be permitted.

Table 210-24 summarizes the requirements for the size of conductors where two or more outlets are required. The first footnote also indicates that these ampacities are for copper conductors where derating is not required. Section 210-3 indicates that branch-circuit conductors rated 15, 20, 30, 40, and 50 A, with two or more outlets, must be protected at their ratings. Section 210-19(a) requires that branch-circuit conductors have an ampacity of not less than the rating of the branch circuit and not less than the maximum load to be served.

These are specific requirements and take precedence over Section 240-3, Exception No. 1 which applies generally. Where the conductor is not part of a multioutlet branch circuit supplying receptacles for cord- and plug-connected portable loads and the conductor ampacities do not correspond to standard ampere ratings of fuses or circuit breakers, the next standard device rating is permitted if this rating does not exceed 800 A.

Exception No. 2: Tap Conductors. Tap conductors as permitted in Sections 210-19(c); 240-21, Exceptions No. 2, 3, 5, 8, 9 and 10; 364-10 and 364-11; and Part D of Article 430.

Exception No. 3: Motor and Motor-Control Circuits. Motor and motor-control circuit conductors protected in accordance with Parts C, D, E, and F of Article 430. Motor-operated appliance circuit conductors protected in accordance with Parts B and D of Article 422. Air-conditioning and refrigerating equipment circuit conductors protected in accordance with Parts C and F of Article 440.

Exception No. 4: Remote Control Circuits. Remote-control circuits shall comply with Article 725.

See Section 725-12 and Exception Nos. 1, 2, and 3.

Exception No. 5: Transformer Secondary Conductors. Conductors supplied by the secondary side of a single-phase transformer having a 2-wire (single-voltage) secondary shall be considered as protected by overcurrent protection provided on the primary (supply) side of the transformer, provided this protection is in accordance with Section 450-3 and does not exceed the value determined by multiplying the secondary conductor ampacity by the secondary-to-primary transformer voltage ratio. Transformer secondary conductors (other than 2 wire) are not considered to be protected by the primary overcurrent protection.

The main rule of Section 240-3 requires that conductors be protected against overcurrent in accordance with their ampacity. Exception No. 5 permits the secondary circuit conductors from a transformer to be protected by overcurrent devices in the primary circuit conductors of the transformer, provided the transformer consists of a 2-wire primary and a 2-wire secondary and is protected in accordance with Section 450-3.

For example, a transformer that has a 2-wire, 480-V primary and a 2-wire, 240-V secondary with overcurrent protection in the primary rated at 50 A is considered to be protection for the secondary circuit conductors whose ampacity is not less than 100 A.

The secondary to primary ratio of the above transformer is 1:2 or 0.5. Multiplying the secondary conductor ampacity by the secondary to primary ratio results in the maximum rating of the overcurrent device permitted in the primary conductors to protect the secondary conductors. Therefore, the length of the secondary conductors is not limited, and no overcurrent protection is required on the secondary side.

If the secondary consists of a 3-wire, 240/120-V system, a line to neutral load (120 V) could draw up to 200 A before the overcurrent device in the primary actuates. This is the result of the 1:4 secondary to primary voltage ratio of the 120-V section of the transformer secondary, thereby causing dangerous overloading of the secondary conductors.

Also, in analyzing the current ratios for a 3-phase transformer, unbalanced loading of the secondary circuit must be considered. Power to a single-phase secondary load will be delivered by all three transformers, but the load is not shared equally. The ratio of the currents in the primary and secondary feeder conductors will not be in accordance with the transformer turns ratio.

Exception No. 6: Capacitor circuits which comply with Article 460.

Exception No. 7: Welders circuits which comply with Article 630.

Exception No. 8: Power Loss Hazard. Conductor overload protection shall not be required where the interruption of the circuit would create a hazard, such as in a material handling magnet circuit. Short-circuit protection shall be provided.

240-4. Protection of Fixture Wires and Cords. Flexible cord, including tinsel cord and extension cords, shall be protected against overcurrent in accordance with their ampacities as specified in Table 400-5. Fixture wire shall be protected against overcurrent in accordance with its ampacity as specified in Table 402-5. Supplementary overcurrent protection as in Section 240-10 shall be permitted to be an acceptable means for providing this protection.

Exception No. 1: When a flexible cord or a tinsel cord approved for and used with a specific listed appliance or portable lamps is connected to a branch circuit of Article 210 in accordance with the following:

20-ampere circuits, tinsel cord or No. 18 cord and larger.

30-ampere circuits, No. 16 cord and larger.

40-ampere circuits, cord of 20-ampere capacity and over.

50-ampere circuits, cord of 20-ampere capacity and over.

Exception No. 2: When fixture wire is connected to 120-volt or higher branch circuit of Article 210 in accordance with the following:

20-ampere circuits, No. 18 up to 50 feet (15.2 m) of run length.

20-ampere circuits, No. 16 up to 100 feet (30.5 m) of run length.

20-ampere circuits, No. 14 and larger.

30-ampere circuits, No. 14 and larger.

40-ampere circuits, No. 12 and larger.

50-ampere circuits, No. 12 and larger.

Exception No. 3: Flexible cord used in listed extension cordsets having No. 16 AWG or larger conductors shall be considered to be protected by 20-ampere branch-circuit overcurrent protection.

Section 240-4 clarifies the requirements for overcurrent protection of flexible cords and fixture wire by referencing Table 400-5 for flexible cords and Table 402-5 for fixture wire ampacity.

Exceptions No. 1 and No. 2 permit smaller conductors to be connected to branch circuits of a greater rating where the smaller conductors are approved for and used with a specific listed appliance, portable lamp, or extension cord, or when fixture wire is protected as listed in the exceptions. Exception No. 3 permits listed cord sets No. 16 AWG or larger to be protected by 20-ampere or less branch-circuit overcurrent devices.

240-6. Standard Ampere Ratings. The standard ampere ratings for fuses and inverse time circuit breakers shall be considered 15, 20, 25, 30, 35, 40, 45, 50, 60, 70, 80, 90, 100, 110, 125, 150, 175, 200, 225, 250, 300, 350, 400, 450, 500, 600, 700, 800, 1000, 1200, 1600, 2000, 2500, 3000, 4000, 5000, and 6000.

Exception: Additional standard ratings for fuses shall be considered 1, 3, 6, 10, and 601.

For the purposes of this article, the rating of an adjustable trip circuit breaker having readily accessible external means for adjusting the trip setting shall be the maximum permissible rating or setting.

240-8. Fuses or Circuit Breakers in Parallel. Fuses, circuit breakers, or combinations thereof shall not be connected in parallel.

Exception: Circuit breakers or fuses, factory assembled in parallel, and approved as a unit.

Section 240-8 prohibits the use of fuses or circuit breakers in parallel, and Section 380-17 prohibits the use of fuses in parallel in fused switches.

It is not the intent of this exception to restore the use of standard fuses in parallel in disconnect switches. However, this exception gives recognition to parallel low-voltage circuit breakers or fuses and parallel high-voltage circuit breakers or fuses where tested and factory-assembled in parallel and approved as a unit.

High-voltage fuses have long been recognized in parallel where assembled in an identified common mounting as per Section 710-21(b)(1).

240-9. Thermal Devices. Thermal cutouts, thermal relays, and other devices not designed to open short circuits shall not be used for the protection of conductors against overcurrent due to short circuits or grounds but the use of such devices shall be permitted to protect motor-branch-circuit conductors from overload if protected in accordance with Section 430-40.

Thermal cutouts are overcurrent protective devices consisting of a heater element that senses overloads on motors or motor branch-circuit conductors and opens the circuit by actuating a renewable fusible member. They are not designed to interrupt short-circuit currents.

240-10. Supplementary Overcurrent Protection. Where supplementary overcurrent protection is used for lighting fixtures, appliances, and other equipment or for internal circuits and components of equipment, it shall not be used as a substitute for branch-circuit overcurrent devices or in place of the branch-circuit protection specified in Article 210. Supplementary overcurrent devices shall not be required to be readily accessible.

240-11. Definition of Current-Limiting Overcurrent Protective Device. A current-limiting overcurrent protective device is a device which, when interrupting currents in its current-limiting range, will reduce the current flowing in the faulted circuit to a magnitude substantially less than that obtainable in the same circuit if the device were replaced with a solid conductor having comparable impedance.

Most electrical distribution systems can deliver large short-circuit currents to components, such as conductors, service equipment, etc. These components are not generally able to handle short-circuit currents; they can be damaged or destroyed and serious "burndowns" and fires could result. Properly selected current-limiting overcurrent protective devices will limit the let-through energy to within the rating of the components in spite of high available short-circuit currents. See Figures 240-1 and 240-2.

ARTICLE 240—OVERCURRENT PROTECTION

See Sections 110-9 and 110-10 for interrupting ratings, circuit impedance, and other characteristics requirements.

Figure 240-1. Class R current-limiting fuse with rejection feature to prohibit the installation of noncurrent-limiting fuses. *(Bussman Mfg. Co.)*

Figure 240-2. Current-limiting circuit breaker within UL Class R fuse levels and former Class K-5 levels. *(Square D Co.)*

240-12. Electrical System Coordination. Where an orderly shutdown is required to minimize hazard(s) to personnel and equipment, a system of coordination based on the following two conditions shall be permitted:

(1) Coordinated short-circuit protection.

(2) Overload indication based on monitoring systems or devices.

(FPN): Coordination is defined as properly localizing a fault condition to restrict outages to the equipment affected, accomplished by choice of selective fault-protective devices. The monitoring system may cause the condition to go to alarm allowing corrective action or an orderly shutdown thereby minimizing personnel hazard and equipment damage.

B. Location

240-20. Ungrounded Conductors.

(a) Overcurrent Device Required. A fuse or an overcurrent trip unit of a circuit breaker shall be connected in series with each ungrounded conductor. A combination of a current transformer and overcurrent relay shall be considered equivalent to an overcurrent trip unit.

(FPN): For motor circuits, see Parts C, D, F, and J of Article 430.

(b) Circuit Breaker as Overcurrent Device. Circuit breakers shall open all ungrounded conductors of the circuit.

Exception: Individual single-pole circuit breakers shall be acceptable as the protection for each ungrounded conductor of 3-wire direct-current or single-phase circuits, or for each ungrounded conductor of lighting or appliance branch circuits connected to 4-wire, 3-phase systems or 5-wire, 2-phase systems, provided such lighting or appliance circuits are supplied from a system having a grounded neutral and no conductor in such circuits operates at a voltage greater than permitted in Section 210-6.

In the first part of the exception, the term "3-wire" applies to both "direct current" and "single-phase." See Figure 240-3.

2-wire, 1Φ system

Figure 240-3. Double-pole circuit breaker required because ungrounded two-wire circuit used is not included in the exception.

(c) Closed-Loop Power Distribution Systems. Listed devices providing equivalent overcurrent protection in closed-loop power distribution systems shall be permitted as a substitute for fuses or circuit breakers.

240-21. Location in Circuit. An overcurrent device shall be connected at the point where the conductor to be protected receives its supply.

Exception No. 1: Smaller Conductor Protected. Where the overcurrent device protecting the larger conductor also protects the smaller conductor in accordance with Tables 310-16 through 310-31.

Exception No. 1 is illustrated by Figure 240-8. A smaller 1/0 THW conductor (150 A) is tapped from a larger 3/0 THW feeder conductor (200 A) which is in turn protected by a 150-A circuit breaker that is equal to the ampacity of the 1/0 tap conductor. The circuit breaker protecting the feeder conductors is rated to protect the tap conductors.

3-wire, 1Φ system

Figure 240-4. Single-pole circuit breakers permitted for overcurrent protection because this is a three-wire, single-phase circuit. It is also a multiwire branch circuit supplying both line-to-line and line-to-neutral loads in a single utilization equipment. See Section 210-4(c), Exception No. 1.

4-wire, 3Φ system   3Φ load

Figure 240-5. Three-pole circuit breaker required.

4-wire, 3Φ system

Lighting or appliance branch circuits

Figure 240-6. Single-pole circuit breakers permitted for overcurrent protection.

Exception No. 2: Feeder Taps Not Over 10 Feet (3.05 m) Long. For conductors tapped to a feeder or transformer secondary where all the following conditions are met:

a. The length of the tap conductors does not exceed 10 feet (3.05 m).

b. The ampacity of the tap conductors is:

172

(1) not less than the combined computed loads on the circuits supplied by the tap.conductors, and

(2a) not less than the rating of the device supplied by the tap conductors, or

(2b) not less than the rating of the overcurrent protective device at the termination of the tap conductors.

c. The tap conductors do not extend beyond the switchboard, panelboard, or control devices they supply.

d. Except at the point of connection to the feeder, the tap conductors are enclosed in a raceway, which shall extend from the tap to the enclosure of an enclosed switchboard, panelboard, or control devices, or to the back of an open switchboard.

(FPN): See Section 384-16(a) for lighting and appliance branch-circuit panelboards.

Exception No. 2 permits a tap from a feeder or from a transformer secondary without requiring overcurrent protection at the point where the tap conductor receives its supply, provided the tap conductor (1) is not more than 10 ft long, (2) is enclosed in a raceway, (3) does not extend beyond the switchboard, panelboard, or control devices that it supplies, and (4) has an ampacity not less than the combined computed loads supplied and not less than the ampere rating of the switchboard, panelboard, or control devices supplied, except where the tap conductor terminates in an overcurrent protective device which does not exceed the ampacity of the tap conductor.

Figure 240-7. Single-pole circuit breakers permitted for overcurrent protection.

Figure 240-8. Section 240-21, Exception No. 1 permits the circuit breaker protecting the feeder conductors to protect the tap conductors to the cabinet.

ARTICLE 240—OVERCURRENT PROTECTION

Exception No. 3: Feeder Taps Not Over 25 Feet (7.62 m) Long. For conductors tapped to a feeder where all of the following conditions are met:

a. The length of the tap conductors does not exceed 25 feet (7.62 m).

b. The ampacity of the tap conductors is not less than ⅓ that of the feeder conductors or overcurrent protection from which they are tapped.

c. The tap conductors terminate with a single circuit breaker or a single set of fuses that will limit the load to the ampacity of the tap conductors. This single overcurrent device shall be permitted to supply any number of additional overcurrent devices on its load side.

d. The tap conductors are suitably protected from physical damage and are enclosed in a raceway.

Exception No. 3 is illustrated in Figure 240-9. Three No. 3/0 THW copper tap conductors are protected from physical damage in a raceway. The lengths of the tap conductors are not more than 25 ft between terminations. They are tapped from a 500 MCM feeder and terminate in a circuit breaker.

Note: A No. 3/0 THW copper conductor (200 A) is more than ⅓ the ampacity of a 500 MCM THW (380 A) copper conductor. See Table 310-16 for ampacity of copper conductors in conduit above ground.

200 A
circuit breaker

No. 3/0 CU, type THW tap
not over 25 ft long

Junction
box

500 MCM
CU,
type THW
feeder

To load

Figure 240-9. Feeder taps terminating in a single circuit breaker. See Exception No. 3.

Exception No. 4: Service Conductors. For service-entrance conductors where protected in accordance with Section 230-91.

Exception No. 5: Branch-Circuit Taps. Taps to individual outlets and circuit conductors supplying a single household electric range shall be considered as protected by the branch-circuit overcurrent devices when in accordance with the requirements of Sections 210-19, 210-20, and 210-24.

Exception No. 6: Motor Circuit Taps. For motor-branch-circuit conductors where protected in accordance with Sections 430-28 and 430-53.

Exception No. 7: Busway Taps. For busways where protected in accordance with Sections 364-10 through 364-14.

Exception No. 8: Transformer Feeder Taps with Primary Plus Secondary Not Over 25 Feet (7.62 m) Long. Where all of the following conditions are met:

a. The conductors supplying the primary of a transformer have an ampacity at least ⅓ that of the conductors or overcurrent protection from which they are tapped.

b. The conductors supplied by the secondary of the transformer have an ampacity that, when multiplied by the ratio of the secondary-to-primary voltage, is at least ⅓ the ampacity of the conductors or overcurrent protection from which the primary conductors are tapped.

c. The total length of one primary plus one secondary conductor, excluding any portion of the primary conductor that is protected at its ampacity, is not over 25 feet (7.62 m).

d. The primary and secondary conductors are suitably protected from physical damage.

e. The secondary conductors terminate in a single circuit breaker or set of fuses which will limit the load to that allowed in Tables 310-16 through 310-31.

Exception No. 8 is illustrated in Figure 240-10.

Figure 240-10. Transformer feeder taps (primary plus secondary) not over 25 ft long, as per Section 240-21, Exception No. 8. Also applies to overcurrent protection requirements of Sections 384-16(a) and 450-3(b).

Exception No. 9: Conductors from generator terminals to the first overcurrent device as covered in Section 445-5.

Exception No. 10: Feeder Taps Over 25 Feet (7.62 m) Long. In high bay manufacturing buildings over 35 feet (10.67 m) high at walls, where conditions of maintenance and supervision assure that only qualified persons will service the systems, conductors tapped to a feeder shall be permitted to be not over 25 feet (7.62 m) long horizontally and not over 100 feet (30.5 m) total length where all of the following conditions are met.

a. The ampacity of the tap conductors is not less than ⅓ that of the overcurrent device from which they are supplied.

b. The tap conductors terminate with a single circuit breaker or a single set of fuses that will limit the load to the ampacity of the tap conductors. This single overcurrent device shall be permitted to supply any number of additional overcurrent devices on its load side.

c. The tap conductors are suitably protected from physical damage and are installed in raceways.

d. The tap conductors are continuous from end-to-end and contain no splices.

e. The tap conductors shall be No. 6 AWG copper or No. 4 AWG aluminum or larger.

f. The tap conductors shall not penetrate walls, floors, or ceilings.

g. The tap shall be made no less than 30 feet (9.14 m) from the floor.

See Figure 240-11.

Figure 240-11. Section 240-21, Exception No. 10 permits a tap rule of 100 ft for manufacturing buildings with walls over 35 ft high. The tap connection is not less than 30 ft from the floor, and conditions of maintenance and supervision must ensure that only qualified persons will service these systems.

Exception No. 11: Transformer Secondary Conductors of Separately Derived Systems for Industrial Installations. For conductors connected to a transformer secondary of a separately derived system where all of the following conditions are met:

a. The length of the secondary conductors does not exceed 25 feet (7.62 m).

b. The ampacity of the conductors is not less than the secondary current rating of the transformer and the sum of the overcurrent devices will limit the load to this capacity.

c. All overcurrent devices are grouped.

d. The tap conductors are suitably protected from physical damage.

Exception No. 11 is new in the 1987 *NEC*.

240-22. Grounded Conductors. No overcurrent device shall be connected in series with any conductor that is intentionally grounded.

Exception No. 1: Where the overcurrent device opens all conductors of the circuit, including the grounded conductor, and is so designed that no pole can operate independently.

Exception No. 2: Where required by Sections 430-36 and 430-37 for motor overload protection.

240-23. Change in Size of Grounded Conductor. Where a change occurs in the size of the ungrounded conductor, a similar change shall be permitted to be made in the size of the grounded conductor.

This section acknowledges that the size of a grounded conductor may be increased or reduced to correspond to a change made in the size of an ungrounded conductor, such as in tap conductors, where all are of the same circuit.

240-24. Location in or on Premises.

(a) Readily Accessible. Overcurrent devices shall be readily accessible.

This section is intended to correlate with Section 230-91, i.e., the service overcurrent device shall be an integral part of the service disconnecting means or shall be located immediately adjacent thereto. See comments following Section 230-91(a).

Exception No. 1: For busways as provided in Section 364-12.

Exception No. 2: For supplementary overcurrent protection as described in Section 240-10.

Exception No. 3: For service overcurrent devices as described in Section 230-92.

(b) Occupant to Have Ready Access. Each occupant shall have ready access to all overcurrent devices protecting the conductors supplying that occupancy.

Exception: In a multiple-occupancy building where electric service and electrical maintenance are provided by the building management and where these are under continuous building management supervision, the service overcurrent devices and feeder overcurrent devices supplying more than one occupancy shall be permitted to be accessible to authorized management personnel only.

(c) Not Exposed to Physical Damage. Overcurrent devices shall be located where they will not be exposed to physical damage.

(d) Not in Vicinity of Easily Ignitible Material. Overcurrent devices shall not be located in the vicinity of easily ignitible material such as in clothes closets.

Clothes closets are only one example of a location where easily ignitible materials may be present. See Section 550-6(a) for the requirements for overcurrent devices that are an integral part of a listed distribution panelboard located just inside a closet entry in mobile homes.

C. Enclosures

240-30. General. Overcurrent devices shall be enclosed in cabinets or cutout boxes.

Exception No. 1: Where a part of an assembly that provides equivalent protection.

Exception No. 2: Where mounted on open-type switchboards, panelboards, or control boards that are in rooms or enclosures free from dampness and easily ignitible material and accessible only to qualified personnel.

Exception No. 3: The operating handle of a circuit breaker shall be permitted to be accessible without opening a door or cover.

Properly selected overcurrent protective devices are designed to open a circuit before an overcurrent condition can seriously damage conductor insulation, and requirements that overcurrent devices be enclosed in cabinets or cutout boxes are to ensure that electrical disturbances in the vicinity will be kept to a minimum.

Overcurrent devices mounted on open-type switchboards, panelboards, or controlboards and having exposed live parts are to be located where accessible only to qualified persons.

240-32. Damp or Wet Locations. Enclosures for overcurrent devices in damp or wet locations shall be identified for use in such locations and shall be mounted so there is at least ¼-inch (6.35-mm) air space between the enclosure and the wall or other supporting surface.

240-33. Vertical Position. Enclosures for overcurrent devices shall be mounted in a vertical position.

Exception: Where this is shown to be impracticable and complies with Section 240-81.

This section indicates that a wall-mounted, vertical position is desirable to achieve easier access, natural hand-operation, normal swing or closing of doors or covers, and legibility of manufacturer's markings.

D. Disconnecting and Guarding

240-40. Disconnecting Means for Fuses and Thermal Cutouts. Disconnecting means shall be provided on the supply side of all fuses or thermal cutouts in circuits of over 150 volts to ground and cartridge fuses in circuits of any voltage, where accessible to other than qualified persons, so that each individual circuit containing fuses or thermal cutouts can be independently disconnected from the source of electric energy.

Exception No. 1: A device provided for current limiting on the supply side of the service disconnecting means as permitted by Section 230-82.

Exception No. 2: A single disconnecting means shall be permitted on the supply side of more than one set of fuses as provided by Section 430-112 for group operation of motors and in Section 424-22 for fixed electric space heating equipment.

Plug fuses are classified at not more than 125 V and 30 A and below [see Section 240-51(a)].

Cartridge fuses of the nonrenewable type are classified 0-600 A at not more than 250 V, 0-600 A at not more than 300 V, and 0-6000 A at not more than 600 V (see Section 240-61). A disconnecting means must be provided whenever cartridge fuses are accessible to other than qualified persons.

Note: Cartridge fuseholders have live parts openly exposed to personnel during replacement of fuses.

240-41. Arcing or Suddenly Moving Parts. Arcing or suddenly moving parts shall comply with (a) and (b) below.

(a) Location. Fuses and circuit breakers shall be so located or shielded that persons will not be burned or otherwise injured by their operation.

(b) Suddenly Moving Parts. Handles or levers of circuit breakers, and similar parts which may move suddenly in such a way that persons in the vicinity are likely to be injured by being struck by them, shall be guarded or isolated.

Arcing or suddenly moving parts are usually associated with switchboards or controlboards which may be of the open type and which should be under competent supervision and accessible only to qualified persons. Fuses or circuit breakers are required to be so located or shielded that under an abnormal condition the subsequent arc across the opening device will not injure persons in the vicinity.

Guardrails may be provided in the vicinity of disconnecting means. Modern switchboards, etc., are equipped with removable handles, but sudden-moving handles may be capable of causing injury.

See Article 100 for definition of "guarded." See also Section 110-17.

E. Plug Fuses, Fuseholders, and Adapters

240-50. General.

(a) Maximum Voltage. Plug fuses and fuseholders shall not be used in circuits exceeding 125 volts between conductors.

Exception: In circuits supplied by a system having a grounded neutral and having no conductor at over 150 volts to ground.

This permits plug fuses to protect 240-V and 208-V loads on circuits supplied by 120/240-V single-phase, 3-wire systems and 208Y/120-V, 3-phase, 4-wire systems.

(b) Marking. Each fuse, fuseholder, and adapter shall be marked with its ampere rating.

(c) Hexagonal Configuration. Plug fuses of 15-ampere and lower rating shall be identified by a hexagonal configuration of the window, cap, or other prominent part to distinguish them from fuses of higher ampere ratings.

(d) No Live Parts. Plug fuses, fuseholders, and adapters shall have no exposed live parts after fuses or fuses and adapters have been installed.

(e) Screw Shell. The screw shell of a plug-type fuseholder shall be connected to the load side of the circuit.

240-51. Edison-Base Fuses.

(a) Classification. Plug fuses of the Edison-base type shall be classified at not over 125 volts and 30 amperes and below.

(b) Replacement Only. Plug fuses of the Edison-base type shall be used only for replacements in existing installations where there is no evidence of overfusing or tampering.

240-52. Edison-Base Fuseholders. Fuseholders of the Edison-base type shall be installed only where they are made to accept Type S fuses by the use of adapters.

240-53. Type S Fuses. Type S fuses shall be of the plug type and shall comply with (a) and (b) below.

(a) Classification. Type S fuses shall be classified at not over 125 volts and 0 to 15 amperes, 16 to 20 amperes, and 21 to 30 amperes.

(b) Noninterchangeable. Type S fuses of an ampere classification as specified in (a) above shall not be interchangeable with a lower ampere classification. They shall be so designed that they cannot be used in any fuseholder other than a Type S fuseholder or a fuseholder with a Type S adapter inserted.

240-54. Type S Fuses, Adapters, and Fuseholders.

(a) **To Fit Edison-Base Fuseholders.** Type S adapters shall fit Edison-base fuseholders.

(b) **To Fit Type S Fuses Only.** Type S fuseholders and adapters shall be so designed that either the fuseholder itself or the fuseholder with a Type S adapter inserted cannot be used for any fuse other than a Type S fuse.

(c) **Nonremovable.** Type S adapters shall be so designed that once inserted in a fuseholder, they cannot be removed.

(d) **Nontamperable.** Type S fuses, fuseholders, and adapters shall be so designed that tampering or shunting (bridging) would be difficult.

(e) **Interchangeability.** Dimensions of Type S fuses, fuseholders, and adapters shall be standardized to permit interchangeability regardless of the manufacturer.

F. Cartridge Fuses and Fuseholders

240-60. General.

(a) **Maximum Voltage — 300-Volt Type.** Cartridge fuses and fuseholders of the 300-volt type shall not be used in circuits of over 300 volts between conductors.

Exception: In circuits supplied by a system having a grounded neutral and having no conductor at over 300 volts to ground.

(b) **Noninterchangeable — 0-6000 Ampere Cartridge Fuseholders.** Fuseholders shall be so designed that it will be difficult to put a fuse of any given class into a fuseholder that is designed for a current lower, or voltage higher, than that of the class to which it belongs. Fuseholders for current-limiting fuses shall not permit insertion of fuses that are not current limiting.

(c) **Marking.** Fuses shall be plainly marked, either by printing on the fuse barrel or by a label attached to the barrel, showing the following: (1) ampere rating; (2) voltage rating; (3) interrupting rating where other than 10,000 amperes; (4) "current limiting" where applicable; (5) the name or trademark of the manufacturer.

Exception: Interrupting rating marking shall not be required on fuses used for supplementary protection.

240-61. Classification. Cartridge fuses and fuseholders shall be classified according to voltage and amperage ranges. Fuses rated 600 volts, nominal, or less, shall be permitted to be used for voltages at or below their ratings.

See Section 710-21(b) for application of high-voltage fuses.

G. Circuit Breakers

240-80. Method of Operation. Circuit breakers shall be trip free and capable of being closed and opened by manual operation. Their normal method of operation by other than manual means such as electrical or pneumatic shall be permitted if means for manual operation is also provided.

Exception: As provided in Section 230-76(2) for circuit breakers used as service disconnecting means.

240-81. Indicating. Circuit breakers shall clearly indicate whether they are in the open "off" or closed "on" position.

Where circuit breaker handles on switchboards or in panelboards are operated vertically rather than rotationally or horizontally, the "up" position of the handle shall be the "on" position.

> See Sections 240-83(d), 380-11, and 410-81(a) for requirements on circuit breakers used as switches.

240-82. Nontamperable. A circuit breaker shall be of such design that any alteration of its trip point (calibration) or the time required for its operation will require dismantling of the device or breaking of a seal for other than intended adjustments.

240-83. Marking.

(a) Durable and Visible. Circuit breakers shall be marked with their ampere rating in a manner that will be durable and visible after installation. Such marking shall be permitted to be made visible by removal of a trim or cover.

(b) Location. Circuit breakers rated at 100 amperes or less and 600 volts or less shall have the ampere rating molded, stamped, etched, or similarly marked into their handles or escutcheon areas.

(c) Interrupting Rating. Every circuit breaker having an interrupting rating other than 5000 amperes shall have its interrupting rating shown on the circuit breaker.

Exception: Interrupting rating marking shall not be required on circuit breakers used for supplementary protection.

> Class H-type cartridge fuses have an interrupting capacity (IC) rating of 10,000 A, and this rating need not be marked on the fuse. However, Class G, J, K, L, R, and T cartridge fuses have over a 10,000 A IC rating and must be marked with the IC rating. See Section 240-60(c).
>
> Section 240-83(c) requires that the IC rating for circuit breakers for other than 5,000 A be indicated on the circuit breaker.
>
> Fuses or circuit breakers used for supplementary protection of fluorescent fixtures, semiconductor rectifiers, motor-operated appliances, etc., need not be marked for IC.

(d) Circuit Breakers Used as Switches. Where used as switches in 120-volt and 277-volt fluorescent lighting circuits, circuit breakers shall be approved for such switching duty and shall be marked "SWD."

> Switching duty circuit breakers (SWD) are required where the breakers are used as switches for 120-V and 277-V fluorescent lighting. Switching duty circuit breakers generally have heavier-duty contacts.

H. Overcurrent Protection Over 600 Volts, Nominal

240-100. Feeders. Feeders shall have a short-circuit protective device in each ungrounded conductor or comply with Section 230-208(d)(2) or (d)(3). The protective device(s) shall be capable of detecting and interrupting all values of current which can occur at their location in excess of their trip setting or melting point. In no case shall the fuse rating in continuous amperes exceed three times, or the long-time trip element setting of a breaker six times, the ampacity of the conductor.

Conductors tapped to a feeder shall be permitted to be protected by the feeder overcurrent device where that overcurrent device also protects the tap conductors.

(FPN): The operating time of the protective device, the available short-circuit current, and the conductor used will need to be coordinated to prevent damaging or dangerous temperatures in conductors or conductor insulation under short-circuit conditions.

240-101. Branch Circuits.   Branch circuits shall have a short-circuit protective device in each ungrounded conductor or comply with Section 230-208(d)(2) or (d)(3). The protective device(s) shall be capable of detecting and interrupting all values of current which can occur at their location in excess of their trip setting or melting point.

ARTICLE 250 — GROUNDING

Contents

M. Grounding of Systems and Circuits of 1 kV and Over (High Voltage)

250-150. General.
250-151. Derived Neutral Systems.
250-152. Solidly Grounded Neutral Systems.
  (a) Neutral Conductor.
  (b) Multiple Grounding.
250-153. Impedance Grounded Neutral Systems.
  (a) Location.
  (b) Identified and Insulated.
  (c) System Neutral Connection.

(d) Equipment Grounding Conductors.
250-154. Grounding of Systems Supplying Portable or Mobile Equipment.
  (a) Portable or Mobile Equipment.
  (b) Exposed Noncurrent-Carrying Metal Parts.
  (c) Ground-Fault Current.
  (d) Ground-Fault Detection and Relaying.
  (e) Isolation.
  (f) Trailing Cable and Couplers.
250-155. Grounding of Equipment.

A. General

250-1. Scope. This article covers general requirements for grounding and bonding of electrical installations, and specific requirements in (a) through (f) below.

(a) Systems, circuits, and equipment required, permitted, or not permitted to be grounded.

(b) Circuit conductor to be grounded on grounded systems.

(c) Location of grounding connections.

(d) Types and sizes of grounding and bonding conductors and electrodes.

(e) Methods of grounding and bonding.

(f) Conditions under which guards, isolation, or insulation may be substituted for grounding.

(FPN): Systems and circuit conductors are grounded to limit voltages due to lightning, line surges, or unintentional contact with higher voltage lines, and to stabilize the voltage to ground during normal operation. Systems and circuit conductors are solidly grounded to facilitate overcurrent device operation in case of ground faults.

See Figure 250-1.

(FPN): Conductive materials enclosing electrical conductors or equipment, or forming part of such equipment, are grounded to limit the voltage to ground on these materials and to facilitate overcurrent device operation in case of ground faults. See Section 110-10.

250-2. Application of Other Articles. In other articles applying to particular cases of installation of conductors and equipment, there are requirements that are in addition to those of this article or are modifications of them:

	Article	Section
Agricultural Buildings		547-8
Appliances		422-16
Branch Circuits		210-5
		210-6
		210-7
Cablebus		365-9
Circuits and Equipment Operating at Less Than 50 Volts	720	
Class 1, Class 2, and Class 3 Circuits		725-20
		725-43
Closed-Loop and Programmed Power Distribution		780-3
		780-4(a)

Equipment ground
(Grounding bus)

System ground
(Grounded service
conductor)

Neutral bus

Grounding electrode
conductor

Grounding
electrode

Figure 250-1. Typical grounding system for single-phase, 3-wire service.

B. Circuit and System Grounding

250-3. Direct-Current Systems.

(a) Two-Wire Direct Current Systems. Two-wire dc systems supplying premises wiring shall be grounded.

Exception No. 1: A system equipped with a ground detector and supplying only industrial equipment in limited areas.

Exception No. 2: A system operating at 50 volts or less between conductors.

Exception No. 3: A system operating at over 300 volts between conductors.

Exception No. 4: A rectifier-derived dc system supplied from an ac system complying with Section 250-5.

Exception No. 5: DC fire protective signaling circuits having a maximum current of 0.030 amperes as specified in Article 760, Part C.

(b) Three-Wire Direct-Current Systems. The neutral conductor of all 3-wire dc systems supplying premises wiring shall be grounded.

250-5. Alternating-Current Circuits and Systems to Be Grounded. AC circuits and systems shall be grounded as provided for in (a), (b), (c), or (d) below. Other circuits and systems shall be permitted to be grounded.

(a) Alternating-Current Circuits of Less than 50 Volts. AC circuits of less than 50 volts shall be grounded under any of the following conditions:

(1) Where supplied by transformers if the transformer supply system exceeds 150 volts to ground.

(2) Where supplied by transformers if the transformer supply system is ungrounded.

(3) Where installed as overhead conductors outside of buildings.

(b) Alternating-Current Systems of 50 Volts to 1000 Volts. AC systems of 50 volts to 1000 volts supplying premises wiring and premises wiring systems shall be grounded under any of the following conditions:

(1) Where the system can be so grounded that the maximum voltage to ground on the ungrounded conductors does not exceed 150 volts.

See Figure 250-2.

120 V, 1Φ, 2 wire

240/120 V, 1Φ, 3 wire

208/120 V, 3Φ, 4 wire

Figure 250-2. Typical systems required to be grounded by Section 250-5(b)(1).

(2) Where the system is nominally rated 480Y/277-volt, 3-phase, 4-wire in which the neutral is used as a circuit conductor.

(3) Where the system is nominally rated 240/120-volt, 3-phase, 4-wire in which the midpoint of one phase is used as a circuit conductor.

See Figure 250-3.

120 V

240 V

N

120 V

208 V

"High leg"

240/120 V, 3Φ, 4 wire

Figure 250-3. Grounding is required. See Sections 215-8, 230-56, and 384-3(e) for identification of the "high leg."

(4) Where a service conductor is uninsulated in accordance with Sections 230-22, 230-30, 230-41.

Exception No. 1: Electric systems used exclusively to supply industrial electric furnaces for melting, refining, tempering, and the like.

Exception No. 2: Separately derived systems used exclusively for rectifiers supplying only adjustable speed industrial drives.

Exception No. 3: Separately derived systems supplied by transformers that have a primary voltage rating less than 1000 volts provided that all of the following conditions are met:

a. The system is used exclusively for control circuits.

b. The conditions of maintenance and supervision assure that only qualified persons will service the installation.

c. Continuity of control power is required.

d. Ground detectors are installed on the control system.

Exception No. 4: Isolated systems as permitted in Article 517.

(FPN): The proper use of suitable ground detectors on ungrounded systems can provide additional protection.

Exception No. 5: High-impedance grounded neutral systems in which a grounding impedance, usually a resistor, limits the ground-fault current to a low value. High impedance grounded neutral systems shall be permitted for three-phase ac systems of 480 volts to 1000 volts where all of the following conditions are met:

a. The conditions of maintenance and supervision assure that only qualified persons will service the installation.

b. Continuity of power is required.

189

c. Ground detectors are installed on the system.

d. Line-to-neutral loads are not served.

See Section 250-27 for the requirements for high-impedance grounded neutral systems.

(c) Alternating-Current Systems of 1 kV and Over. AC systems of 1 kV and over supplying mobile or portable equipment shall be grounded as specified in Section 250-154. Where supplying other than portable equipment, such systems shall be permitted to be grounded. Where such systems are grounded, they shall comply with the applicable provisions of this article.

(d) Separately Derived Systems. A premises wiring system whose power is derived from generator, transformer, or converter windings and has no direct electrical connection, including a solidly connected grounded circuit conductor, to supply conductors originating in another system, if required to be grounded as in (a) or (b) above, shall be grounded as specified in Section 250-26.

Transformers are the most common source for a separately derived system. However, not all transformers become the source of such a system, even though they have the secondary winding isolated electrically from the primary winding. The secondary must supply a premises wiring system before the transformer becomes the source of a separately derived system. A step-down transformer that is part of electrical equipment, and that does not supply premises wiring (see definition of "premises wiring" in Article 100), is not the source of a separately derived system.

(FPN): An alternate alternating-current power source such as an on-site generator is not a separately derived system if the neutral is solidly interconnected to a service-supplied system neutral.

Figures 250-4 and 250-5 depict a 120Y/208-V electrical service supplying a service disconnecting means to a building. The system is fed through a transfer switch that is connected to a generator intended to provide power for an emergency or standby system.

Figure 250-4 does not have the neutral conductor connected to the 3-pole transfer switch; thus there is a direct electrical connection of the grounded circuit conductor (neutral) to the generator. Therefore, the system supplied by the generator is not a separately derived system, and there are no requirements for grounding the neutral at the generator. Under these conditions it is necessary to run an equipment grounding conductor from the service equipment to the 3-pole transfer switch and from the 3-pole transfer switch to the generator.

Figure 250-5 shows the grounded conductor (neutral) connected to a 4-pole transfer switch. Therefore, the generator system does not have a direct electrical connection to the grounded circuit conductor (neutral), and the generator is a separately derived system required to be grounded in accordance with Section 250-26.

Section 250-26 requires that a bonding jumper be installed and connected from the generator frame to the grounded circuit conductor (neutral). The grounding electrode conductor from the generator is required to be connected to a grounding electrode. This conductor should be located as close to the generator as practical. The preferred grounding electrode is the nearest effectively grounded structural metal member or the nearest available effectively grounded metal water pipe, if they are available. If neither of these preferred grounding electrodes is available, then other electrodes specified in Sections 250-81 and 250-83 are permitted to be used.

Figure 250-4. Installation has a direct electrical connection of the grounded circuit conductor (neutral) to the generator; therefore, the generator is not a separately derived system, and there are no requirements for grounding the neutral.

Figure 250-5. Installation does not have a direct electrical connection of the grounded circuit conductor (neutral); therefore, the generator is a separately derived system and is grounded in accordance with Section 250-26.

(FPN): For systems that are not separately derived and are not required to be grounded as specified in Section 250-26, see Section 445-5 for minimum size of conductors which must carry fault current.

ARTICLE 250—GROUNDING

250-6. Portable and Vehicle-Mounted Generators.

(a) Portable Generators. Under the following conditions the frame of a portable generator shall not be required to be grounded and shall be permitted to serve as the grounding electrode for a system supplied by the generator:

(1) The generator supplies only equipment mounted on the generator and/or cord- and plug-connected equipment through receptacles mounted on the generator, and

(2) The noncurrent-carrying metal parts of equipment and the equipment grounding conductor terminals of the receptacles are bonded to the generator frame.

(b) Vehicle-Mounted Generators. Under the following conditions the frame of a vehicle shall be permitted to serve as the grounding electrode for a system supplied by a generator located on the vehicle:

(1) The frame of the generator is bonded to the vehicle frame, and

(2) The generator supplies only equipment located on the vehicle and/or cord- and plug-connected equipment through receptacles mounted on the vehicle or on the generator, and

(3) The noncurrent-carrying metal parts of equipment and the equipment grounding conductor terminals of the receptacles are bonded to the generator frame, and

(4) The system complies with all other provisions of this article.

(c) Neutral Conductor Bonding. A neutral conductor shall be bonded to the generator frame when the generator is a component of a separately derived system. The bonding of any conductor other than a neutral within the generator to its frame shall not be required.

(FPN): For grounding of portable generators supplying fixed wiring systems, see Section 250-5(d).

250-7. Circuits Not to Be Grounded. The following circuits shall not be grounded:

(a) Cranes. Circuits for electric cranes operating over combustible fibers in Class III locations, as provided in Section 503-13.

(b) Health Care Facilities. Circuits as provided in Article 517.

C. Location of System Grounding Connections

250-21. Objectionable Current over Grounding Conductors.

(a) Arrangement to Prevent Objectionable Current. The grounding of electric systems, circuit conductors, surge arresters, and conductive noncurrent-carrying materials and equipment shall be installed and arranged in a manner that will prevent an objectionable flow of current over the grounding conductors or grounding paths.

(b) Alterations to Stop Objectionable Current. If the use of multiple grounding connections results in an objectionable flow of current, one or more of the following alterations shall be made:

(1) Discontinue one or more such grounding connections.

(2) Change the locations of the grounding connections.

(3) Interrupt the continuity of the conductor or conductive path interconnecting the grounding connections.

(4) Take other suitable remedial action satisfactory to the authority having jurisdiction.

Section 250-21(b) is not intended to permit deletion of all grounding connections.

(c) Temporary Currents Not Classified as Objectionable Currents. Temporary currents resulting from accidental conditions, such as ground-fault currents, that occur only while the grounding conductors are performing their intended protective functions shall not be classified as objectionable current for the purposes specified in (a) and (b) above.

250-22. Point of Connection for Direct-Current Systems. DC systems to be grounded shall have the grounding connection made at one or more supply stations. A grounding connection shall not be made at individual services nor at any point on premises wiring.

Exception: Where the dc system source is located on the premises a grounding connection shall be made at the source or the first system disconnecting means or overcurrent device.

Figure 250-6. The neutral is shown grounded at the off-premises generator site in this 3-wire dc distribution system. Grounding of a 2-wire dc system would be accomplished in the same manner. For an on-premises generator, the grounding connection is required to be at the source of the first system disconnecting means or overcurrent device.

3-wire 120/240-V DC distribution system

3-wire 120/240-V AC single-phase secondary distribution system

Figure 250-7. On a 2-wire or 3-wire single-phase ac secondary distribution system, grounding connections are made on the secondary side of the transformer and on the supply side of the service disconnecting means.

250-23. Grounding Service-Supplied Alternating-Current Systems.

(a) System Grounding Connections. A premises wiring system that is supplied by an ac service and is required to be grounded by Section 250-5 shall have at each service a grounding

Transformers

Primary

4-wire, 3-phase 208Y/120-V secondary distribution system

Figure 250-8. The neutral is grounded at each service and also on the secondary side of the transformer on this 4-wire, 3-phase, 208Y/120-V secondary distribution system. When 3-wire, 3-phase service equipment is installed for power purposes on this type of ac system, the grounded (neutral) conductor is required to be run to the service equipment. See Section 250-23(b).

electrode conductor connected to a grounding electrode which complies with Part H of Article 250. The grounding electrode conductor shall be connected to the grounded service conductor at any accessible point from the load end of the service drop or service lateral to and including the terminal or bus to which the grounded service conductor is connected at the service disconnecting means. Where the transformer supplying the service is located outside the building, at least one additional grounding connection shall be made from the grounded service conductor to a grounding electrode, either at the transformer or elsewhere outside the building. A grounding connection shall not be made to any grounded circuit conductor on the load side of the service disconnecting means.

The power for ac premises wiring systems is either separately derived in accordance with Section 250-5(d), or is supplied by the service (see definition of "service" in Article 100). Section 250-26 covers grounding requirements for separately derived ac systems. Section 250-23(a) covers system grounding requirements for service-supplied ac systems.

Section 250-23(a) covers a premises wiring system that is supplied by an ac service, and the system is required to be grounded by Section 250-5. See Section 250-26 for similar requirements.

This type of system is required to have a grounding electrode conductor at each service connected to a grounding electrode which meets the requirements in Part H. Note the grounding electrode requirements for a separately derived system are specified in Section 250-26(c).

The grounding electrode conductor connection to the grounded conductor is accurately specified. First, the connection is required to be made to the grounded service conductor. Second, the *Code* describes where this connection is permitted to be made to the grounded service conductor.

Where the transformer supplying the service is located outside the building, the additional grounding connection to the grounded service conductor is required to be made outside the building. It is unnecessary to specify that this connection is to be made on the secondary side of the transformer because of the definition of "service conductors" in Article 100.

The main rule is that a grounding connection shall not be made to any grounded circuit conductor on the load side of the service disconnecting means. See Exception Nos. 1 through 6 below.

(FPN): See definition of Service Drop and Service Lateral; also Section 230-21.

Exception No. 1: A grounding electrode conductor shall be connected to the grounded conductor of a separately derived system in accordance with the provisions of Section 250-26(b).

Where a separately derived system is required to be grounded, a grounding electrode conductor is required to be connected to the grounded conductor of the derived system as specified in Section 250-26(b).

Exception No. 2: A grounding conductor connection shall be made at each separate building where required by Section 250-24.

Exception No. 3: For ranges, counter-mounted cooking units, wall-mounted ovens, clothes dryers, and meter enclosures as permitted by Section 250-61.

Exception No. 4: For services that are dual fed (double ended) in a common enclosure or grouped together in separate enclosures and employing a secondary tie, a single grounding electrode connection to the tie point of the grounded circuit conductors from each power source shall be permitted.

Exception No. 5: Where the main bonding jumper specified in Sections 250-53(b) and 250-79 is a wire or busbar, and is installed from the neutral bar or bus to the equipment grounding terminal bar or bus in the service equipment, the grounding electrode conductor shall be permitted to be connected to the equipment grounding terminal bar or bus to which the main bonding jumper is connected.

Where a ground-return-type sensor is used for ground-fault protection of equipment (see Article 100 for definition of "ground-fault protection of equipment"), the sensor is required to be installed on the main bonding jumper, and the grounding electrode conductor is required to be connected to the equipment grounding bus or terminal bar so that ground-fault current can be accurately sensed. Where the service equipment is power switchgear, it is often more practical to connect the grounding electrode conductor to the grounding bus inside the switchgear. See Figures 230-19 and 230-20.

Exception No. 6: As covered in Section 250-27 for high-impedance grounded neutral systems grounding connection requirements.

(b) Grounded Conductor Brought to Service Equipment. Where an ac system operating at less than 1000 volts is grounded at any point, the grounded conductor shall be run to each service. This conductor shall be routed with the phase conductors and shall not be smaller than the required grounding electrode conductor specified in Table 250-94 and, in addition, for service phase conductors larger than 1100 MCM copper or 1750 MCM aluminum, the grounded conductor shall not be smaller than 12 ½ percent of the area of the largest phase conductor. Where the service phase conductors are paralleled, the size of the grounded conductor shall be based on the equivalent area for parallel conductors as indicated in this section.

Exception No. 1: The grounded conductor shall not be required to be larger than the largest ungrounded service conductor or equivalent area for paralleled conductors.

Exception No. 2: As covered in Section 250-27 for high-impedance grounded neutral systems grounding connection requirements.

250-24. Two or More Buildings or Structures Supplied from a Common Service.

(a) Grounded Systems. Where two or more buildings or structures are supplied from a common service, the grounded system in each building or structure shall have a grounding electrode as described in Part H connected to the metal enclosure of the building disconnecting means and to the ac system grounded circuit conductor on the supply side of the building or structure disconnecting means.

Figure 250-9. On a 4-wire, 3-phase, 240-V delta secondary system, a mid-phase tap is made at one transformer to provide a neutral for a 3-wire 120/240-V system for lighting and 125-V receptacles. This neutral is grounded at the transformer and at each individual service. This neutral is also required to be run to service equipment supplied from the above-mentioned secondary system, even though installed for 3-wire, 3-phase power purposes. Also, on a 3-wire, 3-phase, 240-V distribution system without a neutral, but with one phase conductor grounded, it is required to ground that phase conductor at each individual service.

Exception No. 1: A grounding electrode at separate buildings or structures shall not be required where only one branch circuit is supplied and there is no equipment in the building or structure that requires grounding.

Exception No. 2: A grounded circuit conductor connection to the grounding electrode shall not be required at a separate building or structure if an equipment grounding conductor is run with the circuit conductors for grounding any noncurrent-carrying equipment, interior metal piping systems and building or structural metal frames and the equipment grounding conductor is bonded at a separate building or structure disconnecting means to existing grounding electrodes described in Part H. Where there are no existing electrodes, a grounding electrode meeting the requirements of Part H shall be installed where the building or structure supplies more than one branch circuit. Where livestock is housed, that portion of the equipment grounding conductor run underground to the disconnecting means shall be insulated or covered copper.

(b) Ungrounded Systems. Where two or more buildings or structures are supplied by a common service from an ungrounded system, each building or structure shall have a grounding electrode as described in Part H connected to the metal enclosure of the building or structure disconnecting means.

Exception No. 1: A grounding electrode at separate buildings or structures shall not be required where only one branch circuit is supplied and there is no equipment in the building or structure that requires grounding.

Exception No. 2: A grounding electrode and grounding electrode conductor connection to the metal enclosure of the building or structure disconnecting means shall not be required provided all of the following conditions are met.

Service drop from distribution
line or transformer

Overhead
conductors

Building 1   Building 2   Building 3

Main grounding electrode

Figure 250-10. Where a single service (grounded system) supplies three buildings, each building is required to have a grounding electrode installed, unless conditions prevail as described in the exceptions to Section 250-24(a). See Figure 250-11.

a. An equipment grounding conductor is run with the circuit conductors to the building or structure disconnecting means for grounding any noncurrent-carrying equipment, interior metal piping systems, and building or structural metal frames.

b. There are no existing grounding electrodes as described in Part H.

c. The building or structure supplies only one branch circuit.

d. Where livestock is housed, that portion of the equipment grounding conductor run underground to the disconnecting means shall be insulated or covered copper.

250-25. Conductor to Be Grounded — Alternating-Current Systems. For ac premises wiring systems, the conductor to be grounded shall be as specified in (1) through (5) below.

(1) Single-phase, 2-wire: one conductor.

(2) Single-phase, 3-wire: the neutral conductor.

(3) Multiphase systems having one wire common to all phases: the common conductor.

(4) Multiphase systems requiring one grounded phase: one phase conductor.

(5) Multiphase systems in which one phase is used as in (2) above: the neutral conductor.

Grounded conductors shall be identified by the means specified in Article 200.

250-26. Grounding Separately Derived Alternating-Current Systems. A separately derived ac system that is required to be grounded by Section 250-5 shall be grounded as specified in (a) through (d) below.

(a) Bonding Jumper. A bonding jumper, sized in accordance with Section 250-79(c) for the derived phase conductors, shall be used to connect the equipment grounding conductors of the derived system to the grounded conductor. Except as permitted by Exception No. 4 of Section 250-23(a), this connection shall be made at any point on the separately derived system from the source to the first system disconnecting means or overcurrent device; or it shall be made at the source of a separately derived system which has no disconnecting means or overcurrent devices.

The intent here is to permit this connection at the transformer, etc., or at the first disconnecting means or overcurrent device where there is likely to be more

197

Figure 250-11. Conditions under which a grounding electrode at a separate building or structure is not required for a grounded system.

standard arrangements incorporated (as in a panelboard suitable for service equipment).

Exception: The size of the bonding jumper for a system that supplies a Class 1 circuit, and is derived from a transformer rated not more than 1000 volt-amperes, shall not be smaller than the derived phase conductors and shall not be smaller than No. 14 copper or No. 12 aluminum.

Section 250-79(c) requires the bonding jumper to be not smaller than the sizes given in Table 250-94, e.g., not smaller than No. 8 AWG copper. This exception permits a bonding jumper for a Class 1 circuit to be not smaller than No. 14 AWG copper.

Grounded service
conductor

Bonding jumper

Main bonding
jumper (screw)

———————— Bonding jumper (Section 250-79)

— — — — Grounded service conductor (neutral)

— — — — Grounding electrode conductor

Figure 250-12. Grounding and bonding at an individual service.

Service
entrance

Figure 250-13. The grounding and bonding arrangement for six switches that serve as the service disconnecting means for an individual service.

(b) Grounding Electrode Conductor. A grounding electrode conductor, sized in accordance with Section 250-94 for the derived phase conductors, shall be used to connect the grounded conductor of the derived system to the grounding electrode as specified in (c) below. Except as permitted by Exception No. 4 of Section 250-23(a), this connection shall be made at any point on the separately derived system from the source to the first system disconnecting means or overcurrent device; or it shall be made at the source of a separately derived system which has no disconnecting means or overcurrent devices.

Exception: A grounding electrode conductor shall not be required for a system that supplies a Class 1 circuit, and is derived from a transformer rated not more than 1000 volt-amperes, provided the system grounded conductor is bonded to the transformer frame or enclosure by a jumper sized in accordance with the Exception for (a), above, and the transformer frame or enclosure is grounded by one of the means specified in Section 250-57.

See commentary following Section 250-26(a), Exception.

(c) Grounding Electrode. The grounding electrode shall be as near as practicable to and preferably in the same area as the grounding conductor connection to the system. The grounding

199

Figure 250-14. Grounding separately derived ac system.

electrode shall be: (1) the nearest available effectively grounded structural metal member of the structure; or (2) the nearest available effectively grounded metal water pipe; or (3) other electrodes as specified in Sections 250-81 and 250-83 where electrodes specified by (1) or (2) above are not available.

(d) Grounding Methods. In all other respects, grounding methods shall comply with requirements prescribed in other parts of this Code.

A separately derived system is a premises wiring system where power is derived from a generator, a transformer, or converter windings and has no direct electrical connection, including a solidly grounded circuit conductor, to supply conductors originating in another system. See comments following Section 250-5(d).

The requirements of Section 250-26 are most commonly applied to 480Y/277-V transformers which are used to transform a 480-V supply to a 208Y/120-V system to supply lighting and appliance loads.

These requirements provide for a low-impedance path to ground so that line-to-ground faults from ungrounded conductors will create sufficient current to operate the overcurrent devices. These requirements also apply to generators or systems derived from converter windings, but do not have the same wide use as dry-type transformers.

Figure 250-15 shows a typical diagram of a dry-type transformer supplied from a 480-V, 3-phase feeder to derive a 208Y/120-V secondary. As indicated in Section 250-26(a), the bonding jumper connection is required to be sized according to Section 250-79(c) and is to be made at the source of the separately derived system or the first system disconnecting means or overcurrent device and, as illustrated, would be at the transformer enclosure. With the grounding electrode conductor, the bonding jumper, and the bonding of the grounded circuit conductor (neutral) connected at the transformer enclosure, line-to-ground fault currents are permitted to return to the supply source rather than going through the earth. In this way, a path of low impedance is provided which facilitates the operation of overcurrent devices in accordance with Section 250-51(3).

The grounding electrode conductor from the secondary grounded circuit conductor is sized according to Section 250-94.

Section 250-26(c) requires that the grounding electrode be as near as practicable to the grounding conductor connection to the system in order to keep the impedance to ground to a minimum. If there is an effectively grounded structural

200

480 V

Dry-type transformer

Grounding electrode nearby, preferably the structural metal

Disconnecting means

Neutral

208Y/120V

Figure 250-15. A grounding arrangement for a separately derived system. The bonding jumper connection is permitted at the transformer, as illustrated, or at the first system disconnecting means.

metal member of the (building) structure, or an effectively grounded metal water pipe available, Section 250-26(c) requires that this grounding electrode be used rather than a concrete-encased electrode, ground ring, or made electrode such as a ground rod. The practice of grounding the secondary of an isolating transformer to a ground rod, or running the grounding electrode conductor back to the service ground (usually to reduce electrical noise on data processing systems), is prohibited if Items (1) or (2) of Section 250-26(c) are available.

250-27. High-Impedance Grounded Neutral System Connections. High-impedance grounded neutral systems shall comply with the provisions of (a) through (f) below.

Section 250-27 covers high-impedance grounded neutral systems of 50-1000 volts. Such systems rated over 1000 volts are covered in Section 250-153. For information on the differences between solidly grounded systems and high-impedance grounded neutral systems, see *Grounding for Emergency and Standby Power Systems* by Robert B. West, IEEE Transactions on Industry Applications, Vol. IA-15, No. 2, March/April, 1979.

(a) Grounding Impedance Location. The grounding impedance shall be installed between the grounding electrode conductor and the system neutral. Where a neutral is not available, the grounding impedance shall be installed between the grounding electrode conductor and the neutral derived from a grounding transformer.

(b) Neutral Conductor. The neutral conductor from the neutral point of the transformer or generator to its connection point to the grounding impedance shall be fully insulated.

201

(c) System Neutral Connection. The system neutral conductor shall not be connected to ground except through the grounding impedance.

(FPN): The impedance is normally selected to limit the ground-fault current to a value slightly greater than or equal to the capacitive charging current of the system. This value of impedance will also limit transient overvoltages to safe values. For guidance, refer to criteria for limiting transient overvoltages in Recommended Practice for Grounding of Industrial and Commercial Power Systems, ANSI/IEEE Standard 142-1982.

Additional information may be found in:

(1) *Charging Current Data for Guesswork-Free Design of High-Resistance Grounded Systems* by D.S. Baker, IEEE Transactions on Industry Applications, Vol. IA-15, No. 2, March/April, 1979;

(2) *High-Resistance Grounding* by Baldwin Bridger, Jr., IEEE Transactions on Industry Applications, Vol. IA-19, No. 1, January/February, 1983.

(d) Neutral Conductor Routing. The conductor connecting the neutral point of the transformer or generator to the grounding impedance shall be permitted to be installed in a separate raceway. It shall not be required to run this conductor with the phase conductors to the first system disconnecting means or overcurrent device.

(e) Equipment Bonding Jumper. The equipment bonding jumper (the connection between the equipment grounding conductors and the grounding impedance) shall be an unspliced conductor run from the first system disconnecting means or overcurrent device to the grounded side of the grounding impedance.

(f) Grounding Electrode Conductor Location. The grounding electrode conductor shall be attached at any point from the grounded side of the grounding impedance to the equipment grounding connection at the service equipment or first system disconnecting means.

D. Enclosure Grounding

250-32. Service Raceways and Enclosures. Metal enclosures for service conductors and equipment shall be grounded.

250-33. Other Conductor Enclosures. Metal enclosures for other than service conductors shall be grounded.

This section requires bonding, grounding, and electrical continuity of metal raceways and thus requires connectors, couplings, or other such fittings that provide bonding and grounding continuity between the fitting and the raceway metal (such as would be required for liquidtight flexible metal conduit). Metal enclosures are required to be grounded so that any fault between an ungrounded (hot) conductor and a metal enclosure will not allow the enclosure to become energized and remain so, and thus present a shock hazard to persons.

Exception No. 1: Metal enclosures for conductors added to existing installations of open wire, knob-and-tube wiring, and nonmetallic-sheathed cable, which do not provide an equipment ground, if in runs of less than 25 feet (7.62 m), if free from probable contact with ground, grounded metal, metal lath, or other conductive material, and if guarded against contact by persons shall not be required to be grounded.

Exception No. 2: Short sections of metal enclosures used to provide support or protection of cable assemblies from physical damage shall not be required to be grounded.

E. Equipment Grounding

250-42. Equipment Fastened in Place or Connected by Permanent Wiring Methods (Fixed). Exposed noncurrent-carrying metal parts of fixed equipment likely to become energized shall be grounded under any of the conditions in (a) through (f) below.

(a) Vertical and Horizontal Distances. Where within 8 feet (2.44 m) vertically or 5 feet (1.52 m) horizontally of ground or grounded metal objects and subject to contact by persons.

Exposed noncurrent-carrying metal parts of fixed equipment not likely to become energized are not required to be grounded. This includes some metal nameplates on nonmetallic enclosures, and small parts such as bolts and screws so located that they are not likely to become energized.

Snap and dimmer switches in nonmetallic boxes indoors with nonmetallic faceplates, or even with metal faceplates, are not usually considered likely to become energized, and therefore are usually not required to be grounded. There is no evidence that this widespread practice has resulted in any problems.

(b) Wet or Damp Locations. Where located in a wet or damp location and not isolated.

(c) Electrical Contact. Where in electrical contact with metal.

(d) Hazardous (Classified) Locations. Where in a hazardous (classified) location as covered by Articles 500 through 517.

(e) Wiring Methods. Where supplied by a metal-clad, metal-sheathed, metal-raceway, or other wiring method which provides an equipment ground, except as permitted by Section 250-33 for short sections of metal enclosures.

(f) Over 150 Volts to Ground. Where equipment operates with any terminal at over 150 volts to ground.

Exception No. 1: Enclosures for switches or circuit breakers used for other than service equipment and accessible to qualified persons only.

Exception No. 2: Metal frames of electrically heated appliances, exempted by special permission, in which case the frames shall be permanently and effectively insulated from ground.

Exception No. 3: Distribution apparatus, such as transformer and capacitor cases, mounted on wooden poles, at a height exceeding 8 feet (2.44 m) above ground or grade level.

Exception No. 4: Listed information processing and listed office equipment protected by a system of double insulation, or its equivalent, shall not be required to be grounded. Where such a system is employed, the equipment shall be distinctively marked.

250-43. Fastened in Place or Connected by Permanent Wiring Methods (Fixed) — Specific. Exposed, noncurrent-carrying metal parts of the kinds of equipment described in (a) through (j) below, regardless of voltage, shall be grounded.

(a) Switchboard Frames and Structures. Switchboard frames and structures supporting switching equipment.

Exception: Frames of two-wire dc switchboards where effectively insulated.

(b) Organs. Generator and motor frames in an electrically operated organ.

Exception: Where the generator is effectively insulated from ground and from the motor driving it.

(c) Motor Frames. Motor frames, as provided by Section 430-142.

(d) Enclosures for Motor Controllers. Enclosures for motor controllers.

Exception: Lined covers of snap switches.

(e) Elevators and Cranes. Electric equipment for elevators and cranes.

(f) Garages, Theaters, and Motion Picture Studios. Electric equipment in garages, theaters, and motion picture studios.

Exception: Pendant lampholders supplied by circuits not over 150 volts to ground.

(g) Electric Signs. Electric signs and associated equipment.

Exception: Where insulated from ground and from other conductive objects and accessible only to qualified persons.

(h) Motion Picture Projection Equipment. Motion picture projection equipment.

(i) Class 1, Class 2, and Class 3 Circuits. Equipment supplied by Class 1, Class 2, and Class 3 remote-control and signaling circuits where required to be grounded by Part B of this article.

(j) Lighting Fixtures. Lighting fixtures as provided in Part E of Article 410.

250-44. Nonelectric Equipment. The metal parts of nonelectric equipment described in (a) through (e) below shall be grounded.

(a) Cranes. Frames and tracks of electrically operated cranes.

(b) Elevator Cars. Frames of nonelectrically driven elevator cars to which electric conductors are attached.

(c) Electric Elevators. Hand-operated metal shifting ropes or cables of electric elevators.

(d) Metal Partitions. Metal partitions, grill work, and similar metal enclosures around equipment of 1 kV and over between conductors except substations or vaults under the sole control of the supply company.

(e) Mobile Homes and Recreational Vehicles. Mobile homes and recreational vehicles as required in Articles 550 and 551.

(FPN): Where extensive metal in or on buildings may become energized and is subject to personal contact, adequate bonding and grounding will provide additional safety.

This fine print note is addressing such constructions as metal siding on buildings. As this is not electric equipment, it is outside the scope of the *National Electrical Code* [see Section 90-2(a)], and the *Code* cannot require that it be grounded. Grounding of metal siding that is likely to become energized and is subject to contact by persons is, however, an excellent safety precaution.

See Section 547-8 for grounding and bonding of agricultural buildings.

250-45. Equipment Connected by Cord and Plug. Under any of the conditions described in (a) through (d) below, exposed noncurrent-carrying metal parts of cord- and plug-connected equipment likely to become energized shall be grounded.

(a) In Hazardous (Classified) Locations. In hazardous (classified) locations (see Articles 500 through 517).

(b) Over 150 Volts to Ground. Where operated at over 150 volts to ground.

Exception No. 1: Motors, where guarded.

Exception No. 2: Metal frames of electrically heated appliances, exempted by special permission, in which case the frames shall be permanently and effectively insulated from ground.

Exception No. 3: Listed information processing and listed office equipment protected by a system of double insulation, or its equivalent, shall not be required to be grounded. Where such a system is employed, the equipment shall be distinctively marked.

(c) In Residential Occupancies. In residential occupancies: (1) refrigerators, freezers, and air conditioners; (2) clothes-washing, clothes-drying, dish-washing machines, sump pumps, electrical aquarium equipment; (3) hand-held motor-operated tools; (4) motor-operated appliances of the following types: hedge clippers, lawn mowers, snow blowers, and wet scrubbers; (5) portable handlamps.

Exception: Listed tools and listed appliances protected by a system of double insulation, or its equivalent, shall not be required to be grounded. Where such a system is employed, the equipment shall be distinctively marked.

(d) In Other than Residential Occupancies. In other than residential occupancies: (1) refrigerators, freezers, and air conditioners; (2) clothes-washing, clothes-drying, dish-washing machines, electronic computer/data processing equipment, sump pumps, electrical aquarium equipment; (3) hand-held motor-operated tools; (4) motor-operated appliances of the following types: hedge clippers, lawn mowers, snow blowers, and wet scrubbers; (5) cord- and plug-connected appliances used in damp or wet locations or by persons standing on the ground or on metal floors or working inside of metal tanks or boilers; (6) tools likely to be used in wet and conductive locations; and (7) portable handlamps.

Exception No. 1: Tools and portable handlamps likely to be used in wet and conductive locations shall not be required to be grounded where supplied through an isolating transformer with an ungrounded secondary of not over 50 volts.

Figure 250-16. Lighting equipment supplied through an isolating transformer operating at 6 or 12 V provides safe illumination for work inside of boilers, tanks, and similar locations that may be metal and/or wet. (*Daniel Woodhead Co.*)

Exception No. 2: Listed portable tools and listed appliances protected by an approved system of double insulation, or its equivalent, shall not be required to be grounded. Where such a system is employed, the equipment shall be distinctively marked.

(FPN): With reference to (c) and (d), portable tools or appliances are not intended to be used in damp, wet or conductive locations unless they are grounded, double insulated or supplied through an isolating transformer.

Tools are required to be grounded by an equipment grounding conductor in a cord or cable supplying the tool, except where supplied by an isolating transformer as permitted by Exception No. 1. Portable tools and appliances protected by an approved system of double insulation are required to be listed by a qualified electrical testing laboratory as being suitable for the purpose, and the equipment is required to be distinctively marked as double insulated.

Cord-connected portable tools or appliances are not intended to be used in damp, wet, or conductive locations, unless supplied by an isolation transformer or protected by an approved system of double insulation.

250-46. Spacing from Lightning Rods. Metal raceways, enclosures, frames, and other noncurrent-carrying metal parts of electric equipment shall be kept at least 6 feet (1.83 m) away from lightning rod conductors, or they shall be bonded to the lightning rod conductors.

(FPN): See Sections 250-86 and 800-31(b)(5). For further information see the Lightning Protection Code, NFPA 78-1983 (ANSI), which contains detailed information on grounding lightning protection systems.

F. Methods of Grounding

250-50. Equipment Grounding Conductor Connections. Equipment grounding conductor connections at the source of separately derived systems shall be made in accordance with Section 250-26(a). Equipment grounding conductor connections at service equipment shall be made as indicated in (a) or (b) below.

(a) For Grounded System. The connection shall be made by bonding the equipment grounding conductor to the grounded service conductor and the grounding electrode conductor.

See Figure 250-17.

Figure 250-17. Grounding for grounded systems, showing connection of equipment grounding bus to the enclosures and the grounded conductor.

(b) For Ungrounded System. The connection shall be made by bonding the equipment grounding conductor to the grounding electrode conductor.

Exception for (a) and (b) above: For replacement of nongrounding-type receptacles with grounding-type receptacles and for branch-circuit extensions only in existing installations that do not have an equipment grounding conductor in the branch circuit, the grounding conductor of a grounding-type receptacle outlet shall be permitted to be grounded to a water pipe which is bonded in accordance with Section 250-80(a).

See Figure 250-18.

Figure 250-18. Branch-circuit extension to existing installation per Section 250-50, Exception for (a) and (b).

(FPN): See Section 210-7(d), Exception, for the use of a ground-fault circuit-interrupter type of receptacle.

250-51. Effective Grounding Path.   The path to ground from circuits, equipment, and conductor enclosures shall: (1) be permanent and continuous; (2) have capacity to conduct safely any fault current likely to be imposed on it; and (3) have sufficiently low impedance to limit the voltage to ground and to facilitate the operation of the circuit protective devices in the circuit. The earth shall not be used as the sole equipment grounding conductor.

This statement, while new in Section 250-51 for the 1987 *NEC*, is not a new requirement. See Section 250-91(c), where the same statement has appeared for many years.

250-53. Grounding Path to Grounding Electrode at Services.

(a) Grounding Electrode Conductor.   A grounding electrode conductor shall be used to connect the equipment grounding conductors, the service-equipment enclosures and, where the system is grounded, the grounded service conductor to the grounding electrode.

(FPN): See Section 250-23(a).

Reference to Section 250-23(a) directs the reader to more detailed specifications for connecting the grounding electrode conductor.

(b) Main Bonding Jumper.   For a grounded system, an unspliced main bonding jumper shall be used to connect the equipment grounding conductor and the service-equipment enclosure to the grounded conductor of the system within the service equipment or within the service conductor enclosure.

250-54. Common Grounding Electrode.   Where an ac system is connected to a grounding electrode in or at a building as specified in Sections 250-23 and 250-24, the same electrode shall be used to ground conductor enclosures and equipment in or on that building. Where separate services supply a building and are required to be connected to a grounding electrode, the same grounding electrode shall be used.

Two or more grounding electrodes that are effectively bonded together shall be considered as a single grounding electrode system in this sense.

250-55. Underground Service Cable.   Where served from a continuous underground metal-sheathed cable system, the sheath or armor of underground service cable metallically connected to the underground system, or underground service conduit containing a metal-sheathed cable bonded to the underground system, shall not be required to be grounded at the building and shall be permitted to be insulated from the interior conduit or piping.

250-56. Short Sections of Raceway.   Isolated sections of metal raceway or cable armor, where required to be grounded, shall be grounded in accordance with Section 250-57.

250-57. Equipment Fastened in Place or Connected by Permanent Wiring Methods (Fixed) — Grounding.   Noncurrent-carrying metal parts of equipment, raceways, and other enclosures, where required to be grounded, shall be grounded by one of the methods indicated in (a) or (b) below.

Exception: Where equipment, raceways, and enclosures are grounded by connection to the grounded circuit conductor as permitted by Sections 250-24, 250-60, and 250-61.

This exception eliminates any possible conflict between Section 250-57, which requires an equipment grounding conductor to be used for equipment grounding, and Sections 250-24, 250-60, and 250-61, which permit the grounded circuit conductor to be used for equipment grounding if certain specified conditions are met.

(a) **Equipment Grounding Conductor Types.**   By any of the equipment grounding conductors permitted by Section 250-91(b).

(b) **With Circuit Conductors.**   By an equipment grounding conductor contained within the same raceway, cable, or cord or otherwise run with the circuit conductors. Bare, covered or insulated equipment grounding conductors shall be permitted. Individually covered or insulated equipment grounding conductors shall have a continuous outer finish that is either green, or green with one or more yellow stripes.

It is necessary to run the equipment grounding conductor with the circuit conductors on alternating current circuits to keep the ac impedance of the equipment grounding conductor as low as possible.

Exception No. 1: An insulated or covered conductor larger than No. 6 copper or aluminum shall, at the time of installation, be permitted to be permanently identified as an equipment grounding conductor at each end and at every point where the conductor is accessible. Identification shall be accomplished by one of the following:

a. Stripping the insulation or covering from the entire exposed length,

b. Coloring the exposed insulation or covering green, or

c. Marking the exposed insulation or covering with green colored tape or green colored adhesive labels.

Exception No. 2: For direct-current circuits only, the equipment grounding conductor shall be permitted to be run separately from the circuit conductors.

See commentary following Section 250-57(b). The same problems occur on dc circuits.

Exception No. 3: Where the conditions of maintenance and supervision assure that only qualified persons will service the installation, an insulated conductor in a multiconductor cable shall, at the time of installation, be permitted to be permanently identified as an equipment grounding conductor at each end and at every point where the conductor is accessible by one of the following means:

a. Stripping the insulation from the entire exposed length,

b. Coloring the exposed insulation green, or

c. Marking the exposed insulation with green tape or green colored adhesive labels.

(FPN): See Section 250-79 for equipment bonding jumper requirements.

(FPN): See Section 400-7 for use of cords for fixed equipment.

250-58. Equipment Considered Effectively Grounded.   Under the conditions specified in (a) and (b) below, the noncurrent-carrying metal parts of the equipment shall be considered effectively grounded.

(a) Equipment Secured to Grounded Metal Supports.   Electric equipment secured to and in electrical contact with a metal rack or structure provided for its support and grounded by one of the means indicated in Section 250-57. The structural metal frame of a building shall not be used as the required equipment grounding conductor for ac equipment.

See Figure 250-19.

Figure 250-19. Example of equipment grounding on metal rack.

(b) Metal Car Frames.   Metal car frames supported by metal hoisting cables attached to or running over metal sheaves or drums of elevator machines which are grounded by one of the methods indicated in Section 250-57.

250-59. Cord- and Plug-Connected Equipment.   Noncurrent-carrying metal parts of cord- and plug-connected equipment, where required to be grounded, shall be grounded by one of the methods indicated in (a), (b), or (c) below.

(a) By Means of the Metal Enclosure. By means of the metal enclosure of the conductors supplying such equipment if a grounding-type attachment plug with one fixed grounding contact is used for grounding the metal enclosure, and if the metal enclosure of the conductors is secured to the attachment plug and to equipment by approved connectors.

Exception: A self-restoring grounding contact shall be permitted on grounding-type attachment plugs used on the power supply cord of portable hand-held, hand-guided, or hand-supported tools or appliances.

(b) By Means of a Grounding Conductor. By means of an equipment grounding conductor run with the power supply conductors in a cable assembly or flexible cord properly terminated in grounding-type attachment plug with one fixed grounding contact. An uninsulated equipment grounding conductor shall be permitted but, if individually covered, the covering shall have a continuous outer finish that is either green or green with one or more yellow stripes.

Exception: A self-restoring grounding contact shall be permitted on grounding-type attachment plugs used on the power supply cord of portable hand-held, hand-guided, or hand-supported tools or appliances.

(c) Separate Flexible Wire or Strap. By means of a separate flexible wire or strap, insulated or bare, protected as well as practicable against physical damage, where part of equipment.

250-60. Frames of Ranges and Clothes Dryers. Frames of electric ranges, wall-mounted ovens, counter-mounted cooking units, clothes dryers, and outlet or junction boxes which are part of the circuit for these appliances shall be grounded in the manner specified by Section 250-57 or 250-59; or, except for mobile homes and recreational vehicles, shall be permitted to be grounded to the grounded circuit conductor if all of the conditions indicated in (a) through (d) below are met.

(a) The supply circuit is 120/240-volt, single-phase, 3-wire; or 208Y/120-volt derived from a 3-phase, 4-wire, wye-connected system.

(b) The grounded conductor is not smaller than No. 10 copper or No. 8 aluminum.

(c) The grounded conductor is insulated; or the grounded conductor is uninsulated and part of a Type SE service-entrance cable and the branch circuit originates at the service equipment.

(d) Grounding contacts of receptacles furnished as part of the equipment are bonded to the equipment.

The grounded circuit conductor (neutral) is permitted to be used to ground the frame of an electric range, wall-mounted oven, or counter-mounted cooking unit, provided all the conditions of (a) through (d) are met. The grounded circuit conductor is also permitted to be used to ground any junction boxes in the circuit supplying the appliance, and a 3-wire pigtail and range receptacle is permitted to be used regardless of whether or not the circuit to the receptacle contains a separate equipment grounding conductor.

The use of the grounded circuit conductor for grounding purposes is contrary to other requirements of the *Code*. See commentary following Section 250-61(b). However, it has been allowed for many years because of the good safety record of these particular appliances that are grounded through the grounded circuit conductor and because an open splice or break in the grounded circuit conductor would normally render the appliance inoperable. A subcommittee reevaluated this requirement for the 1984 *NEC* and verified the continued good safety record.

Where service-entrance cable with an uninsulated neutral is used, it is required that the circuit originate from the service equipment in order to avoid multiple grounding from downstream panelboards. Multiple grounding downstream would raise the potential of all exposed dead metal parts of equipment using this downstream grounding point for equipment grounding by an amount equal to the voltage drop along the neutral, a current-carrying conductor. Thus, under normal conditions adjacent exposed "dead metal" parts could be at a potential difference of several volts.

250-61. Use of Grounded Circuit Conductor for Grounding Equipment.

(a) Supply-Side Equipment. A grounded circuit conductor shall be permitted to ground noncurrent-carrying metal parts of equipment, raceways, and other enclosures on the supply side of the service disconnecting means, and on the supply side of the main disconnecting means for separate buildings as provided in Section 250-24.

(b) Load-Side Equipment. A grounded circuit conductor shall not be used for grounding noncurrent-carrying metal parts of equipment on the load side of the service disconnecting means or on the load side of a separately derived system disconnecting means or the overcurrent devices for a separately derived system not having a main disconnecting means.

One major reason that the grounded circuit conductor is not permitted (except as noted in Section 250-60) to be grounded on the load side of the service is that, should the grounded service conductor become disconnected at any point on the line side of the ground, the equipment grounding conductor and all conductive parts connected to this equipment grounding conductor will carry the neutral current, raising the potential to ground of exposed metal parts not normally intended to carry current. This could result in arcing in concealed spaces, and it could be a severe shock hazard, particularly should a single point in the path be opened inadvertently by a workman, a plumber for example. However, even without an open grounded conductor (usually referred to as an open neutral), the equipment grounding conductor path will become a parallel path with the grounded conductor, and there will be some potential drop on exposed and concealed dead metal parts, the size of this potential drop being determined by the relative impedances of the equipment grounding path and grounded conductor circuits. Not only would the equipment grounding conductor path be affected, but all parallel paths not depended upon as an equipment grounding conductor. This could involve current flowing through metal building structures, piping, and ducts.

Exception No. 1: The frames of ranges, wall-mounted ovens, counter-mounted cooking units, and clothes dryers under the conditions specified by Section 250-60.

Exception No. 2: As permitted in Section 250-24 for separate buildings.

Exception No. 3: It shall be permissible to ground meter enclosures by connection to the grounded circuit conductor on the load-side of the service disconnect if:

a. No service ground-fault protection is installed; and

b. All meter enclosures are located near the service disconnecting means.

Exception No. 4: As required in Sections 710-72(e)(1) and 710-74.

250-62. Multiple Circuit Connections.
Where equipment is required to be grounded, and is supplied by separate connection to more than one circuit or grounded premises wiring system, a means for grounding shall be provided for each such connection as specified in Sections 250-57 and 250-59.

G. Bonding

250-70. General. Bonding shall be provided where necessary to assure electrical continuity and the capacity to conduct safely any fault current likely to be imposed.

250-71. Service Equipment.

(a) Bonding of Service Equipment. The noncurrent-carrying metal parts of equipment indicated in (1), (2) and (3) below shall be effectively bonded together.

(1) Except as permitted in Section 250-55, the service raceways, cable trays, or service cable armor or sheath.

Figure 250-20. Two different types of grounding and bonding arrangements. On the left is shown a grounding electrode conductor at the meter housing with the service equipment enclosure bonded to the grounded service conductor. On the right is shown the grounding electrode conductor at the service equipment and the meter housing bonded to the grounded service conductor.

(2) All service equipment enclosures containing service conductors, including meter fittings, boxes, or the like, interposed in the service raceway or armor.

(3) Any metallic raceway or armor enclosing a grounding electrode conductor as permitted in Section 250-92(a).

(b) Bonding to Other Systems. At dwellings, an accessible means external to enclosures for connecting intersystem bonding and grounding conductors shall be provided at the service by at least one of the following means:

(1) Exposed metallic service raceways.

(2) Exposed grounding electrode conductor.

(3) Approved means for the external connection of a bonding, or grounding conductor to the service raceway or equipment.

(FPN): A No. 6 copper conductor with one end bonded to the service raceway or equipment and with 6 inches (152 mm) or more of the other end made accessible on the outside wall of the dwelling is an example of the approved means covered in (b)(3).

See Figure 250-22 for another means.

(FPN): See Sections 800-31 and 820-22 for bonding and grounding requirements for communication and CATV circuits.

The *Code* requires that separate systems be bonded together to reduce differences of potential between them, which can result from lightning or power contacts. Interconnection is required for lightning rod systems (Section 250-46), communications systems [Section 800-31(b)(5)], and CATV systems [Section 820-22(f)]. Lack of interconnection can result in a severe shock and fire hazard.

The reason for this is as follows. See Figure 250-21, which shows a CATV cable with the jacket grounded to a separate ground rod and not bonded to the power ground. This cable is connected to the tuner of a television set inside a home. Also connected to the tuner is the 120-volt supply, with one conductor grounded at the service (the power ground). In each case there will be a DC resistance to ground at the grounding electrode, as shown in the equivalent circuit. This resistance to ground will vary widely, depending on soil conditions and the type of grounding electrode. The resistance at the CATV ground is likely to be higher than the power ground resistance because the power ground is often an underground metal water piping system or concrete-encased electrode, whereas the CATV ground is commonly a 4-ft ground rod.

Assume that there is a current induced in the power line by a switching surge or a nearby lightning strike so that a momentary current of 1,000 amperes flows over the power line to the power line ground. This amount of current is not unusual under such circumstances. It could be, and often is, considerably more. Also assume that the power ground has a resistance (Rp) of 10 ohms, a *very* low value in most circumstances. A single ground rod in average soil has a resistance to ground in the neighborhood of 40 ohms. According to Ohm's law, point B will be raised momentarily to a potential of $1,000 \times 10 = 10,000$ volts, resulting in a potential of 10,000 volts between points A and B, and anything connected to them, in this case parts within the tuner. This voltage would also exist between the grounded conductor within the CATV cable and grounded surfaces in the walls of the home, such as water pipes (which are connected to the power ground), and over which the cable runs. This potential could also appear across a person with one hand on the CATV cable and the other on a metal surface connected to the power ground (a radiator or refrigerator, for example). The 10,000 volts calculated above is more likely to be many times this value, as extremely low (below normal) values were assumed for both the resistance to ground and the current. However, most insulation systems are not designed to withstand even 10,000 V. Even if the insulation system does withstand this voltage surge, it is likely to be damaged. Breakdown of the insulation system will result in sparking.

The same situation would exist if the current surge was on the CATV cable or on a telephone line. The only difference would be the voltage involved, depending on the individual resistance to ground of the grounding electrodes.

The solution is to bond between points A and B, or to connect the CATV cable jacket to the power ground, and this is exactly what the *Code* requires. Thus, even though point A is raised to some very high voltage above ground, so is point B, and no voltage exists between the two grounding systems.

These rules are provided because of the difficulties encountered by communications and CATV installers in trying to comply with *Code* grounding and bonding requirements, particularly in residences, because of the increasing use of plastic for water pipe, fittings, water meters, and service conduit. In the past, bonding between communications, CATV, and power systems was usually achieved by connecting the communications protector grounds or cable shield to an interior metallic water pipe, because the pipe was often used as the power grounding electrode. Thus, the requirement that the power, communications, CATV cable shield, and metallic water piping systems be bonded together was easily satisfied. In the event that the power was grounded to one of the other electrodes permitted by the *Code*, usually by use of a made electrode such as a ground rod, the bond was connected to the power grounding electrode conductor or to a metallic service

213

Figure 250-21. Illustration of why bonding between different systems is necessary. See commentary above.

raceway, since at least one of these was usually accessible. With the growing proliferation of plastic water pipe, the increasing tendency for the service equipment to be installed in finished areas where the grounding electrode conductor is often concealed (and flush-mounted service equipment installed), as well as the use of plastic service-entrance conduit, communications and CATV installers no longer have access to a point for connecting bonding jumpers or grounding conductors. See Figure 250-22. See also the commentary to Section 820-22(h).

250-72. Method of Bonding Service Equipment. Electrical continuity at service equipment shall be assured by one of the methods specified in (a) through (e) below.

(a) Grounded Service Conductor. Bonding equipment to the grounded service conductor in a manner provided in Section 250-113.

(b) Threaded Couplings. Threaded couplings and threaded bosses on enclosures with joints shall be made up wrenchtight where rigid metal conduit and intermediate metal conduit are involved.

(c) Threadless Couplings and Connectors. Threadless couplings and connectors made up tight for rigid metal conduit, intermediate metal conduit and electrical metallic tubing. Standard locknuts or bushings shall not be used for the bonding required by this section.

External
connection

Figure 250-22. An external accessible means for
connecting intersystem bonding and grounding
conductors for dwellings to provide a bonding
point for such systems as communication and
CATV circuits.

(d) Bonding Jumpers. Bonding jumpers meeting the other requirements of this article
shall be used around concentric or eccentric knockouts that are punched or otherwise formed so
as to impair the electrical connection to ground.

(e) Other Devices. Other approved devices, such as bonding-type locknuts and bushings.

Note that paragraph (e) requires bonding-type locknuts. Standard locknuts or
sealing locknuts are not acceptable for bonding at service equipment.

Bonding bushings for use with rigid or intermediate metal conduit are provided
with means (usually one or more setscrews) for reliably bonding the bushing (and
the conduit on which it is threaded) to the metal equipment enclosure or box.
When means for connecting a grounding conductor or bonding jumper are not
provided, and there is need for such a conductor, a grounding-type bushing is
required to be used.

Grounding-type bushings used with rigid or intermediate metal conduit have
provisions for the connection of a bonding jumper or have means for mounting a
wire connector available from the manufacturer. This type of bushing may also
have means (usually one or more setscrews) which are used for reliably bonding the
bushing to the metal equipment enclosure or box in the same manner that is
accomplished by a bonding jumper.

Figure 250-23. A grounding bushing used to connect a copper
bonding or grounding wire to a conduit. (*The Thomas & Betts Co.,
Inc.*)

250-73. Metal Armor or Tape of Service Cable. The metal covering of service cable having
an uninsulated grounded service conductor in continuous electrical contact with its metallic
armor or tape shall be considered to be grounded.

Figures 250-24 and 250-25. Figure 250-24 (left) shows a grounding wedge lug for providing an electrical connection between a conduit and a box. Figure 250-25 (right) shows the manner in which the lug is installed. (*The Thomas & Betts Co., Inc.*)

Figure 250-26. A threaded grounding bushing showing openings for set screws to assure electrical and mechanical connection. (*General Electric Co.*)

250-74. Connecting Receptacle Grounding Terminal to Box. An equipment bonding jumper shall be used to connect the grounding terminal of a grounding-type receptacle to a grounded box.

Exception No. 1: Where the box is surface mounted, direct metal-to-metal contact between the device yoke and the box shall be permitted to ground the receptacle to the box. This Exception shall not apply to cover-mounted receptacles unless the box and cover combination are listed as providing satisfactory ground continuity between the box and the receptacle.

Exception No. 2: Contact devices or yokes designed and listed for the purpose shall be permitted in conjunction with the supporting screws to establish the grounding circuit between the device yoke and flush-type boxes.

See Figure 250-27.

Exception No. 3: Floor boxes designed for and listed as providing satisfactory ground continuity between the box and the device.

To ground →

Nonmetallic cable
(Can also be used with
metallic cable)

Spring-type grounding
strap for holding
mounting screw

Bonding jumper
eliminated

Box ground
screw

Grounding
strap

Figure 250-27. Receptacle designed with spring-type grounding strap which holds mounting screw captive and eliminates a bonding jumper to box in accordance with Exception No. 2 of Section 250-74.

Exception No. 4: Where required for the reduction of electrical noise (electromagnetic interference) on the grounding circuit, a receptacle in which the grounding terminal is purposely insulated from the receptacle mounting means shall be permitted. The receptacle grounding terminal shall be grounded by an insulated equipment grounding conductor run with the circuit conductors. This grounding conductor shall be permitted to pass through one or more panelboards without connection to the panelboard grounding terminal as permitted in Section 384-27, Exception No. 1, so as to terminate directly at an equipment grounding conductor terminal of the applicable derived system or service.

It is essential to run the equipment grounding conductor with the circuit conductors to maintain low alternating current impedance in the grounding path.

(FPN): Use of an isolated equipment grounding conductor does not relieve the requirement for grounding the raceway system and outlet box.

This fine print note is a reminder that metallic raceways and boxes are still required to be grounded in the usual manner. This could require a separate grounding conductor, for example, to ground a metal box in a nonmetallic raceway system, or to ground flexible metal conduit. Use of an existing equipment grounding conductor as the isolated receptacle grounding conductor, when replacing an ordinary grounding-type receptacle with an isolated ground receptacle, could effectively defeat or seriously compromise the required box or raceway equipment ground.

250-75. Bonding Other Enclosures. Metal raceways, cable trays, cable armor, cable sheath, enclosures, frames, fittings, and other metal noncurrent-carrying parts that are to serve as grounding conductors with or without the use of supplementary equipment grounding conductors shall be effectively bonded where necessary to assure electrical continuity and the capacity to conduct safely any fault current likely to be imposed on them. Any nonconductive paint, enamel, or similar coating shall be removed at threads, contact points, and contact surfaces or be connected by means of fittings so designed as to make such removal unnecessary.

250-76. Bonding for Over 250 Volts. For circuits of over 250 volts to ground, the electrical continuity of metal raceways and cables with metal sheaths that contain any conductor other than

217

service conductors shall be assured by one or more of the methods specified for services in Section 250-72(b) through (e).

Exception: Where oversized, concentric, or eccentric knockouts are not encountered, the following methods shall be permitted:

a. Threadless couplings and connectors for cables with metal sheaths.

b. Two locknuts, on rigid metal conduit, or intermediate metal conduit, one inside and one outside of boxes and cabinets.

c. Fittings with shoulders that seat firmly against the box or cabinet, such as electrical metallic tubing connectors, flexible metallic conduit connectors and cable connectors, with one locknut on the inside of boxes and cabinets.

The methods in a., b., and c. are permitted *only* where there are no oversize, concentric, or eccentric knockouts. Also, when these conditions are met, fittings, such as EMT connectors, cable connectors, etc., that have their shoulders firmly seated against the full metal of a box or cabinet are permitted to have only one locknut located on the inside of the box.

250-77. Bonding Loosely Jointed Metal Raceways. Expansion joints and telescoping sections of raceways shall be made electrically continuous by equipment bonding jumpers or other means.

250-78. Bonding in Hazardous (Classified) Locations. Regardless of the voltage of the electrical system, the electrical continuity of noncurrent-carrying metal parts of equipment, raceways, and other enclosures in any hazardous (classified) location as defined in Article 500 shall be assured by any of the methods specified for services in Section 250-72(b) through (e) that are approved for the wiring method used.

250-79. Main and Equipment Bonding Jumpers.

(a) Material. Main and equipment bonding jumpers shall be of copper or other corrosion-resistant material. A main bonding jumper shall be a wire, bus, screw, or similar suitable conductor.

(b) Attachment. Main and equipment bonding jumpers shall be attached in the manner specified by the applicable provisions of Section 250-113 for circuits and equipment and by Section 250-115 for grounding electrodes.

(c) Size — Equipment Bonding Jumper on Supply Side of Service and Main Bonding Jumper. The bonding jumper shall not be smaller than the sizes given in Table 250-94 for grounding electrode conductors. Where the service-entrance phase conductors are larger than 1100 MCM copper or 1750 MCM aluminum, the bonding jumper shall have an area not less than 12½ percent of the area of the largest phase conductor except that where the phase conductors and the bonding jumper are of different materials (copper or aluminum), the minimum size of the bonding jumper shall be based on the assumed use of phase conductors of the same material as the bonding jumper and with an ampacity equivalent to that of the installed phase conductors. Where the service-entrance conductors are paralleled in two or more raceways or cables, the equipment bonding jumper, where routed with the raceways or cables, shall be run in parallel. The size of the bonding jumper for each raceway or cable shall be based on the size of the service-entrance conductors in each raceway or cable.

Types MI and MC cable are also permitted to be used for services. See Section 230-43.

The size required for the equipment bonding jumper and the main bonding jumper on the supply side of a service is the same as the required size for the grounding electrode conductor taken from Table 250-94 (including the 12½ percent requirement for phase conductors larger than 1100 MCM copper or 1750 MCM aluminum).

Example: In applying the bonding requirements of Figure 250-13, if one of the switches is rated 100 A and the supply conductors are No. 2 AWG Type THW copper conductors, Table 250-94 requires a grounding electrode conductor sized at No. 8 AWG copper or No. 6 AWG aluminum or copper-clad aluminum. The bonding jumper would also be sized at No. 8 AWG copper or No. 6 AWG aluminum or copper-clad aluminum.

If another switch is rated at 200 A and the conductors supplying it are No. 3/0 AWG Type THW copper, the grounding electrode conductor and the bonding jumper are required to be sized at a minimum of No. 4 AWG copper or No. 2 AWG aluminum or copper-clad aluminum.

To apply the bonding jumper requirements, each switch should be treated as separate service equipment, and Table 250-94 should be used to determine the size of the bonding jumper.

In some instances, the bonding jumper may be required to be larger than the grounding electrode conductor. Section 250-79(c) indicates that, where the service-entrance conductors are larger than 1100 MCM copper or 1750 MCM aluminum, the bonding jumper is required to have a cross-sectional area of not less than 12½ percent of the cross-sectional area of the largest phase conductor. For example, if a service is supplied by four 500 MCM conductors in parallel for each phase, the minimum cross-sectional area of the bonding jumper is required to be 250 MCM (4 × 500 MCM = 2000 MCM × .125). See Table 8, Conductor Properties, in Chapter 9 for area in circular mils of AWG and MCM conductors.

(d) Size — Equipment Bonding Jumper on Load Side of Service. The equipment bonding jumper on the load side of the service overcurrent devices shall not be smaller than the sizes listed by Table 250-95 for equipment grounding conductors. A single common continuous equipment bonding jumper shall be permitted to bond two or more raceways or cables where the bonding jumper is sized in accordance with Table 250-95 for the largest overcurrent device supplying circuits therein.

Exception: The equipment bonding jumper shall not be required to be larger than the circuit conductors supplying the equipment, but shall not be smaller than No. 14 AWG.

(e) Installation — Equipment Bonding Jumper. The equipment bonding jumper shall be permitted to be installed inside or outside of a raceway or enclosure. Where installed on the outside, the length of the equipment bonding jumper shall not exceed 6 feet (1.83 m) and shall be routed with the raceway or enclosure. Where installed inside of a raceway, the equipment bonding jumper shall comply with the requirements of Section 310-12(b).

In many applications it is necessary to install equipment bonding jumpers on the outside of metal raceways and enclosures. For example, it would be impractical to install the bonding jumper for a conduit expansion joint on the inside of the conduit. For some metal raceway and rigid conduit systems and conduit systems in hazardous (classified) locations, it is desirable to install the bonding jumper where it is visible and is accessible for inspection and maintenance. An external bonding jumper will have a higher impedance than an internal bonding jumper. However, by limiting the length to 6 ft and routing it with the raceway, there will not be a significant increase in the total impedance of the equipment grounding circuit. For example, this rule permits an exterior bonding jumper where run around a section

219

of flexible metal conduit. See Figure 250-28. Since the function of a bonding jumper is readily apparent, color identification is not necessary.

Figure 250-28. Bonding around outside of flexible metal conduit.

250-80. Bonding of Piping Systems.

(a) Metal Water Piping. The interior metal water piping system shall be bonded to the service equipment enclosure, the grounded conductor at the service, the grounding electrode conductor where of sufficient size, or to the one or more grounding electrodes used. The bonding jumper shall be sized in accordance with Table 250-94. The points of attachment of the bonding jumper shall be accessible.

This section requires a single connection to the interior metal water piping system. However, some judgment must be exercised in each specific case. Where it cannot reasonably be concluded that the hot and cold water pipes are reliably interconnected, then an electrical bonding jumper is required to assure that this connection is made.

Exception: In buildings of multiple occupancy, where the interior metal water piping system for the individual occupancies is metallically isolated from all other occupancies by use of nonmetallic water piping, the interior metal water piping system for each occupancy shall be permitted to be bonded to the panelboard or switchboard enclosure (other than service equipment) supplying that occupancy. The bonding jumper shall be sized in accordance with Table 250-95.

The intent of the exception is to recognize the fact that increased use of nonmetallic water piping systems underground makes it virtually impossible to comply with the main rule of Section 250-80 in the circumstances described.

(b) Other Metal Piping. Interior metal piping which may become energized shall be bonded to the service equipment enclosure, the grounded conductor at the service, the grounding electrode conductor where of sufficient size, or to the one or more grounding electrodes used. The bonding jumper shall be sized in accordance with Table 250-95 using the rating of the circuit which may energize the piping.

The equipment grounding conductor for the circuit which may energize the piping shall be permitted to serve as the bonding means.

(FPN): Bonding all piping and metal air ducts within the premises will provide additional safety.

Paragraph 3.14a. of the *National Fuel Gas Code*, NFPA 54-1984, ANSI Z223.1-1984, requires that each aboveground portion of a gas piping system upstream from the equipment shutoff valve shall be electrically continuous and bonded to any grounding electrode, as defined by the *National Electrical Code*, ANSI/NFPA 70.

H. Grounding Electrode System

250-81. Grounding Electrode System. If available on the premises at each building or structure served, each item (a) through (d) below shall be bonded together to form the grounding electrode system. The bonding jumper shall be installed in accordance with Section 250-92(a), shall be sized in accordance with Section 250-94, and shall be connected in the manner specified in Section 250-115. The unspliced grounding electrode conductor shall be permitted to run to any convenient grounding electrode available in the grounding electrode system. It shall be sized for the largest grounding electrode conductor required among all the available electrodes.

(a) Metal Underground Water Pipe. A metal underground water pipe in direct contact with the earth for 10 feet (3.05 m) or more (including any metal well casing effectively bonded to the pipe) and electrically continuous (or made electrically continuous by bonding around insulating joints or sections or insulating pipe) to the points of connection of the grounding electrode conductor and the bonding conductors. Continuity of the grounding path or the bonding connection to interior piping shall not rely on water meters. A metal underground water pipe shall be supplemented by an additional electrode of a type specified in Section 250-81 or in Section 250-83. The supplemental electrode shall be permitted to be bonded to the grounding electrode conductor, the grounded service-entrance conductor, the grounded service raceway, any grounded service enclosure, or the interior metal water piping at any convenient point.

The connection of a supplemental grounding electrode conductor to "any service" enclosure on the supply side of the service disconnecting means in reality connects the grounding electrode conductor to the grounded service-entrance conductor.

Where the supplemental electrode is a made electrode as in Section 250-83(c) or (d), that portion of the bonding jumper which is the sole connection to the supplemental grounding electrode shall not be required to be larger than No. 6 copper wire or No. 4 aluminum wire.

This paragraph correlates with Section 250-83(c) or (d) and Section 250-94. If a "made electrode" is utilized, the size of the "sole" bonding jumper between the service equipment grounded conductor and, for example, a ground rod does not have to be larger than No. 6 AWG copper or No. 4 AWG aluminum.

The requirement to supplement the metal water pipe is based on the practice of using a plastic pipe for replacement when the original metal water pipe fails from corrosion, which leaves the system without a grounding electrode where the supplementary electrode is not provided.

(b) Metal Frame of the Building. The metal frame of the building, where effectively grounded.

(c) Concrete-Encased Electrode. An electrode encased by at least 2 inches (50.8 mm) of concrete, located within and near the bottom of a concrete foundation or footing that is in direct contact with the earth, consisting of at least 20 feet (6.1 m) of one or more steel reinforcing bars or rods of not less than ½ inch (12.7 mm) diameter, or consisting of at least 20 feet (6.1 m) of bare copper conductor not smaller than No. 4 AWG.

(d) Ground Ring. A ground ring encircling the building or structure, in direct contact with the earth at a depth below earth surface not less than 2½ feet (762 mm), consisting of at least 20 feet (6.1 m) of bare copper conductor not smaller than No. 2 AWG.

Grounding
electrode
conductor

Bolted-type
connection device
or exothermic weld

Grounding
electrode

Nonmetallic
protective
sleeve

Concrete foundation

No. 4 AWG or larger bare
copper conductor or steel
reinforcing bar or rod not
less than ½-inch diameter

2 in.
minimum

20 ft
minimum

Direct contact
with earth

Figure 250-29. A concrete-encased electrode.

Section 250-81 requires the metal underground water pipe, the metal frame of the building, a concrete-encased electrode, and a ground-ring type of electrode, only when they are available, to be bonded together to form the grounding electrode system. See Figure 250-30. Where a metal underground water pipe is the only grounding electrode available, it must be supplemented by one of the grounding electrodes specified in Section 250-81 or Section 250-83.

There has always been a degree of misunderstanding as to whether metal water piping systems should be used as a grounding electrode, and a number of years ago the electrical industry and the water works industry formed a committee of all the affected interests to evaluate the use of metal underground water piping systems as the grounding electrode. Based on their findings, the committee issued an authoritative report on this subject. The International Association of Electrical Inspectors published the "Interim Report of the American Research Committee on Grounding" in January 1944 and had reprints made in March 1949.

The National Bureau of Standards in Washington, D.C., has monitored the electrolysis of metal systems because a flow of current at a grounding electrode on dc systems can cause displacement of metal. The results of this monitoring have shown that problems are minimal.

250-83. Made and Other Electrodes. Where none of the electrodes specified in Section 250-81 is available, one or more of the electrodes specified in (a) through (d) below shall be used. Where practicable, made electrodes shall be embedded below permanent moisture level. Made electrodes shall be free from nonconductive coatings, such as paint or enamel. Where more than one electrode is used, each electrode of one grounding system (including that used for lightning rods) shall not be less than 6 feet (1.83 m) from any other electrode of another grounding system.

(FPN): Two or more electrodes that are effectively bonded together are to be treated as a single electrode system in this sense.

(a) Metal Underground Gas Piping System. An electrically continuous metal underground gas piping system that is uninterrupted with insulating sections or joints and without an outer nonconductive coating, and then only if acceptable to and expressly permitted by both the serving gas supplier and the authority having jurisdiction.

Figure 250-30. A grounding electrode system.

Figure 250-31. Section 250-83 requires a spacing of 6 ft between electrodes of different systems. Section 250-84 requires a 6-ft spacing between electrodes of the same system.

Paragraph 3.14b. of the *National Fuel Gas Code*, NFPA 54-1984, ANSI Z223.1-1984, indicates that gas piping shall not be used as a grounding electrode.

(b) Other Local Metal Underground Systems or Structures. Other local metal underground systems or structures, such as piping systems and underground tanks.

(c) Rod and Pipe Electrodes. Rod and pipe electrodes shall not be less than 8 feet (2.44 m) in length and shall consist of the following materials, and shall be installed in the following manner:

(1) Electrodes of pipe or conduit shall not be smaller than ¾-inch trade size and, where of iron or steel, shall have the outer surface galvanized or otherwise metal-coated for corrosion protection.

(2) Electrodes of rods of steel or iron shall be at least ⅝ inch (15.87 mm) in diameter. Nonferrous rods or their equivalent shall be listed and shall be not less than ½ inch (12.7 mm) in diameter.

(3) The electrode shall be installed such that at least 8 feet (2.44 m) of length is in contact with the soil. It shall be driven to a depth of not less than 8 feet (2.44 m) except that where rock bottom is encountered, the electrode shall be driven at an oblique angle not to exceed 45 degrees from the vertical or shall be buried in a trench that is at least 2½ feet (762 mm) deep. The upper end of the electrode shall be flush with or below ground level unless the aboveground end and the grounding electrode conductor attachment are protected against physical damage as specified in Section 250-117.

Figure 250-32. All pipe and rod electrodes must have 8 ft of length in contact with soil regardless of rock bottom and to provide that the upper end of the electrode be flush with or below ground level unless the aboveground portion is protected against physical damage.

(d) Plate Electrodes.   Each plate electrode shall expose not less than 2 square feet (0.186 sq m) of surface to exterior soil. Electrodes of iron or steel plates shall be at least ¼ inch (6.35 mm) in thickness. Electrodes of nonferrous metal shall be at least 0.06 inch (1.52 mm) in thickness.

250-84. Resistance of Made Electrodes.   A single electrode consisting of a rod, pipe, or plate which does not have a resistance to ground of 25 ohms or less shall be augmented by one additional electrode of any of the types specified in Section 250-81 or 250-83. Where multiple rod, pipe, or plate electrodes are installed to meet the requirements of this section, they shall be not less than 6 feet (1.83 m) apart.

(FPN): The paralleling efficiency of rods longer than 8 feet (2.44 m) is improved by spacing greater than 6 feet (1.83 m).

250-86. Use of Lightning Rods.   Lightning rod conductors and driven pipes, rods, or other made electrodes used for grounding lightning rods shall not be used in lieu of the made grounding electrodes required by Section 250-83 for grounding wiring systems and equipment. This provision shall not prohibit the required bonding together of grounding electrodes of different systems.

(FPN): See Sections 250-46, 800-31(b)(7), and 820-22(h).

(FPN): Bonding together of all separate grounding electrodes will limit potential differences between them and between their associated wiring systems.

J. Grounding Conductors

250-91. Material.   The material for grounding conductors shall be as specified in (a), (b), and (c) below.

Figure 250-33. The resistance to ground of a driven grounding electrode can be measured by a ground tester used in this manner.

(a) Grounding Electrode Conductor. The grounding electrode conductor shall be of copper, aluminum, or copper-clad aluminum. The material selected shall be resistant to any corrosive condition existing at the installation or shall be suitably protected against corrosion. The conductor shall be solid or stranded, insulated, covered, or bare and shall be installed in one continuous length without a splice or joint.

Exception No. 1: Splices in busbars shall be permitted.

Exception No. 2: Where a service consists of more than a single enclosure as permitted in Section 230-40, Exception No. 2, it shall be permissible to connect taps to the grounding electrode conductor. Each such tap conductor shall extend to the inside of each such enclosure. The grounding electrode conductor shall be sized in accordance with Section 250-94, but the tap conductors shall be permitted to be sized in accordance with the grounding electrode conductors specified in Section 250-94 for the largest conductor serving the respective enclosures.

The grounding electrode (tap) conductors are required to be sized using Table 250-94 and are based on the size of the largest conductors serving each enclosure. The grounding electrode conductor is determined by the size of the largest service-entrance conductor or equivalent cross-sectional area for parallel conductors as per Table 250-94. See Figure 250-34.

(b) Types of Equipment Grounding Conductors. The equipment grounding conductor run with or enclosing the circuit conductors shall be one or more or a combination of the following: (1) a copper or other corrosion-resistant conductor. This conductor shall be solid or stranded; insulated, covered, or bare; and in the form of a wire or a busbar of any shape; (2) rigid metal conduit; (3) intermediate metal conduit; (4) electrical metallic tubing; (5) flexible metal conduit where both the conduit and fittings are listed for grounding; (6) armor of Type AC cable; (7) the sheath of mineral-insulated, metal-sheathed cable; (8) the metallic sheath or the combined

Figure 250-34. The tap method eliminates the difficulties found in looping grounding electrode conductors from one enclosure to another.

metallic sheath and grounding conductors of Type MC cable; (9) cable trays as permitted in Sections 318-3(c) and 318-7; (10) other electrically continuous metal raceways listed for grounding.

Exception No. 1: Flexible metal conduit and flexible metallic tubing shall be permitted for grounding if all the following conditions are met:

a. The length in any ground return path does not exceed 6 feet (1.83 m).

b. The circuit conductors contained therein are protected by overcurrent devices rated at 20 amperes or less.

c. The conduit or tubing is terminated in fittings listed for grounding.

Exception No. 2: Liquidtight flexible metal conduit shall be permitted as a grounding means in the 1¼-inch and smaller trade sizes if the total length of any ground return path is 6 feet (1.83 m) or less, the conduit is terminated in fittings listed for grounding, and the circuit conductors contained therein are protected by overcurrent devices rated at 20 amperes or less for ⅜-inch and ½-inch trade sizes and 60 amperes or less for ¾-inch through 1¼-inch trade sizes.

Exception No. 3: For direct-current circuits only, the equipment grounding conductor shall be permitted to be run separately from the circuit conductors.

The various types of conductors, armored or metal-sheathed cables, or metal raceways that are considered as suitable for use as equipment grounding conductors are described in Section 250-91(b).

Flexible metal conduit and flexible metallic tubing are recognized in Exception No. 1 as equipment grounding conductors, where termination fittings approved for grounding are used, if the total length is not over 6 ft in any ground return path (the sum of all lengths of flexible metal conduit and flexible metallic tubing in the ground return path from the part to be grounded to the branch-circuit overcurrent protection), and the contained circuit conductors are protected by overcurrent devices rated at 20 A or less.

Liquidtight flexible metal conduit is recognized as an equipment grounding conductor by Exception No. 2 where used with termination fittings approved for grounding in sizes not over 1¼ in., and in lengths not over 6 ft in any ground return path.

Exception No. 2 adds limitations on the overcurrent protection provided for the circuit conductors, thus providing overcurrent protection for the conduit when used as an equipment grounding conductor. Field experience and laboratory tests indicated that it was possible to overload the grounding path provided in the ⅜ in. through 1¼-in. trade sizes of UL-listed liquidtight flexible metal conduit under certain fault conditions, causing the liquidtight outer jacket to melt and emit smoke. This led to a study by UL and the electrical industry to determine the practical limits for the use of this type of conduit as a grounding conductor. Ground-fault current tests were conducted, and it was determined that overcurrent protection as now specified would maintain the integrity of the outer jacket and the equipment grounding circuit.

The overcurrent protection limitations for the circuit conductors are not required if the conduit is not used as an equipment grounding conductor.

Termination fittings that are approved for grounding may be determined by a qualified electrical testing laboratory, inspection agency, or other organization concerned with product evaluation as part of its listing and labeling program. See the definitions for "approved," "identified," "listed," and "labeled" in Article 100. For grounding requirements, see also Sections 349-16, 350-5, and 351-9.

(c) Supplementary Grounding. Supplementary grounding electrodes shall be permitted to augment the equipment grounding conductors specified in Section 250-91(b), but the earth shall not be used as the sole equipment grounding conductor.

Grounding electrodes (ground rods, etc.) connected to equipment are not permitted to be used in lieu of the equipment grounding conductor, but may be used for supplementary protection, for example, for lightning protection or to equalize potentials in the area of the equipment. See also Section 250-51, second paragraph.

250-92. Installation. Grounding conductors shall be installed as specified in (a), (b), and (c) below.

(a) Grounding Electrode Conductor. A grounding electrode conductor or its enclosure shall be securely fastened to the surface on which it is carried. A No. 4, copper or aluminum, or larger conductor shall be protected if exposed to severe physical damage. A No. 6 grounding conductor that is free from exposure to physical damage shall be permitted to be run along the surface of the building construction without metal covering or protection where it is securely fastened to the construction; otherwise, it shall be in rigid metal conduit, intermediate metal conduit, rigid nonmetallic conduit, electrical metallic tubing, or cable armor. Grounding conductors smaller than No. 6 shall be in rigid metal conduit, intermediate metal conduit, rigid nonmetallic conduit, electrical metallic tubing, or cable armor.

Aluminum or copper-clad aluminum grounding conductors shall not be used where in direct contact with masonry or the earth or where subject to corrosive conditions. Where used outside, aluminum or copper-clad aluminum grounding conductors shall not be installed within 18 inches (457 mm) of the earth.

(b) Enclosures for Grounding Electrode Conductors. Metal enclosures for grounding conductors shall be electrically continuous from the point of attachment to cabinets or equipment to the grounding electrode, and shall be securely fastened to the ground clamp or fitting. Metal enclosures that are not physically continuous from cabinet or equipment to the grounding electrode shall be made electrically continuous by bonding each end to the grounding conductor. Where intermediate metal conduit is used for protection for a grounding conductor, the installation shall comply with the requirements of Article 345. Where rigid metal conduit is used as protection for a grounding conductor, the installation shall comply with the requirements of Article 346. Where rigid nonmetallic conduit is used as protection for a grounding conductor, the installation shall comply with the requirements of Article 347. Where electrical metallic tubing is used, the installation shall comply with the requirements of Article 348.

227

(c) Equipment Grounding Conductor. An equipment grounding conductor shall be installed as follows.

(1) Where it consists of a raceway, cable tray, cable armor, or cable sheath or where it is a wire within a raceway or cable, it shall be installed in accordance with the applicable provisions in this Code using fittings for joints and terminations approved for use with the type raceway or cable used. All connections, joints, and fittings shall be made tight using suitable tools.

(2) Where it is a separate equipment grounding conductor as provided in the Exception for Section 250-50(a) and (b), it shall be installed in accordance with (a) above in regard to restrictions for aluminum and also in regard to protection from physical damage.

Exception: Sizes smaller than No. 6 shall not be required to be enclosed in a raceway or armor where run in the hollow spaces of a wall or partition or where otherwise installed so as not to be subject to physical damage.

250-93. Size of Direct-Current System Grounding Conductor. The size of the grounding conductor for a dc system shall be as specified in (a) through (c) below.

(a) Not Be Smaller than the Neutral Conductor. Where the dc system consists of a 3-wire balancer set or a balancer winding with overcurrent protection as provided in Section 445-4(d), the grounding conductor shall not be smaller than the neutral conductor.

(b) Not Be Smaller than the Largest Conductor. Where the dc system is other than as in (a) above, the grounding conductor shall not be smaller than the largest conductor supplied by the system.

(c) Not Be Smaller than No. 8. In no case shall the grounding conductor be smaller than No. 8 copper or No. 6 aluminum.

250-94. Size of Alternating-Current Grounding Electrode Conductor. The size of the grounding electrode conductor of a grounded or ungrounded ac system shall not be less than given in Table 250-94.

Exception No. 1: Grounded Systems.

a. Where connected to made electrodes as in Section 250-83 (c) or (d), that portion of the grounding electrode conductor which is the sole connection to the grounding electrode shall not be required to be larger than No. 6 copper wire or No. 4 aluminum wire.

b. Where connected to a concrete-encased electrode as in Section 250-81(c), that portion of the grounding electrode conductor which is the sole connection to the grounding electrode shall not be required to be larger than No. 4 copper wire.

c. Where connected to a ground ring as in Section 250-81(d), that portion of the grounding electrode conductor which is the sole connection to the grounding electrode shall not be required to be larger than the conductor used for the ground ring.

Exception No. 2: Ungrounded Systems.

a. Where connected to made electrodes as in Section 250-83 (c) or (d), that portion of the grounding electrode conductor which is the sole connection to the grounding electrode shall not be required to be larger than No. 6 copper wire or No. 4 aluminum wire.

b. Where connected to a concrete-encased electrode as in Section 250-81(c), that portion of the grounding electrode conductor which is the sole connection to the grounding electrode shall not be required to be larger than No. 4 copper wire.

Table 250-94
Grounding Electrode Conductor for AC Systems

Size of Largest Service-Entrance Conductor or Equivalent Area for Parallel Conductors		Size of Grounding Electrode Conductor	
Copper	Aluminum or Copper-Clad Aluminum	Copper	*Aluminum or Copper-Clad Aluminum
2 or smaller	0 or smaller	8	6
1 or 0	2/0 or 3/0	6	4
2/0 or 3/0	4/0 or 250 MCM	4	2
Over 3/0 thru 350 MCM	Over 250 MCM thru 500 MCM	2	0
Over 350 MCM thru 600 MCM	Over 500 MCM thru 900 MCM	0	3/0
Over 600 MCM thru 1100 MCM	Over 900 MCM thru 1750 MCM	2/0	4/0
Over 1100 MCM	Over 1750 MCM	3/0	250 MCM

Where there are no service-entrance conductors, the grounding electrode conductor size shall be determined by the equivalent size of the largest service-entrance conductor required for the load to be served.
*See installation restrictions in Section 250-92(a).
(FPN): See Section 250-23(b).

c. Where connected to a ground ring as in Section 250-81(d), that portion of the grounding electrode conductor which is the sole connection to the grounding electrode shall not be required to be larger than the conductor used for the ground ring.

If a grounding electrode conductor is run from the service equipment or separately derived system to a water pipe or structural metal building member, and from there to one of the electrodes mentioned in Section 250-94, Exception No. 1, that portion of the grounding electrode between the service equipment or separately derived system to the water pipe or structural metal building member must be a full-sized conductor sized per Table 250-94. See Figure 250-35.

250-95. Size of Equipment Grounding Conductors. The size of copper, aluminum, or copper-clad aluminum equipment grounding conductors shall not be less than given in Table 250-95.

Where conductors are run in parallel in multiple raceways, as permitted in Section 310-4, the equipment grounding conductor, where used, shall be run in parallel. Each parallel equipment grounding conductor shall be sized on the basis of the ampere rating of the overcurrent device protecting the circuit conductors in the raceway in accordance with Table 250-95.

A full-sized equipment grounding conductor is needed in each raceway of an array of raceways enclosing paralleled phase conductors to prevent overloading and possible burn-out of the grounding conductor should there be a ground fault condition along one of the parallel branches. The installation conditions for paralleled conductors prescribed in Section 310-4 result in proportional distribution of the current-time duty among the several paralleled grounding conductors only for overcurrent conditions downstream of the paralleled array.

Figure 250-36 shows a parallel array of three nonmetallic conduits installed underground. For clarity, only phase A and the grounding conductors are shown. A short-circuit at point "X" due to a dig-in, for example, will cause the equipment grounding conductor in conduit no. 1 to carry more than its proportionate share of current. Note that point "X" is fed by three different conductors of phase A, one from the left and two from the right. The lowest impedance path to ground is the equipment grounding conductor in conduit no. 1 from the supply panelboard to point "X." The grounding path from point "X" through conduits no. 2 and no. 3

Figure 250-35. Illustration of Section 250-94, Exception No. 1. If the grounding electrode conductor from the service equipment were run first to (for example) the ground rod, and then to the water pipe, the conductor to the ground rod would also have to be full sized per Table 250-94.

is three times as long as the grounding path from point "X" to the supply panelboard.

When conductors are adjusted in size to compensate for voltage drop, equipment grounding conductors, where required, shall be adjusted proportionally according to circular mil area.

Where a single equipment grounding conductor is run with multiple circuits in the same raceway, it shall be sized for the largest overcurrent device protecting conductors in the raceway.

A single equipment grounding conductor is required to be sized for the largest overcurrent device and is not required to be sized for the composite of all the circuits in the raceway. For example, three 3-phase circuits protected by overcurrent devices at 30, 60 and 100 A installed in the same raceway would require only one equipment grounding conductor sized according to the largest (100 A in this case) overcurrent device. Therefore, a No. 8 AWG copper or No. 6 AWG aluminum or copper-clad aluminum is required by Table 250-95.

Exception No. 1: An equipment grounding conductor not smaller than No. 18 copper and not smaller than the circuit conductors if an integral part of a listed flexible cord assembly shall be permitted for grounding cord-connected equipment where the equipment is protected by overcurrent devices not exceeding 20-ampere rating.

Exception No. 2: The equipment grounding conductor shall not be required to be larger than the circuit conductors supplying the equipment.

Figure 250-36. Grounding paths for ground fault at point "X" in parallel array of nonmetallic raceways, illustrating reason for requirement in second paragraph of Section 250-95.

Exception No. 3: Where a raceway or a cable armor or sheath is used as the equipment grounding conductor, as provided in Sections 250-57(a) and 250-91(b).

Table 250-95. Minimum Size Equipment Grounding Conductors for Grounding Raceway and Equipment

Rating or Setting of Automatic Overcurrent Device in Circuit Ahead of Equipment, Conduit, etc., Not Exceeding (Amperes)	Size	
	Copper Wire No.	Aluminum or Copper-Clad Aluminum Wire No.*
15	14	12
20	12	10
30	10	8
40	10	8
60	10	8
100	8	6
200	6	4
300	4	2
400	3	1
500	2	1/0
600	1	2/0
800	0	3/0
1000	2/0	4/0
1200	3/0	250 MCM
1600	4/0	350 "
2000	250 MCM	400 "
2500	350 "	600 "
3000	400 "	600 "
4000	500 "	800 "
5000	700 "	1200 "
6000	800 "	1200 "

*See installation restrictions in Section 250-92(a).

250-97. Outline Lighting. Isolated noncurrent-carrying metal parts of outline lighting systems shall be permitted to be bonded together by a No. 14 copper or No. 12 aluminum conductor protected from physical damage, where a conductor complying with Section 250-95 is used to ground the group.

250-99. Equipment Grounding Conductor Continuity.

(a) Separable Connections. Separable connections such as those provided in draw-out equipment or attachment plugs and mating connectors and receptacles shall provide for first-make, last-break of the equipment grounding conductor.

Exception: Interlocked equipment, plugs, receptacles and connectors which preclude energization without grounding continuity.

(b) Switches. No automatic cutout or switch shall be placed in the equipment grounding conductor of a premises wiring system.

Exception: Where the opening of the cutout or switch disconnects all sources of energy.

Figure 250-37. Shown is one example of the various sizes of enclosing metal conduits used as equipment grounding conductors as they apply to a service and feeder system.

K. Grounding Conductor Connections

250-112. To Grounding Electrode. The connection of a grounding electrode conductor to a grounding electrode shall be accessible and made in a manner that will assure a permanent and effective ground. Where necessary to assure this for a metal piping system used as a grounding electrode, effective bonding shall be provided around insulated joints and sections and around any equipment that is likely to be disconnected for repairs or replacement.

A water meter is typical of equipment likely to be disconnected for repairs or replacement.

Exception: An encased or buried connection to a concrete-encased, driven, or buried grounding electrode shall not be required to be accessible.

When the exposed portion of an encased, driven, or buried electrode is used for the termination of a grounding electrode conductor, the connection between them is required to be accessible. However, if the connection is buried or encased it is not required to be accessible. Note that ground clamps and other connectors which are suitable for use where buried in earth or embedded in concrete are identified for such use, either by a marking on the connector or by a tag attached to the connector.

See Figures 250-29 and 250-31.

250-113. To Conductors and Equipment. Grounding conductors and bonding jumpers shall be connected by exothermic welding, listed pressure connectors, listed clamps, or other listed means. Connection devices or fittings that depend solely on solder shall not be used.

See Figures 250-23 through 250-26.

250-114. Continuity and Attachment of Branch-Circuit Equipment Grounding Conductors to Boxes. Where more than one equipment grounding conductor enters a box all such conductors shall be spliced or joined within the box or to the box with devices suitable for the use. Connections depending solely on solder shall not be used. Splices shall be made in accordance with Section 110-14(b) except that insulation shall not be required. The arrangement of grounding connections shall be such that the disconnection or the removal of a receptacle, fixture, or other device fed from the box will not interfere with or interrupt the grounding continuity.

This section permits either of two arrangements for the termination of equipment grounding conductors. The first method is shown in Figure 250-39. The second method is for each equipment grounding conductor to terminate under, for example, separate ground clips such as the one shown in Figure 250-38 or under a separate grounding screw such as shown in Figure 250-40. Metal outlet or device boxes provided with only one 10-32 tapped hole marked GR are intended for the connection of only one equipment grounding conductor.

Figure 250-38. A clip used to connect a copper grounding conductor to a box.

(a) Metal Boxes. A connection shall be made between the one or more equipment grounding conductors and a metal box by means of a grounding screw which shall be used for no other purpose, or a listed grounding device.

(b) Nonmetallic Boxes. One or more equipment grounding conductors brought into a nonmetallic outlet box shall be so arranged that a connection can be made to any fitting or device in that box requiring grounding.

250-115. Connection to Electrodes. The grounding conductor shall be connected to the grounding fitting by exothermic welding, listed lugs, listed pressure connectors, listed clamps, or other listed means. Connections depending on solder shall not be used. Ground clamps shall be listed for the materials of the grounding electrode and the grounding electrode conductor and where used on pipe, rod or other buried electrodes shall also be listed for direct soil burial. Not

Figure 250-39. An application of a grounding clip.

Figure 250-40. Grounding conductors may be attached to a box by a variety of methods, such as a screw, as show here, or with a grounding clip as shown in Figure 250-38.

more than one conductor shall be connected to the grounding electrode by a single clamp or fitting unless the clamp or fitting is listed for multiple conductors. One of the methods indicated in (a), (b), (c), or (d) below shall be used.

(a) Bolted Clamp. A listed bolted clamp of cast bronze or brass, or plain or malleable iron.

(b) Pipe Fitting, Pipe Plug, etc. A pipe fitting, pipe plug, or other approved device screwed into a pipe or pipe fitting.

(c) Sheet-Metal-Strap Type Ground Clamp. A listed sheet-metal-strap type ground clamp having a rigid metal base that seats on the electrode and having a strap of such material and dimensions that it is not likely to stretch during or after installation.

(d) Other Means. An equally substantial approved means.

Consideration concerning the suitability of ground clamps for direct soil burial should be given when used on ground rod or pipe electrodes or other buried electrodes. See commentary following Section 250-112, Exception.

Figure 250-41. A listed ground clamp generally used with No. 8 through No. 4 grounding electrode conductors. Exothermic welds are also acceptable. Kits are commercially available for this purpose.

Figure 250-42. Listed U-bolt ground clamps are available for all pipe sizes and all grounding electrode conductor sizes. Where grounding electrode conductors are run in conduits, conduit hubs may be bolted to the threaded portion of the U-bolt.

When a ground clamp is used and terminates on, for example, a galvanized water pipe, it is required to be of material that is compatible with steel so as to prevent corrosion. The same type of compatability requirement applies to ground clamps on copper water pipe.

See Section 250-83(c)(3) for rod and pipe electrode installation requirements.

250-117. Protection of Attachment. Ground clamps or other fittings shall be approved for general use without protection or shall be protected from ordinary physical damage as indicated in (a) or (b) below.

(a) Not Likely to Be Damaged. Installations where they are not likely to be damaged.

(b) Protective Covering. Enclosing in metal, wood, or equivalent protective covering.

250-118. Clean Surfaces. Nonconductive coatings (such as paint, lacquer, and enamel) on equipment to be grounded shall be removed from threads and other contact surfaces to assure good electrical continuity.

L. Instrument Transformers, Relays, etc.

250-121. Instrument Transformer Circuits. Secondary circuits of current and potential instrument transformers shall be grounded where the primary windings are connected to circuits of 300 volts or more to ground, and where on switchboards, shall be grounded irrespective of voltage.

Exception: Circuits where the primary windings are connected to circuits of less than 1000 volts with no live parts or wiring exposed or accessible to other than qualified persons.

250-122. Instrument Transformer Cases. Cases or frames of instrument transformers shall be grounded where accessible to other than qualified persons.

Exception: Cases or frames of current transformers, the primaries of which are not over 150 volts to ground and which are used exclusively to supply current to meters.

250-123. Cases of Instruments, Meters, and Relays — Operating at Less than 1000 Volts. Instruments, meters, and relays operating with windings or working parts at less than 1000 volts shall be grounded as specified in (a), (b), or (c) below.

(a) Not on Switchboards. Instruments, meters, and relays not located on switchboards, operating with windings or working parts at 300 volts or more to ground, and accessible to other than qualified persons, shall have the cases and other exposed metal parts grounded.

(b) On Dead-Front Switchboards. Instruments, meters, and relays (whether operated from current and potential transformers, or connected directly in the circuit) on switchboards having no live parts on the front of the panels shall have the cases grounded.

(c) On Live-Front Switchboards. Instruments, meters, and relays (whether operated from current and potential transformers, or connected directly in the circuit) on switchboards having exposed live parts on the front of panels shall not have their cases grounded. Mats of insulating rubber or other suitable floor insulation shall be provided for the operator where the voltage to ground exceeds 150.

250-124. Cases of Instruments, Meters, and Relays — Operating Voltage 1 kV and Over. Where instruments, meters, and relays have current-carrying parts of 1 kV and over to ground, they shall be isolated by elevation or protected by suitable barriers, grounded metal or insulating covers or guards. Their cases shall not be grounded.

Exception: Cases of electrostatic ground detectors where the internal ground segments of the instrument are connected to the instrument case and grounded and the ground detector is isolated by elevation.

250-125. Instrument Grounding Conductor. The grounding conductor for secondary circuits of instrument transformers and for instrument cases shall not be smaller than No. 12 copper or No. 10 aluminum. Cases of instrument transformers, instruments, meters, and relays which are mounted directly on grounded metal surfaces of enclosures or grounded metal switchboard panels shall be considered to be grounded and no additional grounding conductor will be required.

M. Grounding of Systems and Circuits of 1 kV and Over (High Voltage)

250-150. General. Where high-voltage systems are grounded, they shall comply with all applicable provisions of the preceding sections of this article and with the following sections which supplement and modify the preceding sections.

250-151. Derived Neutral Systems. A system neutral derived from a grounding transformer shall be permitted to be used for grounding a high-voltage system.

250-152. Solidly Grounded Neutral Systems.

(a) Neutral Conductor. The neutral of a solidly grounded neutral system shall comply with (1) and (2) below.

(1) The minimum insulation level for neutral conductors of solidly grounded systems shall be 600 volts.

Exception No. 1: Bare copper conductors shall be permitted to be used for the neutral of service entrances and the neutral of direct buried portions of feeders.

Exception No. 2: Bare conductors shall be permitted for the neutral of overhead portions installed outdoors.

(FPN): See Section 225-4 for conductor covering where within 10 feet (3.05 m) of any building or other structure.

(2) The neutral grounding conductor shall be permitted to be a bare conductor if isolated from phase conductors and protected from physical damage.

(b) Multiple Grounding. The neutral of a solidly grounded neutral system shall be permitted to be grounded at more than one point for:

(1) Services.

(2) Direct buried portions of feeders employing a bare copper neutral.

(3) Overhead portion installed outdoors.

250-153. Impedance Grounded Neutral Systems. Impedance grounded neutral systems shall comply with the provisions of (a) through (d) below.

(a) Location. The grounding impedance shall be inserted in the grounding conductor between the grounding electrode of the supply system and the neutral point of the supply transformer or generator.

(b) Identified and Insulated. Where the neutral conductor of an impedance grounded neutral system is used, it shall be identified, as well as fully insulated with the same insulation as the phase conductors.

(c) System Neutral Connection. The system neutral shall not be connected to ground, except through the neutral grounding impedance.

(d) Equipment Grounding Conductors. Equipment grounding conductors shall be permitted to be bare and shall be connected to the ground bus and grounding electrode conductor at the service-entrance equipment and extended to the system ground.

250-154. Grounding of Systems Supplying Portable or Mobile Equipment. Systems supplying portable or mobile high-voltage equipment, other than substations installed on a temporary basis, shall comply with (a) through (e) below.

"Portable" means equipment that is easily carried, while "mobile" means equipment that is easily moved, as on wheels, treads, etc.

(a) Portable or Mobile Equipment. Portable or mobile high-voltage equipment shall be supplied from a system having its neutral grounded through an impedance. Where a delta-connected high-voltage system is used to supply portable or mobile equipment, a system neutral shall be derived.

(b) Exposed Noncurrent-Carrying Metal Parts. Exposed noncurrent-carrying metal parts of portable or mobile equipment shall be connected by an equipment grounding conductor to the point at which the system neutral impedance is grounded.

(c) Ground-Fault Current. The voltage developed between the portable or mobile equipment frame and ground by the flow of maximum ground-fault current shall not exceed 100 volts.

(d) Ground-Fault Detection and Relaying. Ground-fault detection and relaying shall be provided to automatically de-energize any high-voltage system component which has developed a ground fault. The continuity of the equipment grounding conductor shall be continuously monitored so as to de-energize automatically the high-voltage feeder to the portable or mobile equipment upon loss of continuity of the equipment grounding conductor.

(e) Isolation. The grounding electrode to which the portable or mobile equipment system neutral impedance is connected shall be isolated from and separated in the ground by at least 20 feet (6.1 m) from any other system or equipment grounding electrode, and there shall be no direct connection between the grounding electrodes, such as buried pipe, fence, etc.

(f) Trailing Cable and Couplers. High voltage trailing cable and couplers for interconnection of portable or mobile equipment shall meet the requirements of Part C of Article 400 for cables and Section 710-45 for couplers.

250-155. Grounding of Equipment. All noncurrent-carrying metal parts of fixed, portable, and mobile equipment and associated fences, housings, enclosures, and supporting structures shall be grounded.

Exception No. 1: Where isolated from ground and located so as to prevent any person who can make contact with ground from contacting such metal parts when the equipment is energized.

Exception No. 2: Pole-mounted distribution apparatus as provided in Section 250-42, Exception No. 3.

Grounding conductors not an integral part of a cable assembly shall not be smaller than No. 6 copper or No. 4 aluminum.

ARTICLE 280 — SURGE ARRESTERS

Contents

280-23. Circuits of 1 kV and Over— Surge Arrester Conductors.
280-24. Circuits of 1 kV and Over— Interconnections.
  (a) Metallic Interconnections.

(b) Through Spark Gap or Device.
(c) By Special Permission.
280-25. Grounding.

Voltage surges with peaks of several thousand volts, even on 120-V circuits, are not uncommon. These surges occur because of induced voltages in power and transmission lines resulting from lightning strikes in the vicinity of the line. They also occur as a result of switching inductive circuits on the premises. Surge arresters for installation as part of an electric service and for use with cord- and plug-connected solid-state electronic equipment are commercially available. See Figures 280-1 and 280-2.

Figure 280-1. Lightning surge protector for service-entrance installation. This device is suitable for mounting in a panel knockout. (*General Electric Co.*)

Figure 280-2. Voltage spike protector suitable for use with 120-V cord- and plug-connected electronic equipment such as TV sets, small computers, medical equipment, and electronic organs. (*General Electric Co.*)

ARTICLE 280—SURGE ARRESTERS

A. General

280-1. Scope. This article covers general requirements, installation requirements, and connection requirements for surge arresters installed on premises wiring systems.

280-2. Definition. A surge arrester is a protective device for limiting surge voltages by discharging or bypassing surge current, and it also prevents continued flow of follow current while remaining capable of repeating these functions.

280-3. Number Required. Where used at a point on a circuit, a surge arrester shall be connected to each ungrounded conductor. A single installation of such surge arresters shall be permitted to protect a number of interconnected circuits provided that no circuit is exposed to surges while disconnected from the surge arresters.

Means are required to be provided to protect circuits that may be disconnected from the generating station bus. A switch with double-throw action used to disconnect the outside circuits from the station generator and alternatively connect these circuits to ground would satisfy the condition of a single set of arresters protecting more than one circuit.

280-4. Surge Arrester Selection.

(a) On Circuits of Less than 1000 Volts. The rating of the surge arrester shall be equal to or greater than the maximum continuous phase-to-ground power frequency voltage available at the point of application.

(b) On Circuits of 1 kV and Over — Silicon Carbide Types. The rating of a silicon carbide-type surge arrester shall be not less than 125 percent of the maximum continuous phase-to-ground voltage available at the point of application.

(FPN): For further information on selection of surge arresters, see Guide for the Application of Valve-Type Surge Arresters for Alternating-Current Systems (ANSI C62.2-1981).

(FPN): Metal oxide surge arrester ratings are based on the magnitude and duration of overvoltage at the arrester location as affected by phase-to-ground faults, system grounding techniques, switching surges, and other causes. See manufacturer's application rules for the specific arrester to be used at a particular location.

B. Installation

280-11. Location. Surge arresters shall be permitted to be located indoors or outdoors and shall be made inaccessible to unqualified persons.

Exception: Surge arresters listed for installation in accessible locations.

See Figures 280-1 and 280-2 for examples of surge arresters listed for installation in accessible locations.

280-12. Routing of Surge Arrester Connections. The conductor used to connect the surge arrester to line or bus and to ground shall not be any longer than necessary and shall avoid unnecessary bends.

Arrester conductors should be as short and run as straight as practicable, avoiding any sharp bends and turns which would increase the impedance high-frequency currents, such as common to lightning discharges, and tend to reduce the effectiveness of a grounding conductor.

C. Connecting Surge Arresters

280-21. Installed at Services of Less than 1000 Volts. Line and ground connecting conductors shall not be smaller than No. 14 copper or No. 12 aluminum. The arrester grounding conductor shall be connected to one of the following: (1) the grounded service conductor; (2) the grounding electrode conductor; (3) the grounding electrode for the service; or (4) the equipment grounding terminal in the service equipment.

Single-phase or 3-phase grounded or ungrounded services are permitted to have the surge arrester grounded to the equipment grounding terminal in the service equipment. Figure 280-3 shows three methods of grounding the ground terminals of surge arresters at service entrances.

Figure 280-3. Three locations of grounding surge arresters at service entrances. Left, arrester connected to neutral service conductor; center, arrester connected to a grounding electrode conductor; and right, arrester connected to a grounding electrode conductor of an ungrounded system.

280-22. Installed on the Load Side of Services of Less than 1000 Volts. Line and ground connecting conductors shall not be smaller than No. 14 copper or No. 12 aluminum. A surge arrester shall be permitted to be connected between any two conductors (ungrounded conductor(s), grounded conductor, grounding conductor). The grounded conductor and the grounding conductor shall be interconnected only by the normal operation of the surge arrester during a surge.

280-23. Circuits of 1 kV and Over — Surge-Arrester Conductors. The conductor between the surge arrester and the line and surge arrester and the grounding connection shall not be smaller than No. 6 copper or aluminum.

280-24. Circuits of 1 kV and Over — Interconnections. The grounding conductor of a surge arrester protecting a transformer that supplies a secondary distribution system shall be interconnected as specified in (a) or (b) below.

(a) Metallic Interconnections. A metallic interconnection shall be made to the secondary grounded circuit conductor or the secondary circuit grounding conductor provided that, in addition to the direct grounding connection at the surge arrester:

(1) The grounded conductor of the secondary has elsewhere a grounding connection to a continuous metal underground water piping system. However, in urban water-pipe areas where there are at least four water-pipe connections on the neutral and not less than four such connections in each mile of neutral, the metallic interconnection shall be permitted to be made to the secondary neutral with omission of the direct grounding connection at the surge arrester.

(2) The grounded conductor of the secondary system is a part of a multiground neutral system of which the primary neutral has at least four ground connections in each mile of line in addition to a ground at each service.

(b) Through Spark Gap or Device. Where the surge arrester grounding conductor is not connected as in (a) above or where the secondary is not grounded as in (a) above but is otherwise grounded as in Sections 250-81 and 250-83, an interconnection shall be made through a spark gap or listed device as follows:

(1) For ungrounded or unigrounded primary systems, the spark gap or listed device shall have a 60 hertz breakdown voltage of at least twice the primary circuit voltage but not necessarily more than 10 kV, and there shall be at least one other ground on the grounded conductor of the secondary not less than 20 feet (6.1 m) distant from the surge arrester grounding electrode.

(2) For multigrounded neutral primary systems, the spark gap or listed device shall have a 60 hertz breakdown or not more than 3 kV, and there shall be at least one other ground on the grounded conductor of the secondary not less than 20 feet (6.1 m) distant from the surge arrester grounding electrode.

(c) By Special Permission. An interconnection of the surge arrester ground and the secondary neutral, other than as provided in (a) or (b) above, shall be permitted to be made only by special permission.

280-25. Grounding. Except as indicated in this article, surge arrester grounding connections shall be made as specified in Article 250. Grounding conductors shall not be run in metal enclosures unless bonded to both ends of such enclosure.

3 Wiring Methods and Materials

ARTICLE 300 — WIRING METHODS

Contents

ARTICLE 300—WIRING METHODS

300-22. Wiring in Ducts, Plenums, and Other Air-Handling Spaces.
  (a) Ducts for Dust, Loose Stock, or Vapor Removal.
  (b) Ducts or Plenums Used for Environmental Air.
  (c) Other Space Used for Environmental Air.
  (d) Data Processing Systems.

B. Requirements for Over 600 Volts, Nominal
300-31. Covers Required.
300-32. Conductors of Different Systems.
300-34. Conductor Bending Radius.
300-35. Protection Against Induction Heating.
300-36. Grounding.

A. General Requirements

300-1. Scope.

(a) All Wiring Installations. This article covers wiring methods for all wiring installations.

Exception No. 1: Only those sections referenced in Article 725 shall apply to Class 1, Class 2, and Class 3 circuits.

Exception No. 2: Only those sections referenced in Article 760 shall apply to fire protective signaling circuits.

Exception No. 3: Only those sections referenced in Article 770 shall apply to optical fiber cables.

Exception No. 4: Only those sections referenced in Article 800 shall apply to communication systems.

Exception No. 5: Only those sections referenced in Article 820 shall apply to community antenna television and radio distribution systems.

The five exceptions clearly indicate that Article 300 is not applicable to Articles 725, 760, 770, 800, and 820. For example, the requirement of Section 300-15(a) is not applicable to a power-limited fire protective signaling system wired in accordance with Section 760-28(b)(1), so a box is not necessary at the "outlet" for a heat detector head on such a system. However, certain parts of Article 300 are applicable where they are referenced in Articles 725, 760, 770, 800, 810, and 820. For example, see Sections 725-2(b), 760-2(b), 800-3(b)(3), and 820-15(c), which reference Section 300-22. See also the exceptions to these sections.

(b) Integral Parts of Equipment. The provisions of this article are not intended to apply to the conductors which form an integral part of equipment, such as motors, controllers, motor control centers, or factory-assembled control equipment.

300-2. Limitations.

(a) Voltage. Wiring methods specified in Chapter 3 shall be used for voltages 600 volts, nominal, or less where not specifically limited in some section of Chapter 3. They shall be permitted for voltages over 600 volts, nominal, where specifically permitted elsewhere in this Code.

(b) Temperature. Temperature limitation of conductors shall be in accordance with Section 310-10.

300-3. Conductors.

(a) Single Conductors. Single conductors specified in Table 310-13 shall only be permitted to be installed where part of a recognized wiring method of Chapter 3.

(b) Conductors of the Same Circuit. All conductors of the same circuit and, where used, the neutral and all equipment grounding conductors shall be contained within the same raceway, cable tray, trench, cable, or cord.

Exception to (a) and (b): As permitted in Sections 250-57(b), 250-79(e), 300-5(i), 300-20(a), 318-8(d), and 339-3(a)(2).

This exception recognizes that some types of grounding and bonding conductors can be run as single conductors. For example, see Sections 250-79(e) and 300-5(i).

(c) Conductors of Different Systems.

(1) 600 Volts, Nominal, or Less. Conductors of 600 volts, nominal, or less, alternating current and direct current circuits, shall be permitted to occupy the same equipment wiring enclosure, cable, or raceway. All conductors shall have an insulation rating equal to at least the maximum nominal circuit voltage rating of any conductor within the enclosure, cable, or raceway.

This section makes it clear that it is the maximum circuit voltage in the raceway, not the maximum insulation voltage rating of the conductors in the raceway, that determines the minimum voltage rating of conductors for 600 V or less systems.

The conductors of a 3-phase, 4-wire, 208Y/120-V ac circuit; a 3-phase, 4-wire, 480Y/277-V ac circuit; and a 3-wire, 120/240-V dc circuit may occupy the same equipment wiring enclosure, cable, or raceway where all conductors are insulated for the maximum circuit voltage of any conductor. In this case, the maximum circuit voltage would be 480 V, and 600-V insulation would be required for all of the conductors.

Where a 2-wire, 120-V circuit is included in the same raceway with a 3-wire, 120/240-V circuit having 600-V conductors, the 2-wire, 120-V circuit conductors could utilize 300-V insulation.

Exception: For solar photovoltaic systems in accordance with Section 690-4(b).

Section 690-4(b) prohibits solar photovoltaic circuits within the same enclosure as conductors of other systems, unless the conductors are separated by a partition or are connected together.

(FPN): See Section 725-38(a)(2) for Class 2 and Class 3 circuit conductors.

Section 725-38(a)(2) prohibits Class 2 and Class 3 circuit conductors in the same enclosure, cable, or raceway as Class 1, electric light, and power conductors, with some exceptions.

(2) Over 600 Volts, Nominal. Conductors of circuits rated over 600 volts, nominal, shall not occupy the same equipment wiring enclosure, cable, or raceway with conductors of circuits rated 600 volts, nominal, or less.

(FPN): See Section 300-32, Conductors of Different Systems — over 600 volts, nominal.

Exception No. 1: Secondary wiring to electric-discharge lamps of 1000 volts or less, if insulated for the secondary voltage involved, shall be permitted to occupy the same fixture enclosure as the branch-circuit conductors.

Exception No. 2: Primary leads of electric-discharge lamp ballasts, insulated for the primary voltage of the ballast, when contained within the individual wiring enclosure, shall be permitted to occupy the same fixture enclosure as the branch-circuit conductors.

Exception No. 3: Excitation, control, relay, and ammeter conductors used in connection with any individual motor or starter shall be permitted to occupy the same enclosure as the motor circuit conductors.

300-4. Protection Against Physical Damage.   Where subject to physical damage, conductors shall be adequately protected.

(a) Cables and Raceways Through Wood Members.

(1) Bored Holes.   In both exposed and concealed locations, where a cable or raceway-type wiring method is installed through bored holes in joists, rafters, or wood members, holes shall be bored so that the edge of the hole is not less than 1¼ inches (31.8 mm) from the nearest edge of the wood member. Where this distance cannot be maintained the cable or raceway shall be protected from penetration by screws or nails by a steel plate or bushing, at least ¹⁄₁₆ inch (1.59 mm) thick, and of appropriate length and width installed to cover the area of the wiring.

Figure 300-1. Steel plate to protect nonmetallic-sheathed cables within 1¼ in. of the edge of a stud. *(RACO)*

The intent of this section is to prevent nails from being driven into cables. By keeping the edge of the drilled hole 1¼ in. from the nearest edge of the stud, nails would not be likely to penetrate the stud far enough to injure the cables. The model building codes provide maximum requirements for bored or notched holes in studs, and Section 300-4(a)(2) indicates that consideration should be given to the size of notches in studs so as not to affect the strength of the structure. See Figure 300-1.

Exception: Raceways as covered in Articles 345, 346, 347, and 348.

(2) Notches in Wood.   Where there is no objection because of weakening the building structure, in both exposed and concealed locations, cables or raceways shall be permitted to be laid in notches in wood studs, joists, rafters, or other wood members where the cable or raceway at those points is protected against nails or screws by a steel plate at least ¹⁄₁₆ inch (1.59 mm) thick installed before the building finish is applied.

Exception: Raceways as covered in Articles 345, 346, 347, and 348.

The exceptions to Sections 300-4(a)(1) and 300-4(a)(2) permit intermediate metal conduit, rigid metal conduit, rigid nonmetallic conduit, and electrical metallic tubing to be installed through bored holes or laid in notches less than 1¼ in. from the nearest edge of the stud without a steel plate or bushing.

(b) Cables and Electrical Nonmetallic Tubing Through Metal Framing Members.

(1) In both exposed and concealed locations where nonmetallic-sheathed cables pass through either factory or field punched, cut or drilled slots or holes in metal members, the cable shall be protected by bushings or grommets securely fastened in the opening prior to installation of the cable.

(2) Where nails or screws are likely to penetrate nonmetallic-sheathed cable or electrical nonmetallic tubing, a steel sleeve, steel plate or steel clip not less than ⅟₁₆ inch (1.59 mm) in thickness shall be used to protect the cable or tubing.

(c) Cables Through Spaces Behind Panels Designed to Allow Access.   Cables, or raceway-type wiring methods, installed behind panels designed to allow access shall be supported according to their applicable articles.

Cable- or raceway-type wiring methods above suspended ceilings with lift-up panels cannot be laid on the suspended ceiling. They are required to be supported according to the requirements in the article applicable to the wiring method involved. This rule does not apply, however, to many low-voltage cable wiring systems, such as most computer, telephone, and cable TV systems, because there is no fire or shock hazard if such wiring is disturbed. See Section 90-3 and Section 300-1(a), Exceptions No. 1 through 5.

300-5. Underground Installations.

(a) Minimum Cover Requirements.   Direct buried cable or conduit or other raceways shall be installed to meet the minimum cover requirements of Table 300-5.

Cover: Cover is defined as the shortest distance measured between a point on the top surface of any direct buried conductor, cable, conduit, or other raceway and the finished grade.

Table 300-5
Minimum Cover Requirements, 0 to 600 Volts, Nominal

Wiring Method	Minimum Burial (Inches)
Direct Buried Cables	24
Rigid Metal Conduit	6
Intermediate Metal Conduit	6
Rigid Nonmetallic Conduit Approved for	
Direct Burial without Concrete Encasement	18
Other Approved Raceways*	18

For SI units: one inch = 25.4 millimeters.
*Note: Raceways approved for burial only when concrete encased shall require a concrete envelope not less than 2 inches (50.8 mm) thick.

Exception No. 1: The minimum cover requirements for other than rigid metal conduit and intermediate metal conduit shall be permitted to be reduced by 6 inches (152 mm) for installations where a 2-inch (50.8-mm) thick concrete pad or equivalent in physical protection is placed in the trench over the underground installation.

See Exception No. 2 for the exception to the Table 300-5 rule applicable to rigid metal conduit, intermediate metal conduit, and other raceways.

Exception No. 2: The minimum cover requirements shall not apply to conduits or other raceways which are located under a building or exterior concrete slab not less than 4 inches (102 mm) in thickness and extending not less than 6 inches (152 mm) beyond the underground installation.

Exception No. 3: Areas subject to vehicular traffic such as streets, highways, roads, alleys, driveways, and parking lots shall have a minimum cover of 24 inches (610 mm).

Exception No. 3 applies to all wiring methods listed in Table 300-5, and does not permit them to be installed at a depth of less than 24 in. where buried below areas subject to any vehicular traffic, including residential driveways.

Exception No. 4: Residential branch circuits rated 300 volts or less and provided with overcurrent protection of not more than 30 amperes shall be permitted with a cover requirement of 12 inches (305 mm).

For example, a Type UF cable used for a 125-V, 15-A branch circuit for a lamp post on residential property is permitted to be buried 12 in. deep, providing that 24 in. is maintained under areas subject to vehicular traffic.

Exception No. 5: Lesser depths shall be permitted where cables and conductors rise for terminations or splices or where access is otherwise required.

See Section 300-5(d) and Figure 300-2.

Figure 300-2. Type UF cable buried in compliance with Section 300-5. Note the protective bushing where the cable is used with metal conduit.

Exception No. 6: In airport runways, including adjacent defined areas where trespass is prohibited, cable shall be permitted to be buried not less than 18 inches (457 mm) deep and without raceways, concrete encasement or equivalent.

Exception No. 7: Raceways installed in solid rock shall be permitted to be buried at a lesser depth when covered by 2 inches (50.8 mm) or more of concrete over the installation and extending down to the rock surface.

Exception No. 8: Circuits for the control of irrigation and landscape lighting systems which are limited to not more than 30 volts and are installed with Type UF or other identified cable or raceway shall be permitted with a minimum cover of 6 inches (152 mm).

(b) Grounding. All underground installations shall be grounded and bonded in accordance with Article 250 of this Code.

(c) Underground Cables Under Buildings. Underground cable installed under a building shall be in a raceway that is extended beyond the outside walls of the building.

(d) Protection from Damage. Direct buried conductors and cables emerging from the ground shall be protected by enclosures or raceways extending from the minimum cover distance required by Section 300-5(a) in Table 300-5 below grade to a point at least 8 feet (2.44 m) above finished grade. In no case shall the protection be required to exceed 18 inches (457 mm) below finished grade.

Figure 300-3. PVC rigid nonmetallic conduit buried in compliance with Section 300-5 and installed in accordance with Section 300-5(d).

Protection is to extend at least 18 in. below grade.

Note that Section 230-49 requires underground service-entrance conductors to be protected against physical damage in accordance with Section 300-5.

Conductors entering a building shall be protected to the point of entrance.

Where the enclosure or raceway is subject to physical damage the conductors shall be installed in rigid metal conduit, intermediate metal conduit, Schedule 80 rigid nonmetallic conduit or equivalent.

(e) Splices and Taps. Direct buried conductors or cables shall be permitted to be spliced or tapped without the use of splice boxes. The splices or taps shall be made by approved methods and with identified materials.

(f) Backfill. Backfill containing large rock, paving materials, cinders, large or sharply angular substance, or corrosive material shall not be placed in an excavation where materials may

Figure 300-4. Electrical splicing kit for nonshielded single cables up to 5 kV and multiconductor cables up to 600 V. (*3M Company*)

damage raceways, cables, or other substructures or prevent adequate compaction of fill or contribute to corrosion of raceways, cables or other substructures.

Where necessary to prevent physical damage to the raceway or cable, protection shall be provided in the form of granular or selected material, suitable running boards, suitable sleeves, or other approved means.

(g) Raceway Seals. Conduits or raceways through which moisture may contact energized live parts shall be sealed or plugged at either or both ends.

(FPN): Presence of hazardous gases or vapors may also necessitate sealing of underground conduits or raceways entering buildings.

Figure 300-5. Conduit sealing bushing to prevent the entrance of gas or moisture. See Section 230-8 for sealing service raceways. (*O.Z./Gedney Co.*)

(h) Bushing. A bushing, or terminal fitting, with an integral bushed opening shall be used at the end of a conduit or other raceway which terminates underground where the conductors or cables emerge as a direct burial wiring method. A seal incorporating the physical protection characteristics of a bushing shall be permitted to be used in lieu of a bushing.

See Figure 300-2.

(i) Single Conductors. All conductors of the same circuit and, where used, the neutral and all equipment grounding conductors shall be installed in the same raceway or shall be installed in close proximity in the same trench.

Exception No. 1: Conductors in parallel in raceways shall be permitted but each raceway shall contain all conductors of the same circuit including grounding conductors.

This exception permits the installation of paralleled conductors in different raceways. See Section 310-4 for more information.

Exception No. 2: Isolated phase installations shall be permitted in nonmetallic raceways in close proximity where conductors are paralleled as permitted in Section 310-4 and the conditions of Section 300-20 are met.

Isolated phase installations are those in which there is only one phase per raceway. There may be some advantages to such an installation where there are many large conductors in parallel, as it avoids crossing conductors in the close quarters of the termination compartment of a switchboard, or in unit substation and transformer enclosures. The spacing between isolated phase raceways should be as small as possible and the length of the run limited, to avoid the increased circuit impedance and resulting increase in voltage drop inherent in an installation involving alternating-current circuits.

Isolated phase installations present an inherent hazard that must be understood and carefully controlled. The hazard is overheating as a result of induced currents in metal surrounding a raceway with only one phase in the raceway. See Section 300-20(b). The surrounding metal acts as a shorted transformer turn. In underground installations it is unlikely that metal will surround a single raceway or that there will be a fire hazard even if it does. This is not true, however, for aboveground raceways, and is the reason isolated phase installations are not permitted aboveground.

300-6. Protection Against Corrosion. Metal raceways, cable armor, boxes, cable sheathing, cabinets, elbows, couplings, fittings, supports, and support hardware shall be of materials suitable for the environment in which they are to be installed.

(a) General. Ferrous raceways, cable armor, boxes, cable sheathing, cabinets, metal elbows, couplings, fittings, supports, and support hardware shall be suitably protected against corrosion inside and outside (except threads at joints) by a coating of approved corrosion-resistant material such as zinc, cadmium, or enamel. Where protected from corrosion solely by enamel, they shall not be used out-of-doors or in wet locations as described in (c) below. When boxes or cabinets have an approved system of organic coatings and are marked "Raintight," "Rainproof" or "Outdoor Type," they shall be permitted out-of-doors.

Exception: Threads at joints shall be permitted to be coated with an identified electrically conductive compound.

Zinc chromate paste is one type of electrically conductive compound that can be used.

(b) In Concrete or in Direct Contact with the Earth. Ferrous or nonferrous metal raceways, cable armor, boxes, cable sheathing, cabinets, elbows, couplings, fittings, supports, and support hardware shall be permitted to be installed in concrete or in direct contact with the earth, or in areas subject to severe corrosive influences when made of material judged suitable for the condition, or when provided with corrosion protection approved for the condition.

Section 300-6 applies generally. For specific applications, see the particular article covering the various cables, raceways, or enclosures.

(c) Indoor Wet Locations. In portions of dairies, laundries, canneries, and other indoor wet locations, and in locations where walls are frequently washed or where there are surfaces of absorbent materials, such as damp paper or wood, the entire wiring system, including all boxes, fittings, conduits, and cable used therewith, shall be mounted so that there is at least ¼-inch (6.35-mm) air space between it and the wall or supporting surface.

(FPN): In general, areas where acids and alkali chemicals are handled and stored may present such corrosive conditions, particularly when wet or damp. Severe corrosive conditions may also be present in portions of meat-packing plants, tanneries, glue houses, and some stables; installations immediately adjacent to a seashore and swimming pool areas; areas where chemical de-icers are used; and storage cellars or rooms for hides, casings, fertilizer, salt, and bulk chemicals.

Ferrous or nonferrous metal conduit may be installed in concrete, in contact with the earth, or in areas exposed to severe corrosive influences where protected by corrosion protection and judged suitable for the condition. Special precautions are normally necessary for installing aluminum conduits in concrete, and specific approval by the authority having jurisdiction may be necessary.

To help avoid deterioration, metal raceways installed in the earth can be coated with an asphalt compound, plastic sheath, or other equivalent protection. Galvanized rigid steel conduit and steel intermediate metal conduit do not generally require supplementary corrosion protection.

300-7. Raceways Exposed to Different Temperatures.

(a) Sealing. Where portions of an interior raceway system are exposed to widely different temperatures, as in refrigerating or cold-storage plants, circulation of air from a warmer to a colder section through the raceway shall be prevented.

Where a raceway is used to enclose the lighting and refrigeration branch-circuit conductors within a walk-in chest, for example, the circulation of air from a warmer to a colder section through the raceway would cause condensation within the raceway. This can be prevented by sealing the raceway with a suitable, pliable compound at a conduit body or junction box, usually installed in the raceway before it enters the colder section. Special sealing fittings, such as those used in hazardous (classified) locations, are not necessary.

(b) Expansion Joints. Raceways shall be provided with expansion joints where necessary to compensate for thermal expansion and contraction.

300-8. Installation of Conductors with Other Systems. No electric conductor shall be installed in any raceway, cable, or cable tray that contains a pipe, tube, or equal for steam, water, air, gas, drainage, or any service other than electrical.

Exception: Cables approved for the purpose.

Section 300-8 specifically prohibits installation of an electrical conductor in a raceway, cable, or cable tray that includes a drain, water, or air pipe, etc. Although this requirement has been understood by most electrical installers, designers, and inspectors (see fine print note for definition of "raceway" in Article 100), it has not been specifically stated in the *Code* until the 1987 edition, except in Article 513. Cables approved for the purpose include Type IGS cable, Article 325.

300-9. Grounding Metal Enclosures. Metal raceways, boxes, cabinets, cable armor, and fittings shall be grounded as required in Article 250.

300-10. Electrical Continuity of Metal Raceways and Enclosures. Metal raceways, cable armor, and other metal enclosures for conductors shall be metallically joined together into a continuous electric conductor, and shall be so connected to all boxes, fittings, and cabinets as to provide effective electrical continuity. Raceways and cable assemblies shall be mechanically secured to boxes, fittings, cabinets, and other enclosures, except as provided for nonmetallic boxes in Section 370-7(c).

Metal raceways, metal armor or sheaths of cable, metal outlet or junction boxes, and fittings, such as connectors, couplings, locknuts, bushings, etc., must form an effective low-impedance path to ground to conduct safely any fault current and facilitate the operation of overcurrent devices protecting the enclosed circuit conductors.

300-11. Securing and Supporting.

(a) Secured in Place. Raceways, cable assemblies, boxes, cabinets, and fittings shall be securely fastened in place. Support wires that do not provide rigid support shall not be permitted as the sole support.

This section, revised for the 1987 edition, makes it clear that support wires, such as used to hang suspended ceilings, may be used for the support of raceways and cables, but cannot be used as the sole support if the wires do not provide rigid support. See Section 370-13 for support of outlet boxes.

Exception: As permitted elsewhere in this Code.

(b) Raceways Used as Means of Support. Raceways shall not be used as a means of support for other raceways, cables, or nonelectric equipment.

The intent here is to prevent a raceway from being used to support cables or nonelectric equipment such as drop ceilings, water pipe, etc., which could cause a mechanical failure of the raceway. Also, cables, such as telephone cables wrapped around the raceway, can prevent the dissipation of heat from the raceway and affect the temperature of the conductors in the raceway.

Exception No. 1: Where the raceways or means of support are identified for the purpose.

(FPN): See Article 318 for cable trays.

Exception No. 2: Raceways containing power supply conductors for electrically controlled equipment shall be permitted to support Class 2 circuit conductors or cables that are solely for the purpose of connection to the equipment control circuits.

This exception permits, for example, the Class 2 thermostat conductors for an air conditioner unit to be supported by the conduit supplying power to the unit.

Exception No. 3: As permitted in Sections 370-13 for boxes or conduit bodies, or 410-16(f) for fixtures.

300-12. Mechanical Continuity — Raceways and Cables.
Metal or nonmetallic raceways, cable armors, and cable sheaths shall be continuous between cabinets, boxes, fittings, or other enclosures or outlets.

300-13. Mechanical and Electrical Continuity — Conductors.

(a) General. Conductors shall be continuous between outlets, devices, etc., and there shall be no splice or tap within a raceway itself.

Exception No. 1: As provided in Section 374-8 for auxiliary gutters.

Exception No. 2: As provided in Section 362-6 for wireways.

Exception No. 3: As provided in Section 300-15(a), Exception No. 1 for boxes or fittings.

Exception No. 4: As provided in Section 352-7 for surface metal raceways.

Splices or taps are prohibited within a raceway, unless the raceways are equipped with hinged or removable covers according to the four exceptions.

(b) Device Removal. In multiwire circuits the continuity of a grounded conductor shall not be dependent upon device connections, such as lampholders, receptacles, etc., where the removal of such devices would interrupt the continuity.

Grounded (neutral) conductors of multiwire branch circuits supplying receptacles, lampholders, etc., are not permitted to be dependent upon terminal connections for continuity. For such installations (3- or 4-wire circuits), a splice is made and a jumper is connected to the terminal unless "looped" (see comments to Section 300-14); that is, a receptacle or lampholder could be replaced without interrupting the continuity of energized downstream line-to-neutral loads. See Figure 370-1. Opening the neutral could cause unbalanced voltages, and a considerably higher voltage would be impressed on one part of a multiwire branch circuit, especially if the downstream line-to-neutral loads are appreciably unbalanced. This requirement does not apply to individual 2-wire circuits or to other circuits that do not contain a grounded (neutral) conductor.

300-14. Length of Free Conductors at Outlets, Junctions, and Switch Points. At least 6 inches (152 mm) of free conductor shall be left at each outlet, junction, and switch point for splices or the connection of fixtures or devices.

Exception: Conductors that are not spliced or terminated at the outlet, junction, or switch point.

A conductor looping through an outlet box and intended for connection to receptacles, switches, lampholders, etc., requires slack so that terminal connections may be made easily.

Conductors running through a box should have sufficient slack to prevent physical damage from the insertion of devices or from the use of fixture studs, hickeys, or other fixture supports within the box.

300-15. Boxes or Fittings — Where Required.

(a) Box or Fitting. A box or fitting shall be installed at each conductor splice connection point, outlet, switch point, junction point, or pull point for the connection of conduit, electrical metallic tubing, surface raceway, or other raceways.

Exception No. 1: A box or fitting shall not be required for a conductor splice connection in surface raceways, wireways, header-ducts, multi-outlet assemblies, auxiliary gutters, cable trays, and conduit bodies having removable covers which are accessible after installation.

Conduit bodies (Types "T," "L," etc.) are a part of the conduit or tubing system and should not contain more conductors than permitted for the raceway. Conduit bodies having provisions for less than three conduit entries are not permitted to contain splices, taps, or devices unless they are durably and legibly marked with their cubic-inch capacity. The maximum number of conductors that are permitted to be enclosed is to be computed using the volume per conductor listed in Table 370-6(b). See Sections 370-6(b) and (c).

For the use of conductors No. 4 or larger, see Section 370-18(a).

Exception No. 2: As permitted in Section 410-31 where a fixture is used as a raceway.

(b) Box Only. A box shall be installed at each conductor splice connection point, outlet, switch point, junction point, or pull point for the connection of Type AC cable, Type MC cable, mineral-insulated, metal-sheathed cable, nonmetallic-sheathed cable, or other cables, at the connection point between any such cable system and a raceway system and at each outlet and switch point for concealed knob-and-tube wiring.

Exception No. 1: As permitted by Section 336-16 for insulated outlet devices supplied by nonmetallic-sheathed cable.

Exception No. 2: As permitted by Section 410-62 for rosettes.

Exception No. 3: Where accessible fittings are used for straight-through splices in mineral-insulated, metal-sheathed cable.

Exception No. 4: Where cables enter or exit from conduit or tubing which is used to provide cable support or protection against physical damage. A fitting shall be provided on the end(s) of the conduit or tubing, to protect the wires or cables from abrasion.

Exception No. 4 permits conduit or tubing to be used as support and protection against physical damage without terminating in a box. This exception also permits conduit or tubing to be used as physical protection for underground cables exiting from buildings or outdoors on poles, without a box being required on the end of the conduit. A fitting to protect the wires or cables is required on the ends of the conduit or tubing used to provide protection against physical damage. See Figure 300-2. See Sections 250-32 and 250-33 for grounding requirements.

Exception No. 5: A wiring device with integral enclosure identified for the use having brackets that securely fasten the device to walls or ceilings of conventional on-site frame construction for use with nonmetallic-sheathed cable shall be permitted without a separate box.

Exception No. 5 applies to a device with an integral enclosure (boxless device).

(FPN): See Sections 336-15, Exception No. 2; 545-10; 550-10(j); and 551-16(e), Exception No. 1.

Exception No. 6: Where metallic manufactured wiring systems are used.

See Article 604 — Manufactured Wiring Systems.

Exception No. 7: A conduit body shall be permitted in lieu of a box where installed to comply with Section 370-6(c) and Section 370-18.

Exception No. 8: Where a device identified and listed as suitable for installation without a box is used with a closed-loop power distribution system.

See Article 780 — Closed-Loop and Programmed Power Distribution.

Exception No. 9: A fitting identified for the use shall be permitted in lieu of a box where accessible after installation and where the conductors are not spliced or terminated.

This exception permits, for example, a connection between Type AC cable and EMT, with a suitable fitting, where the EMT is to be run down an exposed wall, and the cable jacket is stripped far enough back to allow the conductors to pass through the raceway (the EMT) and enter a device box.

300-16. Raceway or Cable to Open or Concealed Wiring.

(a) Box or Fitting. A box or terminal fitting having a separately bushed hole for each conductor shall be used wherever a change is made from conduit, electrical metallic tubing, nonmetallic-sheathed cable, Type AC cable, Type MC cable, or mineral-insulated, metal-sheathed cable and surface raceway wiring to open wiring or to concealed knob-and-tube wiring. A fitting used for this purpose shall contain no taps or splices and shall not be used at fixture outlets.

(b) Bushing. A bushing shall be permitted in lieu of a box or terminal fitting at the end of a conduit or electrical metallic tubing where the raceway terminates behind an open (unenclosed) switchboard or at an unenclosed control and similar equipment. The bushing shall be of the insulating type for other than lead-sheathed conductors.

300-17. Number and Size of Conductors in Raceway. The number and size of conductors in any raceway shall not be more than will permit dissipation of the heat and ready installation or withdrawal of the conductors without damage to the conductors or to their insulation.

(FPN): See the following sections of this Code: electrical nonmetallic tubing, 331-6; conduit, 345-7 and 346-6; electrical metallic tubing, 348-6; rigid nonmetallic conduit, 347-11; flexible metallic tubing, 349-12; flexible metal conduit, 350-3; liquidtight flexible metal conduit, 351-6; liquidtight nonmetallic flexible conduit, 351-25; surface raceways, 352-4 and 352-25; underfloor raceways, 354-5; cellular metal floor raceways, 356-5; cellular concrete floor raceways, 358-11; wireways, 362-5; auxiliary gutters, 374-5; fixture wire, 402-7; theaters, 520-5; signs, 600-21(d); elevators, 620-33; sound recording, 640-3 and 640-4; Class 1, Class 2, and Class 3 circuits, Article 725; fire protective signaling circuits, Article 760, and optical fiber cables, Article 770.

Listed wire-pulling compounds are available for use to assist in the process of pulling wires into raceways.

300-19. Supporting Conductors in Vertical Raceways.

(a) Spacing Intervals — Maximum. Conductors in vertical raceways shall be supported. One cable support shall be provided at the top of the vertical raceway or as close to the top as practical, plus a support for each additional interval of spacing as specified in Table 300-19(a).

Exception No. 1: If the total vertical riser is less than 25 percent of the spacing specified in Table 300-19(a), no cable support shall be required.

Exception No. 2: Steel wire armor cable shall be supported at the top of the riser with a cable support that clamps the steel wire armor. A safety device shall be permitted at the lower end of the riser to hold the cable in the event there is slippage of the cable in the wire armored cable support. Additional wedge-type supports shall be permitted to relieve the strain on the equipment terminals caused by expansion of the cable under load.

Table 300-19(a). Spacings for Conductor Supports

AWG or Circular-Mil Size of Wire	Conductors Support of Conductors in Vertical Raceways	Aluminum or Copper-Clad Aluminum	Copper
18 AWG thru 8 AWG	Not greater than	100 feet	100 feet
6 AWG thru 0 AWG	" " "	200 feet	100 feet
2/0 AWG thru 4/0 AWG	" " "	180 feet	80 feet
over 4/0 AWG thru 350 MCM	" " "	135 feet	60 feet
over 350 MCM thru 500 MCM	" " "	120 feet	50 feet
over 500 MCM thru 750 MCM	" " "	95 feet	40 feet
over 750 MCM	" " "	85 feet	35 feet

For SI units: one foot = 0.3048 meter.

(b) Support Methods. One of the following methods of support shall be used:

(1) By clamping devices constructed of or employing insulating wedges inserted in the ends of the conduits. Where clamping of insulation does not adequately support the cable, the conductor also shall be clamped.

(2) By inserting boxes at the required intervals in which insulating supports are installed and secured in a satisfactory manner to withstand the weight of the conductors attached thereto, the boxes being provided with covers.

(3) In junction boxes, by deflecting the cables not less than 90 degrees and carrying them horizontally to a distance not less than twice the diameter of the cable, the cables being carried on two or more insulating supports, and additionally secured thereto by tie wires if desired. When this method is used, cables shall be supported at intervals not greater than 20 percent of those mentioned in the preceding tabulation.

(4) By a method of equal effectiveness.

Conductors in long vertical runs are required to be supported to prevent the weight of the conductors from damaging the insulation where leaving the conduit and to prevent the conductors from being pulled out of the terminals. Supports like those shown in Figures 300-6 and 300-7 may be used in addition to many other types of grips manufactured for this purpose.

Example: A vertical raceway contains 1/0 copper conductors. One cable support near the top of the run would be required if the vertical run is from 25 to 100 ft. If the vertical run in this example is less than 25 ft, cable supports are not required.

Figure 300-6. A support bushing located at the top of a vertical conduit at a cabinet or pull box, which prevents the weight of the conductors from damaging the insulation or placing a strain on termination points. *(O.Z./Gedney Co.)*

300-20. Induced Currents in Metal Enclosures or Metal Raceways.

(a) Conductors Grouped Together. Where conductors carrying alternating current are installed in metal enclosures or metal raceways, they shall be so arranged as to avoid heating the surrounding metal by induction. To accomplish this, all phase conductors and, where used, the neutral and all equipment grounding conductors shall be grouped together.

Exception No. 1: As permitted in Section 250-50, Exception for equipment grounding connections.

Exception No. 2: As permitted in Section 427-47 for skin effect heating.

By its very nature, skin effect heating uses induced currents in metal raceways to heat pipelines. Importantly, the temperature of the raceway is known and bears a definite relationship to the pipeline temperature and the overall thermal parameters of the system.

(b) Individual Conductors. Where a single conductor carrying alternating current passes through metal with magnetic properties the inductive effect shall be minimized by: (1) cutting slots in the metal between the individual holes through which the individual conductors pass, or (2) passing all the conductors in the circuit through an insulating wall sufficiently large for all of the conductors of the circuit.

Exception: In the case of circuits supplying vacuum or electric-discharge lighting systems or signs, or X-ray apparatus, the currents carried by the conductors are so small that the inductive heating effect can be ignored where these conductors are placed in metal enclosures or pass through metal.

(FPN): Because aluminum is not a magnetic metal, there will be no heating due to hysteresis; however, induced currents will be present. They will not be of sufficient magnitude to require grouping of conductors or special treatment in passing conductors through aluminum wall sections.

Figure 300-7. Another method of supporting vertical conductors.

300-21. Spread of Fire or Products of Combustion. Electrical installations in hollow spaces, vertical shafts, and ventilation or air-handling ducts shall be so made that the possible spread of fire or products of combustion will not be substantially increased. Openings around electrical penetrations through fire-resistance rated walls, partitions, floors, or ceilings shall be firestopped using approved methods to maintain the fire-resistance rating.

It is the intent of this section that electrical equipment, raceways, cables, etc., be installed in such a manner that they will not contribute to the spread of fire or the products of combustion through the specified component parts of a building. In addition, the fire-stopping method used is required to effectively maintain the fire-resistance rating of the building component that is pierced. See Figures 300-8 and 300-9.

300-22. Wiring in Ducts, Plenums, and Other Air-Handling Spaces. The provisions of this section apply to the installation and uses of electric wiring and equipment in ducts, plenums, and other air-handling spaces.

(FPN): See Article 424, Part F for Electric Duct Heaters.

(a) Ducts for Dust, Loose Stock, or Vapor Removal. No wiring systems of any type shall be installed in ducts used to transport dust, loose stock, or flammable vapors. No wiring system of any type shall be installed in any duct, or shaft containing only such ducts, used for vapor removal or for ventilation of commercial-type cooking equipment.

(b) Ducts or Plenums Used for Environmental Air. Only wiring methods consisting of Type MI cable, Type MC cable employing a smooth or corrugated impervious metal sheath

Figure 300-8. Fire seals used to maintain the integrity of fire-rated walls, floors, partitions, or ceilings as required by Section 300-21. (*O.Z./Gedney Co.*)

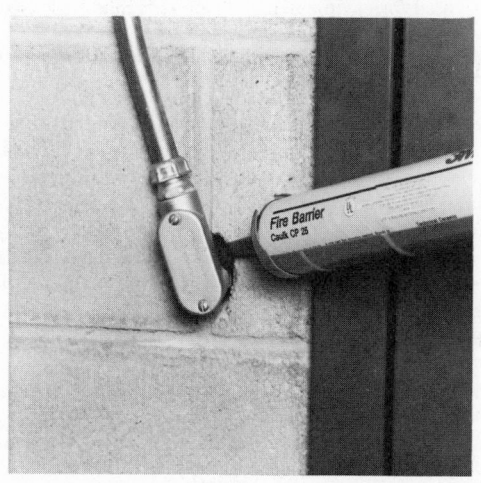

Figure 300-9. Using approved caulking to meet the requirements of Section 300-21. (*Electro Products Div., 3M Co.*)

without an overall nonmetallic covering, electrical metallic tubing, flexible metallic tubing, intermediate metal conduit, or rigid metal conduit shall be installed in ducts or plenums used for environmental air. Flexible metal conduit and liquidtight flexible metal conduit shall be permitted, in lengths not to exceed 4 feet (1.22 m), to connect physically adjustable equipment and devices permitted to be in these ducts and plenum chambers. The connectors used with flexible metal conduit shall effectively close any openings in the connection. Equipment and devices shall be permitted within such ducts or plenum chambers only if necessary for their direct action upon, or sensing of, the contained air. Where equipment or devices are installed and illumination is necessary to facilitate maintenance and repair, enclosed gasketed-type fixtures shall be permitted.

(FPN): The above applies to ducts and plenums specifically fabricated to transport environmental air.

The intent of this section is to limit the materials that would contribute smoke and products of combustion during a fire in an area that handles environmental air,

259

and, in the case of paragraph (b), to provide an effective barrier against the excursion of products of combustion into the duct or plenum.

Paragraph (b) applies to ducts and plenums specifically constructed to transport environmental air, such as sheet metal ducts. Equipment and devices such as lighting fixtures and motors are not normally permitted in ducts or plenums and, for this reason, paragraph (b) wiring methods are different from the wiring methods permitted in paragraph (c).

(c) Other Space Used for Environmental Air. Only wiring methods consisting of Type MI cable, Type MC cable without an overall nonmetallic covering, Type AC cable, or other factory-assembled multiconductor control or power cable which is specifically listed for the use shall be installed in other space used for environmental air.

Other type cables and conductors shall be installed in electrical metallic tubing, flexible metallic tubing, intermediate metal conduit, rigid metal conduit, flexible metal conduit, or where accessible, wireway with metal covers or solid bottom metal cable tray with solid metal covers.

Electric equipment with a metal enclosure or with a nonmetallic enclosure listed for the use and having adequate fire-resistant and low-smoke-producing characteristics, and associated wiring material suitable for the ambient temperature shall be permitted to be installed in other space used for environmental air unless prohibited elsewhere in this Code.

(FPN): The above applies to other spaces such as spaces over hung ceilings which are used for environmental air-handling purposes.

Paragraph (c) applies to other spaces used to transport environmental air that are not specifically manufactured as a duct or plenum, such as suspended (hung) ceilings. Many suspended ceilings are intended to transport return air. Some are also used for supply air, but this use is not nearly so common as those used for return air. As the spaces above suspended ceilings contain lighting fixtures, motors, and other equipment and devices, the wiring methods permitted in paragraph (c) are different from those contained in paragraph (b).

Exception No. 1: Liquidtight flexible metal conduit in single lengths not exceeding 6 feet (1.83 m).

Exception No. 2: Integral fan systems specifically identified for such use.

Exception No. 3: This section does not include habitable rooms or areas of buildings, the prime purpose of which is not air handling.

Exception No. 3 applies to rooms and hallways being used as portions of air-return systems in buildings.

It is not intended that the limitation of wiring methods be applied to these parts of a building the *prime* purpose of which is not air-handling.

If the *prime* purpose of the room or space is air-handling then the requirements of Section 300-22(c) apply whether or not electrical equipment is located in the room [see Section 300-22(c), 3rd paragraph].

If the *prime* purpose is not air-handling then the exception is applicable.

Exception No. 4: Listed prefabricated cable assemblies of metallic manufactured wiring systems without nonmetallic sheath shall be permitted where listed for this use.

Note that the cable assembly is required to be listed for use in space used for environmental air. See Article 604.

Exception No. 5: This section does not include the joist or stud spaces in dwelling units when wiring or equipment passes through such spaces perpendicular to the long dimension of such spaces.

See Figure 300-10.

Figure 300-10. Illustrated is a cable passing through joist spaces of a dwelling unit. The joist space is covered with sheet metal and used as a cold-air return for a forced warm-air central heating system.

Exception No. 6: This section does not include the underfloor area specified in Section 645-2(c)(3).

(d) Data Processing Systems.   Electric wiring in air-handling areas beneath raised floors for data processing systems shall comply with Article 645.

B. Requirements for Over 600 Volts, Nominal

300-31. Covers Required.   Suitable covers shall be installed on all boxes, fittings, and similar enclosures to prevent accidental contact with energized parts or physical damage to parts or insulation.

300-32. Conductors of Different Systems.   Conductors of high-voltage and low-voltage systems shall not occupy the same wiring enclosure or pull and junction boxes.

Exception No. 1: In motors, switchgear and control assemblies and similar equipment.

Exception No. 2: In manholes, if low-voltage conductors are separated from high-voltage conductors.

300-34. Conductor Bending Radius.   The conductor shall not be bent to a radius less than eight times the overall diameter for nonshielded conductors or twelve times the diameter for shielded or lead-covered conductors during or after installation.

300-35. Protection Against Induction Heating.   Metallic raceways and associated conductors shall be so arranged as to avoid heating of the raceway by induction.

300-36. Grounding.   Wiring and equipment installations shall be grounded in accordance with the applicable provisions of Article 250.

ARTICLE 305 — TEMPORARY WIRING

Contents

305-1. Scope. The provisions of this article apply to temporary electrical power and lighting wiring methods which may be of a class less than would be required for a permanent installation.

305-2. Other Articles. Except as specifically modified in this article, all other requirements of this Code for permanent wiring shall apply to temporary wiring installations.

305-3. Time Constraints.

(a) During the Period of Construction. Temporary electrical power and lighting installations shall be permitted during the period of construction, remodeling, maintenance, repair, or demolition of buildings, structures, equipment, or similar activities.

(b) 90 Days. Temporary electrical power and lighting installations shall be permitted for a period not to exceed 90 days for Christmas decorative lighting, carnivals, and similar purposes.

Note that the temporary wiring applications of paragraphs (a) and (c) are not restricted to 90 days. However, see Paragraph (d).

(c) Emergencies and Tests. Temporary electrical power and lighting installations shall be permitted during emergencies and for tests, experiments, and developmental work.

(d) Removal. Temporary wiring shall be removed immediately upon completion of construction or purpose for which the wiring was installed.

305-4. General.

(a) Services. Services shall be installed in conformance with Article 230.

(b) Feeders. Feeders shall be protected as provided in Article 240. They shall originate in an approved distribution center. The conductors shall be permitted within flexible multiconductor cord or cable assemblies of a type identified in Table 400-4 for hard usage or extra hard usage. Where the voltage does not exceed 150 volts to ground and where not subject to physical damage, feeders shall be permitted to be run as open conductors if supported on insulators at intervals of not more than 10 feet (3.05 m).

Exception: Where installed for the purposes specified in Section 305-3(c).

(c) Branch Circuits. All branch circuits shall originate in an approved power outlet or panelboard. Conductors shall be permitted within flexible multiconductor cord or cable assemblies of a type identified in Table 400-4 for hard usage or extra hard usage. All conductors shall be protected as provided in Article 240. Where the voltage does not exceed 150 volts to ground and where not subject to physical damage, branch circuits shall be permitted to be run as open conductors if supported on insulators at intervals of not more than 10 feet (3.05 m). No open wiring branch circuit conductors shall be laid on the floor or ground.

Exception: Where installed for the purposes specified in Section 305-3(c).

> The basic requirement for safety is that temporary wiring is required to be located where it will not be subject to physical damage.
> Note that extension cords are permitted to be laid on the floor.
> The requirement that open conductor wiring be limited to circuits not exceeding 150 volts to ground is new in the 1987 *NEC* for both branch circuits and feeders. Also new is the limitation of flexible cords and cables to those identified in Table 400-4 for hard usage (SJ, SJE, SJT, SJO, etc.) or extra hard usage (S, SE, ST, SO, G, W, etc.)

(d) Receptacles. All receptacles shall be of the grounding type. Unless installed in a continuous grounded metal raceway or metal-covered cable all branch circuits shall contain a separate equipment grounding conductor and all receptacles shall be electrically connected to the equipment grounding conductors. Receptacles on construction sites shall not be installed on branch circuits which supply temporary lighting. Receptacles shall not be connected to the same ungrounded conductor of multiwire circuits which supply temporary lighting.

> The intent of this paragraph is to require installations so that the operation of a fuse or circuit breaker or a ground-fault circuit-interrupter due to a fault or overload of equipment will not deenergize the lighting circuit.

(e) Disconnecting Means. Suitable disconnecting switches or plug connectors shall be installed to permit the disconnection of all ungrounded conductors of each temporary circuit. Multiwire branch circuits shall be provided with a means to disconnect simultaneously all ungrounded conductors at the power outlet or panelboard where the branch circuit originated. Approved handle ties shall be permitted.

(f) Lamp Protection. All lamps for general illumination shall be protected from accidental contact or breakage by a suitable fixture or lampholder with a guard.
Brass shell, paper-lined sockets, or other metal-cased sockets shall not be used unless the shell is grounded.

(g) Splices. On construction sites a box shall not be required for splices or junction connections where the circuit conductors are multiconductor cord or cable assemblies or open conductors. See Sections 110-14(b) and 400-9. A box shall be used wherever a change is made to a raceway system or a cable system which is metal clad or metal sheathed.

(h) Protection from Accidental Damage. Flexible cords and cables shall be protected from accidental damage. Sharp corners and projections shall be avoided. When passing through doorways or other pinch points, protection shall be provided to avoid damage.

> Note that, unlike Section 400-8, Section 305-4(h) permits flexible cords and cables, because of the nature of their use, to pass through doorways.

305-5. Grounding. All grounding shall conform with Article 250.

305-6. Ground-Fault Protection for Personnel. Ground-fault protection for personnel on construction sites shall be provided to comply with (a) or (b) below.

(a) Ground-Fault Circuit-Interrupters. All 125-volt, single-phase, 15- and 20-ampere receptacle outlets which are not a part of the permanent wiring of the building or structure and which are in use by employees shall have ground-fault circuit-interrupter protection for personnel.

Exception: Receptacles on a 2-wire, single-phase portable or vehicle-mounted generator rated not more than 5 kW, where the circuit conductors of the generator are insulated from the generator frame and all other grounded surfaces.

Receptacle outlets that are a part of the permanent wiring of the building are not required to have GFCI protection. However, it is intended that they be used with portable GFCIs or meet the provisions of Section 305-6(b).

Ground-fault circuit-interrupters may be of the portable type (see Figure 210-13), receptacle type (see Figure 210-14), or circuit breaker type. A commonly used temporary power unit is shown in Figure 305-1.

See commentary on GFCIs following Section 210-8.

Figure 305-1. Temporary power outlet units commonly used on construction sites with a variety of configurations. Some are available with ground-fault circuit-interrupter protection. (*Hubbell*)

Figure 305-2. Nuisance tripping of ground-fault circuit-interrupter protective devices by wet or damp weather conditions can be avoided by using watertight plugs and connectors. (*Hubbell*)

(b) Assured Equipment Grounding Conductor Program. A written procedure shall be continuously enforced at the construction site by one or more designated persons to assure that equipment grounding conductors for all cord sets, receptacles which are not a part of the permanent wiring of the building or structure and equipment connected by cord and plug are installed and maintained in accordance with the applicable requirements of Sections 210-7(c), 250-45, 250-59, and 305-4(d).

(1) The following tests shall be performed on all cord sets, receptacles which are not part of the permanent wiring of the building or structure, and cord- and plug-connected equipment required to be grounded.

a. All equipment grounding conductors shall be tested for continuity and shall be electrically continuous.

b. Each receptacle and attachment plug shall be tested for correct attachment of the equipment grounding conductor. The equipment grounding conductor shall be connected to its proper terminal.

c. All required tests shall be performed:

1. Before first use on the construction site.

2. When there is evidence of damage.

3. Before equipment is returned to service following any repairs.

4. At intervals not exceeding 3 months.

(2) The tests required in (1) above shall be recorded and made available to the authority having jurisdiction.

305-7. Guarding. For temporary wiring over 600 volts, nominal, suitable fencing, barriers, or other effective means shall be provided to prevent access of other than authorized and qualified personnel.

ARTICLE 310 — CONDUCTORS FOR GENERAL WIRING

Contents

310-1. Scope. This article covers general requirements for conductors and their type designations, insulations, markings, mechanical strengths, ampacity ratings, and uses. These requirements do not apply to conductors that form an integral part of equipment, such as motors, motor controllers, and similar equipment, or to conductors specifically provided for elsewhere in this Code.

(FPN): For flexible cords and cables, see Article 400. For fixture wires, see Article 402.

310-2. Conductors.

(a) Insulated. Conductors shall be insulated.

Exception: Where covered or bare conductors are specifically permitted elsewhere in this Code.

(FPN): See Section 250-152 for insulation of neutral conductors of a solidly grounded high-voltage system.

(b) Conductor Material. Conductors in this article shall be of aluminum, copper-clad aluminum, or copper unless otherwise specified.

310-3. Stranded Conductors. Where installed in raceways, conductors of size No. 8 and larger shall be stranded.

Exception No. 1: When used as busbars or in mineral-insulated, metal-sheathed cable.

Exception No. 2: Bonding conductors as required in Section 680-22(b).

310-4. Conductors in Parallel. Aluminum, copper-clad aluminum, or copper conductors of size 1/0 and larger, comprising each phase or neutral, shall be permitted to be connected in parallel (electrically joined at both ends to form a single conductor).

Exception No. 1: As permitted in Section 620-12(a)(1), Exception.

Exception No. 2: Conductors in sizes smaller than No. 1/0 AWG shall be permitted to be run in parallel to supply control power to indicating instruments, contactors, relays, solenoids, and similar control devices provided: (a) they are contained within the same raceway or cable; (b) the ampacity of each individual conductor is sufficient to carry the entire load current shared by the parallel conductors; and (c) the overcurrent protection is such that the ampacity of each individual conductor will not be exceeded if one or more of the parallel conductors become inadvertently disconnected.

Exception No. 3: Conductors in sizes smaller than 1/0 shall be permitted to be run in parallel for frequencies of 360 hertz and higher when all of the conditions of Exception No. 2(a), (b), and (c) are met.

For example, in control work and work at higher (360 Hz and higher) frequencies it is sometimes found necessary to reduce cable capacitance effect or voltage drop over long lengths of wire. If a No. 14 AWG conductor is more than enough to carry the load, yet two No. 14 conductors in parallel will reduce the voltage drop to acceptable limits, this should be permissible providing the safeguards indicated in Exception No. 2 are taken.

The paralleled conductors in each phase or neutral shall:

(1) Be the same length;

(2) Have the same conductor material;

(3) Be the same size in circular mil area;

(4) Have the same insulation type;

(5) Be terminated in the same manner.

Where run in separate raceways or cables the raceways or cables shall have the same physical characteristics.

(FPN): Differences in inductive reactance and unequal division of current can be minimized by choice of materials, methods of construction and orientation of conductors. It is not the intent to require that conductors of one phase or neutral be the same as those of another phase or neutral to achieve balance.

For example, the conductors in Phases A and B may be copper, and those in Phase C aluminum. However, all raceways are to be of the same size, material, and length.

When equipment grounding conductors are used with conductors in parallel, they shall comply with the requirements of this section except that they shall be sized as per Section 250-95.

When conductors are used in parallel, space in enclosures shall be given consideration (see Articles 370 and 373).

Conductors installed in parallel shall comply with the provisions of Note 8 to Tables 310-16 through 310-31.

This section permits a practical means for installing large-capacity conductors for feeders or services. The paralleling of two or more conductors in place of one large conductor relies on a number of factors to ensure equal division of current. Therefore, several conditions must be satisfied so as not to overload any of the individual paralleled conductors. Other than as permitted in Section 250-95 and the exceptions to Section 310-4, there does not appear to be any practical need to parallel conductors smaller than size 1/0.

To avoid excessive voltage drop and also to ensure equal division of current, it is essential that separate phase conductors be located close together and that each phase conductor and the neutral and grounding conductors, if used, be grouped together in each conduit. See Section 300-5(i), Exception No. 2 for an exception.

The impedance of a circuit in an aluminum raceway will be different from the impedance of the same circuit in a steel raceway, hence it is required that separate raceways have the same physical characteristics. See Section 300-20.

Note that all of the conductors of each phase or neutral are required to be of the same conductor material. For example, if twelve conductors are paralleled for a 3-phase, 4-wire, 480Y/277-V ac circuit, four conductors could be installed in each of three raceways. The *Code* does not intend that all twelve conductors be of copper or aluminum, but does intend that the individual conductors in parallel for each phase and neutral be of the same material, insulation type, length, etc. Also, it is intended that the three raceways have the same physical characteristics, i.e., three rigid aluminum conduits or three steel IMC conduits or three EMTs or three nonmetallic conduits, not a mixture of two rigid aluminum conduits and one rigid steel conduit.

It is neither economical nor practical to use conductors larger than 1,000 MCM in raceways, unless the conductor size is governed by voltage drop. The ampacity of larger sizes would increase very little in proportion to the increase in the size of the conductor. Therefore, when the size of a conductor increases 50 percent, for example, from 1,000 to 1,500 MCM, a Type THW conductor increases 80 A (less than 15 percent). An increase from 1,000 to 2,000 MCM (100 percent increase) causes an increase of only 120 A (approximately 20 percent). Generally, in situations that call for the use of single conductors larger than 500 MCM, determining the cost of the entire installation using single conductors rather than two (or more) conductors in parallel is beneficial.

310-5. Minimum Size of Conductors. The minimum size of conductors shall be as given in Table 310-5.

Exception No. 1: For flexible cords as permitted by Section 400-12.

Exception No. 2: For fixture wire as permitted by Section 410-24.

Exception No. 3: For fractional horsepower motors as permitted by Section 430-22.

Exception No. 4: For cranes and hoists as permitted by Section 610-14.

Exception No. 5: For elevator control and signaling circuits as permitted by Section 620-12.

Exception No. 6: For Class 1, Class 2, and Class 3 circuits as permitted by Sections 725-16, 725-37, and 725-40.

Table 310-5

Voltage Rating of Conductor—Volts	Minimum Conductor Size—AWG
0 thru 2000	14 Copper 12 Aluminum or Copper-Clad Aluminum
2001 thru 5000	8
5001 thru 8000	6
8001 thru 15000	2 100% Insulation Level* 1 133% Insulation Level*
15001 thru 28000	1
28001 thru 35000	1/0

*See Table 310-64, Definitions.

Exception No. 7: For fire protective signaling circuits as permitted by Sections 760-16, 760-27, and 760-30.

Exception No. 8: For 2001-5000 volt for Types AVA, AVB, and AVL cables, the minimum conductor size is No. 14 AWG copper or No. 12 AWG aluminum or copper-clad aluminum.

Exception No. 9: For Type V cables, the minimum conductor sizes are: No. 12 AWG for 2000-volt rating, No. 10 AWG for 3000-volt rating, and No. 8 AWG for 4000-volt rating.

Exception No. 10: For motor control circuits as permitted by Section 430-72.

310-6. Shielding. Solid dielectric insulated conductors operated above 2000 volts in permanent installations shall have ozone-resistant insulation and shall be shielded. All metallic insulation shields shall be grounded through an effective grounding path meeting the requirements of Section 250-51. Shielding shall be for the purpose of confining the voltage stresses to the insulation.

Exception: Nonshielded insulated conductors listed by a qualified testing laboratory shall be permitted for use up to 8000 volts under the following conditions:

a. Conductors shall have insulation resistant to electric discharge and surface tracking, or the insulated conductor(s) shall be covered with a material resistant to ozone, electric discharge, and surface tracking.

b. Where used in wet locations the insulated conductor(s) shall have an overall nonmetallic jacket or a continuous metallic sheath.

c. Where operated at 5001 to 8000 volts, the insulated conductor(s) shall have a nonmetallic jacket over the insulation. The insulation shall have a specific inductive capacity no greater than 3.6 and the jacket shall have a specific inductive capacity no greater than 10 and no less than 6.

d. Insulation and jacket thicknesses shall be in accordance with Table 310-63.

Permanently installed solid dielectric insulated conductors operated above 2,000 V are to have ozone-resistant insulation and are required to be shielded with a grounded metallic shield (note Exception).

Shielding is the application of a metallic tape or nonmetallic semiconducting tape around the conductor surface, which will prevent corona from forming and will reduce high-voltage stresses. Corona is a faint glow adjacent to the surface of the electrical conductor at high voltage. If there are high-voltage stresses and a charging current flowing between the conductor and ground (usually due to moisture), the surrounding atmosphere is ionized and ozone (which is generated by an electric discharge in ordinary oxygen or air) is formed, which will attack the conductor jacket and insulation and may eventually break them down. The shield is at ground potential; therefore, no voltage above ground is present on the jacket outside of the shield, thus preventing a discharge from the jacket and the subsequent formation of ozone.

Figure 310-1 shows a three-conductor cable of the shielded type.

Figure 310-2 illustrates a stress-relief cone for an indoor cable terminator.

Figure 310-3 illustrates a stress cone on a single-conductor shielded cable terminating inside a pothead. Notice that a clamping ring provides a grounding connection between the copper shielding tape and shield to the metallic base of the pothead.

Specialized training and close adherence to manufacturer's instructions are absolutely essential for high-voltage cable installations.

Figure 310-1. Three-conductor cable of the shielded type.

310-7. Direct Burial Conductors.   Cables rated above 2000 volts shall be shielded. Conductors used for direct burial applications shall be of a type identified for such use.

Exception: Nonshielded multiconductor cables rated 2001-5000 volts shall be permitted if the cable has an overall metallic sheath or armor.

The metallic shield, sheath or armor shall be grounded through an effective grounding path meeting the requirements of Section 250-51.

(FPN): See Sections 300-5 and 710-3(b).

310-8. Wet Locations.

(a) Insulated Conductors.   Insulated conductors used in wet locations shall be (1) lead-covered; (2) Types RHW, TW, THW, THWN, XHHW; or (3) of a type listed for use in wet locations.

(b) Cables.   Cables of one or more conductors used in wet locations shall be of a type listed for use in wet locations.

Conductors used for direct burial applications shall be of a type listed for such use.

310-9. Corrosive Conditions.   Conductors exposed to oils, greases, vapors, gases, fumes, liquids, or other substances having a deleterious effect upon the conductor or insulation shall be of a type suitable for the application.

See commentary following Section 501-13.

310-10. Temperature Limitation of Conductors.   No conductor shall be used in such a manner that its operating temperature will exceed that designated for the type of insulated

269

Figure 310-2. One-piece, premolded stress-relief cone is for indoor cable terminations of up to 35 kV phase-to-phase. (*ITT Blackburn Co.*)

Conductor terminal

Insulator

Solid dielectric rubber or silicone polyethylene
Filling compound
High voltage rubber
insulating tape copper
Shielding tape
Copper shield, tape, wire, sheath
Clamping ring

Figure 310-3. A stress cone on a single-conductor shielded cable terminating inside a pothead.

conductor involved. In no case shall conductors be associated together in such a way with respect to type of circuit, the wiring method employed, or the number of conductors that the limiting temperature of any conductor is exceeded.

Most terminations are normally designed only for 60°C (140°F) or 75°C (167°F) maximum temperatures, although some are now being designed for 90°C (194°F); therefore, the higher rated ampacities for conductors of 90°C (194°F), 110°C (230°F), etc., cannot be utilized unless the terminations have comparable ratings.

Tables 310-16 through 310-31 have ampacity correction factor tables for ambient temperatures that are greater or less than the ambient temperature identified in the table heading. To assign the proper ampacity to a conductor in an ambient above 30°C, the appropriate correction factors must be used. This correction factor is applied in addition to any derating factor, such as in Note 8(a) to Tables 310-16 through 310-31.

Example: No. 2 AWG TW copper conductors are to be installed in a raceway in an ambient temperature of 50°C (122°F). According to Table 310-16, the ampacity of the conductor at 30°C is 95 A which is multiplied by 0.58 (taken from the correction factors at the bottom of the table); thus the ampacity of the No. 2 conductor at 50°C is reduced to 55.1 A (95 A × 0.58 = 55.1 A).

If six of these conductors were run in a raceway, Note 8(a) to the tables would require the ampacity to be reduced to 80 percent, which, in this case, would be 55.1 A × 0.8 = 44.08 A. Under these conditions, the No. 2 conductors would be suitable for a 40-A circuit.

The basis for determining the ampacities of conductors for Tables 310-16 and 310-17 was the "NEMA Report of Determination of Maximum Permissible Current-Carrying Capacity of Code Insulated Wires and Cables for Building Purposes" dated June 27, 1938. The basis for determining the ampacities of conductors for Tables 310-18 through 310-19, and Tables 310-22 through 310-31 was the Neher-McGrath Method. See commentary for Section 310-15(a).

The temperature rating of a conductor (see Table 310-13) is the maximum temperature, at any location along its length, that the conductor can withstand over a prolonged time period without serious degradation.

Conductors that have a rating above the anticipated maximum ambient temperature should be chosen. The operating temperature of conductors should be controlled at or below its rating by coordinating conductor size, number of associated conductors, and ampacity for the particular conductor rating and ambient temperature. All tabulations should be corrected for the anticipated ambient using the ampacity correction factors at the bottom of the tables. Where more than three conductors are associated together, the additional correction given in Note 8(a) to the tables is required to be applied.

(FPN): The temperature rating of a conductor (see Tables 310-13 and 310-61) is the maximum temperature, at any location along its length, that the conductor can withstand over a prolonged time period without serious degradation. Tables 310-16 through 310-31 and 310-69 through 310-84, the correction factors at the bottom of these tables, and the notes to the tables provide guidance for coordinating conductor sizes, types, ampacities, ambient temperatures, and number of associated conductors.

The fine print note is intended to focus attention to the necessity for derating conductors where high ambient temperatures are encountered and to provide users with helpful information in coordinating ampacities, ambient temperatures, conductor size and number, etc., to assure operation at or below rating.

The principal determinants of operating temperature are:

1. Ambient temperature. Ambient temperature may vary along the conductor length as well as from time to time.

2. Heat generated internally in the conductor as the result of load current flow.

3. The rate at which generated heat dissipates into the ambient medium. Thermal insulation which covers or surrounds conductors will affect the rate of heat dissipation.

4. Adjacent load-carrying conductors. Adjacent conductors have the dual effect of raising the ambient temperature and impeding heat dissipation.

310-11. Marking.

(a) Required Information. All conductors and cables shall be marked to indicate the following information, using the applicable method described in (b) below.

271

(1) The maximum rated voltage for which the conductor was listed.

(2) The proper type letter or letters for the type of wire or cable as specified elsewhere in this article, in Tables 310-13 and 310-61, and in Articles 336, 337, 338, 339, 340, and Section 725-40(b)(3).

(3) The manufacturer's name, trademark, or other distinctive marking by which the organization responsible for the product can be readily identified.

(4) The AWG size or circular-mil area.

(b) Method of Marking.

(1) Surface Marking. The following conductors and cables shall be durably marked on the surface at intervals not exceeding 24 inches (610 mm):

a. Single- and multiconductor rubber- and thermoplastic- insulated wire and cable.

b. Nonmetallic-sheathed cable.

c. Service-entrance cable.

d. Underground feeder and branch-circuit cable.

e. Tray cable.

f. Irrigation cable.

g. Power-limited tray cable.

(2) Marker Tape. Metal-covered multiconductor cables shall employ a marker tape located within the cable and running for its complete length.

Exception No. 1: Mineral-insulated, metal-sheathed cable.

Exception No. 2: Type AC cable.

Exception No. 3: The information required in Section 310-11(a)(1), (2), and (4) above shall be permitted to be durably marked on the outer nonmetallic covering of Type MC or Type PLTC cables at intervals not exceeding 24 inches (610 mm).

Exception No. 4: The information required in Section 310-11(a) shall be permitted to be durably marked on a nonmetallic covering under the metallic sheath of Type PLTC cable at intervals not exceeding 24 inches (610 mm).

Type PLTC cable is permitted to have a metallic sheath or armor over a nonmetallic jacketed cable. A second nonmetallic jacket is optional over the metallic sheath. Exception Nos. 3 and 4 will define the marking requirements for either case.

(FPN): Included in the group of metal-covered cables are: Type AC cable (Article 333), Type MC cable (Article 334) and lead-sheathed cable.

(3) Tag Marking. The following conductors and cables shall be marked by means of a printed tag attached to the coil, reel, or carton:

a. Mineral-insulated, metal-sheathed cable.

   b. Switchboard wires.

   c. Metal-covered, single-conductor cables.

   d. Conductors having outer surface of asbestos.

   e. Type AC cable.

(4) Optional Marking of Wire Size. For the following multiconductor cables, the information required in (a) (4) above shall be permitted to be marked on the surface of the individual insulated conductors:

   a. Type MC cable.

   b. Tray cable.

   c. Irrigation cable.

   d. Power-limited tray cable.

(c) Suffixes to Designate Number of Conductors. A type letter or letters used alone shall indicate a single insulated conductor. The following letter suffixes shall indicate the following:
   D—for two insulated conductors laid parallel within an outer nonmetallic covering.
   M—for an assembly of two or more insulated conductors twisted spirally within an outer nonmetallic covering.

310-12. Conductor Identification.

(a) Grounded Conductors. Insulated conductors of No. 6 or smaller, intended for use as grounded conductors of circuits, shall have an outer identification of a white or natural gray color. Multiconductor flat cable No. 4 or larger shall be permitted to employ an external ridge on the grounded conductor.

Exception No. 1: Multiconductor varnished-cloth-insulated cables.

Exception No. 2: Fixture wires as outlined in Article 402.

Exception No. 3: Mineral-insulated, metal-sheathed cable.

Exception No. 4: A conductor identified as required by Section 210-5(a) for branch circuits.

Exception No. 5: Where the conditions of maintenance and supervision assure that only qualified persons will service the installation, grounded conductors in multiconductor cables shall be permitted to be permanently identified at their terminations at the time of installation by a distinctive white marking or other equally effective means.

For aerial cable the identification shall be as above, or by means of a ridge so located on the exterior of the cable as to identify it.

Wires having their outer covering finished to show a white or natural gray color but having colored tracer threads in the braid, identifying the source of manufacture, shall be considered as meeting the provisions of this section.

(FPN): For identification requirements for conductors larger than No. 6, see Section 200-6.

(b) Equipment Grounding Conductors. Bare, covered or insulated grounding conductors shall be permitted. Individually covered or insulated grounding conductors shall have a continuous outer finish that is either green, or green with one or more yellow stripes.

Exception No. 1: An insulated or covered conductor larger than No. 6 shall, at the time of installation, be permitted to be permanently identified as a grounding conductor at each end and at every point where the conductor is accessible. Identification shall be accomplished by one of the following means:

a. *Stripping the insulation or covering from the entire exposed length;*

b. *Coloring the exposed insulation or covering green; or*

c. *Marking the exposed insulation or covering with green colored tape or green colored adhesive labels.*

Exception No. 2: Where the conditions of maintenance and supervision assure that only qualified persons will service the installation, an insulated conductor in a multiconductor cable shall, at the time of installation, be permitted to be permanently identified as a grounding conductor at each end and at every point where the conductor is accessible by one of the following means:

a. *Stripping the insulation from the entire exposed length;*

b. *Coloring the exposed insulation green; or*

c. *Marking the exposed insulation with green tape or green colored adhesive labels.*

(c) Ungrounded Conductors. Conductors which are intended for use as ungrounded conductors, whether used as single conductors or in multiconductor cables, shall be finished to be clearly distinguishable from grounded and grounding conductors. Ungrounded conductors shall be distinguished by colors other than white, natural gray, or green; or by a combination of color plus distinguishing marking. Distinguishing markings shall also be in a color other than white, natural gray, or green, and shall consist of a stripe or stripes or a regularly spaced series of identical marks. Distinguishing markings shall not conflict in any manner with the surface markings required by Section 310-11(b)(1).

310-13. Conductor Constructions and Applications. Insulated conductors shall comply with the applicable provisions of one or more of the following: Tables 310-13, 310-61, 310-62, 310-63, 310-64, 310-65, 310-66, and 310-67.

These conductors shall be permitted for use in any of the wiring methods recognized in Chapter 3 and as specified in their respective tables.

(FPN): Thermoplastic insulation may stiffen at temperatures colder than minus 10°C (plus 14°F), requiring care be exercised during installation at such temperatures. Thermoplastic insulation may also be deformed at normal temperatures where subjected to pressure, requiring care be exercised during installation and at points of support.

Table 310-13 lists the various types of insulated conductors as covered by the requirements of this *Code*. More detailed wire classification information from sizes Nos. 14 AWG through 2,000 MCM may be obtained from standards or directories, such as those published by the Underwriters Laboratories Inc.

Table 310-13 also includes conductor applications and maximum operating temperatures. Some conductors have dual ratings, such as Type XHHW, rated 90°C (194°F) for dry and damp locations and 75°C (167°F) for wet locations, or Type THW, rated 75°C (167°F) for dry and wet locations and 90°C (194°F) for special applications within electric-discharge lighting equipment.

The maximum continuous ampacities for copper, copper-clad aluminum, and aluminum are listed in Tables 310-16 through 310-31 and accompanying Notes 1 through 11.

Copper-clad aluminum conductors are drawn from a copper-clad aluminum rod with the copper metallurgically bonded to an aluminum core. The copper forms a minimum of 10 percent of the cross-sectional area of a solid conductor or each strand of a stranded conductor. See also comments following Section 110-14.

Tentative Interim Amendment 70-87-4 to

NFPA 70

National Electrical Code®

1987 Edition

Pursuant to Section 15 of the NFPA Regulations Governing Committee Projects, the National Fire Protection Association has issued the following Tentative Interim Amendment to NFPA 70, *National Electrical Code*, 1987 edition. The TIA was processed by the National Electrical Code Committee and was issued by the Standards Council on April 15, 1988.

A Tentative Interim Amendment is tentative because it has not been processed through the entire standards-making procedures. It is interim because it is effective only between editions of the standard. A TIA automatically becomes a Proposal of the proponent for the next edition of the standard; as such, it then is subject to all the procedures of the standards making process.

1.   Add an exception to Section 310-15(b) to read as follows:

Exception: Ampacities for one or more single insulated conductors in underground electrical ducts shall be permitted to be determined from Table 310-16 and its accompanying notes where all of the following conditions are met:

1.   Load calculations have been made in accordance with Article 220.

2.   A minimum of 2-inch (50.8-mm) spacing between raceways is maintained.

3.   Fill medium is compacted to eliminate air pockets and to assure uniform heat dissipation.

(FPN): Where such underground conductors supply loads that are expected to have a maximum demand that exceeds 70 percent of the installed circuit capacity, caution should be exercised when determining conductor sizes.

75M-5-88-FP

The following table compares the characteristics of copper-clad aluminum with copper and aluminum conductors.

Conductor Characteristics

	Copper	Cu/Al	Aluminum
Density lbs/in^3	0.323	0.121	0.098
Density gm/cm^3	8.91	3.34	2.71
Resistivity ohms/CMF	10.37	16.08	16.78
Resistivity Microhm-CM	1.724	2.673	2.790
Conductivity (IACS%)	100	61-63	61
Weight % Copper	100	26.8	. . . .
Tensile K psi-Hard	65.0	30.0	27.0
Tensile kg/mm^2-Hard	45.7	21.1	19.0
Tensile K psi-Annealed	35.0	17.0	17.0*
Tensile kg/mm^2-Annealed	24.6	12.0	12.0
Specific Gravity	8.91	3.34	2.71

*Semi-annealed

310-14. Aluminum Conductor Material. Solid aluminum conductors No. 8, 10, and 12 AWG shall be made of an AA-8000 series electrical grade aluminum alloy conductor material. Stranded aluminum conductors No. 8 AWG through 1000 MCM marked as Type XHHW, THW, THWN, THHN, service entrance Type SE Style U and SE Style R shall be made of an AA-8000 series electrical grade aluminum alloy conductor material.

This section provides proper recognition of approved aluminum alloy conductor material to coordinate with the UL requirements for testing terminations suitable for use with aluminum conductors, such as CO/ALR devices.

310-15. Ampacity.

The term electrical duct(s) as used in Article 310 shall include any of the electrical conduits recognized in Chapter 3 as suitable for use underground; and other raceways, round in cross section, listed for underground use; embedded in earth or concrete.

The term "electrical duct" is used to differentiate from "ducts" used for air handling, for example. It is intended to include nonmetallic electrical ducts commonly used for underground wiring as well as other circular raceways (e.g. rigid metal conduit, intermediate metal conduit, rigid nonmetallic conduit, etc.) listed for use underground in earth or concrete.

(a) Applications Covered by Tables. Ampacities for conductors rated 0 through 2000 volts shall be as specified in Tables 310-16 through 310-31 and their accompanying notes. The ampacity for Types V, AVA, AVB, and AVL conductors rated 2001 through 5000 volts shall be the same as for those conductor types rated 0 through 2000 volts. The ampacities for solid dielectric insulated conductors rated 2001 through 35000 volts shall be as specified in Tables 310-69 through 310-84 and their accompanying notes.

Tables 310-16 and 310-17 are based on a method of calculation developed by Sam J. Rosch and published in March 1938 in a paper entitled: "The Current-Carrying Capacity of Rubber-Insulated Conductors" which appeared in "Electrical Engineering," a monthly publication of the American Institute of Electrical Engineers (predecessor of the Institute of Electrical and Electronic Engineers — IEEE). A copy of the paper was reprinted in the January/February 1981 issue of "IAEI News," a publication of the International Association of Electrical Inspectors.

The ampacities in Tables 310-18, 310-19 and Tables 310-22 through 310-31 are based on the Neher-McGrath method of calculating current-carrying capacity. This is the same method used for calculation of the ampacities of the high-voltage conductors in Tables 310-69 through 310-84. A description of this method of calculation was given in AIEE Paper No. 57-660, "The Calculation of the Temperature Rise and Load Capability of Cable Systems" by J. H. Neher and M. H. McGrath. This paper was presented to the AIEE General Meeting in Montreal, Quebec, Canada on June 24-28, 1956, and was published in "AIEE Transactions," Part III (Power Apparatus and Systems), Vol. 76, October 1957, pp. 752 through 772.

Tables 310-16 through 310-19 have been revised for the 1987 *NEC*. Space has been left for the possible addition of new Tables 310-20 and 310-21 in a future edition of the *Code*. Tables 310-22 through 310-31 are new in the 1987 *NEC*, although most of them appeared in the 1984 *NEC* as proposed tables to be effective January 1, 1987.

Following are the titles of Tables 310-16 through 310-31, followed by commentary on the origin of the tables and, in some cases, the differences from the table in the 1984 *NEC*.

Table 310-16. Ampacities of Not More than Three Single Insulated Conductors, Rated O through 2000 Volts, in Raceway in Free Air and Ampacities of Cable Types AC, NM, NMC and SE Based on Ambient Air Temperature of 30°C (86°F).

Table 310-17. Ampacities of Single Insulated Conductors, Rated O through 2000 Volts, in Free Air Based on Ambient Air Temperature of 30°C (86°F).

Table 310-18. Ampacities of Three Single Insulated Conductors Rated O through 2000 Volts, 110° to 250°C, in Raceway in Free Air Based on Ambient Air Temperature of 40°C (104°F).

Table 310-19. Ampacities for Single Insulated Conductors Rated O through 2000 Volts, 110° to 250°C, in Free Air Based on Ambient Air Temperature of 40°C (104°F).

Table 310-22. Ampacities of Three Insulated Conductors, Rated 0 through 2000 Volts, Within an Overall Covering (Three Conductor Cable), in Raceway in Free Air Based on Ambient Air Temperature of 30°C (86°F).

Table 310-23. Ampacities of Two or Three Single Insulated Conductors, Rated 0 through 2000 Volts, Supported on a Messenger, Based on Ambient Air Temperature of 40°C (104°F).

Table 310-24. Ampacities for Bare or Covered Conductors Based on 40°C Ambient, 80°C Total Conductor Temperature, 2 Feet (610 mm) per Second Wind Velocity.

Table 310-25. Ampacities of Single Insulated Conductors, Rated 0 through 2000 Volts, in Nonmagnetic Underground Electrical Ducts (One Conductor per Electrical Duct) Based on Ambient Earth Temperature of 20°C (68°F), Electrical Duct Arrangement as per Figure 310-1, 100 Percent Load Factor, Thermal Resistance (RHO) of 90, Conductor Temperature 75°C (167°F).

Table 310-26. Ampacities of Three Insulated Conductors, Rated 0 through 2000 Volts, Within an Overall Covering (Three Conductor Cable) in Underground Electrical Ducts (One Cable per Electrical Duct) Based on Ambient Earth Temperature of 20°C (68°F), Electrical Duct Arrangement as per Figure 310-1, 100 Percent Load Factor, Thermal Resistance (RHO) of 90, Conductor Temperature 75°C (167°F).

Table 310-27. Ampacities of Three Single Insulated Conductors, Rated 0 through 2000 Volts, in Underground Electrical Ducts (Three Conductors per Electrical Duct) Based on Ambient Earth Temperature of 20°C (68°F), Electrical Duct Arrangement per Figure 310-1, 100 Percent Load Factor, Thermal Resistance (RHO) of 90, Conductor Temperature 75°C (167°F).

Table 310-28. Ampacities of Two or Three Insulated Conductors, Rated 0 through 2000 Volts, Cabled Within an Overall (Two or Three Conductor) Covering Directly Buried in Earth Based on Ambient Earth Temperature of 20°C (68°F), Arrangement per Figure 310-1, 100 Percent Load Factor, Thermal Resistance (RHO) of 90.

Table 310-29. Ampacities of Three Triplexed Single Insulated Conductors, Rated 0 through 2000 Volts, Directly Buried in Earth Based on Ambient Earth Temperature of 20°C (68°F), Arrangement per Figure 310-1, 100 Percent Load Factor, Thermal Resistance (RHO) of 90.

Table 310-30. Ampacities of Three Single Insulated Conductors, Rated 0 through 2000 Volts, Directly Buried in Earth Based on Ambient Earth Temperature of 20°C (68°F), Arrangement per Figure 310-1, 100 Percent Load Factor, Thermal Resistance (RHO) of 90.

Table 310-31. Ampacities of Multiconductor Cables with not more than Three Insulated Conductors, Rated 0 through 2000 Volts, in Free Air. Based on Ambient Air Temperature of 40°C (104°F) (For TC, MC, MI and SNM cables).

Table 310-16 is essentially the same as Table 310-16 in the 1984 NEC with a few very important exceptions. It no longer includes: (1) the ampacities for raceway or cable in earth (underground wiring); (2) the ampacities for Types MC, MI, SNM, or TC cables; or (3) multiconductor cables in raceway. Also, the ambient correction factors part of the table has been expanded.

Table 310-17 is essentially the same as Table 310-17 in the 1984 NEC. The ambient correction factors part of the table has been expanded.

Table 310-18 is similar to Table 310-18 in the 1984 NEC, except the ampacities have changed, and it is now based on a 40°C (104°F) ambient. Also, it does not include underground wiring.

Table 310-19 is similar to Table 310-19 in the 1984 NEC, except the ampacities have changed and it is now based on a 40°C (104°F) ambient. Also, it does not include bare or covered conductors.

Table 310-22 is based on proposed Table 310-24 in the 1984 NEC. It covers three-conductor cable in raceway in free air, previously covered in Table 310-16 of the 1984 NEC.

Table 310-23 is based on proposed Table 310-22 in the 1984 NEC. It covers messenger supported wiring.

Table 310-24 is based on proposed Table 310-20 in the 1984 NEC. It includes the bare or covered conductors previously covered in Table 310-19 of the 1984 NEC.

Table 310-25 is based on proposed Table 310-25 in the 1984 NEC. It covers single conductors in nonmagnetic underground electrical ducts, previously covered in Table 310-16 in the 1984 NEC. See Code Figure 310-1 and the Notes to Tables 310-25 through 310-27.

Table 310-26 is based on proposed Table 310-26 in the 1984 NEC. It covers three-conductor cable in underground electrical ducts, previously covered in Table 310-16 in the 1984 NEC. See Code Figure 310-1 and the Notes to Tables 310-25 through 310-27.

Table 310-27 is based on proposed Table 310-27 in the 1984 NEC. It covers single insulated conductors in underground electrical ducts, previously covered in Table 310-16 in the 1984 NEC. See Code Figure 310-1 and the Notes to Tables 310-25 through 310-27.

Table 310-28 is based on proposed Table 310-28 in the 1984 NEC. It covers two- or three-conductor cable directly buried in earth, such as Type UF cable, previously covered in Table 310-16 of the 1984 NEC. See Code Figure 310-1.

Table 310-29 is based on proposed Table 310-29 in the 1984 NEC. It covers triplexed single insulated conductor cables directly buried in earth, Types UF and USE, previously covered in Table 310-16 in the 1984 NEC. See Code Figure 310-1.

Table 310-30 is based on proposed Table 310-30 in the 1984 NEC. It covers three single insulated conductors directly buried in earth, Types UF and USE, previously covered in Table 310-16 in the 1984 *NEC*. See Code Figure 310-1.

Table 310-31 is based on proposed Table 310-20A in the 1984 *NEC*. It covers multiconductor cables, Types MC, MI, SNM, and TC, in free air, previously covered in Table 310-16 in the 1984 *NEC*.

(b) Applications Not Covered by Tables. Ampacities not covered by the tables shall be permitted to be calculated under engineering supervision, by means of the following general formula:

$$I = \sqrt{\frac{TC - (TA + DELTA\ TD)}{RDC\ (1 + YC)\ RCA}}$$

TC = Conductor temperature in degrees C
TA = Ambient temperature in degrees C
DELTA TD = Dielectric loss temperature rise
RDC = DC resistance of conductor at temperature TC
YC = Component ac resistance resulting from skin effect and proximity effect
RCA = Effective thermal resistance between conductor and surrounding ambient.

Since the applications covered by Tables 310-16 through 310-31 are much more specific than those covered by Tables 310-16 through 310-19 in the 1984 *NEC*, it is to be expected that the general formula (Neher-McGrath calculation) will be in more general use than it has in the past. It is anticipated that engineering and designing firms, and the engineering departments of major electrical contractors and users of the *Code* will have the formula in computer programs for quick calculation of ampacities for applications not covered by the tables.

(FPN): The ampacities provided by this section are based on temperature alone and do not take voltage drop into consideration.

(FPN): Conductors of circuits as defined in Article 100, sized to prevent a voltage drop exceeding 5 percent, will provide reasonable efficiency of operation.

(c) Selection of Ampacity. When more than one calculated or tabulated ampacity could apply for a given circuit length, the lowest value shall be used.

For example, three No. 500 MCM THW conductors in a rigid nonmetallic conduit are run from a motor control center down the side of a building and underground to a pump motor. When run above ground in a 26°-30°C (79°-84°F) ambient, the conductors have an ampacity of 380 amperes (Table 310-16). When run underground, Table 310-27 is applicable, which shows an ampacity of 427 amperes at the usual earth ambient of 20°C (68°F). The ampacity to be used is therefore 380 amperes.

Table 310-13. Conductor Application and Insulations

Trade Name	Type Letter	Max. Operating Temp.	Application Provisions	Insulation	AWG or MCM	Thickness of Insulation Mils	Outer Covering
Asbestos	A	200°C 392°F	Dry locations only. Only for leads within apparatus or within raceways connected to apparatus. Limited to 300 volts.	Asbestos	14.............. 12-8..........	30 40	Without asbestos braid
Asbestos	AA	200°C 392°F	Dry locations only. Only for leads within apparatus or within raceways connected to apparatus or as open wiring. Limited to 300 volts.	Asbestos	14.............. 12-8.......... 6-2............ 1-4/0..........	30 30 40 60	With asbestos, glass, or other suitable braid material
Asbestos	AI	125°C 257°F	Dry locations only. Only for leads within apparatus or within raceways connected to apparatus. Limited to 300 volts.	Impregnated Asbestos	14.............. 12-8..........	30 40	Without asbestos braid
Asbestos	AIA	125°C 257°F	Dry locations only. Only for leads within apparatus or within raceways connected to apparatus or as open wiring.	Impregnated Asbestos	14.............. 12-8.......... 6-2............ 1-4/0.......... 213–500....... 501–1000......	Sol. Str. 30 30 30 40 40 60 60 75 90 105	With asbestos, glass, or other suitable braid material

Table 310-13 (Continued)

Insulation	Trade Name	Max. Operating Temp.	Application	Insulation	Outer Braid
Asbestos and Varnished Cambric	AVA	110°C 230°F	Dry locations only.	Impregnated Asbestos and Varnished Cambric	AVA-asbestos, glass, or other suitable braid material
Asbestos and Varnished Cambric	AVB	90°C 194°F	Dry locations only.	Impregnated Asbestos and Varnished Cambric	Flame-retardant, cotton braid (switchboard wiring) / Flame-retardant, cotton braid

AVA — Thickness of Insulation

Size	1st Asb.	VC	AVA 2nd Asb.	AVL 2nd Asb.
14–8 (solid only)	—	30	20	25
14–8	10	30	15	25
6–2	15	30	20	25
1–4/0	20	40	30	30
213–500	25	40	40	40
501–1000	30	40	40	40
1001–2000	30	50	50	50

For 1000–5000 volts, see Table 310–67.

AVB — Thickness of Insulation

Size	Asb.	VC	2nd Asb.
18–8	10	30	20
6–2	15	40	30
1–4/0	20	40	40
14–8	10	30	15
6–2	15	30	20
1–4/0	20	30	30
213–500	25	40	40
501–1000	30	40	40
1001–2000	30	50	50

For 1000–5000 volts, see Table 310–67.

Table 310-13 (Continued)

Trade Name	Type Letter	Max. Operating Temp.	Application Provisions	Insulation	AWG or MCM	Thickness of Insulation			Mils	Outer Covering
						1st Asb.	VC	AVA 2nd Asb.	AVL 2nd Asb.	
Asbestos and Varnished Cambric	AVL	110°C 230°F	Dry and wet locations.	Impregnated Asbestos and Varnished Cambric	14–8 (solid only)	—	30	20	25	AVL-lead sheath
					14–8	10	30	15	25	
					6–2	15	30	20	25	
					1–4/0	20	40	30	30	
					213–500	25	40	40	40	
					501–1000	30	40	40	40	
					1001–2000	30	50	50	50	
					For 1000–5000 volts, see Table 310-67.					
Fluorinated Ethylene Propylene	FEP or FEPB	90°C 194°F 200°C 392°F	Dry and damp locations. Dry locations—special applications.†	Fluorinated Ethylene Propylene	14–10				20	None
					8–2				30	
				Fluorinated Ethylene Propylene	14–8				14	Glass braid
					6–2				14	Asbestos or other suitable braid material
Mineral Insulation (Metal Sheathed)	MI	90°C 194°F 250°C 482°F	Dry and wet locations. For special application.†	Magnesium Oxide	16–10				36	Copper
					9–4				50	
					3–250				55	
Moisture-, Heat- and Oil-Resistant Thermoplastic	MTW	60°C 140°F 90°C 194°F	Machine tool wiring in wet locations as permitted in NFPA Standard No. 79. (See Article 670.) Machine tool wiring in dry locations as permitted in NFPA Standard No. 79. (See Article 670.)	Flame-Retardant, Moisture-, Heat- and Oil-Resistant Thermoplastic	22–12	(A) 30			(B) 15	(A) None (B) Nylon jacket or equivalent
					10	30			20	
					8	45			30	
					6	60			30	
					4–2	60			40	
					1–4/0	80			50	
					213–500	95			60	
					501–1000	110			70	

†Where environmental conditions require maximum conductor operating temperatures above 90°C.

281

Table 310-13 (Continued)

Trade Name	Type	Max Operating Temp	Application Provisions	Insulation	AWG or kcmil / Thickness (mils)	Outer Covering
Paper		85°C 185°F	For underground service conductors, or by special permission.	Paper		Lead sheath
Perfluoroalkoxy	PFA	90°C 194°F / 200°C 392°F	Dry and damp locations. / Dry locations—special applications.†	Perfluoroalkoxy	14-10........20, 8-2........30, 1-4/0........45	None
Perfluoroalkoxy	PFAH	250°C 482°F	Dry locations only. Only for leads within apparatus or within raceways connected to apparatus. (Nickel or nickel-coated copper only.)	Perfluoroalkoxy	14-10........20, 8-2........30, 1-4/0........45	None
Heat-Resistant Rubber	RH	75°C 167°F	Dry and damp locations.	Heat-Resistant Rubber	**14-12........30, 10........45, 8-2........60, 1-4/0........80, 213-500........95, 501-1000........110, 1001-2000........125, For 601-2000 volts, see Table 310-62.	*Moisture-resistant, flame-retardant, non-metallic covering
Heat-Resistant Rubber	RHH	90°C 194°F	Dry and damp locations.			
Moisture- and Heat-Resistant Rubber	RHW	75°C 167°F	Dry and wet locations. For over 2000 volts insulation shall be ozone-resistant.	Moisture- and Heat-Resistant Rubber	14-10........45, 8-2........60, 1-4/0........80, 213-500........95, 501-1000........110, 1001-2000........125, For 601-2000 volts, see Table 310-62.	*Moisture-resistant, flame-retardant, non-metallic covering

*Some rubber insulations do not require an outer covering.
**For 14-12 sizes RHH shall be 45 mils thickness insulation.
†Where environmental conditions require maximum conductor operating temperatures above 90°C.

Table 310-13 (Continued)

Trade Name	Type Letter	Max. Operating Temp.	Application Provisions	Insulation	AWG or MCM	Thickness of Insulation	Mils	Outer Covering
Silicone-Asbestos	SA	90°C 194°F / 125°C 257°F	Dry and damp locations. / For special application.†	Silicone Rubber	14–10 / 8–2 / 1–4/0 / 213–500 / 501–1000 / 1001–2000		45 / 60 / 80 / 95 / 110 / 125	Asbestos, glass or other suitable braid material
Synthetic Heat-Resistant	SIS	90°C 194°F	Switchboard wiring only.	Heat-Resistant Rubber	14–10 / 8 / 6–2 / 1–4/0		30 / 45 / 60 / 80	None
Thermoplastic and Asbestos	TA	90°C 194°F	Switchboard wiring only.	Thermoplastic and Asbestos	14–8 / 6–2 / 1–4/0	Th'pl'. .20 / .30 / .40	Asb. 20 / 25 / 30	Flame-retardant, nonmetallic covering
Thermoplastic and Fibrous Outer Braid	TBS	90°C 194°F	Switchboard wiring only.	Thermoplastic	14–10 / 8 / 6–2 / 1–4/0		30 / 45 / 60 / 80	Flame-retardant, nonmetallic covering
Extruded Polytetrafluoroethylene	TFE	250°C 482°F	Dry locations only. Only for leads within apparatus or within raceways connected to apparatus, or as open wiring. (Nickel or nickel-coated copper only.)	Extruded Polytetrafluoroethylene	14–10 / 8–2 / 1–4/0		20 / 30 / 45	None

†Where environmental conditions require maximum conductor operating temperatures above 90°C.

Table 310-13 (Continued)

Trade Name	Type	Max. Operating Temperature	Application Provisions	Insulation	AWG MCM	Thickness of Insulation (mils)	Outer Covering
Heat-Resistant Thermoplastic	THHN	90°C 194°F	Dry and damp locations.	Flame-Retardant, Heat-Resistant Thermoplastic	14–12 10 8–6 4–2 1–4/0 250–500 501–1000	15 20 30 40 50 60 70	Nylon jacket or equivalent
Moisture- and Heat-Resistant Thermoplastic	THW	75°C 167°F 90°C 194°F	Dry and wet locations. Special applications within electric discharge lighting equipment. Limited to 1000 open-circuit volts or less. (Size 14–8 only as permitted in Section 410-31.)	Flame-Retardant, Moisture- and Heat-Resistant Thermoplastic	14–10 8–2 1–4/0 213–500 501–1000 1001–2000	45 60 80 95 110 125	None
Moisture- and Heat-Resistant Thermoplastic	THWN	75°C 167°F	Dry and wet locations.	Flame-Retardant, Moisture- and Heat-Resistant Thermoplastic	14–12 10 8–6 4–2 1–4/0 250–500 501–1000	15 20 30 40 50 60 70	Nylon jacket or equivalent
Moisture-Resistant Thermoplastic	TW	60°C 140°F	Dry and wet locations.	Flame-Retardant, Moisture-Resistant Thermoplastic	14–10 8 6–2 1–4/0 213–500 501–1000 1001–2000	30 45 60 80 95 110 125	None

Table 310-13 (Continued)

Trade Name	Type Letter	Max. Operating Temp.	Application Provisions	Insulation	AWG or MCM	Thickness of Insulation Mils	Outer Covering
Underground Feeder & Branch-Circuit Cable-Single Conductor. (For Type UF cable employing more than one conductor, see Article 339.)	UF	60°C 140°F	See Article 339.	Moisture-Resistant	14-10 8-2 1-4/0	*60 *80 *95	Integral with insulation
		**75°C 167°F		Moisture- and Heat-Resistant			
Underground Service-Entrance Cable-Single Conductor. (For Type USE cable employing more than one conductor, see Article 338.)	USE	75°C 167°F	See Article 338.	Heat- and Moisture-Resistant	12-10 8-2 1-4/0 213-500 501-1000 1001-2000	45 60 80 ***95 110 125	Moisture-resistant non-metallic covering [See 338-1 (b).]

*Includes integral jacket.

**For ampacity limitation, see Section 339-5.

***Insulation thickness shall be permitted to be 80 mils for listed Type USE conductors that have been subjected to special investigations.

The nonmetallic covering over individual rubber-covered conductors of aluminum-sheathed cable and of lead-sheathed or multiconductor cable shall not be required to be flame retardant. For Type MC cable, see Section 334-20. For nonmetallic-sheathed cable, see Section 336-25. For Type UF cable, see Section 339-1.

Table 310-13 (Continued)

Trade Name	Type Letter	Max. Operating Temperature	Application Provisions	Insulation	AWG/MCM	Nonmetallic covering or lead sheath
Varnished Cambric	V	85°C 185°F	Dry locations only. Smaller than No. 6 by special permission.	Varnished Cambric	14–8 .... 45 6–2 .... 60 1–4/0 .... 80 213–500 .... 95 500–1000 .... 110 1001–2000 .... 125 For 1000–5000 volts, see Table 310-65 or 310-66.	Nonmetallic covering or lead sheath
Moisture- and Heat-Resistant Cross-Linked Synthetic Polymer	XHHW	90°C 194°F 75°C 167°F	Dry and damp locations. Wet locations.	Flame-Retardant Cross-linked Synthetic Polymer	14–10 .... 30 8–2 .... 45 1–4/0 .... 55 213–500 .... 65 501–1000 .... 80 1001–2000 95	None
Modified Ethylene Tetrafluoroethylene	Z	90°C 194°F 150°C 302°F	Dry and damp locations. Dry locations—special applications.†	Modified Ethylene Tetrafluoroethylene	14–12 .... 15 10 .... 20 8–4 .... 25 3–1 .... 35 1/0–4/0 45	None
Modified Ethylene Tetrafluoroethylene	ZW	75°C 167°F 90°C 194°F 150°C 302°F	Wet locations. Dry and damp locations. Dry locations—special applications.†	Modified Ethylene Tetrafluoroethylene	14–10 .... 30 8–2 45	None

†Where environmental conditions require maximum conductor operating temperatures above 90°C.

286

Table 310-16. Ampacities of Not More than Three Single Insulated Conductors, Rated 0 through 2000 Volts, in Raceway in Free Air and Ampacities of Cable Types AC, NM, NMC and SE

Based on Ambient Air Temperature of 30°C (86°F).

Size	Temperature Rating of Conductor. See Table 310-13.								Size
	60°C (140°F)	75°C (167°F)	85°C (185°F)	90°C (194°F)	60°C (140°F)	75°C (167°F)	85°C (185°F)	90°C (194°F)	
AWG MCM	TYPES †TW, †UF	TYPES †FEPW, †RH, †RHW, †THW, †THWN, †XHHW, †USE, †ZW	TYPE V	TYPES TA, TBS, SA, AVB, SIS, †FEP, †FEPB, †RHH, †THHN, †XHHW*	TYPES †TW, †UF	TYPES †RH, †RHW, †THW, †THWN, †XHHW, †USE	TYPE V	TYPES TA, TBS, SA, AVB, SIS, †RHH, †THHN, †XHHW*	AWG MCM
	COPPER				ALUMINUM OR COPPER-CLAD ALUMINUM				
18	....	....	....	14	....	....	....	....	....
16	....	....	18	18	....	....	....	....	....
14	20†	20†	25	25†	....	....	....	....	....
12	25†	25†	30	30†	20†	20†	25	25†	12
10	30	35†	40	40†	25	30†	30	35†	10
8	40	50	55	55	30	40	40	45	8
6	55	65	70	75	40	50	55	60	6
4	70	85	95	95	55	65	75	75	4
3	85	100	110	110	65	75	85	85	3
2	95	115	125	130	75	90	100	100	2
1	110	130	145	150	85	100	110	115	1
1/0	125	150	165	170	100	120	130	135	1/0
2/0	145	175	190	195	115	135	145	150	2/0
3/0	165	200	215	225	130	155	170	175	3/0
4/0	195	230	250	260	150	180	195	205	4/0
250	215	255	275	290	170	205	220	230	250
300	240	285	310	320	190	230	250	255	300
350	260	310	340	350	210	250	270	280	350
400	280	335	365	380	225	270	295	305	400
500	320	380	415	430	260	310	335	350	500
600	355	420	460	475	285	340	370	385	600
700	385	460	500	520	310	375	405	420	700
750	400	475	515	535	320	385	420	435	750
800	410	490	535	555	330	395	430	450	800
900	435	520	565	585	355	425	465	480	900
1000	455	545	590	615	375	445	485	500	1000
1250	495	590	640	665	405	485	525	545	1250
1500	520	625	680	705	435	520	565	585	1500
1750	545	650	705	735	455	545	595	615	1750
2000	560	665	725	750	470	560	610	630	2000

AMPACITY CORRECTION FACTORS

Ambient Temp. °C	For ambient temperatures other than 30°C (86°F), multiply the ampacities shown above by the appropriate factor shown below.								Ambient Temp. °F
21–25	1.08	1.05	1.04	1.04	1.08	1.05	1.04	1.04	70–77
26–30	1.00	1.00	1.00	1.00	1.00	1.00	1.00	1.00	79–86
31–35	.91	.94	.95	.96	.91	.94	.95	.96	88–95
36–40	.82	.88	.90	.91	.82	.88	.90	.91	97–104
41–45	.71	.82	.85	.87	.71	.82	.85	.87	106–113
46–50	.58	.75	.80	.82	.58	.75	.80	.82	115–122
51–55	.41	.67	.74	.76	.41	.67	.74	.76	124–131
56–60	....	.58	.67	.71	....	.58	.67	.71	133–140
61–70	....	.33	.52	.58	....	.33	.52	.58	142–158
71–80	....	....	.30	.41	....	....	.30	.41	160–176

† Unless otherwise specifically permitted elsewhere in this Code, the overcurrent protection for conductor types marked with an obelisk (†) shall not exceed 15 amperes for 14 AWG, 20 amperes for 12 AWG, and 30 amperes for 10 AWG copper; or 15 amperes for 12 AWG and 25 amperes for 10 AWG aluminum and copper-clad aluminum after any correction factors for ambient temperature and number of conductors have been applied.

* For dry and damp locations only. See 75°C column for wet locations.

Table 310-17. Ampacities of Single Insulated Conductors, Rated 0 through 2000 Volts, In Free Air

Based on Ambient Air Temperature of 30°C (86°F).

Size	Temperature Rating of Conductor. See Table 310-13.								Size
	60°C (140°F)	75°C (167°F)	85°C (185°F)	90°C (194°F)	60°C (140°F)	75°C (167°F)	85°C (185°F)	90°C (194°F)	
AWG MCM	TYPE †TW	TYPES †FEPW, †RH, †RHW, †THW, †THWN, †XHHW, †ZW	TYPE V	TYPES TA, TBS, SA, AVB, SIS, †FEP, †FEPB, †RHH, †THHN, †XHHW*, MI	TYPE †TW	TYPES †RH, †RHW, †THW, †THWN, †XHHW	TYPE V	TYPES TA, TBS, SA, AVB, SIS, †RHH, †THHN, †XHHW*, MI	AWG MCM
	COPPER				ALUMINUM OR COPPER-CLAD ALUMINUM				
18	....	....	....	18	....	....	....	....	
16	....	....	23	24	....	....	....	....	
14	25†	30†	30	35†	....	....	....	....	
12	30†	35†	40	40†	25†	30†	30	35†	12
10	40†	50†	55	55†	35†	40†	40	40†	10
8	60	70	75	80	45	55	60	60	8
6	80	95	100	105	60	75	80	80	6
4	105	125	135	140	80	100	105	110	4
3	120	145	160	165	95	115	125	130	3
2	140	170	185	190	110	135	145	150	2
1	165	195	215	220	130	155	165	175	1
1/0	195	230	250	260	150	180	195	205	1/0
2/0	225	265	290	300	175	210	225	235	2/0
3/0	260	310	335	350	200	240	265	275	3/0
4/0	300	360	390	405	235	280	305	315	4/0
250	340	405	440	455	265	315	345	355	250
300	375	445	485	505	290	350	380	395	300
350	420	505	550	570	330	395	430	445	350
400	455	545	595	615	355	425	465	480	400
500	515	620	675	700	405	485	525	545	500
600	575	690	750	780	455	540	595	615	600
700	630	755	825	855	500	595	650	675	700
750	655	785	855	885	515	620	675	700	750
800	680	815	885	920	535	645	700	725	800
900	730	870	950	985	580	700	760	785	900
1000	780	935	1020	1055	625	750	815	845	1000
1250	890	1065	1160	1200	710	855	930	960	1250
1500	980	1175	1275	1325	795	950	1035	1075	1500
1750	1070	1280	1395	1445	875	1050	1145	1185	1750
2000	1155	1385	1505	1560	960	1150	1250	1335	2000

AMPACITY CORRECTION FACTORS

Ambient Temp. °C	For ambient temperatures other than 30°C (86°F), multiply the ampacities shown above by the appropriate factor shown below.								Ambient Temp. °F
21–25	1.08	1.05	1.04	1.04	1.08	1.05	1.04	1.04	70–77
26–30	1.00	1.00	1.00	1.00	1.00	1.00	1.00	1.00	79–86
31–35	.91	.94	.95	.96	.91	.94	.95	.96	88–95
36–40	.82	.88	.90	.91	.82	.88	.90	.91	97–104
41–45	.71	.82	.85	.87	.71	.82	.85	.87	106–113
46–50	.58	.75	.80	.82	.58	.75	.80	.82	115–122
51–55	.41	.67	.74	.76	.41	.67	.74	.76	124–131
56–60	....	.58	.67	.71	....	.58	.67	.71	133–140
61–70	....	.33	.52	.58	....	.33	.52	.58	142–158
71–80	....	....	.30	.41	....	....	.30	.41	160–176

†Unless otherwise specifically permitted elsewhere in this Code, the overcurrent protection for conductor types marked with an obelisk (†) shall not exceed 15 amperes for 14 AWG, 20 amperes for 12 AWG, and 30 amperes for 10 AWG copper; or 15 amperes for 12 AWG and 25 amperes for 10 AWG aluminum and copper-clad aluminum.

*For dry and damp locations only. See 75°C column for wet locations.

Table 310-18. Ampacities of Three Single Insulated Conductors, Rated 0 through 2000 Volts, 110° to 250°C, in Raceway in Free Air

Based on Ambient Air Temperature of 40°C (104°F).

Size	Temperature Rating of Conductor. See Table 310-13.									Size
	110°C (230°F)	125°C (257°F)	150°C (302°F)	200°C (392°F)	250°C (482°F)	110°C (230°F)	125°C (257°F)	150°C (302°F)	200°C (392°F)	
AWG MCM	TYPES AVA, AVL	TYPES AI, AIA	TYPE Z	TYPES A, AA, FEP, FEPB, PFA	TYPES PFAH, TFE	TYPES AVA, AVL	TYPES AI, AIA	TYPE Z	TYPES A, AA	AWG MCM
	COPPER				NICKEL OR NICKEL-COATED COPPER	ALUMINUM OR COPPER-CLAD ALUMINUM				
14	29	31	34	36	39	....	....	....	....	14
12	36	39	43	45	54	25	27	30	35	12
10	46	50	55	60	73	37	40	44	47	10
8	64	69	76	83	93	48	52	57	65	8
6	81	87	96	110	117	63	68	75	86	6
4	109	118	120	125	148	85	92	94	98	4
3	129	139	143	152	166	96	104	109	119	3
2	143	154	160	171	191	111	120	124	133	2
1	168	181	186	197	215	131	141	145	154	1
1/0	193	208	215	229	244	150	162	169	183	1/0
2/0	229	247	251	260	273	179	193	198	208	2/0
3/0	263	284	288	297	308	205	221	227	238	3/0
4/0	301	325	332	346	361	235	253	260	275	4/0
250	345	372	....	....	....	270	291	....	....	250
300	391	422	....	....	....	306	330	....	....	300
350	436	470	....	....	....	342	369	....	....	350
400	468	505	....	....	....	368	397	....	....	400
500	531	573	....	....	....	421	454	....	....	500
600	588	634	....	....	....	471	508	....	....	600
700	645	696	....	....	....	520	561	....	....	700
750	673	726	....	....	....	545	588	....	....	750
800	699	754	....	....	....	566	610	....	....	800
1000	785	846	....	....	....	651	701	....	....	1000
1500	961	....	....	....	....	795	....	....	....	1500
2000	1109	....	....	....	....	919	....	....	....	2000

AMPACITY CORRECTION FACTORS

Ambient Temp. °C	For ambient temperatures other than 40°C (104°F), multiply the ampacities shown above by the appropriate factor shown below.									Ambient Temp. °F
41–50	.93	.94	.95	.97	.98	.93	.94	.95	.97	106–122
51–60	.85	.87	.90	.94	.95	.85	.87	.90	.94	124–140
61–70	.76	.80	.85	.90	.93	.76	.80	.85	.90	142–158
71–80	.65	.73	.80	.87	.90	.65	.73	.80	.90	160–176
81–90	.53	.64	.74	.83	.87	.53	.64	.74	.83	177–194
91–100	.38	.54	.67	.79	.85	.38	.54	.67	.79	195–212
101–120	....	.24	.52	.71	.79	....	.24	.52	.71	213–248
121–140	....	....	.30	.61	.72	....	....	.30	.61	249–284
141–160	....	....	....	.50	.65	....	....	....	.50	285–320
161–180	....	....	....	.35	.58	....	....	....	.35	321–356
181–200	....	....	....	....	.49	....	....	....	....	357–392
201–225	....	....	....	....	.35	....	....	....	....	393–437

Table 310-19. Ampacities for Single Insulated Conductors, Rated 0 through 2000 Volts, 110° to 250°C, in Free Air

Based on Ambient Air Temperature of 40°C (104°F).

Size	Temperature Rating of Conductor. See Table 310-13.									Size
	110°C (230°F)	125°C (257°F)	150°C (302°F)	200°C (392°F)	250°C (482°F)	110°C (230°F)	125°C (257°F)	150°C (302°F)	200°C (392°F)	
AWG MCM	TYPES AVA, AVL	TYPES AI, AIA	TYPE Z	TYPES A, AA, FEP, FEPB, PFA	TYPES PFAH, TFE	TYPES AVA, AVL	TYPES AI, AIA	TYPE Z	TYPES A, AA	AWG MCM
	COPPER				NICKEL OR NICKEL-COATED COPPER	ALUMINUM OR COPPER-CLAD ALUMINUM				
14	39	42	46	54	59	. . . .	. . . .	. . . .	. . . .	14
12	51	55	60	68	78	40	43	47	54	12
10	67	72	80	90	107	53	57	63	71	10
8	90	97	106	124	142	70	75	83	96	8
6	121	131	155	165	205	95	102	112	128	6
4	160	172	190	220	278	125	135	148	171	4
3	180	194	214	252	327	144	155	170	196	3
2	215	232	255	293	381	167	180	198	227	2
1	247	266	293	344	440	193	208	228	267	1
1/0	286	309	339	399	532	222	239	263	310	1/0
2/0	329	355	390	467	591	257	277	305	363	2/0
3/0	380	410	451	546	708	296	319	351	443	3/0
4/0	446	481	529	629	830	347	374	411	490	4/0
250	493	532	. . . .	. . . .	. . . .	384	414	. . . .	. . . .	250
300	552	595	. . . .	. . . .	. . . .	431	464	. . . .	. . . .	300
350	611	659	. . . .	. . . .	. . . .	477	514	. . . .	. . . .	350
400	663	715	. . . .	. . . .	. . . .	518	559	. . . .	. . . .	400
500	767	827	. . . .	. . . .	. . . .	600	647	. . . .	. . . .	500
600	860	928	. . . .	. . . .	. . . .	674	727	. . . .	. . . .	600
700	953	1028	. . . .	. . . .	. . . .	749	808	. . . .	. . . .	700
750	1000	1079	. . . .	. . . .	. . . .	786	848	. . . .	. . . .	750
800	1039	1121	. . . .	. . . .	. . . .	818	882	. . . .	. . . .	800
1000	1197	1291	. . . .	. . . .	. . . .	947	1021	. . . .	. . . .	1000
1500	1465	1580	. . . .	. . . .	. . . .	1160	1251	. . . .	. . . .	1500
2000	1692	1825	. . . .	. . . .	. . . .	1340	1444	. . . .	. . . .	2000

AMPACITY CORRECTION FACTORS

Ambient Temp. °C	For ambient temperatures other than 40°C (104°F), multiply the ampacities shown above by the appropriate factor shown below.									Ambient Temp. °F
41–50	.93	.94	.95	.97	.98	.93	.94	.95	.97	106–122
51–60	.85	.87	.90	.94	.95	.85	.87	.90	.94	124–140
61–70	.76	.80	.85	.90	.93	.76	.80	.85	.90	142–158
71–80	.65	.73	.80	.87	.90	.65	.73	.80	.87	160–176
81–90	.53	.64	.74	.83	.87	.53	.64	.74	.83	177–194
91–100	.38	.54	.67	.79	.85	.38	.54	.67	.79	195–212
101–120	. . . .	.24	.52	.71	.79	. . . .	.24	.52	.71	213–248
121–140	. . . .	. . . .	.30	.61	.72	. . . .	. . . .	.30	.61	249–284
141–160	. . . .	. . . .	. . . .	.50	.65	. . . .	. . . .	. . . .	.50	285–320
161–180	. . . .	. . . .	. . . .	.35	.58	. . . .	. . . .	. . . .	.35	321–356
181–200	. . . .	. . . .	. . . .	. . . .	.49	. . . .	. . . .	. . . .	. . . .	357–392
201–225	. . . .	. . . .	. . . .	. . . .	.35	. . . .	. . . .	. . . .	. . . .	393–437

Table 310-22.   Ampacities of Three Insulated Conductors, Rated 0 through 2000 Volts, Within an Overall Covering (Three Conductor Cable), in Raceway in Free Air

Based on Ambient Air Temperature of 30°C (86°F).

Size	Temperature Rating of Conductor. See Table 310-13.						Size
	60°C (140°F)	75°C (167°F)	90°C (194°F)	60°C (140°F)	75°C (167°F)	90°C (194°F)	
AWG MCM	TYPE †TW	TYPES †RH, †RHW, †THW, †THWN, †XHHW*, †ZW	TYPES †THHN, †RHH, †XHHW*	TYPE †TW	TYPES †RH, †RHW, †THW, †THWN, †XHHW	TYPES †THHN, †RHH, †XHHW*	AWG MCM
		COPPER			ALUMINUM OR COPPER-CLAD ALUMINUM		
14	16†	18†	21†	. . . .	. . . .	. . . .	14
12	20†	24†	27†	16†	18†	21†	12
10	27†	33†	36†	21†	25†	28†	10
8	36	43	48	28	33	37	8
6	48	58	65	38	45	51	6
4	66	79	89	51	61	69	4
3	76	90	102	59	70	79	3
2	88	105	119	69	83	93	2
1	102	121	137	80	95	106	1
1/0	121	145	163	94	113	127	1/0
2/0	138	166	186	108	129	146	2/0
3/0	158	189	214	124	147	167	3/0
4/0	187	223	253	147	176	197	4/0
250	205	245	276	160	192	217	250
300	234	281	317	185	221	250	300
350	255	305	345	202	242	273	350
400	274	328	371	218	261	295	400
500	315	378	427	254	303	342	500
600	343	413	468	279	335	378	600
700	376	452	514	310	371	420	700
750	387	466	529	321	384	435	750
800	397	479	543	331	397	450	800
900	415	500	570	350	421	477	900
1000	448	542	617	382	460	521	1000
Ambient Temp. °C	For ambient temperatures other than 30°C (86°F), multiply the ampacities shown above by the appropriate factor shown below.						Ambient Temp. °F
21–25	1.08	1.05	1.04	1.08	1.05	1.04	70–77
26–30	1.00	1.00	1.00	1.00	1.00	1.00	79–86
31–35	.91	.94	.96	.91	.94	.96	88–95
36–40	.82	.88	.91	.82	.88	.91	97–104
41–45	.71	.82	.87	.71	.82	.87	106–113
46–50	.58	.75	.82	.58	.75	.82	115–122
51–55	.41	.67	.76	.41	.67	.76	124–131
56–60	. . . .	.58	.71	. . . .	.58	.71	133–140
61–70	. . . .	.33	.58	. . . .	.33	.58	142–158
71–80	. . . .	. . . .	.41	. . . .	. . . .	.41	160–176

† Unless otherwise specifically permitted elsewhere in this Code, the overcurrent protection for conductor types marked with an obelisk (†) shall not exceed 15 amperes for 14 AWG, 20 amperes for 12 AWG, and 30 amperes for 10 AWG copper; or 15 amperes for 12 AWG and 25 amperes for 10 AWG aluminum and copper-clad aluminum.

* For dry and damp locations only. See 75°C column for wet locations.

Table 310-23. Ampacities of Two or Three Single Insulated Conductors, Rated 0 through 2000 Volts, Supported on a Messenger

Based on Ambient Air Temperature of 40°C (104°F).

Size	Temperature Rating of Conductor. See Table 310-13.				Size
	75°C (167°F)	90°C (194°F)	75°C (167°F)	90°C (194°F)	
AWG MCM	TYPES RH, RHW, THW, THWN, XHHW, ZW	TYPES THHN, RHH, XHHW*	TYPES RH, RHW, THW, THWN, XHHW	TYPES THHN, RHH, XHHW*	AWG MCM
	COPPER		ALUMINUM OR COPPER-CLAD ALUMINUM		
8	57	66	44	51	8
6	76	89	59	69	6
4	101	117	78	91	4
3	118	138	92	107	3
2	135	158	106	123	2
1	158	185	123	144	1
1/0	183	214	143	167	1/0
2/0	212	247	165	193	2/0
3/0	245	287	192	224	3/0
4/0	287	335	224	262	4/0
250	320	374	251	292	250
300	359	419	282	328	300
350	397	464	312	364	350
400	430	503	339	395	400
500	496	580	392	458	500
600	553	647	440	514	600
700	610	714	488	570	700
750	638	747	512	598	750
800	660	773	532	622	800
900	704	826	572	669	900
1000	748	879	612	716	1000

Ambient Temp. °C	For ambient temperatures other than 40°C (104°F), multiply the ampacities shown above by the appropriate factor shown below.				Ambient Temp. °F
21–25	1.20	1.14	1.20	1.14	70–77
26–30	1.13	1.10	1.13	1.10	79–86
31–35	1.07	1.05	1.07	1.05	88–95
36–40	1.00	1.00	1.00	1.00	97–104
41–45	.93	.95	.93	.95	106–113
46–50	.85	.89	.85	.89	119–122
51–55	.76	.84	.76	.84	124–131
56–60	.65	.77	.65	.77	133–140
61–70	.38	.63	.38	.63	142–158
71–80	. . . .	.45	. . . .	.45	160–176

* For dry and damp locations only. See 75°C column for wet locations.

CONDUCTORS FOR GENERAL WIRING—ARTICLE 310

Table 310-24. Ampacities for Bare or Covered Conductors

Based on 40°C Ambient, 80°C Total Conductor Temperature,
2 Feet (610 mm) per Second Wind Velocity

Bare Copper Conductors		Covered Copper Conductors	
AWG MCM	AMPS	AWG MCM	AMPS
8	98	8	103
6	124	6	130
4	155	4	163
2	209	2	219
1/0	282	1/0	297
2/0	329	2/0	344
3/0	382	3/0	401
4/0	444	4/0	466
250	494	250	519
300	556	300	584
500	773	500	812
750	1000	750	1050
1000	1193	1000	1253

Bare AAC Aluminum Conductor		Covered AAC Aluminum	
AWG MCM	AMPS	AWG MCM	AMPS
8	76	8	80
6	96	6	101
4	121	4	127
2	163	2	171
1/0	220	1/0	231
2/0	255	2/0	268
3/0	297	3/0	312
4/0	346	4/0	364
266.8	403	266.8	423
336.4	468	336.4	492
397.5	522	397.5	548
477.0	588	477.0	617
556.5	650	556.5	682
636.0	709	636.0	744
795.0	819	795.0	860
954.0	920		
1033.5	968	1033.5	1017
1272	1103	1272	1201
1590	1267	1590	1381
2000	1454	2000	1527

ARTICLE 310—CONDUCTORS FOR GENERAL WIRING

Table 310-25.   Ampacities of Single Insulated Conductors, Rated 0 through 2000 Volts, in Nonmagnetic Underground Electrical Ducts (One Conductor per Electrical Duct)

Based on Ambient Earth Temperature of 20°C (68°F), Electrical Duct Arrangement as per Figure 310-1, 100 Percent Load Factor, Thermal Resistance (RHO) of 90, Conductor Temperature 75°C (167°F)

Size							Size
	3 Electrical Ducts (Fig. 310-1 Detail 2)	6 Electrical Ducts (Fig. 310-1 Detail 3)	9 Electrical Ducts (Fig. 310-1 Detail 4)	3 Electrical Ducts (Fig. 310-1 Detail 2)	6 Electrical Ducts (Fig. 310-1 Detail 3)	9 Electrical Ducts (Fig. 310-1 Detail 4)	
MCM	TYPES RHW, THW, THWN, XHHW, USE	TYPES RHW, THW, THWN, XHHW, USE	TYPES RHW, THW, THWN, XHHW, USE	TYPES RHW, THW, THWN, XHHW, USE	TYPES RHW, THW, THWN, XHHW, USE	TYPES RHW, THW, THWN, XHHW, USE	MCM
	COPPER			ALUMINUM OR COPPER-CLAD ALUMINUM			
250	344	295	270	269	230	211	250
350	418	355	322	327	277	252	350
500	511	431	387	401	337	305	500
750	640	534	469	505	421	375	750
1000	745	617	533	593	491	432	1000
1250	832	686	581	668	551	478	1250
1500	907	744	619	736	604	517	1500
1750	970	793	651	796	651	550	1750
2000	1027	836	683	850	693	581	2000

Ambient Temp. °C	For ambient temperatures other than 20°C (68°F), multiply the ampacities shown above by the appropriate factor shown below.						Ambient Temp. °F
6–10	1.09	1.09	1.09	1.09	1.09	1.09	43–50
11–15	1.04	1.04	1.04	1.04	1.04	1.04	52–59
16–20	1.00	1.00	1.00	1.00	1.00	1.00	61–68
21–25	.95	.95	.95	.95	.95	.95	70–77
26–30	.90	.90	.90	.90	.90	.90	79–86

Notes to Tables 310-25 through 310-27

1. Ampacity of Electrical Duct Bank with Two Electrical Ducts. To obtain the ampacity of cables installed in two electrical ducts in one horizontal row with 7.5-inch (190.7-mm) center-to-center spacing between electrical ducts, similar to Detail 1, Figure 310-1, multiply the ampacity shown for one electrical duct in Tables 310-26 and 310-27 by 0.88.

2. Ampacity of Electrical Duct Bank with Four Electrical Ducts. To obtain the ampacity of cables installed in four electrical ducts in one horizontal row with 7.5-inch (190.7-mm) center-to-center spacing between electrical ducts, similar to Detail 2, Figure 310-1, multiply the ampacity shown for three electrical ducts in Tables 310-26 and 310-27 by 0.94.

3. Electrical Ducts Utilized in Figure 310-1 Include any of the Electrical Conduits Recognized in Chapter 3 as Suitable for Use Underground. When metal conduit is used as an electrical duct in Figure 310-1, the minimum burial depth for all details is 6 inches (152 mm) as permitted by Table 300-5.

Table 310-26. Ampacities of Three Insulated Conductors, Rated 0 through 2000 Volts, Within an Overall Covering (Three Conductor Cable) in Underground Electrical Ducts (One Cable per Electrical Duct)

Based on Ambient Earth Temperature of 20°C (68°F), Electrical Duct Arrangement as per Figure 310-1, 100 Percent Load Factor, Thermal Resistance (RHO) of 90, Conductor Temperature 75°C (167°F)

Size	1 Electrical Duct (Fig. 310-1 Detail 1)	3 Electrical Ducts (Fig. 310-1 Detail 2)	6 Electrical Ducts (Fig. 310-1 Detail 3)	1 Electrical Duct (Fig. 310-1 Detail 1)	3 Electrical Ducts (Fig. 310-1 Detail 2)	6 Electrical Ducts (Fig. 310-1 Detail 3)	Size
AWG MCM	TYPES RHW, THW, THWN, XHHW, USE	TYPES RHW, THW, THWN, XHHW, USE	TYPES RHW, THW, THWN, XHHW, USE	TYPES RHW, THW, THWN, XHHW, USE	TYPES RHW, THW, THWN, XHHW, USE	TYPES RHW, THW, THWN, XHHW, USE	AWG MCM
	COPPER			ALUMINUM OR COPPER-CLAD ALUMINUM			
14	23†	21†	19†	. . . .	. . . .	. . . .	14
12	29†	26†	24†	. . . .	. . . .	. . . .	12
10	39†	34†	31†	. . . .	. . . .	. . . .	10
8	54	48	42	42	37	32	8
6	71	63	54	55	49	42	6
4	93	81	69	72	63	54	4
2	121	105	89	94	82	70	2
1	140	121	102	109	94	79	1
1/0	160	137	116	125	107	90	1/0
2/0	183	156	131	143	122	102	2/0
3/0	210	178	148	164	139	116	3/0
4/0	240	202	168	187	158	131	4/0
250	265	222	184	207	174	144	250
350	321	267	219	252	209	172	350
500	389	320	261	308	254	207	500
750	478	388	314	386	314	254	750
1000	539	435	351	447	361	291	1000

Ambient Temp. °C	For ambient temperatures other than 20°C (68°F), multiply the ampacities shown above by the appropriate factor shown below.						Ambient Temp. °F
6–10	1.09	1.09	1.09	1.09	1.09	1.09	43–50
11–15	1.04	1.04	1.04	1.04	1.04	1.04	52–59
16–20	1.00	1.00	1.00	1.00	1.00	1.00	61–68
21–25	.95	.95	.95	.95	.95	.95	70–77
26–30	.90	.90	.90	.90	.90	.90	79–86

† Unless otherwise specifically permitted elsewhere in this Code, the overcurrent protection for conductor types marked with an obelisk (†) shall not exceed 15 amperes for 14 AWG, 20 amperes for 12 AWG and 30 amperes for 10 AWG copper; or 15 amperes for 12 AWG and 25 amperes for 10 AWG aluminum and copper-clad aluminum.

ARTICLE 310—CONDUCTORS FOR GENERAL WIRING

Table 310-27. Ampacities of Three Single Insulated Conductors, Rated 0 through 2000 Volts, in Underground Electrical Ducts (Three Conductors per Electrical Duct)

Based on Ambient Earth Temperature of 20°C (68°F), Electrical Duct Arrangement per Figure 310-1, 100 Percent Load Factor, Thermal Resistance (RHO) of 90, Conductor Temperature 75°C (167°F)

Size	1 Electrical Duct (Fig. 310-1 Detail 1)	3 Electrical Ducts (Fig. 310-1 Detail 2)	6 Electrical Ducts (Fig. 310-1 Detail 3)	1 Electrical Duct (Fig. 310-1 Detail 1)	3 Electrical Ducts (Fig. 310-1 Detail 2)	6 Electrical Ducts (Fig. 310-1 Detail 3)	Size
AWG MCM	TYPES †RHW, †THW, †THWN, †XHHW, †USE	TYPES †RHW, †THW, †THWN, †XHHW, †USE	TYPES †RHW, †THW, †THWN, †XHHW, †USE	TYPES †RHW, †THW, †THWN, †XHHW, †USE	TYPES †RHW, †THW, †THWN, †XHHW, †USE	TYPES †RHW, †THW, †THWN, †XHHW, †USE	AWG MCM
	COPPER			ALUMINUM OR COPPER-CLAD ALUMINUM			
14	24†	22†	16†	. . . .	. . . .	. . . .	14
12	36†	31†	24†	28†	22†	18†	12
10	46†	41†	32†	36†	31†	25†	10
8	58	51	44	45	40	34	8
6	77	67	56	60	52	44	6
4	100	86	73	78	67	57	4
3	116	99	83	91	77	65	3
2	132	112	93	103	87	73	2
1	153	128	106	119	100	83	1
1/0	175	146	121	136	114	94	1/0
2/0	200	166	136	156	130	106	2/0
3/0	228	189	154	178	147	121	3/0
4/0	263	215	175	205	168	137	4/0
250	290	236	192	227	185	150	250
300	321	260	210	252	204	165	300
350	351	283	228	276	222	179	350
400	376	302	243	297	238	191	400
500	427	341	273	338	270	216	500
600	468	371	296	373	296	236	600
700	509	402	319	408	321	255	700
750	529	417	330	425	334	265	750
800	544	428	338	439	344	273	800
900	575	450	355	466	365	288	900
1000	605	472	372	494	385	304	1000

Ambient Temp. °C	For ambient temperatures other than 20°C (68°F), multiply the ampacities shown above by the appropriate factor shown below.						Ambient Temp. °F
6–10	1.09	1.09	1.09	1.09	1.09	1.09	43–50
11–15	1.04	1.04	1.04	1.04	1.04	1.04	52–59
16–20	1.00	1.00	1.00	1.00	1.00	1.00	61–68
21–25	.95	.95	.95	.95	.95	.95	70–77
26–30	.90	.90	.90	.90	.90	.90	79–86

† Unless otherwise specifically permitted elsewhere in this Code, the overcurrent protection for conductor types marked with an obelisk (†) shall not exceed 15 amperes for 14 AWG, 20 amperes for 12 AWG and 30 amperes for 10 AWG copper; or 15 amperes for 12 AWG and 25 amperes for 10 AWG aluminum and copper-clad aluminum.

Table 310-28. Ampacities of Two or Three Insulated Conductors, Rated 0 through 2000 Volts, Cabled Within an Overall (Two or Three Conductor) Covering Directly Buried in Earth Based on Ambient Earth Temperature of 20°C (68°F), Arrangement per Figure 310-1, 100 Percent Load Factor, Thermal Resistance (RHO) of 90

Size	1 Cable (Fig. 310-1 Detail 5)		2 Cables (Fig. 310-1 Detail 6)		1 Cable (Fig. 310-1 Detail 5)		2 Cables (Fig. 310-1 Detail 6)		Size
	60°C (140°F)	75°C (167°F)	60°C (140°F)	75°C (167°F)	60°C (140°F)	75°C (167°F)	60°C (140°F)	75°C (167°F)	
	TYPES		TYPES		TYPES		TYPES		
AWG MCM	†UF	†RHW, †THW, †THWN, †XHHW, †USE	†UF	†RHW, †THW, †THWN, †XHHW, †USE	†UF	†RHW, †THW, †THWN, †USE	†UF	†RHW, †THW, †THWN, †XHHW, †USE	AWG MCM
	COPPER				ALUMINUM OR COPPER-CLAD ALUMINUM				
14	30†	32†	26†	30†	. . . .	. . . .	. . . .	. . . .	14
12	38†	43†	34†	41†	30†	34†	26†	32†	12
10	47†	56†	43†	52†	38†	45†	34†	41†	10
8	64	75	60	70	51	59	47	55	8
6	85	100	81	95	68	75	60	70	6
4	107	125	100	117	83	97	78	91	4
2	137	161	128	150	107	126	110	117	2
1	155	182	145	170	121	142	113	132	1
1/0	177	208	165	193	138	162	129	151	1/0
2/0	201	236	188	220	157	184	146	171	2/0
3/0	229	269	213	250	179	210	166	195	3/0
4/0	259	304	241	282	203	238	188	220	4/0
250		333		308		261		241	250
350		401		370		315		290	350
500		481		442		381		350	500
750		585		535		473		433	750
1000		657		600		545		497	1000

Ambient Temp. °C	For ambient temperatures other than 20°C (68°F), multiply the ampacities shown above by the appropriate factor shown below.								Ambient Temp. °F
6–10	1.12	1.09	1.12	1.09	1.12	1.09	1.12	1.09	43–50
11–15	1.06	1.04	1.06	1.04	1.06	1.04	1.06	1.04	52–59
16–20	1.00	1.00	1.00	1.00	1.00	1.00	1.00	1.00	61–68
21–25	.94	.95	.94	.95	.94	.95	.94	.95	70–77
26–30	.87	.90	.87	.90	.87	.90	.87	.90	79–86

For ampacities of UF cable in underground electrical ducts, multiply the ampacities shown in the table by 0.74.

† Unless otherwise specifically permitted elsewhere in this Code, the overcurrent protection for conductor types marked with an obelisk (†) shall not exceed 15 amperes for 14 AWG, 20 amperes for 12 AWG and 30 amperes for 10 AWG copper; or 15 amperes for 12 AWG and 25 amperes for 10 AWG aluminum and copper-clad aluminum.

**Table 310-29. Ampacities of Three Triplexed Single Insulated Conductors,
Rated 0 through 2000 Volts, Directly Buried in Earth**

**Based on Ambient Earth Temperature of 20°C (68°F), Arrangement per Figure 310-1,
100 Percent Load Factor, Thermal Resistance (RHO) of 90**

Size	See Fig. 310-1 Detail 7		See Fig. 310-1 Detail 8		See Fig. 310-1 Detail 7		See Fig. 310-1 Detail 8		Size
	60°C (140°F)	75°C (167°F)	60°C (140°F)	75°C (167°F)	60°C (140°F)	75°C (167°F)	60°C (140°F)	75°C (167°F)	
AWG	TYPES		TYPES		TYPES		TYPES		AWG
MCM	†UF	†USE	†UF	†USE	†UF	†USE	†UF	†USE	MCM
	COPPER				ALUMINUM OR COPPER-CLAD ALUMINUM				
14	31†	37†	30†	35†	. . . .	. . . .	. . . .	. . . .	14
12	41†	48†	39†	46†	32†	38†	31†	36†	12
10	54†	63†	50†	59†	42†	49†	39†	46†	10
8	72	84	66	77	55	65	51	60	8
6	91	107	84	99	72	84	66	77	6
4	119	139	109	128	92	108	85	100	4
2	153	179	140	164	119	139	109	128	2
1	173	203	159	186	135	158	124	145	1
1/0	197	231	181	212	154	180	141	165	1/0
2/0	223	262	205	240	175	205	159	187	2/0
3/0	254	298	232	272	199	233	181	212	3/0
4/0	289	339	263	308	226	265	206	241	4/0
250		370		336		289		263	250
350		445		403		349		316	350
500		536		483		424		382	500
750		654		587		525		471	750
1000		744		665		608		544	1000

Ambient Temp. °C	For ambient temperatures other than 20°C (68°F), multiply the ampacities shown above by the appropriate factor shown below.								Ambient Temp. °F
6–10	1.12	1.09	1.12	1.09	1.12	1.09	1.12	1.09	43–50
11–15	1.06	1.04	1.06	1.04	1.06	1.04	1.06	1.04	52–59
16–20	1.00	1.00	1.00	1.00	1.00	1.00	1.00	1.00	61–68
21–25	.94	.95	.94	.95	.94	.95	.94	.95	70–77
26–30	.87	.90	.87	.90	.87	.90	.87	.90	79–86

† Unless otherwise specifically permitted elsewhere in this Code, the overcurrent protection for conductor types marked with an obelisk (†) shall not exceed 15 amperes for 14 AWG, 20 amperes for 12 AWG and 30 amperes for 10 AWG copper; or 15 amperes for 12 AWG and 25 amperes for 10 AWG aluminum and copper-clad aluminum.

Table 310-30. Ampacities of Three Single Insulated Conductors, Rated 0 through 2000 Volts, Directly Buried in Earth

Based on Ambient Earth Temperature of 20°C (68°F), Arrangement per Figure 310-1, 100 Percent Load Factor, Thermal Resistance (RHO) of 90

Size	See Fig. 310-1 Detail 9		See Fig. 310-1 Detail 10		See Fig. 310-1 Detail 9		See Fig. 310-1 Detail 10		Size
	60°C (140°F)	75°C (167°F)	60°C (140°F)	75°C (167°F)	60°C (140°F)	75°C (167°F)	60°C (140°F)	75°C (167°F)	
AWG MCM	TYPES		TYPES		TYPES		TYPES		AWG MCM
	UF	USE	UF	USE	UF	USE	UF	USE	
	COPPER				ALUMINUM OR COPPER-CLAD ALUMINUM				
8	84		78		66		61		8
6	107		101		84		78		6
4	139		130		108		101		4
2	178		165		139		129		2
1	201		187		157		146		1
1/0	230		212		179		165		1/0
2/0	261		241		204		188		2/0
3/0	297		274		232		213		3/0
4/0	336		309		262		241		4/0
250		429		394		335		308	250
350		516		474		403		370	350
500		626		572		490		448	500
750		767		700		605		552	750
1000		887		808		706		642	1000
1250		979		891		787		716	1250
1500		1063		965		862		783	1500
1750		1133		1027		930		843	1750
2000		1195		1082		990		897	2000

Ambient Temp. °C	For ambient temperatures other than 20°C (68°F), multiply the ampacities shown above by the appropriate factor shown below.								Ambient Temp. °F
6–10	1.12	1.09	1.12	1.09	1.12	1.09	1.12	1.09	43–50
11–15	1.06	1.04	1.06	1.04	1.06	1.04	1.06	1.04	52–59
16–20	1.00	1.00	1.00	1.00	1.00	1.00	1.00	1.00	61–68
21–25	.94	.95	.94	.95	.94	.95	.94	.95	70–77
26–30	.87	.90	.87	.90	.87	.90	.87	.90	79–86

Table 310-31. Ampacities of Multiconductor Cables with not more than Three Insulated Conductors, Rated 0 through 2000 Volts, in Free Air

Based on Ambient Air Temperature of 40°C (104°F) (For TC, MC, MI and SNM cables)†

Size	Temperature Rating of Conductor. See Table 310-13.								Size
AWG	60°C (140°F)	75°C (167°F)	85°C (185°F)	90°C (194°F)	60°C (140°F)	75°C (167°F)	85°C (185°F)	90°C (194°F)	AWG
MCM	COPPER				ALUMINUM OR COPPER-CLAD ALUMINUM				MCM
18				11†					18
16				16†					16
14	18†	21†	24†	25†	. . . .	. . . .	. . . .	. . . .	14
12	21†	28†	30†	32†	18†	21†	24†	25†	12
10	28†	36†	41†	43†	21†	28†	30†	32†	10
8	39	50	56	59	30	39	44	46	8
6	52	68	75	79	41	53	59	61	6
4	69	89	100	104	54	70	78	81	4
3	81	104	116	121	63	81	91	95	3
2	92	118	132	138	72	92	103	108	2
1	107	138	154	161	84	108	120	126	1
1/0	124	160	178	186	97	125	139	145	1/0
2/0	143	184	206	215	111	144	160	168	2/0
3/0	165	213	238	249	129	166	185	194	3/0
4/0	190	245	274	287	149	192	214	224	4/0
250	212	274	305	320	166	214	239	250	250
300	237	306	341	357	186	240	268	280	300
350	261	337	377	394	205	265	296	309	350
400	281	363	406	425	222	287	317	334	400
500	321	416	465	487	255	330	368	385	500
600	354	459	513	538	284	368	410	429	600
700	387	502	562	589	306	405	462	473	700
750	404	523	586	615	328	424	473	495	750
800	415	539	604	633	339	439	490	513	800
900	438	570	639	670	362	469	514	548	900
1000	461	601	674	707	385	499	558	584	1000

Ambient Temp. °C	For ambient temperatures other than 40°C (104°F), multiply the ampacities shown above by the appropriate factor shown below.								Ambient Temp. °F
21–25	1.32	1.20	1.15	1.14	1.32	1.20	1.15	1.14	70–77
26–30	1.22	1.13	1.11	1.10	1.22	1.13	1.11	1.10	79–86
31–35	1.12	1.07	1.05	1.05	1.12	1.07	1.05	1.05	88–95
36–40	1.00	1.00	1.00	1.00	1.00	1.00	1.00	1.00	97–104
41–45	.87	.93	.94	.95	.87	.93	.94	.95	106–113
46–50	.71	.85	.88	.89	.71	.85	.88	.89	115–122
51–55	.50	.76	.82	.84	.50	.76	.82	.84	124–131
56–60	. . . .	.65	.75	.77	. . . .	.65	.75	.77	133–140
61–70	. . . .	.38	.58	.63	. . . .	.38	.58	.63	142–158
71–80	. . . .	. . . .	.33	.44	. . . .	. . . .	.33	.44	160–176

† Unless otherwise specifically permitted elsewhere in this Code, the overcurrent protection for conductor types marked with an obelisk (†) shall not exceed 7 amperes for 18 AWG, 10 amperes for 16 AWG, and 15 amperes for 14 AWG, 20 amperes for 12 AWG, and 30 amperes for 10 AWG copper; or 15 amperes for 12 AWG and 25 amperes for 10 AWG aluminum and copper-clad aluminum.

Notes to Tables 310-16 through 310-31

1. **Explanation of Tables.** For explanation of Type Letters, and for recognized size of conductors for the various conductor insulations, see Section 310-13. For installation requirements, see Sections 310-1 through 310-10, and the various articles of this Code. For flexible cords, see Tables 400-4 and 400-5.

3. Three-Wire, Single-Phase Dwelling Services. In dwelling units, conductors, as listed below, shall be permitted to be utilized as three-wire, single-phase, service-entrance conductors and the three-wire, single-phase feeder that carries the total current supplied by that service. Grounded service-entrance conductors shall be permitted to be two AWG sizes smaller than the ungrounded conductors provided the requirements of Section 230-42 are met.

Conductor Types and Sizes
RH-RHH-RHW-THW-THWN-THHN-XHHW

Copper	Aluminum and Copper-Clad AL	Service Rating in Amps
AWG	AWG	
4	2	100
3	1	110
2	1/0	125
1	2/0	150
1/0	3/0	175
2/0	4/0	200

If a single set of 3-wire, single-phase, service-entrance conductors supplies a one-family, two-family, or multifamily dwelling, the reduced conductor size permitted by Note 3 is applicable to the service-entrance conductors only. If there are panelboards on the load side of the main service-entrance equipment supplied by feeders, Note 3 does not permit a reduction in the conductor size for these feeders because they do not carry the total current supplied by the service. See Figures 310-4 and 310-5.

See also Section 550-5(a) for a description of a feeder assembly that carries the total current supplied by the service, and Section 215-2.

Section 230-42 requires that the service-entrance conductors be of sufficient size to carry the loads as computed in Article 220. This means that the load on the grounded (neutral) conductor must also be calculated to be sure it is of sufficient size to carry the load. It should not "automatically" be reduced two sizes. On a 120/240V, 3-wire, single-phase service, the neutral cannot be reduced in size (below the size of the ungrounded conductors) if there are no 240-volt loads, because under the most severe conditions of unbalance the neutral will carry the same current as the ungrounded conductor supplying the load.

5. Bare Conductors. Where bare conductors are used with insulated conductors, their allowable ampacities shall be limited to that permitted for the adjacent insulated conductors.

6. Mineral-Insulated, Metal-Sheathed Cable. The temperature limitation on which the ampacities of mineral-insulated, metal-sheathed cable are based is determined by the insulating materials used in the end seal. Termination fittings incorporating unimpregnated, organic, insulating materials are limited to 90°C operation.

7. Type MTW Machine Tool Wire.

(FPN): For the ampacities of Type MTW wire, see Table 13-1(c) in the Electrical Standard for Industrial Machinery (NFPA 79-1985).

8. Ampacity Adjustment Factors.

(a) More than Three Conductors in a Raceway or Cable. Where the number of conductors in a raceway or cable exceeds three, the ampacities given in Tables 310-16, 310-18, 310-22, 310-26, 310-27, 310-28, 310-29, 310-30, and 310-31 shall be reduced as shown in the following table:

Number of Conductors	Percent of Values in Tables 310-16, 310-18, 310-22, 310-26, 310-27, 310-28, 310-29, 310-30, and 310-31, as Adjusted for Ambient Temperature if Necessary
4 thru 6	80
7 thru 9	70
10 thru 24*	70
25 thru 42*	60
43 and above*	50

*These factors include the effects of a load diversity of 50 percent.

The asterisked note indicates that the figures in the second column are based on a load diversity of 50 percent if there are more than 9 conductors in a raceway or cable. Load diversity of 50 percent means 50 percent of the conductors are fully loaded and 50 percent have no load. It is not uncommon in commercial and industrial occupancies to put more than 9 conductors in a raceway. If a diversity factor of 50 percent or less cannot be assured, the general formula in Section 310-15(b) will provide the correct multiplication factor.

Figure 310-4. The reduced conductor size permitted in Note 3 to Tables 310-16 through 310-31 is applicable to the conductors run to each apartment from the meters.

Figure 310-5. The reduced conductor size permitted in Note 3 to Tables 310-16 through 310-31 is not applicable to the conductors run to each apartment from the service disconnecting means.

Where single conductors or multiconductor cables are stacked or bundled longer than 24 inches (610 mm) without maintaining spacing and are not installed in raceways, the ampacity of each conductor shall be reduced as shown in the above table.

Exception No. 1: When conductors of different systems, as provided in Section 300-3, are installed in a common raceway the derating factors shown above shall apply to the number of power and lighting (Articles 210, 215, 220, and 230) conductors only.

Exception No. 2: For conductors installed in cable trays, the provisions of Section 318-11 shall apply.

Exception No. 2 is not applicable to motor circuit conductors because the so-called "derating factor" for such conductors, as in Section 430-22(a), is not a derating factor. See commentary following Section 430-22(a).

Exception No. 3: Derating factors do not apply to conductors in nipples having a length not exceeding 24 inches (610 mm).

Exception No. 4: Derating factors do not apply to underground conductors entering or leaving an outdoor trench if those conductors have physical protection in the form of rigid metal conduit, intermediate metal conduit or rigid nonmetallic conduit Schedule 80 having a length not exceeding 10 feet (3.05 m) and the number of conductors in a conduit does not exceed 4.

(b) More than One Conduit, Tube, or Raceway. Spacing between conduits, tubing, or raceways shall be maintained.

Spacing is normally maintained between individual conduits in groups of conduit runs from junction box to junction box because of the need to separate the conduits where they enter the junction box to allow room for locknuts and bushings. Field experience has indicated this degree of spacing between runs has not caused any problems.

9. Overcurrent Protection. Where the standard ratings and settings of overcurrent devices do not correspond with the ratings and settings allowed for conductors, the next higher standard rating and setting shall be permitted.

Exception: As limited in Section 240-3.

10. Neutral Conductor.

(a) A neutral conductor which carries only the unbalanced current from other conductors, as in the case of normally balanced circuits of three or more conductors, shall not be counted when applying the provisions of Note 8.

(b) In a 3-wire circuit consisting of 2-phase wires and the neutral of a 4-wire, 3-phase wye-connected system, a common conductor carries approximately the same current as the other conductors and shall be counted when applying the provisions of Note 8.

(c) On a 4-wire, 3-phase wye circuit where the major portion of the load consists of electric-discharge lighting, data processing, or similar equipment, there are harmonic currents present in the neutral conductor and the neutral shall be considered to be a current-carrying conductor.

Third harmonic currents in 3-phase power systems for electronic data processing and similar equipment are capable of causing the current in the neutral to exceed that in the phase conductor.

ARTICLE 310—CONDUCTORS FOR GENERAL WIRING

Third harmonics in this type of equipment are a result of the use of diodes charging capacitors on the input of power supplies. The current waveforms characteristic of such a load are very high in third harmonics. Third harmonics, in contrast to the fundamental, are not reduced by balancing the load. As a result, the neutral, in areas of concentrated electronic loads such as computer installations, production test areas, etc., should not have its current capacity reduced.

11. Grounding or Bonding Conductor. A grounding or bonding conductor shall not be counted when applying the provisions of Note 8.

Notes for all details:

1. Minimum burial depths to top electrical ducts or cables shall be in accordance with Section 300-5. Maximum depth to the top of electrical duct banks shall be 30", and maximum depth to the top of direct buried cables shall be 36".

2. For two and four electrical duct installations with electrical ducts installed in a single row, see the Notes to Tables 310-25 through 310-27.

3. For SI units: one inch = 25.4 millimeters; one foot = 305 millimeters.

Legend

☐ Backfill, maximum Rho = 90 (Earth or concrete)

○ Electrical duct

● Cable or cables

Figure 310-1. Cable Installation Dimensions for Use with
Tables 310-25 through 310-30 and 310-77 through 310-84

Table 310-61. Conductor Application and Insulation

Trade Name	Type Letter	Maximum Operating Temperature	Application Provision	Insulation	Outer Covering
Medium voltage solid dielectric	MV-75 MV-85 MV-90	75C 85C 90C	Dry or wet locations rated 2001 volts and higher	Thermoplastic or Thermosetting	Jacket, Sheath or Armor

Table 310-62. Thickness of Insulation for 601-2000 Volt Nonshielded Types RHH and RHW, in Mils

Conductor Size AWG-MCM	A	B
14–10	80	60
8	80	70
6–2	95	70
1–2/0	110	90
3/0–4/0	110	90
213–500	125	105
501–1000	140	120

Note: Column A insulations are limited to natural, SBR, and butyl rubbers.
Note: Column B insulations are materials such as cross-linked polyethylene, ethylene propylene rubber, and composites thereof.

Table 310-63. Thickness of Insulation and Jacket for Nonshielded Solid Dielectric Insulated Conductors Rated 2001 to 8000 Volts, in Mils

Conductor Size AWG-MCM	2001–5000 Volts						5001–8000 Volts 100 Percent Insulation Level Wet or Dry Locations		
	Dry Locations Single Conductor			Wet or Dry Locations					
	Without Jacket	With Jacket		Single Conductor		Multi-Conductor*	Single Conductor		Multi-Conductor*
	Insulation	Insulation	Jacket	Insulation	Jacket	Insulation	Insulation	Jacket	Insulation
8	110	90	30	125	80	90	180	80	180
6	110	90	30	125	80	90	180	80	180
4–2	110	90	45	125	80	90	180	95	180
1–2/0	110	90	45	125	95	90	180	95	180
3/0–4/0	110	90	65	125	110	90	180	110	180
213–500	120	90	65	140	110	90	210	110	210
501–750	130	90	65	155	125	90	235	125	235
751–1000	130	90	65	155	125	90	250	140	250

*Note: Under a common overall covering such as a jacket, sheath or armor.

Table 310-64. Thickness of Insulation for Shielded Solid Dielectric Insulated Conductors Rated 2001 to 35,000 Volts, in Mils

Conductor Size AWG-MCM	2001–5000 Volts	5001–8000		8001–15,000		15,001–25,000		25,001–28,000	28,001–35,000
		100* Per-cent Insulation level	133* Per-cent Insulation level	100* Per-cent Insulation level	133* Per-cent Insulation level	100* Per-cent Insulation level	133* Per-cent Insulation level	100* Per-cent Insulation level	100* Per-cent Insulation level
8	90	—	—	—	—	—	—	—	—
6–4	90	115	140	—	—	—	—	—	—
2	90	115	140	175	215	—	—	—	—
1	90	115	140	175	215	260	345	280	—
1/0–1000	90	115	140	175	215	260	345	280	345

*Definitions:

100 Percent Insulation Level. Cables in this category shall be permitted to be applied where the system is provided with relay protection such that ground faults will be cleared as rapidly as possible, but in any case within 1 minute. While these cables are applicable to the great majority of cable installations which are on grounded systems, they shall be permitted to be used also on other systems for which the application of cables is acceptable provided the above clearing requirements are met in completely de-energizing the faulted section.

133 Percent Insulation Level. This insulation level corresponds to that formerly designated for ungrounded systems. Cables in this category shall be permitted to be applied in situations where the clearing time requirements of the 100 percent level category cannot be met, and yet there is adequate assurance that the faulted section will be de-energized in a time not exceeding 1 hour. Also they shall be permitted to be used when additional insulation strength over the 100 percent level category is desirable.

Table 310-65. Thickness of Varnished-Cambric Insulation for Single-Conductor Cable, in Mils

Conductor Size AWG or MCM	For Voltages Not Exceeding				
	1000	2000	3000	4000	5000
14	60	—	—	—	—
12	60	80	—	—	—
10	60	80	95	—	—
8–2	60	80	95	110	140
1–4/0	80	95	95	110	140
213–500	95	95	110	125	155
501–1000	110	110	110	125	155
1001–2000	125	125	125	140	155

Table 310-66. Thickness of Varnished-Cambric Insulation for Multiconductor Cable, in Mils

Conductor Size AWG or MCM	For Voltages Not Exceeding									
	1000		2000		3000		4000		5000	
	C	B	C	B	C	B	C	B	C	B
14	60	0	—	—	—	—	—	—	—	—
12	60	0	80	0	—	—	—	—	—	—
10	60	0	80	0	80	30	—	—	—	—
8–2	60	0	80	0	80	30	95	45	95	60
1–4/0	80	0	95	0	95	30	95	45	95	60
213–500	95	0	95	0	95	30	95	45	110	60
501–1000	95	30	95	30	95	45	95	60	110	60
1001–2000	110	30	110	30	110	45	110	60	110	80

The thickness given in columns headed "C" are for the insulation on the individual conductors. Those given in the columns headed "B" are for the thickness of the overall belt of insulation.

Table 310-67

Thickness of Asbestos and Varnished-Cambric Insulation for Single-Conductor Cable, Types AVA, AVB, and AVL, in Mils

Conductor AWG or MCM	Asbestos 1st Wall	Varnished Cambric						Asbestos 2nd Wall
		For Voltages Not Exceeding						
	1000–5000	1000	2000	3000	4000	5000		1000–5000
14–2	15	45	60	80	100	120		25
1–4/0	20	45	60	80	100	120		30
213–500	25	45	60	80	100	120		40
501–1000	30	45	60	80	100	120		40
1001–2000	30	55	75	95	115	140		50

Table 310-69

Ampacities for Insulated Single Copper Conductor Isolated in Air

Based on Conductor Temperature of 90°C and Ambient Air Temperature of 40°C

Conductor Size AWG-MCM	2001–5000 Volts Ampacity	5001–15,000 Volts Ampacity	15,001–35,000 Volts Ampacity
8	83	—	—
6	110	110	—
4	145	150	—
2	190	195	—
1	225	225	225
1/0	260	260	260
2/0	300	300	300
3/0	345	345	345
4/0	400	400	395
250	445	445	440
350	550	550	545
500	695	685	680
750	900	885	870
1000	1075	1060	1040
1250	1230	1210	1185
1500	1365	1345	1315
1750	1495	1470	1430
2000	1605	1575	1535

Table 310-70

Ampacities for Insulated Single Aluminum Conductor Isolated in Air

Based on Conductor Temperature of 90°C and Ambient Air Temperature of 40°C

Conductor Size AWG-MCM	2001–5000 Volts Ampacity	5001–15,000 Volts Ampacity	15,001–35,000 Volts Ampacity
8	64	—	—
6	85	87	—
4	115	115	—
2	150	150	—
1	175	175	175
1/0	200	200	200
2/0	230	235	230
3/0	270	270	270
4/0	310	310	310
250	345	345	345
350	430	430	430
500	545	535	530
750	710	700	685
1000	855	840	825
1250	980	970	950
1500	1105	1085	1060
1750	1215	1195	1165
2000	1320	1295	1265

Table 310-71

Ampacities of an Insulated Three Conductor Copper Cable Isolated in Air

Based on Conductor Temperature of 90°C and Ambient Air Temperature of 40°C

Conductor Size AWG-MCM	2001–5000 Volts Ampacity	5001–35,000 Volts Ampacity
8	59	—
6	79	93
4	105	120
2	140	165
1	160	185
1/0	185	215
2/0	215	245
3/0	250	285
4/0	285	325
250	320	360
350	395	435
500	485	535
750	615	670
1000	705	770

ARTICLE 310—CONDUCTORS FOR GENERAL WIRING

Table 310-72
Ampacities of an Insulated Three Conductor Aluminum Cable Isolated in Air
Based on Conductor Temperature of 90°C and Ambient Air Temperature of 40°C

Conductor Size AWG-MCM	2001–5000 Volts Ampacity	5001–35,000 Volts Ampacity
8	46	—
6	61	72
4	81	95
2	110	125
1	125	145
1/0	145	170
2/0	170	190
3/0	195	220
4/0	225	255
250	250	280
350	310	345
500	385	425
750	495	540
1000	585	635

Table 310-73
Ampacities of an Insulated Triplexed or Three Single Conductor Copper Cables in Isolated Conduit in Air
Based on Conductor Temperature of 90°C and Ambient Air Temperature of 40°C

Conductor Size AWG-MCM	2001–5000 Volts Ampacity	5001–35,000 Volts Ampacity
8	55	—
6	75	83
4	97	110
2	130	150
1	155	170
1/0	180	195
2/0	205	225
3/0	240	260
4/0	280	295
250	315	330
350	385	395
500	475	480
750	600	585
1000	690	675

Table 310-74

Ampacities of Insulated Triplexed or Three Single Conductor Aluminum Cables in Isolated Conduit in Air

Based on Conductor Temperature of 90°C and Ambient Air Temperature of 40°C

Conductor Size AWG-MCM	2001–5000 Volts Ampacity	5001–35,000 Volts Ampacity
8	43	—
6	58	65
4	76	84
2	100	115
1	120	130
1/0	140	150
2/0	160	175
3/0	190	200
4/0	215	230
250	250	255
350	305	310
500	380	385
750	490	485
1000	580	565

Table 310-75

Ampacities of an Insulated Three Conductor Copper Cable in Isolated Conduit in Air

Based on Conductor Temperature of 90°C and Ambient Air Temperature of 40°C

Conductor Size AWG-MCM	2001–5000 Volts Ampacity	5001–35,000 Volts Ampacity
8	52	—
6	69	83
4	91	105
2	125	145
1	140	165
1/0	165	195
2/0	190	220
3/0	220	250
4/0	255	290
250	280	315
350	350	385
500	425	470
750	525	570
1000	590	650

Table 310-76

Ampacities of an Insulated Three Conductor Aluminum Cable in Isolated Conduit in Air
Based on Conductor Temperature of 90°C and Ambient Air Temperature of 40°C

Conductor Size AWG-MCM	2001–5000 Volts Ampacity	5001–35,000 Volts Ampacity
8	41	—
6	53	64
4	71	84
2	96	115
1	110	130
1/0	130	150
2/0	150	170
3/0	170	195
4/0	200	225
250	220	250
350	275	305
500	340	380
750	430	470
1000	505	550

Table 310-77

Ampacities of Three Single Insulated Copper Conductors in Underground Electrical Ducts (Three Conductors per Electrical Duct)

Based on Ambient Earth Temperature of 20°C (68°F), Electrical Duct Arrangement per Figure 310-1, 100% Load Factor, Thermal Resistance (RHO) of 90, Conductor Temperature 90°C (194°F)

One Circuit (See Figure 310-1, Detail 1) Size AWG-MCM	2001–5000 Volts Ampacity	5001–35,000 Volts Ampacity
8	64	—
6	85	90
4	110	115
2	145	155
1	170	175
1/0	195	200
2/0	220	230
3/0	250	260
4/0	290	295
250	320	325
350	385	390
500	470	465
750	585	565
1000	670	640
Three Circuit (See Figure 310-1, Detail 2) Size		
8	56	—
6	73	77
4	95	99
2	125	130
1	140	145
1/0	160	165
2/0	185	185
3/0	210	210
4/0	235	240
250	260	260
350	315	310
500	375	370
750	460	440
1000	525	495
Six Circuit (See Figure 310-1, Detail 3) Size		
8	48	—
6	62	64
4	80	82
2	105	105
1	115	120
1/0	135	135
2/0	150	150
3/0	170	170
4/0	195	190
250	210	210
350	250	245
500	300	290
750	365	350
1000	410	390

Table 310-78

Ampacities of Three Single Insulated Aluminum Conductors in Underground Electrical Ducts (Three Conductors per Electrical Duct)

Based on Ambient Earth Temperature of 20°C (68°F), Electrical Duct Arrangement per Figure 310-1, 100% Load Factor, Thermal Resistance (RHO) of 90, Conductor Temperature 90°C (194°F)

One Circuit (See Figure 310-1, Detail 1) Size AWG-MCM	2001–5000 Volts Ampacity	5001–35,000 Volts Ampacity
8	50	—
6	66	70
4	86	91
2	115	120
1	130	135
1/0	150	155
2/0	170	175
3/0	195	200
4/0	225	230
250	250	250
350	305	305
500	370	370
750	470	455
1000	545	525
Three Circuit (See Figure 310-1, Detail 2) Size		
8	44	—
6	57	60
4	74	77
2	96	100
1	110	110
1/0	125	125
2/0	145	145
3/0	160	165
4/0	185	185
250	205	200
350	245	245
500	295	290
750	370	355
1000	425	405
Six Circuit (See Figure 310-1, Detail 3) Size		
8	38	—
6	48	50
4	62	64
2	80	80
1	91	90
1/0	105	105
2/0	115	115
3/0	135	130
4/0	150	150
250	165	165
350	195	195
500	240	230
750	290	280
1000	335	320

Table 310-79

Ampacities of Three Insulated Copper Conductors Cabled Within an Overall Covering (Three Conductor Cable) in Underground Electrical Ducts (One Cable per Electrical Duct) Based on Ambient Earth Temperature of 20°C (68°F), Electrical Duct Arrangement per Figure 310-1, 100% Load Factor, Thermal Resistance (RHO) of 90, Conductor Temperature 90°C (194°F)

One Circuit (See Figure 310-1, Detail 1) Size AWG-MCM	2001–5000 Volts Ampacity	5001–35,000 Volts Ampacity
8	59	—
6	78	88
4	100	115
2	135	150
1	155	170
1/0	175	195
2/0	200	220
3/0	230	250
4/0	265	285
250	290	310
350	355	375
500	430	450
750	530	545
1000	600	615
Three Circuit (See Figure 310-1, Detail 2) Size		
8	53	—
6	69	75
4	89	97
2	115	125
1	135	140
1/0	150	160
2/0	170	185
3/0	195	205
4/0	225	230
250	245	255
350	295	305
500	355	360
750	430	430
1000	485	485
Six Circuit (See Figure 310-1, Detail 3) Size		
8	46	—
6	60	63
4	77	81
2	98	105
1	110	115
1/0	125	130
2/0	145	150
3/0	165	170
4/0	185	190
250	200	205
350	240	245
500	290	290
750	350	340
1000	390	380

Table 310-80

Ampacities of Three Insulated Aluminum Conductors Cabled Within an Overall Covering (Three Conductor Cable) in Underground Electrical Ducts (One Cable per Electrical Duct)

Based on Ambient Earth Temperature of 20°C (68°F), Electrical Duct Arrangement per Figure 310-1, 100% Load Factor, Thermal Resistance (RHO) of 90, Conductor Temperature 90°C (194°F)

One Circuit (See Figure 310-1, Detail 1) Size AWG-MCM	2001–5000 Volts Ampacity	5001–35,000 Volts Ampacity
8	46	—
6	61	69
4	80	89
2	105	115
1	120	135
1/0	140	150
2/0	160	170
3/0	180	195
4/0	205	220
250	230	245
350	280	295
500	340	355
750	425	440
1000	495	510
Three Circuit (See Figure 310-1, Detail 2) Size		
8	41	—
6	54	59
4	70	75
2	90	100
1	105	110
1/0	120	125
2/0	135	140
3/0	155	160
4/0	175	180
250	190	200
350	230	240
500	280	285
750	345	350
1000	400	400
Six Circuit (See Figure 310-1, Detail 3) Size		
8	36	—
6	46	49
4	60	63
2	77	80
1	87	90
1/0	99	105
2/0	110	115
3/0	130	130
4/0	145	150
250	160	160
350	190	190
500	230	230
750	280	275
1000	320	315

Table 310-81

Ampacities of Single Insulated Copper Conductors Directly Buried in Earth

Based on Ambient Earth Temperature of 20°C (68°F), Arrangement per Figure 310-1, 100% Load Factor, Thermal Resistance (RHO) of 90, Conductor Temperature 90°C (194°F)

Conductor Size AWG-MCM	2001–5000 Volts Ampacity	5001–35,000 Volts Ampacity
One Circuit- 3 Conductors (See Figure 310-1, Detail 9)		
8	110	—
6	140	130
4	180	170
2	230	210
1	260	240
1/0	295	275
2/0	335	310
3/0	385	355
4/0	435	405
250	470	440
350	570	535
500	690	650
750	845	805
1000	980	930
Two Circuits- 6 Conductors (See Figure 310-1, Detail 10)		
8	100	—
6	130	120
4	165	160
2	215	195
1	240	225
1/0	275	255
2/0	310	290
3/0	355	330
4/0	400	375
250	435	410
350	520	495
500	630	600
750	775	740
1000	890	855

For SI units: one inch = 25.4 millimeters.

317

Table 310-82

Ampacities of Single Insulated Aluminum Conductors Directly Buried in Earth

Based on Ambient Earth Temperature of 20°C (68°F), Arrangement per Figure 310-1, 100% Load Factor, Thermal Resistance (RHO) of 90, Conductor Temperature 90°C (194°F)

Conductor Size AWG-MCM	2001–5000 Volts Ampacity	5001–35,000 Volts Ampacity
One Circuit- **3 Conductors** **(See Figure 310-1,** **Detail 9)**		
8	85	—
6	110	100
4	140	130
2	180	165
1	205	185
1/0	230	215
2/0	265	245
3/0	300	275
4/0	340	315
250	370	345
350	445	415
500	540	510
750	665	635
1000	780	740
Two Circuits- **6 Conductors** **(See Figure 310-1,** **Detail 10)**		
8	80	—
6	100	95
4	130	125
2	165	155
1	190	175
1/0	215	200
2/0	245	225
3/0	275	255
4/0	310	290
250	340	320
350	410	385
500	495	470
750	610	580
1000	710	680

For SI units: one inch = 25.4 millimeters.

318

Table 310-83

Ampacities of Three Insulated Copper Conductors Cabled Within an Overall Covering (Three Conductor Cable), Directly Buried in Earth

Based on Ambient Earth Temperature of 20°C (68°F), Arrangement per Figure 310-1, 100% Load Factor, Thermal Resistance (RHO) of 90, Conductor Temperature 90°C (194°F)

Conductor Size AWG-MCM	2001–5000 Volts Ampacity	5001–35,000 Volts Ampacity
One Circuit (See Figure 310-1, Detail 5)		
8	85	—
6	105	115
4	135	145
2	180	185
1	200	210
1/0	230	240
2/0	260	270
3/0	295	305
4/0	335	350
250	365	380
350	440	460
500	530	550
750	650	665
1000	730	750
Two Circuits (See Figure 310-1, Detail 6)		
8	80	—
6	100	105
4	130	135
2	165	170
1	185	195
1/0	215	220
2/0	240	250
3/0	275	280
4/0	310	320
250	340	350
350	410	420
500	490	500
750	595	605
1000	665	675

For SI units: one inch = 25.4 millimeters.

Table 310-84

Ampacities of Three Insulated Aluminum Conductors Cabled Within an Overall Covering
(Three Conductor Cable), Directly Buried in Earth

Based on Ambient Earth Temperature of 20°C (68°F), Arrangement per Figure 310-1, 100% Load Factor, Thermal Resistance (RHO) of 90, Conductor Temperature 90°C (194°F)

Conductor Size AWG-MCM	2001–5000 Volts Ampacity	5001–35,000 Volts Ampacity
One Circuit (See Figure 310-1, Detail 5)		
8	65	—
6	80	90
4	105	115
2	140	145
1	155	165
1/0	180	185
2/0	205	210
3/0	230	240
4/0	260	270
250	285	300
350	345	360
500	420	435
750	520	540
1000	600	620
Two Circuits (See Figure 310-1, Detail 6)		
8	60	—
6	75	80
4	100	105
2	130	135
1	145	150
1/0	165	170
2/0	190	195
3/0	215	220
4/0	245	250
250	265	275
350	320	330
500	385	395
750	480	485
1000	550	560

For SI units: one inch = 25.4 millimeters.

Notes to Tables 310-69 Through 310-84

(FPN): For ampacities calculated in accordance with the following Notes 1 and 2, reference IEEE/ICEA "Power Cable Ampacities" Vols. I and II (IPCEA Pub. No. P-46-426) and "The References" therein for availability of all factors and constants.

1. Ambients Not in Tables. Ampacities at ambient temperatures other than those shown in the tables shall be determined by means of the following formula:

$$I_2 = I_1 \sqrt{\frac{TC - TA_2 - DELTA\ TD}{TC - TA_1 - DELTA\ TD}}$$

320

Where,

I_1 = Ampacity from tables at ambient TA_1
I_2 = Ampacity at desired ambient TA_2
TC = Conductor temperature in degrees C
TA_1 = Surrounding ambient from tables in degrees C
TA_2 = Desired ambient in degrees C
DELTA TD = Dielectric loss temperature rise

2. Grounded Shields. Ampacities shown in Tables 310-69, 310-70, 310-81 and 310-82 are for cable with shields grounded at one point only. When shields are grounded at more than one point, ampacities shall be adjusted to take into consideration the heating due to shield currents.

3. Electrical Duct Bank Configuration. Ampacities shown in Tables 310-77, 310-78, 310-79 and 310-84 shall apply only when the cables are located in the outer electrical ducts of the electrical duct bank. Ampacities for cables located in the inner electrical ducts of the electrical duct bank will have to be determined by special calculations.

ARTICLE 318 — CABLE TRAYS

Contents

ARTICLE 318—CABLE TRAYS

318-12. Number of Type MV and
  Type MC Cables (2001 Volts
  or Over) in Cable Trays.

318-13. Ampacity of Type MV and
  Type MC Cables (2001 Volts
  or Over) in Cable Trays.
 (a) Multiconductor Cables (2001
  Volts or Over).
 (b) Single Conductor Cables (2001
  Volts or Over).

318-1. Scope. This article covers cable tray systems including ladders, troughs, channels, solid bottom trays, and other similar structures.

318-2. Definitions.

Cable Tray System. A unit or assembly of units or sections, and associated fittings, forming a rigid structural system used to support cables.

318-3. Uses Permitted.

(a) Wiring Methods. The following shall be permitted to be installed in cable tray systems under the conditions described in their respective articles:

(1) Mineral-insulated, metal-sheathed cable (Article 330); (2) armored cable (Article 333); (3) metal-clad cable (Article 334); (4) power-limited tray cable (Section 725-40); (5) nonmetallic-sheathed cable (Article 336); (6) shielded, nonmetallic-sheathed cable (Article 337); (7) multiconductor service-entrance cable (Article 338); (8) multiconductor underground feeder and branch-circuit cable (Article 339); (9) power and control tray cable (Article 340); (10) other factory-assembled, multiconductor control, signal, or power cables, which are specifically approved for installation in cable trays; or (11) any approved conduit or raceway with its contained conductors.

(b) In Industrial Establishments. In industrial establishments only, where conditions of maintenance and supervision assure that only qualified persons will service the installed cable tray system, any of the cables in (1) and (2) below shall be permitted to be installed in ladder, ventilated trough, 4-inch (102-mm) ventilated channel-type cable trays, or 6-inch (152-mm) ventilated channel-type cable trays.

(1) Single Conductor. Single conductor cables shall be 250 MCM or larger and shall be of a type listed for use in cable trays. Where exposed to direct rays of the sun, cables shall be identified as being sunlight-resistant.

Exception: Welding cables as permitted in Article 630, Part E.

Cable trays for welding cable are required to be used only for welding cable. See Section 630-42.

(2) Multiconductor. Multiconductor cables Type MV (Article 326) where exposed to direct rays of the sun shall be identified as being sunlight-resistant.

(c) Equipment Grounding Conductors. Metal in cable trays, as defined in Table 318-7(b)(2), shall be permitted to be used as equipment grounding conductors in commercial and industrial establishments, only where continuous maintenance and supervision assure that qualified persons will service the installed cable tray system.

The cross-sectional area of the grounding metal is marked on the outer surface of the sidewall of cable trays listed by UL.

(d) Hazardous (Classified) Locations.   Cable trays in hazardous (classified) locations shall contain only the cable types permitted in Sections 501-4, 502-4, and 503-3.

(FPN): It is not the intent of this article to limit the use of cable trays to industrial establishments only.

(e) Nonmetallic Cable Tray.   Nonmetallic cable tray shall be permitted in corrosive areas and in areas requiring voltage isolation.

Glass fiber cable trays are often used to support cables between an energized cell in an electrochemical cell room (see Article 668) and the grounded frame of the cell room, to assure voltage isolation.

318-4. Uses Not Permitted.   Cable tray systems shall not be used in hoistways or where subject to severe physical damage.

318-5. Construction Specifications.

(a) Strength and Rigidity.   Cable trays shall have suitable strength and rigidity to provide adequate support for all contained wiring.

(b) Smooth Edges.   Cable trays shall not present sharp edges, burrs, or projections which may damage the insulation or jackets of the wiring.

(c) Corrosion Protection.   Cable trays shall be made of corrosion-resistant material or, if made of metal, shall be adequately protected against corrosion.

(d) Side Rails.   Cable trays shall have side rails or equivalent structural members.

(e) Fittings.   Cable trays shall include fittings or other suitable means for changes in direction and elevation of runs.

(f) Nonmetallic Cable Tray.   Nonmetallic cable tray shall be made of flame-retardant material.

318-6. Installation.

(a) Complete System.   Cable trays shall be installed as a complete system. Field bends or modifications shall be so made that the electrical continuity of the cable tray system and support for the cables shall be maintained.

Cable tray is to be installed as a complete system, i.e., unconnected sections are not permitted to support conductors, cables, etc. Manufactured sections or field-adapted sections are to be used for angle turns or for changes in elevation.

(b) Completed Before Installation.   Each run of cable tray shall be completed before the installation of cables.

(c) Supports.   Supports shall be provided to prevent stress on cables where they enter raceways or other enclosures from cable tray systems.

(d) Covers.   In portions of runs where additional protection is required, covers or enclosures providing the required protection shall be of a material compatible with the cable tray.

(e) Multiconductor Cables Rated 600 Volts or Less.   Multiconductor cables rated 600 volts or less shall be permitted to be installed in the same cable tray.

(f) Cables Rated Over 600 Volts.   Cables rated over 600 volts shall not be installed in the same cable tray with cables rated 600 volts or less.

Exception No. 1: Where separated by a solid fixed barrier of a material compatible with the cable tray.

Exception No. 2: Where cables over 600 volts are Type MC.

Figure 318-1. A cable tray installation. The trays are installed as complete systems; any field modifications made must not interfere with the electrical continuity of the system. (*Husky Trough and Ladder*)

(g) Through Partitions and Walls. Cable trays shall be permitted to extend transversely through partitions and walls or vertically through platforms and floors in wet or dry locations where the installations, complete with installed cables, are made in accordance with the requirements of Section 300-21.

See Figure 300-8.

(h) Exposed and Accessible. Cable trays shall be exposed and accessible except as permitted by Section 318-6(g).

(i) Adequate Access. Sufficient space shall be provided and maintained about cable trays to permit adequate access for installing and maintaining the cables.

No specific clearance distance is given. Sufficient spacing is to be provided for cable installation and maintenance.

(FPN): See Section 310-10 for temperature limitation of conductors.

This fine print note is intended to caution the user that the heat dissipation of conductors installed in thermal insulation is reduced.

318-7. Grounding.

(a) Metallic Cable Trays. Metallic cable trays which support electrical conductors shall be grounded as required for conductor enclosures in Article 250.

Much the same as the *Code* requires metal raceways and metal enclosures to be grounded, cable trays made of metal are also required to be grounded. Cable trays are not considered raceways. See definition of "raceway" in Article 100.

(b) Steel or Aluminum Cable Tray Systems. Steel or aluminum cable tray systems shall be permitted to be used as equipment grounding conductors provided that all the following requirements are met:

(1) The cable tray sections and fittings shall be identified for grounding purposes.

(2) The minimum cross-sectional area of cable trays shall conform to the requirements in Table 318-7(b)(2).

(3) All cable tray sections and fittings shall be legibly and durably marked to show the cross-sectional area of metal in channel-type cable trays or cable trays of one-piece construction, and the total cross-sectional area of both side rails for ladder or trough-type cable trays.

(4) Cable tray sections, fittings, and connected raceways shall be bonded in accordance with Section 250-75 using bolted mechanical connectors or bonding jumpers sized and installed in accordance with Section 250-79.

Table 318-7(b)(2)
Metal Area Requirements for Cable Trays Used as Equipment Grounding Conductors

Maximum Fuse Ampere Rating, Circuit Breaker Ampere Trip Setting, or Circuit Breaker Protective Relay Ampere Trip Setting for Ground-Fault Protection of any Cable Circuit in the Cable Tray System	Minimum Cross-Sectional Area of Metal* in Square Inches	
	Steel Cable Trays	Aluminum Cable Trays
60	0.20	0.20
100	0.40	0.20
200	0.70	0.20
400	1.00	0.40
600	1.50**	0.40
1000	—	0.60
1200	—	1.00
1600	—	1.50
2000	—	2.00**

For SI units: one square inch = 645 square millimeters.

*Total cross-sectional area of both side rails for ladder or trough-type cable trays; or the minimum cross-sectional area of metal in channel-type cable trays or cable trays of one-piece construction.

**Steel cable trays shall not be used as equipment grounding conductors for circuits with ground-fault protection above 600 amperes. Aluminum cable trays shall not be used as equipment grounding conductors for circuits with ground-fault protection above 2000 amperes.

318-8. Cable Installation.

(a) Cable Splices. Cable splices made and insulated by approved methods shall be permitted to be located within a cable tray provided they are accessible and do not project above the side rails.

(b) Fastened Securely. In other than horizontal runs, the cables shall be fastened securely to transverse members of the cable trays.

(c) Bushed Conduit. A box shall not be required where cables or conductors are installed in bushed conduit used for support or for protection against physical damage.

(d) Connected in Parallel. Where single conductor cables comprising each phase or neutral of a circuit are connected in parallel as permitted in Section 310-4, the conductors shall be installed in groups consisting of not more than one conductor per phase or neutral, to prevent current unbalance in the paralleled conductors due to inductive reactance.

Single conductors shall be securely bound in circuit groups to prevent excessive movement due to fault-current magnetic forces.

Exception: Where single conductors are cabled together, such as triplexed assemblies.

318-9. Number of Multiconductor Cables, Rated 2000 Volts, Nominal, or Less, in Cable Trays. The number of multiconductor cables, rated 2000 volts, nominal, or less, permitted in a single cable tray shall not exceed the requirements of this section. The conductor sizes herein apply to both aluminum and copper conductors.

(a) Any Mixture of Cables. Where ladder or ventilated trough cable trays contain multiconductor power or lighting cables, or any mixture of multiconductor power, lighting, control, and signal cables, the maximum number of cables shall conform to the following:

(1) Where all of the cables are 4/0 AWG or larger, the sum of the diameters of all cables shall not exceed the cable tray width, and the cables shall be installed in a single layer.

(2) Where all of the cables are smaller than 4/0 AWG, the sum of the cross-sectional areas of all cables shall not exceed the maximum allowable cable fill area in Column 1 of Table 318-9, for the appropriate cable tray width.

(3) Where 4/0 AWG or larger cables are installed in the same cable tray with cables smaller than 4/0 AWG, the sum of the cross-sectional areas of all cables smaller than 4/0 AWG shall not exceed the maximum allowable fill area resulting from the computation in Column 2 of Table 318-9, for the appropriate cable tray width. The 4/0 AWG and larger cables shall be installed in a single layer and no other cables shall be placed on them.

(b) Multiconductor Control and/or Signal Cables Only. Where a ladder or ventilated trough cable tray, having a usable inside depth of 6 inches (152 mm) or less, contains multiconductor control and/or signal cables only, the sum of the cross-sectional areas of all cables at any cross section shall not exceed 50 percent of the interior cross-sectional area of the cable tray. A depth of 6 inches (152 mm) shall be used to compute the allowable interior cross-sectional area of any cable tray which has a usable inside depth of more than 6 inches (152 mm).

(c) Solid Bottom Cable Trays Containing Any Mixture. Where solid bottom cable trays contain multiconductor power or lighting cables, or any mixture of multiconductor power, lighting, control, and signal cables, the maximum number of cables shall conform to the following:

(1) Where all of the cables are 4/0 AWG or larger, the sum of the diameters of all cables shall not exceed 90 percent of the cable tray width, and the cables shall be installed in a single layer.

(2) Where all of the cables are smaller than 4/0 AWG, the sum of the cross-sectional areas of all cables shall not exceed the maximum allowable cable fill area in Column 3 of Table 318-9, for the appropriate cable tray width.

(3) Where 4/0 AWG or larger cables are installed in the same cable tray with cables smaller than 4/0 AWG, the sum of the cross-sectional areas of all cables smaller than 4/0 AWG shall not exceed the maximum allowable fill area resulting from the computation in Column 4 of Table 318-9, for the appropriate cable tray width. The 4/0 AWG and larger cables shall be installed in a single layer and no other cables shall be placed on them.

(d) Solid Bottom Cable Tray Multiconductor Control and/or Signal Cables Only. Where a solid bottom cable tray, having a usable inside depth of 6 inches (152 mm) or less, contains multiconductor control and/or signal cables only, the sum of the cross-sectional areas of all cables at any cross section shall not exceed 40 percent of the interior cross-sectional area of the cable tray. A depth of 6 inches (152 mm) shall be used to compute the allowable interior cross-sectional area of any cable tray which has a usable inside depth of more than 6 inches (152 mm).

Table 318-9. Allowable Cable Fill Area for Multiconductor Cables in Ladder, Ventilated Trough, or Solid Bottom Cable Trays for Cables Rated 2000 Volts or Less

	Maximum Allowable Fill Area in Square Inches for Multiconductor Cables			
	Ladder or Ventilated Trough Cable Trays, Section 318-9(a)		Solid Bottom Cable Trays, Section 318-9(c)	
Inside Width of Cable Tray (Inches)	Column 1 Applicable for Section 318-9(a) (2) Only (Square Inches)	Column 2* Applicable for Section 318-9(a) (3) Only (Square Inches)	Column 3 Applicable for Section 318-9(c) (2) Only (Square Inches)	Column 4* Applicable for Section 318-9(c) (3) Only (Square Inches)
6	7	7–(1.2 Sd)**	5.5	5.5–Sd**
12	14	14–(1.2 Sd)	11.0	11.0–Sd
18	21	21–(1.2 Sd)	16.5	16.5–Sd
24	28	28–(1.2 Sd)	22.0	22.0–Sd
30	35	35–(1.2 Sd)	27.5	27.5–Sd
36	42	42–(1.2 Sd)	33.0	33.0–Sd

For SI units: one square inch = 645 square millimeters.
*The maximum allowable fill areas in Columns 2 and 4 shall be computed. For example, the maximum allowable fill, in square inches, for a 6-inch (152-mm) wide cable tray in Column 2 shall be: 7 minus (1.2 multiplied by Sd).
**The term Sd in Columns 2 and 4 is equal to the sum of the diameters, in inches, of all 4/0 AWG and larger multiconductor cables in the same cable tray with smaller cables.

(e) Ventilated Channel Cable Trays. Where ventilated channel cable trays contain multiconductor cables of any type, the combined cross-sectional area of all cables shall not exceed 1.3 square inches (839 sq mm) in 3-inch (76-mm) wide channel trays, 2.5 square inches (1613 sq mm) in 4-inch (102-mm) wide channel trays, or 3.8 square inches (2452 sq mm) in 6-inch (152-mm) wide channel trays.

Exception: Where only one multiconductor cable is installed in a ventilated channel tray the cross-sectional area of the cable shall not exceed 2.3 square inches (1484 sq mm) in a 3-inch (76-mm) wide channel tray, 4.5 square inches (2903 sq mm) in a 4-inch (102-mm) wide channel tray, or 7.0 square inches (4516 sq mm) in a 6-inch (152-mm) wide channel tray.

Cable trays may be ladder or ventilated trough, solid bottom, ventilated channel type, unventilated, covered, etc., and of various widths and depths. Therefore, inspectors or contractors are not expected to compute the various combinations of cable tray fill in the field. Installation handbooks for cable tray applications are available from various manufacturers.

318-10. Number of Single Conductor Cables, Rated 2000 Volts or Less, in Cable Trays. The number of single conductor cables, nominally rated 2000 volts or less, permitted in a single cable tray section shall not exceed the requirements of this section. The single conductors, or conductor assemblies, shall be evenly distributed across the cable tray. The conductor sizes herein apply to both aluminum and copper conductors.

(a) Ladder or Ventilated Trough Cable Trays. Where ladder or ventilated trough cable trays contain single conductor cables, the maximum number of single conductors shall conform to the following:

(1) Where all of the cables are 1000 MCM or larger, the sum of the diameters of all single conductor cables shall not exceed the cable tray width.

Table 318-10. Allowable Cable Fill Area for Single Conductor Cables in Ladder or Ventilated Trough Cable Trays for Cables Rated 2000 Volts or Less

Inside Width of Cable Tray (Inches)	Maximum Allowable Fill Area in Square Inches for Single Conductor Cables in Ladder or Ventilated Trough Cable Trays	
	Column 1 Applicable for Section 318-10(a) (2) Only (Square Inches)	Column 2* Applicable for Section 318-10(a) (3) Only (Square Inches)
6	6.50	6.50—(1.1 Sd)**
12	13.0	13.0 —(1.1 Sd)
18	19.5	19.5 —(1.1 Sd)
24	26.0	26.0 —(1.1 Sd)
30	32.5	32.5 —(1.1 Sd)
36	39.0	39.0 —(1.1 Sd)

For SI units: one square inch = 645 square millimeters.
*The maximum allowable fill areas in Column 2 shall be computed. For example, the maximum allowable fill, in square inches, for a 6-inch (152-mm) wide cable tray shall be: 6.5 minus (1.1 multiplied by Sd).
**The term Sd in Column 2 is equal to the sum of the diameters, in inches, of all 1000 MCM and larger single conductor cables in the same ladder or ventilated trough cable tray with smaller cables.

(2) Where all of the cables are smaller than 1000 MCM, the sum of the cross-sectional areas of all single conductor cables shall not exceed the maximum allowable cable fill area in Column 1 of Table 318-10, for the appropriate cable tray width.

(3) Where 1000 MCM or larger single conductor cables are installed in the same cable tray with single conductor cables smaller than 1000 MCM, the sum of the cross-sectional areas of all cables smaller than 1000 MCM shall not exceed the maximum allowable fill area resulting from the computation in Column 2 of Table 318-10, for the appropriate cable tray width.

(b) Ventilated Channel-type Cable Trays.   Where 4-inch (102-mm) or 6-inch (152-mm) wide ventilated channel-type cable trays contain single conductor cables, the sum of the diameters of all single conductors shall not exceed the inside width of the channel.

318-11. Ampacity of Cables Rated 2000 Volts or Less in Cable Trays.   The derating factors of Note 8 (a) to Tables 310-16 through 310-31 do not apply to the ampacity of cables in cable trays.

(a) Multiconductor Cables.   The ampacity of multiconductor cables, nominally rated 2000 volts or less, installed according to the requirements of Section 318-9 shall comply with the allowable ampacities of Tables 310-18 and 310-22.

Exception No. 1: Where cable trays are continuously covered for more than 6 feet (1.83 m) with solid unventilated covers, not over 95 percent of the allowable ampacities of Tables 310-22 and 310-31 shall be permitted for multiconductor cables.

Exception No. 2: Where multiconductor cables are installed in a single layer in uncovered trays, with a maintained spacing of not less than one cable diameter between cables, the ampacity shall not exceed the allowable ambient temperature corrected ampacities of Table 310-31.

(b) Single Conductor Cables.   The ampacity of single conductor cables, or single conductors cabled together (triplexed, quadruplexed, etc.), nominally rated 2000 volts or less, shall comply with the following:

(1) Where installed according to the requirements of Section 318-10, the ampacities for 600 MCM and larger single conductor cables in uncovered cable trays shall not exceed 75 percent of the allowable ampacities in Tables 310-17 and 310-19. Where cable trays are continuously covered for more than 6 feet (1.83 m) with solid unventilated covers, the ampacities for 600 MCM and larger cables shall not exceed 70 percent of the allowable ampacities in Tables 310-17 and 310-19.

(2) Where installed according to the requirements of Section 318-10, the ampacities for 250 MCM through 500 MCM single conductor cables in uncovered cable trays shall not exceed 65 percent of the allowable ampacities in Tables 310-17 and 310-19. Where cable trays are continuously covered for more than 6 feet (1.83 m) with solid unventilated covers, the ampacities for 250 MCM through 500 MCM cables shall not exceed 60 percent of the allowable ampacities in Tables 310-17 and 310-19.

(3) Where single conductors are installed in a single layer in uncovered cable trays, with a maintained space of not less than one cable diameter between individual conductors, the ampacity of 250 MCM and larger cables shall not exceed the allowable ampacities in Tables 310-17 and 310-19.

(4) Where single conductors are installed in a triangular configuration in uncovered cable trays, with a maintained space of not less than 2.15 times one conductor diameter (2.15 × O.D.) between circuits, the ampacity of 250 MCM and larger cables shall not exceed the allowable ampacities in Table 310-23.

This section recognizes the use of single conductors in a triangular configuration installed in a cable tray with maintained spacing as having the same ampacity as three single insulated conductors on a messenger. The maintained spacing allows air to circulate around the cable.

318-12. Number of Type MV and Type MC Cables (2001 Volts or Over) in Cable Trays. The number of cables, nominally rated 2001 volts or over, permitted in a single cable tray shall not exceed the requirements of this section.
The sum of the diameters of single conductor and multiconductor cables shall not exceed the cable tray width, and the cables shall be installed in a single layer. Where single conductor cables are triplexed, quadruplexed, or bound together in circuit groups, the sum of the diameters of the single conductors shall not exceed the cable tray width, and these groups shall be installed in single layer arrangement.

318-13. Ampacity of Type MV and Type MC Cables (2001 Volts or Over) in Cable Trays. The ampacity of cables, rated 2001 volts, nominal, or over, installed according to Section 318-12 shall not exceed the requirements of this section.

(a) Multiconductor Cables (2001 Volts or Over). The ampacity of multiconductor cables shall comply with the allowable ampacities of Tables 310-75 and 310-76.

Exception No. 1: Where cable trays are continuously covered for more than 6 feet (1.83 m) with solid unventilated covers, not more than 95 percent of the allowable ampacities of Tables 310-75 and 310-76 shall be permitted for multiconductor cables.

Exception No. 2: Where multiconductor cables are installed in a single layer in uncovered cable trays, with a maintained spacing of not less than one cable diameter between cables, the ampacity shall not exceed the allowable ampacities of Tables 310-71 and 310-72.

(b) Single Conductor Cables (2001 Volts or Over). The ampacity of single conductor cables, or single conductors cabled together (triplexed, quadruplexed, etc.), shall comply with the following:

(1) The ampacities for 250 MCM and larger single conductor cables in uncovered cable trays shall not exceed 75 percent of the allowable ampacities in Tables 310-69 and 310-70. Where the cable trays are covered for more than 6 feet (1.83 m) with solid unventilated covers, the ampacities for 250 MCM and larger single conductor cables shall not exceed 70 percent of the allowable ampacities in Tables 310-69 and 310-70.

(2) Where single conductor cables are installed in a single layer in uncovered cable trays, with a maintained space of not less than one cable diameter between individual conductors, the ampacity of 250 MCM and larger cables shall not exceed the allowable ampacities in Tables 310-69 and 310-70.

(3) Where single conductors are installed in a triangular configuration in uncovered cable trays, with a maintained space of not less than 2.15 times one conductor diameter (2.15 × O.D.) between circuits, the ampacity of 250 MCM and larger cables shall not exceed 105 percent of the allowable ampacities in Tables 310-71 and 310-72.

This section recognizes the use of single conductors in a triangular configuration installed in a cable tray with maintained spacing, which is a common industrial practice.

The increased ampacity over the values in Tables 310-71 and 310-72 was calculated using IEEE S-135/ICEA P. 46-426. The maintained spacing allows free air to circulate around the cables.

ARTICLE 320 — OPEN WIRING ON INSULATORS

Contents

320-1. Definition. Open wiring on insulators is an exposed wiring method using cleats, knobs, tubes, and flexible tubing for the protection and support of single insulated conductors run in or on buildings, and not concealed by the building structure.

"Open wiring on insulators" is an exposed wiring method and is not permitted to be concealed by the structure or finish of the building. It is permitted indoors or outdoors, in dry or wet locations, and where subject to corrosive vapors. Open wiring may be any of the general-use conductors listed in Table 310-13, such as Types RH, TW, and XHHW; the selection, of course, is dependent upon whether the location is wet or dry, temperature considerations, ampacities, etc.

This method of wiring may be used for temporary lighting and power circuits on construction sites, lighting and power circuits in agricultural buildings, and services, and is commonly used for feeders in industrial locations. See Sections 230-43, 305-4, and 547-4.

320-2. Other Articles.   Open wiring on insulators shall comply with this article and also with the applicable provisions of other articles in this Code, especially Articles 225 and 300.

320-3. Uses Permitted.   Open wiring on insulators shall be permitted on systems of 600 volts, nominal, or less, only for industrial or agricultural establishments, indoors or outdoors, in wet or dry locations, where subject to corrosive vapors, and for services.

320-5. Conductors.

(a) Type.   Conductors shall be of a type specified by Article 310.

(b) Ampacity.   The ampacity shall comply with Section 310-15.

See Tables 310-17 and 310-19.

320-6. Conductor Supports.   Conductors shall be rigidly supported on noncombustible, nonabsorbent insulating materials and shall not contact any other objects. Supports shall be installed as follows: (1) within 6 inches (152 mm) from a tap or splice; (2) within 12 inches (305 mm) of a dead-end connection to a rosette, lampholder, or receptacle; (3) at intervals not exceeding 4½ feet (1.37 m) and at closer intervals sufficient to provide adequate support where likely to be disturbed.

Exception No. 1: Supports for conductors No. 8 or larger installed across open spaces shall be permitted up to 15 feet (4.57 m) apart if noncombustible, nonabsorbent insulating spacers are used at least every 4½ feet (1.37 m) to maintain at least 2½ inches (64 mm) between conductors.

Exception No. 2: Where not likely to be disturbed in buildings of mill construction, No. 8 and larger conductors shall be permitted to be run across open spaces if supported from each wood cross member on approved insulators maintaining 6 inches (152 mm) between conductors.

Mill construction is generally considered to be a building where the floors and ceilings are supported on wood beams or wood cross members spaced approximately 15 ft apart. No. 8 and larger conductors may safely span this distance, where the ceilings are high and the conductors are unlikely to contact other objects and are free from obstructions.

Exception No. 3: In industrial establishments only, where conditions of maintenance and supervision assure that only qualified persons will service the system, conductors of size 250 MCM and larger shall be permitted to be run across open spaces where supported on intervals up to 30 feet (9.1 m) apart.

It is common practice in industrial buildings to install open feeders on insulators, which are mounted on the bottom of roof trusses, at every bay location. Many bays are more than 15 ft wide. Therefore, Exception No. 3 permits size 250 MCM and larger conductors to be supported at 30-ft intervals, where it is assured that qualified persons will service the system.

In addition to the ease and economy of installations or alterations of open wiring, it is to be noted that by close spacing of conductors the reactance of a circuit is reduced; hence, the voltage drop is reduced.

ARTICLE 320—OPEN WIRING ON INSULATORS

320-7. Mounting of Conductor Supports. Where nails are used to mount knobs, they shall not be smaller than 10 penny. Where screws are used to mount knobs, or where nails or screws are used to mount cleats, they shall be of a length sufficient to penetrate the wood to a depth equal to at least one-half the height of the knob and fully the thickness of the cleat. Cushion washers shall be used with nails.

320-8. Tie Wires. No. 8 or larger conductors supported on solid knobs shall be securely tied thereto by tie wires having an insulation equivalent to that of the conductor.

320-10. Flexible Nonmetallic Tubing. In dry locations where not exposed to severe physical damage, conductors shall be permitted to be separately enclosed in flexible nonmetallic tubing. The tubing shall be in continuous lengths not exceeding 15 feet (4.57 m) and secured to the surface by straps at intervals not exceeding 4½ feet (1.37 m).

320-11. Through Walls, Floors, Wood Cross Members, etc. Open conductors shall be separated from contact with walls, floors, wood cross members, or partitions through which they pass by tubes or bushings of noncombustible, nonabsorbent insulating material. Where the bushing is shorter than the hole, a waterproof sleeve of noninductive material shall be inserted in the hole and an insulating bushing slipped into the sleeve at each end in such a manner as to keep the conductors absolutely out of contact with the sleeve. Each conductor shall be carried through a separate tube or sleeve.

(FPN): See Section 310-10 for temperature limitation of conductors.

320-12. Clearance from Piping, Exposed Conductors, etc. Open conductors shall be separated at least 2 inches (50.8 mm) from metal raceways, piping, or other conducting material, and from any exposed lighting, power, or signaling conductor, or shall be separated therefrom by a continuous and firmly fixed nonconductor in addition to the insulation of the conductor. Where any insulating tube is used, it shall be secured at the ends. Where practicable, conductors shall pass over rather than under any piping subject to leakage or accumulations of moisture.

The provision for additional protective insulation on open wiring is to prevent contact with metal piping, metal objects, or exposed conductors of other circuits.

320-13. Entering Spaces Subject to Dampness, Wetness, or Corrosive Vapors. Conductors entering or leaving locations subject to dampness, wetness, or corrosive vapors shall have drip loops formed on them and shall then pass upward and inward from the outside of the buildings, or from the damp, wet, or corrosive location, through noncombustible, nonabsorbent insulating tubes.

(FPN): See also Section 230-52.

320-14. Protection from Physical Damage. Conductors within 7 feet (2.13 m) from the floor shall be considered exposed to physical damage. Where open conductors cross ceiling joists and wall studs and are exposed to physical damage, they shall be protected by one of the following methods: (1) by guard strips not less than ⅞ inch (22 mm) in thickness and at least as high as the insulating supports, placed on each side of and close to the wiring; (2) by a substantial running board at least ½ inch (12.7 mm) thick back of the conductors with side protections. Running boards shall extend at least 1 inch (25.4 mm) outside the conductors, but not more than 2 inches (50.8 mm), and the protecting sides shall be at least 2 inches (50.8 mm) high and at least ⅞ inch (22 mm) thick; (3) by boxing made as above and furnished with a cover kept at least 1 inch (25.4 mm) away from the conductors within. Where protecting vertical conductors on side walls, the boxing shall be closed at the top and the holes through which the conductors pass shall be bushed; (4) by rigid metal conduit, intermediate metal conduit, rigid nonmetallic conduit, or electrical metallic tubing, in which case the rules of Article 345, 346, 347, or 348 shall apply; or by metal piping, in which case the conductors shall be encased in continuous lengths of approved flexible tubing. The conductors passing through metal enclosures shall be so grouped that current in both directions is approximately equal.

320-15. Unfinished Attics and Roof Spaces.   Conductors in unfinished attics and roof spaces shall comply with (a) or (b) below.

(a) Accessible by Stairway or Permanent Ladder.   Conductors shall be installed along the side of or through bored holes in floor joists, studs, or rafters. Where run through bored holes, conductors in the joists and in studs or rafters to a height of not less than 7 feet (2.13 m) above the floor or floor joists shall be protected by substantial running boards extending not less than 1 inch (25.4 mm) on each side of the conductors. Running boards shall be securely fastened in place. Running boards and guard strips shall not be required for conductors installed along the sides of joists, studs, or rafters.

(b) Not Accessible by Stairway or Permanent Ladder.   Conductors shall be installed along the sides of or through bored holes in floor joists, studs, or rafters.

Exception: In buildings completed before wiring is installed and having head room at all points of less than 3 feet (914 mm).

320-16. Switches.   Surface-type snap switches shall be mounted in accordance with Section 380-10(a), and boxes shall not be required. Other type switches shall be installed in accordance with Section 380-4.

ARTICLE 321 — MESSENGER SUPPORTED WIRING

Contents

321-1. Definition.   Messenger supported wiring is an exposed wiring support system using a messenger wire to support insulated conductors by any one of the following: (1) a messenger with rings and saddles for conductor support; (2) a messenger with a field-installed lashing material for conductor support; (3) factory-assembled aerial cable; (4) multiplex cables utilizing a bare conductor, factory assembled and twisted with one or more insulated conductors, such as duplex, triplex, or quadruplex type of construction.

Messenger supported wiring systems have been manufactured and have been used successfully for many years in industrial installations. They have also been used for many years as service drops by utilities for commercial and residential installations.

See reference to messenger supported wiring in Section 225-6(b), Exception.

321-2. Other Articles.   Messenger supported wiring shall comply with this article and also with the applicable provisions of other articles in this Code, especially Articles 225 and 300.

321-3. Uses Permitted.

(a) Cable Types.   The following shall be permitted to be installed in messenger supported wiring under the conditions described in the article for each: (1) mineral-insulated, metal-sheathed cable (Article 330); (2) metal-clad cable (Article 334); (3) multiconductor service-entrance cable (Article 338); (4) multiconductor underground feeder and branch-circuit cable (Article 339); (5) power and control tray cable (Article 340); (6) power-limited tray cable (Section 725-40); (7) other factory-assembled, multiconductor control, signal, or power cables which are identified for the use.

(b) In Industrial Establishments. In industrial establishments only, where conditions of maintenance and supervision assure that only competent individuals will service the installed messenger supported wiring, the following shall be permitted:

(1) Any of the conductor types given in Table 310-13 or Table 310-62.

Some of the triplex and quadruplex used by utilities as service-drop cable does not utilize conductors of the type covered in Table 310-13 and does not meet the requirements of Article 310. Such triplex and quadruplex would, therefore, not be acceptable in accordance with this section.

(2) MV Cable.

Where exposed to weather, conductors shall be listed for use in wet locations. Where exposed to direct rays of the sun, conductors or cables shall be sunlight-resistant.

(c) Hazardous (Classified) Locations. Messenger supported wiring shall be permitted to be used in hazardous (classified) locations where the contained cables are permitted for such use in Sections 501-4, 502-4, and 503-3.

321-4. Uses Not Permitted. Messenger supported wiring shall not be used in hoistways or where subject to severe physical damage.

321-5. Ampacity. The ampacity shall be determined by Section 310-15.

See Tables 310-23 and 310-31.

321-6. Messenger Support. The messenger shall be supported at dead ends and at intermediate locations so as to eliminate tension on the conductors. The conductors shall not be permitted to come into contact with the messenger supports or any structural members, walls, or pipes.

321-7. Grounding. The messenger shall be grounded as required by Sections 250-32 and 250-33 for enclosure grounding.

321-8. Conductor Splices and Taps. Conductor splices and taps made and insulated by approved methods shall be permitted in messenger supported wiring.

ARTICLE 324 — CONCEALED
KNOB-AND-TUBE WIRING

Contents

324-1. Definition. Concealed knob-and-tube wiring is a wiring method using knobs, tubes, and flexible nonmetallic tubing for the protection and support of single insulated conductors concealed in hollow spaces of walls and ceilings of buildings.

Open wiring on insulators (Article 320) is an "exposed" wiring method, whereas knob-and-tube wiring is a "concealed" method. Conductors used for knob-and-tube work may be of any general-use type specified by Article 310.

324-2. Other Articles. Concealed knob-and-tube wiring shall comply with this article and also with the applicable provisions of other articles in this Code, especially Article 300.

324-3. Uses Permitted. Concealed knob-and-tube wiring shall be permitted to be used only for extensions of existing installations and elsewhere only by special permission under the following conditions:

(1) In the hollow spaces of walls and ceilings.

(2) In unfinished attic and roof spaces as provided in Section 324-11.

Knob-and-tube wiring is permitted to be installed for extensions of existing installations where special permission is granted by the authority having jurisdiction of enforcement of the *Code*. See definition of "special permission" in Article 100.

324-4. Uses Not Permitted. Concealed knob-and-tube wiring shall not be used in commercial garages, theaters and similar locations, motion picture studios, hazardous (classified) locations or in the hollow spaces of walls, ceilings and attics when such spaces are insulated by loose or rolled insulating material.

Concealed knob-and-tube wiring is designed for use in hollow spaces of walls, ceilings, and attics, and utilizes the free air in such spaces for heat dissipation. Weatherization of hollow spaces by blown-in insulation or rolled insulation prevents the dissipation of heat into the free air space. This will result in higher conductor temperature which could cause insulation breakdown and possible ignition of the insulation.

324-5. Conductors.

(a) Type. Conductors shall be of a type specified by Article 310.

(b) Ampacity. The ampacity shall be determined by Section 310-15.

See Tables 310-17 and 310-19.

324-6. Conductor Supports. Conductors shall be rigidly supported on noncombustible, nonabsorbent insulating materials and shall not contact any other objects. Supports shall be installed as follows: (1) within 6 inches (152 mm) of each side of each tap or splice, and (2) at intervals not exceeding 4½ feet (1.37 m).

Exception: If it is not practicable to provide supports in dry locations it shall be permissible to fish conductors through hollow spaces if each conductor is individually enclosed in flexible nonmetallic tubing. The tubing shall be in continuous lengths between supports, between boxes, or between a support and a box.

324-7. Tie Wires. Where solid knobs are used, conductors shall be securely tied thereto by tie wires having insulation equivalent to that of the conductor.

324-8. Conductor Clearances. A clearance of not less than 3 inches (76 mm) shall be maintained between conductors and of not less than 1 inch (25.4 mm) between the conductor and the surface over which it passes.

Exception: Where space is too limited to provide the above minimum clearances, such as at meters, panelboards, outlets, and switch points, the conductors shall be individually enclosed in flexible nonmetallic tubing, which shall be in continuous lengths between the last support or box and the terminal point.

324-9. Through Walls, Floors, Wood Cross Members, etc. Conductors shall comply with Section 320-11 where passing through holes in structural members. Where passing through wood cross members in plastered partitions, conductors shall be protected by noncombustible, nonabsorbent, insulating tubes extending not less than 3 inches (76 mm) beyond the wood member.

The provision for insulated tubes for use with knob-and-tube wiring where passing through wood cross members in plastered partitions is to protect the wire from contact with plaster which is likely to accumulate on horizontal wood members.

324-10. Clearance from Piping, Exposed Conductors, etc. Conductors shall comply with Section 320-12 for clearances from other exposed conductors, piping, etc.

324-11. Unfinished Attics and Roof Spaces. Conductors in unfinished attics and roof spaces shall comply with (a) or (b) below.

(FPN): See Section 310-10 for temperature limitation of conductors.

(a) Accessible by Stairway or Permanent Ladder. Conductors shall be installed along the side of or through bored holes in floor joists, studs, or rafters. Where run through bored holes, conductors in the joists and in studs or rafters to a height of not less than 7 feet (2.13 m) above the floor or floor joists shall be protected by substantial running boards extending not less than 1 inch (25.4 mm) on each side of the conductors. Running boards shall be securely fastened in place. Running boards and guard strips shall not be required where conductors are installed along the sides of joists, studs, or rafters.

(b) Not Accessible by Stairway or Permanent Ladder. Conductors shall be installed along the sides of or through bored holes in floor joists, studs, or rafters.

Exception: In buildings completed before wiring is installed and having head room at all points of less than 3 feet (914 mm).

Figure 324-1 illustrates the "running board" method of protecting open-type conductors in an accessible attic. This method is applied in attics that are accessible by stairways or permanent ladders and where such spaces are generally used for storage.

Figure 324-1. Open wiring in accessible attic. Wires run through rafters and through joists where there is no floor.

324-12. Splices.   Splices shall be soldered unless approved splicing devices are used. In-line or strain splices shall not be used.

324-13. Boxes.   Outlet boxes shall comply with Article 370.

324-14. Switches.   Switches shall comply with Sections 380-4 and 380-10(b).

ARTICLE 325 — INTEGRATED GAS SPACER CABLE

Type IGS

Contents

A. General

325-1. Definition.   Type IGS cable is a factory assembly of one or more conductors, each individually insulated and enclosed in a loose fit nonmetallic flexible conduit as an integrated gas spacer cable rated 0-600 volts.

Type IGS conductors consist of solid aluminum rods, 250 MCM minimum. These conductors are insulated with dry Kraft paper and are factory-installed in a medium-density polyethylene gas pipe, 2 in. minimum trade size, which is then filled with sulfur hexafluoride gas at a pressure of approximately 20 psi. See Figure 325-1.

ARTICLE 325—INTEGRATED GAS SPACER CABLE

Figure 325-1. Cross section of single-conductor, 4,750 MCM, Type IGS cable.

325-2. Other Articles. The Type IGS cable shall comply with this article and also with the applicable provisions of other articles in this Code.

325-3. Uses Permitted. The Type IGS cable shall be permitted for use underground, including direct burial in the earth, as service-entrance conductors, or as feeder or branch-circuit conductors.

325-4. Uses Not Permitted. The Type IGS cable shall not be used as interior wiring or exposed in contact with buildings.

B. Installation

325-11. Bending Radius. Where the coilable nonmetallic conduit and cable is bent for installation purposes or is flexed or bent during shipment or installation, the radii of bends measured to the inside of the bend shall not be less than specified in Table 325-11.

Table 325-11. Minimum Radii of Bends

Conduit Trade Size	Minimum Radii
2 Inch	24 Inches (610 mm)
3 Inch	35 Inches (889 mm)
4 Inch	45 Inches (1.14 m)

325-12. Bends. A run of Type IGS cable between pull boxes or terminations shall not contain more than the equivalent of four quarter bends (360 degrees, total), including those bends located immediately at the pull box or terminations.

325-13. Fittings. Terminations and splices for the Type IGS cable shall be identified as a type which is suitable for maintaining the gas pressure within the conduit. A valve and cap shall be provided for each length of the cable and conduit to check the gas pressure or to inject gas into the conduit.

325-14. Ampacity. The ampacity of the Type IGS cable and conduit shall not exceed values shown in Table 325-14 for single conductor or multiconductor cable.

C. Construction Specifications

325-20. Conductors. The conductors shall be solid aluminum rods, laid parallel, consisting of one to nineteen ½-inch (12.7-mm) diameter rods.

The minimum conductor size shall be 250 MCM and the maximum size shall be 4750 MCM.

Table 325-14. Ampacity Type IGS

Size MCM	Amperes
250	119
500	168
750	206
1000	238
1250	266
1500	292
1750	315
2000	336
2250	357
2500	376
3000	412
3250	429
3500	445
3750	461
4000	476
4250	491
4500	505
4750	519

325-21. Insulation. The insulation shall be dry kraft paper tapes and a pressurized sulfur hexafluoride gas (SF^6), both approved for electrical use. The nominal gas pressure shall be 20 pounds per square inch gage (psig) (138 kPa gage).

The thickness of the paper spacer shall be as specified in Table 325-21.

Table 325-21. Paper Spacer Thickness

Size MCM	Thickness Inches (mm)
250–1000	.040 (1.02)
1250–4750	.060 (1.52)

325-22. Conduit. The conduit shall be an approved medium density polyethylene identified as suitable for use with natural gas rated pipe in 2 inches, 3 inches, 4 inches trade size. The percent fill dimensions for the conduit are given in Table 325-22.

The size of the conduit permitted for each conductor size shall be calculated for a percent fill not to exceed Table 1, Chapter 9.

Table 325-22. Conduit Dimensions

Conduit Trade Size, Inches	Outside Diameter, Inches (mm)	Inside Diameter, Inches (mm)
2	2.375 (60)	1.947 (49.46)
3	3.500 (89)	2.886 (73.30)
4	4.500 (114)	3.710 (94.23)

325-23. Grounding. The Type IGS cable shall comply with Article 250.

325-24. Marking. The provisions of Section 310-11 shall apply for the Type IGS cable.

339

ARTICLE 326 — MEDIUM VOLTAGE CABLE

Type MV

Contents

326-1. Definition. Type MV is a single or multiconductor solid dielectric insulated cable rated 2001 volts or higher.

Medium voltage cables are rated 2001 to 35,000 V. Cables rated 2001 to 8000 V may be shielded or nonshielded. All insulated conductors 8001 V and higher have electrostatic shielding.

326-2. Other Articles. In addition to the provisions of this article, Type MV cable shall comply with the applicable provisions of this Code, especially Articles 300, 305, 310, 318, 501, and 710.

326-3. Uses Permitted. Type MV cables shall be permitted for use on power systems rated up to 35,000 volts, nominal, in wet or dry locations, in raceways, cable trays as specified in Section 318-3(b), or directly buried in accordance with Section 710-3(b) and in messenger supported wiring.

326-4. Uses Not Permitted. Type MV cable shall not be used unless identified for the use (1) where exposed to direct sunlight, and (2) in cable trays.

Cables intended for installation in cable trays in accordance with Article 318 are marked "for CT Use" or "for use in cable trays."

326-5. Construction. Type MV cables shall have copper, aluminum, or copper-clad aluminum conductors and shall be constructed in accordance with Article 310.

Cables with aluminum conductors are marked with the word "aluminum" or the letters "AL."

326-6. Ampacity. The ampacity of Type MV cable shall be in accordance with Section 310-15.

Exception: The ampacity of Type MV cable installed in cable tray shall be in accordance with Section 318-13.

This exception is required to provide the correct ampacities for conductors and multiconductor cables where installed in cable tray.

326-7. Marking. Medium voltage cable shall be marked as required in Section 310-11.

Cables are marked with their conductor size, voltage rating, and insulation level (100 percent or 133 percent).

ARTICLE 328 — FLAT CONDUCTOR CABLE TYPE FCC

Contents

A. General

328-1. Scope. This article covers a field-installed wiring system for branch circuits incorporating Type FCC cable and associated accessories as defined by the article. The wiring system is designed for installation under carpet squares.

The flat conductor cable system is designed to provide a completely accessible, flexible power system. It also provides an easy method for reworking obsolete wiring systems currently in use in many office facilities. See Figure 328-1.

The carpet squares are not permitted to be larger than 36 in. by 36 in. See Section 328-10. This limitation is judged necessary to provide ready access to the cable by lifting a carpet square. It also reduces the likelihood of someone accessing the cable by cutting through the carpet over the cable with a knife or razor blade, and possibly penetrating the top shield of the cable in the process.

328-2. Definitions.

Type FCC Cable. Type FCC cable consists of three or more flat copper conductors placed edge-to-edge and separated and enclosed within an insulating assembly.

FCC System. A complete wiring system for branch circuits that is designed for installation under carpet squares. The FCC system includes Type FCC cable and associated shielding, connectors, terminators, adapters, boxes, and receptacles.

Cable Connector. A connector designed to join Type FCC cables without using a junction box.

341

Figure 328-1. Installing flat conductor cable. *(AMP Products Corp.)*

Insulating End.   An insulator designed to electrically insulate the end of a Type FCC cable.

Top Shield.   A grounded metal shield covering undercarpet components of the FCC system for the purposes of providing protection against physical damage.

Bottom Shield.   A protective layer which is installed between the floor and Type FCC flat conductor cable to protect the cable from physical damage and may or may not be incorporated as an integral part of the cable.

Transition Assembly.   An assembly to facilitate connection of the FCC system to other approved wiring systems, incorporating (1) a means of electrical interconnection, and (2) a suitable box or covering for providing electrical safety and protection against physical damage.

Metal Shield Connections.   Means of connection designed to electrically and mechanically connect a metal shield to another metal shield, to a receptacle housing or self-contained device, or to a transition assembly.

328-3. Other Articles.   The FCC systems shall conform with applicable provisions of Articles 210, 220, 240, 250 and 300.

328-4. Uses Permitted.

(a) Branch Circuits.   Use of FCC systems shall be permitted both for general-purpose and appliance branch circuits, and for individual branch circuits.

(b) Floors.   Use of FCC systems shall be permitted on hard, sound, smooth, continuous floor surfaces made of concrete, ceramic, or composition flooring, wood, and similar materials.

(c) Walls.   Use of FCC systems shall be permitted on wall surfaces in surface metal raceways.

(d) Damp Locations.   Use of FCC systems in damp locations shall be permitted.

(e) Heated Floors.   Materials used for floors heated in excess of 30°C (86°F) shall be identified as suitable for use at these temperatures.

328-5. Uses Not Permitted. FCC systems shall not be used: (1) outdoors or in wet locations; (2) where subject to corrosive vapors; (3) in any hazardous (classified) location; or (4) in residential, school, and hospital buildings.

Section 328-5(4) prohibits Type FCC wiring systems throughout school and hospital buildings, even though parts of these buildings may be office or administrative spaces.

328-6. Branch-Circuit Ratings.

(a) Voltage. Voltage between ungrounded conductors shall not exceed 300 volts. Voltage between ungrounded conductors and grounded conductor shall not exceed 150 volts.

(b) Current. General-purpose and appliance branch circuits shall have ratings not exceeding 20 amperes. Individual branch circuits shall have ratings not exceeding 30 amperes.

B. Installation

328-10. Coverings. Floor-mounted Type FCC cable, cable connectors, and insulating ends shall be covered with carpet squares no larger than 36 inches (914 mm) square. Those carpet squares that are adhered to the floor shall be attached with release-type adhesives.

328-11. Cable Connections and Insulating Ends. All Type FCC cable connections shall use connectors identified for their use, installed such that electrical continuity, insulation, and sealing against dampness and liquid spillage are provided. All bare cable ends shall be insulated and sealed against dampness and liquid spillage using listed insulating ends.

328-12. Shields.

(a) Top Shield. A metal top shield shall be installed over all floor-mounted Type FCC cable, connectors, and insulating ends. The top shield shall completely cover all cable runs, corners, connectors, and ends.

(b) Bottom Shield. A bottom shield shall be installed beneath all Type FCC cable, connectors, and insulating ends.

328-13. Enclosure and Shield Connections. All metal shields, boxes, receptacle housings, and self-contained devices shall be electrically continuous to the equipment grounding conductor of the supplying branch circuit. All such electrical connections shall be made with connectors identified for this use. The electrical resistivity of such shield system shall not be more than that of one conductor of the Type FCC cable used in the installation.

328-14. Receptacles. All receptacles, receptacle housings, and self-contained devices used with the FCC system shall be identified for this use and shall be connected to the Type FCC cable and metal shields. Connection from any grounding conductor of the Type FCC cable shall be made to the shield system at each receptacle.

328-15. Connection to Other Systems. Power feed, grounding connection, and shield system connection between the FCC system and other wiring systems shall be accomplished in a transition assembly identified for this use.

328-16. Anchoring. All FCC system components shall be firmly anchored to the floor or wall using an adhesive or mechanical anchoring system identified for this use. Floors shall be prepared to assure adherence of the FCC system to the floor until the carpet squares are placed.

328-17. Crossings. Crossings of two Type FCC cable runs shall be permitted. Crossings of a Type FCC cable over or under a flat telephone cable shall be permitted. In each case, a grounded layer of metal shielding shall separate the two cables.

328-18. System Height. Any portion of an FCC system with a height above floor level exceeding 0.090 inches (2.29 mm) shall be tapered or feathered at the edges to floor level.

328-19. FCC Systems Alterations. Alterations to FCC systems shall be permitted. New cable connectors shall be used at new connection points to make alterations. It shall be permitted to leave unused cable runs and associated cable connectors in place and energized. All cable ends shall be covered with insulating ends.

328-20. Polarization of Connections. All receptacles and connections shall be constructed and installed so as to maintain proper polarization of the system.

C. Construction

328-30. Type FCC Cable. Type FCC cable shall be approved for use with the FCC system and shall consist of three, four, or five flat copper conductors, one of which shall be an equipment grounding conductor. The insulating material of the cable shall be moisture-resistant and flame-retardant.

328-31. Markings. Type FCC cable shall be clearly and durably marked on both sides at intervals of not more than 24 inches (610 mm), with the information required by Section 310-11(a) and with the following additional information: (1) material of conductors; (2) maximum temperature rating; and (3) ampacity.

328-32. Conductor Identification.

    (a) Colors. Conductors shall be clearly and durably marked on both sides throughout their length as specified in Section 310-12.

    (b) Order. For a two-wire FCC system with grounding, the grounding conductor shall be central.

328-33. Corrosion Resistance. Metal components of the system shall be either: (1) corrosion-resistant; (2) coated with corrosion-resistant materials; or (3) insulated from contact with corrosive substances.

328-34. Insulation. All insulating materials in the FCC systems shall be identified for their use.

328-35. Shields.

    (a) Materials and Dimensions. All top and bottom shields shall be of designs and materials identified for their use. Top shields shall be metal. Both metallic and nonmetallic materials shall be permitted for bottom shields.

    (b) Resistivity. Metal shields have cross-sectional areas that provide for electrical resistivity of not more than that of one conductor of the Type FCC cable used in the installation.

    (c) Metal-Shield Connectors. Metal shields shall be connected to each other and to boxes, receptacle housings, self-contained devices, and transition assemblies using metal-shield connectors.

328-36. Receptacles and Housings. Receptacle housings and self-contained devices designed either for floor mounting or for in- or on-wall mounting shall be permitted for use with the FCC system. Receptacle housings and self-contained devices shall incorporate means for facilitating entry and termination of Type FCC cable, and for electrically connecting the housing or device with the metal shield. Receptacles and self-contained devices shall comply with Section

210-7. Power and communications outlets installed together in common housing shall be permitted in accordance with Section 800-3(a)(2), Exception No. 1.

328-37. Transition Assemblies. All transition assemblies shall be identified for their use. Each assembly shall incorporate means for facilitating entry of the Type FCC cable into the assembly, for connecting the Type FCC cable to grounded conductors, and for electrically connecting the assembly to the metal cable shields and to equipment grounding conductors.

ARTICLE 330 — MINERAL-INSULATED, METAL-SHEATHED CABLE

Type MI

Contents

A. General

330-1. Definition. Type MI mineral-insulated, metal-sheathed cable is a factory assembly of one or more conductors insulated with a highly compressed refractory mineral insulation and enclosed in a liquidtight and gastight continuous copper sheath.

330-2. Other Articles. Type MI cable shall comply with this article and also with the applicable provisions of other articles in this Code, especially Article 300.

Mineral-insulated, metal-sheathed cable consists of one or more solid copper conductors insulated with highly compressed magnesium oxide and enclosed in a continuous copper sheath. It is labeled by Underwriters Laboratories Inc. in sizes 16 AWG to 250 MCM one conductor, 16 to 4 AWG two and three conductor, 16 to 6 AWG four conductor, and 16 to 10 AWG seven conductor. The cable is rated 600 V.

Terminations especially investigated for use with this cable are listed by Underwriters Laboratories Inc. as "Mineral-Insulated Cable Fittings."

Supplementary nonmetallic coatings presently used have not been investigated by UL for resistance to corrosion.

Fittings for use on mineral-insulated cable Type MI and small-diameter mineral-insulated cable are suitable for use at a maximum operating temperature of 85°C (185°F) in dry locations and 60°C (140°F) in wet locations. A complete box connector consists of a connector body and a screw-on potting fitting.

The screw-on potting fitting to be used with the connector may be used separately as an end fitting for change to open wiring. The screw-on potting fitting is to be assembled with a special tool and consists of a screw-on pot, insulating cap, insulating sleeving, anchoring bead, and sealing compound. See Figure 330-1.

Figure 330-1. Type MI cable fitting used for terminating cable at box or equipment. (*Pyrotenaz USA, Inc.*)

330-3. Uses Permitted. Type MI cable shall be permitted as follows: (1) for services, feeders, and branch circuits; (2) in dry, wet, or continuously moist locations; (3) indoors or outdoors; (4) where exposed or concealed; (5) embedded in plaster, concrete, fill or other masonry, whether above or below grade; (6) in any hazardous (classified) location; (7) where exposed to oil and gasoline; (8) where exposed to corrosive conditions not deteriorating to its sheath; (9) in underground runs where suitably protected against physical damage and corrosive conditions.

Mineral-insulated, metal-sheathed cable (Type MI) is suitable for all power and control circuits up to 600 V and may be used for services, feeders, and branch circuits in exposed and concealed work; in dry and wet locations; for underplaster extensions and embedment in plaster; in masonry, concrete, or fill; for underground runs; or where exposed to weather, continuous moisture, oil in any hazardous (classified) location, or other conditions not having a deteriorating effect on the metal sheath.

330-4. Uses Not Permitted. Type MI cable shall not be used where exposed to destructive corrosive conditions.

Exception: Where protected by materials suitable for the conditions.

B. Installation

330-10. Wet Locations. Where installed in wet locations, Type MI cable shall comply with Section 300-6(c).

330-11. Through Joists, Studs, or Rafters. Type MI cable shall comply with Section 300-4 where installed through studs, joists, rafters, or similar wood members.

330-12. Supports. Type MI cable shall be securely supported at intervals not exceeding 6 feet (1.83 m) by straps, staples, hangers, or similar fittings so designed and installed as not to damage the cable.

Exception: Where cable is fished in.

330-13. Bends. Bends in Type MI cable shall be so made as not to damage the cable. The radius of the inner edge of any bend shall not be less than five times the cable diameter.

330-14. Fittings. Fittings used for connecting Type MI cable to boxes, cabinets, or other equipment shall be identified for such use. Where single-conductor cables enter ferrous metal boxes or cabinets, the installation shall comply with Section 300-20 to prevent inductive heating.

330-15. Terminal Seals. Where Type MI cable terminates, an approved seal shall be provided immediately after stripping to prevent the entrance of moisture into the insulation. The conductors extending beyond the sheath shall be individually provided with an approved insulating material.

C. Construction Specifications

330-20. Conductors. Type MI cable conductors shall be of solid copper with a cross-sectional area corresponding to standard AWG sizes.

330-21. Insulation. The conductor insulation in Type MI cable shall be a highly compressed refractory mineral that will provide proper spacing for the conductors.

330-22. Outer Sheath. The outer sheath shall be of a continuous copper construction to provide mechanical protection, a moisture seal, and an adequate path for grounding purposes.

ARTICLE 331 — ELECTRICAL NONMETALLIC TUBING

Contents

A. General

331-1. Definition. Electrical nonmetallic tubing is a pliable corrugated raceway of circular cross-section with integral or associated couplings, connectors and fittings listed for the installation of electric conductors. It is composed of a material that is resistant to moisture, chemical atmospheres, and is flame-retardant.

Electrical nonmetallic tubing (ENT) is made of the same material (PVC) used for rigid nonmetallic conduit suitable for aboveground use (see Article 347). Because of the corrugations, the raceway can be bent by hand, but it is not intended for use where flexibility is necessary, as at motor terminations to prevent transmission of noise and vibration. See Figure 331-1.

ENT is suitable for the installation of conductors having a temperature rating as indicated on the product. The maximum ambient is 50°C (122°F).

The outside diameters of ENT are such that standard couplings and other fittings for rigid PVC conduit can be employed if the conduit is also constructed of PVC.

A pliable raceway is a raceway which can be bent by hand with a reasonable force, but without other assistance.

331-2. Other Articles. Installations for electrical nonmetallic tubing shall comply with the

347

Figure 331-1. Electrical nonmetallic tubing is permitted in ½-, ¾-, and 1-in. trade sizes only. (*Carlon, an Indian Head Co.*)

provisions of the applicable sections of Article 300. Where equipment grounding is required by Article 250, a separate equipment grounding conductor shall be installed in the raceway.

331-3. Uses Permitted. The use of electrical nonmetallic tubing and fittings shall be permitted:

(1) Concealed within walls, floors, and ceilings where the walls, floors, and ceilings provide a thermal barrier of material which has at least a 15-minute finish rating as identified in listings of fire-rated assemblies.

Interior finish is generally considered to consist of those materials or combinations of materials that form the exposed interior surface of walls and ceilings in a building. Common interior finish materials include plaster, gypsum wallboard, wood, plywood paneling, fibrous ceiling tiles, and a variety of wall coverings. Ordinary paint, wallpaper, or other similar wall coverings not exceeding ⅛ in. (0.6 mm) in thickness are not generally considered as interior finish, except where the authority having jurisdiction deems them to be a hazard.

The finish rating of a wall finish is the time it takes the side not exposed to the fire to reach an average temperature above ambient of 121°C (250°F) (temperature rise) with a temperature rise at any one point not exceeding 163°C (325°F), when the assembly is tested in accordance with NFPA 251, *Standard Methods of Fire Tests of Building Construction and Materials* (also known as UL 263 and ANSI 2.1).

The finish rating of wall assemblies tested and rated by UL will be found in the UL *Fire Resistance Directory* immediately following the assembly rating, just below the design number. However, only assemblies containing combustible support members are given finish ratings.

For walls and finishes not tested and rated, or not given a finish rating because they include no combustible supports, see the following chart.

The fire resistance rating of an assembly or finish is the time period the finish or assembly withstood the fire test without the unexposed side exceeding an average temperature rise of 121°C (250°F) [163°C (325°F) single point]. It is, in effect, the finish rating.

The following chart reproduced from the NFPA *Fire Protection Handbook* (16th edition) provides fire-resistance ratings for common finishes over wood frame.

Material	Fire Resistance Rating* Min
Fiberboard, ½ in. thick	5
Fiberboard, flameproofed, ½ in. thick	10
Fiberboard, ½ in. thick, with ½ in. 1:2, 1:2 gypsum-sand plaster	15
Gypsum wallboard, ⅜ in. thick	10
Gypsum wallboard, ½ in. thick	15
Gypsum wallboard, ⅝ in. thick	20
Gypsum wallboards, laminated, two ⅜ in. thick	28
Gypsum wallboards, laminated, one ⅜ in. plus one ½ in. thick	37
Gypsum wallboards, laminated, two ½ in. thick	47
Gypsum wallboards, laminated, two ⅝ in. thick	60
Gypsum lath, plain or indented, ⅜ in. thick, with ½ in. 1:2, 1:2 gypsum-sand plaster	20
Gypsum lath, perforated, ⅜ in. thick, with ½ in. 1:2, 1:2 gypsum-sand plaster	30
Gypsum-sand plaster, 1:2, 1:3, ½ in. thick, on wood lath	15
Lime-sand plaster, 1:5, 1:7.5, ½ in. thick, on wood lath	15
Gypsum-sand plaster, 1:2, 1:2, ¾ in. thick, on metal lath (no paper backing)	15
Neat gypsum plaster, ¾ in. thick on metal lath (no paper backing)†	30
Neat gypsum plaster, 1 in. thick, on metal lath (no paper backing)†	35
Lime-sand plaster, 1:5, 1:7.5, ¾ in. thick, on metal lath (no paper backing)	10
Portland cement plaster, ¾ in. thick, on metal lath (no paper backing)	10
Gypsum-sand plaster, 1:2, 1:3, ¾ in. thick, on paper-backed metal lath	20

* From National Bureau of Standards, BMS-92.
† Unsanded wood-fiber plaster.
SI units: 1 in. = 25.4 mm.

(2) In locations subject to severe corrosive influences as covered in Section 300-6 and where subject to chemicals for which the materials are specifically approved.

(3) In concealed, dry, and damp locations not prohibited by Section 331-4.

(4) Above suspended ceilings where the suspended ceilings provide a thermal barrier of material which has at least a 15-minute finish rating as identified in listings of fire-rated assemblies.

(5) Embedded in poured concrete, provided fittings identified for this purpose are used for connections.

(FPN): Extreme cold may cause some types of nonmetallic conduits to become brittle and, therefore, more susceptible to damage from physical contact.

This section was revised for the 1987 *Code*. The prohibition on the use of electrical nonmetallic tubing in buildings over three floors above grade has been removed. In addition, ENT may now be used embedded in poured concrete where fittings identified for the purpose are used for connections.

331-4. Uses Not Permitted. Electrical nonmetallic tubing shall not be used:

(1) In hazardous (classified) locations.

(2) For the support of fixtures and other equipment.

(3) Where subject to ambient temperatures exceeding those for which the tubing is approved.

(4) For conductors whose insulation temperature limitations would exceed those for which the tubing is listed.

(5) For direct earth burial.

(6) Where the voltage is over 600 volts.

(7) In exposed locations except as permitted by Section 331-3(4).

B. Installation

331-5. Size.

(a) Minimum. Tubing smaller than ½-inch electrical trade size shall not be used.

(b) Maximum. Tubing larger than 1-inch electrical trade size shall not be used.

331-6. Number of Conductors in Tubing. The number of conductors in a single tubing shall not exceed that permitted by the percentage fill in Table 1, Chapter 9.

331-7. Trimming. All cut ends of tubing shall be trimmed inside and outside to remove rough edges.

331-8. Joints. All joints between lengths of tubing and between tubing and couplings, fittings and boxes shall be by an approved method.

331-9. Bends — How Made. Bends of electrical nonmetallic tubing shall be so made that the tubing will not be damaged and that the internal diameter of the tubing will not be effectively reduced. Bends shall be permitted to be made manually without auxiliary equipment and the radius of the curve of the inner edge of such bends shall not be less than shown in Table 346-10.

331-10. Bends — Number in One Run.   A run of tubing between outlet and outlet or outlet and fitting shall not contain more than the equivalent of four quarter bends (360 degrees, total) including those bends located immediately at the outlet or fitting.

331-11. Supports.   Electrical nonmetallic tubing shall be installed as a complete system as provided in Article 300 and shall be securely fastened in place. Tubing shall be firmly fastened within 3 feet (914 mm) of each outlet box, junction box, cabinet or fitting. Tubing shall be secured at least every 3 feet (914 mm).

331-12. Boxes and Fittings.   Boxes and fittings shall comply with the applicable provisions of Article 370.

331-13. Splices and Taps.   Splices and taps shall be made only in junction boxes, outlet boxes or conduit bodies. See Article 370.

331-14. Bushings.   Where a tubing enters a box or other fitting, a bushing or adapter shall be provided to protect the wire from abrasion unless the design of the box or fitting is such as to provide equivalent protection.

(FPN): See Section 373-6(c) for the protection of conductors No. 4 AWG or larger.

C. Construction Specifications

331-15. General.   Electrical nonmetallic tubing shall be clearly and durably marked at least every 10 feet (3.05 m) as required in the first sentence of Section 110-21. The type of material shall also be included in the marking.

ARTICLE 333 — ARMORED CABLE

Type AC Cable

Contents

333-1. Definition.   Type AC cable is a fabricated assembly of insulated conductors in a flexible metallic enclosure. See Section 333-4.

Armored cable is listed by Underwriters Laboratories Inc. in sizes No. 14 through No. 1 AWG copper and No. 12 through No. 1 AWG aluminum or copper-clad aluminum and is rated at 600 V or less.

ARTICLE 333—ARMORED CABLE

333-2. Other Articles. Type AC cable shall comply with this article and also with the applicable provisions of other articles in this Code, especially Article 300.

333-3. Marking. The provisions of Section 310-11 shall apply, except that Type AC cable shall have ready identification of the maker by distinctive external markers on the cable sheath throughout its entire length.

333-4. Construction. Type AC cable shall be an approved cable with acceptable metal covering. The insulated conductors shall conform with Section 333-5.

Type AC cables are branch-circuit and feeder cables with armor of flexible metal tape. Cables of the AC type, except ACL, shall have an internal bonding strip of copper or aluminum, in intimate contact with the armor for its entire length.

The armor of Type AC cable is recognized as an equipment grounding conductor by Section 250-91(b). The required internal bonding strip can be simply cut off at the termination of the armored cable, or it can be bent back on the armor. It is not necessary to connect it to an equipment grounding terminal. Its use is to supplement the effectiveness of the spiral armor as an equipment grounding means. Many installers use this strip to help prevent the insulating bushing required by Section 333-9 (the "red head") from falling out during rough wiring.

333-5. Conductors. Insulated conductors shall be of a type listed in Table 310-13 or ones which are identified for use in this cable. In addition, the conductors shall have an overall moisture-resistant and fire-retardant fibrous covering. For Type ACT, a moisture-resistant fibrous covering shall be required only on the individual conductors. The ampacity shall be determined by Section 310-15.

Exception: Armored cable installed in thermal insulation shall have conductors rated at 90°C (194°F). The ampacity of cable installed in these applications shall be that of 60°C (140°F) conductors.

UL data refers to the marking of cables as follows. ACT indicates an armored cable employing conductors having thermoplastic insulation. AC indicates an armored cable employing conductors having thermosetting insulation. No suffix indicates 60°C (140°F) rating. H indicates 75°C (167°F) rating. HH indicates 90°C (194°F) rating.

The exception recognizes the decrease in heat dissipation capability of cables installed in a space that is provided with thermal insulation.

333-6. Use.

(a) Uses Permitted. Except where otherwise specified elsewhere in this Code, and where not subject to physical damage, Type AC cable shall be permitted for branch circuits and feeders in both exposed and concealed work.

Type AC cable shall be permitted in dry locations; for underplaster extensions as provided in Article 344; and embedded in plaster finish on brick or other masonry, except in damp or wet locations. It shall be permissible to run or fish this cable in the air voids of masonry block or tile walls; where such walls are exposed or subject to excessive moisture or dampness or are below grade line, Type ACL cable shall be used. This cable shall contain lead-covered conductors (Type ACL) if used where exposed to the weather or to continuous moisture; for underground runs in raceways; where embedded in masonry, concrete, or fill in buildings in course of construction; or where exposed to oil, or other conditions having a deteriorating effect on the insulation.

(b) Uses Not Permitted. Type AC cable shall not be used where prohibited elsewhere in this Code, including (1) in theaters and similar locations, except as provided in Article 518, Places of Assembly; (2) in motion picture studios; (3) in any hazardous (classified) locations; (4) where exposed to corrosive fumes or vapors; (5) on cranes or hoists, except as provided in Section

352

610-11, Exception No. 3; (6) in storage battery rooms; (7) in hoistways or on elevators, except as provided in Section 620-21; or (8) in commercial garages where prohibited in Article 511.

Exception: See Section 501-4(b), Exception.

The exception permits Type AC cable and other wiring methods, including nonmetallic-sheathed cable, for the wiring of intrinsically safe and nonincendive circuits. See Sections 500-2, paragraph after FPN No. 1, and 501-4(b), Exception.

Type ACL cable shall not be used for direct burial in the earth.

The designation "L" indicates that a lead covering has been applied over the conductor assembly.

333-7. Supports. Type AC cable shall be secured by approved staples, straps, hangers, or similar fittings so designed and installed as not to damage the cable at intervals not exceeding 4 ½ feet (1.37 m) and within 12 inches (305 mm) from every outlet box, junction box, cabinet, or fitting.

This section requires that the cable be SECURED. Simply draping the cable over air ducts, lower members of bar joists, pipes, and ceiling grid members is not permitted except as noted in Exception No. 1, or Exception No. 3 which permits lengths up to 6 ft from certain outlets above accessible (suspended) ceilings. See also Section 300-4(c).

Exception No. 1: Where cable is fished.

Exception No. 2: Lengths of not more than 2 feet (610 mm) at terminals where flexibility is necessary.

Exception No. 3: Lengths of not more than 6 feet (1.83 m) from an outlet for connections within an accessible ceiling to lighting fixtures or equipment.

333-8. Bends. All bends shall be made so that the cable will not be damaged, and the radius of the curve of the inner edge of any bend shall not be less than five times the diameter of the Type AC cable.

333-9. Boxes and Fittings. At all points where the armor of AC cable terminates, a fitting shall be provided to protect wires from abrasion, unless the design of the outlet boxes or fittings is such as to afford equivalent protection, and, in addition, an approved insulating bushing or its equivalent approved protection shall be provided between the conductors and the armor. The connector or clamp by which the Type AC cable is fastened to boxes or cabinets shall be of such design that the insulating bushing or its equivalent will be visible for inspection. This bushing shall not be required with lead-covered cables where so installed that the lead sheath will be visible for inspection. Where change is made from Type AC cable to other cable or raceway wiring methods, a box, fitting or conduit body shall be installed at junction points as required in Section 300-15.

Armored cable connectors are considered suitable for equipment grounding.

333-10. Through Studs, Joists, and Rafters. Type AC cable shall comply with Section 300-4 where installed through studs, joists, rafters, or similar wood members.

333-11. Exposed Work. Exposed runs of cable shall closely follow the surface of the building finish or of running boards.

Exception No. 1: Lengths of not more than 24 inches (610 mm) at terminals where flexibility is necessary.

Exception No. 2: On the underside of floor joists in basements where supported at each joist and so located as not to be subject to physical damage.

This exception does not apply to Type NM or NMC cable.

333-12. In Accessible Attics. Type AC cables in accessible attics or roof spaces shall be installed as specified in (a) and (b) below.

(a) Where Run Across the Top of Floor Joists. Where run across the top of floor joists, or within 7 feet (2.13 m) of floor or floor joists across the face of rafters or studding, in attics and roof spaces which are accessible, the cable shall be protected by substantial guard strips which are at least as high as the cable. Where this space is not accessible by permanent stairs or ladders, protection shall only be required within 6 feet (1.83 m) of the nearest edge of the scuttle hole or attic entrance.

(b) Where Carried Along the Sides of Floor Joists. Where cable is carried along the sides of rafters, studs, or floor joists, neither guard strips nor running boards shall be required.

ARTICLE 334 — METAL-CLAD CABLE

Contents

334-1. Definition. Type MC cable is a factory assembly of one or more conductors, each individually insulated and enclosed in a metallic sheath of interlocking tape, or a smooth or corrugated tube.

Type MC cable is available in three designs: (1) interlocked metal tape, (2) corrugated tube, and (3) smooth tube. All are intended for aboveground use, except when marked for direct burial. Cables which are suitable for use in cable trays, directly buried, or in direct sunlight are so marked. Type MC cables include Type CS (copper sheath) and Type ALS (aluminum sheath).

334-2. Other Articles. Metal-clad cable shall comply with this article and also with the applicable provisions of other articles in this Code, especially Article 300.

Type MC cable shall be permitted for systems in excess of 600 volts, nominal. See Section 300-2(a).

Type MC cable is rated for use up to 5000 V and listed in sizes No. 18 AWG and larger for copper and No. 12 AWG and larger for aluminum or copper-clad aluminum. It employs thermoset, thermoplastic, varnished cloth, or composite varnished cloth-thermoplastic insulated conductors. The latter is designated as Type VT and rated 85°C (185°F).

334-3. Uses Permitted. Except where otherwise specified in this Code and where not subject to physical damage, Type MC cables shall be permitted as follows: (1) for services, feeders, and branch circuits; (2) for power, lighting, control, and signal circuits; (3) indoors or outdoors; (4) where exposed or concealed; (5) direct buried when identified for such use; (6) in cable tray; (7) in any approved raceway; (8) as open runs of cable; (9) as aerial cable on a messenger; (10) in hazardous (classified) locations as permitted in Articles 501, 502, and 503; (11) in dry locations; and (12) in wet locations when any of the following conditions are met:

(1) The metallic covering is impervious to moisture.

(2) A lead sheath or moisture impervious jacket is provided under the metal covering.

(3) The insulated conductors under the metallic covering are approved for use in wet locations.

Exception: See Section 501-4(b), Exception.

(FPN): See Section 300-6 for protection against corrosion.

334-4. Uses Not Permitted. Type MC cable shall not be used where exposed to destructive corrosive conditions, such as direct burial in the earth, in concrete, or where exposed to cinder fills, strong chlorides, caustic alkalis, or vapors of chlorine or of hydrochloric acids.

Exception: Where the metallic sheath is suitable for the conditions or is protected by material suitable for the conditions.

B. Installation

334-10. Installation. Type MC cable shall be installed in compliance with Articles 300, 710, and 725 as applicable.

(a) Support. Type MC cable shall be supported and secured at intervals not exceeding 6 feet (1.83 m).

(b) Cable Tray. Type MC cable installed in cable tray shall comply with Article 318.

(c) Direct Buried. Direct buried cable shall comply with Section 300-5 or 710-3, as appropriate.

(d) Installed as Service-Entrance Cable. Type MC cable installed as service-entrance cable shall comply with Article 230.

(e) Installed Outside of Buildings or as Aerial Cable. Type MC cable installed outside of buildings or as aerial cable shall comply with Article 225 and Article 321.

334-11. Bending Radius. All bends shall be so made that the cable will not be damaged, and the radius of the curve of the inner edge of any bend shall not be less than shown below.

ARTICLE 334—METAL-CLAD CABLE

(a) Smooth Sheath.

(1) Ten times the external diameter of the metallic sheath for cable not more than ¾ inch (19 mm) in external diameter;

(2) Twelve times the external diameter of the metallic sheath for cable more than ¾ inch (19 mm) but not more than 1½ inches (38 mm) in external diameter; and

(3) Fifteen times the external diameter of the metallic sheath for cable more than 1 ½ inches (38 mm) in external diameter.

(b) Interlocked-type Armor or Corrugated Sheath. Seven times the external diameter of the metallic sheath.

(c) Shielded Conductors. Twelve times the overall diameter of one of the individual conductors or seven times the overall diameter of the multiconductor cable, whichever is greater.

The minimum bending radius of twelve times the overall diameter of a single shielded conductor is consistent with ICEA (formerly IPCEA) requirements and good engineering practice; however, the same minimum on a multiconductor cable would be excessive.

For example, consider 5000 MCM, 15 kV, 100 percent insulation level (0.175 in. insulation):

	O.D.	12 × O.D.	7 × O.D.
Single Conductor	1.50 in.	18 in.	—
Three Conductor	3.15 — 3.50 in.	38 — 42 in.	22 — 24 in.

334-12. Fittings. Fittings used for connecting Type MC cable to boxes, cabinets, or other equipment shall be identified for such use. Where single-conductor cables enter ferrous metal boxes or cabinets, the installation shall comply with Section 300-20 to prevent inductive heating.

Connectors should be selected in accordance with the size and type of cable for which they are designed. Bronze connectors are intended for use only with cable employing corrugated copper armor.

334-13. Ampacity. The ampacity of Type MC cable shall be in accordance with Section 310-15.

Exception: The ampacities for Type MC cable installed in cable tray shall be determined in accordance with Sections 318-11 and 318-13.

This section is required to correctly identify the allowable ampacities for Type MC cable depending on the installation, i.e., in free air, direct buried, in raceway underground, on a messenger, or in cable tray.

(FPN): See Section 310-10 for temperature limitation of conductors.

C. Construction Specifications

334-20. Conductors. The conductors shall be of copper, aluminum, or copper-clad aluminum, solid or stranded.

The minimum conductor size shall be No. 18 copper and No. 12 aluminum or copper-clad aluminum.

334-21. Insulation. The insulated conductors shall comply with (a) or (b) below.

(a) 600 Volts. Insulated conductors in sizes No. 18 and 16 shall be of a type listed in Table 402-3, with a maximum operating temperature not less than 90°C (194°F), and as permitted by Section 725-16. Conductors larger than No. 16 shall be of a type listed in Table 310-13 or of a type identified for use in MC cable.

(b) Over 600 Volts. Insulated conductors shall be of a type listed in Tables 310-61 through 310-67.

334-22. Metallic Sheath. The metallic covering shall be one of the following types: smooth metallic sheath, welded and corrugated metallic sheath, interlocking metal tape armor. The metallic sheath shall be continuous and close fitting.

Supplemental protection of an outer covering of corrosion-resistant material shall be permitted, and shall be required where such protection is needed. The sheath shall not be used as a current-carrying conductor.

(FPN): See Section 300-6 for protection against corrosion.

334-23. Grounding. Type MC cable shall provide an adequate path for equipment grounding as required by Article 250.

The armor of interlocking Type MC cable is not UL approved as the sole means of providing an equipment grounding circuit but may be used to supplement the internal grounding conductor.

334-24. Marking. The provisions of Section 310-11 shall apply.

Type MC cable is required to be marked with the maximum working voltage, proper type letter or letters for the type of wire, and the AWG size or circular mil area. This marking may be on a marker tape located within the cable running for its complete length, or, if the metallic covering is of smooth construction which permits surface marking, the MC cable may be durably marked on the outer covering at intervals not exceeding 24 in. See Section 310-11 for marking requirements.

ARTICLE 336 — NONMETALLIC-SHEATHED CABLE

Types NM and NMC

Contents

ARTICLE 336—NONMETALLIC-SHEATHED CABLE

336-14. Bends.
336-15. Supports.
336-16. Devices of Insulating Material.
336-17. Boxes of Insulating Material.
336-18. Devices with Integral Enclosures.

C. Construction Specifications
336-25. Construction.
  (a) Type NM.
  (b) Type NMC.
336-26. Conductors.
336-27. Marking.

There has been a reorganization of Article 336 for the 1987 *NEC*. The following chart may be used to correlate the requirements between the 1984 and 1987 *NEC* editions.

Changes in Section Numbering for Article 336, 1987 *NEC*

1984 *NEC*	1987 *NEC*
336-2, paragraphs 1 and 2	336-25, -26
336-2(a)	336-25(a)
336-2(b)	336-25(b)
336-2(c)	336-27
336-3, paragraph 1	336-3, -4
336-3(a)	336-3(a), -4(b)
336-3(c)	336-4(a)
336-4	336-2
336-5	336-15
336-6	336-10
336-6(a)	336-10(a)
336-6(b)	336-10(b)
336-7	336-11
336-8	336-12
336-9	336-13
336-10	336-14
336-11	336-16
336-12	336-17
336-13	336-18

A. General

336-1. Definition. Nonmetallic-sheathed cable is a factory assembly of two or more insulated conductors having an outer sheath of moisture-resistant, flame-retardant, nonmetallic material.

Nonmetallic-sheathed cable may be used for either exposed or concealed wiring. It was first recognized in the 1928 *NEC* as a substitute for concealed knob-and-tube wiring (Article 324) and open wiring on insulators (Article 320). The basic advantages of nonmetallic-sheathed cable (Type NM and Type NMC) are that the outer sheath provides continuous protection in addition to the insulation applied to the conductors; the cable is easily fished in partitions of finished buildings; no insulating supports are required; and only one hole need be bored which can accommodate more than one cable passing through a wood cross member. If cables are bunched through a single hole, see Note 8(a) to Tables 310-16 through 310-31, second paragraph.

Where the cable passes through factory- or field-punched holes in metal studs or similar members, it is to be protected by bushings or grommets securely fastened in the opening, unless the slots or holes are formed so that no metal edge can cut or tear the cable. See Section 300-4(b).

336-2. Other Articles. In addition to the provisions of this article, installations of nonmetallic-sheathed cable shall comply with the other applicable provisions of this Code, especially Articles 300 and 310.

The second paragraph of Note 8(a) to Tables 310-16 through 310-31 states: "Where single conductors or multiconductor cables are stacked or bundled longer than 24 inches (610 mm) without maintaining spacing and are not installed in raceways, the ampacity of each conductor shall be reduced as shown in the above table."

Failure to comply with the appropriate ampacity derating called for by Note 8(a), where Types NM and NMC cables may be stacked or bundled, can lead to overheating of conductors.

The requirements of Note 8 apply to other wiring methods as they do to nonmetallic-sheathed cables.

336-3. Uses Permitted. Type NM and Type NMC cables shall be permitted to be used in one- and two-family dwellings, multifamily dwellings and other structures, except as prohibited in Section 336-4.

Type NM and Type NMC cables are permitted for dwellings and other structures such as stores, professional offices, motels, industrial occupancies, etc., providing these dwellings or structures do not exceed three floors above grade. See Figure 336-1. The word "floor" as used in Section 336-4 means the entire "story" of the building, from floor to ceiling.

(FPN): See Section 310-10 for temperature limitation of conductors.

This fine print note referencing Section 310-10 alerts the installer to temperature limitations along the entire length of the cable.

(a) Type NM. Type NM cable shall be permitted for both exposed and concealed work in normally dry locations. It shall be permissible to install or fish Type NM cable in air voids in masonry block or tile walls where such walls are not exposed or subject to excessive moisture or dampness.

(b) Type NMC. Type NMC cable shall be permitted: (1) for both exposed and concealed work in dry, moist, damp, or corrosive locations; (2) in outside and inside walls of masonry block or tile; (3) in a shallow chase in masonry, concrete, or adobe and covered with plaster, adobe, or similar finish.

Type NMC (corrosion-resistant) cable is required for installations in dairy barns and similar farm buildings (see Article 547) where ordinary types of nonmetallic cables have in some cases deteriorated rapidly due to ammonia fumes or the growth of fungus or mold.

In addition to the insulated conductors, nonmetallic-sheathed cable may have an insulated, covered, or bare conductor for equipment grounding purposes only. See Section 250-57 and Table 250-95.

336-4. Uses Not Permitted.

(a) Type NM or NMC. Types NM and NMC cables shall not be used: (1) in any dwelling or structure exceeding three floors above grade; (2) as service-entrance cable; (3) in commercial

359

garages having hazardous (classified) locations as provided in Section 511-3; (4) in theaters and similar locations, except as provided in Article 518, Places of Assembly; (5) in motion picture studios; (6) in storage battery rooms; (7) in hoistways; (8) embedded in poured cement, concrete, or aggregate; or (9) in any hazardous (classified) location except as permitted by Section 501-4(b), Exception. For the purpose of this article, the first floor of a building shall be that floor which is designed for human habitation and which has 50 percent or more of its perimeter level with or above finished grade of the exterior wall line.

(b) Type NM. Type NM cable shall not be installed: (1) where exposed to corrosive fumes or vapors; (2) where embedded in masonry, concrete, adobe, fill, or plaster; (3) in a shallow chase in masonry, concrete, or adobe and covered with plaster, adobe, or similar finish.

Figure 336-1. A representation of a first floor of a building which is level with or above finished grade of the exterior wall line of 50 percent or more of its perimeter.

For concealed work, nonmetallic-sheathed cable should be installed where it is protected from the physical damage that can often be caused by nails or screws. Where practical, care should be taken to avoid areas where trim, door and window casings, baseboards, moldings, etc., may be nailed. See Section 300-4.

B. Installation

336-10. Exposed Work — General. In exposed work, except as provided in Sections 336-12 and 336-13, the cable shall be installed as specified in (a) and (b) below.

(a) To Follow Surface. The cable shall closely follow the surface of the building finish or of running boards.

(b) Protection from Physical Damage. The cable shall be protected from physical damage where necessary by conduit, electrical metallic tubing, pipe, guard strips, or other means. Where passing through a floor the cable shall be enclosed in rigid metal conduit, intermediate metal conduit, electrical metallic tubing, or other metal pipe extending at least 6 inches (152 mm) above the floor.

336-11. Through Studs, Joists, and Rafters. The cable shall comply with Section 300-4 where installed through studs, joists, rafters, and similar members.

336-12. In Unfinished Basements. Where the cable is run at angles with joists in unfinished basements, it shall be permissible to secure cables not smaller than two No. 6 or three No. 8 conductors directly to the lower edges of the joists. Smaller cables shall either be run through bored holes in joists or on running boards. Where run parallel to the joists, cable of any size shall be secured to the sides or faces of the joists.

Figure 336-2. Nonmetallic-sheathed cable as installed in an unfinished basement. The cable can be run through joists (A), and attached to the side or face of joists or beams (B) and to the running boards (C).

336-13. In Accessible Attics. The installation of cable in accessible attics or roof spaces shall also comply with Section 333-12.

336-14. Bends. Bends in cable shall be so made, and other handling shall be such, that the protective coverings of the cable will not be damaged, and no bend shall have a radius less than five times the diameter of the cable.

336-15. Supports. Nonmetallic-sheathed cable shall be secured by staples, straps, or similar fittings so designed and installed as not to damage the cable. Cable shall be secured in place at intervals not exceeding 4½ feet (1.37 m) and within 12 inches (305 mm) from every cabinet, box, or fitting.

This section requires that the cable be SECURED. Simply draping the cable over air ducts, lower members of bar joists, pipes, and ceiling grid members is not permitted except as noted in Exception No. 1. See also Section 300-4(c).

Exception No. 1: For concealed work in finished buildings, or finished panels for prefabricated buildings where such supporting is impracticable, it shall be permissible to fish the cable between access points.

Exception No. 2: A wiring device identified for the use, without a separate outlet box, incorporating an integral cable clamp shall be permitted when the cable is secured in place at intervals not exceeding 4½ feet (1.37 m) and within 12 inches (305 mm) from the wiring device wall opening, and there shall be at least a 12-inch (305-mm) loop of unbroken cable or 6 inches (152 mm) of a cable end available on the interior side of the finished wall to permit replacement.

336-16. Devices of Insulating Material. Switch, outlet, and tap devices of insulating material shall be permitted to be used without boxes in exposed cable wiring, and for rewiring in existing buildings where the cable is concealed and fished. Openings in such devices shall form a close fit around the outer covering of the cable, and the device shall fully enclose that part of the cable from which any part of the covering has been removed.

Where connections to conductors are by binding-screw terminals, there shall be available as many terminals as conductors.

Exception: Where cables are clamped within the structure, and terminals are of a type identified for use with multiconductors.

336-17. Boxes of Insulating Material. Nonmetallic outlet boxes shall be permitted as provided in Section 370-3.

Nonmetallic boxes and nonmetallic wiring systems are desired in corrosive atmospheres. See Sections 370-3, 370-7(c), 555-6, and Article 547.

336-18. Devices with Integral Enclosures. Wiring devices with integral enclosures identified for such use shall be permitted as provided in Section 300-15(b), Exception No. 5.

The *Code* recognizes wiring devices with integral enclosures in conventional on-site frame construction.

C. Construction Specifications

336-25. Construction. The insulated conductors of Type NM and NMC cable shall be in conformity with Section 336-26. The conductors shall be sizes No. 14 through 2 with copper conductors or sizes No. 12 through 2 with aluminum or copper-clad aluminum conductors. In addition to the insulated conductors, the cable shall be permitted to have an insulated or bare conductor for equipment grounding purposes only. When provided, the grounding conductor shall be sized in accordance with Article 250.

(a) Type NM. The overall covering shall be flame-retardant and moisture-resistant.

(b) Type NMC. The overall covering shall be flame-retardant, moisture-resistant, fungus-resistant, and corrosion-resistant.

336-26. Conductors. The insulated conductors shall be one of the types listed in Table 310-13 which is suitable for branch-circuit wiring or one which is identified for use in these cables.

Conductors shall be rated at 90°C (194°F). The ampacity of Types NM and NMC cable shall be that of 60°C (140°F) conductors and shall comply with Section 310-15.

Cables with conductors rated 90°C (194°F) are designated by testing agencies as Type NMB or NMC-B. The ampacities of nonmetallic-sheathed cable types, regardless of the conductor temperature rating, are limited to those of 60°C (140°F) conductors.

336-27. Marking. In addition to the provisions of Section 310-11, the cable shall have a distinctive marking on the exterior for its entire length specifying the cable type.

ARTICLE 337 — SHIELDED NONMETALLIC-SHEATHED CABLE

Type SNM

Contents

337-1. Definition.
337-2. Other Articles.
337-3. Uses Permitted.
337-4. Bends.
337-5. Handling.

337-6. Fittings.
337-7. Bonding.
337-8. Construction.
337-9. Marking.

337-1. Definition. Type SNM shielded nonmetallic-sheathed cable is a factory assembly of two or more insulated conductors in an extruded core of moisture-resistant, flame-resistant nonmetallic material, covered with an overlapping spiral metal tape and wire shield and jacketed with an extruded moisture-, flame-, oil-, corrosion-, fungus-, and sunlight-resistant nonmetallic material.

Type SNM cables are multiconductor cables in an extruded core of nonmetallic material covered with an overlapping spiral metal tape and wire shield with an overall nonmetallic material jacketing and are basically used in cable trays or in raceways. See Section 337-3.

Figure 337-1 is a simplified illustration of a Type SNM cable, and Figure 337-2 is an expanded view illustrating fittings for connecting such a cable to rigid metal conduit or intermediate metal conduit.

Figure 337-1. A seven-conductor No. 12 Type SNM cable typical for use in cable trays or raceways.

Figure 337-2. Connection-type fitting used where Type SNM cable enters a ¾-in. rigid metal conduit in Class I or Class II, Division 2 hazardous (classified) locations.

363

337-2. Other Articles. In addition to the provisions of this article, installation of Type SNM cable shall conform to other applicable provisions, such as Articles 300, 318, 501, and 502.

337-3. Uses Permitted. Type SNM cable shall be used only as follows: (1) where operating temperatures do not exceed the rating marked on the cable; (2) in cable trays or in raceways; or (3) in hazardous (classified) locations where permitted in Articles 500 through 516.

(FPN): See Section 310-10 for temperature limitation of conductors.

337-4. Bends. Bends in Type SNM cable shall be so made as not to damage the cable or its covering. The radius of the inner edge shall not be less than five times the cable diameter.

337-5. Handling. Type SNM cable shall be handled in such a manner as not to damage the cable or its covering.

337-6. Fittings. Fittings for connecting Type SNM cable to enclosures or equipment shall be identified for this use.

337-7. Bonding. The wire shield shall be bonded to the frame or enclosure of the utilization equipment and to the ground bus or connection at the power supply point. This bonding shall be accomplished using fittings (Section 337-6) or by other Code-approved bonding methods (Section 501-16(a)).

337-8. Construction. The conductors of Type SNM cable shall be Type TFN, TFFN, THHN or THWN in sizes No. 18 through No. 2 copper and No. 12 through No. 2 in aluminum or copper-clad aluminum. Conductor sizes may be mixed in individual cables. The flat overlapping metal tapes shall be spiraled with a long lay. The shield wires shall have a total cross-sectional area as required by Article 250 and not less than the largest circuit conductor in the cable.

The outer jacket shall be water-, oil-, flame-, corrosion-, fungus-, and sunlight-resistant, and suitable for installation in cable trays.

337-9. Marking. Type SNM cable shall have a distinctive marking on its exterior surface for its entire length indicating its type and maximum operating temperature. It shall comply with the general marking requirements of Section 310-11.

The conductors shall each be numbered for identification from each other by durable marking on two sides 180 degrees apart every 6 inches (152 mm) of length, with alternate legends inverted to facilitate reading from both sides.

ARTICLE 338 — SERVICE-ENTRANCE CABLE

Types SE and USE

Contents

338-1. Definition. Service-entrance cable is a single conductor or multiconductor assembly provided with or without an overall covering, primarily used for services and of the following types:

(a) Type SE. Type SE, having a flame-retardant, moisture-resistant covering.

(b) Type USE. Type USE, identified for underground use, having a moisture-resistant covering, but not required to have a flame-retardant covering.

Cabled single-conductor Type USE constructions recognized for underground use may have a bare copper conductor cabled with the assembly. Type USE single, parallel, or cabled conductor assemblies recognized for underground use may have a bare copper concentric conductor applied. These constructions do not require an outer overall covering.

(FPN): See Section 230-41, Exception b.

(c) One Uninsulated Conductor. If Type SE or USE cable consists of two or more conductors, one shall be permitted to be uninsulated.

Service-entrance cable is labeled in sizes No. 12 AWG and larger for copper and No. 10 AWG and larger for aluminum or copper-clad aluminum with Type RH, RHW, RHH or XHHW conductors. If the type designation for the conductors is marked on the outside surface of the cable, the temperature rating of the cable corresponds to the rating of the individual conductors. When this marking does not appear, the temperature rating of the cable is 75°C (167°F).

The cables are classified as follows:

Type SE—Cable for aboveground installation.

Type USE—Cable for underground installation including burial directly in the earth. Type USE size 4/0 and smaller when used as a branch circuit or feeder for underground installation, including direct burial, is required to have all circuit conductors insulated. The equipment grounding conductor (when required) is permitted to be bare. See Section 230-41 for service-entrance conductor insulation requirements.

338-2. Uses Permitted as Service-Entrance Conductors. Service-entrance cable used as service-entrance conductors shall be installed as required by Article 230.

338-3. Uses Permitted as Branch Circuits or Feeders.

(a) Grounded Conductor Insulated. Type SE service-entrance cables shall be permitted in interior wiring systems where all of the circuit conductors of the cable are of the rubber-covered or thermoplastic type.

(b) Grounded Conductor Not Insulated. Type SE service-entrance cables without individual insulation on the grounded circuit conductor shall not be used as a branch circuit or as a feeder within a building, except a cable that has a final nonmetallic outer covering and is supplied by alternating current at not over 150 volts to ground shall be permitted: (1) as a branch circuit to supply only a range, wall-mounted oven, counter-mounted cooking unit, or clothes dryer as covered in Section 250-60, or (2) as a feeder to supply only other buildings on the same premises.

Type SE service-entrance cable shall be permitted for interior use where the fully insulated conductors are used for circuit wiring and the uninsulated conductor is used for equipment grounding purposes.

According to the UL *Electrical Construction Materials Directory*, based upon tests which have been made involving the maximum heating that can be produced, an uninsulated conductor employed in a service cable assembly is considered to have the same current-carrying capacity as the insulated conductors even though it may be smaller in size.

(c) Temperature Limitations. Type SE service-entrance cable used to supply appliances shall not be subject to conductor temperatures in excess of the temperature specified for the type of insulation involved.

338-4. Installation Methods.

(a) Interior Wiring. In addition to the provisions of this article, Type SE service-entrance cable used for interior wiring shall comply with the applicable provisions of Article 300.

(b) Unarmored Cable. Unarmored cable shall be installed in accordance with the provisions of Article 336.

Section 336-4 prohibits the use of nonmetallic-sheathed cables in dwellings and other structures exceeding three floors above grade. Type SE cable (unarmored), which is similar in construction to Types NM and NMC, where used for interior branch circuits and feeders, should also meet the provisions of Sections 336-3 and 4.

The same restriction applies to Type UF where used for interior wiring. See Section 339-3(a)(4).

(c) Through Studs, Joists, Rafters, or Similar Members. Cables shall comply with Section 300-4 where installed through studs, joists, rafters, or similar members.

(FPN): See Section 310-10 for temperature limitation of conductors.

338-5. Marking. Service-entrance cable shall be marked as required in Section 310-11. Cable with the neutral conductor smaller than the ungrounded conductors shall be so marked.

ARTICLE 339 — UNDERGROUND FEEDER AND BRANCH-CIRCUIT CABLE

Type UF

Contents

339-1. Description and Marking.

(a) Description. Underground feeder and branch-circuit cable shall be an approved Type UF cable in sizes No. 14 copper or No. 12 aluminum or copper-clad aluminum through No. 4/0. The conductors of Type UF shall be one of the moisture-resistant types listed in Table 310-13 which is suitable for branch-circuit wiring or one which is identified for such use. In addition to the insulated conductors, the cable shall be permitted to have an approved size of insulated or bare conductor for equipment grounding purposes only. The overall covering shall be flame-retardant, moisture-, fungus-, and corrosion-resistant, and suitable for direct burial in the earth.

(b) Marking. In addition to the provisions of Section 310-11, the cable shall have a distinctive marking on the exterior for its entire length specifying the cable type.

339-2. Other Articles. In addition to the provisions of this article, installations of underground feeder and branch-circuit cable (Type UF) shall comply with other applicable provisions of this Code, especially Article 300 and Section 310-13.

Underground feeder and branch-circuit cable is rated for use at 60°C (140°F), 600 V, and is labeled in sizes No. 14 to 4/0 AWG, copper, and No. 12 to 4/0 AWG, aluminum or copper-clad aluminum, for single and multiple conductor cables.

Submersible water pump cable is a multiconductor cable in which 2, 3, or 4 single-conductor Type UF cables are twisted together without an outer covering. The cable is labeled in sizes from 14 AWG to 4/0 AWG, copper, and from 12 AWG to 4/0 AWG, aluminum or copper-clad aluminum. The cable is tag marked: For use within the well casing for wiring deep-well water pumps where the cable is not subject to repetitive handling caused by frequent servicing of the pump units. The insulation may be surface-marked "Submersible Water Pump Cable" or "Pump Cable."

This cable may employ copper, aluminum, or copper-clad aluminum conductors. Cables with copper-clad aluminum conductors are surface-printed "AL (CU-CLAD)" or "Cu-Clad Al."

If single-conductor Type UF cable is terminated with a fitting not specifically recognized for use with single-conductor cable, special care should be taken to assure it is properly secured and not subject to damage.

339-3. Use.

(a) Uses Permitted.

(1) Type UF cable shall be permitted for use underground, including direct burial in the earth, as feeder or branch-circuit cable where provided with overcurrent protection of the rated ampacity as required in Section 339-4.

(2) Where single-conductor cables are installed, all cables of the feeder circuit, subfeeder circuit, or branch circuit, including the neutral conductor, if any, shall be run together in the same trench or raceway.

Exception: For solar photovoltaic systems in accordance with Section 690-31.

(3) For underground requirements, see Section 300-5.

(4) Type UF cable shall be permitted for interior wiring in wet, dry, or corrosive locations under the recognized wiring methods of this Code, and where installed as nonmetallic-sheathed cable, the installation and conductor requirements shall comply with the provisions of Article 336 and shall be of the multiconductor type.

See commentary following Sections 336-3 and 338-4(b).

Exception: Single-conductor cables shall be permitted as the nonheating leads for heating cables as provided in Section 424-43 and in solar photovoltaic systems in accordance with Section 690-31.

Type UF cable supported by cable trays shall be of the multiconductor type.

(FPN): See Section 310-10 for temperature limitation of conductors.

(b) Uses Not Permitted. Type UF cable shall not be used: (1) as service-entrance cables; (2) in commercial garages; (3) in theaters; (4) in motion picture studios; (5) in storage battery rooms; (6) in hoistways; (7) in any hazardous (classified) location; (8) embedded in poured cement, concrete, or aggregate, except where embedded in plaster as nonheating leads as provided in Article 424; (9) where exposed to direct rays of the sun, unless identified as sunlight-resistant.

Exception: See Section 501-4(b), Exception.

Type UF cables suitable for exposure to the direct rays of the sun are indicated by tag marking and marking on the surface of the cable with the designation "Sunlight Resistant."

339-4. Overcurrent Protection. Overcurrent protection shall be provided in accordance with provisions of Section 240-3.

339-5. Ampacity. The ampacity of Type UF cable shall be that of 60°C (140°F) conductors in accordance with Section 310-15.

ARTICLE 340 — POWER AND CONTROL TRAY CABLE

Type TC

Contents

340-1. Definition.
340-2. Other Articles.
340-3. Construction.
340-4. Use Permitted.

340-5. Uses Not Permitted.
340-6. Marking.
340-7. Ampacity.

340-1. Definition. Type TC power and control tray cable is a factory assembly of two or more insulated conductors, with or without associated bare or covered grounding conductors under a nonmetallic sheath, approved for installation in cable trays, in raceways, or where supported by a messenger wire.

340-2. Other Articles. In addition to the provisions of this article, installations of Type TC tray cable shall comply with other applicable articles of this Code, especially Articles 300 and 318.

340-3. Construction. The insulated conductors of Type TC tray cable shall be in sizes 18 AWG through 1000 MCM copper and sizes 12 AWG through 1000 MCM aluminum or copper-clad aluminum. Insulated conductors of size 14 AWG and larger copper and size 12 AWG and larger aluminum or copper-clad aluminum shall be one of the types listed in Table 310-13 or 310-62, which is suitable for branch circuit and feeder circuits or one which is identified for such use. Insulated conductors of size No. 18 and No. 16 AWG copper shall be in accordance with Section 725-16. The outer sheath shall be a flame-retardant, nonmetallic material. A metallic sheath shall not be permitted either under or over the nonmetallic sheath. Where installed in wet locations, Type TC cable shall be resistant to moisture and corrosive agents.

340-4. Use Permitted. Type TC tray cable shall be permitted to be used: (1) for power, lighting, control, signal, and communication circuits; (2) in cable trays, or in raceways, or where supported in outdoor locations by a messenger wire; (3) in cable trays in hazardous (classified) locations as permitted in Articles 318 and 501 in industrial establishments where the conditions of maintenance and supervision assure that only qualified persons will service the installation; (4) for Class 1 circuits as permitted in Article 725.

The restriction that requires the condition of maintenance and supervision to ensure that only qualified persons will service the installation of Type TC cable applies only where the cable is to be used in a hazardous (classified) location.

(FPN): See Section 310-10 for temperature limitation of conductors.

340-5. Uses Not Permitted. Type TC tray cable shall not be: (1) installed where they will be exposed to physical damage; (2) installed as open cable on brackets or cleats; (3) used where exposed to direct rays of the sun, unless identified as sunlight-resistant; (4) direct buried, unless identified for such use.

Where identified for the use, Type TC cable is permitted to be directly buried. See definition of "identified" in Article 100.

340-6. Marking. The cable shall be marked in accordance with Section 310-11.

340-7. Ampacity. The ampacities of the conductors of Type TC tray cable shall be determined from Section 400-5 for conductors smaller than No. 14, and Section 318-11.

ARTICLE 342 — NONMETALLIC EXTENSIONS

Contents

342-1. Definition. Nonmetallic extensions are an assembly of two insulated conductors within a nonmetallic jacket or an extruded thermoplastic covering. The classification includes both surface extensions, intended for mounting directly on the surface of walls or ceilings, and aerial cable, containing a supporting messenger cable as an integral part of the cable assembly.

342-2. Other Articles. In addition to the provisions of this article, nonmetallic extensions shall be installed in accordance with the applicable provisions of this Code.

342-3. Uses Permitted. Nonmetallic extensions shall be permitted only where all of the following conditions are met:

(a) From an Existing Outlet. The extension is from an existing outlet on a 15- or 20-ampere branch circuit in conformity with the requirements of Article 210.

(b) Exposed and in a Dry Location. The extension is run exposed and in a dry location.

(c) Nonmetallic Surface Extensions. For nonmetallic surface extensions, the building is occupied for residential or office purposes, and does not exceed the height limitations specified in Section 336-4(a).

Nonmetallic surface extensions are limited to residential or office locations. However, it is permitted as an aerial cable in industrial occupancies where a highly flexible means for connecting equipment is necessary. See Sections 342-4(a) and 342-7(b).

(c1) [Alternate to (c)] For aerial cable, the building is occupied for industrial purposes, and the nature of the occupancy requires a highly flexible means for connecting equipment.

(FPN): See Section 310-10 for temperature limitation of conductors.

A nonmetallic extension is an assembly of two insulated circuit conductors with or without an equipment grounding conductor within a nonmetallic jacket or extruded thermoplastic covering. Assemblies without a grounding conductor are marked "intended for replacement use only."

342-4. Uses Not Permitted. Nonmetallic extensions shall not be used:

(a) Aerial Cable. As aerial cable to substitute for one of the general wiring methods specified by this Code.

(b) Unfinished Areas. In unfinished basements, attics, or roof spaces.

(c) Voltage Between Conductors. Where the voltage between conductors exceeds 150 volts for nonmetallic surface extension and 300 volts for aerial cable.

(d) Corrosive Vapors. Where subject to corrosive vapors.

(e) Through a Floor or Partition. Where run through a floor or partition, or outside the room in which it originates.

342-5. Splices and Taps. Extensions shall consist of a continuous unbroken length of the assembly, without splices, and without exposed conductors between fittings. Taps shall be permitted where approved fittings completely covering the tap connections are used. Aerial cable and its tap connectors shall be provided with an approved means for polarization. Receptacle-type tap connectors shall be of the locking-type.

342-6. Fittings. Each run shall terminate in a fitting that covers the end of the assembly. All fittings and devices shall be of a type identified for the use.

342-7. Installation. Nonmetallic extensions shall be installed as specified in (a) and (b) below.

(a) Nonmetallic Surface Extensions.

(1) One or more extensions shall be permitted to be run in any direction from an existing outlet, but not on the floor or within 2 inches (50.8 mm) from the floor.

(2) Nonmetallic surface extensions shall be secured in place by approved means at intervals not exceeding 8 inches (203 mm).

Exception: Where connection to the supplying outlet is made by means of an attachment plug, the first fastening shall be permitted 12 inches (305 mm) or less from the plug.

There shall be at least one fastening between each two adjacent outlets supplied. An extension shall be attached only to woodwork or plaster finish, and shall not be in contact with any metal work or other conductive material other than with metal plates on receptacles.

(3) A bend that reduces the normal spacing between the conductors shall be covered with a cap to protect the assembly from physical damage.

(b) Aerial Cable.

(1) Aerial cable shall be supported by its messenger cable, securely attached at each end with approved clamps and turnbuckles. Intermediate supports shall be provided at not more than

20-foot (6.1-m) intervals. Cable tension shall be adjusted to eliminate excessive sag. The cable shall have a clearance of not less than 2 inches (50.8 mm) from steel structural members or other conductive material.

(2) Aerial cable shall have a clearance of not less than 10 feet (3.05 m) above floor areas accessible to pedestrian traffic, and not less than 14 feet (4.27 m) above floor areas accessible to vehicular traffic.

(3) Cable suspended over work benches, not accessible to pedestrian traffic, shall have a clearance of not less than 8 feet (2.44 m) above the floor.

(4) Aerial cables shall be permitted as a means to support lighting fixtures when the total load on the supporting messenger cable does not exceed that for which the assembly is intended.

(5) The supporting messenger cable, when installed in conformity with the applicable provisions of Article 250 and when properly identified as an equipment grounding conductor, shall be permitted to ground equipment. The messenger cable shall not be used as a branch-circuit conductor.

342-8. Marking. Nonmetallic extensions shall be marked in accordance with Section 110-21.

ARTICLE 344 — UNDERPLASTER EXTENSIONS

Contents

344-1. Use. An underplaster extension installed as permitted by this article shall be permitted only for extending an existing branch circuit in a building of fire-resistive construction.

It is sometimes very difficult or impossible to fish cables into voids or hollow spaces of fire-resistive construction, and, in these instances, underplaster extensions have been a suitable alternative. An underplaster extension, as specified in Sections 344-2 and 344-5, is buried in the plaster finish of ceilings and walls.

344-2. Materials. Such extension shall be run in rigid metal conduit, flexible metal conduit, Type AC cable, intermediate metal conduit, rigid nonmetallic conduit, electrical metallic tubing, Type MC cable, electrical nonmetallic tubing, Type MI cable, or metal raceways. Standard sizes of cables and raceways shall be used.

Exception: For a single conductor only, conduit or tubing having not less than 5/16 inch inside diameter, single-conductor Type AC cable, or single-conductor Type MI cable shall be permitted.

344-3. Boxes and Fittings. Boxes and fittings shall comply with the applicable provisions of Article 370.

344-4. Installation. An underplaster extension shall be laid on the face of masonry or other material and buried in the plaster finish of ceilings or walls. The methods of installation of the raceway or cable for such extension shall be as specified elsewhere in this Code for the particular type of material used.

344-5. Extension to Another Floor. No such extension shall extend beyond the floor on which it originates unless installed in a standard size of rigid metal conduit, intermediate metal conduit, electrical metallic tubing, Type AC cable, or Type MI cable.

Underplaster extensions are permitted in buildings of fire-resistive construction, such as concrete and brick buildings, where fishing cables in hollow spaces is virtually impossible.

This type of installation is permitted only for extending an existing branch circuit and is limited to the wiring methods specified in Sections 344-2 and 344-5.

ARTICLE 345 — INTERMEDIATE METAL CONDUIT

Contents

A. General

345-1. Definition. Intermediate metal conduit is a metal raceway of circular cross section with integral or associated couplings, connectors and fittings approved for the installation of electrical conductors.

Intermediate metal conduit (IMC) is a thinner-walled rigid metal conduit and is satisfactory for use in all locations where rigid metal conduit may be used. Also, threaded and unthreaded fittings, couplings, connectors, etc., are interchangeable for either IMC or rigid metal conduit.

Galvanized IMC installed in concrete does not require supplementary corrosion protection. Wherever ferrous metal conduit runs directly from concrete encasement to soil burial, severe corrosive effects are likely to occur on the metal in contact with the soil. In the absence of specific local experience, soils producing severe corrosive effects are generally characterized by low resistivity, less than 2000 ohm-centimeters.

345-2. Other Articles. Installations for intermediate metal conduit shall comply with the provisions of the applicable sections of Article 300.

345-3. Uses Permitted.

(a) All Atmospheric Conditions and Occupancies. Use of intermediate metal conduit shall be permitted under all atmospheric conditions and occupancies. Where practicable, dissimilar metals in contact anywhere in the system shall be avoided to eliminate the possibility of galvanic action. Intermediate metal conduit shall be permitted as an equipment grounding conductor.

(FPN): See Section 250-91(b) for types of equipment grounding conductors.

Exception: Aluminum fittings and enclosures shall be permitted to be used with steel intermediate metal conduit.

(b) Corrosion Protection. Intermediate metal conduit, elbows, couplings, and fittings shall be permitted to be installed in concrete, in direct contact with the earth, or in areas subject to severe corrosive influences when protected by corrosion protection and judged suitable for the condition.

(FPN): See Section 300-6 for protection against corrosion.

(c) Cinder Fill. Intermediate metal conduit shall be permitted to be installed in or under cinder fill where subject to permanent moisture when protected on all sides by a layer of noncinder concrete not less than 2 inches (50.8 mm) thick; when the conduit is not less than 18 inches (457 mm) under the fill; or when protected by corrosion protection and judged suitable for the condition.

(FPN): See Section 300-6 for protection against corrosion.

B. Installation

345-5. Wet Locations. All supports, bolts, straps, screws, etc., shall be of corrosion-resistant materials or protected against corrosion by corrosion-resistant materials.

(FPN): See Section 300-6 for protection against corrosion.

345-6. Size.

(a) Minimum. Conduit smaller than ½-inch electrical trade size shall not be used.

(b) Maximum. Conduit larger than 4-inch electrical trade size shall not be used.

345-7. Number of Conductors in Conduit. The number of conductors in a single conduit shall not exceed that permitted by the percentage fill specified in Table 1, Chapter 9, using the conduit dimensions of Table 4, Chapter 9.

345-8. Reaming and Threading. All cut ends of conduits shall be reamed or otherwise finished to remove rough edges. Where conduit is threaded in the field, a standard cutting die with a ¾-inch (19-mm) taper per foot (305 mm) shall be used.

See commentary following Section 348-11.

(FPN): See Standards for Pipe Threads, General Purpose (Inch) ANSI/ASME B.1.20.1-1983.

345-9. Couplings and Connectors.

(a) Threadless. Threadless couplings and connectors used with conduit shall be made tight. Where buried in masonry or concrete, they shall be the concretetight type. Where installed in wet locations, they shall be the raintight type.

(b) Running Threads. Running threads shall not be used on conduit for connection at couplings.

See commentary following Section 346-9.

345-10. Bends — How Made. Bends of intermediate metal conduit shall be so made that the conduit will not be damaged, and that the internal diameter of the conduit will not be effectively reduced. The radius of the curve of the inner edge of any field bend shall not be less than indicated in Table 346-10.

Exception: For field bends for conductors without lead sheath and made with a single operation (one shot) bending machine designed for the purpose, the minimum radius shall not be less than that indicated in Table 346-10 Exception.

See commentary following Section 346-10.

345-11. Bends — Number in One Run. A run of conduit between outlet and outlet, between fitting and fitting, or between outlet and fitting, shall not contain more than the equivalent of four quarter bends (360 degrees, total), including those bends located immediately at the outlet or fitting.

See commentary following 346-11.

345-12. Supports. Intermediate metal conduit shall be installed as a complete system as provided in Article 300 and shall be securely fastened in place. Conduit shall be firmly fastened within 3 feet (914 mm) of each outlet box, junction box, cabinet, or fitting. Conduit shall be supported at least every 10 feet (3.05 m).

See commentary following Section 348-12.

Exception No. 1: If made up with threaded couplings, it shall be permissible to support straight runs of intermediate metal conduit in accordance with Table 346-12, provided such supports prevent transmission of stresses to termination where conduit is deflected between supports.

Exception No. 2: The distance between supports shall be permitted to be increased to 20 feet (6.1 m) for exposed vertical risers from industrial machinery, provided that the conduit is made up with threaded couplings firmly supported at the top and bottom of the riser, and no other means of intermediate support is readily available.

345-13. Boxes and Fittings. See Article 370.

345-14. Splices and Taps. Splices and taps shall be made only in junction boxes, outlet boxes or conduit bodies. See Article 370.

345-15. Bushings. Where a conduit enters a box, fitting, or other enclosure, a bushing shall be provided to protect the wire from abrasion unless the design of the box, fitting, or enclosure is such as to afford equivalent protection.

(FPN): See Section 373-6(c) for the protection of conductors No. 4 AWG and larger at bushings.

See commentary following Section 373-6.

C. Construction Specifications

345-16. General. Intermediate metal conduit shall comply with (a) through (c) below.

(a) Standard Lengths. Intermediate metal conduit as shipped shall be in standard lengths of 10 feet (3.05 m) including coupling, one coupling to be furnished with each length. For specific applications or use, it shall be permissible to ship lengths shorter or longer than 10 feet (3.05 m), with or without couplings.

(b) Corrosion-Resistant Material. Nonferrous conduit of corrosion-resistant material shall have suitable markings.

(c) **Marking.** Each length shall be clearly and durably identified at 2½-foot (762-mm) intervals with the letters IMC. Each length shall be marked as required in the first sentence of Section 110-21.

ARTICLE 346 — RIGID METAL CONDUIT

Contents

346-1. Use. The use of rigid metal conduit shall be permitted under all atmospheric conditions and occupancies subject to the following:

(a) **Protected by Enamel.** Ferrous raceways and fittings protected from corrosion solely by enamel shall be permitted only indoors and in occupancies not subject to severe corrosive influences.

(b) **Dissimilar Metals.** Where practicable, dissimilar metals in contact anywhere in the system shall be avoided to eliminate the possibility of galvanic action.

Exception: Aluminum fittings and enclosures shall be permitted to be used with steel rigid metal conduit, and also, steel fittings and enclosures shall be permitted to be used with aluminum rigid metal conduit.

(c) **Corrosion Protection.** Ferrous or nonferrous metal conduit, elbows, couplings, and fittings shall be permitted to be installed in concrete, in direct contact with the earth, or in areas subject to severe corrosive influences where protected by corrosion protection and judged suitable for the condition.

(FPN): See Section 300-6 for protection against corrosion.

This section indicates the permitted uses for ferrous and nonferrous conduit, including their use in concrete, in direct contact with the earth, and in corrosive areas. The fine print note references Section 300-6 for additional information on protection against corrosion and specific types of corrosion-resistant materials.

The exception to Section 346-1(b) makes it clear that aluminum rigid conduit can be used with steel fittings and enclosures as well as aluminum fittings and enclosures with steel rigid conduit. It has been shown by test that the galvanic corrosion at steel and aluminum interfaces is minor in comparison to the natural corrosion on the combination of steel and steel or aluminum and aluminum.

It is advisable to consult with the authority enforcing this *Code* for the approval of corrosion-resistant materials and/or for requirements prior to the installation of nonferrous metal (aluminum) conduit in concrete since chloride additives in the concrete mix have caused corrosion.

346-2. Other Articles. Installations of rigid metal conduit shall comply with the applicable provisions of Article 300.

A. Installation

346-3. Cinder Fill. Conduit shall not be used in or under cinder fill where subject to permanent moisture.

Exception No. 1: Where of corrosion-resistant material suitable for the purpose.

Exception No. 2: Where protected on all sides by a layer of noncinder concrete at least 2 inches (50.8 mm) thick.

Exception No. 3: Where the conduit is at least 18 inches (457 mm) under the fill.

Although cinder fill is not commonly used in modern construction, it is still encountered in older building basement slabs. Care should be taken to install rigid metal conduit as required by the exceptions, because cinders contain sulfur, and sulfuric acid is formed which can corrode metal raceways.

346-4. Wet Locations. All supports, bolts, straps, screws, etc., shall be of corrosion-resistant materials or protected against corrosion by corrosion-resistant materials.

(FPN): See Section 300-6 for protection against corrosion.

346-5. Minimum Size. Conduit smaller than ½-inch electrical trade size shall not be used.

Exception No. 1: For underplaster extensions as permitted in Section 344-2.

Exception No. 2: For enclosing the leads of motors as permitted in Section 430-145(b).

346-6. Number of Conductors in Conduit. The number of conductors permitted in a single conduit shall not exceed the percentage fill specified in Table 1, Chapter 9.

(FPN): For conductor cross-sectional area see Tables 5, 5A, 6, 7, 8 and the applicable Notes to Tables at the beginning of Chapter 9.

Tables 3A, 3B, and 3C in Chapter 9 are based on the allowable percentages of Table 1, Chapter 9, for conduit or tubing fill, that is, 53 percent for 1 conductor, 31 percent for 2 conductors, and 40 percent for 3 or more conductors. Percentages for lead-covered conductors vary, somewhat, from other conductor types (see Table 1).

346-7. Reaming and Threading.

(a) Reamed. All cut ends of conduits shall be reamed or otherwise finished to remove rough edges.

See commentary following Section 348-11.

(b) Threaded. Where conduit is threaded in the field, a standard conduit cutting die with a ¾-inch (19-mm) taper per foot (305 mm) shall be used.

(FPN): See Standards for Pipe Threads, General Purpose (Inch) ANSI/ASME, B.1.20.1-1983.

346-8. Bushings. Where a conduit enters a box, fitting, or other enclosure, a bushing shall be provided to protect the wire from abrasion unless the box, fitting, or enclosure design provides equivalent protection.

(FPN): See Section 373-6(c) for the protection of conductors at bushings.

346-9. Couplings and Connectors.

(a) Threadless. Threadless couplings and connectors used with conduit shall be made tight. Where buried in masonry or concrete, they shall be of the concretetight type. Where installed in wet locations, they shall be of the raintight type.

(b) Running Threads. Running threads shall not be used on conduit for connection at couplings.

Figure 346-1 illustrates a threadless connection integral to a conduit body, FS box, etc. This type of connection may be separate from the conduit body or box as an individual fitting of the compression type (raintight) suitable for wet locations or of the set-screw type (concretetight).

Threadless connections are not intended for use over threads as the fitting will not properly seat. The threaded end of the conduit should be cut off and reamed before using at a threadless connection.

Figure 346-2 illustrates an Erickson coupling (the electrical equivalent of a pipe union) which is used to join two lengths of conduit where it is impossible to turn either length, such as in underground or concrete-slab construction. Bolted split couplings may also be used. Running threads are not permitted to join two conduits, but may be permitted to join two boxes where electrical and mechanical connections are assured (locknuts and bushings).

Figure 346-1. Conduit body with threadless connector. (*Appleton Electric Co.*)

Figure 346-2. Erickson or union-type coupling. (*Appleton Electric Co.*)

346-10. Bends — How Made. Bends of rigid metal conduit shall be so made that the conduit will not be damaged, and that the internal diameter of the conduit will not be effectively reduced. The radius of the curve of the inner edge of any field bend shall not be less than shown in Table 346-10.

Exception: For field bends for conductors without lead sheath and made with a single operation (one shot) bending machine designed for the purpose, the minimum radius shall not be less than indicated in Table 346-10 Exception.

The term "field bend" means any bend or offset made by installers using proper tools and equipment, during the installation of conduit systems.

Table 346-10. Radius of Conduit Bends (Inches)

Size of Conduit (In.)	Conductors Without Lead Sheath (In.)	Conductors With Lead Sheath (In.)
½	4	6
¾	5	8
1	6	11
1¼	8	14
1½	10	16
2	12	21
2½	15	25
3	18	31
3½	21	36
4	24	40
5	30	50
6	36	61

For SI units: (Radius) one inch = 25.4 millimeters.

Table 346-10 Exception. Radius of Conduit Bends (Inches)

Size of Conduit (In.)	Radius to Center of Conduit (In.)
½	4
¾	4½
1	5¾
1¼	7¼
1½	8¼
2	9½
2½	10½
3	13
3½	15
4	16
5	24
6	30

For SI units: (Radius) one inch = 25.4 millimeters.

346-11. Bends — Number in One Run. A run of conduit between outlet and outlet, fitting and fitting, or outlet and fitting shall not contain more than the equivalent of four quarter bends (360 degrees, total), including those bends located immediately at the outlet or fitting.

Limiting the number of bends in a conduit run reduces pulling tension on conductors and helps ensure easy insertion or removal of conductors during later phases of construction when the conduit may be permanently enclosed by the finish of the building. Adjustments during that time are often impossible.

346-12. Supports. Rigid metal conduit shall be installed as a complete system as provided in Article 300 and shall be securely fastened in place. Conduit shall be firmly fastened within 3 feet

(914 mm) of each outlet box, junction box, cabinet, or fitting. Conduit shall be supported at least every 10 feet (3.05 m).

See commentary following Section 348-12.

Exception No. 1: If made up with threaded couplings, it shall be permissible to support straight runs of rigid metal conduit in accordance with Table 346-12, provided such supports prevent transmission of stresses to termination where conduit is deflected between supports.

Exception No. 2: The distance between supports shall be permitted to be increased to 20 feet (6.1 m) for exposed vertical risers from industrial machinery, provided that the conduit is made up with threaded couplings, is firmly supported at the top and bottom of the riser, and no other means of intermediate support is readily available.

Table 346-12. Supports for Rigid Metal Conduit

Conduit Size (Inches)	Maximum Distance Between Rigid Metal Conduit Supports (Feet)
½–¾	10
1	12
1¼–1½	14
2–2½	16
3 and larger	20

For SI units: (Supports) one foot = 0.3048 meter.

346-13. Boxes and Fittings. Boxes and fittings shall comply with the applicable provisions of Article 370.

346-14. Splices and Taps. Splices and taps shall be made only in junction boxes, outlet boxes or conduit bodies. See Article 370.

B. Construction Specifications

346-15. General. Rigid metal conduit shall comply with (a) through (c) below.

(a) Standard Lengths. Rigid metal conduit as shipped shall be in standard lengths of 10 feet (3.05 m) including coupling, one coupling to be furnished with each length. Each length shall be reamed and threaded on each end. For specific applications or uses, it shall be permissible to ship standard lengths or lengths shorter or longer than 10 feet (3.05 m) with or without couplings and with or without threads.

(b) Corrosion-Resistant Material. Nonferrous conduit of corrosion-resistant material shall have suitable markings.

(c) Durably Identified. Each length shall be clearly and durably identified in every 10 feet (3.05 m) as required in the first sentence of Section 110-21.

ARTICLE 347 — RIGID NONMETALLIC CONDUIT

Contents

347-1. Description. This article shall apply to a type of conduit and fittings of suitable nonmetallic material that is resistant to moisture and chemical atmospheres. For use aboveground, it shall also be flame-retardant, resistant to impact and crushing, resistant to distortion from heat under conditions likely to be encountered in service, and resistant to low temperature and sunlight effects. For use underground, the material shall be acceptably resistant to moisture and corrosive agents and shall be of sufficient strength to withstand abuse, such as by impact and crushing, in handling and during installation. Where intended for direct burial, without encasement in concrete, the material shall also be capable of withstanding continued loading that is likely to be encountered after installation.

(FPN): Materials that have been recognized as having suitable physical characteristics when properly formed and treated include fiber, asbestos cement, soapstone, rigid polyvinyl chloride, fiberglass epoxy, and high-density polyethylene for underground use, and rigid polyvinyl chloride for use aboveground.

Three types of rigid nonmetallic conduit are listed by UL: (1) rigid nonmetallic plastic Schedule 40 and 80 PVC; (2) rigid nonmetallic underground plastic; and (3) rigid nonmetallic underground other than plastic, fiber type. Only the rigid nonmetallic plastic Schedule 40 and 80 PVC is suitable for use above ground.

Rigid nonmetallic plastic Schedule 40 and 80 PVC, unless marked for a higher temperature, is intended for use with wires rated 75°C (167°F) or less including where it is encased in concrete within buildings and where ambient temperature is 50°C (122°F) or less. Where encased in concrete in trenches outside of buildings it is suitable for use with wires rated 90°C (194°F) or less.

The UL listings of rigid nonmetallic underground plastic include three types: (1) polyvinyl chloride (PVC) Type A or Type EB; (2) high-density polyethylene (HDPE) Schedule 40; and (3) fiberglass reinforced epoxy. The various conduit types differ in their inside and outside diameters.

This type of conduit is designed for use in underground work under the following conditions, as indicated on the product: (1) when laid with its entire length in concrete (Type A); (2) when laid with its entire length in concrete in outdoor trenches (Type EB); and (3) direct burial with or without being encased in concrete (HDPE Schedule 40 and fiberglass reinforced epoxy). This type of conduit is intended for use in ambient temperatures of 50°C (122°F) or less, and, unless marked otherwise, Type A and HDPE Schedule 40 conduit are intended for use with wires rated 75°C (167°F) or less. Type EB conduit, and Type A conduit encased in concrete in trenches outside of buildings, may be used with wires rated 90°C (194°F) or less. HDPE Schedule 40 conduit, when directly buried or encased in concrete, may be used with wire rated 90°C (194°F) or less. Fiberglass-reinforced epoxy conduit may be used with wires rated 90°C (194°F) or less.

The underground fiber conduit is listed in two types: Type I for use when laid with its entire length in concrete, and Type II for use without concrete encasement.

Rigid nonmetallic conduit is listed in sizes ½ to 6 in. inclusive.

Listed PVC conduit is inherently resistant to atmosphere containing common industrial corrosive agents and will also withstand vapors or mist of caustic, pickling acids, plating baths, and hydrofluoric and chromic acids.

PVC conduit is designed for connection to couplings, fittings, and boxes by the use of a suitable solvent-type cement. Instructions supplied by the manufacturer describe the method of assembly and precautions to be followed.

For use of Schedule 80, see Sections 300-5(d), 551-51(b), and 710-3(b)(1).

347-2. Uses Permitted. The use of rigid nonmetallic conduit and fittings shall be permitted under the following conditions:

(FPN): Extreme cold may cause some nonmetallic conduits to become brittle and therefore more suceptible to damage from physical contact.

(a) Concealed. In walls, floors, and ceilings.

(b) Corrosive Influences. In locations subject to severe corrosive influences as covered in Section 300-6 and where subject to chemicals for which the materials are specifically approved.

(c) Cinders. In cinder fill.

(d) Wet Locations. In portions of dairies, laundries, canneries, or other wet locations and in locations where walls are frequently washed, the entire conduit system including boxes and fittings used therewith shall be so installed and equipped as to prevent water from entering the conduit. All supports, bolts, straps, screws, etc., shall be of corrosion-resistant materials or be protected against corrosion by approved corrosion-resistant materials.

(e) Dry and Damp Locations. In dry and damp locations not prohibited by Section 347-3.

(f) Exposed. For exposed work where not subject to physical damage if identified for such use.

(g) Underground Installations. For underground installations, see Sections 300-5 and 710-3(b).

347-3. Uses Not Permitted. Rigid nonmetallic conduit shall not be used:

(a) Hazardous (Classified) Locations. In hazardous (classified) locations, except as covered in Sections 514-8 and 515-5; and Class I, Division 2 locations as permitted in the Exception to Section 501-4(b).

(b) Support of Fixtures. For the support of fixtures or other equipment.

(c) Physical Damage. Where subject to physical damage unless identified for such use.

(d) Ambient Temperatures. Where subject to ambient temperatures exceeding those for which the conduit is approved.

ARTICLE 347—RIGID NONMETALLIC CONDUIT

See commentary following Section 347-1.

(e) Insulation Temperature Limitations. For conductors whose insulation temperature limitations would exceed those for which the conduit is approved.

See commentary following Section 347-1.

Nonmetallic conduits are not permitted to be installed in ducts, plenums, and other air-handling spaces. See Section 300-22.

In addition, nonmetallic conduits should not be used where their use would substantially increase the possible spread of fire or products of combustion through fire-rated, fire-resistant or fire-stopped walls, partitions, ceilings and floors, hollow spaces, vertical shafts, and ventilating or air-handling ducts. See Section 300-21 for requirements covering the prevention of the spread of fire or products of combustion.

347-4. Other Articles. Installation of rigid nonmetallic conduit shall comply with the applicable provisions of Article 300. Where equipment grounding is required by Article 250, a separate equipment grounding conductor shall be installed in the conduit.

A. Installations

347-5. Trimming. All cut ends shall be trimmed inside and outside to remove rough edges.

See commentary following Section 348-11.

347-6. Joints. All joints between lengths of conduit, and between conduit and couplings, fittings, and boxes, shall be made by an approved method.

347-8. Supports. Rigid nonmetallic conduit shall be secured as required by Table 347-8. In addition, conduit shall be securely fastened within 3 feet (914 mm) of each box, cabinet, or other conduit termination.

Table 347-8. Support of Rigid Nonmetallic Conduit

Conduit Size (Inches)	Maximum Spacing Between Supports (Feet)
½–1	3
1¼–2	5
2½–3	6
3½–5	7
6	8

For SI units: (Supports) one foot = 0.3048 meter.

The requirement in Section 347-8 for a support within 3 ft of each conduit termination is consistent with the minimum support spacing in Table 347-8.

It is recognized that these requirements are fairly stringent because they are based on ambient temperatures higher than normally encountered and utilize horizontal support tests only.

347-9. Expansion Joints. Expansion joints for rigid nonmetallic conduit shall be provided to compensate for thermal expansion and contraction.

Expansion joints or expansion couplings are generally provided in exposed runs of nonmetallic rigid conduit where (1) the run is long, (2) the run is subjected to large temperature variations during installation or afterwards, and (3) expansion and contraction measures are provided for the building structure. Rigid nonmetallic conduit exhibits a considerably greater change in length per degree change in temperature than metal raceway systems.

The normal expansion range of most larger sizes of rigid nonmetallic conduit expansion couplings is generally 6 in. Information concerning installation and application of this type of coupling may be obtained from manufacturer's instructions.

Expansion couplings are seldom used underground where temperatures are relatively constant. Where rigid nonmetallic conduit is buried or covered immediately, expansion and contraction are not a problem.

347-10. Minimum Size. No conduit smaller than ½-inch electrical trade size shall be used.

347-11. Number of Conductors. The number of conductors permitted in a single conduit shall not exceed the percentage fill specified in Table 1, Chapter 9.

Schedule 80 PVC conduit has less cross-sectional area than Schedule 40, rigid metal conduit, or EMT, so Chapter 9 Tables 3A, 3B, and 3C are not applicable to Schedule 80.

(FPN): For conductor cross-sectional area see Tables 5, 5A, 6, 7, 8 and the applicable Notes to Tables at the beginning of Chapter 9.

See commentary following Section 346-6.

347-12. Bushings. Where a conduit enters a box or other fitting, a bushing or adapter shall be provided to protect the wire from abrasion unless the design of the box or fitting is such as to provide equivalent protection.

(FPN): See Section 373-6(c) for the protection of conductors No. 4 AWG and larger at bushings.

347-13. Bends — How Made. Bends of rigid nonmetallic conduit shall be so made that the conduit will not be damaged and that the internal diameter of the conduit will not be effectively reduced. Field bends shall be made only with bending equipment identified for the purpose, and the radius of the curve of the inner edge of such bends shall not be less than shown in Table 346-10.

See commentary following Section 346-10.

347-14. Bends — Number in One Run. A run of conduit between outlet and outlet, fitting and fitting, or outlet and fitting shall not contain more than the equivalent of four quarter bends (360 degrees, total), including those bends located immediately at the outlet or fitting.

347-15. Boxes and Fittings. Boxes and fittings shall comply with the applicable provisions of Article 370.

347-16. Splices and Taps. Splices and taps shall be made only in junction boxes, outlet boxes or conduit bodies. See Article 370.

B. Construction Specifications

347-17. General. Rigid nonmetallic conduit shall comply with the following:

Marking. Each length of nonmetallic conduit shall be clearly and durably marked at least every 10 feet (3.05 m) as required in the first sentence of Section 110-21. The type of material shall also be included in the marking unless it is visually identifiable. For conduit recognized for use aboveground these markings shall be permanent. For conduit limited to underground use only, these markings shall be sufficiently durable to remain legible until the material is installed.

ARTICLE 348 — ELECTRICAL METALLIC TUBING

Contents

348-1. Use. The use of electrical metallic tubing shall be permitted for both exposed and concealed work. Electrical metallic tubing shall not be used: (1) where, during installation or afterward, it will be subject to severe physical damage; (2) where protected from corrosion solely by enamel; (3) in cinder concrete or cinder fill where subject to permanent moisture unless protected on all sides by a layer of noncinder concrete at least 2 inches (50.8 mm) thick or unless the tubing is at least 18 inches (457 mm) under the fill. Where practicable, dissimilar metals in contact anywhere in the system shall be avoided to eliminate the possibility of galvanic action.

Exception: Aluminum fittings and enclosures shall be permitted to be used with steel electrical metallic tubing.

Ferrous or nonferrous electrical metallic tubing, elbows, couplings, and fittings shall be permitted to be installed in concrete, in direct contact with the earth, or in areas subject to severe corrosive influences when protected by corrosion protection and judged suitable for the condition.

Galvanized steel electrical metallic tubing installed in concrete on grade or above grade generally requires no supplementary corrosion protection. EMT installed in concrete below grade level or installed in contact with soil generally requires supplementary corrosion protection.

(FPN): See Section 300-6 for protection against corrosion.

348-2. Other Articles. Installations of electrical metallic tubing shall comply with the applicable provisions of Article 300.

A. Installation

348-4. Wet Locations. All supports, bolts, straps, screws, etc., shall be of corrosion-resistant materials or protected against corrosion by corrosion-resistant materials.

(FPN): See Section 300-6 for protection against corrosion.

348-5. Size.

(a) Minimum. Tubing smaller than ½-inch electrical trade size shall not be used.

Exception No. 1: For underplaster extensions as permitted in Section 344-2.

Exception No. 2: For enclosing the leads of motors as permitted in Section 430-145(b).

(b) Maximum.   The maximum size of tubing shall be the 4-inch electrical trade size.

348-6. Number of Conductors in Tubing.   The number of conductors permitted in a single tubing shall not exceed the percentage fill specified in Table 1, Chapter 9.

(FPN): For conductor cross-sectional area see Tables 5, 5A, 6, 7, 8 and the applicable Notes to Tables at the beginning of Chapter 9.

348-7. Threads.   Electrical metallic tubing shall not be threaded. Where integral couplings are utilized, such couplings shall be permitted to be factory threaded.

348-8. Couplings and Connectors.   Couplings and connectors used with tubing shall be made up tight. Where buried in masonry or concrete, they shall be concretetight type. Where installed in wet locations, they shall be of the raintight type.

UL-listed fittings that are suitable for use in poured concrete or where exposed to rain are so indicated on the fitting or carton. The term "raintight" or the equivalent on the carton indicates suitability for use where directly exposed to rain. The term "concretetight" or equivalent on the carton indicates suitability for use in poured concrete. See Sections 225-22 and 230-53.

Fittings have been tested for use only with steel tubing unless marked on the device or carton to indicate suitability for use with aluminum or other material.

Indentor-type fittings are for use with metallic-coated electrical metallic tubing only and require a special tool supplied by the manufacturer for proper installation. Diametrically opposed indentor-type tools require two sets of indentations nominally 90 degrees apart. Triple indent tools require one set of indentations.

348-9. Bends — How Made.   Bends in the tubing shall be so made that the tubing will not be damaged and that the internal diameter of the tubing will not be effectively reduced. The radius of the curve of the inner edge of any field bend shall not be less than shown in Table 346-10.

Exception: For field bends made with a bending machine designed for the purpose, the minimum radius shall not be less than indicated in Table 346-10 Exception.

348-10. Bends — Number in One Run.   A run of electrical metallic tubing between outlet and outlet, fitting and fitting, or outlet and fitting shall not contain more than the equivalent of four quarter bends (360 degrees, total), including those bends located immediately at the outlet or fitting.

See commentary following Section 346-11.

348-11. Reaming.   All cut ends of electrical metallic tubing shall be reamed or otherwise finished to remove rough edges.

In addition to a reamer, a half-round file has proved practical to remove rough edges with excellent results.

348-12. Supports.   Electrical metallic tubing shall be installed as a complete system as provided in Article 300 and shall be securely fastened in place at least every 10 feet (3.05 m) and within 3 feet (914 mm) of each outlet box, junction box, cabinet, or fitting.

By definition (see Article 100) a coupling is a fitting. See Figure 348-1 for the minimum level of support required. If this does not result in a "secure" fastening, additional support may be necessary.

Figure 348-1. Minimum support required. Note that support is not required within 3 ft on each side of a coupling.

348-13. Boxes and Fittings.   Boxes and fittings shall comply with the applicable provisions of Article 370.

348-14. Splices and Taps.   Splices and taps shall be made only in junction boxes, outlet boxes or conduit bodies. See Article 370.

B. Construction Specifications

348-15. General.   Electrical metallic tubing shall comply with (a) through (c) below.

(a) Cross Section.   The tubing, and elbows and bends for use with the tubing, shall have a circular cross section.

(b) Finish.   Tubing shall have such a finish or treatment of outer surfaces as will provide an approved durable means of readily distinguishing it, after installation, from rigid metal conduit.

(c) Connectors.   Where the tubing is coupled together by threads, the connector shall be so designed as to prevent bending of the tubing at any part of the thread.

ARTICLE 349 — FLEXIBLE METALLIC TUBING

Contents

A. General

349-1. Scope. The provisions of this article apply to a raceway for electric conductors which is circular in cross section, flexible, metallic, and liquidtight without a nonmetallic jacket.

Flexible metallic tubing is a raceway used for certain specific applications, particularly for use under the requirements of Section 300-22(b) and (c) for wiring in ducts, plenums, and other air-handling spaces. Flexible metallic tubing is a material that is readily flexed and is rarely affected by conditions of vibration or other movement. It is an effective barrier to gases and products of combustion when installed with matching fittings and is of adequate mechanical strength for use where not exposed to physical damage. Similarly, flexible metallic tubing has the necessary properties for use as required for tap conductors for lighting fixtures where outlet boxes are placed 1 ft from the fixture. Flexible metallic tubing has advantages over the use of liquidtight flexible metal conduit in ducts and plenums because it does not have a nonmetallic (PVC) outer sheath that would introduce a probable source of smoke and products of combustion into the ventilation system in the event of a fire situation.

349-2. Other Articles. Installations of flexible metallic tubing shall comply with the provisions of the applicable sections of Article 300.

349-3. Uses Permitted. Flexible metallic tubing shall be permitted to be used: (1) in dry locations; (2) in accessible locations when protected from physical damage or concealed such as above suspended ceilings; (3) for 1000 volts maximum; and (4) in branch circuits.

A common application of flexible metallic tubing is as a wiring method for equipment or lighting fixtures mounted on, or above, suspended ceilings.

349-4. Uses Not Permitted. Flexible metallic tubing shall not be used: (1) in hoistways; (2) in storage battery rooms; (3) in hazardous (classified) locations unless otherwise permitted under other articles in this Code; (4) underground for direct earth burial, or embedded in poured concrete or aggregate; (5) where subject to physical damage; and (6) in lengths over 6 feet (1.83 m).

Unlike flexible metal conduit or liquidtight flexible metal conduit, flexible metallic tubing is limited to 6 ft in length.

B. Construction and Installation

349-10. Size.

(a) Minimum. Flexible metallic tubing smaller than ½-inch electrical trade size shall not be used.

Exception No. 1: ⅜-inch trade size shall be permitted to be installed in accordance with Section 300-22(b) and (c).

Exception No. 2: ⅜-inch trade size shall be permitted in lengths not in excess of 6 feet (1.83 m) as part of an approved assembly or for lighting fixtures. See Section 410-67(c).

(b) Maximum. The maximum size of flexible metallic tubing shall be the ¾-inch trade size.

349-12. Number of Conductors.

(a) ½-Inch and ¾-Inch Flexible Metallic Tubing. The number of conductors permitted in ½-inch and ¾-inch trade sizes of flexible metallic tubing shall not exceed the percentage of fill specified in Table 1, Chapter 9.

(b) ⅜-Inch Flexible Metallic Tubing. The number of conductors permitted in ⅜-inch trade size flexible metallic tubing shall not exceed that permitted in Table 350-3.

(FPN): For conductor cross-sectional area see Tables 5, 5A, 6, 7, 8 and the applicable Notes to Tables at the beginning of Chapter 9.

349-16. Grounding. See Section 250-91(b), Exception No. 1.

349-18. Fittings. Flexible metallic tubing shall be used only with approved terminal fittings. Fittings shall effectively close any openings in the connection.

(FPN): See Sections 300-22(b) and (c) for use in ducts, plenums, and other spaces used for environmental air.

349-20. Bends.

(a) Infrequent Flexing Use. Where the flexible metallic tubing shall be infrequently flexed in service after installation, the radii of bends measured to the inside of the bend shall not be less than specified in Table 349-20(a).

(b) Fixed Bends. Where the flexible metallic tubing is bent for installation purposes and is not flexed or bent as required by use after installation, the radii of bends measured to the inside of the bend shall not be less than specified in Table 349-20(b).

Table 349-20(a). Minimum Radii for Flexing Use

Trade Size	Minimum Radii
⅜ inch	10 inches
½ inch	12½ inches
¾ inch	17½ inches

For SI units: (Radii) one inch = 25.4 millimeters.

Table 349-20(b). Minimum Radii for Fixed Bends

Trade Size	Minimum Radii
⅜ inch	3½ inches
½ inch	4 inches
¾ inch	5 inches

For SI units: (Radii) one inch = 25.4 millimeters.

ARTICLE 350 — FLEXIBLE METAL CONDUIT

Contents

350-1. Other Articles. Installations of flexible metal conduit shall comply with the applicable provisions of Articles 300, 333, and 346.

350-2. Use. Flexible metal conduit shall not be used: (1) in wet locations unless conductors are of lead-covered type or of other types approved for the specific conditions and the installation is such that water is not likely to enter other raceways or enclosures to which the conduit is connected; (2) in hoistways, other than provided in Section 620-21; (3) in storage-battery rooms; (4) in any hazardous (classified) location other than permitted in Section 501-4(b); (5) where rubber-covered conductors are exposed to oil, gasoline, or other materials having a deteriorating effect on rubber; nor (6) underground or embedded in poured concrete or aggregate.

Flexible metal conduit is permitted for use in wet locations provided the completed installation prevents water from entering other raceways or enclosures to which the conduit is connected, and the conductors are suitable for wet locations. See Figure 350-1.

Figure 350-1. An example of one acceptable application of flexible metal conduit on the exterior of a building. The branch-circuit supply conductors are suitable for use in a wet location, and the junction box is listed for use in a wet location.

350-3. Minimum Size. Flexible metal conduit less than ½-inch electrical trade size shall not be used.

Exception No. 1: For underplaster extensions as permitted in Section 344-2.

Exception No. 2: For enclosing the leads of motors as permitted in Section 430-145(b).

Exception No. 3: Flexible metal conduit of ⅜-inch nominal trade size shall be permitted in lengths not in excess of 6 feet (1.83 m) as a part of an approved assembly, or for tap connections to lighting fixtures as required in Section 410-67(c), or for lighting fixtures.

This exception makes it clear that ⅜-in. flexible metal conduit is permitted to be used as the factory- or field-installed metal raceway (4 to 6 ft in length) to enclose tap conductors from the outlet box to the fixture terminal housing of recessed lighting fixtures.

389

Also, flexible metal conduit is permitted to be used, for example, as a 6-ft fixture "whip" from an outlet box to a lighting fixture secured to, and supported on, a suspended ceiling.

Exception No. 4: Flexible metal conduit of ⅜-inch nominal trade size shall be permitted for manufactured wiring systems as permitted in Section 604-6(a).

This exception permits a smaller minimum size for manufactured wiring systems because the conductors are not as prone to physical damage when installed under factory-controlled conditions.

Exception No. 5: As permitted in Section 620-21, Exception No. 5.

Table 350-3
Maximum Number of Insulated Conductors in ⅜-Inch Flexible Metal Conduit*

Col. A = With fitting inside conduit.
Col. B = With fitting outside conduit.

Size AWG	Types RFH-2, SF-2		Types TF, T, XHHW, AF, TW, RUH, RUW		Types TFN, THHN, THWN		Types FEP, FEPB, PF, PGF	
	A	B	A	B	A	B	A	B
18	..	3	3	7	4	8	5	8
16	..	2	2	4	3	7	4	8
14	..	..	..	4	3	7	3	7
12	..	..	..	3	..	4	..	4
10	..	..	..	..	..	2	..	3

* In addition, one uninsulated equipment grounding conductor of the same size shall be permitted.

350-4. Supports. Flexible metal conduit shall be secured by an approved means at intervals not exceeding 4½ feet (1.37 m) and within 12 inches (305 mm) on each side of every outlet box, junction box, cabinet, or fitting.

Exception No. 1: Where flexible metal conduit is fished.

Exception No. 2: Lengths not exceeding 3 feet (914 mm) at terminals where flexibility is necessary.

Exception No. 3: Lengths not exceeding 6 feet (1.83 m) from a fixture terminal connection for tap connections to lighting fixtures as required in Section 410-67(c).

Flexible metal conduit is permitted to be concealed or rendered inaccessible by the finish of a building. However, unlike other raceways, such as rigid metal conduit, intermediate metal conduit, or electrical metallic tubing, which are required to be supported every 10 ft and within 3 ft of every box or fitting, flexible metal conduit is required to be supported at least every 4½ ft and within 12 in. of every box or fitting. See Sections 345-12, 346-12, and 348-12. Similar to other raceways, a run of flexible metal conduit installed between boxes, conduit bodies, etc., is not permitted to contain more than the equivalent of four quarter bends (360 degrees total). Adequate shaping and support of this flexible wiring method will assure that conductors can be easily installed or withdrawn at any time.

350-5. Grounding. Flexible metal conduit shall be permitted as a grounding means as covered in Section 250-91(b). Where an equipment bonding jumper is required around flexible metal conduit, it shall be installed in accordance with Section 250-79.

Where flexible metal conduit and fittings have not been specifically approved as a grounding means, a separate equipment grounding or bonding conductor (insulated or bare) is required to be run inside or outside the conduit. Where run outside as an equipment bonding jumper, the jumper is required to be 6 ft or less in length, routed with the raceway, and bonded at each end of the flexible metal conduit to which it is connected.

When used in hazardous (classified) locations, a bonding jumper is specifically required. See Sections 501-16(b), 502-16(b), and 503-16(b).

Exception No. 1: Flexible metal conduit shall be permitted as a grounding means if the total length in any ground return path is 6 feet (1.83 m) or less, the conduit is terminated in fittings approved for grounding, and the circuit conductors contained therein are protected by overcurrent devices rated at 20 amperes or less.

Flexible metal conduit is permitted as an equipment grounding means where it is installed in 6-ft lengths so that a ground fault anywhere in the circuit will not have to traverse through more than 6 ft of flexible metal conduit before the fault current returns to the overcurrent device protecting the circuit. When flexible metal conduit is not cut squarely, so as to provide a proper fit into fittings which clamp around the conduit or are screwed into the conduit, the effectiveness of the grounding path may be reduced. See the commentary following Section 250-91(b). See Figure 350-2.

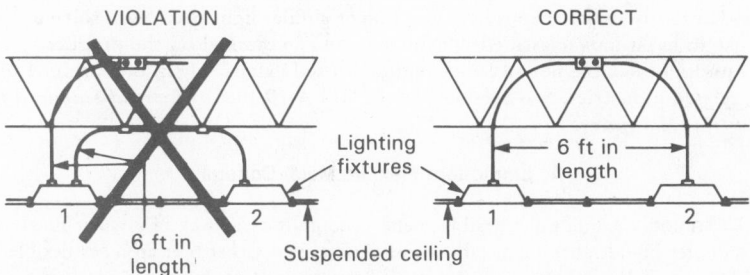

Figure 350-2. The sketch on the right shows the proper application of flexible metal conduit where the total length of any ground return path is limited to 6 ft. The sketch on the left shows an application that is in violation, as the ground return for fixture No. 2 is 12 ft.

Exception No. 2: Where used to connect equipment where flexibility is required, a grounding conductor shall be installed.

Flexibility is required where flexible metal conduit is used to connect to vibrating equipment or equipment that is not fixed in one place, such as motors. Under these conditions, a separate grounding conductor is required to be installed.

350-6. Bends. A run of conduit between outlet and outlet, fitting and fitting, or outlet and fitting shall not contain more than the equivalent of four quarter bends (360 degrees, total), including those bends located immediately at the outlet or fitting.

Angle connectors shall not be used for concealed raceway installations.

ARTICLE 351 — LIQUIDTIGHT FLEXIBLE METAL CONDUIT AND LIQUIDTIGHT FLEXIBLE NONMETALLIC CONDUIT

Contents

351-1. Scope. This article covers liquidtight flexible metal conduit and liquidtight flexible nonmetallic conduit.

Liquidtight flexible metal conduit is intended for use in wet locations or where exposed to mineral oil, both at a maximum temperature of 60°C (140°F). It is not intended for use where exposed to gasoline or similar light petroleum solvents nor for use in hazardous (classified) locations unless so marked on the product.

Liquidtight flexible nonmetallic conduit is used extensively in the machine tool and related industries. See Section 15-6 in NFPA 79-1985, *Electrical Standard for Industrial Machinery*.

A. Liquidtight Flexible Metal Conduit

351-2. Definition. Liquidtight flexible metal conduit is a raceway of circular cross section having an outer liquidtight, nonmetallic, sunlight-resistant jacket over an inner flexible metal core with associated couplings, connectors, and fittings and approved for the installation of electric conductors.

351-3. Other Articles. Installations of liquidtight flexible metal conduit shall comply with the applicable provisions of Article 300 and with the specific sections of Articles 350, 501, 502, 503, and 553 referenced below.

351-4. Use.

(a) Permitted. The use of listed and marked liquidtight flexible metal conduit shall be permitted for direct burial in earth and for exposed and concealed work:

(1) Where conditions of installation, operation, or maintenance require flexibility or protection from liquids, vapors, or solids.

(2) As permitted by Sections 501-4(b), 502-4, and 503-3, and in other hazardous (classified) locations where specifically approved, and by Section 553-7(b).

"Listed and marked" liquidtight flexible metal conduit is permitted for direct burial in the earth. It should be noted that the requirements of Section 300-5 are applicable to liquidtight flexible metal conduit where installed underground.

(b) Not Permitted. Liquidtight flexible metal conduit shall not be used:

(1) Where subject to physical damage.

(2) Where any combination of ambient and/or conductor temperature will produce an operating temperature in excess of that for which the material is approved.

351-5. Size.

(a) Minimum. Liquidtight flexible metal conduit smaller than ½-inch electrical trade size shall not be used.

Exception: ⅜-inch size shall be permitted as covered in Section 350-3.

(b) Maximum. The maximum size of liquidtight flexible metal conduit shall be the 4-inch trade size.

351-6. Number of Conductors.

(a) Single Conduit. The number of conductors permitted in a single conduit, ½- through 4-inch trade sizes, shall not exceed the percentage of fill specified in Table 1, Chapter 9.

(b) ⅜-Inch Liquidtight Flexible Metal Conduit. The number of conductors permitted in ⅜-inch liquidtight flexible metal conduit shall not exceed that permitted in Table 350-3.

351-7. Fittings. Liquidtight flexible metal conduit shall be used only with approved terminal fittings.

351-8. Supports. Where liquidtight flexible metal conduit is installed as a fixed raceway, it shall be secured at intervals not exceeding 4½ feet (1.37 m) and within 12 inches (305 mm) on each side of every outlet box, junction box, cabinet, or fitting.

Exception No. 1: Where liquidtight flexible metal conduit is fished.

Exception No. 2: Lengths not exceeding 3 feet (914 mm) at terminals where flexibility is necessary.

Exception No. 3: Lengths not exceeding 6 feet (1.83 m) from a fixture terminal connection for tap conductors to lighting fixtures as required in Section 410-67(c).

351-9. Grounding. Liquidtight flexible metal conduit shall be permitted as a grounding conductor where both the conduit and the fittings are approved for grounding. Where an equipment bonding jumper is required around liquidtight flexible metal conduit, it shall be installed in accordance with Section 250-79.

Exception No. 1: Liquidtight flexible metal conduit shall be permitted as a grounding means in the 1¼-inch and smaller trade sizes if the total length of all liquidtight flexible metal conduit in any ground return path is 6 feet (1.83 m) or less, the conduit is terminated in fittings listed for grounding, and the circuit conductors contained therein are protected by overcurrent devices rated at 20 amperes or less for ⅜-inch and ½-inch trade sizes and 60 amperes or less for ¾-inch through 1¼-inch trade sizes.

See commentary following Section 250-91(b), Exception No. 2.

Exception No. 2: When used to connect equipment where flexibility is required, an equipment grounding conductor shall be installed.

ARTICLE 351—LIQUIDTIGHT FLEXIBLE CONDUIT

See commentary following Section 350-5, Exception No. 2.

(FPN): See Sections 501-16(b), 502-16(b), and 503-16(b) for types of equipment grounding conductors.

Where liquidtight flexible metal conduit is installed in hazardous (classified) locations, a bonding jumper is required.

351-10. Bends. A run of conduit between outlet and outlet, fitting and fitting, or outlet and fitting shall not contain more than the equivalent of four quarter bends (360 degrees, total), including those bends located immediately at the outlet or fitting.

Angle connectors shall not be used for concealed raceway installations.

B. Liquidtight Flexible Nonmetallic Conduit

351-22. Definition. Liquidtight flexible nonmetallic conduit is a raceway of circular cross section having a smooth inner surface with integral reinforcement within the conduit wall. This conduit is flame-resistant and with fittings is approved for the installation of electrical conductors.

351-23. Use.

(a) Permitted. Liquidtight flexible nonmetallic conduit shall be permitted to be used in exposed locations:

(FPN): Extreme cold may cause some types of nonmetallic conduits to become brittle and therefore more susceptible to damage from physical contact.

(1) Where flexibility is required for installation, operation, or maintenance;

(2) Where protection of the contained conductors is required from vapors, liquids, or solids;

(3) For outdoor locations where listed and marked as suitable for the purpose.

(b) Not Permitted. Liquidtight flexible nonmetallic conduit shall not be used:

(1) Where subject to physical damage;

(2) Where any combination of ambient and conductor temperatures is in excess of that for which the liquidtight flexible nonmetallic conduit is approved;

(3) In lengths longer than 6 feet (1.83 m);

Exception: Where approved for special installations.

(4) Where voltage of the contained conductors is in excess of 600 volts, nominal.

351-24. Size. The sizes of liquidtight flexible nonmetallic conduit shall be electrical trade sizes ½ inch to 2 inch inclusive.

Exception: ⅜-inch size for enclosing the leads of motors as permitted in Section 430-145(b).

351-25. Number of Conductors. The number of conductors permitted in a single conduit shall be in accordance with the percentage fill specified in Table 1, Chapter 9.

351-26. Fittings. Liquidtight flexible nonmetallic conduit shall be used only with terminal fittings identified for such use.

351-27. Equipment Grounding. Where an equipment grounding conductor is required for the circuits installed in liquidtight flexible nonmetallic conduit, it shall be permitted to be installed on the inside or outside of the conduit. Where installed on the outside, the length of the equipment grounding conductor shall not exceed 6 feet (1.83 m) and shall be routed with the raceway or enclosure. Fittings and boxes shall be bonded or grounded in accordance with Article 250.

ARTICLE 352 — SURFACE METAL RACEWAYS AND SURFACE NONMETALLIC RACEWAYS

Contents

A. Surface Metal Raceways

352-1. Use. The use of surface metal raceways shall be permitted in dry locations. They shall not be used: (1) where subject to severe physical damage unless otherwise approved; (2) where the voltage is 300 volts or more between conductors unless the metal has a thickness of not less than .040 inch (1.02 mm); (3) where subject to corrosive vapors; (4) in hoistways; (5) in any hazardous (classified) location except Class I, Division 2 locations as permitted in the Exception to Section 501-4(b); nor (6) concealed except as follows:

Exception No. 1: Surface metal raceways shall be permitted for underplaster extensions where identified for such use.

Exception No. 2: As permitted in Section 645-2(c)(2).

(FPN): See definition of "Exposed — (As applied to wiring methods)" in Article 100.

352-2. Other Articles. Surface metal raceways shall comply with the applicable provisions of Article 300.

352-3. Size of Conductors. No conductor larger than that for which the raceway is designed shall be installed in surface metal raceway.

The number, type, and size of conductors that are permitted to be installed in a listed raceway is marked on the raceway or on the package in which it is shipped.

Raceways, which have been listed for use with lighting fixtures and/or other devices, are marked to this effect on the raceway or on the package in which it is shipped.

The UL Listing Mark is applied to each length or package of complete raceway, raceway cover, or raceway base.

Figure 352-1. Surface metal raceway used as an extension from an existing receptacle. This installation is typical of how surface raceways can be used.

Figure 352-2. A shallow switch box used with a surface raceway.

Some lighting fixtures covered under the UL categories of "fixtures" and "recessed-type fixtures" are suitable for use as raceways. See Section 250-91(b)(10).

See Figures 352-3 and 352-4.

352-4. Number of Conductors in Raceways. The number of conductors installed in any raceway shall be no greater than the number for which the raceway is designed.

The derating factors in Note 8 (a) to Tables 310-16 through 310-31 shall not apply to conductors installed in surface metal raceways when all of the following conditions are met: (1) the cross-sectional area of the raceway exceeds 4 square inches (2580 sq mm); (2) the current-carrying conductors do not exceed thirty in number; (3) the sum of the cross-sectional area of all contained conductors does not exceed 20 percent of the interior cross-sectional area of the surface metal raceway.

(FPN): For conductor cross-sectional area see Tables 5, 5A, 6, 7, 8 and the applicable Notes to Tables at the beginning of Chapter 9.

352-5. Extension Through Walls and Floors. It shall be permissible to extend unbroken lengths of surface metal raceways through dry walls, dry partitions, and dry floors.

(FPN): See Section 353-3 for multioutlet assemblies.

352-6. Combination Raceways. Where combination surface metal raceways are used both for signaling and for lighting and power circuits, the different systems shall be run in separate compartments identified by sharply contrasting colors of the interior finish, and the same relative position of compartments shall be maintained throughout the premises.

352-7. Splices and Taps. Splices and taps shall be permitted in surface metal raceway having a removable cover that is accessible after installation. The conductors, including splices and taps, shall not fill the raceway to more than 75 percent of its area at that point. Splices and taps in surface metal raceways without removable covers shall be made only in junction boxes. All splices and taps shall be made by approved methods.

352-8. Construction. Surface metal raceways shall be of such construction as will distinguish them from other raceways. Surface metal raceways and their elbows, couplings, and similar fittings shall be so designed that the sections can be electrically and mechanically coupled together without subjecting the wires to abrasion. Holes for screws or bolts inside the raceway shall be so designed that when screws or bolts are installed the heads will be flush with the metal surface.
  Where covers and accessories of nonmetallic materials are used on surface metal raceways, they shall be identified for such use.

B. Surface Nonmetallic Raceways

352-21. Description. Part B of this article shall apply to a type of surface nonmetallic raceway and fittings of suitable nonmetallic material that is resistant to moisture and chemical atmospheres. It shall also be flame-retardant, resistant to impact and crushing, resistant to distortion from heat under conditions likely to be encountered in service, and resistant to low-temperature effects.

352-22. Use. The use of surface nonmetallic raceways shall be permitted in dry locations. They shall not be used: (1) where concealed; (2) where subject to severe physical damage; (3) where the voltage is 300 volts or more between conductors; (4) in hoistways; (5) in any hazardous (classified) location except Class I, Division 2 locations as permitted in the Exception to Section 501-4(b); (6) where subject to ambient temperature exceeding 50°C; nor (7) for conductors whose insulation temperature exceeds 75°C.

352-23. Other Articles. Surface nonmetallic raceways shall comply with the applicable provisions of Article 300.

352-24. Size of Conductors. No conductor larger than that for which the raceway is designed shall be installed in surface nonmetallic raceway.

352-25. Number of Conductors in Raceways. The number of conductors installed in any raceway shall be no greater than the number for which the raceway is designed.

352-26. Combination Raceways. Where combination surface nonmetallic raceways are used both for signaling and for lighting and power circuits, the different systems shall be run in

Type of Raceway	Wire Size Gage No.	Types RHH, RHW	Type THW	Type TW	Types THHN, THWN
			Number of Wires		
No. 200	12		2	3	3
	14		2	3	5
No. 500	8			2	2
	10	2	2	3	4
	12	2	3	4	7
	14	2	4	6	9
No. 700	6				2
	8		2	2	3
	10	2	3	4	5
	12	2	4	6	8
	14	3	5	7	11
No. 1500	6				2
	8			2	3
	10	2	3	4	5
	12	2	3	5	7
	14	2	4	6	10
No. 2000†	12			7	7
	14			7	7
No. 2100†	6	2	4	4	6
	8	4	6	8	10
	10	7	10	14	17
	12	8	13	19	28
	14	10	15	24	37
No. 2200†	6	5	7	3* 7	11
	8	8	11	7* 14	19
	10	13	19	10* 26	32
	12	15	23	10* 34	51
	14	18	29	10* 44	69
No. 2600	6	2	3	3	5
	8	4	5	7	9
	10	6	9	12	15
	12	7	11	16	24
	14	9	14	21	33
G-3000	6	4* 11	6* 19	6* 17	6* 27
	8	6* 18	8* 26	8* 34	8* 44
	10	10* 30	10* 45	10* 62	10* 76
	12	14* 36	18* 55	18* 81	18* 119
	14	16* 42	26* 67	26* 103	26* 160
G-4000 — With Divider	2	- 7	- 10	- 10	- 12
	3	- 8	- 11	- 11	- 15
	4	- 9	- 13	- 13	- 17
	6	4* 12	4* 18	4* 18	7* 28.
	8	7* 19	7* 28	7* 36	8* 47
	10	11* 32	11* 48	11* 66	15* 81
	12	15* 39	15* 59	15* 86	24* 128
	14	17* 45	17* 72	17* 110	32* 171
Without Divider	2	- 14	- 20	- 20	- 25
	3	- 16	- 23	- 23	- 30
	4	- 18	- 27	- 27	- 35
	6	8* 24	8* 36	8* 36	10* 57
	8	10* 39	10* 57	10* 78	15* 94
	10	15* 65	15* 96	12* 133	18* 163
	12	21* 78	21* 119	16* 174	34* 256
	14	21* 91	21* 145	17* 222	34* 344
G-6000	2/0	10* 17	12* 22	12* 22	15* 27
	1/0	11* 20	14* 26	14* 26	18* 33
	1	12* 23	17* 31	17* 31	21* 39
	2	16* 30	23* 43	23* 43	29* 53
	3	19* 34	27* 50	27* 50	34* 63
	4	21* 39	32* 58	32* 58	40* 74
	6	27* 51	42* 77	42* 77	66* 122
	8	40* 74	57* 106	73* 134	92* 169
	10	75* 137	111* 203	154* 282	187* 343
	12	90* 164	137* 252	200* 368	295* 540
	14	105* 193	167* 307	255* 469	396* 726

† Figures for Nos. 2000, 2100, 2200, G-3000, G-4000, and G-6000 are *without receptacles*, except where noted.
*With receptacles.

Figure 352-3. Wiremold surface metal raceway. (*The Wiremold Co.*)

Type of Raceway	Wire Size Gage No.	Types RHH, RHW	Type RH	Type THW	Types T, TW	Types THHN, THWN
No. 111 (17/64 in. × 33/64 in.)	12				2	3
	14				2	3
No. 222 (3/8 in. × 7/8 in.)	8				2	2
	10	2		2	4	4
	12	2		3	5	7
	14	3		4	6	10
No. 333 (7/16 in. × 1 in.)	6					2
	8			2	2	3
	10	2	2	3	5	6
	12	2	4	4	6	9
	14	3	4	5	8	12
No. 888 (11/16 in. × 1 23/64 in.)	6	2	2	3	3	5
	8	3	3	5	7	9
	10	6	6	9	13	16
	12	7	10	11	17	25
	14	9	12	14	22	34
No. 711 (3/8 in. × 1 1/8 in.)	8				2	2
	10			2	3	4
	12	2	2	3	4	7
	14	2	3	4	6	9
No. 733 (11/16 in. × 2 1/32 in.)	6	3	3	4	4	7
	8	4	4	7	9	11
	10	8	8	11	16	20
	12	9	13	14	21	31
	14	11	16	17	27	42
No. 1700† (1 5/8 in. × 2 1/8 in.)	6	3* 8	3* 8	5* 13	5* 13	8* 21
	8	5* 14	5* 14	8* 21	10* 27	13* 34
	10	9* 24	9* 24	13* 35	19* 49	23* 60
	12	11* 28	15* 39	17* 43	24* 64	36* 94
	14	13* 33	18* 48	20* 53	31* 81	49* 126
No. 3400	Catalog No. 3400 is a raceway consisting of two No. 1700 housings in a common cover. Each channel has the same wire fill as 1700.					
No. 5100	Catalog No. 5100 is a raceway consisting of three No. 1700 housings in a common cover. Each channel has the same wire fill at 1700.					

†Figures for No. 1700 are *without devices*, except where noted.
*With devices.

Figure 352-4. Types of surface metal raceways. (*Walker Div. of Butler Mfg. Co.*)

separate compartments, identified by printed legend or by sharply contrasting colors of the interior finish, and the same relative position of compartments shall be maintained throughout the premises.

352-27. General. Surface nonmetallic raceways shall be of such construction as will distinguish them from other raceways. Surface nonmetallic raceways and their elbows, couplings, and similar fittings shall be so designed that the sections can be mechanically coupled together without subjecting the wires to abrasion. Holes for screws or bolts inside the raceway shall be so designed that when screws or bolts are installed the heads will be flush with the nonmetallic surface.

ARTICLE 353 — MULTIOUTLET ASSEMBLY

Contents

353-1. Other Articles. A multioutlet assembly shall comply with applicable provisions of Article 300.

(FPN): See definition in Article 100.

Multioutlet assemblies are metal raceways that are usually surface mounted and designed to contain branch-circuit conductors and receptacles. Receptacles may be spaced at desired intervals and may be assembled at the factory or in the field. See Section 220-3(c), Exception No. 1 and Figure 220-4.

353-2. Use. The use of multioutlet assembly shall be permitted in dry locations. It shall not be installed: (1) where concealed, except that it shall be permissible to surround the back and sides of a metal multioutlet assembly by the building finish or recess a nonmetallic multioutlet assembly in a baseboard; (2) where subject to severe physical damage; (3) where the voltage is 300 volts or more between conductors unless the assembly is of metal having a thickness of not less than .040 inch (1.02 mm); (4) where subject to corrosive vapors; (5) in hoistways; nor (6) in any hazardous (classified) locations except Class I, Division 2 locations as permitted in the Exception to Section 501-4(b).

353-3. Metal Multioutlet Assembly Through Dry Partitions. It shall be permissible to extend a metal multioutlet assembly through (not run within) dry partitions, if arrangements are made for removing the cap or cover on all exposed portions and no outlet is located within the partitions.

ARTICLE 354 — UNDERFLOOR RACEWAYS

Contents

354-1. Other Articles. Underfloor raceways shall comply with the applicable provisions of Article 300.

354-2. Use. The installation of underfloor raceways shall be permitted beneath the surface of concrete or other flooring material or in office occupancies, where laid flush with the concrete floor and covered with linoleum or equivalent floor covering. Underfloor raceways shall not be installed (1) where subject to corrosive vapors, nor (2) in any hazardous (classified) location except Class I, Division 2 locations as permitted in the Exception to Section 501-4(b). Unless made of a material judged suitable for the condition or unless corrosion protection approved for the condition is provided, ferrous or nonferrous metal underfloor raceways, junction boxes, and fittings shall not be installed in concrete, or in areas subject to severe corrosive influences.

An underfloor raceway is a practical means of bringing light, power, and signal systems to desks, work benches, or tables that are not located adjacent to wall space. This wiring method offers great flexibility in layout when used with movable partitions and is commonly used in large retail stores and office buildings to supply power at any desired location.

Underfloor raceways are permitted beneath the surface of concrete, wood, or other flooring material. The wiring method between cabinets, raceway junction boxes, and outlet boxes may be rigid metal conduit, intermediate metal conduit, rigid nonmetallic conduit, or EMT. Flexible metal conduit may be used when not installed in concrete.

354-3. Covering. Raceway coverings shall comply with (a) through (d) below.

(a) Raceways Not Over 4 Inches (102 mm) Wide. Half-round and flat-top raceways not over 4 inches (102 mm) in width shall have not less than ¾ inch (19 mm) of concrete or wood above the raceway.

Exception: As permitted in (c) below for flat-top raceways.

(b) Raceways Over 4 Inches (102 mm) Wide but Not Over 8 Inches (203 mm) Wide. Flat-top raceways over 4 inches (102 mm) but not over 8 inches (203 mm) wide with a minimum of 1 inch (25.4 mm) spacing between raceways shall be covered with concrete to a depth of not less than 1 inch (25.4 mm). Raceways spaced less than 1 inch (25.4 mm) apart shall be covered with concrete to a depth of 1½ inches (38 mm).

(c) Trench-type Raceways Flush with Concrete. Trench-type flush raceways with removable covers shall be permitted to be laid flush with the floor surface. Such approved raceways shall be so designed that the cover plates will provide adequate mechanical protection and rigidity equivalent to junction box covers.

Approved flush-type underfloor raceways may be installed flush with the floor surface provided they have covers at least equal to those of junction box covers. Coverings for underfloor raceways are illustrated in Figures 354-1, 354-2, and 354-3.

(d) Other Raceways Flush with Concrete. In office occupancies, approved metal flat-top raceways, if not over 4 inches (102 mm) in width, shall be permitted to be laid flush with the concrete floor surface provided they are covered with substantial linoleum not less than 1/16 inch (1.59 mm) in thickness or with equivalent floor covering. Where more than one and not more than three single raceways are each installed flush with the concrete, they shall be contiguous with each other and joined to form a rigid assembly.

354-4. Size of Conductors. No conductor larger than that for which the raceway is designed shall be installed in underfloor raceways.

354-5. Maximum Number of Conductors in Raceway. The combined cross-sectional area of all conductors or cables shall not exceed 40 percent of the interior cross-sectional area of the raceway.

(FPN): For conductor cross-sectional area see Tables 5, 5A, 6, 7, 8 and the applicable Notes to Tables at the beginning of Chapter 9.

Figure 354-1. A ¾-in. wood or concrete covering is required over underfloor raceways, except for trench-type flush raceways. See Section 354-3(a). (*Walker Div. of Butler Mfg. Co.*)

Figure 354-2. Flat-top underfloor raceways over 4 in. in width and spaced less than 1 in. apart must be covered with at least 1½ in. of concrete. See Section 354-3(b). (*Walker Div. of Butler Mfg. Co.*)

Figure 354-3. A receptacle outlet supplied from an underfloor raceway by the "loop" method of wiring.

354-6. Splices and Taps.   Splices and taps shall be made only in junction boxes.

For the purposes of this section, so-called loop wiring (continuous, unbroken conductor connecting the individual outlets) shall not be considered to be a splice or tap.

Exception: Splices and taps shall be permitted in trench-type flush raceway having a removable cover that is accessible after installation. The conductors, including splices and taps, shall not fill the raceway more than 75 percent of its area at that point.

354-7. Discontinued Outlets.   When an outlet is abandoned, discontinued, or removed, the sections of circuit conductors supplying the outlet shall be removed from the raceway. No splices or reinsulated conductors, such as would be the case with abandoned outlets on loop wiring, shall be allowed in raceways.

Loop wiring (continuous, unbroken conductors) is recognized when it runs from the underfloor raceway up to the terminals of attached receptacles, back into the raceway, and then on to the next device. See Figure 354-3.

When an outlet is removed, the sections of conductors supplying the outlet must be removed from the raceway as well. As would be the case with abandoned outlets on loop wiring, reinsulated or spliced conductors are not allowed in the raceways except trench-type raceways as covered in the exception to Section 354-6. See Section 300-15(a).

354-8. Laid in Straight Lines. Underfloor raceways shall be laid so that a straight line from the center of one junction box to the center of the next junction box will coincide with the center line of the raceway system. Raceways shall be firmly held in place to prevent disturbing this alignment during construction.

354-9. Markers at Ends. A suitable marker shall be installed at or near each end of each straight run of raceways to locate the last insert.

354-10. Dead Ends. Dead ends of raceways shall be closed.

354-13. Junction Boxes. Junction boxes shall be leveled to the floor grade and sealed to prevent the free entrance of water or concrete. Junction boxes used with metal raceways shall be metal and shall be electrically continuous with the raceways.

354-14. Inserts. Inserts shall be leveled and sealed to prevent the entrance of concrete. Inserts used with metal raceways shall be metal and shall be electrically continuous with the raceway. Inserts set in or on fiber raceways before the floor is laid shall be mechanically secured to the raceway. Inserts set in fiber raceways after the floor is laid shall be screwed into the raceway. In cutting through the raceway wall and setting inserts, chips and other dirt shall not be allowed to remain in the raceway, and tools shall be used that are so designed as to prevent the tool from entering the raceway and damaging conductors that may be in place.

354-15. Connections to Cabinets and Wall Outlets. Connections between raceways and distribution centers and wall outlets shall be made by means of flexible metal conduit when not installed in concrete, rigid metal conduit, intermediate metal conduit, electrical metallic tubing, or approved fittings. Where a metallic underfloor raceway system provides for the termination of an equipment grounding conductor, rigid nonmetallic conduit or electrical nonmetallic tubing shall be permitted.

ARTICLE 356 — CELLULAR METAL FLOOR RACEWAYS

Contents

356-1. Definitions. For the purposes of this article, a "cellular metal floor raceway" shall be defined as the hollow spaces of cellular metal floors, together with suitable fittings, which may be approved as enclosures for electric conductors. A "cell" shall be defined as a single, enclosed tubular space in a cellular metal floor member, the axis of the cell being parallel to the axis of the metal floor member. A "header" shall be defined as a transverse raceway for electric conductors, providing access to predetermined cells of a cellular metal floor, thereby permitting the installation of electric conductors from a distribution center to the cells.

Cellular metal floor raceways are a form of metal floor deck construction, designed for use in steel frame buildings, and consist of sheet metal formed into shapes combining to form cells or raceways. The cells extend across the building and, depending on the structural strength required, can have various shapes and sizes.

One type of cellular metal floor is illustrated in Figure 356-1. See Figure 356-2 for installation of header ducts (one for power conductors and one for telephone conductors) prior to the concrete being poured.

Figure 356-1. One type of cellular metal floor construction as viewed in the so-called "slab" stage of installation. (*Square D Co.*)

356-2. Use. Conductors shall not be installed in cellular metal floor raceways (1) where subject to corrosive vapor; (2) in any hazardous (classified) location except Class I, Division 2 locations as permitted in the Exception to Section 501-4(b); nor (3) in commercial garages, other than for supplying ceiling outlets or extensions to the area below the floor but not above.

(FPN): See Section 300-8 for installation of conductors with other systems.

Section 300-8 prohibits the installation of electric conductors in raceways, cables, or cable trays containing any pipes, tubes, etc. for steam, water, air, gas, drainage, or any service other than electrical.

356-3. Other Articles. Cellular metal floor raceways shall comply with the applicable provisions of Article 300.

A. Installation

356-4. Size of Conductors. No conductor larger than No. 1/0 shall be installed, except by special permission.

Figure 356-2. Telephone and power header ducts feeding Cellufloor distribution system. (*Square D Co.*)

356-5. Maximum Number of Conductors in Raceway. The combined cross-sectional area of all conductors or cables shall not exceed 40 percent of the interior cross-sectional area of the cell or header.

(FPN): For conductor cross-sectional area see Tables 5, 5A, 6, 7, 8 and the applicable Notes to Tables at the beginning of Chapter 9.

Connections to the cells are made by means of headers extending across the cells and connecting only to those cells that are to be used as raceways for the conductors. Two or three separate headers, connecting to different sets of cells, may be used for different systems, such as light and power systems, signaling systems, and communication systems.

Figure 356-3 shows the cells with a header in place. The header is extended up to a cabinet or distribution center on a wall or column by means of a special elbow fitting. A junction box or access fitting is provided at each point where the header crosses a cell to which it connects.

See Figure 354-3 and commentary following Section 354-7.

356-6. Splices and Taps. Splices and taps shall be made only in header access units or junction boxes.

For the purposes of this section, so-called loop wiring (continuous unbroken conductor connecting the individual outlets) shall not be considered to be a splice or tap.

356-7. Discontinued Outlets. When an outlet is abandoned, discontinued, or removed, the sections of circuit conductors supplying the outlet shall be removed from the raceway. No splices or reinsulated conductors, such as would be the case with abandoned outlets on loop wiring, shall be allowed in raceways.

356-8. Markers. A suitable number of markers shall be installed for the future locating of cells.

Figure 356-3. A typical cellular metal floor raceway installation showing cells, header ducts, junction boxes, and special elbow fittings. (*Square D Co.*)

Markers are brass flat-head screws set into the top side of the cells and so adjusted that their heads, flush with the floor finish, are exposed to locate cells for future installations.

356-9. Junction Boxes. Junction boxes shall be leveled to the floor grade and sealed against the free entrance of water or concrete. Junction boxes used with these raceways shall be of metal and shall be electrically continuous with the raceway.

356-10. Inserts. Inserts shall be leveled to the floor grade and sealed against the entrance of concrete. Inserts shall be of metal and shall be electrically continuous with the raceway. In cutting through the cell wall and setting inserts, chips and other dirt shall not be allowed to remain in the raceway, and tools shall be used that are designed to prevent the tool from entering the cell and damaging the conductors.

Figure 356-3 illustrates cells connected to "headers" with junction boxes for future access and a special elbow fitting for connecting the "header" to a cabinet. Connections to wall outlets are to be made with metal raceways unless there are provisions for equipment grounding termination (see Section 356-11).

Installation instructions are supplied by the manufacturer for the use of the general contractor, erector, electrical contractor, inspector, and others concerned with the installation.

Figure 356-4 illustrates a preset dual insert, installed prior to concrete being applied, used with cellular metal floor raceways. To install an insert after concrete has been applied, markers should be checked to locate a cell (see Section 356-8). Then, a properly sized concrete-boring drill is used to cut through the concrete to expose the top of the cell. At this point a properly sized metal-cutting hole saw is used to cut through the cell wall. The saw depth is preset to prevent the tool from entering the cell and injuring the conductors. The metal insert threads into the hole providing an electrical, mechanical, and bushed connection.

Figure 356-4. A preset dual insert used with a cellular metal floor raceway to provide access to the power and telephone/signal cells in the floor. Note separation. (*Square D Co.*)

356-11. Connection to Cabinets and Extensions from Cells. Connections between raceways and distribution centers and wall outlets shall be made by means of flexible metal conduit when not installed in concrete, rigid metal conduit, intermediate metal conduit, electrical metallic tubing, or approved fittings. Where there are provisions for the termination of an equipment grounding conductor, nonmetallic conduit or electrical nonmetallic tubing shall be permitted.

B. Construction Specifications

356-12. General. Cellular metal floor raceways shall be so constructed that adequate electrical and mechanical continuity of the complete system will be secured. They shall provide a complete enclosure for the conductors. The interior surfaces shall be free from burrs and sharp edges, and surfaces over which conductors are drawn shall be smooth. Suitable bushings or fittings having smooth rounded edges shall be provided where conductors pass.

ARTICLE 358 — CELLULAR CONCRETE FLOOR RACEWAYS

Contents

358-1. Scope. This article covers cellular concrete floor raceways, the hollow spaces in floors constructed of precast cellular concrete slabs, together with suitable metal fittings designed to provide access to the floor cells.

Cellular concrete floor raceways are a form of floor deck construction and are commonly used in high-rise office buildings. This method is very similar in design, application, and adaptation to cellular metal floor raceways.

Basically, this wiring method consists of floor cells (which are part of the structural floor system); header ducts, laid at right angles to the cells and which are used to carry conductors from cabinets to cells; and junction boxes as shown in Figure 358-1.

ARTICLE 358—CELLULAR CONCRETE FLOOR RACEWAYS

Figure 358-1. Standard underfloor duct used on precast cellular concrete floor raceway. *(Square D Co.)*

358-2. Definitions. A "cell" shall be defined as a single, enclosed tubular space in a floor made of precast cellular concrete slabs, the direction of the cell being parallel to the direction of the floor member. A "header" shall be defined as transverse metal raceways for electric conductors, providing access to predetermined cells of a precast cellular concrete floor, thereby permitting the installation of electric conductors from a distribution center to the floor cells.

358-3. Other Articles. Cellular concrete floor raceways shall comply with the applicable provisions of Article 300.

358-4. Use. Conductors shall not be installed in precast cellular concrete floor raceways (1) where subject to corrosive vapor; (2) in hazardous (classified) locations except Class I, Division 2 locations as permitted in the Exception to Section 501-4(b); nor (3) in commercial garages, other than for supplying ceiling outlets or extensions to the area below the floor but not above.

(FPN): See Section 300-8 for installation of conductors with other systems.

Section 300-8 prohibits the installation of electric conductors in raceways, cables, or cable trays containing any pipes, tubes, etc. for steam, water, air, gas, drainage, or any service other than electrical.

358-5. Header. The header shall be installed in a straight line, at right angles to the cells. The header shall be mechanically secured to the top of the precast cellular concrete floor. The end joints shall be closed by a metallic closure fitting and sealed against the entrance of concrete. The header shall be electrically continuous throughout its entire length and shall be electrically bonded to the enclosure of the distribution center.

358-6. Connection to Cabinets and Other Enclosures. Connections from headers to cabinets and other enclosures shall be made by means of metal raceways and approved fittings.

358-7. Junction Boxes. Junction boxes shall be leveled to the floor grade and sealed against the free entrance of water or concrete. Junction boxes shall be of metal and shall be mechanically and electrically continuous with the header.

408

Figure 358-2 illustrates a trench-type raceway with a rigid cover plate extending at a right angle across the cells, with access to predetermined cells.

Figure 358-2. Trench-type raceway with removable cover shown extending at right angles across the cells of cellular concrete floor construction. (*Bargar Metal Fabricating Co.*)

358-8. Markers. A suitable number of markers shall be installed for the future location of cells.

358-9. Inserts. Inserts shall be leveled and sealed against the entrance of concrete. Inserts shall be of metal and shall be fitted with receptacles of the grounded type. A grounding conductor shall connect the insert receptacles to a positive ground connection provided on the header. In cutting through the cell wall for setting inserts or other purposes (such as providing access openings between header and cells), chips and other dirt shall not be allowed to remain in the raceway, and the tool used shall be so designed as to prevent the tool from entering the cell and damaging the conductors.

358-10. Size of Conductors. No conductor larger than No. 1/0 shall be installed, except by special permission.

358-11. Maximum Number of Conductors. The combined cross-sectional area of all conductors or cables shall not exceed 40 percent of the cross-sectional area of the cell or header.

358-12. Splices and Taps. Splices and taps shall be made only in header access units or junction boxes.
   For the purposes of this section, so-called loop wiring (continuous unbroken conductor connecting the individual outlets) shall not be considered to be a splice or tap.

358-13. Discontinued Outlets. When an outlet is abandoned, discontinued, or removed, the sections of circuit conductors supplying the outlet shall be removed from the raceway. No splices or reinsulated conductors, such as would be the case with abandoned outlets on loop wiring, shall be allowed in raceways.

ARTICLE 362 — WIREWAYS

Contents

362-1. Definition. Wireways are sheet-metal troughs with hinged or removable covers for housing and protecting electric wires and cable and in which conductors are laid in place after the wireway has been installed as a complete system.

Wireways are sheet-metal enclosures equipped with hinged or removable covers and are manufactured in lengths from 1 to 10 ft and various widths and depths. Couplings, elbows, end plates, and accessories, such as "T" and "X" fittings, are available.

Unlike auxiliary gutters, which are not permitted to extend more than 30 ft from the equipment they supplement, wireways may be run throughout an entire area, as shown in Figure 362-1.

The total of the cross-sectional areas of all conductors is not permitted to exceed 20 percent of the interior cross-sectional area of the wireway. Where not more than thirty conductors are installed, the derating factors of Note 8(a) of Tables 310-16 to 310-31 are not applicable

Example: a wireway contains twenty-four TW conductors, eight No. 3/0 (8 × 0.3288 = 2.6304), three No. 6 (3 × 0.0819 = 0.2457), three No. 8 (3 × 0.0471 = 0.1413), and ten No. 12 (10 × 0.0172 = 0.172), which total 3.1894 sq in. (dimensions of conductors are from Table 5, Chapter 9). Twenty percent of the cross-sectional area of the wireway is required to be 3.19 sq in. or greater. Therefore, 3.19 sq in. ÷ 0.20 = 15.95 sq in. A 4-in. × 4-in. wireway or greater is permitted to contain these conductors.

362-2. Use. Wireways shall be permitted only for exposed work. Wireways installed in wet locations shall be of raintight construction. Wireways shall not be installed (1) where subject to severe physical damage or corrosive vapor, nor (2) in any hazardous (classified) location, except Class I, Division 2 and Class II, Division 2 locations as permitted in Sections 501-4(b) and 502-4(b).

Exception: Wireways shall be permitted in concealed spaces in accordance with Section 640-4, Exception c.

This exception permits wireways to be used in concealed spaces for sound recording and similar equipment, provided they are run in a straight line between outlets or junction boxes. In addition, covers of the boxes must be accessible, and all sharp edges which could cause abrasion of the cable must be smoothed.

362-3. Other Articles. Installations of wireways shall comply with the applicable provisions of Article 300.

362-4. Size of Conductors. No conductor larger than that for which the wireway is designed shall be installed in any wireway.

362-5. Number of Conductors. Wireways shall not contain more than thirty current-carrying conductors at any cross section. Conductors for signaling circuits or controller conductors

Figure 362-1. A worker installing conductors in a sheet metal wireway after the complete wireway has been installed. (*Square D Co.*)

between a motor and its starter and used only for starting duty shall not be considered as current-carrying conductors.

The sum of cross-sectional areas of all contained conductors at any cross section of the wireway shall not exceed 20 percent of the interior cross-sectional area of the wireway.

The derating factors specified in Note 8 (a) to Tables 310-16 through 310-31 shall not be applicable to the thirty current-carrying conductors at 20 percent fill specified above.

Exception No. 1: Where the derating factors specified in Note 8 (a) to Tables 310-16 through 310-31 are applied, the number of current-carrying conductors shall not be limited but the sum of the cross-sectional area of all contained conductors at any cross section of the wireway shall not exceed 20 percent of the interior cross-sectional area of the wireway.

Exception No. 2: As provided in Section 520-5, the thirty conductor limitation does not apply for theaters and similar locations.

Exception No. 3: As provided in Section 620-32, the 20 percent fill limitation does not apply for elevators and dumbwaiters.

(FPN): For conductor cross-sectional area see Tables 5, 5A, 6, 7, 8 and the applicable Notes to Tables at the beginning of Chapter 9.

362-6. Splices and Taps. Splices and taps shall be permitted within a wireway provided they are accessible. The conductors, including splices and taps, shall not fill the wireway to more than 75 percent of its area at that point.

Conductors in wireways are accessible through hinged or removable covers. Circuits, taps, or splices may be added or altered, if necessary.

See Section 362-5. See also Table 5 in Chapter 9 for the dimensions of all common sizes of conductors.

362-7. Supports. Wireways shall be securely supported at intervals not exceeding 5 feet (1.52 m), unless specially approved for supports at greater intervals, but in no case shall the distance between supports exceed 10 feet (3.05 m).

Exception: Vertical runs of wireways shall be securely supported at intervals not exceeding 15 feet (4.57 m) and shall have not more than one joint between supports. Adjoining wireway sections shall be securely fastened together to provide a rigid joint.

362-8. Extension Through Walls. Unbroken lengths of wireway shall be permitted to pass transversely through walls if in unbroken lengths where passing through.

362-9. Dead Ends. Dead ends of wireways shall be closed.

362-10. Extensions from Wireways. Extensions from wireways shall be made with rigid or flexible metal conduit, intermediate metal conduit, rigid nonmetallic conduit, electrical nonmetallic tubing, electrical metallic tubing, surface metal raceway, Type MI cable, liquidtight flexible metal conduit, cord pendants, or metal-clad cable. Where rigid nonmetallic conduit or electrical nonmetallic tubing is used, connection of equipment grounding conductors in the nonmetallic raceway to the wireway shall comply with Sections 250-113 and 250-118.

Extensions are required to be made from metal raceways or metal-clad cables through knockouts which are provided on the wireway or which may be field-punched. Rigid nonmetallic conduit and electrical nonmetallic tubing may also be used. In this case, the equipment grounding conductor in the rigid nonmetallic conduit or electrical nonmetallic tubing is required to be connected to the metal wireway in accordance with Sections 250-113 and 250-118.

Sections of wireways, including accessory fittings (elbows, endplates, flanges, etc.), are bolted together assuring a rigid mechanical and electrical connection.

See Section 250-91(b)(10).

362-11. Marking. Wireways shall be marked so that their manufacturer's name or trademark will be visible after installation.

362-12. Grounding. Grounding shall be according to the provisions of Article 250.

ARTICLE 363 — FLAT CABLE ASSEMBLIES

Type FC

Contents

363-15. Supports.
363-16. Rating.
363-17. Marking.

363-18. Protective Covers.
363-19. Identification.
363-20. Terminal Block Identification.

363-1. Definition. Type FC, a flat cable assembly, is an assembly of parallel conductors formed integrally with an insulating material web specifically designed for field installation in surface metal raceway.

Type FC cable is an assembly of two, three, or four parallel No. 10 AWG special stranded copper wires formed integrally with an insulating material web. The cable is marked with the size of the maximum branch circuit to which it may be connected, the cable type designation, manufacturer's identification, maximum working voltage, conductor size, and temperature rating. A marking accompanying the cable on a tag or reel indicates the special metal raceways and specific type of FC cable fittings with which the cable is intended to be used.

Figures 363-1 and 363-2 show the basic components of this wiring method.

INSULATING END CAP

FIXTURE HANGER

TERMINAL BOX
With color-coded
terminal block

SPLICE
PLATE

CABLE PULL-IN GUIDE

Figure 363-1. The basic components and accessories used for an installation of Type FC (flat) cable assembly. (*The Wiremold Co.*)

363-2. Other Articles. In addition to the provisions of this article, installation of Type FC cable shall conform with the applicable provisions of Articles 210, 220, 250, 300, 310, and 352.

363-3. Uses Permitted. Flat cable assemblies shall be permitted only as branch circuits to supply suitable tap devices for lighting, small appliances, or small power loads. Flat cable assemblies shall be installed for exposed work only. Flat cable assemblies shall be installed in locations where they will not be subjected to severe physical damage.

363-4. Uses Not Permitted. Flat cable assemblies shall not be installed: (1) where subject to corrosive vapors unless suitable for the application; (2) in hoistways; (3) in any hazardous (classified) location; or (4) outdoors or in wet or damp locations unless identified for use in wet locations.

363-5. Installation. Flat cable assemblies shall be installed in the field only in surface metal raceways identified for the use. The channel portion of the surface metal raceway systems shall be installed as complete systems before the flat cable assemblies are pulled into the raceways.

363-6. Number of Conductors. The flat cable assemblies shall consist of either two, three, or four conductors.

363-7. Size of Conductors. Flat cable assemblies shall have conductors of No. 10 special stranded copper wires.

Figure 363-2. Fixture hanger
used with Type FC cable
assembly. (*The Wiremold Co.*)

363-8. Conductor Insulation. The entire flat cable assembly shall be formed to provide a suitable insulation covering all of the conductors and using one of the materials recognized in Table 310-13 for general branch-circuit wiring.

363-9. Splices. Splices shall be made in approved junction boxes using approved wiring methods.

363-10. Taps. Taps shall be made between any phase conductor and the neutral or any other phase conductor by means of devices and fittings identified for the use. Tap devices shall be rated at not less than 15 amperes or more than 300 volts and they shall be color-coded in accordance with the requirements of Section 363-20.

363-11. Dead Ends. Each flat cable assembly dead end shall be terminated in an end-cap device identified for the use.
The dead-end fitting for the enclosing metal surface raceway shall be identified for the use.

363-12. Fixture Hangers. Fixture hangers installed with the flat cable assemblies shall be identified for the use.

363-13. Fittings. Fittings to be installed with flat cable assemblies shall be designed and installed to prevent physical damage to the cable assemblies.

363-14. Extensions. All extensions from flat cable assemblies shall be made by approved wiring methods, within the junction boxes, installed at either end of the flat cable assembly runs.

363-15. Supports. The flat cable assemblies shall be supported by means of their special design features, within the surface metal raceways.
The surface metal raceways shall be supported as required for the specific raceway to be installed.

363-16. Rating. The rating of the branch circuit shall not exceed 30 amperes.

363-17. Marking. In addition to the provisions of Section 310-11, Type FC cable shall have the temperature rating durably marked on the surface at intervals not exceeding 24 inches (610 mm).

363-18. Protective Covers. When a flat cable assembly is installed less than 8 feet (2.44 m) from the floor, it shall be protected by a metal cover identified for the use.

363-19. Identification. The grounded conductor shall be identified throughout its length by means of a distinctive and durable white or natural gray marking.

363-20. Terminal Block Identification. Terminal blocks identified for the use shall have distinctive and durable markings for color or word coding. The neutral section shall have a white marking or other suitable designation. The next adjacent section of the terminal block shall have a black marking or other suitable designation. The next section shall have a red marking or other suitable designation. The final or outer section, opposite the neutral section of the terminal block, shall have a blue marking or other suitable designation.

ARTICLE 364 — BUSWAYS

Contents

A. General Requirements

364-1. Scope. This article covers service-entrance, feeder, and branch-circuit busways and associated fittings.

364-2. Definition. For the purpose of this article a busway is considered to be a grounded metal enclosure containing factory mounted, bare or insulated conductors which are usually copper or aluminum bars, rods, or tubes.

(FPN): For cablebus, refer to Article 365.

The maximum rating of UL-listed busway is 600 V.

A busway that has been investigated to determine its suitability for installation in a specified position, or for use in vertical runs, or for support at intervals greater than 5 ft, or for outdoor use is so marked.

A busway that is intended to supply and support industrial and commercial lighting fixtures is classified as "lighting busway" and is so marked. Trolley busway is marked "trolley busway" and is additionally marked "lighting busway" if

415

intended to supply and support industrial and commercial lighting fixtures. A busway with provision for insertion of plug-in devices at any point along the length of the busway and intended for general use is classified as "continuous plug-in busway" and is so marked.

Short-run busways are marked to limit the run to 30 ft or less, and no more than 10 ft vertically, and are intended primarily for a feed to switchboards. Except for transformer stubs, short-run busways are not intended to have intermediate taps. Short-run busways are not ventilated and may be marked for outdoor use.

A busway marked "lighting busway" and protected by overcurrent devices rated in excess of 20 A is intended for use only with fixtures employing heavy-duty lampholders unless additional overcurrent protection is provided for the fixture in accordance with this *Code*.

A "trolley busway" should be installed out of the reach of persons, or it should be otherwise installed to prevent accidental contact with exposed conductors. See Figures 364-1 and 364-2.

Figure 364-1. A trolley busway with the trolley in place. (*Midland Ross*)

364-3. Other Articles.   Installations of busways shall comply with the applicable provisions of Article 300.

364-4. Use.

(a) **Use Permitted.**   Busways shall be installed only where they are located in the open and are visible.

416

Figure 364-2. A plug-in device for stationary use on a trolley busway. (*Midland Ross*)

Exception: Busways shall be permitted to be installed behind panels if means of access are provided and if all the following conditions are met.

a. No overcurrent devices are installed on the busway other than for an individual fixture.

b. The space behind the access panels is not used for air-handling purposes.

c. The busway is totally enclosed, nonventilating type.

d. Busway is so installed that the joints between sections and fittings are accessible for maintenance purposes.

The exception permits busways to be located behind panels that are designed to allow access, such as suspended ceilings not used for air-handling purposes, provided the busway is totally enclosed, joints and fittings are accessible for maintenance, and no overcurrent device (other than for an individual fixture) is installed.

Busways are commonly used as feeders, mounted horizontally in industrial buildings, or mounted vertically in high-rise buildings.

Where busways are employed for ungrounded systems, an abnormal potential may build up on one of the conductors and could cause a "flashover" on the system. Figure 364-3 is a diagram of a "potentializer plug" and its connection to a busway. This device is a complete assembly in a metal enclosure designed to plug into a busway. It consists of three 18,000-ohm resistors which serve to maintain each of the conductors at a normal potential to ground. A tap is connected to each resistor, providing 120 V to three 7.5-W lamps which serve as ground detectors.

See Figure 100-1.

(b) Use Prohibited. Busways shall not be installed: (1) where subject to severe physical damage or corrosive vapors; (2) in hoistways; (3) in any hazardous (classified) location, unless

417

specifically approved for such use [see Section 501-4(b)]; nor (4) outdoors or in wet or damp locations unless identified for such use.

Figure 364-3. A schematic of a "potentializer plug" and its connections to a busway.

364-5. Support. Busways shall be securely supported at intervals not exceeding 5 feet (1.52 m) unless otherwise designed and marked.

364-6. Through Walls and Floors. It shall be permissible to extend unbroken lengths of busway through dry walls. It shall be permissible to extend busways vertically through dry floors if totally enclosed (unventilated) where passing through and for a minimum distance of 6 feet (1.83 m) above the floor to provide adequate protection from physical damage.

364-7. Dead Ends. A dead end of a busway shall be closed.

364-8. Branches from Busways. Branches from busways shall be made with busways, rigid metal conduit, intermediate metal conduit, rigid nonmetallic conduit, electrical nonmetallic tubing, flexible metal conduit, electrical metallic tubing, metal surface raceway or metal-clad cable; or with suitable cord assemblies approved for hard usage for the connection of portable equipment or for the connection of stationary equipment to facilitate their interchange. Flexible cord assembly connections shall be permitted to be made directly to the load end terminals of a busway plug-in device, providing the connection includes a suitable tension take-up device on the cord. Where a nonmetallic raceway is used, connection of equipment grounding conductors in the nonmetallic raceway to the busway shall comply with Sections 250-113 and 250-118.

364-9. Overcurrent Protection. Overcurrent protection shall be provided in accordance with Sections 364-10 through 364-14.

364-10. Rating of Overcurrent Protection — Feeders and Subfeeders. Where the allowable current rating of the busway does not correspond to a standard rating of the overcurrent device, the next higher rating shall be permitted.

The rated ampacity of a busway is based on the allowable temperature rise of the conductors and can be determined in the field only by reference to the nameplate data.

364-11. Reduction in Size of Busway.   Omission of overcurrent protection shall be permitted at points where busways are reduced in size, provided that the smaller busway does not extend more than 50 feet (15.2 m) and has a current rating at least equal to ⅓ the rating or setting of the overcurrent device next back on the line, and provided further that such busway is free from contact with combustible material.

Where the smaller busway is kept within the specified limits, the additional cost of providing overcurrent protection at the point where the size is changed is not warranted. For example, busway protected by a 1200-A overcurrent device may be reduced in size, provided the smaller busway has a current rating of 400 A (⅓ of 1,200 A) and does not extend more than 50 ft. In this case, overcurrent protection would be required if the smaller busway were rated less than 400 A, that is, 200 A, 300 A, etc.

364-12. Subfeeder or Branch Circuits.   Where a busway is used as a feeder, devices or plug-in connections for tapping off subfeeder or branch circuits from the busway shall contain the overcurrent devices required for the protection of the subfeeder or branch circuits. The plug-in device shall consist of an externally operable circuit breaker or an externally operable fusible switch. Where such devices are mounted out of reach and contain disconnecting means, suitable means such as ropes, chains, or sticks shall be provided for operating the disconnecting means from the floor.

Exception No. 1: As permitted in Section 240-21 for taps.

Exception No. 2: For fixed or semi-fixed lighting fixtures, where the branch-circuit overcurrent device is part of the fixture cord plug on cord-connected fixtures.

Exception No. 3: Where fixtures without cords are plugged directly into the busway and the overcurrent device is mounted on the fixture.

Externally operated fused switches and circuit breakers plugged into busways, which are mounted out of reach, are to be considered accessible when operated by means such as ropes, chains, or hooksticks.

An appliance, without individual overcurrent protection, may be connected directly to a busway as permitted in Section 210-23; however, a motor-driven appliance must also meet all of the applicable requirements of Article 430.

364-13. Rating of Overcurrent Protection — Branch Circuits.   A busway shall be permitted as a branch circuit of any one of the types described in Article 210. When so used, the rating or setting of the overcurrent device protecting the busway shall determine the ampere rating of the branch circuit, and the circuit shall in all respects conform with the requirements of Article 210 that apply to branch circuits of that rating.

364-14. Length of Busways Used as Branch Circuits.   Busways which are used as branch circuits and which are so designed that loads can be connected at any point shall be limited to such lengths as will provide that in normal use the circuits will not be overloaded.

364-15. Marking.   Busways shall be marked with the voltage and current rating for which they are designed, and with the manufacturer's name or trademark in such manner as to be visible after installation.

B. Requirements for Over 600 Volts, Nominal

364-21. Identification. Each bus run shall be provided with a permanent nameplate on which the following information shall be provided: (1) rated voltage; (2) rated continuous current; if bus is forced-cooled, both the normal forced-cooled rating and the self-cooled (not forced-cooled) rating for the same temperature rise shall be given; (3) rated frequency; (4) rated impulse withstand voltage; (5) rated 60-Hz withstand voltage (dry); (6) rated momentary current; and (7) manufacturer's name or trademark.

(FPN): See Switchgear Assemblies, ANSI C37.20-1969 (R1981), for construction and testing requirements for metal-enclosed buses.

364-22. Grounding. Metal-enclosed bus shall be grounded in accordance with Article 250.

364-23. Adjacent and Supporting Structures. Metal-enclosed busways shall be installed so that temperature rise from induced circulating currents in any adjacent metallic parts will not be hazardous to personnel or constitute a fire hazard.

Figure 364-4. A 10-ft section of feeder busway. (*Square D Co.*)

364-24. Neutral. Neutral bus, where required, shall be sized to carry all neutral load current, including harmonic currents, and shall have adequate momentary and short-circuit rating consistent with system requirements.

364-25. Barriers and Seals. Bus runs having sections located both inside and outside of buildings shall have a vapor seal at the building wall to prevent interchange of air between indoor and outdoor sections.

Fire barriers shall be provided where fire walls, floors, or ceilings are penetrated.

See also Section 300-21.

Exception: Vapor seals shall not be required in forced-cooled bus.

364-26. Drain Facilities. Drain plugs, filter drains, or similar methods shall be provided to remove condensed moisture from low points in bus run.

364-27. Ventilated Bus Enclosures. Ventilated bus enclosures shall be installed in accordance with Article 710, Part D, unless designed so that foreign objects inserted through any opening will be deflected from energized parts.

364-28. Terminations and Connections. Where bus enclosures terminate at machines cooled by flammable gas, seal-off bushings, baffles, or other means shall be provided to prevent accumulation of flammable gas in the bus enclosures.

Flexible or expansion connections shall be provided in long, straight runs of bus to allow for temperature expansion or contraction, or where the bus run crosses building vibration insulation joints.

All conductor termination and connection hardware shall be accessible for installation, connection, and maintenance.

364-29. Switches. Switching devices or disconnecting links provided in the bus run shall have the same momentary rating as the bus. Disconnecting links shall be plainly marked to be removable only when bus is de-energized. Switching devices which are not load break shall be interlocked to prevent operation under load, and disconnecting link enclosures shall be interlocked to prevent access to energized parts.

364-30. Low-Voltage Wiring. Secondary control devices and wiring which are provided as part of the metal-enclosed bus run shall be insulated by fire-retardant barriers from all primary circuit elements with the exception of short lengths of wire, such as at instrument transformer terminals.

ARTICLE 365 — CABLEBUS

Contents

365-1. Definition. Cablebus is an approved assembly of insulated conductors with fittings and conductor terminations in a completely enclosed, ventilated protective metal housing. The assembly is designed to carry fault current and to withstand the magnetic forces of such current.

Cablebus consists of a metal structure or framework which is installed in a manner similar to a cable tray support system. Insulated conductors, No. 1/0 or larger, are field-installed within the framework on special insulating blocks at specified intervals to provide controlled spacing between conductors. To completely enclose the conductors, a ventilated top cover is attached to the framework. See Figure 365-1.

(FPN): Cablebus is ordinarily assembled at the point of installation from components furnished or specified by the manufacturer in accordance with instructions for the specific job.

365-2. Use.

(a) 600 Volts or Less. Cablebus shall be permitted at any voltage or current for which spaced conductors are rated and shall be installed for exposed work only. Cablebus installed

Figure 365-1. A section of cablebus with conductors in place and the ventilated top cover ready to be attached to the busway frame. (*Husky Cabl-Bus*)

outdoors or in corrosive, wet, or damp locations shall be identified for such use. Cablebus shall not be installed in hoistways or hazardous (classified) locations unless specifically approved for such use. Cablebus shall be permitted to be used for branch circuits, feeders, and services.

Cablebus framework, where adequately bonded, shall be permitted as the equipment grounding conductor for branch circuits and feeders.

(b) Over 600 Volts. Cablebus shall be permitted for systems in excess of 600 volts, nominal. See Section 710-3(a).

365-3. Conductors.

(a) Types of Conductors. The current-carrying conductors in cablebus shall have an insulation rating of 75°C or higher of an approved type and suitable for the application in accordance with Articles 310 and 710.

(b) Ampacity of Conductors. The ampacity of conductors in cablebus shall be in accordance with Tables 310-17 and 310-19.

(c) Size and Number of Conductors. The size and number of conductors shall be that for which the cablebus is designed, and in no case smaller than No. 1/0.

(d) Conductor Supports. The insulated conductors shall be supported on blocks or other mounting means designed for the purpose.

The individual conductors in a cablebus shall be supported at intervals not greater than 3 feet (914 mm) for horizontal runs and 1½ feet (457 mm) for vertical runs. Vertical and horizontal spacing between supported conductors shall not be less than one conductor diameter at the points of support.

365-5. Overcurrent Protection. When the allowable ampacity of cablebus conductors does not correspond to a standard rating of an overcurrent device, the next higher ampere rated overcurrent device shall be permitted.

365-6. Support and Extension Through Walls and Floors.

(a) Support. Cablebus shall be securely supported at intervals not exceeding 12 feet (3.66 m).

Exception: Where spans longer than 12 feet (3.66 m) are required, the structure shall be specifically designed for the required span length.

(b) Transversely Routed. It shall be permissible to extend cablebus transversely through partitions or walls, other than fire walls, provided the section within the wall is continuous, protected against physical damage, and unventilated.

(c) Through Dry Floors and Platforms. Except where fire stops are required, it shall be permissible to extend cablebus vertically through dry floors and platforms, provided the cablebus is totally enclosed at the point where it passes through the floor or platform and for a distance of 6 feet (1.83 m) above the floor or platform.

(d) Through Floors and Platforms in Wet Locations. Except where fire stops are required, it shall be permissible to extend cablebus vertically through floors and platforms in wet locations where (1) there are curbs or other suitable means to prevent waterflow through the floor or platform opening, and (2) where the cablebus is totally enclosed at the point where it passes through the floor or platform and for a distance of 6 feet (1.83 m) above the floor or platform.

365-7. Fittings. A cablebus system shall include approved fittings for: (1) changes in horizontal or vertical direction of the run; (2) dead ends; (3) terminations in or on connected apparatus or equipment or the enclosures for such equipment; and (4) additional physical protection where required, such as guards for severe mechanical exposure.

365-8. Conductor Terminations. Approved terminating means shall be used for connections to cablebus conductors.

365-9. Grounding. Sections of cablebus shall be electrically bonded either by inherent design of the mechanical joints or by applied bonding means.

(FPN): See Section 250-75 for bonding of metal noncurrent-carrying parts.

A cablebus installation shall be grounded in accordance with Sections 250-32 and 250-33.

365-10. Marking. Each section of cablebus shall be marked with the manufacturer's name or trade designation and the maximum diameter, number, voltage rating, and ampacity of the conductors to be installed. Markings shall be so located as to be visible after installation.

ARTICLE 370 — OUTLET, DEVICE, PULL AND JUNCTION BOXES, CONDUIT BODIES AND FITTINGS

Contents

A. Scope and General

370-1. Scope. This article covers the installation and use of all boxes, conduit bodies, and fittings as required by Section 300-15, and boxes, conduit bodies, and fittings referred to in Section 300-15 used as outlet, junction, or pull boxes, depending on their use. Cast, sheet metal, nonmetallic, and other boxes such as FS, FD, and larger boxes are not classified as conduit bodies. Fittings such as capped elbows and service-entrance elbows are not classified as conduit bodies.

(FPN): For systems over 600 volts, nominal, see Part D of this article.

A device box is designed to accept the installation of a device such as a snap switch, receptacle, or dimmer. An outlet box requires the use of a plaster ring or special cover in order to be adapted for use as a device box.

Fittings such as capped elbows and service-entrance elbows are not classified as conduit bodies [see Section 370-7(b)]. Therefore, the rules covering the use of

424

conduit bodies in this article are not applicable to these types of fittings. See the definitions of "conduit body," "fitting," and "outlet" in Article 100.

370-2. Round Boxes. Round boxes shall not be used where conduits or connectors requiring the use of locknuts or bushings are to be connected to the side of the box.

This rule requires the use of rectangular or octagonal boxes having a flat bearing surface at each knockout for locknuts and bushings to ensure effective grounding continuity. However, round boxes can be used where the conduit or cable is secured by clamps within the box, or the cable does not need attachment to the box [see Section 370-7(c), Exception].

370-3. Nonmetallic Boxes. Nonmetallic boxes shall be permitted only with open wiring on insulators, concealed knob-and-tube wiring, nonmetallic-sheathed cable, electrical nonmetallic tubing, and with rigid nonmetallic conduit.

In addition thereto, nonmetallic boxes over 100 cubic inches shall be permitted to be used with metal raceways and metal-sheathed cables. Integral bonding means shall be provided between all threaded entries for metal raceways or metal-sheathed cables.

370-4. Metal Boxes. All metal boxes shall be grounded in accordance with the provisions of Article 250.

B. Installation

370-5. Damp, Wet, or Hazardous (Classified) Locations.

(a) Damp or Wet Locations. In damp or wet locations, boxes, conduit bodies, and fittings shall be so placed or equipped as to prevent moisture from entering or accumulating within the box, conduit body, or fitting. Boxes, conduit bodies, and fittings installed in wet locations shall be listed for use in wet locations.

(b) Hazardous (Classified) Locations. Installations in hazardous (classified) locations shall conform to Articles 500 through 517.

(FPN): For boxes in floors, see Section 370-17(b).

(FPN): For protection against corrosion, see Section 300-6.

Article 100 defines "weatherproof" as "so constructed or protected that exposure to the weather will not interfere with successful operation." Rainproof, raintight, or watertight equipment can fulfill the requirements for weatherproof where varying weather conditions other than wetness, such as snow, ice, dust, or temperature extremes, are not a factor.

A "weatherhead" fitting is considered to be weatherproof because the openings for the conductors are placed in a downward position so that rain or snow cannot enter the fitting.

See definitions of "damp location" and "wet location" under "location" in Article 100.

370-6. Number of Conductors in Outlet, Device, and Junction Boxes, and Conduit Bodies. Boxes shall be of sufficient size to provide free space for all conductors enclosed in the box.

The provisions of this section shall not apply to terminal housings supplied with motors. See Section 430-12.

Boxes and conduit bodies containing conductors, size No. 4 or larger, shall also comply with the provisions of Section 370-18.

ARTICLE 370—BOXES AND FITTINGS

(a) Standard Boxes. The maximum number of conductors permitted in standard boxes shall be as is listed in Table 370-6(a). See Section 370-18 where boxes or conduit bodies are used as junction or pull boxes.

When conductors of different sizes terminate in a box, the requirements of Section 370-6(b) are applicable. For example, the size of a box without clamps, which contains two 3-wire, No. 12 AWG multiwire branch circuits installed in conduit, used to supply four fixtures with eight No. 14 AWG fixture tap conductors would require a box which is sized at 6 × 2.25 cu in. plus 8 × 2.0 cu in. = 29.5 cu in. minimum. Table 370-6(a) indicates that a 4^{11}/₁₆ × 1½ square (29.5 cu in.), 4 × 2⅛ square (30.3 cu in.), or 4^{11}/₁₆ × 2⅛ square (42.0 cu in.) box would satisfy this arrangement.

If the fixture tap conductors were No. 18 AWG, the box would be sized at 6 × 2.25 cu in. plus 8 × 1.5 cu in. = 25.5 cu in. minimum.

(1) Table 370-6(a) shall apply where no fittings or devices, such as fixture studs, cable clamps, hickeys, switches, or receptacles, are contained in the box and where no grounding conductors are part of the wiring within the box. Where one or more of these types of fittings, such as fixture studs, cable clamps, or hickeys are contained in the box, the number of conductors shown in the table shall be reduced by one for each type of fitting; an additional deduction of one conductor shall be made for each strap containing one or more devices; and a further deduction of one conductor shall be made for one or more grounding conductors entering the box. Where a second set of equipment grounding conductors, as permitted by Section 250-74, Exception No. 4, is present in the box, then an additional deduction of one conductor shall be made. A conductor running through the box shall be counted as one conductor, and each conductor originating outside of the box and terminating inside the box is counted as one conductor. Conductors, no part of which leaves the box, shall not be counted. The volume of a wiring enclosure (box) shall be the total volume of the assembled sections, and, where used, the space provided by plaster rings, domed covers, extension rings, etc., that are marked with their volume in cubic inches, or are made from boxes the dimensions of which are listed in Table 370-6(a).

Section 250-74, Exception No. 4 permits a grounding-type receptacle to have its grounding terminal isolated from the box in which it is mounted to help relieve electrical noise problems. Therefore, it is likely there will be two sets of equipment grounding conductors in the box, one for grounding the receptacle (running back to the ground for the service or separately derived system) and the other for grounding the box itself. This section requires each of these two sets of equipment grounding conductors to be counted as a conductor in the box.

A conductor, no part of which leaves the box, is usually some type of jumper, such as the grounding jumper shown in Figure 370-1.

(2) For combinations of conductor sizes shown in Table 370-6(a), the maximum number of conductors permitted shall be computed using the volume per conductor listed in Table 370-6(b), with the deductions provided for in Section 370-6(a)(1) and these volume deductions shall be based on the largest conductor entering the box. The maximum number and size of conductors listed in Table 370-6(a) shall not be exceeded.

Where conductors of different sizes are in a box and deductions are required by Section 370-6(a)(1) because of a fixture stud, cable clamps, etc., the deductions are to be based on the largest conductor entering the box. For example, if a box contains two No. 12 AWG circuit conductors, two No. 14 AWG circuit conductors, two equipment grounding conductors (one for each of the two circuits), two clamps, and one fixture stud, the minimum required volume would be calculated as follows:

```
2 No. 12 AWG circuit conductors  ...................................... 2 × 2.25 cu in. =   4.5
2 No. 14 AWG circuit conductors  ...................................... 2 × 2    cu in. =   4.0
2 equipment grounding conductors ...................................... 1 × 2.25 cu in. =   2.25
2 clamps  ............................................................. 1 × 2.25 cu in. =   2.25
1 fixture stud  ...................................................... 1 × 2.25 cu in. =   2.25
                                                                    Total       15.25
```

A 4 × 1½-in. round or octagonal metal box, listed in Table 370-6(a) as having a minimum 15.5 cu in. capacity, would be acceptable in this application.

Table 370-6(a). Metal Boxes

Box Dimension, Inches Trade Size or Type	Min. Cu. In. Cap.	No. 18	No. 16	No. 14	No. 12	No. 10	No. 8	No. 6
4 × 1¼ Round or Octagonal	12.5	8	7	6	5	5	4	0
4 × 1½ Round or Octagonal	15.5	10	8	7	6	6	5	0
4 × 2⅛ Round or Octagonal	21.5	14	12	10	9	8	7	0
4 × 1¼ Square	18.0	12	10	9	8	7	6	0
4 × 1½ Square	21.0	14	12	10	9	8	7	0
4 × 2⅛ Square	30.3	20	17	15	13	12	10	6*
4¹¹⁄₁₆ × 1¼ Square	25.5	17	14	12	11	10	8	0
4¹¹⁄₁₆ × 1½ Square	29.5	19	16	14	13	11	9	0
4¹¹⁄₁₆ × 2⅛ Square	42.0	28	24	21	18	16	14	6
3 × 2 × 1½ Device	7.5	5	4	3	3	3	2	0
3 × 2 × 2 Device	10.0	6	5	5	4	4	3	0
3 × 2 × 2¼ Device	10.5	7	6	5	4	4	3	0
3 × 2 × 2½ Device	12.5	8	7	6	5	5	4	0
3 × 2 × 2¾ Device	14.0	9	8	7	6	5	4	0
3 × 2 × 3½ Device	18.0	12	10	9	8	7	6	0
4 × 2⅛ × 1½ Device	10.3	6	5	5	4	4	3	0
4 × 2⅛ × 1⅞ Device	13.0	8	7	6	5	5	4	0
4 × 2⅛ × 2⅛ Device	14.5	9	8	7	6	5	4	0
3¾ × 2 × 2½ Masonry Box/Gang	14.0	9	8	7	6	5	4	0
3¾ × 2 × 3½ Masonry Box/Gang	21.0	14	12	10	9	8	7	0
FS—Minimum Internal Depth 1¾ Single Cover/Gang	13.5	9	7	6	6	5	4	0
FD—Minimum Internal Depth 2⅜ Single Cover/Gang	18.0	12	10	9	8	7	6	3
FS—Minimum Internal Depth 1¾ Multiple Cover/Gang	18.0	12	10	9	8	7	6	0
FD—Minimum Internal Depth 2⅜ Multiple Cover/Gang	24.0	16	13	12	10	9	8	4

* Not to be used as a pull box. For termination only.

Table 370-6(a) lists the maximum number of conductors permitted in a metal box before the deductions provided for in Section 370-6(a)(1) are considered. Figure 370-1 illustrates one ¹⁴⁄₂ and one ¹⁴⁄₃ nonmetallic-sheathed cable, each with bare equipment grounding conductors installed in a device box. This arrangement would be counted as follows:

Two nonmetallic-sheathed cables (circuit conductors)	5
Two grounding conductors	1
Internal clamp(s) (hickeys or studs)	1
Receptacle (strap containing one or more devices)	1
Total	8

Column No. 1 in Table 370-6(a) lists a device box (3 × 2 × 3½ in.) which is adequate for nine No. 14 conductors. However, this box may be too deep for shallower partitions; thus, a smaller device box (3 × 2 × 2½ in.) is permitted with a domed side bracket (marked with its volume in cubic inches) and the maximum number of conductors is required to be computed as per Table 370-6(b). A 4 × 1¼ in. square box and plaster ring combination would also be permitted.

The phrase in the last sentence of Section 370-6(a)(1) "or are made from boxes the dimensions of which are listed in Table 370-6(a)" means that extension rings made from boxes having the dimensions tabulated in Table 370-6(a) do not have to be marked with their cubic inch volume to be considered as having volume.

Extension rings or boxes, domed covers or plaster rings, etc., that are marked with their volume in cubic inches are considered as having usable conductor space.

(b) Other Boxes. Boxes 100 cubic inches or less other than those described in Table 370-6(a), conduit bodies having provision for more than two conduit entries and nonmetallic boxes shall be durably and legibly marked by the manufacturer with their cubic inch capacity. The maximum number of conductors permitted shall be computed using the volume per conductor listed in Table 370-6(b), with the deductions provided for in Section 370-6(a)(1), and these volume deductions shall be based on the largest conductor entering the box. Boxes described in Table 370-6(a) that have a larger cubic inch capacity than is designated in the table shall be permitted to have their cubic inch capacity marked as required by this section and the maximum number of conductors permitted shall be computed using the volume per conductor listed in Table 370-6(b).

Table 370-6(b). Volume Required per Conductor

Size of Conductor	Free Space Within Box for Each Conductor
No. 18	1.5 cubic inches
No. 16	1.75 cubic inches
No. 14	2. cubic inches
No. 12	2.25 cubic inches
No. 10	2.5 cubic inches
No. 8	3. cubic inches
No. 6	5. cubic inches

Table 370-6(a) lists the cubic inch capacities and the maximum number of conductors (No. 18 through No. 6) permitted in most commonly used metal boxes.

Table 370-6(b) lists the volume that is required for conductors (No. 18 through No. 6) used in boxes 100 cu in. or less, other than those described in Table 370-6(a). Such boxes are required to be marked with their cubic inch capacity. These provisions assure that free space for all conductors will be provided. A conductor running through a box without a splice or tap is counted as one conductor.

(c) Conduit Bodies. Conduit bodies enclosing No. 6 conductors or smaller shall have a cross-sectional area not less than twice the cross-sectional area of the largest conduit to which it is attached. The maximum number of conductors permitted shall be the maximum number permitted by Table 1, Chapter 9, for the conduit to which it is attached.

14/2 nonmetallic with ground

14/3 nonmetallic with ground

Split receptacle

Figure 370-1. Device box, with a domed side, providing sufficient space for all conductors, clamp, and receptacle in compliance with Section 370-6(b).

Conduit bodies having provisions for less than three conduit entries shall not contain splices, taps, or devices unless they comply with the provisions of Section 370-6(b) and are supported in a rigid and secure manner.

This section requires that conduit bodies be supported in a rigid and secure manner so that they will not turn in place. See Section 370-13(e). Where conduit bodies have provisions for two or less conduit entries and contain splices, taps, or devices, they are required to be durably and legibly marked with their cubic inch capacity. The maximum number of conductors permitted in a conduit body is computed by using the volume for conductors listed in Table 370-6(b). See Section 370-18 for requirements when conduit bodies are used as pull and junction boxes.

370-7. Conductors Entering Boxes, Conduit Bodies, or Fittings. Conductors entering boxes, conduit bodies or fittings shall be protected from abrasion, and shall comply with (a) through (d) below.

(a) Openings to Be Closed. Openings through which conductors enter shall be adequately closed.

(b) Metal Boxes, Conduit Bodies, and Fittings. Where metal outlet boxes, conduit bodies or fittings are installed with open wiring or concealed knob-and-tube wiring, conductors shall enter through insulating bushings or, in dry places, through flexible tubing extending from the last insulating support and firmly secured to the box, conduit body or fitting. Where raceway or cable is installed with metal outlet boxes, conduit bodies or fittings, the raceway or cable shall be secured to such boxes, conduit bodies and fittings. Fittings such as capped elbows and service-entrance elbows shall not contain splices, taps, or devices and shall be of sufficient size to provide free space for all conductors enclosed in the fitting.

Capped elbows and service-entrance elbows are fittings intended to permit a sharp bend in a raceway system and still provide for pulling of conductors.

429

(c) Nonmetallic Boxes. Nonmetallic boxes shall be suitable for the lowest temperature rated conductor entering the box. Where nonmetallic boxes are used with open wiring or concealed knob-and-tube wiring, the conductors shall enter the box through individual holes. Where flexible tubing is used to encase the conductors, the tubing shall extend from the last insulating support to no less than ¼ inch (6.35 mm) inside the box. Where nonmetallic-sheathed cable is used, the cable assembly, including the sheath, shall extend into the box no less than ¼ inch (6.35 mm) through a nonmetallic-sheathed cable knockout opening. In all instances all permitted wiring methods shall be secured to the boxes.

Standard nonmetallic boxes are permitted for use with 90°C (194°F) insulated conductors. However, where insulated conductors rated at higher temperatures are installed within a nonmetallic box, the box is required to be suitably identified by marking on the box or in the listing of the box. See Section 110-3(b). A nonmetallic box used for splicing a higher temperature rated conductor to a conductor of a lower temperature rating is required to be identified as suitable for the temperature rating of the lower rated conductor.

Exception: Where nonmetallic-sheathed cable is used with boxes no larger than a nominal size 2¼ inch by 4 inch mounted in walls and where the cable is fastened within 8 inches (203 mm) of the box measured along the sheath and where the sheath extends into the box no less than ¼ inch (6.35 mm), securing the cable to the box shall not be required.

Securing means are required in ceiling boxes and all other boxes larger than 2¼ in. by 4 in. The requirement is based on the width of the box and the likelihood of the cable being pushed back out of the box when the conductors and device, if any, are folded back into the box during installation of receptacles, switches, etc.

(d) Conductors No. 4 AWG or Larger. Installation shall comply with Section 373-6(c).

370-8. Unused Openings. Unused openings in boxes, conduit bodies and fittings shall be effectively closed to afford protection substantially equivalent to that of the wall of the box, conduit body or fitting. Metal plugs or plates used with nonmetallic boxes, conduit bodies or fittings shall be recessed at least ¼ inch (6.35 mm) from the outer surface.

370-9. Boxes Enclosing Flush Devices. Boxes used to enclose flush devices shall be of such design that the devices will be completely enclosed on back and sides, and that substantial support for the devices will be provided. Screws for supporting the box shall not be used in attachment of the device contained therein.

370-10. In Wall or Ceiling. In walls or ceilings of concrete, tile, or other noncombustible material, boxes and fittings shall be so installed that the front edge of the box or fitting will not set back of the finished surface more than ¼ inch (6.35 mm). In walls and ceilings constructed of wood or other combustible material, outlet boxes and fittings shall be flush with the finished surface or project therefrom.

Plaster and gypsum board are "other noncombustible materials." A wall with wood studs covered by plaster or gypsum board is considered a "wall of noncombustible material" for the purposes of Section 370-10.

370-11. Repairing Plaster and Drywall or Plasterboard. Plaster, drywall or plasterboard surfaces that are broken or incomplete shall be repaired so there will be no gaps or open spaces greater than ⅛ inch (3.18 mm) at the edge of the box or fitting.

370-12. Exposed Surface Extensions. In making an exposed surface extension from an existing outlet of concealed wiring, a box or extension ring shall be mounted over the original box and mechanically secured to it. Extensions shall not be made from the cover. Where required, equipment grounding shall be in accordance with Article 250.

Figure 370-2. Extension boxes are secured to existing boxes in concealed construction for additions or alterations to the wiring system.

Figure 370-2 illustrates an extension box that is mounted to an existing box, assuring mechanical and electrical continuity.

The use of a blank box cover attached to an existing flush device, outlet or junction box, with a knockout in the cover used to connect a cable or flexible-type raceway, would not meet the requirements of this section. Also, grounding continuity would not be maintained with the cover removed.

370-13. Supports.   Enclosures within the scope of Article 370 shall be rigidly and securely fastened in place in accordance with (a) through (h) below.

(a) Surface Mounting.   They shall be fastened to the surface upon which they are mounted unless such surface does not provide adequate support in which case they shall be supported in accordance with (b).

Support of a box on an acoustical tile suspended-type ceiling is one example of where a rod should be attached to the box and structural member.

(b) Structural Mounting.   They shall be rigidly supported from a structural member of the building either directly or by using a metal or wood brace. Support wires that do not provide rigid support shall not be permitted as the sole support.

Figure 370-3 illustrates one method of supporting a box where the ceiling construction affords no support. See also Section 410-16(a).

(1) Nails, where used as a fastening means, shall be permitted to pass through the interior of the enclosure if located within ¼ inch (6.35 mm) of the back or ends of the enclosure.

This prevents the nails from interfering with the installation of devices. Permitting nails within ¼ in. of the ends of the box prevents splitting of the smaller wooden studs used in some frame-type construction, which sometimes occurs when nails are within ¼ in. of the back of the box.

(2) Metal braces shall be protected against corrosion and formed from metal not less than .020 inch (508 micrometers) thick uncoated. Wood braces shall have a cross section not less than nominal 1 inch (25.4 mm) by 2 inch (50.8 mm).

431

Box rod and plate hanger used when a fixture weighing more than 50 lbs. is to be installed, or when a box is installed in a large opening of a tile ceiling.

Figure 370-3. A plate and threaded-rod hanger used to support an outlet box in a tile arch ceiling.

(c) Nonstructural Mounting. It shall be permissible to make a flush installation in existing covered surfaces where adequate support is provided by clamps, anchors, or fittings. Framing members of suspended ceiling systems shall be permitted as the support if the framing members are adequately supported and securely fastened to each other and to the building structure. Enclosures so supported shall be fastened to the framing member by mechanical means such as bolts, screws, or rivets. Clips identified for use with the type of ceiling framing member(s) and enclosure(s) shall also be permitted.

Where there are no structural members, or where cut into existing walls, boxes are permitted to be secured by clamps or anchors. See Figure 370-4 for one example of an acceptable mounting method.

(d) Raceway Supported Enclosure(s), Without Devices. Threaded enclosures not over 100 cubic inches that do not contain devices, receptacles or switches and do not support fixtures shall be considered to be adequately supported if two or more conduits are threaded into the enclosure wrenchtight and are supported within 3 feet (914 mm) of the enclosure on two or more sides so as to provide the rigid and secure installation intended by this section of the Code.

Exception: Conduit or electrical metallic tubing shall be permitted to support conduit bodies provided the conduit bodies are not larger than the largest trade size of the conduit or electrical metallic tubing.

Such enclosures shall also be considered to be adequately supported if they comply with subsection (e) following.

Boxes are not permitted to be supported by rigid raceways using a locknut and bushing connection, nor is a box permitted to be supported by a single raceway.

432

(e) Raceway Supported Enclosures, With Devices. Threaded enclosures not over 100 cubic inches that contain devices, receptacles or switches shall be considered to be adequately supported if two or more conduits are threaded into the enclosure wrenchtight and if each conduit is supported within 18 inches (457 mm) of the enclosure so as to provide the rigid and secure installation intended by this section of the Code.

Exception: Conduit shall be permitted to support conduit bodies provided the conduit bodies are not larger than the largest trade size of the conduit.

See commentary under 370-13(d).

(f) Enclosure(s) in Concrete or Masonry. Enclosure(s) shall be permitted to be supported by being embedded.

Boxes are permitted to be embedded in masonry or concrete provided they are rigid and secure. See Figure 370-5.

(g) Nonthreaded Nonmetallic Conduit Supported Enclosures. Nonthreaded nonmetallic enclosures shall be permitted to be installed in accordance with instructions contained in the listing or labeling provided the two or more conduit support distances comply with (d) or (e) above.

(h) Pendant Boxes. Boxes shall be supported from a multiconductor cable in some satisfactory manner that protects the conductors against strain, such as a strain relief connector threaded into a box with a hub.

See Sections 517-101(b)(3), Exception No. 2 and 517-101(c)(1), Exception for examples of locations where pendant boxes may be used. They are also commonly used around cranes and hoists, and in many industrial applications.

370-14. Depth of Outlet Boxes. No box shall have an internal depth of less than ½ inch (12.7 mm). Boxes intended to enclose flush devices shall have an internal depth of not less than $^{15}/_{16}$ inch (23.8 mm).

Figure 370-4. Top view of inserting and securing a box with a mounting bracket through an opening cut in an existing wall finish.

Figure 370-5. A "mud" box installed in a concrete ceiling. Additional support is not required.

The use of a shallow box may become necessary because of old work or existing construction where very narrow partitions, plumbing pipes, or ductwork is encountered within the partition, etc. The selection of a box used in this type of situation is required to be based on its having sufficient cubic inch capacity.

370-15. Covers and Canopies.   In completed installations each outlet box shall have a cover, faceplate, or fixture canopy.

(a) Nonmetallic or Metal Covers and Plates.   Nonmetallic or metal covers and plates shall be permitted with nonmetallic outlet boxes. Where metal covers or plates are used, they shall comply with the grounding requirements of Section 250-42.

(FPN): See Sections 410-18(a) and 410-56(c) for metal faceplates.

(b) Exposed Combustible Wall or Ceiling Finish.   Where a fixture canopy or pan is used, any combustible wall or ceiling finish exposed between the edge of the canopy or pan and the outlet box shall be covered with noncombustible material.

Because of the possibility that heat from a short circuit or overlamping or ground fault within a fixture canopy or pan could create a fire hazard, any exposed combustible wall or ceiling space between the edge of the outlet box and the perimeter of the fixture is required to be covered with noncombustible material. The noncombustible material need not be metal. Glass fiber pads commonly provided as thermal barriers on ceiling pan fixtures can be used to meet this requirement. Where the wall or ceiling finish is concrete, tile, plaster, or other noncombustible material, the requirements of this section do not apply. See Section 370-11.

(c) Flexible Cord Pendants.   Covers of outlet boxes and conduit bodies having holes through which flexible cord pendants pass shall be provided with bushings designed for the purpose or shall have smooth, well-rounded surfaces on which the cords may bear. So-called hard-rubber or composition bushings shall not be used.

370-17. Outlet Boxes.

(a) Boxes at Lighting Fixture Outlets.   Boxes used at lighting fixture outlets shall be designed for the purpose. At every outlet used exclusively for lighting, the box shall be so designed or installed that a lighting fixture may be attached.

Device boxes are designed for the mounting of devices such as snap-switches and receptacles, usually by 6-32 screws. They are not suitable for the support of other than very lightweight lighting fixtures, such as some wall-bracket types. See Section 410-16.

(b) Floor Boxes. Boxes listed specifically for this application shall be used for receptacles located in the floor.

Exception: Boxes located in elevated floors of show windows and similar locations where the authority having jurisdiction judges them to be free from physical damage, moisture, and dirt.

(c) Boxes at Fan Outlets. Outlet boxes shall not be used as the sole support for ceiling (paddle) fans.

Exception: Boxes listed for the application shall be permitted as the sole means of support.

See also Section 422-18.
One method of supporting a ceiling fan so that the box does not serve as the sole support is shown in Figure 370-6.

Figure 370-6. Supporting ceiling fan without depending on box for sole support.

370-18. Pull and Junction Boxes. Boxes and conduit bodies used as pull or junction boxes shall comply with (a) through (d) of this section.

(a) Minimum Size. For raceways ¾ inch trade size or larger, containing conductors of No. 4 or larger, and for cables containing conductors of No. 4 or larger, the minimum dimensions of pull or junction boxes installed in a raceway or cable run shall comply with the following:

(1) Straight Pulls. In straight pulls the length of the box shall not be less than eight times the trade diameter of the largest raceway.

(2) Angle or U Pulls. Where angle or U pulls are made, the distance between each raceway entry inside the box and the opposite wall of the box shall not be less than six times the trade diameter of the largest raceway. This distance shall be increased for additional entries by the amount of the maximum sum of the diameters of all other raceway entries in any one row on the same wall of the box. The row that provides the maximum distance shall be used in this calculation.

Exception: Where a conduit or cable entry is in the wall of a box or conduit body opposite to a removable cover and where the distance from that wall to the cover is in conformance with the column for one wire per terminal in Table 373-6(a).

The distance between raceway entries enclosing the same conductor shall not be less than six times the trade diameter of the larger raceway.

435

When transposing cable size into raceway size in (a)(1) and (a)(2) above, the minimum trade size raceway required for the number and size of conductors in the cable shall be used.

(3) Boxes of dimensions less than those required in (a)(1) and (a)(2) above shall be permitted for installations of combinations of conductors that are less than the maximum conduit fill (of conduits being used) permitted by Table 1, Chapter 9, provided the box has been approved for and is permanently marked with the maximum number and maximum size of conductors permitted.

Exception: Terminal housings supplied with motors which shall comply with the provisions of Section 430-12.

(b) Conductors in Pull or Junction Boxes. In pull boxes or junction boxes having any dimension over 6 feet (1.83 m), all conductors shall be cabled or racked up in an approved manner.

(FPN): See Section 373-6(c) for insulation of conductors at bushings.

(c) Covers. All pull boxes, junction boxes, conduit bodies, and fittings shall be provided with covers compatible with the box, conduit body or fitting construction and suitable for the conditions of use. Where metal covers are used, they shall comply with the grounding requirements of Section 250-42.

(d) Permanent Barriers. Where permanent barriers are installed in a box, each section shall be considered as a separate box.

This section applies to minimum dimensions of pull or junction boxes used with raceways (¾ in. or larger) or cables, where they contain conductors No. 4 AWG or larger.

For straight pulls, for example, a 2-in. conduit containing four 4/0 AWG conductors (see Table 3B in Chapter 9) requires a 16-in.-long pull box [8 × 2 in. = 16 in. as per 370-18 (a)(1)]. It should be understood that 16 in. is the required minimum length; however, for maximum ease in handling this size of conductor, a longer length pull box may be desired.

For angle pulls or U pulls, 370-18 (a)(2) indicates two methods for computing the box dimensions. The largest dimension computed by either of the two methods is, of course, the one that should be used. If there is more than one row of raceway entry in one wall, the row that provides the maximum distance is to be used.

First method:

$$
\begin{aligned}
6 \times 4 \text{ in.} &= 24 \text{ in.} \\
2 \times 3 \text{ in.} &= 6 \\
4 \times 2\tfrac{1}{2} \text{ in.} &= \underline{10} \\
\text{Total } & 40 \text{ in.}
\end{aligned}
$$

Second method:

Figure 370-7 illustrates a box in which the conduits enter and leave in the same order, that is, there is no crossover of conductors. The 2½-in. conduit in the top, left corner must be spaced not less than 15 in. (6 × 2½ in. = 15 in.) (dimension A, measured center to center). By calculation, or by sketching the layout of the box and conduits on paper, it is determined that distance C is approximately 10½ in. and, by practical installation methods for the spacing of conduits, distance B is approximately 32½ in. (10½ in. + 32½ in. = 43 in.); therefore, the second method determining the larger box would be applied in this case.

Larger sizes of conductors are generally formed in circuit groups and "tie wrapped" together, or sufficient space should be allowed to provide for insulated racks that will support conductors in an orderly manner. Conductors are required to be prevented from resting directly on metal inside the box, and insulating bushings are required to be provided unless part of enclosures have an integral threaded hub or boss that provides a smoothly rounded or flared entry for conductors. See Section 373-6(c).

Figure 370-7. Raceways in a right-angle turn with no crossover of conductors within the pull box.

370-19. Junction, Pull and Outlet Boxes to Be Accessible. Junction, pull and outlet boxes shall be so installed that the wiring contained in them can be rendered accessible without removing any part of the building or in underground circuits without excavating sidewalks, paving, earth, or other substance that is to be used to establish the finished grade.

Exception: Listed boxes shall be permitted where covered by gravel, light aggregate, or noncohesive granulated soil if their location is effectively identified and accessible for excavation.

Consideration should also be given to the accessibility of junction boxes installed on a structural ceiling above a suspended ceiling.

ARTICLE 370—BOXES AND FITTINGS

A covered box is permitted to be used at any point for the connection of conduit, tubing, or cable, provided it is not rendered inaccessible. See Article 100 for definition of "accessible (as applied to wiring methods)." See also Section 300-15.

C. Construction Specifications

370-20. Metal Boxes, Conduit Bodies, and Fittings.

(a) Corrosion-Resistant. Metal boxes, conduit bodies, and fittings shall be corrosion-resistant or shall be well galvanized, enameled, or otherwise properly coated inside and out to prevent corrosion.

(FPN): See Section 300-6 for limitation in the use of boxes and fittings protected from corrosion solely by enamel.

(b) Thickness of Metal. Sheet steel boxes not over 100 cubic inches in size shall be made from steel not less than 0.0625 inch (1.59 mm) thick. The wall of a malleable iron box and a die-cast or permanent-mold cast aluminum, brass or bronze box shall not be less than 3/32 inch (2.38 mm) thick. Other cast metal boxes shall have a wall thickness not less than 1/8 inch (3.17 mm).

UL-listed cast metal boxes suitable for field drilling and tapping of holes for conduit connections and mounting are marked to indicate the location and trade size of the openings.

(c) Metal Boxes Over 100 Cubic Inches. Metal boxes over 100 cubic inches in size shall be constructed so as to be of ample strength and rigidity. If of sheet steel the metal shall not be less than 0.053 inch (1.35 mm) uncoated.

(d) Grounding Provisions. A means shall be provided in each metal box, designed for use with nonmetallic raceways and nonmetallic cable systems, for the connection of an equipment grounding conductor.

The "means provided" by the box manufacturer is usually in the form of a 10-32 tapped hole marked "GR" or "GRD" or the equivalent, next to the hole. It should be noted, however, that the "means provided" may not necessarily be utilized. See Figure 250-38 and the commentary following Section 250-114.

370-21. Covers. Metal covers shall be of a thickness not less than that specified for the walls of the box or fitting of the same material and with which they are designed to be used, or shall be lined with firmly attached insulating material not less than 1/32 inch (0.79 mm) in thickness. Covers of porcelain or other approved insulating material shall be permitted if of such form and thickness as to afford the required protection and strength.

370-22. Bushings. Covers of outlet boxes, conduit bodies and outlet fittings having holes through which flexible cord pendants may pass shall be provided with approved bushings or shall have smooth, well-rounded surfaces, upon which the cord may bear. Where conductors other than flexible cord may pass through a metal cover, a separate hole equipped with a bushing of suitable insulating material shall be provided for each conductor. Such separate holes shall be connected by a slot as required by Section 300-20.

(FPN): For alternating current conductors, see Section 300-20(b).

370-23. Nonmetallic Boxes. Provisions for supports or other mounting means for nonmetallic boxes shall be outside of the box, or the box shall be so constructed as to prevent contact between the conductors in the box and the supporting screws.

Nonmetallic boxes considered as being suitable for use with nonmetallic conduit are marked as per Section 110-3(b) and are usually intended for support by conduit.

438

These types of boxes are not recognized for the support of fixtures or other equipment nor are they designed to accommodate heat-producing equipment.

370-24. Marking. All boxes and conduit bodies, covers, extension rings, plaster rings, and the like shall be durably and legibly marked with the manufacturer's name or trademark.

D. Pull and Junction Boxes for Use on Systems Over 600 Volts, Nominal

370-50. General. In addition to the generally applicable provisions of Article 370, the rules in Sections 370-51 and 370-52 shall apply.

370-51. Size of Pull and Junction Boxes. Pull and junction boxes shall provide adequate space and dimensions for the installation of conductors in accordance with the following:

(a) For Straight Pulls. The length of the box shall not be less than forty-eight times the outside diameter, over sheath, of the largest shielded or lead-covered conductor or cable entering the box. The length shall not be less than thirty-two times the outside diameter of the largest nonshielded conductor or cable.

(b) For Angle or U Pulls. The distance between each cable or conductor entry inside the box and the opposite wall of the box shall not be less than thirty-six times the outside diameter, over sheath, of the largest cable or conductor. This distance shall be increased for additional entries by the amount of the sum of the outside diameters, over sheath, of all other cables or conductor entries through the same wall of the box.

The distance between a cable or conductor entry and its exit from the box shall be not less than thirty-six times the outside diameter, over sheath, of that cable or conductor.

Exception No. 1: Where cables are nonshielded and not lead-covered, the distance of thirty-six times the outside diameter shall be permitted to be reduced to twenty-four times the outside diameter.

Exception No. 2: Where a conductor or cable entry is in the wall of a box opposite to a removable cover and where the distance from that wall to the cover is in conformance with the provisions of Section 300-34.

Exception No. 3: Terminal housings supplied with motors which shall comply with the provisions of Section 430-12.

(c) Removable Sides. One or more sides of any pull box shall be removable.

370-52. Construction and Installation Requirements.

(a) Corrosion Protection. Boxes shall be made of material inherently resistant to corrosion or shall be suitably protected, both internally and externally, by enameling, galvanizing, plating, or other means.

(b) Passing Through Partitions. Suitable bushings, shields, or fittings having smooth rounded edges shall be provided where conductors or cables pass through partitions and at other locations where necessary.

(c) Complete Enclosure. Boxes shall provide a complete enclosure for the contained conductors or cables.

(d) Wiring Is Accessible. Boxes shall be so installed that the wiring is accessible without removing any part of the building. Working space shall be provided in accordance with Section 110-34.

(e) Suitable Covers. Boxes shall be closed by suitable covers securely fastened in place. Underground box covers that weigh over 100 pounds (43.6 kg) shall be considered as meeting

439

this requirement. Covers for boxes shall be permanently marked "HIGH VOLTAGE." The marking shall be on the outside of the box cover and shall be readily visible. Letters shall be block type at least ½ inch (12.7 mm) in height.

(f) Suitable for Expected Handling. Boxes and their covers shall be capable of withstanding the handling to which they may be subjected.

ARTICLE 373 — CABINETS AND CUTOUT BOXES

Contents

373-1. Scope. This article covers the installation and construction specifications of cabinets, cutout boxes, and meter socket enclosures.

See Section 373-6(b)(1) for the requirement in Article 373 relating to meter socket enclosures.

See definitions of "cabinet" and "cutout box" in Article 100. Cabinets and cutout boxes are designed with a swinging door(s) to enclose switches, overcurrent devices, or control equipment. Some cabinets for circuit breaker panelboards or "load centers" do not have doors as permitted by Exception No. 2 to Section 240-30. Cabinets and cutout boxes are required to be of sufficient size to accommodate all devices and conductors without overcrowding or jamming. This condition can be prevented by the use of auxiliary gutters (see Article 374).

A. Installation

373-2. Damp, Wet, or Hazardous (Classified) Locations.

(a) Damp and Wet Locations. In damp or wet locations, cabinets and cutout boxes of the surface type shall be so placed or equipped as to prevent moisture or water from entering and accumulating within the cabinet or cutout box, and shall be mounted so there is at least ¼-inch (6.35-mm) air space between the enclosure and the wall or other supporting surface. Cabinets or cutout boxes installed in wet locations shall be weatherproof.

(FPN): For protection against corrosion, see Section 300-6.

(b) Hazardous (Classified) Locations.   Installations in hazardous (classified) locations shall conform to Articles 500 through 517.

See Section 430-91 for motor controller enclosure selection table for indoor and outdoor use.

373-3. Position in Wall.   In walls of concrete, tile, or other noncombustible material, cabinets shall be so installed that the front edge of the cabinet will not set back of the finished surface more than ¼ inch (6.35 mm). In walls constructed of wood or other combustible material, cabinets shall be flush with the finished surface or project therefrom.

373-4. Unused Openings.   Unused openings in cabinet or cutout boxes shall be effectively closed to afford protection substantially equivalent to that of the wall of the cabinet or cutout box. Where metal plugs or plates are used with nonmetallic cabinets or cutout boxes, they shall be recessed at least ¼ inch (6.35 mm) from the outer surface.

373-5. Conductors Entering Cabinets or Cutout Boxes.   Conductors entering cabinets or cutout boxes shall be protected from abrasion and shall comply with (a) through (c) below.

See Section 373-6(c).

(a) Openings to Be Closed.   Openings through which conductors enter shall be adequately closed.

(b) Metal Cabinets and Cutout Boxes.   Where metal cabinets or cutout boxes are installed with open wiring or concealed knob-and-tube wiring, conductors shall enter through insulating bushings or, in dry places, through flexible tubing extending from the last insulating support and firmly secured to the cabinet or cutout box.

(c) Cables.   Where cable is used, each cable shall be secured to the cabinet or cutout box.

This section prohibits the installation of several cables bunched together and run through a knockout or chase nipple. Individual cable clamps or connectors are required to be used with only one cable per clamp or connector unless the clamp or connector is approved for more than a single cable.

373-6. Deflection of Conductors.   Conductors at terminals or conductors entering or leaving cabinets or cutout boxes and the like shall comply with (a) through (c) below.

(a) Width of Wiring Gutters.   Conductors shall not be deflected within a cabinet or cutout box unless a gutter having a width in accordance with Table 373-6(a) is provided. Conductors in parallel in accordance with Section 310-4 shall be judged on the basis of the number of conductors in parallel.

(b) Wire Bending Space at Terminals.   Wire bending space at each terminal shall be provided in accordance with (1) or (2) below:

(1) Table 373-6(a) shall apply where the conductor does not enter or leave the enclosure through the wall opposite its terminal.

Exception No. 1: A conductor shall be permitted to enter or leave an enclosure through the wall opposite its terminal provided the conductor enters or leaves the enclosure where the gutter joins an adjacent gutter that has a width that conforms to Table 373-6(b) for that conductor.

Exception No. 2: A conductor not larger than 350 MCM shall be permitted to enter or leave an enclosure containing only a meter socket(s) through the wall opposite its terminal provided the terminal is a lay-in type where either:

441

Table 373-6(a). Minimum Wire Bending Space at Terminals and Minimum Width of Wiring Gutters in Inches

AWG or Circular-Mill Size of Wire	Wires per Terminal				
	1	2	3	4	5
14–10	Not Specified	—	—	—	—
8–6	1½	—	—	—	—
4–3	2	—	—	—	—
2	2½	—	—	—	—
1	3	—	—	—	—
0–00	3½	5	7	—	—
000–0000	4	6	8	—	—
250 MCM	4½	6	8	10	—
300–350 MCM	5	8	10	12	—
400–500 MCM	6	8	10	12	14
600–700 MCM	8	10	12	14	16
750–900 MCM	8	12	14	16	18
1000–1250 MCM	10	—	—	—	—
1500–2000 MCM	12	—	—	—	—

For SI units: one inch = 25.4 millimeters.
Bending space at terminals shall be measured in a straight line from the end of the lug or wire connector (in the direction that the wire leaves the terminal) to the wall, barrier, or obstruction.

a. the terminal is directly facing the enclosure wall and offset is not greater than 50 percent of the bending space specified in Table 373-6(a), or

b. the terminal is directed toward the opening in the enclosure and is within a 45-degree angle of directly facing the enclosure wall.

(FPN): Offset is the distance measured along the enclosure wall from the axis of the centerline of the terminal to a line passing through the center of the opening in the enclosure.

(2) Table 373-6(b) shall apply where the conductor enters or leaves the enclosure through the wall opposite its terminal.

Section 373-6(b)(2) and Table 373-6(b) provide the requirements for wire bending space where straight-in wiring or offset (double bends) are employed at terminals. Section 373-6(b)(1) is for use where only 90-degree bends are involved.

The footnotes to Table 373-6(b) are intended to permit a reduction in required bending space for removable and lay-in wire terminals. These terminal wire connectors are required to be of the type that are intended for a single conductor (single barrel). To make wiring easier, one type of terminal may be removed and placed on the stripped end of the conductor, which has been cut to the proper length. The terminal is then crimped or lightly torqued on the conductor as intended, and then remounted. If a mechanical screw connector is involved, the screw should then be torqued to the proper value. See commentary following the fine print note under Section 110-14.

Note that in accordance with the footnotes to Tables 373-6(a) and 373-6(b), bending space is measured in the direction that the wire leaves the terminal when using Table 373-6(a) and in a direction perpendicular to the enclosure wall when using Table 373-6(b).

A lay-in-type terminal is a pressure wire connector in which part of the connector is removeable or swings away so that the stripped end of the conductor can be laid into the fixed portion of the connector. The removeable or swing-away portion is then put back in place and the connector tightened down on the conductor.

See Figures 373-1 and 373-2. See also Figure 430-1.

Table 373-6(b). Minimum Wire Bending Space at Terminals for Section 373-6(b)(2) in Inches

Wire Size	1	Wires per Terminal 2	3	4 or More
14–10	Not Specified	—	—	—
8	1½	—	—	—
6	2	—	—	—
4	3	—	—	—
3	3	—	—	—
2	3½	—	—	—
1	4½	—	—	—
0	5½	5½	7	—
2/0	6	6	7½	—
3/0	6½ (½)	6½ (½)	8	—
4/0	7 (1)	7½ (1½)	8½ (½)	—
250	8½ (2)	8½ (2)	9 (1)	10
300	10 (3)	10 (2)	11 (1)	12
350	12 (3)	12 (3)	13 (3)	14 (2)
400	13 (3)	13 (3)	14 (3)	15 (3)
500	14 (3)	14 (3)	15 (3)	16 (3)
600	15 (3)	16 (3)	18 (3)	19 (3)
700	16 (3)	18 (3)	20 (3)	22 (3)
750	17 (3)	19 (3)	22 (3)	24 (3)
800	18	20	22	24
900	19	22	24	24
1000	20	—	—	—
1250	22	—	—	—
1500	24	—	—	—
1750	24	—	—	—
2000	24	—	—	—

For SI units: one inch = 25.4 millimeters.

Bending space at terminals shall be measured in a straight line from the end of the lug or wire connector in a direction perpendicular to the enclosure wall.

For removable and lay-in wire terminals intended for only one wire, bending space shall be permitted to be reduced by the number of inches shown in parentheses.

(c) Insulated Fittings. Where ungrounded conductors of No. 4 or larger enter a raceway in a cabinet, pull box, junction box, or auxiliary gutter, the conductors shall be protected by a substantial fitting providing a smoothly rounded insulating surface, unless the conductors are separated from the raceway fitting by substantial insulating material securely fastened in place.

Where No. 4 AWG or larger ungrounded conductors enter a cabinet or cutout box from metal raceways, a smoothly rounded insulating bushing or fitting is required to protect the conductors from abrasion during and after installation. See Sections 345-15, 346-8, and 347-12.

Metal conduit bushings or fittings provided with insulated sleeves or linings are commonly used. It is also possible to use a separate insulating sleeve or lining to separate the conductors from the raceway fitting.

UL-listed insulating bushings provided either separately or as part of a fitting are suitable for a temperature of 150°C, if they are colored black or brown, and for 90°C if of any other color unless specifically marked for a higher temperature. See Figure 373-3.

Exception: Where threaded hubs or bosses that are an integral part of an enclosure provide a smoothly rounded or flared entry for conductors.

443

Figure 373-1. The following rules apply when wiring as shown.

T1, Section 373-6(b)(2): Table 373-6(b) applies for conductors M.

T2, Section 373-6(b)(2): Table 373-6(b) applies for conductors BR2 unless in accordance with Section 373-6(b)(1), Exception. Conductors enter a second wiring space G, conforming to Table 373-6(b) for conductors BR2.

T3, Section 373-6(b)(2): Table 373-6(b) applies for conductors BR3.

T4, Section 373-6(b)(1): Table 373-6(a) applies for conductor N.

G1, Section 373-6(a): Table 373-6(a) applies for conductors M. Table 373-6(b) applies for conductors BR2 when T2 does not comply with Table 373-6(b).

G2, Section 373-6(a): Table 373-6(a) applies for conductors BR2.

G3, Section 373-6(a): Table 373-6(a) applies for conductors BR3.

G4, Section 373-6(a): Table 373-6(a) applies for conductor N.

Conduit bushings constructed wholly of insulating material shall not be used to secure a raceway. The insulating fitting or insulating material shall have a temperature rating not less than the insulation temperature rating of the installed conductors.

373-7. Space in Enclosures. Cabinets and cutout boxes shall have sufficient space to accommodate all conductors installed in them without crowding.

373-8. Enclosures for Switches or Overcurrent Devices. Enclosures for switches or overcurrent devices shall not be used as junction boxes, auxiliary gutters, or raceways for conductors feeding through or tapping off to other switches or overcurrent devices.

Exception: Where adequate space is provided so that the conductors do not fill the wiring space at any cross section to more than 40 percent of the cross-sectional area of the space, and so that the conductors, splices, and

444

Figure 373-2. Conditions under which Section 373-6(b)(1), Exception No. 2 are applicable.

Figure 373-3. An insulating bushing to protect conductors from chafing against a metal conduit fitting.

taps do not fill the wiring space at any cross section to more than 75 percent of the cross-sectional area of the space.

Most enclosures are intended to accommodate only those conductors that will be connected to terminals for switches or overcurrent devices within the enclosures themselves. Where adequate space is provided for additional conductors, such as control circuits, the total conductor fill in the enclosure is not permitted to exceed

445

40 percent of the cross section of the wiring space in the enclosure, and no more than 75 percent if splices or taps are necessary.

An example would be if an enclosure had a wiring space of 4 in. × 3 in., the cross-sectional area would be 12 sq in. Thus, the total conductor fill (see Table 5 in Chapter 9 for dimensions of conductors) at any cross section could not exceed 4.8 sq in. (40 percent of 12 sq in.), and the maximum space for conductors and splices or taps at any cross section could not exceed 9 sq in. (75 percent of 12 sq in.).

In general, the best way to avoid overcrowding enclosures is to use properly sized auxiliary gutters (Sections 374-5 and 374-8) or junction boxes (Sections 370-6 and 370-18). See Section 430-10 and commentary for wiring space in enclosures for motor controllers and disconnecting means. See also Section 710-59 for installations over 600 volts.

373-9. Side or Back Wiring Spaces or Gutters.   Cabinets and cutout boxes shall be provided with back wiring spaces, gutters, or wiring compartments as required by Section 373-11(c) and (d).

B. Construction Specifications

373-10. Material.   Cabinets and cutout boxes shall comply with (a) through (c) below.

(a) Metal Cabinets and Cutout Boxes.   Metal cabinets and cutout boxes shall be protected both inside and outside against corrosion.

(FPN): For protection against corrosion, see Section 300-6.

(b) Strength.   The design and construction of cabinets and cutout boxes shall be such as to secure ample strength and rigidity. If constructed of sheet steel, the metal shall not be less than 0.053 inch (1.35 mm) uncoated.

(c) Nonmetallic Cabinets.   Nonmetallic cabinets shall be submitted for approval prior to installation.

373-11. Spacing.   The spacing within cabinets and cutout boxes shall comply with (a) through (d) below.

(a) General.   Spacing within cabinets and cutout boxes shall be sufficient to provide ample room for the distribution of wires and cables placed in them, and for a separation between metal parts of devices and apparatus mounted within them as follows:

(1) Base.   Other than at points of support, there shall be an air space of at least ¹⁄₁₆ inch (1.59 mm) between the base of the device and the wall of any metal cabinet or cutout box in which the device is mounted.

(2) Doors.   There shall be an air space of at least 1 inch (25.4 mm) between any live metal part, including live metal parts of enclosed fuses, and the door.

Exception: Where the door is lined with an approved insulating material or is of a thickness of metal not less than No. 12 MSG, the air space shall not be less than ½ inch (12.7 mm).

(3) Live Parts.   There shall be an air space of at least ½ inch (12.7 mm) between the walls, back, gutter partition, if of metal, or door of any cabinet or cutout box and the nearest exposed current-carrying part of devices mounted within the cabinet where the voltage does not exceed 250. This spacing shall be increased to at least 1 inch (25.4 mm) for voltages 251 to 600, nominal.

Exception: As permitted in (2) above.

(b) Switch Clearance. Cabinets and cutout boxes shall be deep enough to allow the closing of the doors when 30-ampere branch-circuit panelboard switches are in any position; when combination cutout switches are in any position; or when other single-throw switches are opened as far as their construction will permit.

(c) Wiring Space. Cabinets and cutout boxes that contain devices or apparatus connected within the cabinet or box to more than eight conductors, including those of branch circuits, meter loops, subfeeder circuits, power circuits, and similar circuits, but not including the supply circuit or a continuation thereof, shall have back-wiring spaces or one or more side-wiring spaces, side gutters, or wiring compartments.

(d) Wiring Space — Enclosure. Side-wiring spaces, side gutters, or side-wiring compartments of cabinets and cutout boxes shall be made tight enclosures by means of covers, barriers, or partitions extending from the bases of the devices, contained in the cabinet to the door, frame, or sides of the cabinet.

Exception: Where the enclosure contains only those conductors that are led from the cabinet at points directly opposite their terminal connections to devices within the cabinet.

Partially enclosed back-wiring spaces shall be provided with covers to complete the enclosure. Wiring spaces that are required by (c) above, and that are exposed when doors are open, shall be provided with covers to complete the enclosure. Where adequate space is provided for feed-through conductors and for splices as required in Section 373-8, Exception, additional barriers shall not be required.

ARTICLE 374 — AUXILIARY GUTTERS

Contents

374-1. Use. Auxiliary gutters shall be permitted to supplement wiring spaces at meter centers, distribution centers, switchboards, and similar points of wiring systems and may enclose conductors or busbars, but shall not be used to enclose switches, overcurrent devices, appliances, or other similar equipment.

Auxiliary gutter sections and associated fittings are identical to those of wireways, and, if listed by UL, each bears the single UL listing mark "Listed Wireway or Auxiliary Gutter." They differ only in their intended use. See commentary following Section 362-1. Gutters (and wireways) are required to be constructed and installed to assure adequate electrical and mechanical continuity of the complete system. See Section 250-91(b)(10).

ARTICLE 374—AUXILIARY GUTTERS

Auxiliary gutters for outdoor use are required to be of "raintight" construction. See Section 620-35 for elevator uses and Section 640-4, for sound-recording equipment uses.

374-2. Extension Beyond Equipment. An auxiliary gutter shall not extend a greater distance than 30 feet (9.14 m) beyond the equipment which it supplements.

Exception: As provided in Section 620-35 for elevators.

(FPN): For wireways, see Article 362. For busways, see Article 364.

374-3. Supports. Gutters shall be supported throughout their entire length at intervals not exceeding 5 feet (1.52 m).

374-4. Covers. Covers shall be securely fastened to the gutter.

374-5. Number of Conductors. Auxiliary gutters shall not contain more than thirty current-carrying conductors at any cross section. The sum of the cross-sectional areas of all contained conductors at any cross section of an auxiliary gutter shall not exceed 20 percent of the interior cross-sectional area of the auxiliary gutter.

Exception No. 1: As provided in Section 620-35 for elevators.

Exception No. 2: Conductors for signaling circuits or controller conductors between a motor and its starter and used only for starting duty shall not be considered as current-carrying conductors.

Exception No. 3: Where the correction factors specified in Note 8(a) to Tables 310-16 through 310-31 are applied, there shall be no limit on the number of current-carrying conductors, but the sum of the cross-sectional area of all contained conductors at any cross section of the auxiliary gutter shall not exceed 20 percent of the interior cross-sectional area of the auxiliary gutter.

(FPN): For conductor cross-sectional area see Tables 5, 5A, 6, 7, 8 and the applicable Notes to Tables at the beginning of Chapter 9.

The dimensions of rubber- and thermoplastic-insulated conductors given in Tables 5 and 5A in Chapter 9 may be used to compute the size of gutters required to contain a given combination of such conductors.

Where auxiliary gutters contain thirty or fewer current-carrying conductors, the correction factors of Note 8(a) (Tables 310-16 through 310-31) do not apply. There is no limit on the number of current-carrying conductors if Note 8(a) is applied; however, the contained conductors are not permitted to exceed 20 percent of the interior cross-sectional area of the gutter. See example given in the commentary following Section 362-1 for method of calculating number of conductors within a wireway which is also applicable to auxiliary gutters.

No limit is placed on the size of conductors that may be installed in an auxiliary gutter; however, see Section 374-6 for limitations of bare copper or aluminum busbars enclosed in gutters.

374-6. Ampacity of Conductors. Where the number of current-carrying conductors contained in the auxiliary gutter is thirty or less, the correction factors specified in Note 8(a) to Tables 310-16 through 310-31 shall not apply. The current carried continuously in bare copper bars in auxiliary gutters shall not exceed 1000 amperes per square inch (645 sq mm) of cross section of the conductor. For aluminum bars, the current carried continuously shall not exceed 700 amperes per square inch (645 sq mm) of cross section of the conductor.

374-7. Clearance of Bare Live Parts. Bare conductors shall be securely and rigidly supported so that the minimum clearance between bare current-carrying metal parts of opposite polarities mounted on the same surface will not be less than 2 inches (50.8 mm), nor less than 1 inch (25.4 mm) for parts that are held free in the air. A clearance not less than 1 inch (25.4 mm) shall be secured between bare current-carrying metal parts and any metal surface. Adequate provisions shall be made for the expansion and contraction of busbars.

374-8. Splices and Taps. Splices and taps shall comply with (a) through (d) below.

(a) Within Gutters. Splices or taps shall be permitted within gutters when they are accessible by means of removable covers or doors. The conductors, including splices and taps, shall not fill the gutter to more than 75 percent of its area.

(b) Bare Conductors. Taps from bare conductors shall leave the gutter opposite their terminal connections and conductors shall not be brought in contact with uninsulated current-carrying parts of opposite polarity.

(c) Suitably Identified. All taps shall be suitably identified at the gutter as to the circuit or equipment which they supply.

(d) Overcurrent Protection. Tap connections from conductors in auxiliary gutters shall be provided with overcurrent protection as required in Section 240-21.

Precautions are required to be taken by providing suitable bushings, shields, etc., where conductors pass around bends, or between gutters and cabinets and other locations to prevent abrasion of the conductor insulation. Also, conductors are required to be shaped or formed in a permanent manner so that they are not in contact with bare busbars within the gutter.

Per subparagraphs (c) and (d), all taps from gutters are required to be identified (as to circuits or equipment) and be protected with overcurrent devices per Section 240-21.

374-9. Construction and Installation. Auxiliary gutters shall comply with (a) through (e) below.

(a) Electrical and Mechanical Continuity. Gutters shall be so constructed and installed that adequate electrical and mechanical continuity of the complete system will be secured.

(b) Substantial Construction. Gutters shall be of substantial construction and shall provide a complete enclosure for the contained conductors. All surfaces, both interior and exterior, shall be suitably protected from corrosion. Corner joints shall be made tight and, where the assembly is held together by rivets or bolts shall be spaced not more than 12 inches (305 mm) apart.

(c) Smooth Rounded Edges. Suitable bushings, shields, or fittings having smooth rounded edges shall be provided where conductors pass between gutters, through partitions, around bends, between gutters and cabinets or junction boxes, and at other locations where necessary to prevent abrasion of the insulation of the conductors.

(d) Deflected Insulated Conductors. Where insulated conductors are deflected within an auxiliary gutter, either at the ends or where conduits, fittings, or other raceways or cables enter or leave the gutter, or where the direction of the gutter is deflected greater than 30 degrees, dimensions corresponding to Section 373-6 shall apply.

(e) Outdoor Use. Auxiliary gutters installed in wet locations shall be of raintight construction.

This section correlates with Section 362-2 and provides for auxiliary gutters which may be installed in locations which may not be outdoors, for example, in a vehicle car washing area inside of a building.

ARTICLE 380 — SWITCHES

Contents

A. Installation

380-1. Scope. The provisions of this article shall apply to all switches, switching devices, and circuit breakers where used as switches.

380-2. Switch Connections.

(a) Three-Way and Four-Way Switches. Three-way and four-way switches shall be so wired that all switching is done only in the ungrounded circuit conductor. Where in metal raceways, wiring between switches and outlets shall be in accordance with Section 300-20(a).

Exception: Switch loops shall not require a grounded conductor.

Although the *NEC* does not specifically prohibit use of two 2-conductor nonmetallic-sheathed cables for wiring three-way and four-way switches instead of a single 3-conductor cable, use of two 2-conductor cables could easily result in a violation of Section 300-20 if steel boxes are used and the cables enter the box through separate knockouts. Use of the same clamp or section of a clamp for both cables would, in most cases, be in violation of Section 110-3(b) because clamps have been tested for only one cable per clamp or section of clamp.

The grounded conductor is not needed [see Section 300-20(a)] because the ungrounded conductor both enters and leaves the enclosure in the same cable or raceway, thus avoiding inductive heating.

(b) Grounded Conductors. Switches or circuit breakers shall not disconnect the grounded conductor of a circuit.

Exception No. 1: Where the switch or circuit breaker simultaneously disconnects all conductors of the circuit.

Exception No. 2: Where the switch or circuit breaker is so arranged that the grounded conductor cannot be disconnected until all the ungrounded conductors of the circuit have been disconnected.

380-3. Enclosure. Switches and circuit breakers shall be of the externally operable type mounted in an enclosure listed for the intended use. The minimum wire bending space at terminals and minimum gutter space provided in switch enclosures shall be as required in Section 373-6.

Exception: Pendant- and surface-type snap switches and knife switches mounted on an open-face switchboard or panelboard.

380-4. Wet Locations. A switch or circuit breaker in a wet location or outside of a building shall be enclosed in a weatherproof enclosure or cabinet that shall comply with Section 373-2(a).

380-5. Time Switches, Flashers, and Similar Devices. Time switches, flashers, and similar devices need not be of the externally operable type. They shall be enclosed in metal boxes or cabinets.

Exception No. 1: Where mounted in switchboards, control panels, or enclosures and so located that any live terminals, located within 6 inches (152 mm) of the manually adjustable clock dial or "on-off" switch, are covered by suitable barriers.

Exception No. 2: Where enclosed in approved individual housings with no live parts exposed to the operator.

Time switches, flashers, etc., are required to be mounted in metal enclosures to prevent sparks or thermal energy from the natural operation of such automatic switching devices from contacting any combustible material in the area.

380-6. Position of Knife Switches.

(a) Single-Throw Knife Switches. Single-throw knife switches shall be so placed that gravity will not tend to close them. Single-throw knife switches, approved for use in the inverted position, shall be provided with a locking device that will ensure that the blades remain in the open position when so set.

(b) Double-Throw Knife Switches. Double-throw knife switches shall be permitted to be mounted so that the throw will be either vertical or horizontal. Where the throw is vertical, a locking device shall be provided to hold the blades in the open position when so set.

(c) Connection of Knife Switches. Single-throw knife switches shall be so connected that the blades are deenergized when the switch is in the open position.

Exception: Where the load side of the switch is connected to circuits or equipment, the inherent nature of which may provide a backfeed source of power. For such installations, a permanent sign shall be installed on the switch enclosure or immediately adjacent to open switches reading: "WARNING—LOAD SIDE OF SWITCH MAY BE ENERGIZED BY BACKFEED."

Typical backfeed sources are batteries, generators, and double-ended switchboard ties. These may cause the switch blades to be energized when the switch is in the open position, a condition inherent to the circuitry.

380-7. Indicating. General-use and motor-circuit switches and circuit breakers, where mounted in an enclosure as described in Section 380-3, shall clearly indicate whether they are in the open "off" or closed "on" position.

Where these switch or circuit breaker handles are operated vertically rather than rotationally or horizontally, the up position of the handle shall be the "on" position.

Exception: Double-throw switches.

451

ARTICLE 380—SWITCHES

380-8. Accessibility and Grouping.

(a) Location. All switches and circuit breakers used as switches shall be so located that they may be operated from a readily accessible place. They shall be so installed that the center of the grip of the operating handle of the switch or circuit breaker, when in its highest position, will not be more than 6½ feet (1.98 m) above the floor or working platform.

Exception No. 1: On busway installations, fused switches and circuit breakers shall be permitted to be located at the same level as the busway. Suitable means shall be provided to operate the handle of the device from the floor.

Exception No. 2: Switches installed adjacent to motors, appliances, or other equipment which they supply shall be permitted to be located higher than specified in the foregoing and to be accessible by portable means.

Exception No. 3: Hookstick operable isolating switches shall be permitted at heights of more than 6½ feet (1.98 m).

(b) Voltage Between Adjacent Switches. Snap switches shall not be grouped or ganged in outlet boxes unless they can be so arranged that the voltage between adjacent switches does not exceed 300, or unless they are installed in boxes equipped with permanently installed barriers between adjacent switches.

380-9. Faceplates for Flush-Mounted Snap Switches.
Flush snap switches, that are mounted in ungrounded metal boxes and located within reach of conducting floors or other conducting surfaces, shall be provided with faceplates of nonconducting, noncombustible material. Metal faceplates shall be of ferrous metal not less than 0.030 inch (0.762 mm) in thickness or of nonferrous metal not less than 0.040 inch (1.016 mm) in thickness. Faceplates of insulating material shall be noncombustible and not less than 0.10 inch (2.54 mm) in thickness but they shall be permitted to be less than 0.10 inch (2.54 mm) in thickness if formed or reinforced to provide adequate mechanical strength. Faceplates shall be installed so as to completely cover the wall opening and seat against the wall surface.

Switch plates attached to outlets supplied by a wiring method which does not provide a ready means for grounding are required to be made of insulating material and are required to have no exposed conductive parts.

380-10. Mounting of Snap Switches.

(a) Surface-type. Snap switches used with open wiring on insulators shall be mounted on insulating material that will separate the conductors at least ½ inch (12.7 mm) from the surface wired over.

(b) Box Mounted. Flush-type snap switches mounted in boxes that are set back of the wall surface as permitted in Section 370-10 shall be installed so that the extension plaster ears are seated against the surface of the wall. Flush-type snap switches mounted in boxes that are flush with the wall surface or project therefrom shall be so installed that the mounting yoke or strap of the switch is seated against the box.

Cooperation is necessary among the building trades (carpenters, dry-wall installers, plasterers, etc.) in order for electricians to properly set device boxes flush with the finish surface, thereby ensuring a secure seating of the switch yoke and permitting the maximum projection of switch handles through the installed switch plate.

380-11. Circuit Breakers as Switches.
A hand-operable circuit breaker equipped with a lever or handle, or a power-operated circuit breaker capable of being opened by hand in the event of

a power failure, shall be permitted to serve as a switch if it has the required number of poles. Note: See provisions contained in Section 240-81.

Circuit breakers capable of being hand-operated are required to clearly indicate whether they are in the open "off" or closed "on" position.
See Section 240-83(d) for marking (SWD) for circuit breakers used as switches for 120-V and 277-V fluorescent lighting circuits. Also see Section 380-7.

380-12. Grounding of Enclosures. Enclosures for switches or circuit breakers shall be grounded as specified in Article 250. Where nonmetallic enclosures are used with metal-sheathed cables or metallic conduits, provision shall be made for grounding continuity.

380-13. Knife Switches.

(a) Isolating Switches. Knife switches rated at over 1200 amperes at 250 volts or less, and at over 600 amperes at 251 to 600 volts, shall be used only as isolating switches and shall not be opened under load.

(b) To Interrupt Currents. To interrupt currents over 1200 amperes at 250 volts, nominal, or less, or over 600 amperes at 251 to 600 volts, nominal, a circuit breaker or a switch of special design listed for such purpose shall be used.

(c) General-Use Switches. Knife switches of ratings less than specified in (a) and (b) above shall be considered general-use switches.

(FPN): See definition of general-use switch in Article 100.

(d) Motor-Circuit Switches. Motor-circuit switches shall be permitted to be of the knife-switch type.

(FPN): See definition of a motor-circuit switch in Article 100.

380-14. Rating and Use of Snap Switches. Snap switches shall be used within their ratings and as indicated in (a) through (c) below:

(a) AC General-Use Snap Switch. A form of general-use snap switch suitable only for use on alternating-current circuits for controlling the following:

(1) Resistive and inductive loads, including electric-discharge lamps, not exceeding the ampere rating of the switch at the voltage involved.

(2) Tungsten-filament lamp loads not exceeding the ampere rating of the switch at 120 volts.

(3) Motor loads not exceeding 80 percent of the ampere rating of the switch at its rated voltage.

(b) AC-DC General-Use Snap Switch. A form of general-use snap switch suitable for use on either ac or dc circuits for controlling the following:

(1) Resistive loads not exceeding the ampere rating of the switch at the voltage applied.

(2) Inductive loads not exceeding 50 percent of the ampere rating of the switch at the applied voltage. Switches rated in horsepower are suitable for controlling motor loads within their rating at voltage applied.

(3) Tungsten-filament lamp loads not exceeding the ampere rating of the switch at the applied voltage if "T" rated.

(FPN): For switches on signs and outline lighting, see Section 600-2.

(FPN): For switches controlling motors, see Sections 430-83, 430-109, and 430-110.

(c) CO/ALR Snap Switches. Snap switches rated 20 amperes or less directly connected to aluminum conductors shall be listed and marked CO/ALR.

B. Construction Specifications

380-15. Marking. Switches shall be marked with the current and voltage and, if horsepower rated, the maximum rating for which they are designed.

380-16. 600-Volt Knife Switches. Auxiliary contacts of a renewable or quick-break type or the equivalent shall be provided on all knife switches rated 600 volts designed for use in breaking current over 200 amperes.

380-17. Fused Switches. A fused switch shall not have fuses in parallel.

(FPN): See Section 240-8, Exception.

380-18. Wire Bending Space. The wire bending space required by Section 380-3 shall meet Table 373-6(b) spacings to the enclosure wall opposite the line and load terminals.

ARTICLE 384 — SWITCHBOARDS AND PANELBOARDS

Contents

(d) Supplied Through a
Transformer.
(e) Delta Breakers.
384-17. Panelboards in Damp or Wet
Locations.
384-18. Enclosure.
384-19. Relative Arrangement of
Switches and Fuses.

384-21. Busbars.
384-22. Protection of Instrument
Circuits.
384-23. Component Parts.
384-24. Knife Switches.
384-25. Wire Bending Space in
Panelboards.
384-26. Minimum Spacings.
384-27. Grounding of Panelboards.

C. Construction Specifications
384-20. Panels.

384-1. Scope. This article covers (1) all switchboards, panelboards, and distribution boards installed for the control of light and power circuits, and (2) battery-charging panels supplied from light or power circuits.

Exception: Switchboards or portions thereof used exclusively to control signaling circuits operated by batteries.

384-2. Other Articles. Switches, circuit breakers, and overcurrent devices used on switchboards, panelboards, and distribution boards, and their enclosures, shall comply with this article and also with the requirements of Articles 240, 250, 370, 380, and other articles that apply. Switchboards and panelboards in hazardous (classified) locations shall comply with the requirements of Articles 500 through 517.

See definitions of "panelboard" and "switchboard" in Article 100.

384-3. Support and Arrangement of Busbars and Conductors.

(a) Conductors and Busbars on a Switchboard, Panelboard, or Control Board. Conductors and busbars on a switchboard, panelboard, or control board shall be so located as to be free from physical damage and shall be held firmly in place. Other than the required interconnections and control wiring, only those conductors that are intended for termination in a vertical section of a switchboard shall be located in that section. Barriers shall be placed in all service switchboards that will isolate the service busbars and terminals from the remainder of the switchboard.

Exception: Conductors shall be permitted to travel horizontally through vertical sections of switchboards where such conductors are isolated from busbars by a barrier.

It is often impractical to disconnect or deenergize the service conductors supplying a service switchboard. For this reason, qualified electricians work on these switchboards with the service bus energized. Barriers are required in all UL-listed service switchboards to isolate the service busbars and terminals from the remainder of the switchboard, thus providing some measure of safety against contact with line energized parts during maintenance and installation of new feeders or branch circuits. It must be remembered that deenergizing the load side of a switchboard, by operation of the disconnecting means, does not deenergize the ungrounded service conductors. Installers should also be careful to remove tools that may have been left on the inside of the gear in order to prevent serious ground faults or short circuits due to the tools coming in contact with busbars.

The exception permits conductors to travel horizontally through vertical sections of a switchboard where barriers are provided to isolate the conductors from the busbars.

(b) Overheating and Inductive Effects. The arrangement of busbars and conductors shall be such as to avoid overheating due to inductive effects.

(c) Used as Service Equipment. Each switchboard, switchboard section, or panelboard, if used as service equipment, shall be provided with a main bonding jumper sized in accordance with Section 250-79(c) or the equivalent placed within the service disconnect section for connecting the grounded service conductor on its supply side to the switchboard or panelboard frame. All sections of a switchboard shall be bonded together using an equipment grounding conductor sized in accordance with Table 250-95.

(d) Load Terminals. Load terminals in switchboards and panelboards shall be so located that it will be unnecessary to reach across or beyond an ungrounded line bus in order to make load connections.

(e) High-Leg Marking. On a switchboard or panelboard supplied from a 4-wire delta-connected system, where the midpoint of one phase is grounded, that phase busbar or conductor having the higher voltage to ground shall be durably and permanently marked by an outer finish that is orange in color, or by other effective means.

The "high leg" marking is intended to prevent problems due to the lack of complete standardization, where metered and nonmetered equipment are installed in the same installation. Electricians should always be cautious and test each phase to ground, with suitable equipment, in order to know exactly where this "high leg" is located in the system.

(f) Phase Arrangement. The phase arrangement on three-phase buses shall be A, B, C from front to back, top to bottom, or left to right, as viewed from the front of the switchboard or panelboard. The B phase shall be that phase having the higher voltage to ground on 3-phase, 4-wire delta-connected systems. Other busbar arrangements shall be permitted for additions to existing installations and shall be marked.

Exception: Equipment within the same single section or multisection switchboard or panelboard as the meter on 3-phase, 4-wire delta-connected systems shall be permitted to have the same phase configuration as the metering equipment.

The exception requires that the phase leg having the higher voltage to ground $(120 \times 1.73 = 208$ V on a 120/240-V, 3-phase, 4-wire delta-connected system; see Figure 250-3) maintain the center position (B phase) in all panelboards or switchboards or at least maintain a standardized position in existing installations to avoid the hazards associated with running a 2-wire 208-V branch circuit when a 2-wire 120-V circuit is intended. The exception recognizes the fact that metering compartments have been standardized with the "high leg" at the right (C phase) position and the exception makes it unnecessary to transpose the busbar arrangement before and after a metering compartment. See also Sections 215-8 and 230-56.

(g) Minimum Wire Bending Space. The minimum wire bending space at terminals and minimum gutter space provided in panelboards and switchboards shall be as required in Section 373-6.

This section requires that installations in the field comply with Section 373-6. See also commentary following Section 384-25 which covers the size of the enclosure.

384-4. Installation. Equipment within the scope of Article 384 shall be located in rooms or spaces dedicated to such equipment. Such space shall include that space described in Section 110-16, and in addition shall include an exclusively dedicated space extending from floor to structural ceiling with a width and depth that of the equipment. No piping, ducts, or equipment foreign to the electrical equipment or architectural appurtenances shall be permitted to be installed in, enter or pass through such spaces or rooms.

(FPN): It is not the intent to mandate a dedicated room.

The following Formal Interpretation No. 81-3 for Section 384-2 (Section 384-4 in this edition) was issued in June, 1981 for the 1981 edition of the *National Electrical Code*.

Statement: A building has one or more closets located so as to feed electric and communication services to areas of the building. Each closet is entered by one door and it has no partitions. A portion of the closet is dedicated to a panelboard serving branch circuits for that area. Another portion of the closet is dedicated to telephone equipment. The telephone equipment and wiring do not encroach on the dedicated space for the panelboard.

Question: Is it the intent of Section 384-2 of the 1981 *National Electrical Code* to prohibit such an installation?

Answer: No.

Statement: It has been common practice to flush-mount panelboards in the walls of corridors and hallways in buildings and residences.

Question: Is it the intent of Section 384-2 of the 1981 *National Electrical Code* to prohibit such installation?

Answer: No.

(FPN): This section is not intended to prohibit sprinkler protection for the electrical installation.

Exception No. 1: Control equipment which by its very nature or because of other rules of this Code must be adjacent to or within sight of its operating machinery.

Exception No. 2: Ventilating, heating, or cooling equipment that serves the electrical rooms or spaces.

Exception No. 3: Equipment located throughout industrial plants which is isolated from foreign equipment by height or physical enclosures or covers which will afford adequate mechanical protection from vehicular traffic, accidental contact by unauthorized personnel, or accidental spillage or leakage from piping systems.

Exception No. 4: Outdoor electrical equipment located in weatherproof enclosures protected from accidental contact by unauthorized personnel or vehicular traffic or accidental spillage or leakage from piping systems.

The required space includes the space described in Section 110-16 and an exclusively dedicated space extending to the ceiling over the equipment. See Figures 384-1 and 384-2. A suspended ceiling over the equipment would not be considered as being the structural ceiling described in this section.

The following Formal Interpretation No. 81-5 was issued in August, 1982, for the 1981 edition of the *National Electrical Code*.

Question: Is it the intent of Section 384-2 (Section 384-4 of this edition) of the *National Electrical Code* to prohibit automatic sprinkler protection in rooms containing switchboards and panelboards?

Answer: No.

457

Figure 384-1. This figure illustrates the space in front of the panelboard required by Section 110-16. This is working space. See Figure 384-2 for additional space required by Section 384-4.

Figure 384-2. This figure illustrates the additional exclusively dedicated space required over and under the panelboard by Section 384-4. This space is for the cables, raceways, etc., to and from the panelboard.

Automatic sprinklers and their associated piping are permitted in rooms dedicated exclusively to panelboards and switchboards if they are for protection of the panelboards and switchboards. See the second fine print note following the main rule. If the entire room is not dedicated to panelboards and switchboards, automatic sprinklers are permitted in the room if they do not enter the space in the room dedicated to the panelboards or switchboards. If an electrical equipment room contains electrical equipment not within the scope of Article 384, such as motors and motor controllers (Article 430), or switches (Article 380), it is not dedicated exclusively to equipment within the scope of Article 384.

A. Switchboards

384-5. Location of Switchboards. Switchboards that have any exposed live parts shall be located in permanently dry locations and then only where under competent supervision and accessible only to qualified persons. Switchboards shall be so located that the probability of damage from equipment or processes is reduced to a minimum.

384-6. Wet Locations. Where a switchboard is in a wet location or outside of a building, it shall be enclosed in a weatherproof enclosure or cabinet installed to comply with Section 373-2(a).

384-7. Location Relative to Easily Ignitible Material. Switchboards shall be so placed as to reduce to a minimum the probability of communicating fire to adjacent combustible materials. Where installed over a combustible floor, suitable protection thereto shall be provided.

Installation of switchboards on a combustible wood floor is prohibited. One method of compliance with this rule would be to form and set a piece of sheet steel or other suitable noncombustible material on the floor under the equipment.

384-8. Clearances.

(a) From Ceiling. A space of 3 feet (914 mm) or more shall be provided between the top of any switchboard and any combustible ceiling.

Exception No. 1: Where a noncombustible shield is provided between the switchboard and the ceiling.

Exception No. 2: Totally enclosed switchboards.

Building designers should consider these rules when designing areas in which switchboards will be located.

(b) Around Switchboards. Clearances around switchboards shall comply with the provisions of Section 110-16.

Sufficient access and working space is required to permit ready and safe operation and maintenance of such equipment. Table 110-16(a) indicates minimum working clearances from 0 to 600 V.
For work space clearances of switchboards operating at over 600 V, see Table 110-34(a).

384-9. Conductor Insulation. An insulated conductor used within a switchboard shall be listed, flame-retardant and shall be rated not less than the voltage applied to it and not less than the voltage applied to other conductors or busbars with which it may come in contact.

384-10. Clearance for Conductors Entering Bus Enclosures. Where conduits or other raceways enter a switchboard, floor standing panelboard, or similar enclosure at the bottom, sufficient space shall be provided to permit installation of conductors in the enclosure. The wiring space shall not be less than shown in the following table where the conduit or raceways enter or leave the enclosure below the busbars, their supports, or other obstructions. The conduit or raceways, including their end fittings, shall not rise more than 3 inches (76 mm) above the bottom of the enclosure.

Conductor	Minimum Spacing Between Bottom of Enclosure and Busbars, their Supports, or other Obstructions (Inches)
Insulated busbars, their supports, or other obstructions	8 (203mm)
Noninsulated busbars	10 (254mm)

ARTICLE 384—SWITCHBOARDS AND PANELBOARDS

This section should be carefully considered when installing underground conduit or raceways which will terminate in the bottom of an open switchboard. For example, if larger sizes of conduit are employed for service laterals or feeders and terminate where they extend more than 3 in. above the bottom of the enclosure, it will be difficult to cut them after it is discovered that they are too long. On the other hand, conduits or raceways should not be installed where flush with the finished floor under switchboards where located on the outside of buildings or in other locations where water could enter the raceways.

384-11. Grounding Switchboard Frames. Switchboard frames and structures supporting switching equipment shall be grounded.

Exception: Frames of direct-current, single-polarity switchboards shall not be required to be grounded if effectively insulated.

384-12. Grounding of Instruments, Relays, Meters, and Instrument Transformers on Switchboards. Instruments, relays, meters, and instrument transformers located on switchboards shall be grounded as specified in Sections 250-121 through 250-125.

B. Panelboards

384-13. General. All panelboards shall have a rating not less than the minimum feeder capacity required for the load computed in accordance with Article 220. Panelboards shall be durably marked by the manufacturer with the voltage and the current rating and the number of phases for which they are designed and with the manufacturer's name or trademark in such a manner as to be visible after installation, without disturbing the interior parts or wiring.

Some panelboards are suitable for use as service equipment and are so marked.
UL-listed panelboards are for use with copper conductors unless marked to indicate which terminals are suitable for use with aluminum conductors. Such marking is required to be independent of any marking on terminal connectors and is required to be on a wiring diagram or other readily visible location. If all terminals are suitable for use with aluminum conductors as well as with copper conductors, the panelboard will be marked "Use Copper or Aluminum Wire." A panelboard employing terminals or main or branch-circuit units individually marked "AL-CU" will be marked as noted above or "Use Copper Wire Only." The latter marking indicates that wiring space or other factors make the panelboard unsuitable for aluminum conductors. See Section 110-14(a).
Panelboards to which units (circuit breakers, switches, etc.) may be added in the field are marked with the name or trademark of the manufacturer and the catalog number or equivalent of those units intended for installation in the field.
Unless the panelboard is marked to indicate otherwise, the termination provisions are based on the use of 60°C (140°F) ampacities for wire sizes No. 14-1 AWG, and 75°C (167°F) ampacities for wire sizes No. 1/0 AWG and larger.

384-14. Lighting and Appliance Branch-Circuit Panelboard. For the purposes of this article, a lighting and appliance branch-circuit panelboard is one having more than 10 percent of its overcurrent devices rated 30 amperes or less, for which neutral connections are provided.

A lighting and appliance branch-circuit panelboard is a panelboard having not more than 42 overcurrent devices (the maximum — see Section 384-15), where more than 10 percent of the installed overcurrent devices (10 percent of 42 = 4.2; round off to 5) are rated 30 A or less and for which circuit and neutral connections are provided. Lighting circuits rated 30 A or less without a neutral connection are not considered.

384-15. Number of Overcurrent Devices on One Panelboard. Not more than forty-two overcurrent devices (other than those provided for in the mains) of a lighting and appliance branch-circuit panelboard shall be installed in any one cabinet or cutout box.

A lighting and appliance branch-circuit panelboard shall be provided with physical means to prevent the installation of more overcurrent devices than that number for which the panelboard was designed, rated, and approved.

For the purposes of this article, a 2-pole circuit breaker shall be considered two overcurrent devices; a 3-pole breaker shall be considered three overcurrent devices.

Class CTL panelboards are identified by the words "Class CTL" on the Underwriters Laboratories Inc. "Listing Mark."

Class CTL panelboards incorporate physical features which, in conjunction with the physical size, configuration, or other means provided in Class CTL circuit breakers, fuseholders, or fusible switches, are designed to prevent the installation of more overcurrent protective poles than that number for which the device is designed and rated.

Class CTL is the Underwriters Laboratories Inc. designation for the *Code* requirement for circuit limitation within a lighting and appliance branch-circuit panelboard and means "circuit limiting."

Figure 384-3 shows a panelboard with a 200-A main circuit breaker. Figure 384-4 shows a panelboard without main overcurrent protection, but which may be protected by overcurrent protection as illustrated in Figure 384-5.

384-16. Overcurrent Protection.

(a) Lighting and Appliance Branch-Circuit Panelboard Individually Protected. Each lighting and appliance branch-circuit panelboard shall be individually protected on the supply side by not more than two main circuit breakers or two sets of fuses having a combined rating not greater than that of the panelboard.

Exception No. 1: Individual protection for a lighting and appliance panelboard shall not be required if the panelboard feeder has overcurrent protection not greater than the rating of the panelboard.

Main overcurrent protection may be an integral part of a panelboard or located remote from the panelboard. See Figures 384-3, 384-4, and 384-5. See also commentary following Section 384-15.

Exception No. 2: For existing installations, individual protection for lighting and appliance branch-circuit panelboards is not required where such panelboards are used as service equipment in supplying an individual residential occupancy.

The phrase "for existing installations" in Exception No. 2 means the existing panelboard. It is not intended that a split-bus panelboard used in an individual dwelling occupancy be replaced if a circuit is added to the existing panelboard. However, it does mean that for installation of new panelboards in new or existing residential occupancies, a split-bus six disconnect panelboard (with more than two circuit breakers or sets of fuses protecting the panelboard) is not permitted for the service equipment.

An individual residential occupancy could be a dwelling unit in a multifamily dwelling where the panelboard is used as service equipment. See the definition of "dwelling unit" in Article 100.

461

Figure 384-3. A lighting and appliance branch circuit panelboard (with main circuit breaker) suitable for use as service equipment. (*Square D Co.*)

Figure 384-4. A distribution panelboard with main lugs only. (*Square D Co.*)

(b) Snap Switches Rated at 30 Amperes or Less. Panelboards equipped with snap switches rated at 30 amperes or less shall have overcurrent protection not in excess of 200 amperes.

This requirement is limited to snap switches; it does not apply to panelboards equipped with circuit breakers.

Figure 384-5. An arrangement of three individual lighting and appliance branch-circuit panelboards with main overcurrent protection remote from the panelboards. Note that the panelboard feeders have overcurrent protection not greater than the rating of the panelboard.

Figure 384-6. Panel on left has two 100-A main breakers installed as disconnecting means and 200-A main lugs. Panel on right is a split-bus panel with 150-A main lugs and six main breaker disconnecting means. The 150-A panelboard on the right is suitable for use as service equipment only if it is not a lighting and appliance panelboard or if it presently exists in an individual residential occupancy.

(c) Continuous Load. The total load on any overcurrent device located in a panelboard shall not exceed 80 percent of its rating where in normal operation the load will continue for 3 hours or more.

Exception: Where the assembly including the overcurrent device is approved for continuous duty at 100 percent of its rating.

(d) Supplied through a Transformer. Where a panelboard is supplied through a transformer, the overcurrent protection required in (a) and (b) above shall be located on the secondary side of the transformer.

463

Figure 384-7. A split-bus lighting and appliance branch-circuit panelboard supplying an individual residential occupancy.

Exception: A panelboard supplied by the secondary side of a single-phase transformer having a two-wire (single-voltage) secondary shall be considered as protected by overcurrent protection provided on the primary (supply) side of the transformer, provided this protection is in accordance with Section 450-3(b)(1) and does not exceed the value determined by multiplying the panelboard rating by the secondary-to-primary voltage ratio.

(e) Delta Breakers. A three-phase disconnect or overcurrent device shall not be connected to the bus of any panelboard that has less than three-phase buses.

(FPN): This is intended to prohibit the use of "delta breakers" in panelboards.

384-17. Panelboards in Damp or Wet Locations. Panelboards in damp or wet locations shall be installed to comply with Section 373-2(a).

384-18. Enclosure. Panelboards shall be mounted in cabinets, cutout boxes, or enclosures designed for the purpose and shall be dead front.

Exception: Panelboards other than of the dead front externally operable type shall be permitted where accessible only to qualified persons.

384-19. Relative Arrangement of Switches and Fuses. In panelboards, fuses of any type shall be installed on the load side of any switches.

Exception: As provided in Section 230-94 for use as service equipment.

Section 230-94 permits the service switch on either the supply side or load side of fuses. Where fuses of panelboards are accessible to other than qualified persons, such as occupants of a multifamily dwelling, Section 240-40 requires that disconnecting means be located on the supply side of all fuses in circuits of over 150 V to ground and cartridge-type fuses in circuits of any voltage. Thus, when the disconnect switch is opened, the fuses are deenergized and danger from shock is reduced.

C. Construction Specifications

384-20. Panels. The panels of switchboards shall be made of moisture-resistant, noncombustible material.

384-21. Busbars. Insulated or bare busbars shall be rigidly mounted.

384-22. Protection of Instrument Circuits. Instruments, pilot lights, potential transformers, and other switchboard devices with potential coils shall be supplied by a circuit that is protected by standard overcurrent devices rated 15 amperes or less.

Exception No. 1: Where the operation of the overcurrent device might introduce a hazard in the operation of devices.

Exception No. 2: For ratings of 2 amperes or less, special types of enclosed fuses shall be permitted.

384-23. Component Parts. Switches, fuses, and fuseholders used on panelboards shall comply with the applicable requirements of Articles 240 and 380.

384-24. Knife Switches. Exposed blades of knife switches shall be deenergized when open.

384-25. Wire Bending Space in Panelboards. The enclosure for a panelboard shall have the top and bottom wire bending space sized in accordance with Table 373-6(b) for the largest conductor entering or leaving the enclosure. Side wire bending space shall be in accordance with Table 373-6(a) for the largest conductor to be terminated in that space.

Exception No. 1: Either the top or bottom wire bending space shall be permitted to be sized in accordance with Table 373-6(a) for a lighting and appliance branch-circuit panelboard rated 225 amperes or less.

Exception No. 2: Either the top or bottom wire bending space for any panelboard shall be permitted to be sized in accordance with Table 373-6(a) where at least one side wire bending space is sized in accordance with Table 373-6(b) for the largest conductor to be terminated in any side wire bending space.

Exception No. 3: The top and bottom wire bending space shall be permitted to be sized in accordance with Table 373-6(a) spacings if the panelboard is designed and constructed for wiring using only one single 90 degree bend for each conductor including the neutral and the wiring diagram shows and specifies the method of wiring that shall be used.

Exception No. 4: Either the top or the bottom wire bending space, but not both, shall be permitted to be sized in accordance with Table 373-6(a) where there are no conductors terminated in that space.

This section covers the size of the enclosure for a panelboard. With reference to Figure 373-1 (see Section 373-6), the general rule calls for wire bending space T1 and T4 to be in accordance with Table 373-6(b) for conductors M (assuming these are the largest conductors entering the enclosure). Side wire bending space T2 shall be in accordance with Table 373-6(a) for the wire size to be used with the largest rated unit facing that side space, and T3 shall be similarly sized for the largest rated unit facing the right side of the enclosure. Exception No. 1 of Section 384-25 permits either T1 or T4 (not both) to be reduced to the space required by Table 373-6(a) for size M conductors for a panelboard rated 225 A or less. Exception No. 2 of Section 384-25 permits either T1 or T4 (not both) to be reduced to the space required by Table 373-6(a) for size M conductors for *any* panelboard where either T2 or T3 (or both) is sized in accordance with Table 373-6(b) for the largest conductor to be terminated in either the left or right side spaces. Under the construction rules of Section 384-25, a panelboard enclosure might not be of adequate size for all manner of wiring, and Section 373-6 must be considered when wiring is planned.

Exception No. 3 of Section 384-25 permits both the top and bottom wire bending space to be reduced as noted. A single 90 degree bend, meaning one and only one 90 degree bend, is required to be present for the ungrounded conductors. A grounded conductor is permitted to be wired straight in if Table 373-6(b) spacing is provided for the grounded conductor.

Exception No. 4 permits reduction of the top or bottom space to Table 373-6(a) spacings where there are no terminals facing that space. In this case, the space is a gutter space and measurement is on a line perpendicular to the wall of the enclosure and to the closest barrier post or side of a switch, fuse, or circuit breaker unit that is, or may be, installed.

ARTICLE 384—SWITCHBOARDS AND PANELBOARDS

384-26. Minimum Spacings. The distance between bare metal parts, busbars, etc., shall not be less than specified in Table 384-26.

Exception No. 1: At switches or circuit breakers.

Exception No. 2: Inherent spacings in listed components.

Where close proximity does not cause excessive heating, parts of the same polarity at switches, enclosed fuses, etc., shall be permitted to be placed as close together as convenience in handling will allow.

Table 384-26. Minimum Spacings Between Bare Metal Parts

	Opposite Polarity Where Mounted on the Same Surface	Opposite Polarity Where Held Free in Air	*Live Parts to Ground
Not over 125 volts, nominal..................	¾ inch	½ inch	½ inch
Not over 250 volts, nominal..................	1¼ inch	¾ inch	½ inch
Not over 600 volts, nominal..................	2 inches	1 inch	1 inch

For SI units: one inch = 25.4 millimeters.
*For spacing between live parts and doors of cabinets, see Section 373-11(a) (1), (2), and (3).

384-27. Grounding of Panelboards. Panelboard cabinets shall be grounded in the manner specified in Article 250 or Section 384-3(c). An approved terminal bar for equipment grounding conductors shall be provided and secured inside of the cabinet for the attachment of all the feeder and branch-circuit equipment grounding conductors, where the panelboard is used with nonmetallic raceway or cable, or where separate grounding conductors are provided. The terminal bar shall be bonded to the cabinet or panelboard frame, or at the first system disconnecting means or overcurrent device for a separately derived system, and shall not be connected to the neutral bar in other than service equipment.

A separate equipment grounding conductor terminal bar is required to be installed and bonded to the panelboard for the termination of feeder and branch-circuit equipment grounding conductors. Where installed within service equipment, this terminal is permitted to be bonded to the neutral terminal bar. Any other connection between the equipment grounding terminal bar and the neutral bar, other than as permitted by Exception No. 2, would raise the potential of all exposed dead metal parts of equipment since current flow in the neutral or grounded conductor would allow a potential difference of several volts, and would also permit neutral current to take two paths back to the service equipment — one being through the equipment grounding conductor (the raceway, for example). This is important when subpanels are used, since arcing and/or loose connections at connectors, raceway fittings, etc., could serve to create a potential fire or shock hazard.

Exception No. 1: Where an isolated equipment grounding conductor is provided as permitted by Section 250-74, Exception No. 4, this insulated equipment grounding conductor which is run with the circuit conductors shall be permitted to pass through the panelboard without being connected to the panelboard's equipment grounding terminal bar.

Exception No. 2: The terminal bar for equipment grounding conductors shall be permitted to be connected to the neutral bar at separate buildings in accordance with the provisions of Section 250-24.

Electronic equipment, which is often used in data processing systems, hospitals, laboratories, etc., may fail to perform properly due to electromagnetic interference present in the electrical supply.

Where required for the reduction of electrical noise (electromagnetic interference) on the grounding circuit, an isolated equipment grounding terminal is permitted. This equipment grounding terminal is required to be grounded by an insulated equipment grounding conductor that is run with the circuit conductors. It is also permitted to pass through one or more panelboards (without connection to the panelboard grounding terminal), but it is very important that it terminate directly at the applicable derived system or service grounding terminal. Connection only to a separate grounding electrode places earth in the fault return path and may prevent sufficient current to open overcurrent protection when a ground fault occurs. See commentary following 250-74 fine print note and 250-91(c).

4 Equipment for General Use

ARTICLE 400 — FLEXIBLE CORDS AND CABLES

Contents

A. General

400-1. Scope. This article covers general requirements, applications, and construction specifications for flexible cords and flexible cables.

Flexible cords and cables as covered by Article 400 are not considered a wiring method. Wiring methods are covered in Chapter 3 of the *Code*.

400-2. Other Articles. Flexible cords and flexible cables shall comply with this article and with the applicable provisions of other articles of this Code.

400-3. Suitability. Flexible cords and cables and their associated fittings shall be suitable for the conditions of use and location.

400-4. Types. Flexible cords and flexible cables shall conform to the description in Table 400-4. Types of flexible cords and flexible cables other than those listed in the table shall be the subject of special investigation.

Table 400-4. Flexible Cords and Cables (See Section 400-4)

Trade Name	Type Letter	Size AWG	No. of Conductors	Insulation	Nominal *Insulation Thickness		Braid on Each Conductor	Outer Covering	Use		
					AWG	Mils					
Asbestos-Covered Heat-Resistant Cord	AFC AFPD	18–10	2 or 3	Impregnated Asbestos	18–14	30	Cotton or Rayon	None	Pendant	Dry Locations	Not Hard Usage
	AFPO		2		12–10	45	None	Cotton, Rayon, or Saturated Asbestos			
Thermoset-Jacketed Heat-Resistant Cord	AFS	18–10	2 or 3	Impregnated Asbestos	18–14	30	None	Thermoset	Portable Heaters	Damp Locations	Extra Hard Usage
	AFSJ	18–16									Hard Usage
Lamp Cord	C	18–10	2 or more	Thermoset or Thermoplastic	18–16	30	Cotton	None	Pendant or Portable	Dry Locations	Not Hard Usage
					14–10	45					
Data Processing Cable	DP See Note 2.	32 Min.	2 or More	Thermoplastic, Thermoset or Crosslinked Synthetic Polymer	32–27 (50V)	8	None	Thermoplastic, Thermoset or Crosslinked Synthetic Polymer	Data Processing Systems	Dry Locations	Power and Signaling Circuits
					26–23 (50V)	12					
					22–20 (50V)	16					
					32–16 (300V)	20					
					14–10 (300V)	30					
					8–2 (300V)	60					

See Notes 1 through 9.
* See Note 9.

Table 400-4 (Continued)

Elevator Cable	E See Note 6.	20–14	2 or More	Thermoset	20–16	20	Cotton	Three Cotton, Outer one Flame-Retardant & Moisture-Resist. See Note 4.	Elevator Lighting and Control	Nonhazardous Locations
	EN See Note 6.				20–16	20	Flexible Nylon Jacket	One Cotton and a Neoprene or Thermoplastic Jacket See Note 4.	Elevator Lighting and Control	Hazardous (Classified) Locations
Elevator Cable	EO See Note 6.	20–14	2 or More	Thermoset	20–16	20	Cotton	Three Cotton, Outer one Flame-Retardant & Moisture-Resist. See Note 4.		Nonhazardous Locations
					14	30		One Cotton and a Neoprene Jacket See Note 4.	Elevator Lighting and Control	Hazardous (Classified) Locations
Elevator Cable	ET See Note 6.	20–14	2 or More	Thermoplastic	20–16	20	Rayon	Three Cotton, Outer one Flame-Retardant & Moisture-Resist. See Note 4.		Nonhazardous Locations
	ETLB See Note 6.				14	30	None			
	ETP See Note 6.			Thermoplastic			Rayon	Thermoplastic		
	ETT See Note 6.			Thermoplastic			None	One Cotton and a Thermoplastic jacket		Hazardous (Classified) Locations

See Notes 1 through 9.
* See Note 9.

Table 400-4 (Continued)

Trade Name	Type Letter	Size AWG	No. of Conductors	Insulation	Nominal *Insulation Thickness AWG	Mils	Braid on Each Conductor	Outer Covering	Use
Portable Power Cable	G	8–500 MCM	2–6 plus Grounding Conductor(s)	Thermoset	8–2 / 1–4/0 / 250 MCM–500 MCM	60 / 80 / 95		Oil-Resistant Thermoset	Portable, Extra Hard Usage, and as Permitted in Sections 520-68 and 530-12.
Heater Cord	HPD	18–12	2, 3, or 4	Thermoset with Asbestos or All Thermoset	Thermoset / 18–16 / 14–12	15 / 30	None	Cotton or Rayon	Dry Locations, Portable Heaters, Not Hard Usage
Parallel Heater Cord	HPN See Note 7.	18–12	2 or 3	Thermosetting	18–16 / 14 / 12	45 / 80 / 95	None	Thermosetting	Portable, Damp Locations, Not Hard Usage
Thermoset Jacketed Heater Cord	HS	14–12		Thermoset with Asbestos or All Thermoset	18–16 (Thermoset/Asbestos)	15	None	Cotton and Thermoset	Portable or Portable Heaters, Damp Locations, Extra Hard Usage
	HSJ See Note 8.		2, 3 or 4		18–16 (All Thermoset)	30			
	HSJO See Note 8.	18–12			14–12 (Thermoset/Asbestos)	30		Cotton and Oil-Resistant	Hard Usage
	HSO	14–12			14–12 (All Thermoset)	45			Extra Hard Usage
Twisted Portable Cord	PD	18–10	2 or more	Thermoset or Thermoplastic	18–16 / 14–10	30 / 45	Cotton	Cotton or Rayon	Pendant or Portable, Dry Locations, Not Hard Usage

See Notes 1 through 9.
* See Note 9.

Table 400-4 (Continued)

Trade Name	Type Letter	Size AWG	Number of Conductors	Insulation	AWG	Nominal Insulation Thickness (mils)	Braid on Each Conductor	Outer Covering	Pendant or Portable	Damp Locations	Use
Hard Service Cord	S See Note 5.	18-2	2 or more	Thermoset	18-16	30	None	Thermoset	Pendant or Portable	Damp Locations	Extra Hard Usage
	SE See Note 5.			Thermo-plastic Elastomer	14-10	45		Thermoplastic Elastomer			
	SEO See Note 5.				8-2	60		Oil-Resistant Thermoplastic Elastomer			
Junior Hard Service Cord	SJ	18-10	2, 3, 4, or 5	Thermoset	18-12	30	None	Thermoset	Pendant or Portable	Damp Locations	Hard Usage
	SJE			Thermo-plastic Elastomer				Thermoplastic Elastomer			
	SJEO							Oil-Resistant Thermoplastic Elastomer			
	SJO			Thermoset	10	45		Oil-Resistant Thermoset			
	SJOO			Oil-Resistant Thermoset				Oil-Resistant Thermoset			
	SJT			Thermo-plastic or Thermoplastic				Thermoplastic			
	SJTO			Thermoset or Thermoplastic				Oil-Resistant Thermoplastic			
	SJTOO			Oil-Resistant Thermo-plastic or Thermoset				Oil-Resistant Thermoplastic			

See Notes 1 through 9.
* See Note 9.

473

Table 400-4   (Continued)

Trade Name	Type Letter	Size AWG	No. of Conductors	Insulation	Nominal *Insulation Thickness AWG	Mils	Braid on Each Conductor	Outer Covering	Use		
Hard Service Cord	SO See Note 5.	18–2	2 or more	Thermoset	18–16	30		Oil-Resistant Thermoset	Pendant or Portable	Damp Locations	Extra Hard Usage
	SOO See Note 5.			Oil-Resistant Thermoset	14–10	45		Oil-Resistant Thermoset			
					8–2	60					
All Thermoset Parallel Cord	SP-1 See Note 7.	18	2 or 3	Thermoset	18	30	None	Thermoset	Pendant or Portable	Damp Locations	Not Hard Usage
	SP-2 See Note 7.	18–16			18–16	45					
	SP-3 See Note 7.	18–12		Thermoset	18–16	60	None	Thermoset	Refrigerators, Room Air Conditioners and as permitted in Section 422-8(d)	Damp Locations	Not Hard Usage
					14	80					
					12	95					
					10	110					

See Notes 1 through 9.
* See Note 9.

Table 400-4 (Continued)

Trade Name	Type Letter	Size AWG	Number of Conductors	Insulation	AWG		Braid	Outer Covering	Use		
All Elastomer (Thermoplastic) Parallel Cord	SPE-1 See Note 7.	18		Thermoplastic Elastomer	18	30	None	Thermoplastic Elastomer	Pendant or Portable	Damp Locations	Not Hard Usage
	SPE-2 See Note 7.	18–16	2 or 3		18–16	45					
	SPE-3 See Note 7.	18–12			18–16 14 12 10	60 80 95 110	None	Thermoplastic Elastomer	Refrigerators, Room Air Conditioners and as permitted in Section 422-8(d)	Damp Locations	Not Hard Usage
All Plastic Parallel Cord	SPT-1 See Note 7.	18		Thermoplastic	18	30	None	Thermoplastic	Pendant or Portable	Damp Locations	Not Hard Usage
	SPT-2 See Note 7.	18–16	2 or 3		18–16	45					
	SPT-3 See Note 7.	18–10			18–16 14 12 10	60 80 95 110	None	Thermoplastic	Refrigerators, Room Air Conditioners and as permitted in Section 422-8(d)	Damp Locations	Not Hard Usage

See Notes 1 through 9.
* See Note 9.

Table 400-4 (Continued)

Trade Name	Type Letter	Size AWG	No. of Conductors	Insulation	Nominal *Insulation Thickness AWG	Mils	Braid on Each Conductor	Outer Covering	Use		
Range, Dryer Cable	SRD	10–4	3 or 4	Thermoset	10–4	45	None	Thermoset	Portable	Damp Locations	Ranges, Dryers
	SRDE	10–4	3 or 4	Thermo-plastic Elastomer			None	Thermoplastic Elastomer	Portable	Damp Locations	Ranges, Dryers
	SRDT	10–4	3 or 4	Thermo-plastic			None	Thermoplastic	Portable	Damp Locations	Ranges, Dryers
Hard Service Cord	ST See Note 5.	18–2	2 or more	Thermo-plastic or Thermoset	18–16 14–10 8– 2	30 45 60	None	Thermoplastic	Pendant or Portable	Damp Locations	Extra Hard Usage
	STO See Note 5.							Oil-Resistant Thermoplastic			
	STOO See Note 5.			Oil-Resistant Thermo-plastic or Thermoset							
Vacuum Cleaner Cord	SV See Note 7.	18–17	2 or 3	Thermoset	18–17	15	None	Thermoset	Pendant or Portable	Damp Locations	Not Hard Usage
	SVE See Note 7.			Thermo-plastic Elastomer				Thermoplastic Elastomer			
	SVO			Thermoset				Oil-Resistant Thermoset			
	SVOO			Oil-Resistant Thermoset				Oil-Resistant Thermoset			

See Notes 1 through 9.
*See Note 9.

Table 400-4 (Continued)

Trade Name	Type Letter	Size AWG	No. of Conductors	Insulation (Material)	Insulation (AWG)	Insulation (mils)	Braid on Each Conductor	Outer Covering	Pendant or Portable	Damp Locations	Not Hard Usage
Vacuum Cleaner Cord	SVT See Note 7.	18–17	2 or 3	Thermoset or Thermoplastic	18–17	15	None	Thermoplastic			Not Hard Usage
	SVTO See Note 7.			Thermoset or Thermoplastic				Oil-Resistant Thermoplastic			
	SVTOO			Oil-Resistant Thermoplastic or Thermoset				Oil-Resistant Thermoplastic			
Parallel Tinsel Cord	TPT See Note 3.	27	2	Thermoplastic	27	30	None	Thermoplastic	Attached to an Appliance	Damp Locations	Not Hard Usage
Jacketed Tinsel Cord	TS See Note 3.	27	2	Thermoset			None	Thermoset	Attached to an Appliance	Damp Locations	Not Hard Usage
	TST See Note 3.	27	2	Thermoplastic	27	15	None	Thermoplastic	Attached to an Appliance	Damp Locations	Not Hard Usage
Portable Power Cable	W	8–500 MCM	1–6	Thermoset	8–2, 1–4/0, 250MCM–500MCM	60, 80, 95		Oil-Resistant Thermoset	Portable, Extra Hard Usage, and as Permitted in Sections 520-68 and 530-12.		

See Notes 1 through 9.
*See Note 9.

ARTICLE 400—FLEXIBLE CORDS AND CABLES

Notes to Table 400-4

1. Except for Types SP-1, SPE-1, SP-2, SPE-2, AFPO, SP-3, SPE-3, SPT-1, SPT-2, SPT-3, HPN, TPT, and 3-conductor parallel versions of SRD, SRDE, SRDT, individual conductors are twisted together.

2. Cables constructed differently than specified herein and listed as component parts of a data processing system shall be permitted.

3. Types TPT, TS, and TST shall be permitted in lengths not exceeding 8 feet (2.44 m) when attached directly, or by means of a special type of plug, to a portable appliance rated at 50 watts or less and of such nature that extreme flexibility of the cord is essential.

4. Rubber-filled or varnished cambric tapes shall be permitted as a substitute for the inner braids.

5. Types S, SO, SE, SEO, SOO, ST, STO, STOO, G, and W shall be permitted for use on theater stages, in garages, and elsewhere where flexible cords are permitted by this Code.

6. Elevator traveling cables for operating control and signal circuits shall contain nonmetallic fillers as necessary to maintain concentricity. Cables exceeding 100 feet (30.5 m) between supports shall have steel supporting members. In locations subject to excessive moisture or corrosive vapors or gases, supporting members of other materials shall be permitted. Where steel supporting members are used, they shall run straight through the center of the cable assembly and shall not be cabled with the copper strands of any conductor.

In addition to conductors used for control and signaling circuits, Types E, EO, EN, ET, ETP, ETLB and ETT elevator cables shall be permitted to incorporate in the construction one or more No. 20 AWG telephone conductor pairs and/or one or more coaxial cables. The No. 20 AWG conductor pairs shall be permitted to be covered with suitable shielding for telephone, audio or higher frequency communication circuits; the coaxial cables consist of a center conductor, insulation and shield for use in video or other radio frequency communication circuits. The insulation of the conductors shall be rubber or thermoplastic of thickness not less than specified for the other conductors of the particular type of cable. Metallic shields shall have their own protective covering. Where used, these components shall be permitted to be incorporated in any layer of the cable assembly but shall not run straight through the center.

7. A third conductor in these cables is for grounding purposes only.

8. The individual conductors of all cords, except those of heat-resistant cords (Types AFC, AFPD, AFPO, AFS, and AFSJ), shall have a thermoset or thermoplastic insulation, except that the grounding conductor where used shall be in accordance with Section 400-23(b). Unvulcanized rubber compounds shall be permitted to be used for all sizes of heater cord Types HSJ and HSJO, and for sizes 18 and 16 AWG Type HPD.

9. Where the voltage between any two conductors exceeds 300, but does not exceed 600, flexible cord of No. 10 and smaller shall have thermoset or thermoplastic insulation on the individual conductors at least 45 mils in thickness, unless Type S, SO, SE, SEO, SOO, ST, STO, or STOO cord is used.

400-5. Ampacity of Flexible Cords and Cables. Table 400-5 gives the allowable ampacity for not more than three current-carrying copper conductors in a cord. If the number of current-carrying conductors in a cord exceeds three, the ampacity of each conductor shall be reduced from the 3-conductor rating as shown in the following table:

Number of Conductors	Percent of Values in Table 400-5
4 through 6	80
7 through 24	70
25 through 42	60
43 and above	50

Subheading C of Table 400-5 gives the allowable ampacity for single-conductor Type W cable only where the individual conductors are not installed in raceways and are not in physical contact with each other except in lengths not to exceed 24 inches when passing through the wall of an enclosure.

A neutral conductor which carries only the unbalanced current from other conductors, as in the case of normally balanced circuits of three or more conductors, shall not be considered as a current-carrying conductor.

In a 3-wire circuit consisting of 2 phase wires and the neutral of a 4-wire, 3-phase wye-connected system, a common conductor carries approximately the same current as the other conductors and shall be considered a current-carrying conductor.

On a 4-wire, 3-phase wye circuit where the major portion of the load consists of electric-discharge lighting, data processing, or similar equipment, there are harmonic currents present in the neutral conductor and the neutral shall be considered to be a current-carrying conductor.

An equipment grounding conductor shall not be considered a current-carrying conductor.

Where a single conductor is used for both equipment grounding and to carry unbalanced current from other conductors, as provided for in Section 250-60 for electric ranges and electric clothes dryers, it shall not be considered as a current-carrying conductor.

400-6. Marking. Flexible cords and cables shall be marked by means of a printed tag attached to the coil reel or carton. The tag shall contain the information required in Section 310-11(a).

Types SJ, SJE, SJO, SJEO, SJT, SJTO, SJTOO, S, SE, SEO, SO, SOO, ST, STO and STOO flexible cords and G and W flexible cables shall be durably marked on the surface at intervals not exceeding 24 inches (610 mm) with the type designation, size, and number of conductors.

400-7. Uses Permitted.

(a) Uses. Flexible cords and cables shall be used only for (1) pendants; (2) wiring of fixtures; (3) connection of portable lamps or appliances; (4) elevator cables; (5) wiring of cranes and hoists; (6) connection of stationary equipment to facilitate their frequent interchange; (7) prevention of the transmission of noise or vibration; (8) appliances where the fastening means and mechanical connections are designed to permit removal for maintenance and repair; (9) data processing cables as permitted by Section 645-2; (10) connection of moving parts; or (11) temporary wiring as permitted in Sections 305-4(b) and 305-4(c).

(b) Attachment Plugs. Where used as permitted in subsections (a)(3), (a)(6), and (a)(8) of this section, each flexible cord shall be equipped with an attachment plug and shall be energized from a receptacle outlet.

The flexible cords and cables referred to in this article are not limited to use with portable equipment. However, they are not permitted to be used as a substitute for the fixed wiring of a structure or where concealed behind building walls, ceilings, or floors. See Section 400-8. Also see Article 305 for the requirement for the use of extension cords as temporary wiring. See Section 240-4 for overcurrent protection requirements for flexible cord.

400-8. Uses Not Permitted. Unless specifically permitted in Section 400-7 flexible cords and cables shall not be used (1) as a substitute for the fixed wiring of a structure; (2) where run through holes in walls, ceilings, or floors; (3) where run through doorways, windows, or similar openings; (4) where attached to building surfaces; or (5) where concealed behind building walls, ceilings, or floors.

Table 400-5. Ampacity of Flexible Cords and Cables
[Based on Ambient Temperature of 30°C (86°F). See Section 400-13 and Table 400-4.]

Size AWG	Thermoset Type TS Thermoplastic Types TPT, TST	Thermoset Types C, E, EN, EO, G, PD, S, SJ, SJO, SJOO, SO, SOO, SP, SP-1, SP-2, SP-3, SRD, SV, SVO, SVOO, W Thermoplastic Types ET, ETT, ETLB, ETP, SE, SEO, SJE, SJEO, SJT, SJTO, SJTOO, SPE-1, SPE-2, SPE-3, SPT, SPT-1, SPT-2, SPT-3, ST, STO, STOO, SRDE, SRDT, SVE, SVEO, SVT, SVTO, SVTOO			Types AFS, AFSJ, HPD, HPN, HS, HSJ, HSJO, HSO	Asbestos Types AFC* AFPD* AFPO
		A†	B†	C		
27**	0.5	. .	. .	. .	. .	. .
20	. .	5***	7***	. .	. .	. .
18	. .	7	10	. .	10	6
17	. .	. .	12	. .	. .	. .
16	. .	10	13	. .	15	8
15	. .	. .	. .	. .	17	. .
14	. .	15	18	. .	20	17
12	. .	20	25	. .	30	23
10	. .	25	30	. .	35	28
8	. .	35	40	60	. .	. .
6	. .	45	55	80	. .	. .
4	. .	60	70	105	. .	. .
2	. .	80	95	140	. .	. .
1	. .	90	110	165	. .	. .
1/0	. .	100	125	195	. .	. .
2/0	. .	115	145	225	. .	. .
3/0	. .	130	165	260	. .	. .
4/0	. .	155	195	300	. .	. .
250 MCM	. .	170	215	340	. .	. .
300 MCM	. .	190	240	375	. .	. .
350 MCM	. .	210	260	420	. .	. .
400 MCM	. .	225	280	455	. .	. .
500 MCM	. .	255	320	515	. .	. .

* These types are used almost exclusively in fixtures where they are exposed to high temperatures and ampere ratings are assigned accordingly.

** Tinsel cord.

*** Elevator cables only.

† The ampacities under sub-heading A apply to 3-conductor cords and other multiconductor cords connected to utilization equipment so that only 3 conductors are current carrying. The ampacities under sub-heading B apply to 2-conductor cords and other multiconductor cords connected to utilization equipment so that only 2 conductors are current carrying.

NOTE. Ultimate Insulation Temperature. In no case shall conductors be associated together in such a way with respect to the kind of circuit, the wiring method used, or the number of conductors that the limiting temperature of the conductors will be exceeded.

400-9. Splices. Flexible cord shall be used only in continuous lengths without splice or tap when initially installed in applications permitted by Section 400-7(a). The repair of hard service cord (see Column 1, Table 400-4) No. 14 and larger shall be permitted if conductors are spliced in accordance with Section 110-14(b) and the completed splice retains the insulation, outer sheath properties, and usage characteristics of the cord being spliced.

400-10. Pull at Joints and Terminals. Flexible cords shall be so connected to devices and to fittings that tension will not be transmitted to joints or terminals.

(FPN): Some methods of preventing pull on a cord from being transmitted to joints or terminals are (1) knotting the cord, (2) winding with tape, and (3) fittings designed for the purpose.

400-11. In Show Windows and Show Cases.   Flexible cords used in show windows and show cases shall be Type S, SO, SE, SEO, SOO, SJ, SJE, SJO, SJEO, SJOO, ST, STO, STOO, SJT, SJTO, SJTOO, or AFS.

Exception No. 1: For the wiring of chain-supported lighting fixtures.

Exception No. 2: As supply cords for portable lamps and other merchandise being displayed or exhibited.

Flexible cords listed for "hard usage" or "extra hard usage" should be used in show windows and show cases, and precautions should be taken to ensure that these cords are maintained in good condition because of possible contact with combustible materials usually present at these locations and because of the wear and tear they are exposed to by continuous housekeeping and display changes.

400-12. Minimum Size.   The individual conductors of a flexible cord or cable shall not be smaller than the sizes in Table 400-4.

400-13. Overcurrent Protection.   Flexible cords not smaller than No. 18, and tinsel cords or cords having equivalent characteristics of smaller size approved for use with specific appliances, shall be considered as protected against overcurrent by the overcurrent devices described in Section 240-4.

400-14. Protection from Damage.   Flexible cords and cables shall be protected by bushings or fittings where passing through holes in covers, outlet boxes, or similar enclosures.

There are a variety of bushings and fittings available for this purpose, both insulated and noninsulated, some including strain-relief means as required in Section 400-10. Many insulating bushings are listed by Underwriters Laboratories Inc. in the product categories Conduit Fittings (bushings and fittings for use on the ends of conduit in boxes, gutters, etc.); Insulating Devices and Materials, Bushings (bushings for the protection of cords where they pass through walls or barriers of metal); or Outlet Bushings and Fittings (bushings and fittings for use on the ends of conduit, EMT, or armored cable where a change to open wiring is made).

B. Construction Specifications

400-20. Labels.   Flexible cords shall be examined and tested at the factory and labeled before shipment.

See definition of "labeled" in Article 100.

400-21. Nominal Insulation Thickness.   The nominal thickness of insulation for conductors of flexible cords and cables shall not be less than specified in Table 400-4.

400-22. Grounded-Conductor Identification.   One conductor of flexible cords which is intended to be used as a grounded circuit conductor shall have a continuous marker readily distinguishing it from the other conductor or conductors. The identification shall consist of one of the methods indicated in (a) through (f) below.

(a) Colored Braid.   A braid finished to show a white or natural gray color and the braid on the other conductor or conductors finished to show a readily distinguishable solid color or colors.

(b) Tracer in Braid.   A tracer in a braid of any color contrasting with that of the braid and no tracer in the braid of the other conductor or conductors. No tracer shall be used in the braid of any conductor of a flexible cord which contains a conductor having a braid finished to show white or natural gray.

Exception: In the case of Types C and PD, and cords having the braids on the individual conductors finished to show white or natural gray. In such cords the identifying marker shall be permitted to consist of the solid white or natural gray finish on one conductor, provided there is a colored tracer in the braid of each other conductor.

(c) Colored Insulation. A white or natural gray insulation on one conductor and insulation of a readily distinguishable color or colors on the other conductor or conductors for cords having no braids on the individual conductors.

For jacketed cords furnished with appliances, one conductor having its insulation colored light blue, with the other conductors having their insulation of a readily distinguishable color other than white or natural gray.

Exception: Cords which have insulation on the individual conductors integral with the jacket.

It shall be permissible to cover the insulation with an outer finish to provide the desired color.

(d) Colored Separator. A white or natural gray separator on one conductor and a separator of a readily distinguishable solid color on the other conductor or conductors of cords having insulation on the individual conductors integral with the jacket.

(e) Tinned Conductors. One conductor having the individual strands tinned and the other conductor or conductors having the individual strands untinned for cords having insulation on the individual conductors integral with the jacket.

(f) Surface Marking. One or more stripes, ridges, or grooves so located on the exterior of the cord as to identify one conductor for cords having insulation on the individual conductors integral with the jacket.

400-23. Grounding-Conductor Identification. A conductor intended to be used as a grounding conductor shall have a continuous identifying marker readily distinguishing it from the other conductor or conductors. Conductors having a continuous green color or a continuous green color with one or more yellow stripes shall not be used for other than grounding purposes. The identifying marker shall consist of one of the methods in (a) or (b) below.

(a) Colored Braid. A braid finished to show a continuous green color or a continuous green color with one or more yellow stripes.

(b) Colored Insulation or Covering. For cords having no braids on the individual conductors, an insulation of a continuous green color or a continuous green color with one or more yellow stripes.

400-24. Attachment Plugs. Where a flexible cord is provided with a grounding conductor and equipped with an attachment plug, the attachment plug shall comply with Section 250-59(a) and (b).

C. Portable Cables Over 600 Volts, Nominal

400-30. Scope. This part applies to multiconductor portable cables used to connect mobile equipment and machinery.

400-31. Construction.

(a) Conductors. The conductors shall be No. 8 AWG copper or larger and shall employ flexible stranding.

(b) Shields. Cables operated at over 2000 volts shall be shielded. Shielding shall be for the purpose of confining the voltage stresses to the insulation.

(c) Grounding Conductor(s). Grounding conductor(s) shall be provided. The total area shall be not less than that of the size of the conductor required in Section 250-95.

400-32. Shielding. All shields shall be grounded.

400-33. Grounding. Grounding conductors shall be connected in accordance with Part K of Article 250.

400-34. Minimum Bending Radii. The minimum bending radii for portable cables during installation and handling in service shall be adequate to prevent damage to the cable.

400-35. Fittings. Connectors used to connect lengths of cable in a run shall be of a type which lock firmly together. Provisions shall be made to prevent opening or closing these connectors while energized. Suitable means shall be used to eliminate tension at connectors and terminations.

400-36. Splices and Terminations. Portable cables shall not be operated with splices unless the splices are of the permanent molded, vulcanized types in accordance with Section 110-14(b). Terminations on high-voltage portable cables shall be accessible only to authorized and qualified personnel.

ARTICLE 402 — FIXTURE WIRES

Contents

402-1. Scope. This article covers general requirements and construction specifications for fixture wires.

402-2. Other Articles. Fixture wires shall comply with this article and also with the applicable provisions of other articles of this Code.

(FPN): For application in lighting fixtures, see Article 410.

402-3. Types. Fixture wires shall be of a type listed in Table 402-3, and they shall comply with all requirements of that table. The fixture wires listed in Table 402-3 are all suitable for service at 600 volts, nominal, unless otherwise specified.

(FPN): Thermoplastic insulation may stiffen at temperatures colder than minus 10°C (plus 14°F), requiring care be exercised during installation at such temperatures. Thermoplastic insulation may also be deformed at normal temperatures where subjected to pressure, requiring care be exercised during installation and at points of support.

Table 402-3.   Fixture Wire

Trade Name	Type Letter	Insulation	AWG	Thickness of Insulation (Mils)	Outer Covering	Max. Operating Temp.	Application Provisions
Heat-Resistant Rubber-Covered Fixture Wire Solid or 7-Strand	RFH-1	Heat-Resistant Rubber	18	15	Nonmetallic Covering	75°C 167°F	Fixture wiring. Limited to 300 volts.
	RFH-2	Heat-Resistant Rubber	18–16	30	Nonmetallic Covering	75°C 167°F	Fixture wiring, and as permitted in Sections 725-16 and 760-16.
		Heat-Resistant Latex Rubber	18–16	18			
Heat-Resistant Cross-Linked Synthetic Polymer-Insulated Fixture Wire—Solid or Stranded	RFHH-2	Cross-Linked Synthetic Polymer	18–16	30	None or Nonmetallic Covering	90°C 194°F	Fixture wiring, and as permitted in Sections 725-16 and 760-16. Multiconductor cable as permitted in Sections 725-16 and 760-16.
	RFHH-3		18–16	45			
Heat-Resistant Rubber-Covered Fixture Wire Flexible Stranding	FFH-2	Heat-Resistant Rubber	18–16	30	Nonmetallic Covering	75°C 167°F	Fixture wiring, and as permitted in Section 725-16.
		Heat-Resistant Latex Rubber	18–16	18			
Thermoplastic-Covered Fixture Wire—Solid or 7-Strand	TF	Thermoplastic	18–16	30	None	60°C 140°F	Fixture wiring, and as permitted in Sections 725-16 and 760-16.
Thermoplastic-Covered Fixture Wire—Flexible Stranding	TFF	Thermoplastic	18–16	30	None	60°C 140°F	Fixture wiring, and as permitted in Section 725-16.

Table 402-3 (Continued)

Name of Wire	Type Letter	Insulation	Size AWG	Thickness of Moisture-Resistant Insulation Mils	Thickness of Asbestos Mils	Outer Covering	Max. Operating Temp.	Application
Heat-Resistant Thermoplastic-Covered Fixture Wire—Solid or 7-Strand	TFN	Thermoplastic	18–16 15			Nylon Jacketed or equivalent	90°C 194°F	Fixture wiring, and as permitted in Sections 725-16 and 760-16.
Heat-Resistant Thermoplastic-Covered Fixture Wire—Flexible Stranded	TFFN	Thermoplastic	18–16 15			Nylon Jacketed or equivalent	90°C 194°F	Fixture wiring, and as permitted in Section 725-16.
Asbestos Covered Heat-Resistant Fixture Wire	AF	Impregnated Asbestos or Moisture-Resistant Insulation and Impregnated Asbestos	18–14	— / 20	30 / 10	None	150°C 302°F	Fixture wiring. Limited to 300 volts and indoor dry locations.
			12–10	— / 25	45 / 20			
Silicone Insulated Fixture Wire Solid or 7-Strand	SF-1	Silicone Rubber	18 15			Nonmetallic Covering	200°C 392°F	Fixture wiring. Limited to 300 volts.
	SF-2	Silicone Rubber	18–14 30			Nonmetallic Covering	200°C 392°F	Fixture wiring, and as permitted in Sections 725-16 and 760-16.
Silicone Insulated Fixture Wire Flexible Stranding	SFF-1	Silicone Rubber	18 15			Nonmetallic Covering	150°C 302°F	Fixture wiring. Limited to 300 volts.
	SFF-2	Silicone Rubber	18–14 30			Nonmetallic Covering	150°C 302°F	Fixture wiring, and as permitted in Section 725-16.

Table 402-3 (Continued)

Trade Name	Type Letter	Insulation	Thickness of Insulation AWG	Mils	Outer Covering	Max. Operating Temp.	Application Provisions
Fluorinated Ethylene Propylene Fixture Wire Solid or 7-Strand	PF	Fluorinated Ethylene Propylene	18–14	 20	None	200°C 392°F	Fixture wiring, and as permitted in Sections 725-16 and 760-16.
	PGF		18–14	 14	Glass Braid		
Fluorinated Ethylene Propylene Fixture Wire Flexible Stranding	PFF	Fluorinated Ethylene Propylene	18–14	 20	None	150°C 302°F	Fixture wiring, and as permitted in Section 725-16.
	PGFF		18–14	 14	Glass Braid		
Tape Insulated Fixture Wire Solid or 7-Strand	KF-1	Aromatic Polyimide Tape	18–10	.... 5.5	None	200°C 392°F	Fixture wiring. Limited to 300 volts.
	KF-2	Aromatic Polyimide Tape	18–10	.... 8.4	None	200°C 392°F	Fixture wiring, and as permitted in Sections 725-16 and 760-16.
Tape Insulated Fixture Wire Flexible Stranding	KFF-1	Aromatic Polyimide Tape	18–10	.... 5.5	None	200°C 392°F	Fixture wiring. Limited to 300 volts.
	KFF-2	Aromatic Polyimide Tape	18–10	.... 8.4	None	200°C 392°F	Fixture wiring, and as permitted in Section 725-16.

Table 402-3 (Continued)

Trade Name	Type	Insulation	AWG	Thickness	Max. Temperature	Application
ECTFE Solid or 7-Strand	HF	Ethylene Chloro Trifluoro Ethylene	18–14 15	None	150°C 302°F	Fixture wiring, and as permitted in Section 725-16.
ECTFE Flexible Stranding	HFF	Ethylene Chloro Trifluoro Ethylene	18–14 15	None	150°C 302°F	Fixture wiring, and as permitted in Section 725-16.
Crosslinked Polyolefin Insulated Fixture Wire Solid or 7-Strand	XF	Crosslinked Polyolefin	18–14 .... 30 12–10 45	None	150°C 302°F	Fixture wiring. Limited to 300 volts.
Crosslinked Polyolefin Insulated Fixture Wire Flexible Stranded	XFF	Crosslinked Polyolefin	18–14 .... 30 12–10 45	None	150°C 302°F	Fixture wiring. Limited to 300 volts.
Modified ETFE Solid or 7-Strand	ZF	Modified Ethylene Tetrafluoro-ethylene	18–14 15	None	150°C 302°F	Fixture wiring, and as permitted in Sections 725-16 and 760-16.
Flexible Stranding	ZFF	Modified Ethylene Tetrafluoro-ethylene	18–14 15	None	150°C 302°F	Fixture wiring, and as permitted in Section 725-16.

Table 402-3 (Continued)

Trade Name	Type Letter	Insulation	Thickness of Insulation AWG	Mils	Outer Covering	Max. Operating Temp.	Application Provisions
Extruded Poly-tetrafluoro-ethylene Solid or 7-Strand (Nickel or Nickel-Coated Copper)	PTF	Extruded Poly-tetrafluoro-ethylene	18–14	20	None	250°C 482°F	Fixture wiring, and as permitted in Sections 725-16 and 760-16. (Nickel or nickel-coated copper)
Extruded Poly-tetrafluoro-ethylene Flexible Stranding (No. 26-36 AWG Silver or Nickel-Coated Copper)	PTFF	Extruded Poly-tetrafluoro-ethylene	18–14	20	None	150°C 302°F	Fixture wiring, and as permitted in Section 725-16. (Silver or nickel-coated copper)
Perfluoro-alkoxy Solid or 7-Strand (Nickel or Nickel-Coated Copper)	PAF	Perfluoroalkoxy	18–14	20	None	250°C 482°F	Fixture wiring, and as permitted in Sections 725-16 and 760-16. (Nickel or nickel-coated copper)
Perfluoro-alkoxy Flexible Stranding	PAFF	Perfluoroalkoxy	18–14	20	None	150°C 302°F	Fixture wiring, and as permitted in Sections 725-16.

402-5. Ampacity of Fixture Wires. The ampacity of fixture wire shall not exceed the following:

Table 402-5

Size (AWG)	Ampacity
18	6
16	8
14	17
12	23
10	28

No conductor shall be used under such conditions that its operating temperature will exceed the temperature specified in Table 402-3 for the type of insulation involved.

(FPN): See Section 310-10 for temperature limitation of conductors.

402-6. Minimum Size. Fixture wires shall not be smaller than No. 18.

402-7. Number of Conductors in Conduit. The number of fixture wires permitted in a single conduit shall be as given in Table 2 of Chapter 9.

402-8. Grounded-Conductor Identification. One conductor of fixture wires which is intended to be used as a grounded conductor shall be identified by means of stripes or by the means described in Section 400-22(a) through (e).

402-9. Marking.

(a) Required Information. All fixture wires shall be marked to indicate the information required in Section 310-11(a).

(b) Method of Marking. Thermoplastic-insulated fixture wire shall be durably marked on the surface at intervals not exceeding 24 inches (610 mm). All other fixture wire shall be marked by means of a printed tag attached to the coil, reel, or carton.

402-10. Uses Permitted. Fixture wires shall be permitted: (1) for installation in lighting fixtures and in similar equipment where enclosed or protected and not subject to bending or twisting in use, or (2) for connecting lighting fixtures to the branch-circuit conductors supplying the fixtures.

402-11. Uses Not Permitted. Fixture wires shall not be used as branch-circuit conductors.

Exception: As permitted by Section 725-16 for Class 1 circuits and Section 760-16 for fire protective signaling circuits.

402-12. Overcurrent Protection. Overcurrent protection for fixture wires shall be as specified in Section 240-4.

ARTICLE 410 — LIGHTING FIXTURES, LAMPHOLDERS, LAMPS, RECEPTACLES, AND ROSETTES

Contents

490

ARTICLE 410—LIGHTING FIXTURES, ETC.

A. General

410-1. Scope. This article covers lighting fixtures, lampholders, pendants, receptacles, and rosettes, incandescent filament lamps, arc lamps, electric-discharge lamps, the wiring and equipment forming part of such lamps, fixtures and lighting installations.

410-2. Application to Other Articles. Equipment for use in hazardous (classified) locations shall conform to Articles 500 through 517.

410-3. Live Parts. Fixtures, lampholders, lamps, rosettes, and receptacles shall have no live parts normally exposed to contact. Exposed accessible terminals in lampholders, receptacles, and switches shall not be installed in metal fixture canopies or in open bases of portable table or floor lamps.

Exception: Cleat-type lampholders, receptacles, and rosettes located at least 8 feet (2.44 m) above the floor shall be permitted to have exposed contacts.

B. Fixture Locations

410-4. Fixtures in Specific Locations.

Underwriters Laboratories Inc. publishes a pamphlet titled: "Fixture Marking Guide." This pamphlet was developed to help authorities having jurisdiction quickly determine whether common types of UL-listed fluorescent and incandescent fixtures are installed correctly. It is available from UL.

(a) Wet and Damp Locations. Fixtures installed in wet or damp locations shall be so installed that water cannot enter or accumulate in wiring compartments, lampholders, or other electrical parts. All fixtures installed in wet locations shall be marked, "Suitable for Wet Locations." All fixtures installed in damp locations shall be marked, "Suitable for Wet Locations" or "Suitable for Damp Locations."

Installations underground or in concrete slabs or masonry in direct contact with the earth, and locations subject to saturation with water or other liquids, such as locations exposed to weather and unprotected, vehicle washing areas, and like locations, shall be considered to be wet locations with respect to the above requirement.

Interior locations protected from weather but subject to moderate degrees of moisture, such as some basements, some barns, some cold-storage warehouses and the like, the partially protected locations under canopies, marquees, roofed open porches, and the like, shall be considered to be damp locations with respect to the above requirement.

(FPN): See Article 680 for lighting fixtures in swimming pools, fountains, and similar installations.

Fixtures marked "Suitable for Wet Locations" are required where exposed to the weather or where subject to water saturation. Construction, design, and installation are to be such as to prevent the entrance of rain, snow, ice, and dust. Outdoor parks and parking lots, outdoor recreational areas (tennis, golf, baseball, etc.), car wash areas, and building exteriors are areas which would be considered wet locations.

Areas protected from the weather and not subject to water saturation, but exposed to moisture, such as the underside of store or gasoline station canopies, or theater marquees, some cold-storage warehouses, some agricultural buildings, some basements, and roofed open porches and carports may be considered damp locations and fixtures are required to be marked "Suitable for Damp Locations." See definitions of "damp location," "dry location," and "wet location," under "location" in Article 100.

(b) Corrosive Locations. Fixtures installed in corrosive locations shall be of a type suitable for such locations.

(FPN): See Section 210-7 for receptacles in fixtures.

(c) In Ducts or Hoods. Fixtures shall be permitted to be installed in cooking hoods of nonresidential occupancies where all of the following conditions are met:

(1) The fixture shall be identified for use within commercial cooking hoods and installed so that the temperature limits of the materials used are not exceeded.

(2) The fixture shall be so constructed that all exhaust vapors, grease, oil or cooking vapors are excluded from the lamp and wiring compartment. Diffusers shall be resistant to thermal shock.

(3) Parts of the fixture exposed within the hood shall be corrosion resistant or protected against corrosion and the surface shall be smooth so as not to collect deposits and facilitate cleaning.

(4) Wiring methods and materials supplying the fixture(s) shall not be exposed within the cooking hood.

(FPN): See Section 110-11.

The requirements for this section were initially taken from NFPA 96, *Standard for the Installation of Equipment for the Removal of Smoke and Grease-Laden Vapors from Commercial Cooking Equipment.* NFPA 96 covers the basic requirements for the design, installation, and use of exhaust system components including (1) hoods, (2) grease-removal devices, (3) exhaust ducts, (4) dampers, (5) air-moving devices, (6) auxiliary equipment, and (7) fire extinguishing equipment for the exhaust system and the cooking equipment used therewith in commercial, industrial, institutional, and similar cooking applications. This standard does not apply to installations for normal residential family use.

Grease can cause short circuits or ground faults in wiring, hence the requirement prohibiting wiring methods and materials (raceways, cables, lampholders, etc.) within ducts or hoods. Conventional enclosed and gasketed fixtures located in the path of travel of exhaust products are not permitted because a fire could result from the high temperatures on grease-coated glass bowls or globes enclosing the lamps. Recessed or surface fixtures intended for location within hoods are required to be identified as suitable for the specific purpose, and should be installed with the required clearances maintained. Note that wiring methods are not permitted to be run exposed within the cooking hood.

(d) Pendants. No parts of cord-connected fixtures, hanging fixtures, or pendants shall be located within a zone measured 3 feet (914 mm) horizontally and 8 feet (2.44 m) vertically from the top of the bathtub rim. This zone is all encompassing and includes the zone directly over the tub.

The intent of this section is to keep the fixture out of reach of a person when standing on the bathtub rim. See Figure 410-1. See Section 680-41 for installation requirements for spas and hot tubs installed indoors.

Figure 410-1. Fixtures located in bathrooms.

410-5. Fixtures Near Combustible Material. Fixtures shall be so constructed, or installed, or equipped with shades or guards that combustible material will not be subjected to temperatures in excess of 90°C (194°F).

410-6. Fixtures Over Combustible Material. Lampholders installed over highly combustible material shall be of the unswitched type. Unless an individual switch is provided for each fixture, lampholders shall be located at least 8 feet (2.44 m) above the floor, or shall be so located or guarded that the lamps cannot be readily removed or damaged.

This section refers to pendants and fixed lighting equipment installed above highly combustible material. Where the lamp cannot be located out of reach, the requirement can be met by equipping the lamp with a suitable guard. This section is not applicable to portable lamps.

410-7. Fixtures in Show Windows. Externally wired fixtures shall not be used in a show window.

Exception: Fixtures of the chain-supported type shall be permitted to be externally wired.

410-8. Fixtures in Clothes Closets.

(a) Location. A fixture in a clothes closet shall be permitted to be installed:

(1) On the wall above the closet door, provided the clearance between the fixture and a storage area where combustible material may be stored within the closet is not less than 18 inches (457 mm), or

(2) On the ceiling over an area which is unobstructed to the floor, maintaining an 18-inch (457-mm) clearance horizontally between the fixture and a storage area where combustible material may be stored within the closet.

A flushed recessed fixture with a solid lens or a ceiling-mounted fluorescent fixture shall be permitted to be installed provided there is a 6-inch (152-mm) clearance, horizontally, between the fixture and the storage area.

(b) Pendants. Pendants shall not be installed in clothes closets.

It is not mandatory to install a lighting fixture in a clothes closet; if one is installed, however, the conditions of installation are as required by this section.

The requirements here apply to lighting, incandescent and fluorescent, in various kinds of occupancies. The intent is to prevent hot lamps from coming in contact with cartons, blankets, etc., stored on shelves and clothing hung in closets which would, of course, constitute a fire hazard. Note that the storage area includes the clothing hanging area.

From Figure 410-2 it is quite obvious that fixtures other than flush recessed types with solid lens and ceiling-mounted fluorescent types cannot be located in shallow clothes closets because proper clearances would not be provided.

Proper lighting may be achieved in small clothes closets by locating fixtures on the outside ceiling in front of the closet door, especially in hallways where such fixtures can serve a dual function. Flush recessed fixtures with a solid lens and ceiling-mounted fluorescent fixtures are to be installed with at least a 6-in. clearance.

410-9. Space for Cove Lighting. Coves shall have adequate space and shall be so located that lamps and equipment can be properly installed and maintained.

Adequate space permits easy access for relamping fixtures or replacing sockets, ballasts, etc., and also improves ventilation.

Figure 410-2. Lighting fixtures are required to be installed in clothes closets so as to maintain the minimum clearances shown above. Pendants are prohibited.

C. Provisions at Fixture Outlet Boxes, Canopies, and Pans

410-10. Space for Conductors. Canopies and outlet boxes taken together shall provide adequate space so that fixture conductors and their connecting devices can be properly installed.

410-11. Temperature Limit of Conductors in Outlet Boxes. Fixtures shall be of such construction or so installed that the conductors in outlet boxes shall not be subjected to temperatures greater than that for which the conductors are rated.

Branch-circuit wiring shall not be passed through an outlet box that is an integral part of an incandescent fixture unless the fixture is identified for through wiring.

Branch-circuit conductors run to a lighting outlet box are not permitted to be subjected to greater temperatures than those for which they are rated. For example, conductors are rated 60°C (140°F) and are to supply a ceiling outlet box for the connection of a surface-mounted incandescent fixture or attached outlet box of a recessed fixture. The design and installation of the fixture should be such that the heat of the incandescent lamps does not subject the conductors to a greater temperature than 60°C (140°F). These types of fixtures are listed by Underwriters Laboratories Inc. based on the heat-contributing factor of the supply conductors at not more than the maximum permitted lamp wattage of the fixture.

Figure 410-3 illustrates recessed fixtures listed by UL for one set of supply conductors, and Figure 410-4 illustrates fixtures listed for a "feed through" installation.

The following paragraph is an excerpt from the Underwriters Laboratories Inc. Electrical Construction Materials Directory:

With the exception of fluorescent-lamp fixtures, recessed fixtures are marked with the required minimum temperature rating of wiring supplying the fixture. Unless marked in combination with the listing mark "Maximum of _____ No. _____ AWG branch-circuit conductors suitable for at least _____°C (_____°F) permitted in junction box," no allowance has been made for any heat contributed by branch-circuit conductors which pass through, or supply and pass through, an outlet box or other splice compartment which is part of the fixture.

Figure 410-3. Branch-circuit conductors terminating at each fixture (no "feed-through").

Figure 410-4. Recessed lighting fixtures that are designed for "feed-through" branch-circuit conductors.

410-12. Outlet Boxes to Be Covered.   In a completed installation, each outlet box shall be provided with a cover unless covered by means of a fixture canopy, lampholder, receptacle, rosette, or similar device.

Lighting fixtures are required to be designed and installed not only to prevent overheating of conductors but also to prevent overheating of adjacent combustible wall or ceiling finishes. Hence, the requirement that any combustible finish between the edge of a fixture canopy and an outlet box be covered with a noncombustible material or fixture accessory. See Section 370-11 for requirements covering noncombustible finishes.

Where lighting fixtures are not directly mounted on outlet boxes, suitable outlet box covers are required.

410-13. Covering of Combustible Material at Outlet Boxes. Any combustible wall or ceiling finish exposed between the edge of a fixture canopy or pan and an outlet box shall be covered with noncombustible material.

See commentary following Section 410-12.

410-14. Connection of Electric-Discharge Lighting Fixtures.

(a) Independently of the Outlet Box. Where electric-discharge lighting fixtures are supported independently of the outlet box, they shall be connected through metal raceways, metal-clad cables, or nonmetallic-sheathed cables.

Exception: Cord-connected fixtures shall be permitted as provided in Sections 410-30(b) and (c).

(b) Access to Boxes. Electric discharge lighting fixtures surface mounted over concealed outlet, pull, or junction boxes shall be installed with suitable openings in back of the fixture to provide access to the boxes.

D. Fixture Supports

410-15. Supports.

(a) General. Fixtures, lampholders, rosettes, and receptacles shall be securely supported. A fixture that weighs more than 6 pounds (2.72 kg) or exceeds 16 inches (406 mm) in any dimension shall not be supported by the screw shell of a lampholder.

(b) Metal Poles Supporting Lighting Fixtures. Metal poles shall be permitted to be used to support lighting fixtures and enclose supply conductors, provided that the following conditions are met.

(1) An accessible handhole not less than 2 inches (50.8 mm) × 4 inches (102 mm) having a raintight cover shall provide access to the supply raceway or cable termination within the pole or pole base. Where raceway risers or cable are not installed within the pole, a threaded fitting or nipple shall be brazed or welded to the pole opposite the handhole, for the supply connection. Other poles shall be permitted to be field welded, brazed, or tapped. Such poles shall be capped or covered.

(2) A terminal for grounding the pole shall be provided; it shall be accessible from the handhole.

(3) Metal raceways or other equipment grounding conductors shall be bonded to the pole with an equipment grounding conductor recognized by Section 250-91(b) and sized in accordance with Section 250-95.

(4) Conductors in vertical metal poles used as raceways shall be supported as provided in Section 300-19.

410-16. Means of Support.

(a) Outlet Boxes. Where the outlet box or fitting will provide adequate support, a fixture shall be attached thereto or be supported as required by Section 370-13 for boxes. A fixture that weighs more than 50 pounds (22.7 kg) shall be supported independently of the outlet box.

(b) Inspection. Fixtures shall be so installed that the connections between the fixture conductors and the circuit conductors can be inspected without requiring the disconnection of any part of the wiring.

Exception: Fixtures connected by attachment plugs and receptacles.

(c) Suspended Ceilings. Framing members of suspended ceiling systems used to support fixtures shall be securely fastened to each other and shall be securely attached to the building structure at appropriate intervals. Fixtures shall be securely fastened to the ceiling framing member by mechanical means, such as bolts, screws, or rivets. Clips identified for use with the type of ceiling framing member(s) and fixture(s) shall also be permitted.

(d) Fixture Studs. Fixture studs that are not a part of outlet boxes, hickeys, tripods, and crowfeet shall be made of steel, malleable iron, or other material suitable for the application.

(e) Insulating Joints. Insulating joints that are not designed to be mounted with screws or bolts shall have an exterior metal casing, insulated from both screw connections.

(f) Raceway Fittings. Raceway fittings used to support lighting fixture(s) shall be capable of supporting the weight of the complete fixture assembly and lamp(s).

Whether a lighting fixture is attached to an outlet box or supported independently of the outlet box, care should be taken to securely and rigidly fasten the outlet box or support the independent rod or pipe hanger (as shown in Figure 370-3).

So-called "drop-in" fixtures or surface-mounted fixtures are required to be securely fastened to the framing members of hung or suspended ceilings by mechanical means, such as bolts, screws, or rivets, or clips identified for use with the type of ceiling framing member(s) and fixture(s), and no other support of the fixture is necessary. However, the suspended ceiling framing members must be securely attached to each other and to the building structure and, also, additional supporting wires, rods, etc., may be necessary to provide ample support of the ceiling in areas where fixtures are installed.

(g) Busways. Fixtures shall be permitted to be connected to busways in accordance with Section 364-12.

E. Grounding

410-17. General. Fixtures and lighting equipment shall be grounded as provided in Part E of this article.

410-18. Exposed Fixture Parts.

(a) With Exposed Conductive Parts. The exposed conductive parts of lighting fixtures and equipment directly wired or attached to outlets supplied by a wiring method which provides an equipment ground shall be grounded.

(b) Made of Insulating Material. Fixtures directly wired or attached to outlets supplied by a wiring method which does not provide a ready means for grounding shall be made of insulating material and shall have no exposed conductive parts.

410-19. Equipment Over 150 Volts to Ground.

(a) Metal Fixtures, Transformers, and Transformer Enclosures. Metal fixtures, transformers, and transformer enclosures on circuits operating at over 150 volts to ground shall be grounded.

(b) Other Exposed Metal Parts.   Other exposed metal parts shall be grounded or insulated from ground and other conducting surfaces and inaccessible to unqualified persons.

Exception: Lamp tie wires, mounting screws, clips, and decorative bands on glass lamps spaced not less than 1½ inches (38 mm) from lamp terminals shall not be required to be grounded.

410-20. Equipment Grounding Conductor Attachment.   Fixtures with exposed metal parts shall be provided with a means for connecting an equipment grounding conductor for such fixtures.

410-21. Methods of Grounding.   Fixtures and equipment shall be considered grounded where mechanically connected to an equipment grounding conductor as specified in Section 250-91(b) and sized in accordance with Section 250-95.

F. Wiring of Fixtures

410-22. Fixture Wiring — General.   Wiring on or within fixtures shall be neatly arranged and shall not be exposed to physical damage. Excess wiring shall be avoided. Conductors shall be so arranged that they shall not be subjected to temperatures above those for which they are rated.

410-23. Polarization of Fixtures.   Fixtures shall be so wired that the screw shells of lampholders will be connected to the same fixture or circuit conductor or terminal. The grounded conductor, where connected to a screw-shell lampholder, shall be connected to the screw shell.

410-24. Conductors.

(a) Insulation.   Fixtures shall be wired with conductors having insulation suitable for the environmental conditions, current, voltage, and temperature to which the conductors will be subjected.

(b) Conductor Size.   Fixture conductors shall not be smaller than No. 18.

(FPN): For ampacity of fixture wire, see Table 402-5.

(FPN): For maximum operating temperature and voltage limitation of fixture wires, see Section 402-3.

410-25. Conductors for Certain Conditions.

(a) Mogul-Base Lampholders.   Fixtures provided with mogul-base, screw-shell lampholders and operating at not over 300 volts between conductors shall be wired with Type AF, SF-1, SF-2, SFF-1, SFF-2, PF, PGF, PFF, PGFF, PTF, PTFF, PAF, PAFF, XF, XFF, ZF or ZFF fixture wire.

(b) Other than Mogul-Base, Screw-Shell Lampholders.   Fixtures provided with other than mogul-base, screw-shell lampholders and operating at not over 300 volts between conductors shall be wired with Type AF, SF-1, SF-2, PF, PGF, PFF, PGFF, PTF, PTFF, PAF, PAFF, XF, XFF, ZF or ZFF fixture wire or Type AFC or AFPD flexible cord.

Exception No. 1: Where temperatures do not exceed 90°C (194°F), Types CF, TFN and TFFN fixture wire or Type CFPD flexible cord shall be permitted.

Exception No. 2: Where temperatures exceed 60°C (140°F) but are not higher than 75°C (167°F), Types RH and RHW rubber-covered wire and Types RFH-1, RFH-2, FFH-1, and FFH-2 fixture wires shall be permitted.

Exception No. 3: Where temperatures do not exceed 60°C (140°F), Type T thermoplastic wire, Types TF and TFF fixture wires shall be permitted, including fixtures of decorative types on which lamps of not over 60-watt rating are used in connection with imitation candles.

(FPN): See Table 402-3 and Section 402-3 for fixture wires and conductors; and Table 400-5 for flexible cords.

410-27. Pendant Conductors for Incandescent Filament Lamps.

(a) Support. Pendant lampholders with permanently attached leads, where used for other than festoon wiring, shall be hung from separate stranded rubber-covered conductors that are soldered directly to the circuit conductors but supported independently thereof.

(b) Size. Such pendant conductors shall not be smaller than No. 14 for mogul-base or medium-base screw-shell lampholders, nor smaller than No. 18 for intermediate or candelabra-base lampholders.

Exception: Listed Christmas tree and decorative lighting outfits shall be permitted to be smaller than No. 18.

(c) Twisted or Cabled. Pendant conductors longer than 3 feet (914 mm) shall be twisted together where not cabled in a listed assembly.

410-28. Protection of Conductors and Insulation.

(a) Properly Secured. Conductors shall be secured in a manner that will not tend to cut or abrade the insulation.

(b) Protection Through Metal. Conductor insulation shall be protected from abrasion where it passes through metal.

(c) Fixture Stems. Splices and taps shall not be located within fixture arms or stems.

(d) Splices and Taps. No unnecessary splices or taps shall be made within or on a fixture.

(FPN): For approved means of making connections, see Section 110-14.

(e) Stranding. Stranded conductors shall be used for wiring on fixture chains and on other movable or flexible parts.

(f) Tension. Conductors shall be so arranged that the weight of the fixture or movable parts will not put a tension on the conductors.

410-29. Cord-Connected Showcases. Individual showcases, other than fixed, shall be permitted to be connected by flexible cord to permanently installed receptacles, and groups of not more than six such showcases shall be permitted to be coupled together by flexible cord and separable locking-type connectors with one of the group connected by flexible cord to a permanently installed receptacle.

The installation shall comply with (a) through (e) of this section.

(a) Cord Requirements. Flexible cord shall be hard-service type, having conductors not smaller than the branch-circuit conductors, having ampacity at least equal to the branch-circuit overcurrent device, and having an equipment grounding conductor.

(FPN): See Table 250-95 for size of grounding conductor.

(b) Receptacles, Connectors, and Attachment Plugs. Receptacles, connectors, and attachment plugs shall be of a listed grounding type rated 15 or 20 amperes.

(c) Support. Flexible cords shall be secured to the undersides of showcases so that: (1) wiring will not be exposed to mechanical damage; (2) a separation between cases not in excess of

2 inches (50.8 mm), nor more than 12 inches (305 mm) between the first case and the supply receptacle will be assured; and (3) the free lead at the end of a group of showcases will have a female fitting not extending beyond the case.

(d) No Other Equipment. Equipment other than showcases shall not be electrically connected to showcases.

(e) Secondary Circuit(s). Where showcases are cord connected, the secondary circuit(s) of electric discharge lighting shall be limited to one showcase.

410-30. Cord-Connected Lampholders and Fixtures.

(a) Lampholders. Where a metal lampholder is attached to a flexible cord, the inlet shall be equipped with an insulating bushing which, if threaded, shall not be smaller than nominal ⅜-inch pipe size. The cord hole shall be of a size appropriate for the cord, and all burrs and fins shall be removed in order to provide a smooth bearing surface for the cord.

Metal (brass-shell and aluminum-shell type) lampholders used with flexible cord pendants should be equipped with smooth and permanently secured insulating bushings. Nonmetallic-type lampholders do not require a bushing because the material and design afford equivalent protection.

Bushing having holes ⁹⁄₃₂ inch (7.14 mm) in diameter shall be permitted for use with plain pendant cord and holes ¹³⁄₃₂ inch (10.3 mm) in diameter with reinforced cord.

(b) Adjustable Fixtures. Fixtures which require adjusting or aiming after installation shall not be required to be equipped with an attachment plug or cord connector provided the exposed cord is of the hard usage or extra-hard usage type and is not longer than that required for maximum adjustment. The cord shall not be subject to strain or physical damage.

(c) Electric-Discharge Fixtures. It shall be permissible to locate cord-equipped fixtures directly below the outlet box, if the cord is continuously visible for its entire length outside the fixture and is not subject to strain or physical damage. Such cord-equipped fixtures shall terminate at the outer end of the cord in a grounding-type attachment plug (cap) or busway plug.
Electric-discharge lighting fixtures provided with mogul-base, screw-shell lampholders shall be permitted to be connected to branch circuits of 50 amperes or less by cords complying with Section 240-4. Receptacles and attachment plugs shall be permitted to be of lower ampere rating than the branch circuit but not less than 125 percent of the fixture full-load current.
Electric-discharge lighting fixtures equipped with a flanged surface inlet shall be permitted to be supplied by cord pendants equipped with cord connectors. Inlets and connectors shall be permitted to be of lower ampere rating than the branch circuit but not less than 125 percent of the fixture load current.

This section permits electric-discharge lighting fixtures to be connected by means of a continuously visible cord only where such cords are not used as a supporting means and the fixtures are suspended directly below the outlet boxes supplying each fixture. Electric-discharge lighting fixtures are not permitted to be supplied by cord where installed in lift-out-type suspended ceilings. Electric-discharge fixtures are permitted to be connected to busways by cords plugged directly into the busway or suspended from the busway as permitted in Section 364-12.

410-31. Fixtures as Raceways. Fixtures shall not be used as a raceway for circuit conductors.

Exception No. 1: Fixtures listed for use as a raceway.

Fixtures listed for use as raceways are labeled by Underwriters Laboratories Inc. as "Fixtures Suitable for Use as Raceways."

Exception No. 2: Fixtures designed for end-to-end assembly to form a continuous raceway or fixtures connected together by recognized wiring methods shall be permitted to carry through conductors of a two-wire or multiwire branch circuit supplying the fixtures.

Exception No. 3: One additional two-wire branch circuit separately supplying one or more of the connected fixtures described in Exception No. 2 shall be permitted to be carried through the fixtures.

Exception No. 3 permits an additional 2-wire circuit to be carried through the fixtures to supply switched night lighting commonly used to conserve energy.

(FPN): See Article 100 for definition of multiwire branch circuit.

Branch-circuit conductors within 3 inches (76 mm) of a ballast within the ballast compartment shall be recognized for use at temperatures not lower than 90°C (194°F), such as Types RHH, THW, THHN, FEP, FEPB, SA, XHHW, and AVA.

See conductor application provisions for these insulation types in Table 310-13. Note the 90°C (194°F) rating that may be applied to THW conductors for special application in electric discharge lighting equipment.

G. Construction of Fixtures

410-34. Combustible Shades and Enclosures. Adequate air space shall be provided between lamps and shades or other enclosures of combustible material.

410-35. Fixture Rating.

(a) Marking. All fixtures requiring ballasts or transformers shall be plainly marked with their electrical rating and the manufacturer's name, trademark, or other suitable means of identification. A fixture requiring supply wire rated higher than 90°C (194°F) shall be so marked, in letters ¼ inch (6.35 mm) high prominently displayed on the fixture and shipping carton or equivalent.

(b) Electrical Rating. The electrical rating shall include the voltage and frequency and shall indicate the current rating of the unit, including the ballast, transformer, or autotransformer.

410-36. Design and Material. Fixtures shall be constructed of metal, wood, or other material suitable for the application and shall be so designed and assembled as to secure requisite mechanical strength and rigidity. Wiring compartments, including their entrances, shall be such that conductors may be drawn in and withdrawn without physical damage.

410-37. Nonmetallic Fixtures. In all fixtures not made entirely of metal or noncombustible material, wiring compartments shall be lined with metal.

Exception: Where armored or lead-covered conductors with suitable fittings are used.

410-38. Mechanical Strength.

(a) Tubing for Arms. Tubing used for arms and stems where provided with cut threads shall not be less than 0.040 inch (0.1 mm) in thickness and where provided with rolled (pressed) threads shall not be less than 0.025 inch (0.635 mm) in thickness. Arms and other parts shall be fastened to prevent turning.

(b) Metal Canopies. Metal canopies supporting lampholders, shades, etc., exceeding 8 pounds (3.63 kg), or incorporating attachment-plug receptacles, shall not be less than 0.020 inch (508 micrometers) in thickness. Other canopies shall not be less than 0.016 inch (406 micrometers) if made of steel and not less than 0.020 inch (508 micrometers) if of other metals.

(c) Canopy Switches. Pull-type canopy switches shall not be inserted in the rims of metal canopies that are less than 0.025 inch (635 micrometers) in thickness unless the rims are reinforced by the turning of a bead or the equivalent. Pull-type canopy switches, whether mounted in the rims or elsewhere in sheet metal canopies, shall not be located more than 3½ inches (89 mm) from the center of the canopy. Double set-screws, double canopy rings, a screw ring, or equal method shall be used where the canopy supports a pull-type switch or pendant receptacle.

The above thickness requirements shall apply to measurements made on finished (formed) canopies.

410-39. Wiring Space. Bodies of fixtures, including portable lamps, shall provide ample space for splices and taps and for the installation of devices, if any. Splice compartments shall be of nonabsorbent, noncombustible material.

410-42. Portable Lamps.

(a) General. Portable lamps shall be wired with flexible cord, recognized by Section 400-4 and an attachment plug of the polarized or grounding type. When used with Edison-based lampholders, the grounded conductor shall be identified and attached to the screw shell and the identified blade of the attachment plug.

Figure 410-5. A portable handlamp with a grounded metallic guard and reflector, and a swivel-type hook that permits positioning the lamp in any location. (*Daniel Woodhead Co.*)

(b) Portable Handlamps. In addition to the provisions of Section 410-42(a), portable handlamps shall comply with the following: (1) metal shell, paperlined lampholders shall not be used; (2) handlamps shall be equipped with a handle of molded composition or other insulating material; (3) handlamps shall be equipped with a substantial guard attached to the lampholder or handle; (4) metallic guards shall be grounded by the means of an equipment grounding conductor run with circuit conductors within the power supply cord.

410-44. Cord Bushings. A bushing or the equivalent shall be provided where flexible cord enters the base or stem of a portable lamp. The bushing shall be of insulating material unless a jacketed type of cord is used.

410-45. Tests. All wiring shall be free from short circuits and grounds and shall be tested for these defects prior to being connected to the circuit.

410-46. Live Parts. Exposed live parts within porcelain fixtures shall be suitably recessed and so located as to make it improbable that wires will come in contact with them. There shall be a spacing of at least ½ inch (12.7 mm) between live parts and the mounting plane of the fixture.

H. Installation of Lampholders

410-47. Screw-Shell Type. Lampholders of the screw-shell type shall be installed for use as lampholders only. Where supplied by a circuit having a grounded conductor, the grounded conductor shall be connected to the screw shell.

Many years ago it was common practice to install screw-shell lampholders with screw-shell adapters in baseboards and walls for connecting cord-connected appliances and lighting equipment. This now-prohibited practice permitted exposed live parts to be contacted by persons when the adapters were removed.
See Section 410-56(a) for permitted uses of receptacles.

410-48. Double-Pole Switched Lampholders. Where supplied by the ungrounded conductors of a circuit, the switching device of lampholders of the switched type shall simultaneously disconnect both conductors of the circuit.

Single-pole switching may be used to interrupt the ungrounded conductor of a 2-wire circuit having one conductor grounded. The grounded conductor is required to be connected to the screw shell of the lampholder.
Where a 2-wire circuit is derived from two ungrounded conductors of a multiwire circuit (3- or 4-wire system), or from the two ungrounded conductors of a 2-wire circuit (3-wire system), and used with switched lampholders, the switching device is required to be double-pole and simultaneously disconnect both ungrounded conductors of the circuit. See Section 410-52.

410-49. Lampholders in Wet or Damp Locations. Lampholders installed in wet or damp locations shall be of the weatherproof type.

J. Construction of Lampholders

410-50. Insulation. The outer metal shell and the cap shall be lined with insulating material which shall prevent the shell and cap from becoming a part of the circuit. The lining shall not extend beyond the metal shell more than ⅛ inch (3.17 mm), but shall prevent any current-carrying part of the lamp base from being exposed when a lamp is in the lampholding device.

410-51. Lead Wires.   Lead wires, furnished as a part of weatherproof lampholders and intended to be exposed after installation, shall be of approved stranded, rubber-covered conductors not less than No. 14 and shall be sealed in place or otherwise made raintight.

Exception: No. 18 rubber-covered conductors shall be permitted for candelabra sockets.

410-52. Switched Lampholders.   Switched lampholders shall be of such construction that the switching mechanism interrupts the electrical connection to the center contact. The switching mechanism shall also be permitted to interrupt the electrical connection to the screw shell if the connection to the center contact is simultaneously interrupted.

K. Lamps and Auxiliary Equipment

410-53. Bases, Incandescent Lamps.   An incandescent lamp for general use on lighting branch circuits shall not be equipped with a medium base if rated over 300 watts, nor with a mogul base if rated over 1500 watts. Special bases or other devices shall be used for over 1500 watts.

410-54. Electric-Discharge Lamp Auxiliary Equipment.

(a) Enclosures.   Auxiliary equipment for electric-discharge lamps shall be enclosed in noncombustible cases and treated as sources of heat.

(b) Switching.   Where supplied by the ungrounded conductors of a circuit, the switching device of auxiliary equipment shall simultaneously disconnect all conductors.

Underwriters Laboratories Inc. provides the following information under Electric-Discharge Lamp Control Equipment, Ballasts, in the UL Electrical Construction Materials Directory.

OPEN TYPE:

Open core and coil constructions (i.e. ballasts without complete metal enclosures) are intended for use within suitable enclosures.

INDOOR BALLAST:

An indoor ballast is suitable for use in an indoor location only.

OUTDOOR BALLAST:

Outdoor Ballast, Type 1—Outdoor ballast, Type 1, is suitable for use in outdoor fixtures and outdoor signs or other outdoor equipment if the ballast is provided with a complete metal enclosure in addition to its own enclosure. Ballasts of this type are marked "Type 1 Outdoor" or "Type 1."Outdoor Ballast, Type 2—Outdoor ballast, Type 2, is suitable for use in outdoor fixtures, outdoor signs, or other outdoor equipment if the ballast is provided with an enclosure (not necessarily metal) in addition to its own enclosure. Ballasts of this type are marked "Type 2 Outdoor" or "Type 2."

WEATHERPROOF BALLAST:

A weatherproof ballast is suitable for use where completely exposed to the weather without an additional enclosure and is marked "Weatherproof" or "WP."

410-55. Arc Lamps.   Arc lamps used in theaters shall comply with Section 520-61, and arc lamps used in projection machines shall comply with Section 540-20. Arc lamps used on constant-current systems shall comply with the general requirements of Article 710.

L. Receptacles, Cord Connectors, and Attachment Plugs (Caps)

410-56. Rating and Type.

(a) Receptacles. Receptacles installed for the attachment of portable cords shall be rated at not less than 15 amperes, 125 volts, or 15 amperes, 250 volts, and shall be of a type not suitable for use as lampholders.

Exception: The use of receptacles of 10-ampere, 250-volt rating used in nonresidential occupancies for the supply of equipment other than portable hand tools, portable handlamps, and extension cords shall be permitted.

(b) CO/ALR Receptacles. Receptacles rated 20 amperes or less and directly connected to aluminum conductors shall be marked CO/ALR.

This requires that 15- and 20-A receptacles directly connected to aluminum conductors be suitable for such use. If the receptacle is not of the CO/ALR type, it can be connected with a copper pigtail to an aluminum branch-circuit conductor if a wire connector suitable for such a connection, and marked with the letters "AL" and "CU," is used. See commentary on Section 110-14(b).

(c) Faceplates. Metal faceplates shall be of ferrous metal not less than 0.030 inch (762 micrometers) in thickness or of nonferrous metal not less than 0.040 inch (1 mm) in thickness. Metal faceplates shall be grounded. Faceplates of insulating material shall be noncombustible and not less than 0.10 inch (2.54 mm) in thickness but shall be permitted to be less than 0.10 inch (2.54 mm) in thickness if formed or reinforced to provide adequate mechanical strength.

(d) Position of Receptacle Faces. After installation, receptacle faces shall be flush with or project from faceplates of insulating material and shall project a minimum of 0.015 inch (381 micrometers) from metal faceplates. Faceplates shall be installed so as to completely cover the opening and seat against the mounting surface. Receptacles mounted in boxes that are set back of the wall surface, as permitted in Section 370-10, shall be installed so that the mounting yoke or strap of the receptacle is held rigidly at the surface of the wall. Receptacles mounted in boxes that are flush with the wall surface or project therefrom shall be so installed that the mounting yoke or strap of the receptacle is seated against the box or raised box cover.

(e) Attachment Plugs. All 15- and 20-ampere attachment plugs and connectors shall be so constructed that there are no exposed current-carrying parts except the prongs, blades, or pins. The cover for wire terminations shall be a part, which is essential for the operation of an attachment plug or connector (dead-front construction).

Paragraph (d) requires boxes to be properly and securely mounted to provide a solid backing for receptacles so that attachment plugs can be inserted or removed without difficulty. This is also intended to provide for secure mounting of the receptacle in order to maintain effective grounding continuity when the box is flush with the wall surface or projects therefrom. See also Section 380-10(b).

The reason for requiring receptacles to project from metal faceplates is to prevent faults caused by attachment plugs with exposed bare terminal screws. The design requirements of paragraph (e) for attachment plugs (dead-front construction) should prevent such faults at metal plates with new devices; however, existing attachment plugs with terminal screws exposed on the face are still in use.

Mounting boxes properly (Sections 370-10 and 370-13) requires the cooperation of other crafts (plasterers, dry-wall applicators, carpenters, building designers, etc.), and the proper installation of receptacles and faceplates assures that attachment plugs can be fully inserted, thus providing a better contact.

(f) Attachment Plug Ejector Mechanisms. Attachment plug ejector mechanisms shall not adversely affect engagement of the blades of the attachment plug with the contacts of the receptacle.

Section 410-56(f) permits a device designed for use by the aged, infirmed, and the blind to reduce the likelihood of damage to the cord when pulling on the cord to remove the plug.

(g) Noninterchangeability. Receptacles, cord connectors, and attachment plugs shall be constructed so that the receptacle or cord connectors will not accept an attachment plug with a different voltage or current rating than that for which the device is intended. Nongrounding-type receptacles and connectors shall not accept grounding-type attachment plugs.

See Figures 210-6 and 210-7 for ANSI C73 Standard configuration chart.

Exception: A 20-ampere T-slot receptacle or cord connector shall be permitted to accept a 15-ampere attachment plug of the same voltage rating.

410-57. Receptacles in Damp or Wet Locations.

(a) Damp Locations. A receptacle installed outdoors in a location protected from the weather or in other damp locations shall have an enclosure for the receptacle that is weatherproof when the receptacle is covered (attachment plug cap not inserted and receptacle covers closed).
An installation suitable for wet locations shall also be considered suitable for damp locations.
A receptacle shall be considered to be in a location protected from the weather where located under roofed open porches, canopies, marquees, and the like, and will not be subjected to a beating rain or water run-off.

(b) Wet Locations. A receptacle installed outdoors where exposed to weather or in other wet locations shall be in a weatherproof enclosure, the integrity of which is not affected when the receptacle is in use (attachment plug cap inserted).

Exception: An enclosure that is weatherproof only when a self-closing receptacle cover is closed shall be permitted to be used for a receptacle installed outdoors where the receptacle is not to be used with other than portable tools or other portable equipment not left connected to the outlet indefinitely.

(c) Protection for Floor Receptacles. Standpipes of floor receptacles shall allow floor-cleaning equipment to be operated without damage to receptacles.

(d) Flush Mounting with Faceplate. The enclosure for a receptacle installed in an outlet box flush-mounted on a wall surface shall be made weatherproof by means of a weatherproof faceplate assembly that provides a watertight connection between the plate and the wall surface.

(e) Installation. A receptacle outlet installed outdoors shall be located so that water accumulation is not likely to touch the outlet cover or plate.

Outdoor receptacle outlets are required for one-family and two-family dwellings and for swimming pool areas and are very common at other locations, such as shopping centers for children's rides and decorative lighting, truck terminals for refrigeration units and motor warmers, marinas, mobile home and recreational vehicle sites, and a variety of other outdoor locations.
In wet locations, the receptacle outlet is required to remain weatherproof with the cover open and the attachment plug inserted, except for temporary uses of portable equipment.

The enclosure for an outdoor receptacle may be flush or surface mounted or supported by conduits and used with a variety of receptacles and covers; however, it is the installer's responsibility to provide a watertight seal. See Figure 410-6.

Figure 410-6. Weatherproof receptacle cover suitable for wet locations. (*Crouse-Hinds*)

410-58. Grounding-type Receptacles, Adapters, Cord Connectors, and Attachment Plugs.

(a) Grounding Poles. Grounding-type receptacles, cord connectors, and attachment plugs shall be provided with one fixed grounding pole in addition to the circuit poles.

Exception: The grounding contacting pole of grounding-type attachment plugs on the power supply cords of portable hand-held, hand-guided, or hand-supported tools or appliances shall be permitted to be of the movable self-restoring type on circuits operating at not over 150 volts between any two conductors nor over 150 volts between any conductor and ground.

(b) Grounding-Pole Identification. Grounding-type receptacles, adapters, cord connections and attachment plugs shall have a means for connection of a grounding conductor to the grounding pole. A terminal for connection to the grounding pole shall be designated by:

(1) A green-colored hexagonal headed or shaped terminal screw or nut, not readily removable; or

(2) A green-colored pressure wire connector body (a wire barrel); or

(3) A similar green-colored connection device in the case of adapters. The grounding terminal of a grounding adapter shall be a green-colored rigid ear, lug, or similar device. The grounding connection shall be so designed that it cannot make contact with current-carrying parts of the receptacle, adapter, or attachment plug. The adapter shall be polarized.

Subparagraph (b)(3) requires the grounding terminal of an adapter to be a green-colored ear, lug, or similar device, thereby prohibiting an adapter with an attached pigtail grounding wire.

(4) If the terminal for the equipment grounding conductor is not visible, the conductor entrance hole shall be marked with the word "Green" or otherwise identified by a distinctive green color.

(c) Grounding Terminal Use. A grounding terminal or grounding-type device shall not be used for purposes other than grounding.

(d) Grounding-Pole Requirements. Grounding-type attachment plugs and mating cord connectors and receptacles shall be so designed that the grounding connection is made before the current-carrying connections. Grounding-type devices shall be designed so grounding poles of attachment plugs cannot be brought into contact with current-carrying parts of receptacles or cord connectors.

The grounding member of the attachment plug cap of most grounding-type combinations is longer to ensure a "make-first break-last" grounding connection. In some non-ANSI pin-and-sleeve types, the grounding contact of the receptacle is closer to the face of the receptacle than other contacts, accomplishing the same purpose.

(e) Use. Grounding-type attachment plugs shall be used only where an equipment ground is to be provided.

M. Rosettes

410-59. Unapproved Types.

(a) Fusible Rosettes. Fusible rosettes shall not be installed.

(b) Separable Rosettes. Separable rosettes that may change polarity shall not be used.

410-60. Rosettes in Damp or Wet Locations. Rosettes installed in damp or wet locations shall be of the weatherproof type.

410-61. Rating. Rosettes shall be rated at 660 watts, 250 volts, with a maximum current rating of 6 amperes.

410-62. Rosettes for Exposed Wiring. Rosettes for exposed wiring shall be provided with bases that shall have at least two holes for supporting screws, shall be high enough to keep the wires and terminals at least ½ inch (12.7 mm) from the surface wired over, and shall have a lug of insulating material under each terminal to prevent the rosette from being placed over projections that would reduce the separation to less than ½ inch (12.7 mm).

410-63. Rosettes for Use with Boxes or Raceways. Rosettes for use with conduit boxes or raceways shall have bases high enough to keep wires and terminals at least ⅜ inch (9.52 mm) from the surface wired over.

The most common use for rosettes is to permit connection of a pendant fixture to open wiring on insulators or nonmetallic-sheathed cable without use of a box. See Section 300-15(b), Exception No. 2.

N. Special Provisions for Flush and Recessed Fixtures

410-64. General.   Fixtures installed in recessed cavities in walls or ceilings shall comply with Sections 410-65 through 410-72.

The following Formal Interpretation, FI No. 81-6, was issued by NFPA in October, 1982 for the 1981 *NEC*:

Question: Is it intended that fixtures installed in suspended ceilings be subject to the requirements of Part N of Article 410?

Answer: Yes.

410-65. Temperature.

(a) Combustible Material.   Fixtures shall be so installed that adjacent combustible material will not be subjected to temperatures in excess of 90°C (194°F).

(b) Fire-Resistant Construction.   Where a fixture is recessed in fire-resistant material in a building of fire-resistant construction, a temperature higher than 90°C (194°F), but not higher than 150°C (302°F), shall be considered acceptable if the fixture is plainly marked that it is listed for that service.

(c) Recessed Incandescent Fixtures.   Incandescent fixtures shall have thermal protection and shall so be identified as thermally protected.

Because many recessed incandescent fixtures are suitable for a wide variety of lamp sizes and types, and finish trims, the temperature close to the lamp can vary widely. Therefore, many manufacturers have chosen to locate their thermal protectors away from the source of heat, such as in the outlet box, and to design the protector so that it will detect a change in temperature resulting from the addition of thermal insulation around the fixture. This prevents "nuisance tripping" of the protector as a result of changing lamp wattage, for example, but still provides protection against excessive overheating as a result of thermal insulation around a fixture that is not designed for such use.

Exception No. 1: Recessed incandescent fixtures identified for use and installed in poured concrete.

Exception No. 2: Listed recessed incandescent fixtures that provide, by construction design, the equivalent temperature performance characteristics of thermally protected fixtures and are so identified.

This exception has been revised for the 1987 NEC. Recessed incandescent fixtures without thermal protection are no longer permitted unless they are listed and identified as providing equivalent temperature performance by construction design.

Figure 410-7. A listed Type IC recessed fixture suitable for use in insulated ceilings in direct contact with thermal insulation. Thermal protection is provided to deactivate the lamp should the fixture be mislamped so that it overheats. (*Thomas Industries Inc.*)

The suspended ceiling type of recessed incandescent fixture (not Type IC) without thermal protection is not acceptable under the requirements of the 1987 *NEC*. This type of fixture was permitted by TIA No. 70-84-4 of the 1984 *NEC*.

410-66. Clearance and Installation.

(a) Clearance. Recessed portions of lighting fixture enclosures, other than at the points of support, shall be spaced at least ½ inch (12.7 mm) from combustible materials.

Exception No. 1: Recessed fixtures identified as suitable for insulation to be in direct contact with the fixture.

Exception No. 2: Recessed fluorescent fixtures.

(b) Installation. Thermal insulation shall not be installed within 3 inches (76 mm) of the recessed fixture enclosure, wiring compartment, or ballast, and shall not be so installed above the fixture so as to entrap heat and prevent the free circulation of air.

Exception No. 1: Recessed fixtures identified as suitable for insulation to be in direct contact with the fixture.

Exception No. 2: Recessed fluorescent fixtures.

Recessed fluorescent fixtures are excepted from the clearance requirements of Section 410-66(a) and the installation requirements of 410-66(b) because of the ballast protection requirements in Section 410-73(e).

410-67. Wiring.

(a) General. Conductors having insulation suitable for the temperature encountered shall be used.

(b) Circuit Conductors. Branch-circuit conductors having an insulation suitable for the temperature encountered shall be permitted to terminate in the fixture.

(c) Tap Conductors. Tap conductors of a type suitable for the temperature encountered shall be permitted to run from the fixture terminal connection to an outlet box placed at least 1 foot (305 mm) from the fixture. Such tap conductors shall be in a suitable raceway of at least 4 feet (1.22 m) but not more than 6 feet (1.83 m) in length.

P. Construction of Flush and Recessed Fixtures

410-68. Temperature. Fixtures shall be so constructed that adjacent combustible material will not be subject to temperatures in excess of 90°C (194°F).

410-69. Enclosure. Sheet metal enclosures shall be protected against corrosion and shall not be less than No. 22 MSG.

Exception: Where a wireway cover is within the No. 22 MSG enclosure, it shall be permitted to be of No. 24 MSG metal.

410-70. Lamp Wattage Marking. Incandescent lamp fixtures shall be marked to indicate the maximum allowable wattage of lamps. The markings shall be permanently installed, in letters at least ¼ inch (6.35 mm) high, and shall be located where visible during relamping.

410-71. Solder Prohibited. No solder shall be used in the construction of a fixture box.

410-72. Lampholders. Lampholders of the screw-shell type shall be of porcelain or other suitable insulating materials. Where used, cements shall be of the high-heat type.

Q. Special Provisions for Electric-Discharge Lighting Systems of 1000 Volts or Less

410-73. General.

(a) Open-Circuit Voltage of 1000 Volts or Less. Equipment for use with electric-discharge lighting systems and designed for an open-circuit voltage of 1000 volts or less shall be of a type intended for such service.

(b) Considered as Alive. The terminals of an electric-discharge lamp shall be considered as alive where any lamp terminal is connected to a circuit of over 300 volts.

(c) Transformers of the Oil-Filled Type. Transformers of the oil-filled type shall not be used.

(d) Additional Requirements. In addition to complying with the general requirements for lighting fixtures, such equipment shall comply with Part Q of this article.

(e) Thermal Protection. Where fluorescent fixtures are installed indoors, the ballasts shall have thermal protection integral within the ballast. Replacement ballasts for all fluorescent fixtures installed indoors shall also have thermal protection integral within the ballast.

Thermal protection integral with the ballast is required for fluorescent fixtures installed indoors. Ballasts not provided with integral thermal protection are not permitted to be used as replacements for such fixtures. Thermally protected ballasts are required as replacements for nonthermally protected ballasts in older fixtures not originally provided with thermally protected ballasts. Thermally protected fluorescent lamp ballasts intended for use in accordance with Section 410-73(e) are marked "Class P."

As different "Class P" ballasts have different heating characteristics, the heating characteristics should be considered when selecting replacements for nonthermally protected ballasts.

This type of ballast protection is set to open the circuit at a predetermined temperature to prevent abnormal ballast heat buildup caused by a fault in one or more of the ballast components, or by some lampholder or wiring faults.

Exception to (e) above: Fluorescent fixtures with simple reactance ballasts.

Figure 410-8 illustrates a reactance-type ballast used in series with a 30-W or less preheat-type fluorescent lamp. This type of ballast does not require thermal protection, and the fixture may be equipped with automatic-type starters (such as used with medicine cabinet fixtures) or a manual momentary contact starter (such as used with desk lamps and some small under-cabinet fixtures).

Figure 410-8. The circuitry for a simple reactance-type ballast for fluorescent lighting.

(f) Recessed High-Intensity Discharge Fixtures. Where recessed high-intensity discharge fixtures are installed indoors, they shall be thermally protected and shall be identified. Where fixtures are operated by remote ballasts, the ballasts shall also be thermally protected.

410-74. Direct-Current Equipment. Fixtures installed on direct-current circuits shall be equipped with auxiliary equipment and resistors especially designed and for direct-current operation, and the fixtures shall be so marked.

410-75. Voltages — Dwelling Occupancies.

(a) Open-Circuit Voltage Exceeding 1000 Volts. Equipment having an open-circuit voltage exceeding 1000 volts shall not be installed in dwelling occupancies.

(b) Open-Circuit Voltage Exceeding 300 Volts. Equipment having an open-circuit voltage exceeding 300 volts shall not be installed in dwelling occupancies unless such equipment is so designed that there will be no exposed live parts when lamps are being inserted, are in place, or are being removed.

Fixtures intended for use in other-than-dwelling occupancies are so marked. This usually indicates that the fixture has maintenance features that are considered to be beyond the capabilities of the ordinary householder or involve voltages in excess of those permitted by this *Code* for dwelling occupancies. See Sections 210-6 and 410-75(a).

410-76. Fixture Mounting.

(a) Exposed Ballasts. Fixtures having exposed ballasts or transformers shall be so installed that such ballasts or transformers will not be in contact with combustible material.

(b) Combustible Low-Density Cellulose Fiberboard. Where a surface-mounted fixture containing a ballast is to be installed on combustible low-density cellulose fiberboard, it shall be listed for this condition or shall be spaced not less than 1½ inches (38 mm) from the surface of the fiberboard. Where such fixtures are partially or wholly recessed, the provisions of Sections 410-64 through 410-72 shall apply.

(FPN): Combustible low-density cellulose fiberboard includes sheets, panels, and tiles that have a density of 20 pounds per cubic foot (320.36 kg/cu m) or less, and that are formed of bonded plant fiber material but does not include solid or laminated wood, nor fiberboard that has a density in excess of 20 pounds per cubic foot (320.36 kg/cu m) or is a material that has been integrally treated with fire-retarding chemicals to the degree that the flame spread in any plane of the material will not exceed 25, determined in accordance with tests for surface burning characteristics of building materials. See Test Method for Surface Burning Characteristics of Building Materials, ANSI/ASTM E84-1984.

Fluorescent lamp fixtures intended for mounting on combustible low-density cellulose fiberboard ceilings have been evaluated with thermal insulation above the ceiling in the vicinity of the fixture and bear the Underwriters Laboratories Inc. listing mark "Suitable for Surface Mounting on Combustible Low-Density Cellulose Fiberboard." Fluorescent lamp fixtures not so marked may be directly mounted against a ceiling surface of other-than-combustible low-density fiberboard or may be spaced not less than 1½ in. from the surface of the low-density fiberboard.

Further information may be obtained from the Underwriters Laboratories Inc. publication, "Building Materials Directory," and also from the American National Standards Institute publication, "Method of Test for Surface Burning Characteristics of Building Materials."

410-77. Equipment Not Integral with Fixture.

(a) Metal Cabinets. Auxiliary equipment, including reactors, capacitors, resistors, and similar equipment, where not installed as part of a lighting fixture assembly, shall be enclosed in accessible, permanently installed metal cabinets.

(b) Separate Mounting. Separately mounted ballasts that are intended for direct connection to a wiring system shall not be required to be separately enclosed.

410-78. Autotransformers. An autotransformer which is used to raise the voltage to more than 300 volts, as part of a ballast for supplying lighting units, shall be supplied only by a grounded system.

410-79. Switches. Snap switches shall comply with Section 380-14.

R. Special Provisions for Electric-Discharge Lighting Systems of More than 1000 Volts

These sections apply to interior electric-discharge "neon-tube"-type lighting (containing neon, helium, or argon gas, with or without mercury, at low vapor pressure), long-length fluorescent tube lighting requiring more than 1,000 V, and cold-cathode fluorescent-lamp installations arranged to operate with several tubes in series.

ARTICLE 410—LIGHTING FIXTURES, ETC.

410-80. General.

(a) Open-Circuit Voltage Exceeding 1000 Volts. Equipment for use with electric-discharge lighting systems and designed for an open-circuit voltage exceeding 1000 volts shall be of a type intended for such service.

(b) Considered as Alive. The terminal of an electric-discharge lamp shall be considered as alive when any lamp terminal is connected to a circuit of over 300 volts.

(c) Additional Requirements. In addition to complying with the general requirements for lighting fixtures, such equipment shall comply with Part R of this article.

(FPN): For signs and outline lighting, see Article 600.

410-81. Control.

(a) Disconnection. Fixtures or lamp installations shall be controlled either singly or in groups by an externally operable switch or circuit breaker that opens all ungrounded primary conductors.

(b) Within Sight or Locked Type. The switch or circuit breaker shall be located within sight from the fixtures or lamps, or it shall be permitted elsewhere if it is provided with a means for locking in the open position.

Providing that the switch or circuit breaker is within view or capable of being locked "off" the service person assures that the disconnecting means will not be closed while servicing the equipment.

410-82. Lamp Terminals and Lampholders. Parts that must be removed for lamp replacement shall be hinged or held captive. Lamps or lampholders will be so designed that there shall be no exposed live parts when lamps are being inserted or are being removed.

410-83. Transformer Ratings. Transformers and ballasts shall have a secondary open-circuit voltage of not over 15,000 volts with an allowance on test of 1000 volts additional. The secondary-current rating shall not be more than 120 milliamperes if the open-circuit voltage is over 7500 volts, and not more than 240 milliamperes if the open-circuit voltage is 7500 volts or less.

410-84. Transformer Type. Transformers shall be enclosed and listed.

410-85. Transformer Secondary Connections.

(a) High-Voltage Windings. The high-voltage windings of transformers shall not be connected in series or in parallel.

Exception: Two transformers, each having one end of its high-voltage winding grounded and connected to the enclosure, shall be permitted to have their high-voltage windings connected in series to form the equivalent of a midpoint grounded transformer.

(b) Grounded Ends of Paralleled Transformers. The grounded ends of paralleled transformers as permitted in (a) above shall be connected by an insulated conductor not smaller than No. 14.

410-86. Transformer Locations.

(a) Accessible. Transformers shall be accessible after installation.

(b) Secondary Conductors. Transformers shall be installed as near to the lamps as practicable to keep the secondary conductors as short as possible.

(c) Adjacent to Combustible Materials. Transformers shall be so located that adjacent combustible materials will not be subjected to temperatures in excess of 90°C (194°F).

410-87. Transformer Loading. The lamps connected to any transformer shall be of such length and characteristics as not to cause a condition of continuous overvoltage on the transformer.

Transformers are required to be enclosed and listed, and should be rated to supply the proper current and voltage for the lamp or tube. See Section 600-32.

410-88. Wiring Method — Secondary Conductors. Conductors shall be installed in accordance with Section 600-31.

Table 310-13, which lists various types of insulated conductors, does not include the type of cable required in Sections 410-88 and 600-31(b). Underwriters Laboratories Inc., however, does have standards for this type of cable. The following information is an excerpt from the Underwriters Laboratories Inc. Electrical Construction Materials Directory:

Gas tube sign and ignition cable may be Type GTO-5 (5,000 volts), GTO-10 (10,000 volts), or GTO-15 (15,000 volts), and is listed in sizes Nos. 18-10 AWG copper and Nos. 12-10 AWG aluminum and copper-clad aluminum. This material is intended for use with gas tube signs, oil burners, and inside lighting.

L used as a suffix in combination with any of the preceding type letter designations indicates that an outer covering of lead has been applied.

The UL symbol on the product and the listing mark of Underwriters Laboratories Inc. on the attached tag, coil, reel or smallest unit container in which the product is packaged is the only method provided by UL to identify these products manufactured under its listing and follow-up service. The listing mark for these products includes the name and/or symbol of Underwriters Laboratories Inc. together with the word "Listed," a control number, and one of the following product names as appropriate: A gas tube sign and ignition cable that contains a copper or copper-clad aluminum conductor has the product name "Gas Tube Sign and Ignition Cable," a gas tube sign and ignition cable that contains an aluminum conductor has the product name "Gas Tube Sign and Ignition Aluminum Cable."

410-89. Lamp Supports. Lamps shall be adequately supported as required in Section 600-33.

410-90. Exposure to Damage. Lamps shall not be located where normally exposed to physical damage.

410-91. Marking. Each fixture or each secondary circuit of tubing having an open-circuit voltage of over 1000 volts shall have a clearly legible marking in letters not less than ¼ inch (6.35 mm) high reading "Caution. . . .volts." The voltage indicated shall be the rated open-circuit voltage.

410-92. Switches. Snap switches shall comply with Section 380-14.

S. Lighting Track

410-100. Definition. Lighting track is a manufactured assembly designed to support and energize lighting fixtures which are capable of being readily repositioned on the track. Its length may be altered by the addition or subtraction of sections of track.

410-101. Installation.

(a) Lighting Track. Lighting track shall be permanently installed and permanently connected to a branch circuit. Only lighting track fittings shall be installed on lighting track.

Lighting track fittings shall not be equipped with general-purpose receptacles.

A lighting track fitting differs from a fitting as defined in Article 100 in that it usually performs both an electrical and a mechanical function.

It is not the intent that such assemblies be a system for locating convenience receptacles or alternative for required receptacles outlets such as the ones required in Section 210-62. Lighting track can be removed and relocated and thus is not a substitute for required outlets.

(b) Connected Load. The connected load on lighting track shall not exceed the rating of the track. Lighting track shall be supplied by a branch circuit having a rating not more than that of the track.

(c) Locations Not Permitted. Lighting track shall not be installed: (1) where subject to physical damage; (2) in wet or damp locations; (3) where subject to corrosive vapors; (4) in storage battery rooms; (5) in hazardous (classified) locations; (6) where concealed; (7) where extended through walls or partitions; (8) less than 5 feet (1.52 m) above the finished floor except where protected from physical damage.

(d) Support. Fittings identified for use on lighting track shall be designed specifically for the track on which they are to be installed. They shall be securely fastened to the track, maintain polarization and grounding, and shall be designed to be suspended directly from the track.

See commentary following Section 410-101(a).

410-102. Track Load. For branch-circuit calculations a maximum of 2 feet (609.6 mm) of lighting track or fraction thereof shall be considered 180 VA. Where multicircuit track is installed, the load requirement of this section shall be considered to be divided equally between the circuits.

410-103. Heavy-Duty Track. Heavy-duty lighting track is lighting track identified for use exceeding 20 amperes. Each fitting attached to a heavy-duty lighting track shall have individual overcurrent protection.

See commentary following Section 410-101(a).

410-104. Fastening. Lighting track shall be securely mounted so that each fastening will be suitable for supporting the maximum weight of fixtures which can be installed. Unless identified for supports at greater intervals, a single section 4 feet (1.22 m) or shorter in length shall have two supports, and when installed in a continuous row each individual section of not more than 4 feet (1.22 m) in length shall have one additional support.

410-105. Construction Requirements.

(a) Construction. The housing for the lighting track system shall be of substantial construction to maintain rigidity. The conductors shall be installed within the track housing permitting insertion of a fixture, and designed to prevent tampering and accidental contact with live parts. Components of lighting track systems of different voltages shall not be interchangeable. The track conductors shall be a minimum No. 12 AWG or equal, and shall be copper. The track system ends shall be insulated and capped.

Exception: Fittings which incorporate an integral device to reduce the line voltage for a lower voltage lamp.

(b) Grounding. Lighting track shall be grounded in accordance with Article 250 and the track sections shall be securely coupled to maintain continuity of the circuitry, polarization and grounding throughout.

ARTICLE 422 — APPLIANCES

Contents

ARTICLE 422—APPLIANCES

E. Marking of Appliances
422-30. Nameplate.
   (a) Nameplate Marking.
   (b) To Be Visible.
422-31. Marking of Heating Elements.

422-32. Appliances Consisting of Motors and Other Loads.
   (a) Marking.
   (b) Alternate Marking Method.

A. General

422-1. Scope. This article covers electric appliances used in any occupancy.

   This article covers electric appliances that may be used in a dwelling unit, and appliances for commercial and industrial locations. It also covers appliances that may be fastened in place or cord- and plug-connected appliances, such as air-conditioning units, dishwashers, heating appliances, water heaters, infrared heating lamps, etc. See Section 422-3 for requirements of other articles. Also see Article 100 for definition of "appliance."

422-2. Live Parts. Appliances shall have no live parts normally exposed to contact.

   Exception: Toasters, grills, or other appliances in which the current-carrying parts at high temperatures are necessarily exposed.

422-3. Other Articles. All requirements of this Code shall apply where applicable. Appliances for use in hazardous (classified) locations shall comply with Articles 500 through 517.
   The requirements of Article 430 shall apply to the installation of motor-operated appliances and the requirements of Article 440 shall apply to the installation of appliances containing hermetic refrigerant motor-compressor(s), except as specifically amended in this article.

B. Branch-Circuit Requirements

422-5. Branch-Circuit Sizing. This section specifies sizes of conductors capable of carrying appliance current without overheating under the conditions specified. This section shall not apply to conductors that form an integral part of an appliance.

   (a) Individual Circuits. The rating of an individual branch circuit shall not be less than the marked rating of the appliance or the marked rating of an appliance having combined loads as provided in Section 422-32.

   Exception No. 1: For motor-operated appliances not having a marked rating the branch-circuit size shall be in accordance with Part B of Article 430.

   Exception No. 2: For an appliance, other than a motor-operated appliance, that is continuously loaded, the branch-circuit rating shall not be less than 125 percent of the marked rating; or not less than 100 percent if the branch-circuit device and its assembly is approved for continuous loading at 100 percent of its rating.

   Exception No. 3: Branch circuits for household cooking appliances shall be permitted to be in accordance with Table 220-19.

   (b) Circuits Supplying Two or More Loads. For branch circuits supplying appliance and other loads, the rating shall be determined in accordance with Section 210-23.

   If a labeled or listed appliance is provided with installation instructions from the manufacturer, the branch-circuit size is not permitted to be less than the minimum size required by the installation instructions. See Section 110-3(b).

422-6. Branch-Circuit Overcurrent Protection. Branch circuits shall be protected in accordance with Section 240-3.

If a protective device rating is marked on an appliance, the branch-circuit overcurrent device rating shall not exceed the protective device rating marked on the appliance.

C. Installation of Appliances

422-7. General. All appliances shall be installed in an approved manner.

422-8. Flexible Cords.

(a) Heater Cords. All cord- and plug-connected smoothing irons and electrically heated appliances that are rated at more than 50 watts and produce temperatures in excess of 121°C (250°F) on surfaces with which the cord is likely to be in contact shall be provided with one of the types of approved heater cords listed in Table 400-4.

(b) Other Heating Appliances. All other cord- and plug-connected electrically heated appliances shall be connected with one of the approved types of cord listed in Table 400-4, selected in accordance with the usage specified in that table.

(c) Other Appliances. Flexible cord shall be permitted: (1) for connection of appliances to facilitate their frequent interchange or to prevent the transmission of noise or vibration, or (2) to facilitate the removal or disconnection of appliances, that are fastened in place, for maintenance or repair.

(d) Specific Appliances.

(1) Electrically operated kitchen waste disposers intended for dwelling unit use and provided with a Type S, SO, ST, STO, SJ, SJO, SJT, SJTO, SP-3, SPE-3, or SPT-3, three-conductor cord terminated with a grounding-type attachment plug shall be permitted where all of the following conditions are met:

a. The length of the cord shall not be less than 18 inches (457 mm) and not over 36 inches (914 mm).

b. Receptacles shall be located to avoid physical damage to the flexible cord.

c. The receptacle shall be accessible.

(2) Built-in dishwashers and trash compactors intended for dwelling unit use and provided with a Type S, SO, ST, STO, SJ, SJO, SJT, SJTO, SP-3, SPE-3, or SPT-3, three-conductor cord terminated with a grounding-type attachment plug shall be permitted where all of the following conditions are met:

a. The length of the cord shall be 3 to 4 feet (0.914 to 1.22 m).

b. Receptacles shall be located to avoid physical damage to the flexible cord.

c. The receptacle shall be located in the space occupied by the appliance or adjacent thereto.

d. The receptacle shall be accessible.

Exception: Listed kitchen waste disposers, dishwashers and trash compactors protected by a system of double insulation, or its equivalent, shall not be required to be grounded. Where such a system is employed, the equipment shall be distinctively marked.

(3) The supply cord conductors and internal wiring of portable high-pressure spray washing machines shall have ground-fault circuit-interrupter protection for personnel. The ground-fault circuit-interrupter shall be identified for use with portable equipment and permitted as an integral part of the attachment plug.

These high-pressure water sprayers are operated in a wet environment, and the requirement for a ground-fault circuit-interrupter is intended to reduce the shock hazard.

422-9. Cord- and Plug-Connected Immersion Heaters. Electric heaters of the cord- and plug-connected immersion type shall be so constructed and installed that current-carrying parts are effectively insulated from electrical contact with the substance in which they are immersed.

422-10. Protection of Combustible Material. Each electrically heated appliance that is intended by size, weight, and service to be located in a fixed position shall be so placed as to provide ample protection between the appliance and adjacent combustible material.

422-11. Stands for Cord- and Plug-Connected Appliances. Each smoothing iron and other cord- and plug-connected electrically heated appliance intended to be applied to combustible material shall be equipped with an approved stand, which shall be permitted to be a separate piece of equipment or a part of the appliance.

422-12. Signals for Heated Appliances. In other than dwelling-type occupancies, each electrically heated appliance or group of appliances intended to be applied to combustible material shall be provided with a signal.

Exception: If an appliance is provided with an integral temperature-limiting device.

A common way to provide a signal light for electrically heated appliances in commercial or industrial locations is to use a red light so connected to and within sight of the appliance as to indicate that the appliance is energized and operating.

No signal is required for an electrically heated appliance provided with a thermostat or equal that limits it to a certain temperature.

422-13. Flatirons. Electrically heated smoothing irons shall be equipped with an identified temperature-limiting means.

422-14. Water Heaters.

(a) Storage- and Instantaneous-type Water Heaters. Each storage- or instantaneous-type water heater shall be equipped with a temperature-limiting means in addition to its control thermostat to disconnect all ungrounded conductors, and such means shall be: (1) installed to sense maximum water temperature and, (2) either a trip-free, manually reset type or a type having a replacement element. Such water heaters shall be marked to require the installation of a temperature and pressure relief valve.

(FPN): See Listing Requirements for Relief Valves and Automatic Gas Shutoff Devices for Hot Water Supply Systems (ANSI Z21.22-1979).

Exception: Water heaters with supply water temperature of 82°C (180°F) or above and a capacity of 60 kW or above and identified as being suitable for this use; and water heaters with a capacity of 1 gallon (3.785 L) or less and identified as being suitable for such use.

(b) Storage-type Water Heaters. A branch circuit supplying a fixed storage-type water heater having a capacity of 120 gallons (454.2 L) or less shall have a rating not less than 125 percent of the nameplate rating of the water heater.

(FPN): For branch-circuit sizing, see Section 422-5(a), Exception No. 2.

422-15. Infrared Lamp Industrial Heating Appliances.

(a) 300 Watts or Less. Infrared heating lamps rated at 300 watts or less shall be permitted with lampholders of the medium-base, unswitched porcelain type or other types identified as suitable for use with infrared heating lamps rated 300 watts or less.

(b) Over 300 Watts. Screw-shell lampholders shall not be used with infrared lamps over 300 watts rating.

Exception: Lampholders identified as suitable for use with infrared heating lamps rated more than 300 watts.

(c) Lampholders. Lampholders shall be permitted to be connected to any of the branch circuits of Article 210 and, in industrial occupancies, shall be permitted to be operated in series on circuits of over 150 volts to ground provided the voltage rating of the lampholders is not less than the circuit voltage.

Each section, panel, or strip carrying a number of infrared lampholders (including the internal wiring of such section, panel, or strip) shall be considered an appliance. The terminal connection block of each such assembly shall be considered an individual outlet.

> Infrared (heat) radiation lamps are tungsten-filament incandescent lamps that are similar in appearance to lighting lamps; however, they are designed to operate at a lower temperature, thus transferring more heat radiation and less light intensity. Infrared lamps are used for a variety of heating and drying purposes in residential, commercial, and industrial locations.

422-16. Grounding.
Appliances required by Article 250 to be grounded shall have exposed noncurrent-carrying metal parts grounded in the manner specified in Article 250.

(FPN): See Sections 250-42, 250-43 and 250-45 for equipment grounding of refrigerators and freezers and Sections 250-57 and 250-60 for equipment grounding of electric ranges, wall-mounted ovens, counter-mounted cooking units, and clothes dryers.

422-17. Wall-Mounted Ovens and Counter-Mounted Cooking Units.

(a) Permitted to Be Cord- and Plug-Connected or Permanently Connected. Wall-mounted ovens and counter-mounted cooking units complete with provisions for mounting and for making electrical connections shall be permitted to be permanently connected or, only for ease in servicing or for installation, cord- and plug-connected.

(b) Separable Connector or a Plug and Receptacle Combination. A separable connector or a plug and receptacle combination in the supply line to an oven or cooking unit shall:

(1) Not be installed as the disconnecting means required by Section 422-20.

(2) Be approved for the temperature of the space in which it is located.

422-18. Support of Ceiling Fans.
Listed ceiling fans that do not exceed 35 pounds in weight, with or without accessories, shall be permitted to be supported by outlet boxes identified for such use and supported in accordance with Sections 370-13 and 370-17.

> See commentary following Section 370-17(c).

422-19. Other Installation Methods.
Appliances employing methods of installation other than covered by this article shall be permitted to be used only by special permission.

D. Control and Protection of Appliances

422-20. Disconnecting Means. A means shall be provided to disconnect each appliance from all ungrounded conductors in accordance with the following sections of Part D. If an appliance is supplied by more than one source, the disconnecting means shall be grouped and identified.

422-21. Disconnection of Permanently Connected Appliances.

(a) Rated at Not Over 300 Volt Amperes or ⅛ Horsepower. For permanently connected appliances rated at not over 300 volt amperes or ⅛ horsepower, the branch-circuit overcurrent device shall be permitted to serve as the disconnecting means.

(b) Permanently Connected Appliances of Greater Rating. For permanently connected appliances of greater rating the branch-circuit switch or circuit breaker shall be permitted to serve as the disconnecting means where readily accessible to the user of the appliance.

(FPN): For motor-driven appliances of more than ⅛ horsepower, see Section 422-26.

Exception: Appliances employing unit switches as permitted by Section 422-24.

422-22. Disconnection of Cord- and Plug-Connected Appliances.

(a) Separable Connector or an Attachment Plug and Receptacle. For cord- and plug-connected appliances, an accessible separable connector or an accessible plug and receptacle shall be permitted to serve as the disconnecting means. Other cord- and plug-connected appliances shall be provided with disconnecting means in accordance with Section 422-21.

(b) Connection at the Rear Base of a Range. For cord- and plug-connected household electric ranges, an attachment plug and receptacle connection at the rear base of a range, if it is accessible from the front by removal of a drawer, shall be considered as meeting the intent of Section 422-22(a).

(c) Rating. The rating of a receptacle or of a separable connector shall not be less than the rating of any appliance connected thereto.

Exception: Demand factors authorized elsewhere in this Code shall be permitted to be applied.

(d) Requirements for Attachment Plugs and Connectors. Attachment plugs and connectors shall conform to the following:

(1) Live Parts. They shall be so constructed and installed as to guard against inadvertent contact with live parts.

(2) Interrupting Capacity. They shall be capable of interrupting their rated current without hazard to the operator.

(3) Interchangeability. They shall be so designed that they will not fit into receptacles of lesser rating.

(4) Polarity. If the appliance is provided with a single-pole switching device, the attachment plug shall be polarized or of the grounding type.

(FPN): See also Section 410-42.

This requirement is new in the 1987 *NEC*.

422-24. Unit Switch(es) as Disconnecting Means. A unit switch(es) with a marked "off" position that is a part of an appliance and disconnects all ungrounded conductors shall be permitted as the disconnecting means required by this article where other means for disconnection are provided in the following types of occupancies:

(a) Multifamily Dwellings. In multifamily dwellings, the other disconnecting means shall be within the dwelling unit, or on the same floor as the dwelling unit in which the appliance is installed, and shall be permitted to control lamps and other appliances.

(b) Two-Family Dwellings. In two-family dwellings, the other disconnecting means shall be permitted either inside or outside of the dwelling unit in which the appliance is installed. In this case, an individual switch or circuit breaker for the dwelling unit shall be permitted and shall also be permitted to control lamps and other appliances.

(c) One-Family Dwellings. In one-family dwellings, the service disconnecting means shall be permitted to be the other disconnecting means.

(d) Other Occupancies. In other occupancies, the branch-circuit switch or circuit breaker, where readily accessible for servicing of the appliance, shall be permitted as the other disconnecting means.

422-25. Switch and Circuit Breaker to Be Indicating. Switches and circuit breakers used as disconnecting means shall be of the indicating type.

422-26. Disconnecting Means for Motor-Driven Appliances. If a switch or circuit breaker serves as the disconnecting means for a permanently connected motor-driven appliance of more than ⅛ horsepower, it shall be located within sight from the motor controller and shall comply with Part H of Article 430.

Exception: A switch or circuit breaker that serves as the other disconnecting means as required in Section 422-24(a), (b), (c) or (d) shall be permitted to be out of sight from the motor controller of an appliance provided with a unit switch(es) with a marked "off" position and which disconnects all ungrounded conductors.

422-27. Overcurrent Protection.

(a) Appliances. Appliances shall be protected against overcurrent in accordance with (b) through (f) below and Sections 422-5 and 422-6.

Exception: Motors of motor-operated appliances shall be provided with overload protection in accordance with Part C of Article 430. Hermetic refrigerant motor-compressors in air-conditioning or refrigerating equipment shall be provided with overload protection in accordance with Part F of Article 440. When appliance overcurrent protective devices separate from the appliance are required, data for selection of these devices shall be marked on the appliance. The minimum marking shall be that specified in Sections 430-7 and 440-4.

(b) Household-type Appliance with Surface Heating Elements. A household-type appliance with surface heating elements having a maximum demand of more than 60 amperes computed in accordance with Table 220-19 shall have its power supply subdivided into two or more circuits, each of which is provided with overcurrent protection rated at not over 50 amperes.

(c) Infrared Lamp Commercial and Industrial Heating Appliances. Infrared lamp commercial and industrial heating appliances shall have overcurrent protection not exceeding 50 amperes.

(d) Open-Coil or Exposed Sheathed-Coil Types of Surface Heating Elements in Commercial-type Heating Appliances. Open-coil or exposed sheathed-coil types of surface heating elements in commercial-type heating appliances shall be protected by overcurrent protective devices rated at not over 50 amperes.

(e) Single Nonmotor-Operated Appliance. If the branch circuit supplies a single nonmotor-operated appliance, the overcurrent device rating shall not exceed a protective device rating marked on the appliance or, if there is no marking, the value specified as follows:

Appliance rating not
exceeding 13.3 amperes . . . . 20 amperes
Appliance rating greater
than 13.3 amperes . . . . 150 percent of appliance rating.

(f) Electric Heating Appliances Employing Resistance-type Heating Elements Rated More than 48 Amperes. Electric heating appliances employing resistance-type heating elements rated more than 48 amperes shall have the heating elements subdivided. Each subdivided load shall not exceed 48 amperes and shall be protected at not more than 60 amperes.

These supplementary overcurrent protective devices shall be: (1) factory installed within or on the heater enclosure or provided as a separate assembly by the heater manufacturer; (2) accessible, but need not be readily accessible; and (3) suitable for branch-circuit protection.

The main conductors supplying these overcurrent protective devices shall be considered branch-circuit conductors.

Exception No. 1: Household-type appliances with surface heating elements as covered in Section 422-27(b) and commercial-type heating appliances as covered in Section 422-27(d).

Exception No. 2: Commercial kitchen and cooking appliances using sheathed-type heating elements not covered in Section 422-27(d) shall be permitted to be subdivided into circuits not exceeding 120 amperes and protected at not more than 150 amperes where one of the following is met:

a. Elements are integral with and enclosed within a cooking surface;

b. Elements are completely contained within an enclosure identified as suitable for this use; or

c. Elements are contained within an ASME rated and stamped vessel.

Exception No. 3: Water heaters and steam boilers employing resistance-type immersion electric heating elements contained in an ASME rated and stamped vessel shall be permitted to be subdivided into circuits not exceeding 120 amperes and protected at not more than 150 amperes.

E. Marking of Appliances

422-30. Nameplate.

(a) Nameplate Marking. Each electric appliance shall be provided with a nameplate, giving the identifying name and the rating in volts and amperes, or in volts and watts. If the appliance is to be used on a specific frequency or frequencies, it shall be so marked.

When motor overload protection external to the appliance is required, the appliance shall be so marked.

(FPN): See Section 422-27(a), Exception for overcurrent protection requirements.

(b) To Be Visible. Marking shall be located so as to be visible or easily accessible after installation.

422-31. Marking of Heating Elements. All heating elements that are rated over one ampere, replaceable in the field, and a part of an appliance shall be legibly marked with the ratings in volts and amperes, or in volts and watts, or with the manufacturer's part number.

422-32. Appliances Consisting of Motors and Other Loads. Appliances shall be marked in accordance with (a) or (b) below.

(a) Marking. In addition to the marking required in Section 422-30, the marking on an appliance consisting of a motor with other load(s) or motors with or without other load(s) shall specify the minimum circuit size and the maximum rating of the circuit overcurrent protective device.

Exception No. 1: Appliances factory-equipped with cords and attachment plugs, complying with Section 422-30.

Exception No. 2: An appliance where both the minimum circuit size and maximum rating of the circuit overcurrent protective device are not more than 15 amperes and complies with Section 422-30.

(b) Alternate Marking Method. An alternate marking method shall be permitted to specify the rating of the largest motor in volts and amperes, and the additional load(s) in volts and amperes, or volts and watts in addition to the marking required in Section 422-30.

Exception No. 1: Appliances factory-equipped with cords and attachment plugs, complying with Section 422-30.

Exception No. 2: The ampere rating of a motor 1/8 horsepower or less or a nonmotor load 1 ampere or less shall be permitted to be omitted unless such loads constitute the principal load.

ARTICLE 424 — FIXED ELECTRIC SPACE HEATING EQUIPMENT

Contents

A. General

424-1. Scope. This article covers fixed electric equipment used for space heating. For the purpose of this article, heating equipment shall include heating cable, unit heaters, boilers, central systems, or other approved fixed electric space heating equipment. This article shall not apply to process heating and room air conditioning.

424-2. Other Articles. All requirements of this Code shall apply where applicable. Fixed electric space heating equipment for use in hazardous (classified) locations shall comply with Articles 500 through 517. Fixed electric space heating equipment incorporating a hermetic refrigerant motor-compressor shall also comply with Article 440.

424-3. Branch Circuits.

(a) Branch-Circuit Requirements. Individual branch circuits shall be permitted to supply any size fixed electric space heating equipment.

Branch circuits supplying two or more outlets for fixed electric space heating equipment shall be rated 15, 20, or 30 amperes.

Exception: In other than residential occupancies, fixed infrared heating equipment shall be permitted to be supplied from branch circuits rated not over 50 amperes.

(b) Branch-Circuit Sizing. The ampacity of the branch-circuit conductors and the rating or setting of overcurrent protective devices supplying fixed electric space heating equipment consisting of resistance elements with or without a motor shall not be less than 125 percent of the total load of the motors and the heaters. The rating or setting of overcurrent protective devices shall be permitted in accordance with Section 240-3, Exception No. 1. A contactor, thermostat, relay, or similar device, approved for continuous operation at 100 percent of its rating, shall be permitted to supply its full-rated load as provided in Section 210-22(c), Exception No. 2.

The size of the branch-circuit conductors and overcurrent protective devices supplying fixed electric space heating equipment including a hermetic refrigerant motor-compressor with or without resistance units shall be computed in accordance with Sections 440-34 and 440-35.

The provisions of this section shall not apply to conductors which form an integral part of approved fixed electric space heating equipment.

The sizing of branch-circuit conductors supplying fixed electric space heating equipment at 125 percent of the total load of the heaters (and motors) is predicated on the need to protect overcurrent devices, particularly in panelboards, from overheating during periods of prolonged operation. See Section 384-16(c). The requirement in this section is phrased so as to avoid arguments as to whether or not the heating equipment is a "continuous load" as defined in Article 100.

B. Installation

424-9. General.   All fixed electric space heating equipment shall be installed in an approved manner.

Heating equipment and systems often have special instructions for installation regarding spacings, types of supply wires, or special control equipment which must be considered in determining the suitability of the installation. See Section 110-3(b). A pamphlet titled "Electrically Operated Central Heating and Cooling Equipment Installation Marking Guide" is available from Underwriters Laboratories Inc. to aid in understanding such special instructions.

424-10. Special Permission.   Fixed electric space heating equipment and systems installed by methods other than covered by this article shall be permitted only by special permission.

424-11. Supply Conductors.   Fixed electric space heating equipment requiring supply conductors with over 60°C insulation shall be clearly and permanently marked. This marking shall be plainly visible after installation and shall be permitted to be adjacent to the field-connection box.

Fixed electric space heating equipment often requires high-temperature supply conductors.

424-12. Locations.

(a) Exposed to Severe Physical Damage.   Fixed electric space heating equipment shall not be used where exposed to severe physical damage unless adequately protected.

(b) Damp or Wet Locations.   Heaters and related equipment installed in damp or wet locations shall be approved for such locations and shall be constructed and installed so that water cannot enter or accumulate in or on wired sections, electrical components, or duct work.

(FPN): See Section 110-11 for equipment exposed to deteriorating agents.

424-13. Spacing from Combustible Materials.   Fixed electric space heating equipment shall be installed to provide the required spacing between the equipment and adjacent combustible material, unless it has been found to be acceptable where installed in direct contact with combustible material.

424-14. Grounding.   All exposed noncurrent-carrying metal parts of fixed electric space heating equipment likely to become energized shall be grounded as required in Article 250.

C. Control and Protection of Fixed Electric Space Heating Equipment

424-19. Disconnecting Means.   Means shall be provided to disconnect the heater, motor controller(s), and supplementary overcurrent protective device(s) of all fixed electric space heating equipment from all ungrounded conductors. Where heating equipment is supplied by more than one source, the disconnecting means shall be grouped and identified.

(a) Heating Equipment with Supplementary Overcurrent Protection.   The disconnecting means for fixed electric space heating equipment with supplementary overcurrent protection

530

Figure 424-1. An electric furnace with cooling
coils for air conditioning.

shall be within sight from and on the supply side of the supplementary overcurrent protective
device(s), and in addition shall comply with either (1) or (2) below.

(1) Heater Containing No Motor Rated Over ⅛ Horsepower. The above disconnecting
means or unit switches complying with Section 424-19(c) shall be permitted to serve as the
required disconnecting means for both the motor controller(s) and heater under either (a) or (b)
below.

a. The disconnecting means provided is also within sight from the motor controller(s) and
the heater; or

b. The disconnecting means provided shall be capable of being locked in the open
position.

(2) Heater Containing a Motor(s) Rated Over ⅛ Horsepower.

a. The above disconnecting means shall be permitted to serve as the required disconnecting means for both the motor controller(s) and heater if this disconnecting means is also in sight
from the motor controller(s) and the heater.

b. Where the disconnecting means is not within sight from the heater a separate
disconnecting means shall be installed, or the disconnecting means shall be capable of being
locked in the open position, or unit switches complying with Section 424-19(c) shall be
permitted.

c. Where the disconnecting means is not within sight from the motor controller location
a disconnecting means complying with Section 430-102 shall be provided.

d. Where the motor is not in sight from the motor controller location, Section 430-102(b)
shall apply.

531

(b) Heating Equipment Without Supplementary Overcurrent Protection.

(1) Without Motor or with Motor Not Over ⅛ Horsepower. For fixed electric space heating equipment without a motor rated over ⅛ horsepower, the branch-circuit switch or circuit breaker shall be permitted to serve as the disconnecting means, where readily accessible for servicing.

(2) Over ⅛ Horsepower. For motor-driven electric space heating equipment with a motor rated over ⅛ horsepower, a disconnecting means shall be located within sight from the motor controller.

Exception: As permitted by Section 424-19(a)(2).

(c) Unit Switch(es) as Disconnecting Means. A unit switch(es) with a marked "off" position that is part of a fixed heater and disconnects all ungrounded conductors shall be permitted as the disconnecting means required by this article where other means for disconnection are provided in the following types of occupancies.

(1) Multifamily Dwellings. In multifamily dwellings, the other disconnecting means shall be within the dwelling unit, or on the same floor as the dwelling unit in which the fixed heater is installed, and shall also be permitted to control lamps and appliances.

(2) Two-Family Dwellings. In two-family dwellings, the other disconnecting means shall be permitted either inside or outside of the dwelling unit in which the fixed heater is installed. In this case, an individual switch or circuit breaker for the dwelling unit shall be permitted and shall also be permitted to control lamps and appliances.

(3) One-Family Dwellings. In one-family dwellings, the service disconnecting means shall be permitted to be the other disconnecting means.

(4) Other Occupancies. In other occupancies, the branch-circuit switch or circuit breaker, where readily accessible for servicing of the fixed heater, shall be permitted as the other disconnecting means.

424-20. Thermostatically Controlled Switching Devices.

(a) Serving as Both Controllers and Disconnecting Means. Thermostatically controlled switching devices and combination thermostats and manually controlled switches shall be permitted to serve as both controllers and disconnecting means provided all of the following conditions are met:

(1) Provided with a marked "off" position.

(2) Directly open all ungrounded conductors when manually placed in the "off" position.

(3) Designed so that the circuit cannot be energized automatically after the device has been manually placed in the "off" position.

(4) Located as specified in Section 424-19.

(b) Thermostats that Do Not Directly Interrupt All Ungrounded Conductors. Thermostats that do not directly interrupt all ungrounded conductors and thermostats that operate remote control circuits shall not be required to meet the requirements of (a). These devices shall not be permitted as the disconnecting means.

424-21. Switch and Circuit Breaker to Be Indicating. Switches and circuit breakers used as disconnecting means shall be of the indicating type.

424-22. Overcurrent Protection.

(a) Branch-Circuit Devices. Electric space heating equipment, other than such motor-operated equipment as required by Articles 430 and 440 to have additional overcurrent protection, shall be permitted to be protected against overcurrent where supplied by one of the branch circuits in Article 210.

(b) Resistance Elements. Resistance-type heating elements in electric space heating equipment shall be protected at not more than 60 amperes. Equipment rated more than 48 amperes and employing such elements shall have the heating elements subdivided, and each subdivided load shall not exceed 48 amperes. Where a subdivided load is less than 48 amperes the rating of the supplementary overcurrent protective device shall comply with Section 424-3(b).

Exception: As provided in Section 424-72(a).

(c) Overcurrent Protective Devices. The supplementary overcurrent protective devices for the subdivided loads specified in (b) above shall be: (1) factory installed within or on the heater enclosure or supplied for use with the heater as a separate assembly by the heater manufacturer; (2) accessible, but shall not be required to be readily accessible; and (3) suitable for branch-circuit protection.

(FPN): See Section 240-10.

Where cartridge fuses are used to provide this overcurrent protection, a single disconnecting means shall be permitted to be used for the several subdivided loads.

(FPN): See Section 240-40.

Where subdivided loads are required, the heating equipment manufacturer is required to furnish the necessary overcurrent protective devices.

The main branch-circuit conductors supplying the overcurrent protective devices for subdivided loads are considered as branch circuits to make it clear that the 125 percent requirement in Section 424-3(b) is for the branch circuit only.

(d) Branch-Circuit Conductors. The conductors supplying the supplementary overcurrent protective devices shall be considered branch-circuit conductors.

Exception: For heaters rated 50 kW or more, the conductors supplying the supplementary overcurrent protective devices specified in (c) above shall be permitted to be sized at not less than 100 percent of the nameplate rating of the heater provided all of the following conditions are met:

a. The heater is marked with a minimum conductor size; and

b. The conductors are not smaller than the marked minimum size; and

c. A temperature-actuated device controls the cyclic operation of the equipment.

(e) Conductors for Subdivided Loads. Field-wired conductors between the heater and the supplementary overcurrent protective devices shall be sized at not less than 125 percent of the load served. The supplementary overcurrent protective devices specified in (c) shall protect these conductors in accordance with Section 240-3.

Exception: For heaters rated 50 kW or more, the ampacity of field-wired conductors between the heater and the supplementary overcurrent protective devices shall be permitted to be not less than 100 percent of the load of their respective subdivided circuits provided all of the following conditions are met:

a. The heater is marked with a minimum conductor size; and b. The conductors are not smaller than the marked minimum size; and

c. A temperature-activated device controls the cyclic operation of the equipment.

D. Marking of Heating Equipment

424-28. Nameplate.

(a) Marking Required. Each unit of fixed electric space heating equipment shall be provided with a nameplate giving the identifying name and the normal rating in volts and watts, or in volts and amperes.

Electric space heating equipment intended for use on alternating current only or direct current only shall be marked to so indicate. The marking of equipment consisting of motors over $\frac{1}{8}$ horsepower and other loads shall specify the rating of the motor in volts, amperes, and frequency, and the heating load in volts and watts, or in volts and amperes.

(b) Location. This nameplate shall be located so as to be visible or easily accessible after installation.

424-29. Marking of Heating Elements.
All heating elements that are replaceable in the field and are a part of an electric heater shall be legibly marked with the ratings in volts and watts, or in volts and amperes.

E. Electric Space Heating Cables

424-34. Heating Cable Construction.
Heating cables shall be furnished complete with factory-assembled nonheating leads at least 7 feet (2.13 m) in length.

424-35. Marking of Heating Cables.
Each unit shall be marked with the identifying name or identification symbol, catalog number, ratings in volts and watts, or in volts and amperes.

Each unit length of heating cable shall have a permanent legible marking on each nonheating lead located within 3 inches (76 mm) of the terminal end. The lead wire shall have the following color identification to indicate the circuit voltage on which it is to be used: 120-volt nominal, yellow; 208-volt nominal, blue; 240-volt nominal, red; and 277-volt nominal, brown.

424-36. Clearances of Wiring in Ceilings.
Wiring located above heated ceilings shall be spaced not less than 2 inches (50.8 mm) above the heated ceiling and shall be considered as operating at an ambient of 50°C. The ampacity of conductors shall be computed on the basis of the correction factors given in Tables 310-16 through 310-31.

Exception: Wiring above heated ceilings and located above thermal insulation having a minimum thickness of 2 inches (50.8 mm) shall not require correction for temperature.

424-37. Location of Branch-Circuit and Feeder Wiring in Exterior Walls.
Wiring methods shall comply with Article 300 and Section 310-10.

424-38. Area Restrictions.

(a) Shall Not Extend Beyond the Room or Area. Heating cables shall not extend beyond the room or area in which they originate.

(b) Uses Prohibited. Cables shall not be installed in closets, over walls or partitions that extend to the ceiling, or over cabinets whose clearance from the ceiling is less than the minimum horizontal dimension of the cabinet to the nearest cabinet edge that is open to the room or area.

Exception: Isolated single runs of cable shall be permitted to pass over partitions where they are embedded.

(c) In Closet Ceilings as Low Temperature Heat Sources to Control Relative Humidity. This provision shall not prevent the use of cable in closet ceilings as low temperature heat sources to control relative humidity, provided they are used only in those portions of the ceiling that are unobstructed to the floor by shelves or other permanent fixtures.

424-39. Clearance from Other Objects and Openings.   Heating elements of cables shall be separated at least 8 inches (203 mm) from the edge of outlet boxes and junction boxes that are to be used for mounting surface lighting fixtures. A clearance of not less than 2 inches (50.8 mm) shall be provided from recessed fixtures and their trims, ventilating openings, and other such openings in room surfaces. Sufficient area shall be provided to assure that no heating cable will be covered by any surface-mounted units.

424-40. Splices.   Embedded cables shall be spliced only where necessary and only by approved means, and in no case shall the length of the heating cable be altered.

424-41. Installation of Heating Cables on Dry Board, in Plaster and on Concrete Ceilings.

  (a) Shall Not Be Installed in Walls.   Cables shall not be installed in walls.

  Exception: Isolated single runs of cable shall be permitted to run down a vertical surface to reach a dropped ceiling.

  (b) Adjacent Runs.   Adjacent runs of cable not exceeding 2¾ watts per foot shall be installed not less than 1½ inches (38 mm) on centers.

  (c) Surfaces to Be Applied.   Heating cables shall be applied only to gypsum board, plaster lath or other fire-resistant material. With metal lath or other electrically conductive surfaces, a coat of plaster shall be applied to completely separate the metal lath or conductive surface from the cable.

  (FPN): See also (f) below.

  (d) Splices.   All heating cables, the splice between the heating cable and nonheating leads, and 3-inch (76-mm) minimum of the nonheating lead at the splice shall be embedded in plaster or dry board in the same manner as the heating cable.

  (e) Ceiling Surface.   The entire ceiling surface shall have a finish of thermally noninsulating sand plaster having a nominal thickness of ½ inch (12.7 mm), or other noninsulating material identified as suitable for this use and applied according to specified thickness and directions.

  (f) Secured.   Cables shall be secured at intervals not exceeding 16 inches (406 mm) by means of approved stapling, tape, plaster, nonmetallic spreaders, or other approved means. Staples or metal fasteners that straddle the cable shall not be used with metal lath or other electrically conductive surfaces.

  Exception: Cables identified to be secured at intervals not to exceed 6 feet (1.83 m).

  (g) Dry Board Installations.   In dry board installations, the entire ceiling below the heating cable shall be covered with gypsum board not exceeding ½ inch (12.7 mm) thickness. The void between the upper layer of gypsum board, plaster lath, or other fire-resistant material and the surface layer of gypsum board shall be completely filled with thermally conductive nonshrinking plaster or other approved material or equivalent thermal conductivity.

  (h) Free from Contact with Conductive Surfaces.   Cables shall be kept free from contact with metal or other electrical conductive surfaces.

  (i) Joists.   In dry board applications, cable shall be installed parallel to the joist, leaving a clear space centered under the joist of 2½ inches (64 mm) (width) between centers of adjacent runs of cable. Surface layer of gypsum board shall be mounted so that the nails or other fasteners do not pierce the heating cable.

(j) **Crossing Joists.** Cables shall cross joists only at the ends of the room.

Exception: Where the cable is required to cross joists elsewhere in order to satisfy the manufacturer's instructions that the installer avoid placing the cable too close to ceiling penetrations and light fixtures.

424-42. Finished Ceilings. Finished ceilings shall not be covered with decorative panels or beams constructed of materials which have thermal insulating properties, such as wood, fiber, or plastic. Finished ceilings shall be permitted to be covered with paint, wallpaper, or other approved surface finishes.

424-43. Installation of Nonheating Leads of Cables.

(a) **Free Nonheating Leads.** Free nonheating leads of cables shall be installed in accordance with approved wiring methods from the junction box to a location within the ceiling. Such installations shall be permitted to be single conductors in approved raceways, single or multiconductor Type UF, Type NMC, Type MI, or other approved conductors.

(b) **Leads in Junction Box.** Not less than 6 inches (152 mm) of free nonheating lead shall be within the junction box. The marking of the leads shall be visible in the junction box.

(c) **Excess Leads.** Excess leads of heating cables shall not be cut but shall be secured to the underside of the ceiling and embedded in plaster or other approved material, leaving only a length sufficient to reach the junction box with not less than 6 inches (152 mm) of free lead within the box.

424-44. Installation of Cables in Concrete or Poured Masonry Floors.

(a) **Watts per Linear Foot.** Heating cables shall not exceed 16½ watts per linear foot (305 mm) of cable.

(b) **Spacing Between Adjacent Runs.** The spacing between adjacent runs of cable shall not be less than 1 inch (25.4 mm) on centers.

(c) **Secured in Place.** Cables shall be secured in place by nonmetallic frames or spreaders or other approved means while the concrete or other finish is applied.
Cables shall not be installed where they bridge expansion joints unless protected from expansion and contraction.

(d) **Spacings Between Heating Cable and Metal Embedded in the Floor.** Spacings shall be maintained between the heating cable and metal embedded in the floor.

Exception: Grounded metal-clad cable shall be permitted to be in contact with metal embedded in the floor.

(e) **Leads Protected.** Leads shall be protected where they leave the floor by rigid metal conduit, intermediate metal conduit, rigid nonmetallic conduit, electrical metallic tubing, or by other approved means.

(f) **Bushings or Approved Fittings.** Bushings or approved fittings shall be used where the leads emerge within the floor slab.

424-45. Inspection and Tests. Cable installations shall be made with due care to prevent damage to the cable assembly and shall be inspected and approved before cables are covered or concealed.

F. Duct Heaters

424-57. General. Part F shall apply to any heater mounted in the air stream of a forced-air system where the air moving unit is not provided as an integral part of the equipment.

Figure 424-2. An insert-type electric duct heater.

424-58. Identification. Heaters installed in an air duct shall be identified as suitable for the installation.

424-59. Air Flow. Means shall be provided to assure uniform and adequate air flow over the face of the heater in accordance with the manufacturer's instructions.

(FPN): Heaters installed within 4 feet (1.22 m) of the outlet of an air-moving device, heat pump, air conditioner, elbows, baffle plates, or other obstructions in duct work may require turning vanes, pressure plates, or other devices on the inlet side of the duct heater to assure an even distribution of air over the face of the heater.

424-60. Elevated Inlet Temperature. Duct heaters intended for use with elevated inlet air temperature shall be identified as suitable for use at the elevated temperatures.

424-61. Installation of Duct Heaters with Heat Pumps and Air Conditioners. Heat pumps and air conditioners having duct heaters closer than 4 feet (1.22 m) to the heat pump or air conditioner shall have both the duct heater and heat pump or air conditioner identified as suitable for such installation and so marked.

424-62. Condensation. Duct heaters used with air conditioners or other air-cooling equipment that may result in condensation of moisture shall be identified as suitable for use with air conditioners.

424-63. Fan Circuit Interlock. Means shall be provided to ensure that the fan circuit is energized when any heater circuit is energized. However, time- or temperature-controlled delay in energizing the fan motor shall be permitted.

424-64. Limit Controls. Each duct heater shall be provided with an approved, integral, automatic-reset temperature-limiting control or controllers to de-energize the circuit or circuits.

In addition, an integral independent supplementary control or controllers shall be provided in each duct heater that will disconnect a sufficient number of conductors to interrupt current flow. This device shall be manually resettable or replaceable.

424-65. Location of Disconnecting Means. Duct heater controller equipment shall be accessible with the disconnecting means installed at or within sight from the controller.

Exception: As permitted by Section 424-19(a).

424-66. Installation. Duct heaters shall be installed in accordance with the manufacturer's instructions in a manner so that operation will not create a hazard to persons or property. Furthermore, duct heaters shall be located with respect to building construction and other equipment so as to permit access to the heater. Sufficient clearance shall be maintained to permit replacement of controls and heating elements and for adjusting and cleaning of controls and other parts requiring such attention. See Section 110-16.

(FPN): For additional installation information, see Air Conditioning and Ventilating Systems, NFPA 90A-1985 (ANSI) and Warm Air Heating and Air Conditioning Systems, NFPA 90B-1984 (ANSI).

G. Resistance-type Boilers

424-70. Scope. The provisions in Part G of this article shall apply to boilers employing resistance-type heating elements. Electrode-type boilers shall not be considered as employing resistance-type heating elements. See Part H of this article.

424-71. Identification. Resistance-type boilers shall be identified as suitable for the installation.

424-72. Overcurrent Protection.

(a) Boiler Employing Resistance-type Immersion Heating Elements in an ASME Rated and Stamped Vessel. A boiler employing resistance-type immersion heating elements contained in an ASME rated and stamped vessel shall have the heating elements protected at not more than 150 amperes. Such a boiler rated more than 120 amperes shall have the heating elements subdivided into loads not exceeding 120 amperes.

Where a subdivided load is less than 120 amperes, the rating of the overcurrent protective device shall comply with Section 424-3(b).

(b) Boiler Employing Resistance-type Heating Elements Rated More than 48 Amperes and Not Contained in an ASME Rated and Stamped Vessel. A boiler employing resistance-type heating elements not contained in an ASME rated and stamped vessel shall have the heating elements protected at not more than 60 amperes. Such a boiler rated more than 48 amperes shall have the heating elements subdivided into loads not exceeding 48 amperes.

Where a subdivided load is less than 48 amperes, the rating of the overcurrent protective device shall comply with Section 424-3(b).

(c) Supplementary Overcurrent Protective Devices. The supplementary overcurrent protective devices for the subdivided loads as required by Section 424-72(a) and (b) shall be: (1) factory installed within or on the boiler enclosure or provided as a separate assembly by the boiler manufacturer; and (2) accessible, but need not be readily accessible; and (3) suitable for branch-circuit protection.

Where cartridge fuses are used to provide this overcurrent protection, a single disconnecting means shall be permitted for the several subdivided circuits. See Section 240-40.

(d) Conductors Supplying Supplementary Overcurrent Protective Devices. The conductors supplying these supplementary overcurrent protective devices shall be considered branch-circuit conductors.

Exception: Where the heaters are rated 50 kW or more, the conductors supplying the overcurrent protective device specified in (c) above shall be permitted to be sized at not less than 100 percent of the nameplate rating of the heater provided all of the following conditions are met:

a. The heater is marked with a minimum conductor size; and

b. The conductors are not smaller than the marked minimum size; and

c. A temperature or pressure-actuated device controls the cyclic operation of the equipment.

(e) Conductors for Subdivided Loads. Field-wired conductors between the heater and the supplementary overcurrent protective devices shall be sized at not less than 125 percent of the load served. The supplementary overcurrent protective devices specified in (c) shall protect these conductors in accordance with Section 240-3.

Exception: For heaters rated 50 kW or more, the ampacity of field-wired conductors between the heater and the supplementary overcurrent protective devices shall be permitted to be not less than 100 percent of the load of their respective subdivided circuits provided all of the following conditions are met:

a. The heater is marked with a minimum conductor size; and

b. The conductors are not smaller than the marked minimum size; and

c. A temperature-activated device controls the cyclic operation of the equipment.

424-73. Over-Temperature Limit Control. Each boiler designed, so that in normal operation there is no change in state of the heat transfer medium, shall be equipped with a temperature sensitive limiting means. It shall be installed to limit maximum liquid temperature and shall directly or indirectly disconnect all ungrounded conductors to the heating elements. Such means shall be in addition to a temperature regulating system and other devices protecting the tank against excessive pressure.

424-74. Over-Pressure Limit Control. Each boiler designed, so that in normal operation there is a change in state of the heat transfer medium from liquid to vapor, shall be equipped with a pressure sensitive limiting means. It shall be installed to limit maximum pressure and shall directly or indirectly disconnect all ungrounded conductors to the heating elements. Such means shall be in addition to a pressure regulating system and other devices protecting the tank against excessive pressure.

424-75. Grounding. All noncurrent-carrying metal parts shall be grounded in accordance with Article 250. Means for connection of equipment grounding conductor(s) sized in accordance with Table 250-95 shall be provided.

H. Electrode-type Boilers

424-80. Scope. The provisions in Part H of this article shall apply to boilers for operation at 600 volts, nominal, or less, in which heat is generated by the passage of current between electrodes through the liquid being heated.

424-81. Identification. Electrode-type boilers shall be identified as suitable for the installation.

424-82. Branch-Circuit Requirements. The size of branch-circuit conductors and overcurrent protective devices shall be calculated on the basis of 125 percent of the total load (motors not included). A contactor, relay or other device, approved for continuous operation at 100 percent of its rating, shall be permitted to supply its full-rated load. See Section 210-22(c), Exception

No. 2. The provisions of this section shall not apply to conductors that form an integral part of an approved boiler.

Exception: For an electrode boiler rated 50 kW or more, the conductors supplying the boiler electrode(s) shall be permitted to be sized at not less than 100 percent of the nameplate rating of the electrode boiler provided all the following conditions are met:

a. The electrode boiler is marked with a minimum conductor size; and

b. The conductors are not smaller than the marked minimum size; and

c. A temperature or pressure-actuated device controls the cyclic operation of the equipment.

424-83. Over-Temperature Limit Control. Each boiler designed, so that in normal operation there is no change in state of the heat transfer medium, shall be equipped with a temperature sensitive limiting means. It shall be installed to limit maximum liquid temperature and shall directly or indirectly interrupt all current flow through the electrodes. Such means shall be in addition to the temperature regulating system and other devices protecting the tank against excessive pressure.

424-84. Over-Pressure Limit Control. Each boiler designed, so that in normal operation there is a change in state of the heat transfer medium from liquid to vapor, shall be equipped with a pressure sensitive limiting means. It shall be installed to limit maximum pressure and shall directly or indirectly interrupt all current flow through the electrodes. Such means shall be in addition to a pressure regulating system and other devices protecting the tank against excessive pressure.

424-85. Grounding. For those boilers designed such that fault currents do not pass through the pressure vessel and the pressure vessel is electrically isolated from the electrodes, all exposed noncurrent-carrying metal parts including the pressure vessel, supply, and return connecting piping shall be grounded in accordance with Article 250.

For all other designs the pressure vessel containing the electrodes shall be isolated and electrically insulated from ground.

424-86. Markings. All electrode-type boilers shall be marked to show: (1) the manufacturer's name; (2) the normal rating in volts, amperes, and kilowatts; (3) the electrical supply required specifying frequency, number of phases, and number of wires; (4) the marking: "Electrode-type Boiler"; (5) a warning marking — "ALL POWER SUPPLIES SHALL BE DISCONNECTED BEFORE SERVICING INCLUDING SERVICING THE PRESSURE VESSEL."

The nameplate shall be located so as to be visible after installation.

J. Electric Radiant Heating Panels and Heating Panel Sets

424-90. Scope. The provisions of Part J of this article shall apply to radiant heating panels and heating panel sets.

424-91. Definitions.

(a) Heating Panel. A heating panel is a complete assembly provided with a junction box or a length of flexible conduit for connection to a branch circuit.

(b) Heating Panel Set. A heating panel set is a rigid or nonrigid assembly provided with nonheating leads or a terminal junction assembly identified as being suitable for connection to a wiring system.

424-92. Markings.

(1) Markings shall be permanent and in a location that is visible prior to application of panel finish.

(2) Each unit shall be identified as suitable for the installation.

(3) Each unit shall be marked with the identifying name or identification symbol, catalog number, rating in volts and watts, or in volts and amperes.

(4) The manufacturers of heating panels or heating panel sets shall provide marking labels which indicate that the space heating installation incorporates heating panels or heating panel sets and instructions that the labels shall be affixed to the panelboards to identify which branch circuits supply the circuits to those space heating installations.

Exception: Heating panels and heating panel set installations that are visible and distinguishable after installation shall not be required to have labels provided.

424-93. Installation.

(a) General.

(1) Heating panels and heating panel sets shall be installed in accordance with the manufacturer's instructions.

(2) The heating portion shall not:

a. Be installed in or behind surfaces where subject to physical damage.

b. Be run through or above walls, partitions, cupboards or similar portions of structures that extend to the ceiling.

c. Be run in or through thermal insulation, but shall be permitted to be in contact with the surface of thermal insulation.

(3) Edges of panels and panel sets shall be separated by not less than 8 inches (203 mm) from the edges of any outlet boxes and junction boxes that are to be used for mounting surface lighting fixtures. A clearance of not less than 2 inches (50.8 mm) shall be provided from recessed fixtures and their trims, ventilating openings and other such openings in room surfaces. Sufficient area shall be provided to assure that no heating panel or heating panel set is to be covered by any surface-mounted units.

Exception: Heating panels and panel sets listed and marked for lesser clearances shall be permitted to be installed at the marked clearances.

(4) After the heating panels or heating panel sets are installed and inspected, it shall be permitted to install a surface which has been identified by the manufacturer's instructions as being suitable for the installation. The surface shall be secured so that the nails or other fastenings do not pierce the heating panels or heating panel sets.

(5) Surfaces permitted by Section 424-93(a)(4) shall be permitted to be covered with paint, wallpaper or other approved surfaces identified in the manufacturer's instructions as being suitable.

(b) Heating Panel Sets.

(1) Heating panel sets shall be permitted to be secured to the lower face of joists or mounted in between joists, headers or nailing strips.

(2) Heating panel sets shall be installed parallel to joists or nailing strips.

(3) Nailing or stapling of heating panel sets shall be done only through the unheated portions provided for this purpose. Heating panel sets shall not be cut through or nailed through any point closer than ¼ inch (6.35 mm) to the element. Nails, staples or other fasteners shall not be used where they penetrate current-carrying parts.

(4) Heating panel sets shall be installed as complete units unless identified as suitable for field cutting in an approved manner.

424-94. Clearances of Wiring in Ceilings. Wiring located above heated ceilings shall be spaced not less than 2 inches (50.3 mm) above the heated ceiling and shall be considered as operating at an ambient of 50°C (122°F). The ampacity shall be computed on the basis of the correction factors given in Tables 310-16 through 310-31.

Exception: Wiring above heated ceilings and located above thermal insulations having a minimum thickness of 2 inches (50.8 mm) shall not require correction for temperature.

424-95. Location of Branch-Circuit and Feeder Wiring in Walls.

(a) Exterior Walls. Wiring methods shall comply with Article 300 and Section 310-10.

(b) Interior Walls. Any wiring behind heating panels or heating panel sets located in interior walls or partitions shall be considered as operating at an ambient of 40°C (104°F) and the ampacity shall be computed on the basis of the correction factors given in Tables 310-16 through 310-31.

424-96. Connection to Branch-Circuit Conductors.

(a) General. Heating panels or heating panel sets assembled together in the field to form a heating installation in one room or area shall be connected in accordance with the manufacturer's instructions.

(b) Heating Panels. Heating panels shall be connected to branch-circuit wiring by an approved wiring method.

(c) Heating Panel Sets.

(1) Heating panel sets shall be connected to branch-circuit wiring by a method identified as being suitable for the purpose.

(2) A heating panel set provided with terminal junction assembly shall be permitted to have the nonheating leads attached at the time of installation in accordance with the manufacturer's instructions.

424-97. Nonheating Leads. Excess nonheating leads of heating panels or heating panel sets shall be permitted to be cut to the required length. They shall meet the installation requirements of the wiring method employed in accordance with Section 424-96. Nonheating leads shall be an integral part of a heating panel and a heating panel set and shall not be subjected to the ampacity requirements of Section 424-3(b) for branch circuits.

424-98. Installation in Concrete or Poured Masonry.

(a) Maximum Heated Area. Heating panels or heating panel sets shall not exceed 33 watts per square foot (0.093 sq m) of heated area.

(b) Secured in Place and Identified as Suitable. Heating panels or heating panel sets shall be secured in place by means specified in the manufacturer's instructions and identified as suitable for the installation.

(c) Expansion Joints. Heating panels or heating panel sets shall not be installed where they bridge expansion joints unless protected from expansion and contraction.

(d) Spacings. Spacings shall be maintained between heating panels or heating panel sets and metal embedded in the floor.

Exception: Grounded metal-clad heating panels shall be permitted to be in contact with metal embedded in the floor.

(e) Protection of Leads. Leads shall be protected where they leave the floor by rigid metal conduit, intermediate metal conduit, rigid nonmetallic conduit, electrical metallic tubing or by other approved means.

(f) Bushings or Fittings Required. Bushings or approved fittings shall be used where the leads emerge within the floor slabs.

424-99. Installation Under Floor Covering.

(a) Identification. Heating panels or heating panel sets for installation under floor covering shall be identified as suitable for installation under floor covering.

(b) Maximum Heated Area. Heating panels or panel sets, installed under floor covering, shall not exceed 15 watts per square foot (0.093 m^2) of heated area.

(c) Installation. Listed heating panels or panel sets, if installed under floor covering, shall be installed on floor surfaces which are smooth and flat in accordance with the manufacturer's instructions and shall also comply with the following:

(1) Expansion Joints. Heating panels or heating panel sets shall not be installed where they bridge expansion joints unless protected from expansion and contraction.

(2) Connection to Conductors. Heating panels and heating panel sets shall be connected to branch-circuit and supply wiring by wiring methods recognized in Chapter 3.

(3) Anchoring. Heating panels and heating panel sets shall be firmly anchored to the floor using an adhesive or anchoring system identified for this use.

(4) Coverings. After heating panels or heating panel sets are installed and inspected, they shall be permitted to be covered by a floor covering which has been identified by the manufacturer as being suitable for the installation. The covering shall be secured to the heating panel or heating panel sets with release-type adhesives.

(5) Fault Protection. A device to open all ungrounded conductors supplying the heating panels or heating panel sets, provided by the manufacturer, shall function when a low or high resistance line to line, line to grounded conductor or line to ground fault occurs such as the result of a penetration of the element/element assembly.

(FPN): An integral grounding shield may be required to provide this protection.

An example of a heating system which could be installed in this fashion would be a system using conductive film heating elements.

ARTICLE 426 — FIXED OUTDOOR ELECTRIC DE-ICING AND SNOW-MELTING EQUIPMENT

Contents

A. General

426-1. Scope. The requirements of this article shall apply to electrically energized heating systems and the installation of these systems.

(a) Embedded. Embedded in driveways, walks, steps, and other areas.

(b) Exposed. Exposed on drainage systems, bridge structures, roofs, and other structures.

544

Article 426 includes requirements for resistance heating elements, impedance heating systems, or skin effect heating systems. These systems are defined in Section 426-2. In addition, specific requirements are provided for exposed resistance heating elements of the type commonly used on residences for gutter and roof de-icing and snow melting. See Sections 426-21 and 426-23. See commentary following Section 426-11.

426-2. Definitions. For the purpose of this article:

Heating System. A complete system consisting of components such as heating elements, fastening devices, nonheating circuit wiring, leads, temperature controllers, safety signs, junction boxes, raceways, and fittings.

Resistance Heating Element. A specific separate element to generate heat which is embedded in or fastened to the surface to be heated.

(FPN): Tubular heaters, strip heaters, heating cable, heating tape, and heating panels are examples of resistance heaters.

Impedance Heating System. A system in which heat is generated in a pipe or rod, or combination of pipes and rods, by causing current to flow through the pipe or rod by direct connection to an ac voltage source from a dual-winding transformer. The pipe or rod shall be permitted to be embedded in the surface to be heated, or constitute the exposed components to be heated.

Skin Effect Heating System. A system in which heat is generated on the inner surface of a ferromagnetic envelope embedded in or fastened to the surface to be heated.

(FPN): Typically, an electrically insulated conductor is routed through and connected to the envelope at the other end. The envelope and the electrically insulated conductor are connected to an ac voltage source from a dual-winding transformer.

426-3. Application of Other Articles. All requirements of this Code shall apply except as specifically amended in this article. Cord- and plug-connected fixed outdoor electric de-icing and snow-melting equipment intended for specific use and identified as suitable for this use shall be installed according to Article 422. Fixed outdoor electric de-icing and snow-melting equipment for use in hazardous (classified) locations shall comply with Articles 500 through 516.

See Sections 422-7 and 422-8.

426-4. Branch-Circuit Sizing. The ampacity of branch-circuit conductors and the rating or setting of overcurrent protective devices supplying fixed outdoor electric de-icing and snow-melting equipment shall not be less than 125 percent of the total load of the heaters. The rating or setting of overcurrent protective devices shall be permitted in accordance with Section 240-3, Exception No. 1.

B. Installation

426-10. General. Equipment for outdoor electric de-icing and snow melting shall be identified as being suitable for:

(1) The chemical, thermal, and physical environment, and

(2) Installation in accordance with the manufacturer's drawings and instructions.

426-11. Use. Electrical heating equipment shall be installed in such a manner as to be afforded protection from physical damage.

ARTICLE 426—FIXED OUTDOOR ELECTRIC DE-ICING

The instructions required by UL for UL-listed mat or cable de-icing and snow-melting equipment intended for burial in concrete specifically indicate that the slab is required to be a double pour (poured in two parts) if that is the only acceptable means of installation. If such a limitation is not specifically mentioned, either a single or double pour may be used. See Section 110-3(b).

426-12. Thermal Protection. External surfaces of outdoor electric de-icing and snow-melting equipment which operate at temperatures exceeding 60°C (140°F) shall be physically guarded, isolated, or thermally insulated to protect against contact by personnel in the area.

See Section 110-17.

426-13. Identification. The presence of outdoor electric de-icing and snow-melting equipment shall be evident by the posting of appropriate caution signs or markings where clearly visible.

426-14. Special Permission. Fixed outdoor de-icing and snow-melting equipment employing methods of construction or installation other than covered by this article shall be permitted only by special permission.

See definition of "special permission" in Article 100.

C. Resistance Heating Elements

426-20. Embedded De-Icing and Snow-Melting Equipment.

(a) Watt Density. Panels or units shall not exceed 120 watts per square foot (0.093 sq m) of heated area.

(b) Spacing. The spacing between adjacent cable runs is dependent upon the rating of the cable, and shall be not less than 1 inch (25.4 mm) on centers.

(c) Cover. Units, panels, or cables shall be installed:

(1) On a substantial asphalt or masonry base at least 2 inches (50.8 mm) thick and have at least 1½ inches (38 mm) of asphalt or masonry applied over the units, panels, or cables; or

(2) They shall be permitted to be installed over other approved bases and embedded within 3½ inches (89 mm) of masonry or asphalt but not less than 1½ inches (38 mm) from the top surface; or

(3) Equipment that has been specially investigated for other forms of installation shall be installed only in the manner for which it has been investigated.

(d) Secured. Cables, units, and panels shall be secured in place by frames or spreaders or other approved means while the masonry or asphalt finish is applied.

(e) Expansion and Contraction. Cables, units, and panels shall not be installed where they bridge expansion joints unless adequately protected from expansion and contraction.

426-21. Exposed De-Icing and Snow-Melting Equipment.

(a) Secured. Heating element assemblies shall be secured to the surface being heated by approved means.

(b) Overtemperature. Where the heating element is not in direct contact with the surface being heated, the design of the heater assembly shall be such that its temperature limitations shall not be exceeded.

(c) Expansion and Contraction. Heating elements and assemblies shall not be installed where they bridge expansion joints unless provision is made for expansion and contraction.

(d) Flexural Capability. Where installed on flexible structures, the heating elements and assemblies shall have a flexural capability compatible with the structure.

426-22. Installation of Nonheating Leads for Embedded Equipment.

(a) Grounding Sheath or Braid. Nonheating leads having a grounding sheath or braid shall be permitted to be embedded in the masonry or asphalt in the same manner as the heating cable without additional physical protection.

(b) Raceways. All but 1 to 6 inches (25.4 to 152 mm) of nonheating leads of Type TW and other approved types not having a grounding sheath shall be enclosed in a rigid conduit, electrical metallic tubing, intermediate metal conduit, or other raceways within asphalt or masonry; and the distance from the factory splice to raceway shall be not less than 1 inch (25.4 mm) or more than 6 inches (152 mm).

(c) Bushings. Insulating bushings shall be used in the asphalt or masonry where leads enter conduit or tubing.

See commentary following Section 373-6(c).

(d) Expansion and Contraction. Leads shall be protected in expansion joints and where they emerge from masonry or asphalt by rigid conduit, electrical metallic tubing, intermediate metal conduit, other raceways, or other approved means.

(e) Leads in Junction Boxes. Not less than 6 inches (152 mm) of free nonheating lead shall be within the junction box.

426-23. Installation of Nonheating Leads for Exposed Equipment.

(a) Nonheating Leads. Power supply nonheating leads (cold leads) for resistance elements shall be suitable for the temperature encountered. Preassembled nonheating leads on approved heaters shall be permitted to be shortened if the markings specified in Section 426-25 are retained. Not less than 6 inches (152 mm) of nonheating leads shall be provided within the junction box.

(b) Protection. Nonheating power supply leads shall be enclosed in a rigid conduit, intermediate metal conduit, electrical metallic tubing, or other approved means.

426-24. Electrical Connection.

(a) Heating Element Connections. Electrical connections, other than factory connections of heating elements to nonheating elements embedded in masonry or asphalt or on exposed surfaces, shall be made with insulated connectors identified for the use.

(b) Circuit Connections. Splices and terminations at the end of the nonheating leads, other than the heating element end, shall be installed in a box or fitting in accordance with Sections 110-14 and 300-15.

426-25. Marking. Each factory-assembled heating unit shall be legibly marked within 3 inches (76 mm) of each end of the nonheating leads with the permanent identification symbol, catalog number, and ratings in volts and watts, or in volts and amperes.

426-26. Corrosion Protection. Ferrous and nonferrous metal raceways, cable armor, cable sheaths, boxes, fittings, supports, and support hardware shall be permitted to be installed in concrete or in direct contact with the earth, or in areas subject to severe corrosive influences, when made of material suitable for the condition, or when provided with corrosion protection identified as suitable for the condition.

426-27. Grounding.

(a) Metal Parts. Exposed noncurrent-carrying metal parts of equipment likely to become energized shall be grounded as required in Article 250.

(b) Grounding Braid or Sheath. Grounding means, such as copper braid, metal sheath, or other approved means, shall be provided as part of the heated section of the cable, panel, or unit.

(c) Bonding and Grounding. All noncurrent-carrying metal parts that are likely to become energized shall be bonded together and connected to an equipment grounding conductor sized in accordance with Table 250-95, extending to the distribution panelboard.

D. Impedance Heating

426-30. Personnel Protection. Exposed elements of impedance heating systems shall be physically guarded, isolated, or thermally insulated with weatherproof jacket to protect against contact by personnel in the area.

426-31. Voltage Limitations. The impedance heating elements shall not operate at a voltage greater than 30 volts ac.

Exception: The voltage shall be permitted to be greater than 30 volts, but not more than 80 volts, if a ground-fault circuit-interrupter for personnel protection is provided.

426-32. Isolation Transformer. A dual-winding transformer with a grounded shield between the primary and secondary windings shall be used to isolate the distribution system from the heating system.

426-33. Induced Currents. All current-carrying components shall be installed in accordance with Section 300-20.

426-34. Grounding. An impedance heating system that is operating at a voltage greater than 30, but not more than 80, shall be grounded at designated point(s).

E. Skin Effect Heating

426-40. Conductor Ampacity. The ampacity of the electrically insulated conductor inside the ferromagnetic envelope shall be permitted to exceed the values shown in Article 310, provided it is identified as suitable for this use.

426-41. Pull Boxes. Where pull boxes are used they shall be accessible without excavation by location in suitable vaults or above grade. Outdoor pull boxes shall be of watertight construction.

426-42. Single Conductor in Enclosure. The provisions of Section 300-20 shall not apply to the installation of a single conductor in a ferromagnetic envelope (metal enclosure).

426-43. Corrosion Protection. Ferromagnetic envelopes, ferrous or nonferrous metal raceways, boxes, fittings, supports, and support hardware shall be permitted to be installed in concrete or in direct contact with the earth, or in areas subjected to severe corrosive influences, where made of material suitable for the condition, or where provided with corrosion protection identified as suitable for the condition. Corrosion protection shall maintain the original wall thickness of the ferromagnetic envelope.

426-44. Grounding. The ferromagnetic envelope shall be grounded at both ends; and, in addition, it shall be permitted to be grounded at intermediate points as required by its design.

The provisions of Section 250-26 shall not apply to the installation of skin effect heating systems.

(FPN): See Section 250-26(d).

F. Control and Protection

426-50. Disconnecting Means.

(a) Disconnection. All fixed outdoor de-icing and snow-melting equipment shall be provided with a means for disconnection from all ungrounded conductors. Where readily accessible to the user of the equipment, the branch-circuit switch or circuit breaker shall be permitted to serve as the disconnecting means. Switches used as the disconnecting means shall be of the indicating type.

(b) Cord- and Plug-Connected Equipment. The factory-installed attachment plug of cord- and plug-connected equipment rated 20 amperes or less and 150 volts or less to ground shall be permitted to be the disconnecting means.

426-51. Controllers.

(a) Temperature Controller with "Off" Position. Temperature controlled switching devices which indicate an "off" position and which interrupt line current shall open all ungrounded conductors when the control device is in the "off" position. These devices shall not be permitted to serve as the disconnecting means unless provided with a positive lockout in the "off" position.

(b) Temperature Controller Without "Off" Position. Temperature controlled switching devices which do not have an "off" position shall not be required to open all ungrounded conductors and shall not be permitted to serve as the disconnecting means.

(c) Remote Temperature Controller. Remote controlled temperature actuated devices shall not be required to meet the requirements of Section 426-51(a). These devices shall not be permitted to serve as the disconnecting means.

(d) Combined Switching Devices. Switching devices consisting of combined temperature actuated devices and manually controlled switches which serve both as the controller and the disconnecting means shall comply with all of the following conditions:

(1) Open all ungrounded conductors when manually placed in the "off" position; and

(2) Be so designed that the circuit cannot be energized automatically if the device has been manually placed in the "off" position; and

(3) Be provided with a positive lockout in the "off" position.

426-52. Overcurrent Protection. Fixed outdoor electric de-icing and snow-melting equipment shall be permitted to be protected against overcurrent where supplied by a branch circuit as specified in Section 426-4.

ARTICLE 427 — FIXED ELECTRIC HEATING EQUIPMENT FOR PIPELINES AND VESSELS

Contents

A. General

427-1. Scope. The requirements of this article shall apply to electrically energized heating systems and the installation of these systems used with pipelines and/or vessels.

Article 427 includes requirements for impedance heating, induction heating, and skin effect heating, in addition to resistance heating elements. Definitions of the various systems are provided in Section 427-2.

427-2. Definitions. For the purpose of this article:

Pipeline. A length of pipe including pumps, valves, flanges, control devices, strainers and/or similar equipment for conveying fluids.

Vessel. A container such as a barrel, drum, or tank for holding fluids or other material.

Integrated Heating System. A complete system consisting of components such as pipelines, vessels, heating elements, heat transfer medium, thermal insulation, moisture barrier, nonheating leads, temperature controllers, safety signs, junction boxes, raceways, and fittings.

550

Resistance Heating Element. A specific separate element to generate heat which is applied to the pipeline or vessel externally or internally.

(FPN): Tubular heaters, strip heaters, heating cable, heating tape, heating blankets, and immersion heaters are examples of resistance heaters.

Impedance Heating System. A system in which heat is generated in a pipeline or vessel wall by causing current to flow through the pipeline or vessel wall by direct connection to an ac voltage source from a dual-winding transformer.

Induction Heating System. A system in which heat is generated in a pipeline or vessel wall by inducing current and hysteresis effect in the pipeline or vessel wall from an external isolated ac field source.

Skin Effect Heating System. A system in which heat is generated on the inner surface of a ferromagnetic envelope attached to a pipeline and/or vessel.

(FPN): Typically, an electrically insulated conductor is routed through and connected to the envelope at the other end. The envelope and the electrically insulated conductor are connected to an ac voltage source from a dual-winding transformer.

427-3. Application of Other Articles. All requirements of this Code shall apply except as specifically amended in this article. Cord-connected pipe heating assemblies intended for specific use and identified as suitable for this use shall be installed according to Article 422. Fixed electric pipeline and vessel heating equipment for use in hazardous (classified) locations shall comply with Articles 500 through 516.

See Sections 422-7 and 422-8.

427-4. Branch-Circuit Sizing. The ampacity of branch-circuit conductors and the rating or setting of overcurrent protective devices supplying fixed electric heating equipment for pipelines and vessels shall be not less than 125 percent of the total load of the heaters. The rating or setting of overcurrent protective devices shall be permitted in accordance with Section 240-3, Exception No. 1.

B. Installation

427-10. General. Equipment for pipeline and vessel electrical heating shall be identified as being suitable for: (1) the chemical, thermal and physical environment; and (2) installation in accordance with the manufacturer's drawings and instructions.

427-11. Use. Electrical heating equipment shall be installed in such a manner as to be afforded protection from physical damage.

427-12. Thermal Protection. External surfaces of pipeline and vessel heating equipment which operate at temperatures exceeding 60°C (140°F) shall be physically guarded, isolated, or thermally insulated to protect against contact by personnel in the area.

427-13. Identification. The presence of electrically heated pipelines and/or vessels shall be evident by the posting of appropriate caution signs or markings at frequent intervals along the pipeline or vessel.

C. Resistance Heating Elements

427-14. Secured. Heating element assemblies shall be secured to the surface being heated by means other than the thermal insulation.

427-15. Not in Direct Contact. Where the heating element is not in direct contact with the pipeline or vessel being heated, means shall be provided to prevent overtemperature of the heating element unless the design of the heater assembly is such that its temperature limitations will not be exceeded.

427-16. Expansion and Contraction. Heating elements and assemblies shall not be installed where they bridge expansion joints unless provisions are made for expansion and contraction.

427-17. Flexural Capability. Where installed on flexible pipelines, the heating elements and assemblies shall have a flexural capability compatible with the pipeline.

427-18. Power Supply Leads.

(a) **Nonheating Leads.** Power supply nonheating leads (cold leads) for resistance elements shall be suitable for the temperature encountered. Preassembled nonheating leads on approved heaters shall be permitted to be shortened if the markings specified in Section 427-20 are retained. Not less than 6 inches (152 mm) of nonheating leads shall be provided within the junction box.

(b) **Power Supply Leads Protection.** Nonheating power supply leads shall be protected where they emerge from electrically heated pipeline or vessel heating units by rigid metal conduit, intermediate metal conduit, electrical metallic tubing, or other raceways identified as suitable for the application.

(c) **Interconnecting Leads.** Interconnecting nonheating leads connecting portions of the heating system shall be permitted to be covered by thermal insulation in the same manner as the heaters.

427-19. Electrical Connections.

(a) **Nonheating Interconnections.** Nonheating interconnections, where required under thermal insulation, shall be made with insulated connectors identified as suitable for this use.

(b) **Circuit Connections.** Splices and terminations outside the thermal insulation shall be installed in a box or fitting in accordance with Sections 110-14 and 300-15.

427-20. Marking. Each factory-assembled heating unit shall be legibly marked within 3 inches (76 mm) of each end of the nonheating leads with the permanent identification symbol, catalog number, and ratings in volts and watts, or in volts and amperes.

427-21. Grounding. Exposed noncurrent-carrying metal parts of electric heating equipment which are likely to become energized shall be grounded as required in Article 250.

427-22. Equipment Protection. Ground-fault protection of equipment shall be provided for branch circuits supplying electric heating equipment not having a metal covering.

The level of ground-fault protection normally used for personnel safety is 5 ma. This level may not be practical for an application where capacitive-type leakage, such as on long runs of heat-tracing cable, may be encountered. The intent of this section is to minimize the possibility of fire by providing equipment ground-fault protection as defined in Article 100, and to provide a degree of personnel safety by rapidly deenergizing a circuit that has developed a ground fault.

D. Impedance Heating

427-25. Personnel Protection. All accessible external surfaces of the pipeline and/or vessel being heated shall be physically guarded, isolated, or thermally insulated (with weatherproof jacket for outside installations) to protect against contact by personnel in the area.

427-26. Voltage Limitations. The pipeline or vessel being heated shall not operate at a voltage greater than 30 volts ac.

Exception: The voltage shall be permitted to be greater than 30 volts but not more than 80 volts if a ground-fault circuit-interrupter for personnel protection is provided.

427-27. Isolation Transformer. A dual-winding transformer with a grounded shield between the primary and secondary windings shall be used to isolate the distribution system from the heating system.

427-28. Induced Currents. All current-carrying components shall be installed in accordance with Section 300-20.

427-29. Grounding. The pipeline and/or vessel being heated which is operating at a voltage greater than 30 but not more than 80 shall be grounded at designated points.

427-30. Secondary Conductor Sizing. The ampacity of the conductors connected to the secondary of the transformer shall be rated at least 100 percent of the total load of the heater.

E. Induction Heating

427-35. Scope. This part covers the installation of line frequency induction heating equipment and accessories for pipelines and vessels.

(FPN): See Article 665 for other applications.

427-36. Personnel Protection. Induction coils that operate or may operate at a voltage greater than 30 volts ac shall be enclosed in a nonmetallic or split metallic enclosure, isolated or made inaccessible by location to protect personnel in the area.

427-37. Induced Current. Induction coils shall be prevented from inducing circulating currents in surrounding metallic equipment, supports, or structures by shielding, isolation, or insulation of the current paths. Stray current paths shall be bonded to prevent arcing.

F. Skin Effect Heating

427-45. Conductor Ampacity. The ampacity of the electrically insulated conductor inside the ferromagnetic envelope shall be permitted to exceed the values given in Article 310 provided it is identified as suitable for this use.

427-46. Pull Boxes. Pull boxes for pulling the electrically insulated conductor in the ferromagnetic envelope shall be permitted to be buried under the thermal insulation providing their locations are indicated by permanent markings on the insulation jacket surface and on drawings. For outdoor installations, pull boxes are to be of watertight construction.

427-47. Single Conductor in Enclosure. The provisions of Section 300-20 shall not apply to the installation of a single conductor in a ferromagnetic envelope (metal enclosure).

427-48. Grounding. The ferromagnetic envelope shall be grounded at both ends and, in addition, it shall be permitted to be grounded at intermediate points as required by its design. The ferromagnetic envelope shall be bonded at all joints to assure electrical continuity.

The provisions of Section 250-26 shall not apply to the installation of skin effect heating systems.

(FPN): See Section 250-26(d).

G. Control and Protection

427-55. Disconnecting Means.

(a) Switch or Circuit Breaker. Means shall be provided to disconnect all fixed electric pipeline or vessel heating equipment from all ungrounded conductors. The branch-circuit switch or circuit breaker, where readily accessible to the user of the equipment, shall be permitted to serve as the disconnecting means. Switches used as disconnecting means shall be of the indicating type, and shall be provided with a positive lockout in the "off" position.

(b) Cord- and Plug-Connected Equipment. The factory-installed attachment plug of cord- and plug-connected equipment rated 20 amperes or less and 150 volts or less to ground shall be permitted to be the disconnecting means.

427-56. Controls.

(a) Temperature Control with "Off" Position. Temperature controlled switching devices which indicate an "off" position and which interrupt line current shall open all ungrounded conductors when the control device is in this "off" position. These devices shall not be permitted to serve as the disconnecting means unless provided with a positive lockout in the "off" position.

(b) Temperature Control Without "Off" Position. Temperature controlled switching devices which do not have an "off" position shall not be required to open all ungrounded conductors and shall not be permitted to serve as the disconnecting means.

(c) Remote Temperature Controller. Remote controlled temperature actuated devices shall not be required to meet the requirements of Section 427-56(a) and (b). These devices shall not be permitted to serve as the disconnecting means.

(d) Combined Switching Devices. Switching devices consisting of combined temperature actuated devices and manually controlled switches which serve both as the controllers and the disconnecting means shall comply with all the following conditions:

(1) Open all ungrounded conductors when manually placed in the "off" position; and

(2) Be so designed that the circuit cannot be energized automatically if the device has been manually placed in the "off" position; and

(3) Be provided with a positive lockout in the "off" position.

427-57. Overcurrent Protection.
Heating equipment shall be considered as protected against overcurrent where supplied by a branch circuit as specified in Section 427-4.

ARTICLE 430 — MOTORS, MOTOR CIRCUITS, AND CONTROLLERS

Contents

A. General

430-1. Motor Feeder and Branch Circuits. The following general requirements cover provisions for motors, motor circuits, and controllers that do not properly fall into the other parts of this article.

(FPN): See Article 440 for air-conditioning and refrigerating equipment.

(FPN): Diagram 430-1 is for information only.

Diagram 430-1 is intended to assist the user in following the provisions of Article 430. It is explanatory material and not a *Code* requirement.

430-2. Adjustable Speed Drive Systems. The incoming branch circuit or feeder to power conversion equipment included as a part of an adjustable speed drive system shall be based on the rated input to the power conversion equipment. If the power conversion equipment provides overload protection for the motor, additional overload protection is not required.

The disconnecting means shall be permitted to be in the incoming line to the conversion equipment and shall have a rating not less than 115 percent of the rated input current of the conversion unit.

430-3. Part-Winding Motors. A part-winding-start induction or synchronous motor is one arranged for starting by first energizing part of its primary (armature) winding and, subsequently, energizing the remainder of this winding in one or more steps. The purpose is to reduce the initial values of the starting current drawn or the starting torque developed by the motor. A standard part-winding-start induction motor is arranged so that one-half of its primary winding can be energized initially and, subsequently, the remaining half can be energized, both halves then carrying equal current. A hermetic refrigerant compressor motor shall not be considered a standard part-winding-start induction motor.

Where separate overload devices are used with a standard part-winding-start induction motor, each half of the motor winding shall be individually protected in accordance with Sections 430-32 and 430-37 with a trip current one-half that specified.

Each motor-winding connection shall have branch-circuit short-circuit and ground-fault protection rated at not more than one-half that specified by Section 430-52.

Exception: A single device having this half rating shall be permitted for both windings if it will allow the motor to start. Where a time-delay (dual-element) fuse is used as a single device for both windings, it shall be permitted to have a rating not exceeding 150 percent of motor full-load current.

430-5. Other Articles. Motors and controllers shall also comply with the applicable provisions of the following:

ARTICLE 430—MOTORS, MOTOR CIRCUITS, CONTROLLERS

430-6. Ampacity and Motor Rating Determination. Conductors supplying equipment covered by this article shall be selected from Tables 310-16 through 310-31. The required ampacity and motor ratings shall be determined as specified in (a), (b) and (c) below.

(a) General Motor Applications. Other than as specified for torque motors in (b) below, where the current rating of a motor is used to determine the ampacity of conductors or ampere ratings of switches, branch-circuit short-circuit and ground-fault protection, etc., the values given in Tables 430-147, 430-148, 430-149, and 430-150, including notes, shall be used instead of the actual current rating marked on the motor nameplate. Separate motor overload protection shall be based on the motor nameplate current rating. Where a motor is marked in amperes, but not horsepower, the horsepower rating shall be assumed to be that corresponding to the value given in Tables 430-147, 430-148, 430-149, and 430-150, interpolated if necessary.

Exception No. 1: Multispeed motors shall be in accordance with Sections 430-22(a) and 430-52.

Exception No. 2: For equipment employing a shaded-pole or permanent-split-capacitor-type fan or blower motor that is marked with the motor type, the full-load current for such motor marked on the nameplate of the equipment in which the fan or blower motor is employed shall be used instead of the horsepower rating to determine the ampacity or rating of the disconnecting means, the branch-circuit conductors, the controller, the branch-circuit short-circuit and ground-fault protection, and the separate overload protection. This marking on the equipment nameplate shall not be less than the current marked on the fan or blower motor nameplate.

(b) Torque Motors. For torque motors the rated current shall be locked-rotor current, and this nameplate current shall be used to determine the ampacity of the branch-circuit conductors covered in Sections 430-22 and 430-24 and the ampere rating of the motor overload protection.

(FPN): For motor controllers and disconnecting means, see Section 430-83, Exception No. 3 and Section 430-110.

(c) AC Adjustable Voltage Motors. For motors used in alternating-current, adjustable voltage, variable torque drive systems, the ampacity of conductors, or ampere ratings of switches, branch-circuit short-circuit and ground-fault protection, etc., shall be based on the maximum operating current marked on the motor and/or control nameplate. If the maximum operating current does not appear on the nameplate, the ampacity determination shall be based on 150 percent of the values given in Tables 430-149 and 430-150.

430-7. Marking on Motors and Multimotor Equipment.

(a) Usual Motor Applications. A motor shall be marked with the following information:

(1) Maker's name.

Part A. General, Sections 430-1 through 430-18.
Part B. Motor Circuit Conductors, Sections 430-21 through 430-29.
Part C. Motor and Branch-Circuit Overload Protection, Sections 430-31 through 430-44.
Part D. Motor Branch-Circuit Short-Circuit and Ground-Fault Protection, Sections 430-51 through 430-58.
Part E. Motor Feeder Short-Circuit and Ground-Fault Protection, Sections 430-61 through 430-63.
Part F. Motor Control Circuits, Sections 430-71 through 430-74.
Part G. Motor Controllers, Sections 430-81 through 430-91.
Part H. Disconnecting Means, Sections 430-101 through 430-113.
Part J. Over 600 Volts, Nominal, Sections 430-121 through 430-127.
Part K. Protection of Live Parts — All Voltages, Sections 430-131 through 430-133.
Part L. Grounding All Voltages, Sections 430-141 through 430-145.
Part M. Tables, Tables 430-147 through 430-152.

To Supply	
Motor Feeder	Part B
	430-24
	430-25 and 430-26
Motor Feeder	Part E
Short-Circuit and Ground-Fault Protection	Part E
Motor Disconnecting Means	Part H
Motor Branch-Circuit Short-Circuit and Ground-Fault Protection	Part D
Motor Circuit Conductor	Part B
Motor Controller	Part G
Motor Control Circuits	Part F
Motor Overload Protection	Part C
Motor	Part A
Thermal Protection	Part C
Secondary Controller	Part B
Secondary Conductors	Sec. 430-23
Secondary	Sec. 430-23
Resistor	Part B
	and Art. 470

(FPN): Diagram 430-1.

(2) Rated volts and full-load amperes. For a multispeed motor full-load amperes for each speed, except shaded-pole and permanent-split capacitor motors where amperes are required only for maximum speed.

(3) Rated frequency and number of phases, if an alternating-current motor.

(4) Rated full-load speed.

(5) Rated temperature rise or the insulation system class and rated ambient temperature.

(6) Time rating. The time rating shall be 5, 15, 30, or 60 minutes, or continuous.

(7) Rated horsepower if ⅛ horsepower or more. For a multispeed motor ⅛ horsepower or more, rated horsepower for each speed, except shaded-pole and permanent-split capacitor motors ⅛ horsepower or more where rated horsepower is required only for maximum speed. Motors of arc welders are not required to be marked with the horsepower rating.

(8) Code letter if an alternating-current motor rated ½ horsepower or more. On polyphase wound-rotor motors the code letter shall be omitted.

(FPN): See (b) below.

(9) Secondary volts and full-load amperes if a wound-rotor induction motor.

(10) Field current and voltage for direct-current excited synchronous motors.

(11) Winding: straight shunt, stabilized shunt, compound, or series, if a direct-current motor. Fractional horsepower dc motors 7 inches (178 mm) or less in diameter shall not be required to be marked.

(12) A motor provided with a thermal protector complying with Section 430-32(a) (2) or (c) (2) shall be marked "Thermally Protected." Thermally protected motors rated 100 watts or less and complying with Section 430-32(c) (2) shall be permitted to use the abbreviated marking, "T.P."

(13) A motor complying with Section 430-32(c) (4) shall be marked "Impedance Protected." Impedance protected motors rated 100 watts or less and complying with Section 430-32(c) (4) shall be permitted to use the abbreviated marking "Z.P."

(b) Locked-Rotor Indicating Code Letters. Code letters marked on motor nameplates to show motor input with locked rotor shall be in accordance with Table 430-7(b).

The code letter indicating motor input with locked rotor shall be in an individual block on the nameplate, properly designated. This code letter shall be used for determining branch-circuit short-circuit and ground-fault protection by reference to Table 430-152, as provided in Section 430-52.

(1) Multispeed motors shall be marked with the code letter designating the locked-rotor kVA per horsepower for the highest speed at which the motor can be started.

Exception: Constant-horsepower multispeed motors shall be marked with the code letter giving the highest locked-rotor kVA per horsepower.

(2) Single-speed motors starting on Y connection and running on delta connections shall be marked with a code letter corresponding to the locked-rotor kVA per horsepower for the Y connection.

(3) Dual-voltage motors that have a different locked-rotor kVA per horsepower on the two voltages shall be marked with the code letter for the voltage giving the highest locked-rotor kVA per horsepower.

(4) Motors with 60- and 50-hertz ratings shall be marked with a code letter designating the locked-rotor kVA per horsepower on 60 hertz.

(5) Part-winding-start motors shall be marked with a code letter designating the locked-rotor kVA per horsepower that is based upon the locked-rotor current for the full winding of the motor.

Table 430-7(b). Locked-Rotor Indicating Code Letters

Code Letter		Kilovolt-Amperes per Horsepower with Locked Rotor
A	....	0 — 3.14
B	....	3.15— 3.54
C	....	3.55— 3.99
D	....	4.0 — 4.49
E	....	4.5 — 4.99
F	....	5.0 — 5.59
G	....	5.6 — 6.29
H	....	6.3 — 7.09
J	....	7.1 — 7.99
K	....	8.0 — 8.99
L	....	9.0 — 9.99
M	....	10.0 —11.19
N	....	11.2 —12.49
P	....	12.5 —13.99
R	....	14.0 —15.99
S	....	16.0 —17.99
T	....	18.0 —19.99
U	....	20.0 —22.39
V	....	22.4 —and up

(c) Torque Motors. Torque motors are rated for operation at standstill and shall be marked in accordance with (a) above.

Exception: Locked-rotor torque shall replace horsepower.

(d) Multimotor and Combination-Load Equipment. Multimotor and combination-load equipment shall be provided with a visible nameplate marked with the maker's name, the rating in volts, frequency, number of phases, minimum supply circuit conductor ampacity, and the maximum ampere rating of the circuit short-circuit and ground-fault protective device. The conductor ampacity shall be computed in accordance with Section 430-25 and counting all of the motors and other loads that will be operated at the same time. The short-circuit and ground-fault protective device rating shall not exceed the value computed in accordance with Section 430-53. Multimotor equipment for use on two or more circuits shall be marked with the above information for each circuit.

Where the equipment is not factory-wired and the individual nameplates of motors and other loads are visible after assembly of the equipment, the individual nameplates shall be permitted to serve as the required marking.

The nameplate marking of the maximum ampere rating of the branch-circuit short-circuit and ground-fault protective device may limit the type of protective device to a fuse by stipulating "fuse" without reference to a circuit breaker. This means that the circuit to the equipment is required to be protected by fuses, such as in a fused disconnect switch. The fused switch could be supplied from a circuit breaker in a panelboard.

430-8. Marking on Controllers. A controller shall be marked with the maker's name or identification, the voltage, the current or horsepower rating, and such other necessary data to properly indicate the motors for which it is suitable. A controller that includes motor overload protection suitable for group motor application shall be marked with the motor overload protection and the maximum branch-circuit short-circuit and ground-fault protection for such applications.

Combination controllers employing adjustable instantaneous trip circuit breakers shall be clearly marked to indicate the ampere settings of the adjustable trip element.

Where a controller is built in as an integral part of a motor or of a motor-generator set, individual marking of the controller shall not be required if the necessary data are on the nameplate. For controllers that are an integral part of equipment approved as a unit, the above marking shall be permitted on the equipment nameplate.

430-9. Terminals.

(a) Markings. Terminals of motors and controllers shall be suitably marked or colored where necessary to indicate the proper connections.

(b) Conductors. Motor controllers and terminals of control circuit devices shall be connected with copper conductors unless identified for use with a different conductor.

Terminals for motor controllers are tested, designed, and listed using copper conductors. This section highlights this limitation while permitting other conductors to be used in future equipment if determined to be suitable and identified as such.

(c) Torque Requirements. Control circuit devices with screw-type pressure terminals used with No. 14 AWG or smaller copper conductors shall be torqued to a minimum of 7 pound-inches (0.79 N-m) unless identified for a different torque value.

Proper torque is essential for safe and reliable connections. This new section enhances safety by providing a minimum torque value for screw-type pressure terminals. The value chosen, 7 pound-inches, is specified in Table 7.5 of UL 486, *Equipment Wiring Terminals*, as the minimum tightening torque for screw-type pressure terminals (unless marked otherwise).

430-10. Wiring Space in Enclosures.

(a) General. Enclosures for motor controllers and disconnecting means shall not be used as junction boxes, auxiliary gutters, or raceways for conductors feeding through or tapping off to the other apparatus unless designs are employed which provide adequate space for this purpose.

(FPN): See Section 373-8 for switch and overcurrent-device enclosures.

During the planning stages of a motor(s) installation, consideration should be given to location and proper working spaces (as required by Sections 110-16 and 110-34) for motor controllers and disconnects, including provisions for the use of auxiliary gutters or junction boxes to assure space for conductor feeding through or tapping off to other apparatus.

For switch and overcurrent device enclosures, see Section 373-8.

(b) Wire Bending Space in Enclosures. Minimum wire bending space within the enclosures for motor controllers shall be in accordance with Table 430-10(b) when measured in a straight line from the end of the lug or wire connector (in the direction the wire leaves the terminal) to the wall or barrier. Where alternate wire termination means is substituted for that supplied by the manufacturer of the controller, it shall be of a type identified by the manufacturer for use with the controller and shall not reduce the minimum wire bending space.

Where the enclosure is a motor control center, the minimum wire bending space shall be in accordance with requirements of Article 373.

See Figure 430-1 for illustration of measurement in accordance with Section 430-10(b).

Figure 430-1. Wire bending space in enclosures for motor controllers.

Table 430-10(b). Minimum Wire Bending Space at the Terminals of Enclosed Motor Controllers (in Inches)

AWG or Circular-Mil Size of Wire	*Wires per Terminal	
	1	2
14–10	Not specified	—
8–6	1½	—
4–3	2	—
2	2½	—
1	3	—
1/0	5	5
2/0	6	6
3/0–4/0	7	7
250	8	8
300	10	10
350–500	12	12
600–700	14	16
750–900	18	19

* Where provision for 3 or more wires per terminal exists the minimum wire bending space shall be in accordance with the requirements of Article 373.

430-11. Protection Against Liquids. Suitable guards or enclosures shall be provided to protect exposed current-carrying parts of motors and the insulation of motor leads where installed directly under equipment, or in other locations where dripping or spraying oil, water, or other injurious liquid may occur, unless the motor is designed for the existing conditions.

Exposed current-carrying parts and insulated leads of motors should be suitably protected from injurious liquids (dripping or sprayed oil or other lubricants, water, or excessive moisture) whose presence may cause an insulation breakdown.

430-12. Motor Terminal Housings.

(a) Material. Where motors are provided with terminal housings, the housings shall be of metal and of substantial construction.

Exception: In other than hazardous (classified) locations, substantial, nonmetallic, nonburning housings shall be permitted provided an internal grounding means between the motor frame and the equipment grounding connection is incorporated within the housing.

This exception was revised for the 1987 *NEC.* The previous rule limited the exception to motors larger than 34 inches in diameter. Nonmetallic terminal housings are now permitted on motors of any size provided the housing material has been determined to be nonburning, for example, a flammability rating of at least 94-5V in accordance with UL 746C - Polymeric Materials—Use in Electrical Equipment Evaluations.

(b) Dimensions and Space — Wire-to-Wire Connections. When these terminal housings enclose wire-to-wire connections, they shall have minimum dimensions and usable volumes in accordance with Table 430-12(b).

Table 430-12(b). Terminal Housings—Wire-to-Wire Connections
Motors 11 Inches in Diameter or Less

HP	Cover Opening, Minimum Dimension, Inches	Usable Volume, Minimum Cubic Inches
1 and smaller*	1⅛	7½
1½, 2 and 3†	1¾	12
5 and 7½	2	16
10 and 15	2½	26

For SI units: one inch = 25.4 millimeters.

* For motors rated 1 horsepower and smaller and with the terminal housing partially or wholly integral with the frame or end shield, the volume of the terminal housing shall be not less than 0.8 cubic inch per wire-to-wire connection. The minimum cover opening dimension is not specified.

† For motors rated 1½, 2 and 3 horsepower and with the terminal housing partially or wholly integral with the frame or end shield, the volume of the terminal housing shall not be less than 1.0 cubic inch per wire-to-wire connection. The minimum cover opening dimension is not specified.

(c) Dimensions and Space — Fixed Terminal Connections. Where these terminal housings enclose rigidly mounted motor terminals, the terminal housing shall be of sufficient size to provide minimum terminal spacings and usable volumes in accordance with Tables 430-12(c)(1) and (c)(2).

(d) Large Wire or Factory Connections. For motors with larger ratings, greater number of leads, or larger wire sizes, or where motors are installed as a part of factory-wired equipment, without additional connection being required at the motor terminal housing during equipment installation, the terminal housing shall be of ample size to make connections, but the foregoing provisions for the volumes of terminal housings shall not be considered applicable.

Motors Over 11 Inches in Diameter
Alternating-Current Motors

Max. Full-load Current for Three-phase Motors with Max. of Twelve Leads Amperes	Terminal Box Minimum Dimension Inches	Usable Volume, Minimum Cubic Inches	Typical Maximum Horsepower Three Phase	
			230 Volt	460 Volt
45	2.5	26	15	30
70	3.3	55	25	50
110	4.0	100	40	75
160	5.0	180	60	125
250	6.0	330	100	200
400	7.0	600	150	300
600	8.0	1100	250	500

For SI units: one inch = 25.4 millimeters.

Direct-Current Motors

Maximum Full-Load Current for Motors with Maximum of Six Leads Amperes	Terminal Box Minimum Dimensions Inches	Usable Volume, Minimum Cubic Inches
68	2.5	26
105	3.3	55
165	4.0	100
240	5.0	180
375	6.0	330
600	7.0	600
900	8.0	1100

For SI units: one inch = 25.4 millimeters.
Auxiliary leads for such items as brakes, thermostats, space heater, exciting fields, etc., may be neglected if their current-carrying area does not exceed 25 percent of the current-carrying area of the machine power leads.

Table 430-12(c)(1). Terminal Spacings—Fixed Terminals

	Minimum Spacing, Inches	
Nominal Volts	Between Line Terminals	Between Line Terminals and Other Uninsulated Metal Parts
240 or less	¼	¼
Over 250 through 600	⅜	⅜

For SI units: one inch = 25.4 millimeters.

Table 430-12(c)(2). Usable Volumes—Fixed Terminals

Power-Suppy Conductor Size, AWG	Minimum Usable Volume per Power-Supply Conductor, Cubic Inches
14	1.0
12 and 10	1¼
8 and 6	2¼

For SI units: one inch = 25.4 millimeters.

565

(e) Equipment Grounding Connections. A means for attachment of an equipment grounding conductor termination in accordance with Section 250-113 shall be provided at motor terminal housings for wire-to-wire connections or fixed terminal connections. The means for such connections shall be permitted to be located either inside or outside the motor terminal housing.

Exception: Where a motor is installed as a part of factory-wired equipment, which is required to be grounded and without additional connection being required at the motor terminal housing during equipment installation, a separate means for motor grounding at the motor terminal housing shall not be required.

430-13. Bushing. Where wires pass through an opening in an enclosure, conduit box, or barrier, a bushing shall be used to protect the conductors from the edges of openings having sharp edges. The bushing shall have smooth well-rounded surfaces where it may be in contact with the conductors. If used where oils, greases, or other contaminants may be present, the bushing shall be made of material not deleteriously affected.

(FPN): For conductors exposed to deteriorating agents, see Section 310-9.

430-14. Location of Motors.

(a) Ventilation and Maintenance. Motors shall be located so that adequate ventilation is provided and so that maintenance, such as lubrication of bearings and replacing of brushes, can be readily accomplished.

(b) Open Motors. Open motors having commutators or collector rings shall be located or protected so that sparks cannot reach adjacent combustible material, but this shall not prohibit the installation of these motors on wooden floors or supports.

430-16. Exposure to Dust Accumulations. In locations where dust or flying material will collect on or in motors in such quantities as to seriously interfere with the ventilation or cooling of motors and thereby cause dangerous temperatures, suitable types of enclosed motors that will not overheat under the prevailing conditions shall be used.

(FPN): Especially severe conditions may require the use of enclosed pipe-ventilated motors, or enclosure in separate dusttight rooms, properly ventilated from a source of clean air.

For motors exposed to combustible dust or readily ignitible flying material, see the requirements of Sections 502-8 and 502-9 (Class II, Divisions 1 and 2) and Sections 503-6 and 503-7 (Class III, Divisions 1 and 2). For classification of locations, see Sections 500-6 (Class II locations) and 500-7 (Class III locations).

430-17. Highest Rated (Largest) Motor. In determining compliance with Sections 430-24, 430-53(b), and 430-53(c), the highest rated (largest) motor shall be considered to be that motor having the highest rated full-load current. The full-load current used to determine the highest rated motor shall be the equivalent value corresponding to the motor horsepower rating selected from Tables 430-147, 430-148, 430-149, and 430-150.

430-18. Nominal Voltage of Rectifier Systems. The nominal value of the ac voltage being rectified shall be used to determine the voltage of a rectifier derived system.

Exception: The nominal dc voltage of the rectifier shall be used if it exceeds the peak value of the ac voltage being rectified.

B. Motor Circuit Conductors

430-21. General. Part B specifies sizes of conductors capable of carrying the motor current without overheating under the conditions specified.

Exception: The provisions of Section 430-124 shall apply over 600 volts, nominal.

The provisions of Articles 250, 300, and 310 shall not apply to conductors that form an integral part of approved equipment, or to integral conductors of motors, motor controllers, and the like.

(FPN): See Sections 300-1(b) and 310-1.

(FPN): See Section 430-9(b) for equipment device terminal requirements.

430-22. Single Motor.

(a) General. Branch-circuit conductors supplying a single motor shall have an ampacity not less than 125 percent of the motor full-load current rating.

In case of a multispeed motor, the selection of branch-circuit conductors on the line side of the controller shall be based on the highest of the full-load current ratings shown on the motor nameplate; selection of branch-circuit conductors between the controller and the motor, which are energized for that particular speed, shall be based on the current rating for that speed.

(FPN): See Example No. 8, Chapter 9 and Diagram 430-1.

Exception No. 1: Conductors for a motor used for short-time, intermittent, periodic, or varying duty shall have an ampacity not less than the percentage of the motor nameplate current rating shown in Table 430-22(a) Exception unless the authority having jurisdiction grants special permission for conductors of smaller size.

Exception No. 2: For direct-current motors operating from a rectified single-phase power supply, the conductors between the controller and the motor shall have an ampacity of not less than the following percent of the motor full-load current rating:

a. Where a rectifier bridge of the single-phase half-wave type is used, 190 percent.

b. Where a rectifier bridge of the single-phase full-wave type is used, 150 percent.

Table 430-22(a) Exception.   Duty-Cycle Service

Classification of Service	Percentages of Nameplate Current Rating			
	5-Minute Rated Motor	15-Minute Rated Motor	30- & 60-Minute Rated Motor	Con-tinuous Rated Motor
Short-Time Duty Operating valves, raising or lowering rolls, etc..............................	110	120	150	. . .
Intermittent Duty Freight and passenger elevators, tool heads, pumps, drawbridges, turntables, etc. For arc welders, see Section 630-21.....................	85	85	90	140
Periodic Duty Rolls, ore- and coal-handling machines, etc.	85	90	95	140
Varying Duty...............................	110	120	150	200

Any motor application shall be considered as continuous duty unless the nature of the apparatus it drives is such that the motor will not operate continuously with load under any condition of use.

ARTICLE 430—MOTORS, MOTOR CIRCUITS, CONTROLLERS

The provision for a conductor with an ampacity of at least 125 percent of the motor full-load current rating is not a conductor derating. It is based on the need to provide for a sustained running current greater than the rated full-load current and for protection of the conductors by the motor overload protective device set above the motor full-load current rating.

The ampacity of the motor branch-circuit conductors is based on the full-load current rating values provided in Tables 430-147 through 430-150.

(b) Separate Terminal Enclosure. The conductors between a stationary motor rated 1 horsepower or less and the separate terminal enclosure permitted in Section 430-145(b) shall be permitted to be smaller than No. 14 but not smaller than No. 18, provided they have an ampacity as specified in (a) above.

Section 240-40 requires a disconnecting means on the supply side of cartridge fuses to disconnect the fuses from the source of electrical energy.

Figure 430-2 illustrates each motor on an individual branch circuit with branch-circuit short-circuit and ground-fault protective devices located at a distribution panel and disconnecting means, controllers, and overload protection at the motor locations.

Figure 430-3 also illustrates each motor on an individual branch circuit, but, unlike Figure 430-2, the branch circuits are tapped from a subfeeder at a convenient location such as a junction box, wireway, or from open wiring. The tap conductors are required to terminate in a branch-circuit protective device located not more than 25 ft from where the taps are connected to the subfeeder in accordance with Section 430-28. Also see Section 430-28, Exception which permits a 100-ft tap under some conditions.

Where motors or motor-operated appliances are connected to a 15- or 20-A branch circuit that also supplies lighting, or other appliance loads, as illustrated in Figure 430-4, the provisions of Articles 210 and 430 apply. Motors rated less than 1 hp may be connected to these circuits and are required to be provided with overload protective devices unless the motors are not permanently installed, are started manually, and are within sight from the controller location. For additional information for the installation of motors (1 hp or less), see Sections 430-32(b) and (c), and 430-53(a).

Figure 430-5 illustrates the essential parts of a motor branch circuit: (1) the branch-circuit conductors, (2) the disconnecting means, (3) the branch-circuit short-circuit and ground-fault protective devices, and (4) the motor overload protective devices. The branch-circuit short-circuit and ground-fault protective device may be fuses or a circuit breaker and is required to be capable of carrying the starting current of the motor without opening the circuit. See Table 430-152.

In general, it is required that every motor be provided with overload protective devices intended to protect motors, motor-control apparatus, and motor branch-circuit conductors against excessive heating due to motor overloads and failure to start. Overload in equipment is defined as operation in excess of normal, full-load rating, which, when it persists for a sufficient length of time, will cause damage or dangerous overheating. Overload in a motor includes stalled rotor, but does not include fault currents due to short circuits or grounds. See Section 430-44 for conditions where providing automatic opening of a motor circuit due to overload may be objectionable.

A motor is considered to be for continuous duty unless the nature of the apparatus it drives is such that the motor cannot operate continuously with load under any condition of use. Conductors for a motor used for short-time, intermittent, periodic, or varying duty are required to have an ampacity in accordance with Table 430-22(a), Exception. Branch-circuit conductors for a motor with a rated horsepower used for 5-minute short-time duty service are permitted to be sized smaller than for the same motor with a 60-minute rating, due to the cooling intervals between operating periods.

When selecting the smallest permissible size branch-circuit conductors for elevator motors, which are generally considered intermittent duty motors, it is safest to be guided by the recommendations of the manufacturer of the equipment. This also applies to feeders of two or more elevator motors or other types of similar equipment.

430-23. Wound-Rotor Secondary.

(a) Continuous Duty. For continuous duty, the conductors connecting the secondary of a

Figure 430-2. Layout showing each motor supplied by an individual branch circuit from a distribution center. (*branch-circuit, short-circuit, and ground-fault protective devices)

Figure 430-3. Layout showing a subfeeder supplying individual branch circuits to each motor.

No. 12 copper or
No. 10 aluminum Mains

20 A

(L) Lighting
(L) load

(M) Motors
(M) (less than 1 hp)

(A)
(A) Appliances

Figure 430-4. Layout showing a 20-A
branch circuit supplying small motors,
lamps, and appliances.

Mains

Protective devices,
fuses, or circuit
breaker

Branch-circuit conductor
ampacity 125% of the
motor full-load current
rating

Disconnecting
means

Controller with motor
overload protection generally
set at 125% of the motor
full-load current rating

Motor

Figure 430-5. A motor branch circuit showing
the three essential parts, that is, the branch-
circuit conductors, branch-circuit overcurrent
protection, and motor overload protection.

wound-rotor alternating-current motor to its controller shall have an ampacity not less than 125 percent of the full-load secondary current of the motor.

(b) Other than Continuous Duty. For other than continuous duty, these conductors shall have an ampacity, in percent of full-load secondary current, not less than that specified in Table 430-22(a) Exception.

(c) Resistor Separate from Controller. Where the secondary resistor is separate from the controller, the ampacity of the conductors between controller and resistor shall not be less than that given in Table 430-23(c).

Wound-rotor ac motors are generally used where speed control is desired, where high starting torque for a rapid smooth acceleration to full load is required, for frequent starting, and for low starting current. These motors are also known as slip-ring motors because three slip rings are mounted on the shaft, and brushes, which are in contact with the slip rings, are connected to field-installed external resistance units and a controller. See Figure 430-6. The resistors are a part of the rotor circuit, and all of the resistance value is in the circuit when starting the motor. This value is reduced gradually until all of it is out of the circuit and the motor is at maximum speed, or until the motor is at a desired speed.

Table 430-23(c). Secondary Conductor

Resistor Duty Classification	Ampacity of Conductor in Percent of Full-Load Secondary Current
Light starting duty	35
Heavy starting duty	45
Extra-heavy starting duty	55
Light intermittent duty	65
Medium intermittent duty	75
Heavy intermittent duty	85
Continuous duty	110

The selection of a controller used for speed regulation, usually a dial-type or a drum-type switch, is basically for two types of loads, that is, constant-torque (machine loads) and variable-torque (fan loads).

The ampacities of the conductors between the controller and the resistor units are the allowable percentages of Table 430-23(c) for the resistor classification of duty.

Figure 430-6. A branch circuit to a wound-rotor induction motor showing a drum controller and separate bank of resistors for motor starting and speed regulation.

430-24. Conductors Supplying Several Motors. Conductors supplying two or more motors shall have an ampacity equal to the sum of the full-load current rating of all the motors plus 25 percent of the highest rated motor in the group.

Where one or more motors of the group are used on short-time, intermittent, periodic, or varying duty, the ampacity of the conductors shall be computed as follows:

(1) Determine the needed ampere rating for each motor used for other than continuous duty from Table 430-22(a) Exception.

(2) Determine the needed ampere rating for each continuous-duty motor based on 100 percent motor full-load current rating.

571

(3) Multiply the largest single motor ampere rating determined from (1) or (2) above by 1.25. Add all other motor ampere ratings from (1) and (2) above and select the conductor ampacity for this total ampere rating.

Exception: Where the circuitry is so interlocked as to prevent the starting and running of a second motor or group of motors, the conductor size shall be determined from the larger motor or group of motors that is to be operated at a given time.

(FPN): See Example No. 8, Chapter 9.

Where the conductors are feeders, the highest rating or setting of the feeder short-circuit and ground-fault protective devices for the minimum size feeder conductor permitted by this section is specified in Section 430-62.

The size of the feeder conductors is required to be increased accordingly where the selection of a feeder protective device of higher rating or setting is based on the simultaneous starting of two or more motors.

These requirements, and those of Section 430-62 for the short-circuit and ground-fault protection of power feeders, are based upon the principle that a power feeder should be of such size that it will have an ampacity equal to 125 percent of the full-load current of the largest motor, plus the full-load currents of all other motors supplied by the feeder. Except when two or more motors may be started simultaneously, the heaviest load that a power feeder will ever be required to carry occurs when the largest motor is started at a time when all the other motors supplied by the same feeder are running and delivering their full-rated horsepower.

Where the conductors are branch-circuit conductors to multimotor equipment, Section 430-53 specifies the maximum rating of the branch-circuit short-circuit and ground-fault protective device. Section 430-7(d) requires the maximum ampere rating of the short-circuit and ground-fault protective device to be marked on the equipment.

430-25. Conductors Supplying Motors and Other Loads.

(a) Combination Load. Conductors supplying a motor load and in addition a lighting or appliance load shall have an ampacity sufficient for the lighting or appliance load computed in accordance with Article 220 and other applicable sections plus the motor load determined in accordance with Section 430-24 or, for a single motor, in accordance with Section 430-22.

Exception: The ampacity of conductors supplying motor-operated fixed electric space heating equipment shall conform with Section 424-3(b).

(b) Multimotor and Combination-Load Equipment. The ampacity of the conductors supplying multimotor and combination-load equipment shall not be less than the minimum circuit ampacity marked on the equipment in accordance with Section 430-7(d).

To compute the load for the minimum allowable conductor size for a combination lighting (or lighting and appliance) load and motor load, the capacity for the lighting load is determined in accordance with Article 220 (and other applicable sections, Article 422, etc.) plus the sum of the motor load, determined in accordance with Section 430-22 (single motor), or Section 430-24 (two or more motors).

430-26. Feeder Demand Factor.

Where reduced heating of the conductors results from motors operating on duty-cycle, intermittently, or from all motors not operating at one time, the authority having jurisdiction may grant permission for feeder conductors to have an ampacity less than specified in Sections 430-24 and 430-25, provided the conductors have sufficient ampacity for the maximum load determined in accordance with the sizes and number of motors supplied and the character of their loads and duties.

The authority having jurisdiction may grant permission to allow a demand factor of less than 100 percent for industrial plants where operational procedures, production demands, or the nature of the work is such that all the motors are not running at one time.

430-27. Capacitors with Motors. Where capacitors are installed in motor circuits, conductors shall comply with Sections 460-8 and 460-9.

430-28. Feeder Taps. Feeder tap conductors shall have an ampacity not less than that required by Part B, shall terminate in a branch-circuit protective device and, in addition, shall meet one of the following requirements: (1) be enclosed by either an enclosed controller or by a raceway and be not more than 10 feet (3.05 m) in length; or (2) have an ampacity of at least one-third that of the feeder conductors, be protected from physical damage and be not more than 25 feet (7.62 m) in length; or (3) have the same ampacity as the feeder conductors.

Short-circuit and ground-fault protection is not required at a point where a tap conductor, equal in size to the feeder conductor from which it is supplied, is used. The tap conductors are required to be protected by the same short-circuit and ground-fault protection (fuses or circuit breakers) protecting the feeder conductors.

In addition to the above, short-circuit and ground-fault protection can be omitted at the point of connection to a feeder where a tap conductor, which may be less than ⅓ of the feeder size, is limited to 10 ft or less in length and enclosed within a controller or raceway, and where a tap conductor, which is at least ⅓ the ampacity of the feeder, is limited to 25 ft or less in length and suitably protected from physical damage. In high-bay manufacturing buildings, feeder taps up to 100 ft long are permitted under Section 430-28, Exception.

Tap conductors are required to terminate in a branch-circuit short-circuit and ground-fault protective device. Conductors from this point to the motor-running protective device and to the motor are required to have an ampacity that is 125 percent of the full-load motor current, as specified in Section 430-22.

Example: A 15-hp 230-V 3-phase motor with autotransformer starter is to be supplied by a tap made to a 250 MCM feeder. Assuming three conductors in an individual raceway, all to be Type THW copper, and no ambient correction factor, the feeder has an ampacity of 255 A (see Table 310-16). Where the tap conductors are not over 25 ft long (see Figure 430-7), No. 4 AWG conductors with an ampacity of 85 A are permitted (⅓ × 255 A = 85 A).

The full-load current of the motor is 42 A and, according to Part D of Article 430, assuming that the motor is not marked with a code letter, the branch-circuit fuses or circuit breakers are permitted to be rated at 90 A (nontime-delay fuse) or less in accordance with Table 430-152 and Section 430-52, Exception No. 1. With the motor overload protection set at 50 A the tap conductors are well protected from overload.

Tap conductors connected to feeders are not permitted to be sized smaller than the ampacity of branch-circuit conductors required by Section 430-22.

Exception: Feeder Taps Over 25 Feet (7.62 m) Long. In high-bay manufacturing buildings {over 35 feet (10.67 m) high at walls} conductors tapped to a feeder shall be permitted to be not over 25 feet (7.62 m) long horizontally and not over 100 feet (30.5) total length where all of the following conditions are met:

a. The ampacity of the tap conductors is not less than one-third that of the feeder conductors.

b. The tap conductors terminate with a single circuit breaker or a single set of fuses conforming with (1) Part D if the tap is a branch circuit or (2) Part E if the tap is a feeder.

Figure 430-7. Protective devices (branch-circuit, short-circuit, and ground-fault) for a branch circuit located not more than 25 ft from the point where the conductors are tapped to the main feeder.

c. The tap conductors are suitably protected from physical damage and are installed in raceways.

d. The tap conductors are continuous from end-to-end and contain no splices.

e. The tap conductors shall be No. 6 AWG copper or No. 4 AWG aluminum or larger.

f. The tap conductors shall not penetrate walls, floors, or ceilings.

430-29. Constant Voltage DC Motors — Power Resistors. Conductors connecting the motor controller to separately mounted power accelerating and dynamic braking resistors in the armature circuit shall have an ampacity not less than the value calculated from Table 430-29 using motor full-load current. If an armature shunt resistor is used, the power accelerating resistor conductor ampacity shall be calculated using the total of motor full-load current and armature shunt resistor current.

Armature shunt resistor conductors shall have an ampacity of not less than that calculated from Table 430-29 using rated shunt resistor current as full-load current.

Table 430-29. Conductor Rating Factors for Power Resistors

| Time in Seconds | | Ampacity of Conductor in Percent |
On	Off	of Full-Load Current
5	75	35
10	70	45
15	75	55
15	45	65
15	30	75
15	15	85
Continuous Duty		110

C. Motor and Branch-Circuit Overload Protection

430-31. General. Part C specifies overload devices intended to protect motors, motor-control apparatus, and motor branch-circuit conductors against excessive heating due to motor overloads and failure to start.

Overload in electrical apparatus is an operating overcurrent which, when it persists for a sufficient length of time, would cause damage or dangerous overheating of the apparatus. It does not include short circuits or ground faults.

These provisions shall not be interpreted as requiring overload protection where it might introduce additional or increased hazards, as in the case of fire pumps.

(FPN): See Installation of Centrifugal Fire Pumps, NFPA 20-1983 (ANSI).

See Section 230-90(a), Exception No. 4 for the commentary on centrifugal fire pumps.

The provisions of Part C shall not apply to motor circuits rated over 600 volts, nominal. See Part J.

(FPN): See Example No. 8, Chapter 9.

NFPA 20-1983, Standard for the Installation of Centrifugal Fire Pumps, contains, in general, the minimum requirements for the selection and installation of centrifugal fire pumps.

Table 430-152 lists the allowable percentages of full-load current for the selection of the maximum rating or setting of motor branch-circuit short-circuit and ground-fault protective devices. The motor branch-circuit, short-circuit and ground-fault protective device is required to be capable of carrying the starting current of the motor without opening the circuit; therefore, the protective device cannot provide overload protection for the motor.

Fire pump motors require circuit breakers and are allowed much larger short-circuit and ground-fault protection than other motors recognizing that the pump should be allowed to operate to failure rather than be removed from the line, under adverse fire conditions. A manually operated fuseless isolating switch is required to be connected ahead (supply side) of the circuit breaker.

For squirrel-cage induction motors, which are generally used, the circuit breaker is required to be of the time-delay type and have a time delay of not over 20 seconds at locked-rotor current (approximately 600 percent of the rated full-load motor current) and is required to be calibrated up to and set at 300 percent of the motor full-load current.

Combined overload protection (special-type fuses), as described in Section 430-55, is permitted as a single protective device. In most cases where motor overload protection is provided, however, the motor controller consists of a switch or contactor to control the circuit to the motor, and the motor-overload protective device is an overload relay with a heater coil selected to match the motor.

430-32. Continuous-Duty Motors.

(a) More than 1 Horsepower. Each continuous-duty motor rated more than 1 horsepower shall be protected against overload by one of the following means:

(1) A separate overload device that is responsive to motor current. This device shall be selected to trip or rated at no more than the following percent of the motor nameplate full-load current rating.

Motors with a marked service factor not less than 1.15 .... 125%
Motors with a marked temperature rise not over 40°C.. 125%
All other motors 115%

Modification of this value shall be permitted as provided in Section 430-34.

For a multispeed motor, each winding connection shall be considered separately.

Where a separate motor overload device is so connected that it does not carry the total current designated on the motor nameplate, such as for wye-delta starting, the proper percentage of nameplate current applying to the selection or setting of the overload device shall be clearly designated on the equipment, or the manufacturer's selection table shall take this into account.

(2) A thermal protector integral with the motor, approved for use with the motor it protects on the basis that it will prevent dangerous overheating of the motor due to overload and failure to start. The ultimate trip current of a thermally protected motor shall not exceed the following percentage of motor full-load current given in Tables 430-148, 430-149, and 430-150.

Motor full-load current not exceeding 9 amperes 170%
Motor full-load current 9.1 to and including 20 amperes 156%
Motor full-load current greater than 20 amperes... 140%

If the motor current-interrupting device is separate from the motor and its control circuit is operated by a protective device integral with the motor, it shall be so arranged that the opening of the control circuit will result in interruption of current to the motor.

Figure 430-8. Line-voltage magnetic starter. (*Square D Co.*)

Type S

Figure 430-9. A Type S nonrenewable plug fuse and adapter.

(3) A protective device integral with a motor that will protect the motor against damage due to failure to start shall be permitted if the motor is part of an approved assembly that does not normally subject the motor to overloads.

(4) For motors larger than 1500 horsepower, a protective device having embedded temperature detectors that cause current to the motor to be interrupted when the motor attains a temperature rise greater than marked on the nameplate in an ambient of 40°C.

(b) One Horsepower or Less, Nonautomatically Started.

(1) Each continuous-duty motor rated at 1 horsepower or less that is not permanently installed, is nonautomatically started, and is within sight from the controller location shall be

permitted to be protected against overload by the branch-circuit short-circuit and ground-fault protective device. This branch-circuit protective device shall not be larger than that specified in Part D of Article 430.

Exception: Any such motor shall be permitted on a nominal 120-volt branch circuit protected at not over 20 amperes.

(2) Any such motor that is not in sight from the controller location shall be protected as specified in Section 430-32(c). Any motor rated at 1 horsepower or less that is permanently installed shall be protected in accordance with Section 430-32(c).

(c) One Horsepower or Less, Automatically Started. Any motor of 1 horsepower or less that is started automatically shall be protected against overload by one of the following means:

(1) A separate overload device that is responsive to motor current. This device shall be selected to trip or rated at no more than the following percentage of the motor nameplate full-load current rating.

Motors with a marked service factor not less than 1.15	125%
Motors with a marked temperature rise not over 40°C	125%
All other motors	115%

For a multispeed motor, each winding connection shall be considered separately. Modification of this value shall be permitted as provided in Section 430-34.

(2) A thermal protector integral with the motor, approved for use with the motor which it protects on the basis that it will prevent dangerous overheating of the motor due to overload and failure to start. Where the motor current interrupting device is separate from the motor and its control circuit is operated by a protective device integral with the motor, it shall be so arranged that the opening of the control circuit will result in interruption of current to the motor.

(3) A protective device integral with a motor that will protect the motor against damage due to failure to start shall be permitted (1) if the motor is part of an approved assembly that does not subject the motor to overloads, or (2) if the assembly is also equipped with other safety controls (such as the safety combustion controls on a domestic oil burner) that protect the motor against damage due to failure to start. Where the assembly has safety controls that protect the motor, it shall be so indicated on the nameplate of the assembly where it will be visible after installation.

(4) In case the impedance of the motor windings is sufficient to prevent overheating due to failure to start, the motor shall be permitted to be protected as specified in Section 430-32(b)(1) for manually started motors if the motor is part of an approved assembly in which the motor will limit itself so that it will not be dangerously overheated.

(FPN): Many alternating-current motors of less than $\frac{1}{20}$ horsepower, such as clock motors, series motors, etc., and also some larger motors such as torque motors, come within this classification. It does not include split-phase motors having automatic switches that disconnect the starting windings.

(d) Wound-Rotor Secondaries. The secondary circuits of wound-rotor alternating-current motors, including conductors, controllers, resistors, etc., shall be permitted to be protected against overload by the motor-overload device.

Operation of a motor in excess of its normal full-load rating for a prolonged period of time causes damage or dangerous overheating which may start a fire. Overload protection is intended to protect the motor and the system components from damaging overload currents.

A continuous-duty motor with a marked service factor not less than 1.15 or with a marked temperature rise not over 40°C can carry a 25 percent overload for an extended period of time without damage to the motor. Other types of motors are those with a service factor less than 1.15 or with a marked temperature rise greater than 40°C and are not capable of withstanding a prolonged overload, and the motor-overload protective device should open the circuit should the motor continue to draw 115 percent of its rated full-load current.

A thermal protector located inside the motor housing is connected in series with the motor winding. This protective device commonly consists of two contacts attached to a bimetallic disk through which the circuit is normally "closed." The thermal protector heating coil (in series with the motor winding) causes the disk to heat rapidly and the heat-actuated disk snaps "open" to protect the motor against failure to start, a sudden heavy overload, or dangerous overheating due to a prolonged overload.

After opening the circuit and after the motor has cooled to a normal temperature, the contacts will automatically close and restart the motor. In some cases this may not be desirable. For such applications the protective device is so designed that it must be returned to the closed position by a manually controlled reset as required by Section 430-43. See Figures 430-10 and 430-11. For larger motors (usually over 1 hp) a similar device is used. This device, upon abnormal overload, acts as a control circuit switch and operates the control circuit of a motor current-interrupting device located separately from the motor, usually a motor contactor or starter. A thermal protector and circuit-interrupting device should be approved for use with the motor it protects and is required to open the circuit on an overcurrent as specified in Section 430-32(a)(2).

Click. . . it's on   Click. . . it's off

Figure 430-10. A thermal protector for a motor. A heat-sensitive, snap-action disk opens contacts and protects the motor against dangerous overheating. (*Texas Instruments, Inc.*)

430-33. Intermittent and Similar Duty. A motor used for a condition of service that is inherently short-time, intermittent, periodic, or varying duty, as illustrated by Table 430-22(a) Exception, shall be permitted to be protected against overload by the branch-circuit short-circuit and ground-fault protective device, provided the protective device rating or setting does not exceed that specified in Table 430-152.

Any motor application shall be considered to be for continuous duty unless the nature of the apparatus it drives is such that the motor cannot operate continuously with load under any condition of use.

Where a motor is selected for duty-cycle service (intermittent, short-time, periodic, or varying), it can be assumed that the motor will not operate continu-

Figure 430-11. Integral mounting of the thermal protective device (Figure 430-10) in a motor housing.

ously due to the nature of the apparatus or machinery it drives. Therefore, prolonged overloads are not likely to occur unless mechanical failure in the driven apparatus stalls the motor; however, in this case the branch-circuit protective device would open the circuit. The omission of overload protective devices for such motors is based upon the type of duty and not upon the time rating of the motor.

430-34. Selection of Overload Relay. Where the overload relay selected in accordance with Section 430-32(a)(1) and (c)(1) is not sufficient to start the motor or to carry the load, the next higher size overload relay shall be permitted to be used provided the trip current of the overload relay does not exceed the following percentage of motor full-load current rating.

Motors with marked service factor not less than 1.15... 140%
Motors with a marked temperature rise not over 40°C... 140%
All other motors 130%

If not shunted during the starting period of the motor as provided in Section 430-35, the overload device shall have sufficient time delay to permit the motor to start and accelerate its load.

430-35. Shunting During Starting Period.

(a) Nonautomatically Started. For a nonautomatically started motor the overload protection shall be permitted to be shunted or cut out of the circuit during the starting period of the motor if the device by which the overload protection is shunted or cut out cannot be left in the starting position and if fuses or inverse time circuit breakers rated or set at not over 400 percent of the full-load current of the motor are so located in the circuit as to be operative during the starting period of the motor.

(b) Automatically Started. The motor overload protection shall not be shunted or cut out during the starting period if the motor is automatically started.

If not shunted during the starting period of the motor, the overload device is required to have sufficient time delay to start and accelerate its load; whereas if shunting is employed, the overload protection is cut out of the circuit during the starting period of the motor. See Figure 430-12.

Where fuses are used as overload protection, they may be shunted or cut out of the circuit during the starting period by a device (in this case a double-throw

Figure 430-12. Arrangement for across-the-line starting of a motor. When the switch is thrown momentarily to the left to start the motor, the running fuses are shunted or cut out of the circuit. The switch is then thrown to the right (running position) and is required to be so designed that it cannot be left in the starting position.

switch designed so that it cannot be left in the starting position). Therefore, during the starting period, the motor is protected only by the branch-circuit fuses that are always rated within the limits of this section. If there are no branch-circuit fuses, as permitted by Section 430-53, then a starter (shunting) device is not allowed during the starting period unless the feeder protection is within the limits of this section (not over 400 percent of the full-load motor current).

Exception: The motor overload protection shall be permitted to be shunted or cut out during the starting period on an automatically started motor where:

(1) The motor starting period exceeds the time delay of available motor overload protective devices, and

(2) Listed means are provided to:

a. Sense motor rotation and to automatically prevent the shunting or cutout in the event that the motor fails to start, and

b. Limit the time of overload protection shunting or cutout to less than the locked rotor time rating of the protected motor, and

c. Provide for shutdown and manual restart if motor running condition is not reached.

430-36. Fuses — In Which Conductor. Where fuses are used for motor overload protection, a fuse shall be inserted in each ungrounded conductor.

A fuse shall also be inserted in the grounded conductor if the supply system is 3-wire, 3-phase ac with one conductor grounded.

430-37. Devices Other than Fuses — In Which Conductor. Where devices other than fuses are used for motor overload protection, Table 430-37 shall govern the minimum allowable number and location of overload units such as trip coils, relays, or thermal cutouts.

All 3-phase motors are required to be provided with three overload units, one in each phase. The exceptions are those protected by other approved means. Specially designed or integral-type detectors, with or without supplementary external protective devices, are some exceptions.

Table 430-37. Overload Units

Kind of Motor	Supply System	Number and location of overload units, such as trip coils, relays, or thermal cutouts
1-phase ac or dc	2-wire, 1-phase ac or dc ungrounded	1 in either conductor
1-phase ac or dc	2-wire, 1-phase ac or dc, one conductor grounded	1 in ungrounded conductor
1-phase ac or dc	3-wire, 1-phase ac or dc, grounded-neutral	1 in either ungrounded conductor
2-phase ac	3-wire, 2-phase ac, ungrounded	2, one in each phase
2-phase ac	3-wire, 2-phase ac, one conductor grounded	2 in ungrounded conductors
2-phase ac	4-wire, 2-phase ac, grounded or ungrounded	2, one per phase in ungrounded conductors
2-phase ac	5-wire, 2-phase ac, grounded neutral or ungrounded	2, one per phase in any ungrounded phase wire
3-phase ac	Any 3-phase	*3, one in each phase

Exception: Where protected by other approved means.

430-38. Number of Conductors Opened by Overload Device.   Motor overload devices other than fuses, thermal cutouts, or thermal protectors shall simultaneously open a sufficient number of ungrounded conductors to interrupt current flow to the motor.

430-39. Motor Controller as Overload Protection.   A motor controller shall also be permitted to serve as an overload device if the number of overload units complies with Table 430-37 and if these units are operative in both the starting and running position in the case of a direct-current motor, and in the running position in the case of an alternating-current motor.

For the purpose of this article, a controller may be a switch, a circuit breaker, a contactor, or other device to start and stop a motor by making and breaking the motor circuit current and is required to be capable of interrupting the stalled-rotor current of the motor and have a hp rating not lower than the hp rating of the motor.

Dual-element fuses can be sized to provide motor overload protection. See Section 430-36. Automatically operated contactors or circuit breakers (with trip units) are governed by the requirements of Sections 430-37 and 430-38.

430-40. Thermal Cutouts and Overload Relays.   Thermal cutouts, overload relays, and other devices for motor overload protection that are not capable of opening short circuits shall be protected by fuses or circuit breakers with ratings or settings in accordance with Section 430-52 or by a motor short-circuit protector in accordance with Section 430-52.

Exception No. 1: Where approved for group installation and marked to indicate the maximum size of fuse or inverse time circuit breaker by which they must be protected.

Exception No. 2: The fuse or circuit breaker ampere rating shall be permitted to be marked on the nameplate of approved equipment in which the thermal cutout or overload relay is used.

ARTICLE 430—MOTORS, MOTOR CIRCUITS, CONTROLLERS

(FPN): For instantaneous trip circuit breakers or motor short-circuit protectors, see Section 430-52.

430-42. Motors on General-Purpose Branch Circuits. Overload protection for motors used on general-purpose branch circuits as permitted in Article 210 shall be provided as specified in (a), (b), (c), or (d) below.

(a) Not Over 1 Horsepower. One or more motors without individual overload protection shall be permitted to be connected to a general-purpose branch circuit only where the installation complies with the limiting conditions specified in Section 430-32(b) and (c) and Section 430-53(a)(1) and (a)(2).

(b) Over 1 Horsepower. Motors of larger ratings than specified in Section 430-53(a) shall be permitted to be connected to general-purpose branch circuits only where each motor is protected by overload protection selected to protect the motor as specified in Section 430-32. Both the controller and the motor overload device shall be approved for group installation with the short-circuit and ground-fault protective device selected in accordance with Section 430-53.

(c) Cord- and Plug-Connected. Where a motor is connected to a branch circuit by means of an attachment plug and receptacle and individual overload protection is omitted as provided in (a) above, the rating of the attachment plug and receptacle shall not exceed 15 amperes at 125 volts or 10 amperes at 250 volts. Where individual overload protection is required as provided in (b) above for a motor or motor-operated appliance that is attached to the branch circuit through an attachment plug and receptacle, the overload device shall be an integral part of the motor or of the appliance. The rating of the attachment plug and receptacle shall determine the rating of the circuit to which the motor may be connected, as provided in Article 210.

(d) Time Delay. The branch-circuit short-circuit and ground-fault protective device protecting a circuit to which a motor or motor-operated appliance is connected shall have sufficient time delay to permit the motor to start and accelerate its load.

Two or more motors, or one or more motors and other loads, may be connected to the same 120-V, 15- or 20-A single-phase lighting circuit. The provision is that each motor is to be rated not more than 1 hp, the full-load rating of each motor is not to exceed 6 A, and the rating of the branch-circuit protective device is not permitted to be exceeded.

Motors with ratings larger than 1 hp or 6 A may be connected to general-purpose branch circuits only if the motor is protected against overload as required by Section 430-32.

It should be understood that the requirements for overload protection, as provided in Section 430-32, are required to be applied in all cases regardless of the number (one or more) of motors or the type of branch circuit.

430-43. Automatic Restarting. A motor overload device that can restart a motor automatically after overload tripping shall not be installed unless approved for use with the motor it protects. A motor that can restart automatically after shutdown shall not be installed if its automatic restarting can result in injury to persons.

An integral motor overload protective device may be of the type that, after tripping and sufficiently cooling, will automatically restart the motor, or it may be of the type that, after tripping, returns to a closed position by use of a manually operated reset button. See commentary following Section 430-32.

430-44. Orderly Shutdown. If immediate automatic shutdown of a motor by a motor overload protective device(s) would introduce additional or increased hazard(s) to a person(s) and continued motor operation is necessary for safe shutdown of equipment or process, a motor overload sensing device(s) conforming with the provisions of Part C of this article shall be permitted to be connected to a supervised alarm instead of causing immediate interruption of the motor circuit, so that corrective action or an orderly shutdown can be initiated.

D. Motor Branch-Circuit Short-Circuit and Ground-Fault Protection

430-51. General. Part D specifies devices intended to protect the motor branch-circuit conductors, the motor control apparatus, and the motors against overcurrent due to short circuits or grounds. They add to or amend the provisions of Article 240. The devices specified in Part D do not include the types of devices required by Sections 210-8, 230-95, and 305-6.

The provisions of Part D do not apply to motor circuits rated over 600 volts, nominal. See Part J.

(FPN): See Example No. 8, Chapter 9.

430-52. Rating or Setting for Individual Motor Circuit. The motor branch-circuit short-circuit and ground-fault protective device shall be capable of carrying the starting current of the motor. A protective device having a rating or setting not exceeding the value calculated according to the values given in Table 430-152 shall be used.

Exception No. 1: Where the values for branch-circuit short- circuit and ground-fault protective devices determined by Table 430-152 do not correspond to the standard sizes or ratings of fuses, nonadjustable circuit breakers, thermal protective devices, or possible settings of adjustable circuit breakers, any of which are adequate to carry the load, the next higher size, rating, or setting shall be permitted.

Exception No. 2: Where the rating specified in Table 430-152 is not sufficient for the starting current of the motor:

a. The rating of a nontime-delay fuse not exceeding 600 amperes shall be permitted to be increased but shall in no case exceed 400 percent of the full-load current.

b. The rating of a time-delay (dual element) fuse shall be permitted to be increased but shall in no case exceed 225 percent of the full-load current.

c. The rating of an inverse time circuit breaker shall be permitted to be increased but shall in no case exceed (1) 400 percent for full-load currents of 100 amperes or less, or (2) 300 percent for full-load currents greater than 100 amperes.

d. The rating of a fuse of 601-6000 ampere classification shall be permitted to be increased but shall in no case exceed 300 percent of the full-load current.

Exception No. 3: Torque motor branch circuits shall be protected at the motor nameplate current rating in accordance with Section 240-3, Exception No. 1.

(FPN): See Section 240-6 for standard ratings of fuses and circuit breakers.

An instantaneous trip circuit breaker shall be used only if adjustable, and if part of a combination controller having motor overload and also short-circuit and ground-fault protection in each conductor. A motor short-circuit protector shall be permitted in lieu of devices listed in Table 430-152 if the motor short-circuit protector is part of a combination controller having both motor overload protection and short-circuit and ground-fault protection in each conductor and if it will operate at not more than 1300 percent of full-load motor current. An instantaneous trip circuit breaker or motor short-circuit protector shall be used only as part of a combination motor controller which provides coordinated motor branch-circuit overload and short-circuit and ground-fault protection.

Exception: Where the setting specified in Table 430-152 is not sufficient for the starting current of the motor, the setting of an instantaneous trip circuit breaker shall be permitted to be increased but shall in no case exceed 1300 percent of the motor full-load current.

For a multispeed motor, a single short-circuit and ground-fault protective device shall be permitted for two or more windings of the motor, provided the rating of the protective device does not exceed the above applicable percentage of the nameplate rating of the smallest winding protected.

Where maximum branch-circuit short-circuit and ground-fault protective device ratings are shown in the manufacturer's overload relay table for use with a motor controller or are otherwise marked on the equipment, they shall not be exceeded even if higher values are allowed as shown above.

(FPN): See Example No. 8 in Chapter 9 and Diagram 430-1.

Suitable fuses shall be permitted in lieu of devices listed in Table 430-152 for an adjustable speed drive system provided that the marking for replacement fuses is provided adjacent to the fuses.

This section defines the maximum allowable ratings or settings of devices (fuses or circuit breakers) acceptable for motor branch-circuit short-circuit and ground-fault protection and states that these devices are expected to carry the starting currents of the motor and to provide short-circuit and ground-fault protection.

For certain exceptions to the maximum rating or setting of these motor branch-circuit protective devices as specified in Table 430-152, see Sections 430-52, 430-53, and 430-54. See Figure 430-2.

Section 430-6 provides that where the current rating of a motor is used to determine the ampacity of conductors or ampere ratings of switches, branch-circuit overcurrent devices, etc., the values given in Tables 430-147 through 430-150 (including notes) are required to be used instead of the actual motor nameplate current rating. Separate motor overload protection is required to be based on the motor nameplate current rating.

Figure 430-5 illustrates a typical motor circuit where the branch-circuit short-circuit and ground-fault protective fuses or circuit breaker rating must carry the starting current and may be sized 150 to 300 percent of the motor full-load current (depending on the type of motor). It should be noted that it is not necessary to size the branch-circuit conductors to the percentages (150 to 300) permitted for the branch-circuit short-circuit and ground-fault protective devices.

The rules for short-circuit and ground-fault protection are specific for particular situations. A short circuit is a fault between two conductors or between phases. A ground fault is a fault to ground. During a short-circuit or phase-to-ground condition, the extreme excess current would cause the protective fuses or circuit breakers to open the circuit. Excess current flow caused by an overload condition must pass through the overload protective device at the motor controller thereby causing this device to open the circuit. Branch-circuit conductors with an ampacity of 125 percent (Note: not 150 to 300 percent) of the motor full-load current are reasonably protected by motor-protective devices set to operate at nearly the same current as the ampacity of the conductors. Branch-circuit short-circuit and ground-fault protective devices will open the circuit under short-circuit conditions and thereby provide short-circuit and ground-fault protection for both the motor and overload protective device; however, the overload protective device is not intended to open short circuits or ground faults.

Section 430-7 provides for information that is required to be marked on motor nameplates. AC motors, rated ½ hp or more, are required to be marked with code letters in accordance with Table 430-7(b) which are used to determine the correct rating of the branch-circuit protective devices. For motors smaller than ½ hp, or for the many motors still in use without code letters, the provisions of Table 430-152 apply.

The rating or setting of the branch-circuit short-circuit and ground-fault protective device should be selected as low as possible for maximum protection;

however, where the rating or setting specified in Table 430-152 is not sufficient for the starting current of the motor, such as in the case of severe starting conditions where the motor and its driven machinery requires an extended period of time to reach its desired speed, it is allowable to use a higher rating or setting as permitted in the exception to Section 430-52.

Two or more small motors, each not over 1 hp and not over 6 A, may be connected to 120-V, 20-A, or 208 through 600-V, 15-A branch circuits if each motor has overload protection and the rating of the branch-circuit protective device does not exceed the rating specified on the motor controller (for the overhead relay heater coil). See Section 430-53(a). Also, if the branch-circuit short-circuit and ground-fault protective device can be selected for the smallest motor in the group, two or more motors may be connected to the same branch circuit. This may be feasible where two motors are very nearly the same size and cannot start simultaneously. See Section 430-53(b).

For other than the conditions specified in Sections 430-53(a) and (b) as described above, the equipment or controllers and protective devices are required to be listed (See Article 100). Where listed multimotor equipment is installed, it is required to be marked with the maximum rating of the branch-circuit short-circuit and ground-fault protective device in accordance with Section 430-7(d), and the protective device is not permitted to exceed this marked rating. Where the short-circuit and ground-fault protective device, the controller and the overload protective device are field installed, they are required to be listed for such use and provided with instructions for use with each other. See Section 430-53(c).

430-53. Several Motors or Loads on One Branch Circuit.   Two or more motors or one or more motors and other loads shall be permitted to be connected to the same branch circuit under the conditions specified in (a), (b), or (c) below.

(a) Not Over 1 Horsepower.   Several motors each not exceeding 1 horsepower in rating shall be permitted on a nominal 120 volt branch circuit protected at not over 20 amperes or a branch circuit of 600 volts, nominal, or less, protected at not over 15 amperes, if all of the following conditions are met:

(1) The full-load rating of each motor does not exceed 6 amperes.

(2) The rating of the branch-circuit short-circuit and ground-fault protective device marked on any of the controllers is not exceeded.

(3) Individual overload protection conforms to Section 430-32.

(b) If Smallest Motor Protected.   If the branch-circuit short-circuit and ground-fault protective device is selected not to exceed that allowed by Section 430-52 for the motor of the smallest rating, two or more motors or one or more motors and other load(s), with each motor having individual overload protection, shall be permitted to be connected to a branch circuit where it can be determined that the branch-circuit short-circuit and ground-fault protective device will not open under the most severe normal conditions of service that might be encountered.

(c) Other Group Installations.   Two or more motors of any rating or one or more motors and other load(s), with each motor having individual overload protection, shall be permitted to be connected to one branch circuit where the motor controller(s) and overload device(s) are (1) installed as a listed factory assembly and the motor branch-circuit short-circuit and ground-fault protective device is either provided as part of the assembly or is specified by a marking on the assembly, or (2) the motor branch-circuit short-circuit and ground-fault protective device, the motor controller(s) and overload device(s) are field-installed as separate assemblies listed for such use and provided with manufacturers' instructions for use with each other, and (3) all of the following conditions are complied with:

(1) Each motor overload device is listed for group installation with a specified maximum rating of fuse and/or inverse time circuit breaker.

(2) Each motor controller is listed for group installation with a specified maximum rating of fuse and/or circuit breaker.

(3) Each circuit breaker is one of the inverse time type and listed for group installation.

(4) The branch circuit shall be protected by fuses or inverse time circuit breakers having a rating not exceeding that specified in Section 430-52 for the largest motor connected to the branch circuit plus an amount equal to the sum of the full-load current ratings of all other motors and the ratings of other loads connected to the circuit. Where this calculation results in a rating less than the ampacity of the supply conductors, it shall be permitted to increase the maximum rating of the fuses or circuit breaker to a value not exceeding that permitted by Section 240-3, Exception No. 1.

(5) The branch-circuit fuses or inverse time circuit breakers are not larger than allowed by Section 430-40 for the thermal cutout or overload relay protecting the smallest motor of the group.

(FPN): See Section 110-10.

Section 110-10 addresses characteristics of components such as impedance and short-circuit withstand ratings. It should be noted that devices with the same ampere rating may have significantly different short-circuit withstand ratings. A proper selection of components includes consideration of the characteristics of all components so that a fault results in minimum damage.

(d) Single Motor Taps. For group installations described above, the conductors of any tap supplying a single motor shall not be required to have an individual branch-circuit short-circuit and ground-fault protective device, provided they comply with either of the following: (1) no conductor to the motor shall have an ampacity less than that of the branch-circuit conductors, or (2) no conductor to the motor shall have an ampacity less than one-third that of the branch-circuit conductors, with a minimum in accordance with Section 430-22; the conductors to the motor overload device being not more than 25 feet (7.62 m) long and being protected from physical damage.

The following two examples describe installations permitting the omission of individual motor branch-circuit short-circuit and ground-fault protective devices. See Figures 430-13 and 430-14.

Figure 430-13 illustrates main branch-circuit conductors supplying a motor that is part of a group installation. The tap conductors have an ampacity equal to the ampacity of the main branch-circuit conductors; therefore, branch-circuit short-circuit and ground-fault protective devices, fuses, or circuit breakers for the conductors in the tap are not required at the point of connection of the tap conductors to the main conductors, provided that the motor controller and motor overload protective device are listed for group installation with the size of main branch-circuit short-circuit and ground-fault protective device used.

Figure 430-14 illustrates main branch-circuit conductors supplying a motor that is part of a group installation. The tap conductors have an ampacity at least one-third the ampacity of the main branch-circuit conductors, are not more than 25 ft in length (as shown in Figure 438-5), and are suitably protected from physical damage. The motor controller and motor overload protective device are required to be listed for group installation with the size of main branch-circuit short-circuit and ground-fault protective device used.

In both examples, the main branch-circuit fuses or circuit breakers would operate in the event of a short circuit, and the overload protective device would operate to protect the motor and the tap conductors under overload conditions.

It should be noted that the tap conductors should never be of a smaller size and ampacity than the branch-circuit conductors required by Section 430-22; that is, a tap conductor (25 ft or less) may be ⅓ the ampacity of the main branch-circuit conductor to which it is connected. However, this ampacity is required to be equal to or larger than 125 percent of the motor full-load current rating (see Section 430-22). For example, a feeder sized at No. 2/0 copper THW typically has an ampacity of 175 A (see Table 310-16) and a tap conductor (25 ft or less) would normally be permitted to be sized at No. 6 copper THW (65 A). However, if a 25-hp, 230-V, 3-phase, squirrel-cage motor is to be supplied from this feeder, a No. 6 tap conductor would not meet the requirements of Section 430-22; that is, 125 percent of the full-load current of the motor is 85 A [1.25 × 68 A (Table 430-150) = 85 A]. Therefore, the branch-circuit tap conductors are not permitted to be smaller than a No. 4 copper THW with a normal ampacity of 85 A (see Table 310-16). Note that the ampacities in Table 310-16 are reduced for ambient temperatures above 30°C and for more than 3 conductors in the raceway or cable.

Figure 430-13. Motor branch-circuit protective devices can be omitted for tap conductors that have the same ampacity as the main branch-circuit conductors.

430-54. Multimotor and Combination-Load Equipment. The rating of the branch-circuit short-circuit and ground-fault protective device for multimotor and combination-load equipment shall not exceed the rating marked on the equipment in accordance with Section 430-7(d).

430-55. Combined Overcurrent Protection. Motor branch-circuit short-circuit and ground-fault protection and motor overload protection shall be permitted to be combined in a single protective device where the rating or setting of the device provides the overload protection specified in Section 430-32.

Either a circuit breaker with inverse time characteristics or a dual-element (time-delay) fuse may serve as both motor overload protection and also as the branch-circuit short-circuit and ground-fault protection. Figures 430-9, 430-15, and 430-16 are examples of dual-element fuses that are able to withstand the normal motor starting current when sized at or near the motor full-load rating, but open on a prolonged overload or "blow" rapidly on a short circuit or ground fault.

Figure 430-9 illustrates a dual-element Type S fuse and adapter that is available up to a 30-A rating and is designed to prevent oversize fusing. See Sections 240-51 through 240-54.

Figure 430-14. Motor branch-circuit protective devices can be omitted when the tap conductors have at least ⅓ the ampacity of the main conductors, are not over 25 ft long, and are protected from physical damage.

Figures 430-15 and 430-16 illustrate time-delay cartridge-type dual-element fuses. The dual-element characteristics, similar to those of the Type S fuse shown in Figure 430-9, are the "thermal cutout element," which permits harmless high-inrush currents to flow for short periods (but would open the circuit during a prolonged period), and the "fuse link element," which has current-limiting ability for short-circuit currents (and would "blow" rapidly). Dual-element fuses may be used in larger sizes to provide only short-circuit and ground-fault protection.

Figure 430-15. A Fusetron cartridge-type fuse. (*Bussmann Mfg. Co.*)

430-56. Branch-Circuit Protective Devices — In Which Conductor.   Branch-circuit protective devices shall comply with the provisions of Section 240-20.

430-57. Size of Fuseholder.   Where fuses are used for motor branch-circuit short-circuit and ground-fault protection, the fuseholders shall not be of a smaller size than required to accommodate the fuses specified by Table 430-152.

Exception: Where fuses having time delay appropriate for the starting characteristics of the motor are used, fuseholders of smaller size than specified in Table 430-152 shall be permitted.

Figure 430-16. Class R dual-element fuse
with physical rejection feature to prevent
interchangeability. (*International
Association of Electrical Inspectors*)

Use of dual-element (time-delay) fuses makes it possible to use smaller sizes of
fuses thereby providing better protection because of the lower ratings. This also
permits a considerable saving in installation cost by using smaller size switches and
panels and allows for easier arrangement of equipment where space is at a
premium at motor control centers.

430-58. Rating of Circuit Breaker.   A circuit breaker for motor branch-circuit short-circuit
and ground-fault protection shall have a current rating in accordance with Sections 430-52 and
430-110.

An instantaneous trip circuit breaker has no intentional time-delay and opens
only in response to currents in excess of its trip setting. Combination motor
controller assemblies (see Section 430-52) are available with either interchangeable
or noninterchangeable instantaneous trip units. In such a combination controller,
the motor overload protective device in each conductor is relied upon to protect
against excessive heating due to motor overloads and failure to start.

E. Motor Feeder Short-Circuit and
Ground-Fault Protection

430-61. General.   Part E specifies protective devices intended to protect feeder conductors
supplying motors against overcurrents due to short circuits or grounds.

(FPN): See Example No. 8, Chapter 9.

430-62. Rating or Setting — Motor Load.

(a) Specific Load.   A feeder supplying a specific fixed motor load(s) and consisting of
conductor sizes based on Section 430-24 shall be provided with a protective device having a rating
or setting not greater than the largest rating or setting of the branch-circuit short-circuit and
ground-fault protective device for any motor of the group (based on Table 430-152, or Section
440-22(a) for hermetic refrigerant motor-compressors), plus the sum of the full-load currents of
the other motors of the group.

This section was modified for the 1987 *Code* to recognize the lower setting for
motor overload devices required for hermetic refrigerant motor-compressors.

Where the same rating or setting of the branch-circuit short-circuit and ground-fault
protective device is used on two or more of the branch circuits of the group, one of the protective
devices shall be considered the largest for the above calculations.

(FPN): See Example No. 8, Chapter 9.

(b) Future Additions.   For large-capacity installations, where heavy-capacity feeders are
installed to provide for future additions or changes, the rating or setting of the feeder protective
devices shall be permitted to be based on the ampacity of the feeder conductors.

ARTICLE 430—MOTORS, MOTOR CIRCUITS, CONTROLLERS

430-63. Rating or Setting — Power and Light Loads. Where a feeder supplies a motor load, and in addition a lighting or a lighting and appliance load, the feeder protective device shall be permitted to have a rating or setting sufficient to carry the lighting or the lighting and appliance load as determined in accordance with Articles 210 and 220, plus for a single motor, the rating permitted by Section 430-52, and for two or more motors, the rating permitted by Section 430-62.

F. Motor Control Circuits

430-71. General. Part F contains modifications of the general requirements and applies to the particular conditions of motor control circuits.

(FPN): See Section 430-9(b).

Definition of Motor Control Circuit: The circuit of a control apparatus or system that carries the electric signals directing the performance of the controller, but does not carry the main power current.

430-72. Overcurrent Protection.

(a) General. A motor control circuit tapped from the load side of a motor branch-circuit short-circuit and ground-fault protective device(s) and functioning to control the motor(s) connected to that branch circuit shall be protected against overcurrent in accordance with Section 430-72. Such a tapped control circuit shall not be considered to be a branch circuit and shall be permitted to be protected by either a supplementary or branch-circuit overcurrent protective device(s). A motor control circuit other than such a tapped control circuit shall be protected against overcurrent in accordance with Section 725-12 or 725-35, as applicable.

(b) Conductor Protection. The overcurrent protection for conductors shall not exceed the values specified in Column A of Table 430-72(b).

Exception No. 1: Conductors which do not extend beyond the motor control equipment enclosure shall require only short-circuit and ground-fault protection and shall be permitted to be protected by the motor branch-circuit short-circuit and ground-fault protective device(s) where the rating of the protective device(s) is not over the value specified in Column B of Table 430-72(b).

Exception No. 2: Conductors which extend beyond the motor control equipment enclosure shall require only short-circuit and ground-fault protection and shall be permitted to be protected by the motor branch-circuit short-circuit and ground-fault protective device(s) where the rating of the protective device(s) is not over the value specified in Column C of Table 430-72(b).

Exception No. 3: Conductors supplied by the secondary side of a single-phase transformer having only a two-wire (single-voltage) secondary shall be permitted to be protected by overcurrent protection provided on the primary (supply) side of the transformer, provided this protection does not exceed the value determined by multiplying the appropriate maximum rating of the overcurrent device for the secondary conductor from Table 430-72(b) by the secondary-to-primary voltage ratio. Transformer secondary conductors (other than two-wire) are not considered to be protected by the primary overcurrent protection.

Exception No. 4: Conductors of control circuits shall require only short-circuit and ground-fault protection and shall be permitted to be protected by the motor branch-circuit short-circuit and ground-fault protective device(s) where the opening of the control circuit would create a hazard as, for example, the control circuit of a fire pump motor, and the like.

(c) Control Circuit Transformer. Where a motor control circuit transformer is provided, the transformer shall be protected in accordance with Article 450.

Exception No. 1: Control circuit transformers rated less than 50 VA and an integral part of the motor controller and located within the motor controller enclosure.

Table 430-72(b).   Maximum Rating of Overcurrent Protective Device-Amperes

Control Circuit Conductor Size, AWG	Column A Basic Rule		Column B Exception No. 1		Column C Exception No. 2	
	Copper	Alum. or Copper-Clad Alum.	Copper	Alum. or Copper-Clad Alum.	Copper	Alum. or Copper-Clad Alum.
18	7	—	25	—	7	—
16	10	—	40	—	10	—
14	Note 1	—	100	—	45	—
12	Note 1	Note 1	120	100	60	45
10	Note 1	Note 1	160	140	90	75
larger than 10	Note 1	Note 1	Note 2	Note 2	Note 3	Note 3

Note 1: Value specified in Tables 310-16 through 310-31, as applicable.
Note 2: 400 percent of value specified in Table 310-17 for 60°C conductors.
Note 3: 300 percent of value specified in Table 310-16 for 60°C conductors.

Exception No. 2: Where the control circuit transformer rated primary current is less than 2 amperes, an overcurrent device rated or set at not more than 500 percent of the rated primary current shall be permitted in the primary circuit.

Exception No. 3: Where the transformer supplies a Class 1 power-limited, circuit {see Section 725-11(a)} Class 2, or Class 3 remote control circuit conforming with the requirements of Article 725 (see Article 725 Part C).

Exception No. 4: Where protection is provided by other approved means.

Exception No. 5: Overcurrent protection shall be omitted where the opening of the control circuit would create a hazard, as, for example, the control circuit of a fire pump motor and the like.

430-73. Mechanical Protection of Conductor.   Where damage to a motor control circuit would constitute a hazard, all conductors of such a remote motor control circuit that are outside the control device itself shall be installed in a raceway or be otherwise suitably protected from physical damage.

Where one side of the motor control circuit is grounded, the motor control circuit shall be so arranged that an accidental ground in the remote-control devices will not start the motor.

Where damage to the motor control circuit conductors would constitute a fire or accident hazard, physical protection of the motor control circuit conductors is extremely important. Conductors are required to be installed in raceways where damage to the control circuit conductors could result in an accidental ground causing the device to operate or breakage of conductors could render the device inoperative. Either condition could constitute a hazard to persons or property. Where boilers or furnaces are equipped with an automatic safety control device, damage to the conductors of the low-voltage (Article 725, Class 2) control circuit (thermostat, etc.) does not constitute a hazard.

The second paragraph of Section 430-73 requires that, if one side of the motor control circuit is grounded, the circuit be arranged so that an accidental ground in the remote-control devices will not start the motor. For example, if the control circuit is a 277-V single-phase circuit derived from a 480-V wye 3-phase system supplying the motor, one side of the control circuit will be the grounded neutral. If the "start" button of the motor control circuit is in the grounded neutral, a ground fault on the coil side of the "start" button can short-circuit the "start" circuit and start the motor. The same condition will exist if the ground fault is in the wiring rather than the control device itself. By locating the "start" button in the ungrounded side of the control circuit, this hazardous condition is avoided. See Figure 430-17.

591

Combinations of ground faults in motor and motor-control circuits can produce the same problem. If the circuit is ungrounded, the first fault may go undetected. One solution is to use double-pole control devices, one pole in each of the two control lines.

Figure 430-17. Control wiring in violation of Paragraph 2, Section 430-73(left) and in compliance with Paragraph 2, Section 430-73 (right).

430-74. Disconnection.

(a) General. Motor control circuits shall be so arranged that they will be disconnected from all sources of supply when the disconnecting means is in the open position. The disconnecting means shall be permitted to consist of two or more separate devices, one of which disconnects the motor and the controller from the source(s) of power supply for the motor, and the other(s), the motor control circuit(s) from its power supply. Where separate devices are used, they shall be located immediately adjacent one to each other.

Exception No. 1: Where more than twelve motor control circuit conductors are required to be disconnected, the disconnecting means shall be permitted to be located other than immediately adjacent one to each other where all of the following conditions are complied with:

a. Access to live parts is limited to qualified persons in accordance with Part K of this article.

b. A warning sign is permanently located on the outside of each equipment enclosure door or cover permitting access to the live parts in the motor control circuit(s), warning that motor control circuit disconnecting means are remotely located and specifying the location and identification of each disconnect. Where live parts are not in an equipment enclosure as permitted by Sections 430-132 and 430-133, an additional warning sign(s) shall be located where visible to persons who may be working in the area of the live parts.

Exception No. 2: Where the opening of one or more motor control circuit disconnect means may result in potentially unsafe conditions for personnel or property and the conditions a. and b. of Exception No. 1 above are complied with.

(b) Control Transformer in Controller. Where a transformer or other device is used to obtain a reduced voltage for the motor control circuit and is located in the controller, such transformer or other device shall be connected to the load side of the disconnecting means for the motor control circuit.

G. Motor Controllers

430-81. General. Part G is intended to require suitable controllers for all motors.

(a) Definition. For definition of "Controller," see Article 100. For the purpose of this article, a controller is any switch or device normally used to start and stop a motor by making and breaking the motor circuit current.

(b) Stationary Motor of ⅛ Horsepower or Less. For a stationary motor rated at ⅛ horsepower or less that is normally left running and is so constructed that it cannot be damaged by overload or failure to start, such as clock motors and the like, the branch-circuit protective device shall be permitted to serve as the controller.

(c) Portable Motor of ⅓ Horsepower or Less. For a portable motor rated at ⅓ horsepower or less, the controller shall be permitted to be an attachment plug and receptacle.

430-82. Controller Design.

(a) Starting and Stopping. Each controller shall be capable of starting and stopping the motor it controls, and shall be capable of interrupting the stalled-rotor current of the motor.

(b) Autotransformer. An autotransformer starter shall provide an "off" position, a running position, and at least one starting position. It shall be so designed that it cannot rest in the starting position or in any position that will render the overload device in the circuit inoperative.

(c) Rheostats. Rheostats shall be in compliance with the following:

(1) Motor-starting rheostats shall be so designed that the contact arm cannot be left on intermediate segments. The point or plate on which the arm rests when in the starting position shall have no electrical connection with the resistor.

(2) Motor-starting rheostats for direct-current motors operated from a constant voltage supply shall be equipped with automatic devices that will interrupt the supply before the speed of the motor has fallen to less than one-third its normal value.

430-83. Rating. The controller shall have a horsepower rating not lower than the horsepower rating of the motor.

Exception No. 1: For a stationary motor rated at 2 horsepower or less, and 300 volts or less, the controller shall be permitted to be a general-use switch having an ampere rating not less than twice the full-load current rating of the motor.

On ac circuits, general-use snap switches suitable only for use on ac (not general-use ac-dc snap switches) shall be permitted to control a motor rated at 2 horsepower or less and 300 volts or less having a full-load current rating not more than 80 percent of the ampere rating of the switch.

Exception No. 2: A branch-circuit inverse time circuit breaker rated in amperes only shall be permitted as a controller. Where this circuit breaker is also used for overload protection, it shall conform to the appropriate provisions of this article governing overload protection.

Exception No. 3: The motor controller for a torque motor shall have a continuous-duty, full-load current rating not less than the nameplate current rating of the motor. For a motor controller rated in horsepower but not marked with the foregoing current rating, the equivalent current rating shall be determined from the horsepower rating by using Tables 430-147, 430-148, 430-149, or 430-150.

A controller, as defined in Section 430-81(a), includes any switch or device normally used to start and stop a motor by making and breaking the motor circuit current. Circuit breakers are suitable for this use; however, circuit breakers used for branch-circuit short-circuit and ground-fault protection are not well adapted for motor overload protective devices.

430-84. Need Not Open All Conductors. The controller shall not be required to open all conductors to the motor.

Exception: Where the controller serves also as a disconnecting means, it shall open all ungrounded conductors to the motor as provided in Section 430-111.

A controller that does not also serve as a disconnecting means is required to open only as many motor-circuit conductors as may be necessary to stop the motor. That is, one conductor for a dc or single-phase motor circuit; two conductors for a 3-phase motor circuit; and three conductors for a 2-phase motor circuit.

430-85. In Grounded Conductors. One pole of the controller shall be permitted to be placed in a permanently grounded conductor, provided the controller is so designed that the pole in the grounded conductor cannot be opened without simultaneously opening all conductors of the circuit.

Generally, one conductor of a 120-V circuit is grounded and a single-pole device is required to be connected in the ungrounded conductor to serve as a controller. A 2-pole controller is permitted for such a circuit, where both conductors (grounded and ungrounded) are opened simultaneously. The same requirement can be applied to other circuits, such as 240-V, 3-wire circuits with one conductor grounded.

430-87. Number of Motors Served by Each Controller. Each motor shall be provided with an individual controller.

Exception: For motors rated 600 volts or less, a single controller rated at not less than the sum of the horsepower ratings of all of the motors of the group shall be permitted to serve the group of motors under any one of the following conditions:

a. Where a number of motors drive several parts of a single machine or piece of apparatus, such as metal and woodworking machines, cranes, hoists, and similar apparatus.

b. Where a group of motors is under the protection of one overcurrent device as permitted in Section 430-53(a).

c. Where a group of motors is located in a single room within sight from the controller location.

These requirements for an individual controller are the same as those specified in Section 430-112 permitting the use of a single disconnecting means for a group of motors.

430-88. Adjustable-Speed Motors. Adjustable-speed motors that are controlled by means of field regulation shall be so equipped and connected that they cannot be started under weakened field.

Exception: Where the motor is designed for such starting.

The speed of a motor will increase or decrease with variations in the amount of magnetic flux passing through the armature. Since the speed of the armature increases until the necessary counterelectromotive force is produced, it is evident that weakening the field by decreasing the current flow through the field magnets will increase the motor speed; and increasing the current flow through the field magnets will decrease the motor speed. Because of excessive starting currents, this type motor is not permitted to be started under a weakened field condition unless the motor is designed for such starting.

430-89. Speed Limitation. Machines of the following types shall be provided with speed limiting devices or other speed limiting means:

(a) Separately Excited DC Motors. Separately excited direct-current motors.

(b) Series Motors. Series motors.

(c) Motor-Generators and Converters. Motor-generators and converters that can be driven at excessive speed from the direct-current end, as by a reversal of current or decrease in load.

Exception No. 1: When the inherent characteristics of the machines, the system, or the load and the mechanical connection thereto are such as to safely limit the speed.

Exception No. 2: When the machine is always under the manual control of a qualified operator.

DC motors are commonly used where speed control is essential such as electric railways and elevators where a smooth start, controlled acceleration, and a smooth stop are necessary.

If the load is removed from a series motor when it is running, the speed of the motor will increase until it is dangerously high. To produce the necessary counterelectromotive force with a weakened field, the armature must turn correspondingly faster. Series motors are commonly used as gear-drive traction motors of electric locomotives and, thus, are continuously loaded.

The Ward Leonard speed control system is widely used to control a separately excited dc motor for the operation of electric elevators or hoists. Figure 430-18 is a simplified diagram of the speed control system where the armatures of two generators (G_1 and G_2) are mounted on a shaft which is driven by a motor (not shown). M is the motor-drive for the elevator. The fields of G_1 and M are excited by G_1. By varying the rheostat R position, the voltage generated by G_2 is also varied and this in turn controls the speed of M. If the field circuit of M were to be accidently opened during a light load, the motor would reach an excessive speed; however, no speed-limiting device is required as the motor is always loaded.

Separately excited dc motors, series motors, motor (compound-wound dc) generators, and (synchronous) converters are required to be provided with speed limiting devices (note Exceptions) such as a centrifugal device on the shaft of the machine or a remotely located overspeed device, which may be set at a predetermined speed to operate a set of contacts and thereby trip a circuit breaker and de-energize the machine.

Figure 430-18. A schematic diagram of the Ward Leonard speed control system.

Rheostat R

430-90. Combination Fuseholder and Switch as Controller. The rating of a combination fuseholder and switch used as a motor controller shall be such that the fuseholder will accommodate the size of the fuse specified in Part C of this article for motor overload protection.

Exception: Where fuses having time delay appropriate for the starting characteristics of the motor are used, fuseholders of smaller size than specified in Part C of this article shall be permitted.

Time-delay (dual element) fuses can commonly be used for both motor overload and branch-circuit short-circuit and ground-fault protection and can be sized in accordance with Section 430-32. See also Sections 430-36, 430-55, and 430-57.

430-91. Motor Controller Enclosure Types. Table 430-91 provides the basis for selecting enclosures for use in specific nonhazardous locations. The enclosures are not intended to protect against conditions such as condensation, icing, corrosion or contamination which may occur within the enclosure or enter via the conduit or unsealed openings. These internal conditions require special consideration by the installer and/or user.

Table 430-91. Motor Controller Enclosure Selection Table

Provides a Degree of Protection Against the Following Environmental Conditions	For Outdoor Use Enclosure Type Number†						
	3	3R	3S	4	4X	6	6P
Incidental contact with the enclosed equipment	X	X	X	X	X	X	X
Rain, snow and sleet	X	X	X	X	X	X	X
Sleet*	—	—	X	—	—	—	—
Windblown dust	X	—	X	X	X	X	X
Hosedown	—	—	—	X	X	X	X
Corrosive agents	—	—	—	—	X	—	X
Occasional temporary submersion	—	—	—	—	—	X	X
Occasional prolonged submersion	—	—	—	—	—	—	X

* Mechanism shall be operable when ice covered.

For Indoor Use

Provides a Degree of Protection Against the Following Environmental Conditions	Enclosure Type Number†										
	1	2	4	4X	5	6	6P	11	12	12K	13
Incidental contact with the enclosed equipment	X	X	X	X	X	X	X	X	X	X	X
Falling dirt	X	X	X	X	X	X	X	X	X	X	X
Falling liquids and light splashing	—	X	X	X	—	X	X	X	X	X	X
Dust, lint, fibers and flyings	—	—	X	X	X	X	X	—	X	X	X
Hosedown and splashing water	—	—	X	X	—	X	X	—	—	—	—
Oil and coolant seepage	—	—	—	—	—	—	—	—	X	X	X
Oil or coolant spraying and splashing	—	—	—	—	—	—	—	—	—	—	X
Corrosive agents	—	—	—	X	—	—	X	X	—	—	—
Occasional temporary submersion	—	—	—	—	—	X	X	—	—	—	—
Occasional prolonged submersion	—	—	—	—	—	—	X	—	—	—	—

† Enclosure type number, except type number 1, shall be marked on the motor controller enclosure.

Enclosure-type numbers are described in greater detail in industry standards such as ANSI/NEMA IC6-1978, NEMA Pub. 250-179, UL 508, and controller manufacturers' literature. For other than general-use Type No. 1 enclosures, the type number is required to be marked on the motor controller enclosure.

H. Disconnecting Means

430-101. General.   Part H is intended to require disconnecting means capable of disconnecting motors and controllers from the circuit.

(FPN): See Diagram 430-1.

(FPN): See Section 110-22 for identification of disconnecting means.

430-102. Location.

(a) Controller.   A disconnecting means shall be located in sight from the controller location.

Exception No. 1: For motor circuits over 600 volts, nominal, the controller disconnecting means shall be permitted to be out of sight of the controller, provided the controller is marked with a warning label giving the location and identification of the disconnecting means to be locked in the open position.

Exception No. 2: A single disconnecting means shall be permitted to be located adjacent to a group of coordinated controllers mounted adjacent one to each other on a multimotor continuous process machine.

(b) Motor.   A disconnecting means shall be located in sight from the motor location and the driven machinery location.

Exception: Where the disconnecting means provided in accordance with Section 430-102(a) is capable of being locked in the open position.

This rule has been revised in the 1987 *Code*. The rule requires that the disconnecting means be in sight from the controller, the motor location, and the driven machinery location. For motors over 600 V, the controller disconnecting means may be out of sight of the controller provided that the controller has a warning label giving the location and identification of the disconnecting means which must be capable of being locked in the open position. See Figure 430-19.

The disconnecting means may be out of sight of the motor if the disconnecting means complying with Section 430-102(a) is capable of being locked in the open position. See Figure 430-20.

A group of coordinated controllers for a multimotor continuous process machine may use a single disconnecting means where the motors are mounted adjacent to one another on the machine. See Figure 430-21.

430-103. To Disconnect Both Motor and Controller.   The disconnecting means shall disconnect the motor and the controller from all ungrounded supply conductors and shall be so designed that no pole can be operated independently. The disconnecting means shall be permitted in the same enclosure with the controller.

(FPN): See Section 430-113 for equipment receiving energy from more than one source.

The *Code* requires that a switch, circuit breaker, or other device serve as a disconnecting means for both the controller and the motor, thereby providing safety during maintenance and inspection shutdown periods. The disconnecting means also disconnects the controller; therefore, it cannot be a part of the controller. However, separate disconnects and controllers may be mounted on the same panel or contained in the same enclosure, such as combination fused-switch, magnetic-starter units.

Depending upon the size of the motor and other conditions, the type of disconnecting means required may be a motor-circuit switch, a circuit breaker, a general-use switch, an isolating switch, an attachment plug and receptacle, or a

Figure 430-19. A motor controller (for motors over 600 V) which is out of sight from the disconnecting means must be marked with a label indicating the location of the disconnecting means. The controller must be capable of being locked in the open position.

Figure 430-20. A controller disconnecting means that is not in sight from the motor must be designed so that it can be locked in the open position.

branch-circuit short-circuit and ground-fault protective device. See Section 430-109.

If a motor is stalled, or under heavy overload, and the motor controller fails to properly open the circuit, the disconnecting means, which is required to be rated to interrupt locked-rotor current, can be used to open the circuit. Switches rated up to 100 hp are readily obtainable, but for motors larger than 100 hp ac or 40 hp dc, the disconnecting means is permitted to be a general-use or isolating switch when plainly marked "Do not operate under load." See Section 430-109, Exception No. 4.

430-104. To Be Indicating. The disconnecting means shall plainly indicate whether it is in the open (off) or closed (on) position.

Figure 430-21. A single disconnecting means located adjacent to a group of coordinated controllers mounted on a multimotor continuous process machine.

Figure 430-22. Heavy-duty safety switches UL listed for use on systems up to 200,000 A fault current rms symmetrical with Class J or Class R fuses installed. (*Square D Co.*)

430-105. Grounded Conductors.   One pole of the disconnecting means shall be permitted to disconnect a permanently grounded conductor, provided the disconnecting means is so designed that the pole in the grounded conductor cannot be opened without simultaneously disconnecting all conductors of the circuit.

430-106. Service Switch as Disconnecting Means. Where an installation consists of a single motor, the service switch may serve as the disconnecting means if it complies with this article and is within sight from the controller location.

430-107. Readily Accessible. One of the disconnecting means shall be readily accessible.

430-108. Every Switch. Every disconnecting means in the motor circuit between the point of attachment to the feeder and the point of connection to the motor shall comply with the requirements of Sections 430-109 and 430-110.

430-109. Type. The disconnecting means shall be a motor-circuit switch rated in horsepower, a circuit breaker, or a molded case switch (nonautomatic circuit interrupter).

Exception No. 1: For stationary motors of ⅛ horsepower or less, the branch-circuit overcurrent device shall be permitted to serve as the disconnecting means.

Exception No. 2: For stationary motors rated at 2 horsepower or less and 300 volts or less, the disconnecting means shall be permitted to be a general-use switch having an ampere rating not less than twice the full-load current rating of the motor.

On ac circuits, general-use snap switches suitable only for use on ac (not general-use ac-dc snap switches) shall be permitted to disconnect a motor rated 2 horsepower or less and 300 volts or less having a full-load current rating not more than 80 percent of the ampere rating of the switch.

Exception No. 3: For motors of over 2 horsepower to and including 100 horsepower, the separate disconnecting means required for a motor with an autotransformer-type controller shall be permitted to be a general-use switch where all of the following provisions are met:

a. The motor drives a generator that is provided with overload protection.

b. The controller (1) is capable of interrupting the locked-rotor current of the motor; (2) is provided with a no-voltage release; and (3) is provided with running overload protection not exceeding 125 percent of the motor full-load current rating.

c. Separate fuses or an inverse time circuit breaker rated or set at not more than 150 percent of the motor full-load current are provided in the motor branch circuit.

Stationary motor
⅛ hp or less

Disconnecting means: branch circuit fuse, may be breaker

Figure 430-23. Exception No. 1: The branch-circuit overcurrent device may serve as the disconnecting means for stationary motors of ⅛ hp or less.

Exception No. 4: For stationary motors rated at more than 40 horsepower direct-current or 100 horsepower alternating-current, the disconnecting means shall be permitted to be a general-use or isolating switch when plainly marked "Do not operate under load."

Exception No. 5: For a cord- and plug-connected motor, a horsepower-rated attachment plug and receptacle having ratings no less than the motor ratings shall be permitted to serve as the disconnecting means.

General case: motor-circuit switch
or circuit breaker, Exception 2: general-use switch

Figure 430-24. Exception No. 2: A general-use switch having an ampere rating not less than twice the motor full-load rating may serve as the disconnecting means for motors rated 2 hp or less and operating at 300 V or less.

Figure 430-25. Exception No. 4: A general-use switch or isolation switch may serve as the disconnecting means for stationary motors rated more than 40 hp dc or 100 hp ac, if marked "Do not operate under load."

A horsepower rated attachment plug and receptacle shall not be required for a cord- and plug-connected appliance in accordance with Section 422-22 or a room air conditioner in accordance with Section 440-63.

Exception No. 6: For torque motors the disconnecting means shall be permitted to be a general-use switch.

Section 430-108 requires every disconnecting means in the motor circuit to comply with Sections 430-109 and 430-110.

The disconnecting means is required to be a circuit breaker, a motor-circuit switch, or a molded case switch (nonautomatic circuit interrupter). A motor-circuit switch is a horsepower-rated switch capable of interrupting the maximum overload current of a motor (see Definition, Article 100). A molded case switch (nonautomatic circuit interrupter) is a circuit breaker-like device without the overcurrent element and automatic trip mechanism. It is rated in amperes and is suitable for use as a motor circuit disconnect based on its ampere rating, like a circuit breaker.

Figures 430-23 through 430-26 illustrate the exceptions to this general requirement.

When horsepower-rated fused switches are required, it is to be noted that marking within the enclosure usually permits a dual horsepower rating. The "standard" horsepower rating is based on the largest nontime-delay (nondual-

601

element) fuse rating which can be used in the switch and which will permit the motor to start. The "maximum" horsepower rating is based on the largest rated time-delay (dual-element) fuse which can be used in the switch and which will permit the motor to start. Thus, when time-delay fuses are used, smaller sized switches and fuseholders can be used. See Section 430-57, Exception.

Figure 430-26. Exception No. 5: An attachment plug and receptacle of the proper rating may serve as the disconnecting means for cord-and-plug connected motors.

430-110. Ampere Rating and Interrupting Capacity.

(a) General. The disconnecting means for motor circuits rated 600 volts, nominal, or less, shall have an ampere rating of at least 115 percent of the full-load current rating of the motor.

(b) For Torque Motors. Disconnecting means for a torque motor shall have an ampere rating of at least 115 percent of the motor nameplate current.

(c) For Combination Loads. Where two or more motors are used together or where one or more motors are used in combination with other loads, such as resistance heaters, and where the combined load may be simultaneous on a single disconnecting means, the ampere and horsepower ratings of the combined load shall be determined as follows:

(1) The rating of the disconnecting means shall be determined from the summation of all currents, including resistance loads, at the full-load condition and also at the locked-rotor condition. The combined full-load current and the combined locked-rotor current so obtained shall be considered as a single motor for the purpose of this requirement as follows:

The full-load current equivalent to the horsepower rating of each motor shall be selected from Table 430-148, 430-149, or 430-150. These full-load currents shall be added to the rating in amperes of other loads to obtain an equivalent full-load current for the combined load.

The locked-rotor current equivalent to the horsepower rating of each motor shall be selected from Table 430-151. The locked-rotor currents shall be added to the rating in amperes of other loads to obtain an equivalent locked-rotor current for the combined load. Where two or more motors and/or other loads cannot be started simultaneously, appropriate combinations of locked-rotor and full-load current shall be permitted to be used to determine the equivalent locked-rotor current for the simultaneous combined loads.

Exception: Where part of the concurrent load is resistance load, and where the disconnecting means is a switch rated in horsepower and amperes, the switch used shall be permitted to have a horsepower rating not less than the combined load of the motor(s), if the ampere rating of the switch is not less than the locked-rotor current of the motor(s) plus the resistance load.

(2) The ampere rating of the disconnecting means shall not be less than 115 percent of the summation of all currents at the full-load condition determined in accordance with (c)(1) above.

(3) For small motors not covered by Tables 430-147, 430-148, 430-149, or 430-150, the locked-rotor current shall be assumed to be six times the full-load current.

A general-use switch, fuse, circuit breaker, molded case switch (nonautomatic circuit interrupter), or attachment plug and receptacle used as a disconnecting means is required to have an ampere rating of not less than 115 percent of the motor full-load current.

430-111. Switch or Circuit Breaker as Both Controller and Disconnecting Means. A switch or circuit breaker complying with Section 430-83 shall be permitted to serve as both controller and disconnecting means if it opens all ungrounded conductors to the motor, if it is protected by an overcurrent device (which shall be permitted to be the branch-circuit fuses) that opens all ungrounded conductors to the switch or circuit breaker, and if it is of one of the following types:

(a) Air-Break Switch. An air-break switch, operable directly by applying the hand to a lever or handle.

(b) Inverse Time Circuit Breaker. An inverse time circuit breaker operable directly by applying the hand to a lever or handle.

(c) Oil Switch. An oil switch used on a circuit whose rating does not exceed 600 volts or 100 amperes, or by special permission on a circuit exceeding this capacity where under expert supervision.

The oil switch or circuit breaker specified above shall be permitted to be both power and manually operable.

The overcurrent device protecting the controller shall be permitted to be part of the controller assembly or shall be permitted to be separate.

An autotransformer-type controller shall be provided with a separate disconnecting means.

Where the controller consists of a manually operable air-break switch, an inverse time circuit breaker, or a 100-A maximum oil switch (higher rating by special permission), the controller is considered to be a satisfactory disconnecting means. It is the intent of this section to permit omission of an additional device to serve as a disconnecting means. See Figure 430-27.

It should be noted that a separate disconnecting means is required to be provided if the controller is of the autotransformer or "compensator" type (this switch may be combined in the same enclosure with a motor overload protective device).

Where used as a controller, the switch or circuit breaker is required to meet all of the requirements for controllers and be protected by branch-circuit short-circuit and ground-fault protective devices (fuses or a circuit breaker), which ensure that all ungrounded conductors will be opened.

430-112. Motors Served by Single Disconnecting Means. Each motor shall be provided with an individual disconnecting means.

Exception: A single disconnecting means shall be permitted to serve a group of motors under any one of the following conditions:

a. Where a number of motors drive several parts of a single machine or piece of apparatus, such as metal and woodworking machines, cranes, and hoists.

b. Where a group of motors is under the protection of one set of branch-circuit protective devices as permitted by Section 430-53(a).

ARTICLE 430—MOTORS, MOTOR CIRCUITS, CONTROLLERS

c. Where a group of motors is in a single room within sight from the location of the disconnecting means.

The single disconnecting means shall have a rating not less than is required by Section 430-110 for a single motor, the rating of which equals the sum of the horsepowers or currents of all the motors of the group.

The exception permits a single disconnecting means to serve a group of motors. The disconnecting means is required to have a rating equal to the sum of the horsepowers or currents of all the motors of the group. If the total horsepower is over 2 hp, a motor-circuit switch (horsepower-rated) is required to be used. Thus, for five 2-hp motors the disconnecting means should be a motor-circuit switch rated at not less than 10 hp.

Exception a. A single disconnecting means may be used where a number of motors drive several parts of a single machine such as cranes (see Sections 610-31 and 610-32), metal or woodworking machines, steel rolling mill machinery, etc. The single disconnecting means for multimotor machinery provides a positive means of simultaneously de-energizing all motor branch circuits, including remote-control circuits, interlocking circuits, limit-switch circuits, and operator control stations.

Exception b. Section 430-53(a) permits a group of motors under the protection of the same branch-circuit device provided the device is rated not more than 20 A at 125 V or 15 A at more than 125 V but not more than 600 V. The motors are required to be rated 1 hp or less, and the full-load current for each motor is not permitted to exceed 6 A. A single disconnecting means is both practical and economical for a group of such small motors.

Exception c. Many times, a group of motors is located in one room, such as a pump room, compressor room, mixer room, etc. It is therefore possible to design the layout of a single disconnecting means with an unobstructed view (not more than 50 ft) from each motor.

These conditions are similar to the requirements in Section 430-87 which permits the use of a single controller for a group of motors.

430-113. Energy from More than One Source. Motor and motor-operated equipment receiving electrical energy from more than one source shall be provided with disconnecting means from each source of electrical energy immediately adjacent to the equipment served. Each source shall be permitted to have a separate disconnecting means.

Exception No. 1: Where a motor receives electrical energy from more than one source, the disconnecting means for the main power supply to the motor shall not be required to be immediately adjacent to the motor provided the controller disconnecting means is capable of being locked in the open position.

Exception No. 2: A separate disconnecting means shall not be required for a Class 2 remote-control circuit conforming with Article 725, rated not more than 30 volts, and which is isolated and ungrounded.

Exception No. 1 applies to large synchronous motors that receive electrical energy from more than one source. Exception No. 2 applies to low-voltage control circuits, such as thermostat circuits used with heating and air-conditioning equipment.

J. Over 600 Volts, Nominal

430-121. General. Part J recognizes the additional hazard due to the use of higher voltages. It adds to or amends the other provisions of this article. Other requirements for circuits and equipment operating at over 600 volts, nominal, are in Article 710.

430-122. Marking on Controllers. In addition to the marking required by Section 430-8, a controller shall be marked with the control voltage.

Overcurrent protection that
opens all ungrounded conductors

Switch
(hand operable)

or

Oilbreak switch not
over 600 V not over
100 A except by
permission*

Oil

Motor

or

Mains

Circuit
breaker*

Figure 430-27. Three alternative arrangements where a switch, or circuit breaker, or oilbreak switch can serve satisfactorily as both the controller and disconnecting means. (*Oilbreak switch or circuit breaker may be hand operated or power operated.)

430-123. Conductor Enclosures Adjacent to Motors. Flexible metal conduit or liquidtight flexible metal conduit not exceeding 6 feet (1.83 m) in length shall be permitted to be employed for raceway connection to a motor terminal enclosure.

430-124. Size of Conductors. Conductors supplying motors shall have an ampacity not less than the current at which the motor overload protective device(s) is selected to trip.

430-125. Motor Circuit Overcurrent Protection.

(a) **General.** The high-voltage circuit for each motor shall include coordinated protection to automatically interrupt overload and fault currents in the motor, the motor circuit conductors, and the motor control apparatus.

Exception: Where a motor is vital to operation of the plant and the motor should operate to failure if necessary to prevent a greater hazard to persons, the sensing device(s) is permitted to be connected to a supervised annunciator or alarm instead of interrupting the motor circuit.

(b) **Overload Protection.**

(1) Each motor shall be protected against dangerous heating due to motor overloads and failure to start by a thermal protector integral with the motor or external current sensing devices, or both.

(2) The secondary circuits of wound-rotor alternating-current motors including conductors, controllers, and resistors rated for the application shall be considered as protected against overcurrent by the motor overload protection means.

(3) Operation of the overload interrupting device shall simultaneously disconnect all ungrounded conductors.

(4) Overload sensing devices shall not automatically reset after trip unless resetting of the overload sensing device does not cause automatic restarting of the motor or there is no hazard to persons created by automatic restarting of the motor and its connected machinery.

(c) Fault-Current Protection.

(1) Fault-current protection shall be provided in each motor circuit by one of the following means:

a. A circuit breaker of suitable type and rating so arranged that it can be serviced without hazard. The circuit breaker shall simultaneously disconnect all ungrounded conductors. The circuit breaker shall be permitted to sense the fault current by means of integral or external sensing elements.

b. Fuses of a suitable type and rating placed in each ungrounded conductor. Fuses shall be used with suitable disconnecting means or they shall be of a type that can also serve as the disconnecting means. They shall be so arranged that they cannot be serviced while they are energized.

(2) Fault-current interrupting devices shall not reclose the circuit automatically.

Exception: Where circuits are exposed to transient faults and where automatic reclosing of the circuit does not create a hazard to persons.

(3) Overload protection and fault-current protection shall be permitted to be provided by the same device.

430-126. Rating of Motor Control Apparatus. Motor controllers and motor branch-circuit disconnecting means shall have a continuous ampere rating not less than the current at which the overload protective device(s) is selected to trip.

430-127. Disconnecting Means. The controller disconnecting means shall be capable of being locked in the open position.

K. Protection of Live Parts — All Voltages

430-131. General. Part K specifies that live parts shall be protected in a manner judged adequate to the hazard involved.

430-132. Where Required. Exposed live parts of motors and controllers operating at 50 volts or more between terminals shall be guarded against accidental contact by enclosure or by location as follows:

(a) In a Room or Enclosure. By installation in a room or enclosure that is accessible only to qualified persons.

(b) On a Suitable Balcony. By installation on a suitable balcony, gallery, or platform, so elevated and arranged as to exclude unqualified persons.

(c) Elevation. By elevation 8 feet (2.44 m) or more above the floor.

Exception: Stationary motors having commutators, collectors, and brush rigging located inside of motor-end brackets and not conductively connected to supply circuits operating at more than 150 volts to ground.

430-133. Guards for Attendants. Where live parts of motors or controllers operating at over 150 volts to ground are guarded against accidental contact only by location as specified in Section 430-132, and where adjustment or other attendance may be necessary during the operation of the apparatus, suitable insulating mats or platforms shall be provided so that the attendant cannot readily touch live parts unless standing on the mats or platforms.

(FPN): For working space, see Sections 110-16 and 110-34.

L. Grounding All Voltages

430-141. General. Part L specifies the grounding of motor and controller frames to prevent a voltage above ground in the event of accidental contact between live parts and frames. Insulation, isolation, or guarding are suitable alternatives to grounding of motors under certain conditions.

430-142. Stationary Motors. The frames of stationary motors shall be grounded under any of the following conditions: (1) where supplied by metal-enclosed wiring; (2) where in a wet location and not isolated or guarded; (3) if in a hazardous (classified) location as covered in Articles 500 through 517; (4) if the motor operates with any terminal at over 150 volts to ground.

Where the frame of the motor is not grounded, it shall be permanently and effectively insulated from the ground.

Any motor in a wet location and subject to contact by personnel constitutes a serious hazard and, unless it is isolated, elevated, or guarded from reach, shall be grounded.

Stationary motors are usually supplied by wiring enclosed in metal raceways (rigid metal conduit, intermediate metal conduit, EMT, flexible metal conduit, etc.) or by cables with metal sheaths (Types AC, MC). Upon being effectively attached to the motor junction box or frame, the metal raceway or cable armor serves as the equipment grounding conductor. See Section 250-91(b).

430-143. Portable Motors. The frames of portable motors that operate at over 150 volts to ground shall be guarded or grounded.

(FPN): See Section 250-45(d) for grounding of portable appliances in other than residential occupancies.

(FPN): See Section 250-59(b) for color of grounding conductor.

430-144. Controllers. Controller enclosures shall be grounded regardless of voltage. Controller enclosures shall have means for attachment of an equipment grounding conductor termination in accordance with Section 250-113.

Exception No. 1: Enclosures attached to ungrounded portable equipment.

Exception No. 2: Lined covers of snap switches.

430-145. Method of Grounding. Where required, grounding shall be done in the manner specified in Article 250.

(a) Grounding Through Terminal Housings. Where the wiring to fixed motors is metal-enclosed cable or in metal raceways, junction boxes to house motor terminals shall be provided, and the armor of the cable or the metal raceways shall be connected to them in the manner specified in Article 250.

(FPN): See Section 430-12(e) for grounding connection means required at motor terminal housings.

(b) Separation of Junction Box from Motor. The junction box required by (a) above shall be permitted to be separated from the motor not more than 6 feet (1.83 m), provided the leads to the motor are Type AC cable or armored cord or are stranded leads enclosed in liquidtight flexible metal conduit, liquidtight flexible nonmetallic conduit, flexible metal conduit, intermediate metal conduit, rigid metal conduit or electrical metallic tubing not smaller than ⅜-inch electrical trade size, the armor or raceway being connected both to the motor and to the box. Where stranded leads are used, protected as specified above, they shall not be larger than No. 10, and shall comply with other requirements of this Code for conductors to be used in raceways.

(c) Grounding of Controller Mounted Devices. Instrument transformer secondaries and exposed noncurrent-carrying metal or other conductive parts or cases of instrument transformers, meters, instruments, and relays shall be grounded as specified in Sections 250-121 through 250-125.

Most motors are subject to vibration, and good wiring practice requires that, in nearly all cases, the wiring to motors that are fixed be installed with a short section of liquidtight flexible metal or nonmetallic conduit, or flexible metal conduit, to the motor terminal housing.

M. Tables

Table 430-147. Full-Load Current in Amperes, Direct-Current Motors

The following values of full-load currents* are for motors running at base speed.

HP	Armature Voltage Rating*					
	90V	120V	180V	240V	500V	550V
¼	4.0	3.1	2.0	1.6		
⅓	5.2	4.1	2.6	2.0		
½	6.8	5.4	3.4	2.7		
¾	9.6	7.6	4.8	3.8		
1	12.2	9.5	6.1	4.7		
1½		13.2	8.3	6.6		
2		17	10.8	8.5		
3		25	16	12.2		
5		40	27	20		
7½		58		29	13.6	12.2
10		76		38	18	16
15				55	27	24
20				72	34	31
25				89	43	38
30				106	51	46
40				140	67	61
50				173	83	75
60				206	99	90
75				255	123	111
100				341	164	148
125				425	205	185
150				506	246	222
200				675	330	294

* These are average direct-current quantities.

Table 430-148.   Full-Load Currents in Amperes
Single-Phase Alternating-Current Motors

The following values of full-load currents are for motors running at usual speeds and motors with normal torque characteristics. Motors built for especially low speeds or high torques may have higher full-load currents, and multispeed motors will have full-load current varying with speed, in which case the nameplate current ratings shall be used.

To obtain full-load currents of 208- and 200-volt motors, increase corresponding 230-volt motor full-load currents by 10 and 15 percent, respectively.

The voltages listed are rated motor voltages. The currents listed shall be permitted for system voltage ranges of 110 to 120 and 220 to 240.

HP	115V	230V
⅙	4.4	2.2
¼	5.8	2.9
⅓	7.2	3.6
½	9.8	4.9
¾	13.8	6.9
1	16	8
1½	20	10
2	24	12
3	34	17
5	56	28
7½	80	40
10	100	50

Table 430-149. Full-Load Current
Two-Phase Alternating-Current Motors (4-Wire)

The following values of full-load current are for motors running at speeds usual for belted motors and motors with normal torque characteristics. Motors built for especially low speeds or high torques may require more running current, and multispeed motors will have full-load current varying with speed, in which case the nameplate current rating shall be used. Current in the common conductor of a 2-phase, 3-wire system will be 1.41 times the value given.

The voltages listed are rated motor voltages. The currents listed shall be permitted for system voltage ranges of 110 to 120, 220 to 240, 440 to 480, and 550 to 600 volts.

HP	Induction Type Squirrel-Cage and Wound-Rotor Amperes				
	115V	230V	460V	575V	2300V
½	4	2	1	.8	
¾	4.8	2.4	1.2	1.0	
1	6.4	3.2	1.6	1.3	
1½	9	4.5	2.3	1.8	
2	11.8	5.9	3	2.4	
3		8.3	4.2	3.3	
5		13.2	6.6	5.3	
7½		19	9	8	
10		24	12	10	
15		36	18	14	
20		47	23	19	
25		59	29	24	
30		69	35	28	
40		90	45	36	
50		113	56	45	
60		133	67	53	14
75		166	83	66	18
100		218	109	87	23
125		270	135	108	28
150		312	156	125	32
200		416	208	167	43

Table 430-150. Full-Load Current*
Three-Phase Alternating-Current Motors

HP	Induction Type Squirrel-Cage and Wound-Rotor Amperes					Synchronous Type †Unity Power Factor Amperes			
	115V	230V	460V	575V	2300V	230V	460V	575V	2300V
½	4	2	1	.8					
¾	5.6	2.8	1.4	1.1					
1	7.2	3.6	1.8	1.4					
1½	10.4	5.2	2.6	2.1					
2	13.6	6.8	3.4	2.7					
3		9.6	4.8	3.9					
5		15.2	7.6	6.1					
7½		22	11	9					
10		28	14	11					
15		42	21	17					
20		54	27	22					
25		68	34	27		53	26	21	
30		80	40	32		63	32	26	
40		104	52	41		83	41	33	
50		130	65	52		104	52	42	
60		154	77	62	16	123	61	49	12
75		192	96	77	20	155	78	62	15
100		248	124	99	26	202	101	81	20
125		312	156	125	31	253	126	101	25
150		360	180	144	37	302	151	121	30
200		480	240	192	49	400	201	161	40

For full-load currents of 208- and 200-volt motors, increase the corresponding 230-volt motor full-load current by 10 and 15 percent, respectively.

* These values of full-load current are for motors running at speeds usual for belted motors and motors with normal torque characteristics. Motors built for especially low speeds or high torques may require more running current, and multispeed motors will have full-load current varying with speed, in which case the nameplate current rating shall be used.

† For 90 and 80 percent power factor the above figures shall be multiplied by 1.1 and 1.25 respectively.

The voltages listed are rated motor voltages. The currents listed shall be permitted for system voltage ranges of 110 to 120, 220 to 240, 440 to 480, and 550 to 600 volts.

Table 430-151. Conversion Table of Locked-Rotor Currents for Selection of Disconnecting Means and Controllers as Determined from Horsepower and Voltage Rating

For use only with Sections 430-110, 440-12 and 440-41.

Motor Locked-Rotor Current Amperes*							
Single Phase		Two or Three Phase					Max. HP
115V	230V	115V	200V	230V	460V	575V	Rating
58.8	29.4	24	18.8	12	6	4.8	½
82.8	41.4	33.6	19.3	16.8	8.4	6.6	¾
96	48	43.2	24.8	21.6	10.8	8.4	1
120	60	62	35.9	31.2	15.6	12.6	1½
144	72	81	46.9	40.8	20.4	16.2	2
204	102	—	66	58	26.8	23.4	3
336	168	—	105	91	45.6	36.6	5
480	240	—	152	132	66	54	7½
600	300	—	193	168	84	66	10
—	—	—	290	252	126	102	15
—	—	—	373	324	162	132	20
—	—	—	469	408	204	162	25
—	—	—	552	480	240	192	30
—	—	—	718	624	312	246	40
—	—	—	897	780	390	312	50
—	—	—	1063	924	462	372	60
—	—	—	1325	1152	576	462	75
—	—	—	1711	1488	744	594	100
—	—	—	2153	1872	936	750	125
—	—	—	2484	2160	1080	864	150
—	—	—	3312	2880	1440	1152	200

* These values of motor locked-rotor current are approximately six times the full-load current values given in Tables 430-148 and 430-150.

Table 430-152.   Maximum Rating or Setting of Motor Branch-Circuit Short-Circuit and Ground-Fault Protective Devices

Type of Motor	Percent of Full-Load Current			
	Nontime Delay Fuse	Dual Element (Time-Delay) Fuse	Instan-taneous Trip Breaker	*Inverse Time Breaker
Single-phase, all types				
No code letter	300	175	700	250
All ac single-phase and polyphase squirrel-cage and synchronous motors† with full-voltage, resistor or reactor starting:				
No code letter	300	175	700	250
Code letter F to V	300	175	700	250
Code letter B to E	250	175	700	200
Code letter A	150	150	700	150
All ac squirrel-cage and synchronous motors† with autotransformer starting:				
Not more than 30 amps				
No code letter	250	175	700	200
More than 30 amps				
No code letter	200	175	700	200
Code letter F to V	250	175	700	200
Code letter B to E	200	175	700	200
Code letter A	150	150	700	150
High-reactance squirrel-cage				
Not more than 30 amps				
No code letter	250	175	700	250
More than 30 amps				
No code letter	200	175	700	200
Wound-rotor—				
No code letter	150	150	700	150
Direct-current (constant voltage)				
No more than 50 hp				
No code letter	150	150	250	150
More than 50 hp				
No code letter	150	150	175	150

For explanation of Code Letter Marking, See Table 430-7(b).

For certain exceptions to the values specified, see Sections 430-52 through 430-54.

* The values given in the last column also cover the ratings of nonadjustable inverse time types of circuit breakers that may be modified as in Section 430-52.

† Synchronous motors of the low-torque, low-speed type (usually 450 rpm or lower), such as are used to drive reciprocating compressors, pumps, etc. that start unloaded, do not require a fuse rating or circuit-breaker setting in excess of 200 percent of full-load current.

613

ARTICLE 440 —AIR-CONDITIONING AND REFRIGERATING EQUIPMENT

Contents

614

A. General

440-1. Scope. The provisions of this article apply to electric motor-driven air-conditioning and refrigerating equipment, and to the branch circuits and controllers for such equipment. It provides for the special considerations necessary for circuits supplying hermetic refrigerant motor-compressors and for any air-conditioning and/or refrigerating equipment which is supplied from an individual branch circuit which supplies a hermetic refrigerant motor-compressor.

440-2. Definitions.

Hermetic Refrigerant Motor-Compressor: A combination consisting of a compressor and motor, both of which are enclosed in the same housing, with no external shaft or shaft seals, the motor operating in the refrigerant.

440-3. Other Articles.

(a) Article 430. These provisions are in addition to, or amendatory of, the provisions of Article 430 and other articles in this Code, which apply except as modified in this article.

(b) Article 422, 424, or 430. The rules of Article 422, 424, or 430, as applicable, shall apply to air-conditioning and refrigerating equipment which does not incorporate a hermetic refrigerant motor-compressor. Examples of such equipment are devices which employ refrigeration compressors driven by conventional motors, furnaces with air-conditioning evaporator coils installed, fan-coil units, remote forced air-cooled condensers, remote commercial refrigerators, etc.

(c) Article 422. Devices such as room air conditioners, household refrigerators and freezers, drinking water coolers, and beverage dispensers shall be considered appliances and the provisions of Article 422 shall also apply.

(d) Other Applicable Articles. Hermetic refrigerant motor-compressors, circuits, controller s, and equipment shall also comply with the applicable provisions of the following:

Garages, Aircraft Hangars, Gasoline Dispensing and Service Stations,
Capacitors ....Section 460-9
Garages, Aircraft Hangars, Gasoline Dispensing and Service Stations,
  Bulk Storage Plants, Spray Application, Dipping and
  Coating Processes, Inhalation Anesthetizing
  Locations ....Articles 511, 513, 514, 515, 516, and 517-G
Hazardous (Classified) Locations ....Articles 500 through 503
Motion-Picture and Television Studios ....Article 530
Resistors and Reactors...Article 470

    Article 440 provides for special considerations necessary for circuits supplying hermetic refrigerant motor-compressors and is in addition to, or amendatory of, the provisions of Article 430 and other applicable articles. However, many requirements, such as disconnecting means, controllers, single or group installations, and sizing of conductors, are the same as, or very similar to, those applied in Article 430.

ARTICLE 440—AIR-CONDITIONING AND REFRIGERATING EQUIPMENT

Article 440 does not apply unless a hermetic refrigerant motor-compressor is supplied. Article 440 must be applied in conjunction with Article 430.

Note the term "rated-load current," defined in the fine print note following Section 440-4(a), and the term "branch-circuit selection current," defined in the fine print note following Section 440-4(c).

When a "branch-circuit selection current" is marked on a nameplate, it is required to be used instead of the "rated-load current" in order to determine the size of the disconnecting means, the controller, the motor branch-circuit conductors, and the overcurrent protective devices for the branch-circuit conductors and the motor. The value of "branch-circuit selection current" will always be greater than the marked "rated-load current."

440-4. Marking on Hermetic Refrigerant Motor-Compressors and Equipment.

(a) Hermetic Refrigerant Motor-Compressor Nameplate. A hermetic refrigerant motor-compressor shall be provided with a nameplate which shall give the manufacturer's name, trademark or symbol; identifying designation; phase; voltage; and frequency. The rated load current in amperes of the motor-compressor shall be marked by the equipment manufacturer on either or both the motor-compressor nameplate and the nameplate of the equipment in which the motor-compressor is used. The locked-rotor current of each single-phase motor-compressor having a rated-load current of more than 9 amperes at 115 volts or more than 4.5 amperes at 230 volts and each polyphase motor-compressor shall be marked on the motor-compressor nameplate. Where a thermal protector complying with Section 440-52(a)(2) and (b)(2) is used, the motor-compressor nameplate or the equipment nameplate shall be marked with the words "Thermally Protected." Where a protective system, complying with Section 440-52(a)(4) and (b)(4), is used and is furnished with the equipment, the equipment nameplate shall be marked with the words, "Thermally Protected System." Where a protective system complying with Section 440-52(a)(4) and (b)(4) is specified, the equipment nameplate shall be appropriately marked.

(FPN): Definition: The rated-load current for a hermetic refrigerant motor-compressor is the current resulting when the motor-compressor is operated at the rated load, rated voltage and rated frequency of the equipment it serves.

(b) Multimotor and Combination-Load Equipment. Multimotor and combination-load equipment shall be provided with a visible nameplate marked with the maker's name, the rating in volts, frequency and number of phases, minimum supply circuit conductor ampacity, and the maximum rating of the branch-circuit short-circuit and ground-fault protective device. The ampacity shall be calculated by using Part D and counting all the motors and other loads which will be operated at the same time. The branch-circuit short-circuit and ground-fault protective device rating shall not exceed the value calculated by using Part C. Multimotor or combination-load equipment for use on two or more circuits shall be marked with the above information for each circuit.

Exception No. 1: Multimotor and combination-load equipment which is suitable under the provisions of this article for connection to a single 15- or 20-ampere, 120-volt, or a 15-ampere, 208- or 240-volt single-phase branch circuit shall be permitted to be marked as a single load.

Exception No. 2: Room air conditioners as provided in Part G of Article 440.

(c) Branch-Circuit Selection Current. Hermetic refrigerant motor-compressors or equipment containing such compressor(s) in which the protection system, approved for use with the motor-compressor which it protects, permits continuous current in excess of the specified percentage of nameplate rated-load current given in Section 440-52(b)(2) or (b)(4) shall also be marked with a branch-circuit selection current that complies with Section 440-52(b)(2) or (b)(4). This marking shall be provided by the equipment manufacturer and shall be on the nameplate(s) where the rated-load current(s) appears.

(FPN): Definition: Branch-circuit selection current is the value in amperes to be used instead of the rated-load current in determining the ratings of motor branch-circuit conductors, disconnecting means, controllers and branch-circuit short-circuit and ground-fault protective devices wherever the running overload protective device permits a sustained current greater than the specified percentage of the rated-load current. The value of branch-circuit selection current will always be equal to or greater than the marked rated-load current.

440-5. Marking on Controllers. A controller shall be marked with the maker's name, trademark, or symbol; identifying designation; the voltage; phase; full-load and locked-rotor current (or horsepower) rating; and such other data as may be needed to properly indicate the motor-compressor for which it is suitable.

440-6. Ampacity and Rating. Conductors for equipment covered by this article shall be selected from Tables 310-16 through 310-31 as applicable. The required ampacity of conductors and rating of equipment shall be determined as follows.

(a) Hermetic Refrigerant Motor-Compressor. For a hermetic refrigerant motor-compressor, the rated-load current marked on the nameplate of the equipment in which the motor-compressor is employed shall be used in determining the rating or ampacity of the disconnecting means, the branch-circuit conductors, the controller, the branch-circuit short-circuit and ground-fault protection, and the separate motor overload protection. Where no rated-load current is shown on the equipment nameplate, the rated-load current shown on the compressor nameplate shall be used. For disconnecting means and controllers, see also Sections 440-12 and 440-41.

Exception No. 1: When so marked, the branch-circuit selection current shall be used instead of the rated-load current to determine the rating or ampacity of the disconnecting means, the branch-circuit conductors, the controller, and the branch-circuit short-circuit and ground-fault protection.

Exception No. 2: As permitted in Section 440-22(b) for branch-circuit short-circuit and ground-fault protection of cord- and plug-connected equipment.

(b) Multimotor Equipment. For multimotor equipment employing a shaded-pole or permanent split-capacitor-type fan or blower motor, the full-load current for such motor marked on the nameplate of the equipment in which the fan or blower motor is employed shall be used instead of the horsepower rating to determine the ampacity or rating of the disconnecting means, the branch-circuit conductors, the controller, the branch-circuit short-circuit and ground-fault protection, and the separate overload protection. This marking on the equipment nameplate shall not be less than the current marked on the fan or blower motor nameplate.

440-7. Highest Rated (Largest) Motor. In determining compliance with this article and with Sections 430-24, 430-53(b) and (c), and 430-62(a), the highest rated (largest) motor shall be considered to be that motor which has the highest rated-load current. Where two or more motors have the same rated-load current, only one of them shall be considered as the highest rated (largest) motor. For other than hermetic refrigerant motor-compressors, and fan or blower motors as covered in Section 440-6(b), the full-load current used to determine the highest rated motor shall be the equivalent value corresponding to the motor horsepower rating selected from Tables 430-148, 430-149, or 430-150.

Exception: When so marked, the branch-circuit selection current shall be used instead of the rated-load current in determining the highest rated (largest) motor-compressor.

440-8. Single Machine. An air-conditioning or refrigerating system shall be considered to be a single machine under the provisions of Section 430-87, Exception and Section 430-112, Exception. The motors shall be permitted to be located remotely from each other.

B. Disconnecting Means

440-11. General. The provisions of Part B are intended to require disconnecting means capable of disconnecting air-conditioning and refrigerating equipment including motor-compressors, and controllers, from the circuit feeder. See Diagram 430-1.

ARTICLE 440—AIR-CONDITIONING AND REFRIGERATING EQUIPMENT

440-12. Rating and Interrupting Capacity.

(a) Hermetic Refrigerant Motor-Compressor. A disconnecting means serving a hermetic refrigerant motor-compressor shall be selected on the basis of the nameplate rated-load current or branch-circuit selection current, whichever is greater, and locked-rotor current, respectively, of the motor-compressor as follows:

(1) The ampere rating shall be at least 115 percent of the nameplate rated-load current or branch-circuit selection current, whichever is greater.

(2) To determine the equivalent horsepower in complying with the requirements of Section 430-109, the horsepower rating shall be selected from Tables 430-148, 430-149, or 430-150 corresponding to the rated-load current or branch-circuit selection current, whichever is greater, and also the horsepower rating from Table 430-151 corresponding to the locked-rotor current. In case the nameplate rated-load current or branch-circuit selection current and locked-rotor current do not correspond to the currents shown in Tables 430-148, 430-149, 430-150, or 430-151, the horsepower rating corresponding to the next higher value shall be selected. In case different horsepower ratings are obtained when applying these tables, a horsepower rating at least equal to the larger of the values obtained shall be selected.

(b) Combination Loads. Where one or more hermetic refrigerant motor-compressors are used together or are used in combination with other motors and/or loads such as resistance heaters and where the combined load may be simultaneous on a single disconnecting means, the rating for the combined load shall be determined as follows:

(1) The horsepower rating of the disconnecting means shall be determined from the summation of all currents, including resistance loads, at the rated-load condition and also at the locked-rotor condition. The combined rated-load current and the combined locked-rotor current so obtained shall be considered as a single motor for the purpose of this requirement as follows:

a. The full-load current equivalent to the horsepower rating of each motor, other than a hermetic refrigerant motor-compressor, and fan or blower motors as covered in Section 440-6(b) shall be selected from Tables 430-148, 430-149, or 430-150. These full-load currents shall be added to the motor-compressor rated-load current(s) or branch-circuit selection current(s), whichever is greater, and to the rating in amperes of other loads to obtain an equivalent full-load current for the combined load.

b. The locked-rotor current equivalent to the horsepower rating of each motor, other than a hermetic refrigerant motor-compressor, shall be selected from Table 430-151, and for fan and blower motors of the shaded-pole or permanent split-capacitor type marked with the locked-rotor current, the marked value shall be used. The locked-rotor currents shall be added to the motor-compressor locked-rotor current(s) and to the rating in amperes of other loads to obtain an equivalent locked-rotor current for the combined load. Where two or more motors and/or other loads cannot be started simultaneously, appropriate combinations of locked-rotor and rated-load current or branch-circuit selection current, whichever is greater, shall be an acceptable means of determining the equivalent locked-rotor current for the simultaneous combined load.

Exception: Where part of the concurrent load is a resistance load and the disconnecting means is a switch rated in horsepower and amperes, the switch used shall be permitted to have a horsepower rating not less than the combined load to the motor-compressor(s) and other motor(s) at the locked-rotor condition, if the ampere rating of the switch is not less than this locked-rotor load plus the resistance load.

(2) The ampere rating of the disconnecting means shall be at least 115 percent of the summation of all currents at the rated-load condition determined in accordance with Section 440-12(b)(1).

(c) Small Motor-Compressors. For small motor-compressors not having the locked-rotor current marked on the nameplate, or for small motors not covered by Tables 430-147, 430-148,

430-149, or 430-150, the locked-rotor current shall be assumed to be six times the rated-load current. See Section 440-3(a).

(d) Every Switch. Every disconnecting means in the refrigerant motor-compressor circuit between the point of attachment to the feeder and the point of connection to the refrigerant motor-compressor shall comply with the requirements of Section 440-12.

(e) Disconnecting Means Rated in Excess of 100 Horsepower. Where the rated-load or locked-rotor current as determined above would indicate a disconnecting means rated in excess of 100 horsepower, the provisions of Section 430-109, Exception No. 4 shall apply.

440-13. Cord-Connected Equipment. For cord-connected equipment such as room air conditioners, household refrigerators and freezers, drinking water coolers, and beverage dispensers, a separable connector or an attachment plug and receptacle shall be permitted to serve as the disconnecting means. See also Section 440-63.

440-14. Location. Disconnecting means shall be located within sight from and readily accessible from the air-conditioning or refrigerating equipment. The disconnecting means shall be permitted to be installed on or within the air-conditioning or refrigerating equipment.

Exception: Cord- and plug-connected appliances.

(FPN): See Parts G and H of Article 430 for additional requirements.

The reference to Parts G and H of Article 430 in the fine print note is intended to call attention to the additional disconnect location requirements in Sections 430-102, 430-107 and 430-113. Since Section 440-3(a) makes the requirements in Article 440 in addition to or amendatory of the provisions of Article 430, the requirement of Section 440-14 mandates equipment disconnecting means within sight from and readily accessible from the equipment, even if there is also a remote disconnect capable of being locked in the open position under the provision of Section 430-102(b), Exception. This special requirement for air-conditioning and refrigeration equipment covered by Article 440 is more stringent than the provisions in Article 430 in order to provide protection for service personnel working on equipment located in an attic, on the roof, or outside in a remote location where it is difficult to gain access to a remote lockable disconnect.

C. Branch-Circuit Short-Circuit and Ground-Fault Protection

440-21. General. The provisions of Part C specify devices intended to protect the branch-circuit conductors, control apparatus and motors in circuits supplying hermetic refrigerant motor-compressors against overcurrent due to short circuits and grounds. They are in addition to or amendatory of the provisions of Article 240.

Where an air conditioner is listed by a qualified electrical testing laboratory with the nameplate stating "maximum fuse size," the listing restricts the use of this unit to fuse protection only and does not cover its use with circuit breakers. If the air conditioner has been evaluated for both fuses and ordinary circuit breakers, or both fuses and "HACR-Type" circuit breakers, it may be so marked. UL-listed circuit breakers which have been found suitable for use with heating, air-conditioning, and refrigeration equipment comprising multimotor or combination loads are marked as "Listed HACR Type." It is the intent of Section 110-3(b) to have any restriction of listing applied to the installation of the equipment in order to comply with the *Code*.

The UL Electrical Appliance and Utilization Equipment Directory states the following under "Air-Conditioners, Central Cooling": "This marked protective device rating is the maximum for which the equipment has been investigated and found acceptable. Where the marking specifies fuses, or 'HACR'-type circuit breakers, the equipment is intended to be protected only by the type of protective device specified." (See Figure 440-1.)

Figure 440-1. Illustrated are three correct wiring methods indicating, where the nameplate specifies fuses, that the equipment is intended to be protected by fuses only.

440-22. Application and Selection.

(a) Rating or Setting for Individual Motor-Compressor. The motor-compressor branch-circuit short-circuit and ground-fault protective device shall be capable of carrying the starting current of the motor. A protective device having a rating or setting not exceeding 175 percent of the motor-compressor rated-load current or branch-circuit selection current, whichever is greater, shall be permitted, provided that where the protection specified is not sufficient for the starting current of the motor, the rating or setting shall be permitted to be increased, but shall not exceed 225 percent of the motor rated-load current or branch-circuit selection current, whichever is greater.

Exception: The rating of the branch-circuit short-circuit and ground-fault protective device shall not be required to be less than 15 amperes.

(b) Rating or Setting for Equipment. The equipment branch-circuit short-circuit and ground-fault protective device shall be capable of carrying the starting current of the equipment. Where the hermetic refrigerant motor-compressor is the only load on the circuit, the protection shall conform with Section 440-22(a). Where the equipment incorporates more than one hermetic refrigerant motor-compressor or a hermetic refrigerant motor-compressor and other motors or other loads, the equipment short-circuit and ground-fault protection shall conform with Section 430-53 and the following:

(1) Where a hermetic refrigerant motor-compressor is the largest load connected to the circuit, the rating or setting of the branch-circuit short-circuit and ground-fault protective device shall not exceed the value specified in Section 440-22(a) for the largest motor-compressor plus the sum of the rated-load current or branch-circuit selection current, whichever is greater, of the other motor-compressor(s) and the ratings of the other loads supplied.

(2) Where a hermetic refrigerant motor-compressor is not the largest load connected to the circuit, the rating or setting of the branch-circuit short-circuit and ground-fault protective device shall not exceed a value equal to the sum of the rated-load current or branch-circuit selection current, whichever is greater, rating(s) for the motor-compressor(s) plus the value specified in Section 430-53(c)(4) where other motor loads are supplied, or the value specified in Section 240-3 where only nonmotor loads are supplied in addition to the motor-compressor(s).

Exception No. 1: Equipment which will start and operate on a 15- or 20-ampere 120-volt, or 15-ampere 208- or 240-volt single-phase branch circuit shall be permitted to be protected by the 15- or 20-ampere overcurrent device protecting the branch circuit, but if the maximum branch-circuit short-circuit and ground-fault protective device rating marked on the equipment is less than these values, the circuit protective device shall not exceed the value marked on the equipment nameplate.

Exception No. 2: The nameplate marking of cord- and plug-connected equipment rated not greater than 250 volts, single-phase, such as household refrigerators and freezers, drinking water coolers, and beverage dispensers, shall be used in determining the branch-circuit requirements, and each unit shall be considered as a single motor unless the nameplate is marked otherwise.

(c) Protective Device Rating Not to Exceed the Manufacturer's Values. Where maximum protective device ratings shown on a manufacturer's heater table for use with a motor controller are less than the rating or setting selected in accordance with Section 440-22(a) and (b), the protective device rating shall not exceed the manufacturer's values marked on the equipment.

D. Branch-Circuit Conductors

440-31. General. The provisions of Part D and Articles 300 and 310 specify sizes of conductors required to carry the motor current without overheating under the conditions specified, except as modified in Section 440-6(a), Exception No. 1.

The provisions of these articles shall not apply to integral conductors of motors, motor controllers and the like, or to conductors which form an integral part of approved equipment.

(FPN): See Sections 300-1(b) and 310-1 for similar requirements.

440-32. Single Motor-Compressor. Branch-circuit conductors supplying a single motor-compressor shall have an ampacity not less than 125 percent of either the motor-compressor rated-load current or the branch-circuit selection current, whichever is greater.

440-33. Motor-Compressor(s) With or Without Additional Motor Loads. Conductors supplying one or more motor-compressor(s) with or without additional load(s) shall have an ampacity not less than the sum of the rated-load or branch-circuit selection current ratings, whichever is larger, of all the motor-compressor(s) plus the full-load currents of the other motor(s), plus 25 percent of the highest motor or motor-compressor rating in the group.

Exception No. 1: When the circuitry is so interlocked as to prevent the starting and running of a second motor-compressor or group of motor-compressors, the conductor size shall be determined from the largest motor-compressor or group of motor-compressors that is to be operated at a given time.

Exception No. 2: Room air conditioners as provided in Part G of Article 440.

440-34. Combination Load. Conductors supplying a motor-compressor load in addition to a lighting or appliance load as computed from Article 220 and other applicable articles shall have an ampacity sufficient for the lighting or appliance load plus the required ampacity for the motor-compressor load determined in accordance with Section 440-33, or, for a single motor-compressor, in accordance with Section 440-32.

Exception: When the circuitry is so interlocked as to prevent simultaneous operation of the motor-compressor(s) and all other loads connected, the conductor size shall be determined from the largest size required for the motor-compressor(s) and other loads to be operated at a given time.

440-35. Multimotor and Combination-Load Equipment. The ampacity of the conductors supplying multimotor and combination-load equipment shall not be less than the minimum circuit ampacity marked on the equipment in accordance with Section 440-4(b).

E. Controllers for Motor-Compressors

440-41. Rating.

(a) Motor-Compressor Controller. A motor-compressor controller shall have both a continuous-duty full-load current rating, and a locked-rotor current rating, not less than the nameplate rated-load current or branch-circuit selection current, whichever is greater, and locked-rotor current, respectively (see Sections 440-6 and 440-7) of the compressor. In case the motor controller is rated in horsepower, but is without one or both of the foregoing current ratings, equivalent currents shall be determined from the ratings as follows: use Tables 430-148, 430-149, or 430-150 to determine the equivalent full-load current rating. Use Table 430-151 to determine the equivalent locked-rotor current ratings.

(b) Controller Serving More than One Load. A controller, serving more than one motor-compressor or a motor-compressor and other loads, shall have a continuous-duty full-load current rating, and a locked-rotor current rating not less than the combined load as determined in accordance with Section 440-12(b).

F. Motor-Compressor and Branch-Circuit Overload Protection

440-51. General. The provisions of Part F specify devices intended to protect the motor-compressor, the motor-control apparatus, and the branch-circuit conductors against excessive heating due to motor overload and failure to start. See Section 240-3, Exception No. 3.

(FPN): Note: Overload in electrically driven apparatus is an operating overcurrent which, when it persists for a sufficient length of time, would cause damage or dangerous overheating. It does not include short circuits or ground faults.

440-52. Application and Selection.

(a) Protection of Motor-Compressor. Each motor-compressor shall be protected against overload and failure to start by one of the following means:

(1) A separate overload relay which is responsive to motor-compressor current. This device shall be selected to trip at not more than 140 percent of the motor-compressor rated-load current.

(2) A thermal protector integral with the motor-compressor, approved for use with the motor-compressor which it protects on the basis that it will prevent dangerous overheating of the motor-compressor due to overload and failure to start. If the current-interrupting device is separate from the motor-compressor and its control circuit is operated by a protective device integral with the motor-compressor, it shall be so arranged that the opening of the control circuit will result in interruption of current to the motor-compressor.

(3) A fuse or inverse time circuit breaker responsive to motor current, which shall also be permitted to serve as the branch-circuit short-circuit and ground-fault protective device. This device shall be rated at not more than 125 percent of the motor-compressor rated-load current. It shall have sufficient time delay to permit the motor-compressor to start and accelerate its load. The equipment or the motor-compressor shall be marked with this maximum branch-circuit fuse or inverse time circuit breaker rating.

(4) A protective system, furnished or specified and approved for use with the motor-compressor which it protects on the basis that it will prevent dangerous overheating of the motor-compressor due to overload and failure to start. If the current interrupting device is separate from the motor-compressor and its control circuit is operated by a protective device which is not integral with the current-interrupting device, it shall be so arranged that the opening of the control circuit will result in interruption of current to the motor-compressor.

(b) Protection of Motor-Compressor Control Apparatus and Branch-Circuit Conductors. The motor-compressor controller(s), the disconnecting means and branch-circuit conductors shall be protected against overcurrent due to motor overload and failure to start by one of the following means which shall be permitted to be the same device or system protecting the motor-compressor in accordance with Section 440-52(a).

Exception: For motor-compressors and equipment on 15- or 20-ampere single-phase branch circuits as provided in Sections 440-54 and 440-55.

(1) An overload relay selected in accordance with Section 440-52(a)(1).

(2) A thermal protector applied in accordance with Section 440-52(a)(2) and which will not permit a continuous current in excess of 156 percent of the marked rated-load current or branch-circuit selection current.

(3) A fuse or inverse time circuit breaker selected in accordance with Section 440-52(a)(3).

(4) A protective system in accordance with Section 440-52(a)(4) and which will not permit a continuous current in excess of 156 percent of the marked rated-load current or branch-circuit selection current.

440-53. Overload Relays. Overload relays and other devices for motor overload protection, which are not capable of opening short circuits, shall be protected by fuses or inverse time circuit breakers with ratings or settings in accordance with Part C unless approved for group installation or for part-winding motors and marked to indicate the maximum size of fuse or inverse time circuit breaker by which they shall be protected.

Exception: The fuse or inverse time circuit breaker size marking shall be permitted on the nameplate of approved equipment in which the overload relay or other overload device is used.

440-54. Motor-Compressors and Equipment on 15- or 20-Ampere Branch Circuits — Not Cord-and-Attachment Plug-Connected. Overload protection for motor-compressors and equipment used on 15- or 20-ampere 120-volt, or 15-ampere 208- or 240-volt single-phase branch circuits as permitted in Article 210 shall be permitted as indicated in (a) and (b) below.

(a) Overload Protection. The motor-compressor shall be provided with overload protection selected as specified in Section 440-52(a). Both the controller and motor overload protective device shall be approved for installation with the short-circuit and ground-fault protective device for the branch circuit to which the equipment is connected.

(b) Time Delay. The short-circuit and ground-fault protective device protecting the branch circuit shall have sufficient time delay to permit the motor-compressor and other motors to start and accelerate their loads.

440-55. Cord-and-Attachment Plug-Connected Motor-Compressors and Equipment on 15- or 20-Ampere Branch Circuits. Overload protection for motor-compressors and equipment that are cord-and-attachment plug-connected and used on 15- or 20-ampere 120-volt, or 15-ampere 208- or 240-volt single-phase branch circuits as permitted in Article 210 shall be permitted as indicated in (a), (b), and (c) below.

(a) Overload Protection. The motor-compressor shall be provided with overload protection as specified in Section 440-52(a). Both the controller and the motor overload protective device shall be approved for installation with the short-circuit and ground-fault protective device for the branch circuit to which the equipment is connected.

(b) Attachment Plug and Receptacle Rating. The rating of the attachment plug and receptacle shall not exceed 20 amperes at 125 volts or 15 amperes at 250 volts.

(c) Time Delay. The short-circuit and ground-fault protective device protecting the branch circuit shall have sufficient time delay to permit the motor-compressor and other motors to start and accelerate their loads.

G. Provisions for Room Air Conditioners

440-60. General. The provisions of Part G shall apply to electrically energized room air conditioners that control temperature and humidity. For the purpose of Part G, a room air conditioner (with or without provisions for heating) shall be considered as an alternating-current appliance of the air-cooled window, console, or in-wall type that is installed in the conditioned room and which incorporates a hermetic refrigerant motor-compressor(s). The provisions of Part G cover equipment rated not over 250 volts, single phase, and such equipment shall be permitted to be cord-and-attachment plug-connected.

A room air conditioner that is rated three phase or rated over 250 volts shall be directly connected to a wiring method recognized in Chapter 3, and provisions of Part G shall not apply.

440-61. Grounding. Room air conditioners shall be grounded in accordance with Sections 250-42, 250-43, and 250-45.

440-62. Branch-Circuit Requirements.

(a) Room Air Conditioner as a Single Motor Unit. A room air conditioner shall be considered as a single motor unit in determining its branch-circuit requirements when all the following conditions are met:

(1) It is cord-and-attachment plug-connected.

(2) Its rating is not more than 40 amperes and 250 volts, single phase.

(3) Total rated-load current is shown on the room air-conditioner nameplate rather than individual motor currents, and

(4) The rating of the branch-circuit short-circuit and ground-fault protective device does not exceed the ampacity of the branch-circuit conductors or the rating of the receptacle, whichever is less.

(b) Where No Other Loads Are Supplied. The total marked rating of a cord-and-attachment plug-connected room air conditioner shall not exceed 80 percent of the rating of a branch circuit where no other loads are supplied.

(c) Where Lighting Units or Other Appliances Are also Supplied. The total marked rating of a cord-and-attachment plug-connected room air conditioner shall not exceed 50 percent of the rating of a branch circuit where lighting units or other appliances are also supplied.

440-63. Disconnecting Means. An attachment plug and receptacle shall be permitted to serve as the disconnecting means for a single-phase room air conditioner rated 250 volts or less if: (1) the manual controls on the room air conditioner are readily accessible and located within 6 feet (1.83 m) of the floor, or (2) an approved manually operable switch is installed in a readily accessible location within sight from the room air conditioner.

440-64. Supply Cords. Where a flexible cord is used to supply a room air conditioner, the length of such cord shall not exceed: (1) 10 feet (3.05 m) for a nominal, 120-volt rating, or (2) 6 feet (1.83 m) for a nominal 208- or 240-volt rating.

ARTICLE 445 — GENERATORS

Contents

445-1. General. Generators and their associated wiring and equipment shall also comply with the applicable provisions of Articles 230, 250, 700, 701, and 702.

445-2. Location. Generators shall be of a type suitable for the locations in which they are installed. They shall also meet the requirements for motors in Section 430-14. Generators installed in hazardous (classified) locations as described in Articles 500 through 503, or in other locations as described in Articles 510 through 517, and in Articles 520, 530, and 665 shall also comply with the applicable provisions of those articles.

445-3. Marking. Each generator shall be provided with a nameplate giving the maker's name, the rated frequency, power factor, number of phases if of alternating current, the rating in kilowatts or kilovolt amperes, the normal volts and amperes corresponding to the rating, rated revolutions per minute, insulation system class and rated ambient temperature or rated temperature rise, and time rating.

445-4. Overcurrent Protection.

(a) Constant-Voltage Generators. Constant-voltage generators, except alternating-current generator exciters, shall be protected from overloads by inherent design, circuit breakers, fuses, or other acceptable overcurrent protective means, suitable for the conditions of use.

(b) Two-Wire Generators. Two-wire, direct-current generators shall be permitted to have overcurrent protection in one conductor only if the overcurrent device is actuated by the entire current generated other than the current in the shunt field. The overcurrent device shall not open the shunt field.

(c) 65 Volts or Less. Generators operating at 65 volts or less and driven by individual motors shall be considered as protected by the overcurrent device protecting the motor if these devices will operate when the generators are delivering not more than 150 percent of their full-load rated current.

(d) Balancer Sets. Two-wire, direct-current generators used in conjunction with balancer sets to obtain neutrals for 3-wire systems shall be equipped with overcurrent devices that will disconnect the 3-wire system in case of excessive unbalancing of voltages or currents.

(e) 3-Wire, Direct-Current Generators. Three-wire, direct-current generators, whether compound or shunt wound, shall be equipped with overcurrent devices, one in each armature lead, and so connected as to be actuated by the entire current from the armature. Such overcurrent devices shall consist either of a double-pole, double-coil circuit breaker, or of a 4-pole circuit breaker connected in the main and equalizer leads and tripped by two overcurrent devices, one in each armature lead. Such protective devices shall be so interlocked that no one pole can be opened without simultaneously disconnecting both leads of the armature from the system.

Exception to (a) through (e): Where deemed by the authority having jurisdiction, a generator is vital to the operation of an electrical system and the generator should operate to failure to prevent a greater hazard to persons, the overload sensing device(s) shall be permitted to be connected to an annunciator or alarm supervised by authorized personnel instead of interrupting the generator circuit.

Alternating-current generators can be designed so that, during short periods of time when the generator may carry an excessive overload, the voltage will fall off sufficiently to limit the current and power output to values that will not damage the generator.

The connection of a 2-wire generator, protected by a single-pole circuit breaker, is illustrated in Figure 445-1. Where two or more dc generators are operated in parallel or multiple, an equalizer conductor lead is connected to the positive terminal of each generator and, in effect, connects the series fields in parallel so as to maintain equal output voltage for each generator. The current could divide at the positive terminal, some flowing through the series field and positive lead and some flowing through the equalizer lead. The entire current generated flows through the negative lead; therefore, the fuse or circuit breaker (or at least the operating coil of a circuit breaker) must be placed in the negative lead. Overcurrent devices are required to be connected so as to be actuated by the entire armature output current.

An overcurrent device should not be placed in the shunt-field circuit because, if this circuit were to open when the field is at full strength, an extremely high voltage would be induced which could damage the field-winding insulation and injure the generator.

Section 445-4(c) indicates that generators operating at 65 V or less are to be thought of as protected by the overcurrent devices that also protect the drive-motor, providing these devices will operate when the generator delivers 150 percent of its rated full-load current.

Figure 445-2 illustrates a double-pole circuit breaker with one pole connected in each lead of the main generator and with the operating coil properly designed to be connected in the neutral lead from the balancer, and so arranged as to be operated by either one of the "A" coils or by the "B" coil. Each of the two generators used as a balancer set carries approximately one-half of the unbalanced load and, thus, is always smaller than the main generator. During an excessive imbalance of the load, the balancer set would be overloaded with no overload on the main generator; hence, a double-pole circuit breaker is connected (as noted) to guard against this condition.

It should be noted that the authority having jurisdiction may judge that the generator should operate to failure rather than providing automatic means to shut it down, which, in many cases, could present a greater hazard to personnel. An overload sensing device(s) would be permitted to be connected to an annunciator or an alarm (instead of interrupting the generator) and allow operating personnel to shut down load-side equipment in a safe and orderly fashion.

445-5. Ampacity of Conductors. The ampacity of the phase conductors from the generator terminals to the first overcurrent device shall not be less than 115 percent of the nameplate current rating of the generator. It shall be permitted to size the neutral conductors in accordance with Section 220-22. Conductors which must carry ground-fault currents shall not be smaller than required by Section 250-23(b).

Exception No. 1: Where the design and operation of the generator prevent overloading, the ampacity of the conductors shall not be less than 100 percent of the nameplate current rating of the generator.

Exception No. 2: Where the generator manufacturer's leads are connected directly to an overcurrent device that is an integral part of the generator set assembly.

445-6. Protection of Live Parts. Live parts of generators operated at more than 50 volts to ground shall not be exposed to accidental contact where accessible to unqualified persons.

Figure 445-1. A schematic diagram of a 2-wire dc generator protected by a single-pole circuit breaker.

Figure 445-2. A schematic diagram of a double-pole circuit breaker (one pole connected in each lead of the main generator) with the opening coil arranged to be connected in the neutral of the balancer set.

445-7. Guards for Attendants. Where necessary for the safety of attendants, the requirements of Section 430-133 shall apply.

445-8. Bushings. Where wires pass through an opening in an enclosure, conduit box, or barrier, a bushing shall be used to protect the conductors from the edges of an opening having sharp edges. The bushing shall have smooth, well-rounded surfaces where it may be in contact with the conductors. If used where oils, grease, or other contaminants may be present, the bushing shall be made of a material not deleteriously affected.

ARTICLE 450 —TRANSFORMERS AND TRANSFORMER VAULTS

(Including Secondary Ties)

Contents

450-1. Scope. This article covers the installation of all transformers.

Exception No. 1: Current transformers.

Exception No. 2: Dry-type transformers that constitute a component part of other apparatus and comply with the requirements for such apparatus.

Exception No. 3: Transformers which are an integral part of an X-ray, high-frequency, or electrostatic-coating apparatus.

Exception No. 4: Transformers used with Class 2 and Class 3 circuits that comply with Article 725.

Exception No. 5: Transformers for sign and outline lighting that comply with Article 600.

Exception No. 6: Transformers for electric-discharge lighting that comply with Article 410.

Exception No. 7: Transformers used for power-limited fire protective signaling circuits that comply with Part C of Article 760.

Exception No. 8: Liquid-filled or dry-type transformers used for research, development, or testing, where effective arrangements are provided to safeguard unqualified persons from contacting high-voltage terminals or energized conductors.

Exception No. 8 permits an exemption for liquid-filled or dry-type transformers because they are usually energized only when tests are being made, are under constant supervision by qualified personnel, and high-voltage circuits are guarded and interlocked to protect against accidental contact by unqualified persons.

This article also covers the installation of transformers in hazardous (classified) locations as modified by Articles 501 through 503.

A. General Provisions

450-2. Definitions. For the purpose of this article:

Transformer: The word transformer is intended to mean an individual transformer, single- or polyphase, identified by a single nameplate, unless otherwise indicated in this article.

450-3. Overcurrent Protection. Overcurrent protection shall comply with (a), (b), or (c) below. As used in this section, the word "transformer" shall mean a transformer or polyphase bank of two or three single-phase transformers operating as a unit.

(a) Transformers Over 600 Volts, Nominal.

(1) Primary and Secondary. Each transformer over 600 volts, nominal, shall have primary and secondary protective devices rated or set to open at no more than the values noted in Table 450-3(a)(1).

Exception No. 1: Where the required fuse rating or circuit breaker setting does not correspond to a standard rating or setting, the next higher standard rating or setting shall be permitted.

Exception No. 2: As provided in (a)(2) below.

(2) Supervised Installations. Where conditions of maintenance and supervision assure that only qualified persons will monitor and service the transformer installation, overcurrent protection as provided in (a)(2) shall be permitted.

Table 450-3(a)(1)
Transformers Over 600 Volts

	Maximum Rating or Setting for Overcurrent Device				
	Primary		Secondary		
	Over 600 Volts		Over 600 Volts		600 Volts or Below
Transformer Rated Impedance	Circuit Breaker Setting	Fuse Rating	Circuit Breaker Setting	Fuse Rating	Circuit Breaker Setting or Fuse Rating
Not more than 6%	600%	300%	300%	250%	125%
More than 6% and not more than 10%	400%	300%	250%	225%	125%

The secondary circuit breaker setting or fuse rating requirements of Table 450-3(a)(1) for transformers with secondaries of 600 volts and below have been changed from the previous edition of the *Code*. The circuit breaker setting or fuse rating has been reduced from 250 percent of the full load rating of the transformer to 125 percent. Exception No. 2 permits the use of a fuse or circuit breaker set at 250 percent where certain conditions of monitoring and maintenance are met. This change is designed to reduce the incidence of transformer overload failures as well as maintain the flexibility of design and operation required in industrial and commercial locations.

a. Primary. Each transformer over 600 volts, nominal, shall be protected by an individual overcurrent device on the primary side. Where fuses are used, their continuous current rating shall not exceed 250 percent of the rated primary current of the transformer. Where circuit breakers are used, they shall be set at not more than 300 percent of the rated primary current of the transformer.

Exception No. 1: Where the required fuse rating or circuit breaker setting does not correspond to a standard rating or setting, the next higher standard rating or setting shall be permitted.

Exception No. 2: An individual overcurrent device shall not be required where the primary circuit overcurrent device provides the protection specified in this section.

Exception No. 3: As provided in (a)(2)b. below:

b. Primary and Secondary. A transformer over 600 volts, nominal, having an overcurrent device on the secondary side rated or set to open at not more than the values noted in Table 450-3(a)(2)b., or a transformer equipped with a coordinated thermal overload protection by the manufacturer, shall not be required to have an individual overcurrent device in the primary connection provided the primary feeder overcurrent device is rated or set to open at not more than the values noted in Table 450-3(a)(2)b.

(b) Transformers 600 Volts, Nominal, or Less.

(1) Primary. Each transformer 600 volts, nominal, or less, shall be protected by an individual overcurrent device on the primary side, rated or set at not more than 125 percent of the rated primary current of the transformer.

Exception No. 1: Where the rated primary current of a transformer is 9 amperes or more and 125 percent of this current does not correspond to a standard rating of a fuse or nonadjustable circuit breaker, the next higher standard rating described in Section 240-6 shall be permitted. Where the rated primary current is less than 9 amperes, an overcurrent device rated or set at not more than 167 percent of the primary current shall be permitted.

Table 450-3(a)(2)b
Transformers Over 600 Volts in Supervised Locations

	Maximum Rating or Setting for Overcurrent Device				
	Primary		Secondary		
	Over 600 Volts		Over 600 Volts		600 Volts or Below
Transformer Rated Impedance	Circuit Breaker Setting	Fuse Rating	Circuit Breaker Setting	Fuse Rating	Circuit Breaker Setting or Fuse Rating
Not more than 6%	600%	300%	300%	250%	250%
More than 6% and not more than 10%	400%	300%	250%	225%	250%

Where the rated primary current is less than 2 amperes, an overcurrent device rated or set at not more than 300 percent shall be permitted.

Exception No. 2: An individual overcurrent device shall not be required where the primary circuit overcurrent device provides the protection specified in this section.

Exception No. 3: As provided in (b)(2) below.

(2) Primary and Secondary. A transformer 600 volts, nominal, or less, having an overcurrent device on the secondary side rated or set at not more than 125 percent of the rated secondary current of the transformer shall not be required to have an individual overcurrent device on the primary side if the primary feeder overcurrent device is rated or set at a current value not more than 250 percent of the rated primary current of the transformer.

A transformer 600 volts, nominal, or less, equipped with coordinated thermal overload protection by the manufacturer and arranged to interrupt the primary current, shall not be required to have an individual overcurrent device on the primary side if the primary feeder overcurrent device is rated or set at a current value not more than six times the rated current of the transformer for transformers having not more than 6 percent impedance, and not more than four times the rated current of the transformer for transformers having more than 6 but not more than 10 percent impedance.

Exception: Where the rated secondary current of a transformer is 9 amperes or more and 125 percent of this current does not correspond to a standard rating of a fuse or nonadjustable circuit breaker, the next higher standard rating described in Section 240-6 shall be permitted.

Where the rated secondary current is less than 9 amperes, an overcurrent device rated or set at not more than 167 percent of the rated secondary current shall be permitted.

(c) Potential (Voltage) Transformers. Potential transformers installed indoors or enclosed shall be protected with primary fuses.

(FPN): See also Section 384-22.

Questions frequently arise as to whether the overcurrent protection required for transformers, as specified in Section 450-3, will provide satisfactory protection for the primary and secondary conductors. Where polyphase transformers are involved, primary and secondary conductors will usually not be properly protected. The rules in Section 450-3 are intended to protect the transformer alone. The primary overcurrent device provides short-circuit protection for the primary conductors and a degree of overload protection for the transformer, and a secondary overcurrent device prevents the transformer and secondary conductors from being overloaded. The transformer is considered the point of supply, and the conductors that it supplies are required to be protected in accordance with their ampacity.

Exceptions to this rule are permitted under special conditions outlined in Section 230-207, and Exception No. 8 of Section 240-21. See Figures 230-25 and 240-10.

Single-phase transformers having a 2-wire (single voltage) secondary may omit the secondary conductor overcurrent protective device if the primary transformer overcurrent protection is provided in accordance with this section, and its rating does not exceed the value determined by multiplying the secondary conductor ampacity by the secondary to primary voltage ratio. See commentary following Section 240-3, Exception No. 5. Single-phase transformers with a 3-wire secondary are not included in Exception No. 5 because of the possibility of a severe unbalanced load which the primary transformer protection would not recognize.

In those cases in which the primary feeder to the transformer incorporates overcurrent protective devices that are rated (or set) at a level not to exceed those prescribed herein, it is not necessary to duplicate them at the transformer.

Primary overcurrent protection (125%) (may be circuit breaker)

Transformer

Panel

Figure 450-1. Transformers of 600 V or less are required to be protected by an individual overcurrent device on the primary side. Exceptions to the basic rule are given in Section 450-3(b)(1).

450-4. Autotransformers 600 Volts, Nominal, or Less.

(a) Overcurrent Protection. Each autotransformer 600 volts, nominal, or less shall be protected by an individual overcurrent device installed in series with each ungrounded input conductor. Such overcurrent device shall be rated or set at not more than 125 percent of the rated full-load input current of the autotransformer. An overcurrent device shall not be installed in series with the shunt winding (the winding common to both the input and the output circuits) of the autotransformer between Points A and B as shown in Diagram 450-4.

An overcurrent device is not permitted between Points A and B in Diagram 450-4, even though use of an overcurrent device in this part of the circuit would provide closer protection of the transformer windings, because of the voltage feedback problem that can occur.

Refer to Figure 450-3, which shows a two-winding, single-phase transformer connected to boost a 208-V supply to 240 V. It is provided with single-pole overcurrent devices in the supply. If an overcurrent device were located between points A and B (OC-2), and this overcurrent device opened, the full 208-V supply voltage would be applied across the 32-V secondary winding in series with the

Primary overcurrent protection (250%) (may be circuit breaker)

Primary overcurrent protection (6 times transformer rating with 6% or less impedance or 4 times transformer rating with more than 6% but not more than 10% impedance)

Secondary overcurrent protection (125%) (may be circuit breaker)

Transformer with factory- installed integral overload protection device (rated to interrupt primary current)

Panel

Panel

Figure 450-2. Overcurrent protection on the primary and secondary sides of transformers rated 600 V or less. Exceptions to the basic rule are given in Section 450-3(b)(2).

-A

SHUNT WINDING(S)

B

Diagram 450-4

load. Under these conditions, a higher than normal voltage would appear across the primary winding. If the load impedance were very low, this voltage could approach $^{208}/_{32} \times 208 = 1352$ V.

Exception: Where the rated input current of an autotransformer is 9 amperes or more and 125 percent of this current does not correspond to a standard rating of a fuse or nonadjustable circuit breaker, the next higher standard rating described in Section 240-6 shall be permitted. Where the rated input current is less than

Figure 450-3. Overcurrent device in series with shunt winding of autotransformer is not permitted by Section 450-4(a).

9 amperes, an overcurrent device rated or set at not more than 167 percent of the input current shall be permitted.

(b) Transformer Field-Connected as an Autotransformer. A transformer field-connected as an autotransformer shall be identified for use at elevated voltage.

(FPN): For information on permitted uses of autotransformers, see Section 210-9.

This requirement is necessary because of the dielectric voltage withstand test requirements applied to transformers. The test is conducted at 2,500 volts for windings rated 250 V or less, and 4,000 V for higher rated windings. A transformer intended for buck or boost operation would require that the test for the low-voltage winding be based on the sum of the primary and secondary voltage ratings.

450-5. Grounding Autotransformers. Grounding autotransformers covered in this section are zig-zag or T-connected transformers connected to 3-phase, 3-wire ungrounded systems for the purpose of creating a 3-phase, 4-wire distribution system or to provide a neutral reference for grounding purposes. Such transformers shall have a continuous per phase current rating and a continuous neutral current rating.

(FPN): The phase current in a grounding autotransformer is one-third the neutral current.

(a) Three-Phase, 4-Wire System. A grounding autotransformer used to create a 3-phase, 4-wire distribution system from a 3-phase, 3-wire ungrounded system shall conform to the following:

(1) Connections. The transformer shall be directly connected to the ungrounded phase conductors and shall not be switched or provided with overcurrent protection which is independent of the main switch and common-trip overcurrent protection for the 3-phase, 4-wire system.

(2) Overcurrent Protection. An overcurrent sensing device shall be provided that will cause the main switch or common-trip overcurrent protection referred to in (a)(1) above to open if the load on the autotransformer reaches or exceeds 125 percent of its continuous current per phase or neutral rating. Delayed tripping for temporary overcurrents sensed at the autotransformer overcurrent device shall be permitted for the purpose of allowing proper operation of branch or feeder protective devices on the 4-wire system.

(3) Transformer Fault Sensing. A fault sensing system that will cause the opening of a main switch or common-trip overcurrent device for the 3-phase, 4-wire system shall be provided to guard against single-phasing or internal faults.

(FPN): This can be accomplished by the use of two subtractive-connected donut-type current transformers installed to sense and signal when an unbalance occurs in the line current to the autotransformer of 50 percent or more of rated current.

240 V, 3-phase, 3-wire
delta service

Figure 450-4. A zig-zag autotransformer used to create a 3-phase, 4-wire distribution system or to provide a neutral reference for grounding purposes.

(4) Rating. The autotransformer shall have a continuous neutral current rating sufficient to handle the maximum possible neutral unbalanced load current of the 4-wire system.

The donut-type current transformers shown as CT-1, CT-2, and CT-3 in Figure 450-5 are intended to trip the main breaker if the current in any phase or the neutral conductor exceeds 125 percent of the rated current [see Section 450-5(a)(2)]. The current transformers CT-2 and CT-3 are also differentially connected to protect against an internal failure of the autotransformer [see Section 450-5(a)(3)].

Figure 450-5 shows the proper method of protecting a grounding autotransformer where used to provide a neutral for a 3-phase system when necessary to supply a group of single-phase, line-to-neutral loads. Separate overcurrent protection is not provided for the autotransformer because there will be no control of the system line-to-neutral voltages if it becomes disconnected; consequently, simultaneous interruption of the power supply to all the line-to-neutral loads is necessary whenever the grounding autotransformer is switched off.

(b) Ground Reference for Fault Protection Devices. A grounding autotransformer used to make available a specified magnitude of ground-fault current for operation of a ground responsive protective device on a 3-phase, 3-wire ungrounded system shall conform to the following requirements:

(1) Rating. The autotransformer shall have a continuous neutral current rating sufficient for the specified ground-fault current.

(2) Overcurrent Protection. An overcurrent protective device of adequate short-circuit rating that will open simultaneously all ungrounded conductors when it operates shall be applied in the grounding autotransformer branch circuit and rated or set at a current not exceeding 125 percent of the autotransformer continuous per phase current rating or 42 percent of the continuous current rating of any series connected devices in the autotransformer neutral connection. Delayed tripping for temporary overcurrents to permit the proper operation of ground responsive tripping devices on the main system shall be permitted, but shall not exceed values which would be more than the short-time current rating of the grounding autotransformer or any series connected devices in the neutral connection thereto.

635

ARTICLE 450—TRANSFORMERS AND VAULTS

Figure 450-5. Zig-zag autotransformer for establishing a neutral connection for a 480Y/277-V, 3-phase ungrounded system to supply single-phase line-to-neutral loads. See Section 450-5(a).

CT-1 is connected to an overload relay responsive to excess neutral current being supplied. See Section 450-5(a)(2).

CT-2 and CT-3 are connected to differential-type fault-current sensing relays responsive to an unbalance of neutral current among the three phases of the grounding autotransformer (indicating an internal fault). See Section 450-5(a)(3).

All three relays are required to be arranged to trip the circuit breaker located upstream of both the autotransformer and the line-to-neutral connected loads to satisfy the requirements of Section 450-5(a)(1).

Figure 450-6. Zig-zag autotransformer for establishing a reference ground-fault current for fault-protective device operation or for damping transitory overvoltage surges. See Section 450-5(b) and (c).

The overcurrent protective device is to have a rating (or setting) not in excess of 125 percent of the rated phase current of the autotransformer (42 percent of the neutral current rating) and not more than 42 percent of the continuous current rating of the neutral grounding resistor or other current-carrying device in the neutral connection. See Section 450-5(b)(2).

636

(c) Ground Reference for Damping Transitory Overvoltages. A grounding autotransformer used to limit transitory overvoltages shall be of suitable rating and connected in accordance with (a)(1) above.

For this case involving a high-resistance grounding package, the *NEC* text seems to suggest that the connections and overcurrent protection should conform with Section 450-5(a)(1), but this is not the case. The functional performance parallels that described in Section 450-5(b), differing only in that the magnitude of available ground-fault current would likely be a lower value. It would be appropriate to employ the connections displayed on Figure 450-6, and conform with the overcurrent protection requirements prescribed in Section 450-5(b)(2).

With any of the grounding autotransformer applications covered by Sections 450-5(a), (b), or (c), it is important to emphasize the use of a ganged 3-pole switching interrupter for connecting and disconnecting the autotransformer in order to accomplish simultaneous connection (and disconnection) of the three line terminals. If at any time one or two of the line connections to the autotransformer should open, which could occur if the protective devices were single-pole, the grounding autotransformer ceases to function in the desired fashion and acts as a high-inductive-reactance connection between the electrical system and ground. The latter connection is prone to create high-value transitory overvoltages, line-to-ground — a most unwanted result.

450-6. Secondary Ties. A secondary tie is a circuit operating at 600 volts, nominal, or less, between phases that connects two power sources or power supply points, such as the secondaries of two transformers. The tie shall be permitted to consist of one or more conductors per phase.

As used in this section, the word "transformer" means a transformer or a bank of transformers operating as a unit.

(a) Tie Circuits. Tie circuits shall be provided with overcurrent protection at each end as required in Article 240.

Exception: Under the conditions described in (a)(1) and (a)(2) below, the overcurrent protection shall be permitted to be in accordance with (a)(3) below.

(1) Loads at Transformer Supply Points Only. Where all loads are connected at the transformer supply points at each end of the tie and overcurrent protection is not provided in accordance with Article 240, the rated ampacity of the tie shall not be less than 67 percent of the rated secondary current of the largest transformer connected to the secondary tie system.

(2) Loads Connected Between Transformer Supply Points. Where load is connected to the tie at any point between transformer supply points and overcurrent protection is not provided in accordance with Article 240, the rated ampacity of the tie shall not be less than 100 percent of the rated secondary current of the largest transformer connected to the secondary tie system.

Exception: As otherwise provided in (a)(4) below.

(3) Tie Circuit Protection. Under the conditions described in (a)(1) and (a)(2) above, both ends of each tie conductor shall be equipped with a protective device that will open at a predetermined temperature of the tie conductor under short-circuit conditions. This protection shall consist of one of the following: (1) a fusible link cable connector, terminal, or lug, commonly known as a limiter, each being of a size corresponding with that of the conductor and of construction and characteristics according to the operating voltage and the type of insulation on the tie conductors, or (2) automatic circuit breakers actuated by devices having comparable current-time characteristics.

(4) Interconnection of Phase Conductors Between Transformer Supply Points. Where the tie consists of more than one conductor per phase, the conductors of each phase shall be interconnected in order to establish a load supply point, and the protection specified in (a)(3) above shall be provided in each tie conductor at this point.

Exception: Loads shall be permitted to be connected to the individual conductors of a paralleled conductor tie without interconnecting the conductors of each phase and without the protection specified in (a)(3) above at load connection points provided the tie conductors of each phase have a combined capacity of not less than 133 percent of the rated secondary current of the largest transformer connected to the secondary tie system; the total load of such taps does not exceed the rated secondary current of the largest transformer; and the loads are equally divided on each phase and on the individual conductors of each phase as far as practicable.

(5) Tie Circuit Control. Where the operating voltage exceeds 150 volts to ground, secondary ties provided with limiters shall have a switch at each end that, when open, will de-energize the associated tie conductors and limiters. The current rating of the switch shall not be less than the rated current of the conductors connected to the switch. It shall be capable of opening its rated current, and it shall be constructed so that it will not open under the magnetic forces resulting from short-circuit current.

(b) Overcurrent Protection for Secondary Connections. Where secondary ties are used, an overcurrent device rated or set at not more than 250 percent of the rated secondary current of the transformers shall be provided in the secondary connections of each transformer. In addition, an automatic circuit breaker actuated by a reverse-current relay set to open the circuit at not more than the rated secondary current of the transformer shall be provided in the secondary connection of each transformer.

The rules of Section 450-6 apply specifically to network systems for power distribution that are commonly employed where the load density is high and reliability of service is important. Such a system is illustrated in Figure 450-9. This type of distribution system introduces a variety of problems not encountered in the more common radial-type distribution system and must be designed by experienced electrical engineers. The sketch shows a typical 3-phase network system for an industrial plant fed by two primary feeders, preferably from separate substations, which are energized at any standard voltage up to 34,500 V. Each of the transformers is supplied by the two primary feeders which are arranged by means of a double-throw switch at the transformer so that either feeder may supply it.

Each of the network transformers is rated in the range of 300 kVA to 1,000 kVA and is required to be protected as illustrated in Figure 450-7. The primary and secondary protection is in accordance with Section 450-3, but an additional protective device is also required to be provided on the secondary side known as a network protector consisting of a circuit breaker and a reverse-power relay. This operates on reverse current to prevent power being fed back into the transformer through the secondary ties should a fault occur in the transformer or in a primary feeder. The reverse-power relay is set to trip the circuit breaker at a current value not more than the rated secondary current of the transformer. The relay is not designed to trip the circuit breaker in the event of an overload on the secondary of the transformer.

The secondary ties shown in Figure 450-9 are required to be protected at each end with an overcurrent device in accordance with Section 450-6(a)(3). The overcurrent device most commonly provided for this purpose is a special type of fuse known as a current limiter (see Figure 450-8). This is a high-interrupting capacity device designed to provide short-circuit protection only for the secondary ties and will open safely before temperatures damaging to the cable insulation are reached. See Section 240-11 for definition of current-limiting overcurrent protective device. See also commentary following Section 240-11. The secondary ties form a closed loop that is equipped with switching devices so that any part of the loop may be isolated when repairs are needed or a current limiter must be replaced.

Figure 450-7. Primary and secondary overcurrent protection for a transformer in a network system showing a network protector (an automatic circuit breaker actuated by a reverse-current relay).

Figure 450-8. A current-limiter is a special type of high-interrupting capacity fuse.

450-7. Parallel Operation. Transformers shall be permitted to be operated in parallel and switched as a unit provided that the overcurrent protection for each transformer meets the requirements of Section 450-3 (a)(1) or (b)(2).

450-8. Guarding. Transformers shall be guarded as specified in (a) through (d) below.

(a) **Mechanical Protection.** Appropriate provisions shall be made to minimize the possibility of damage to transformers from external causes where the transformers are exposed to physical damage.

ARTICLE 450—TRANSFORMERS AND VAULTS

Figure 450-9. A typical 3-phase network system for an industrial plant fed by two primary feeders.

One example of mechanical protection is 3-in. to 4-in. inside diameter vertical steel pipes embedded in the ground and filled with concrete. This method can be used where transformers may otherwise be subjected to damage by vehicles.

(b) Case or Enclosure. Dry-type transformers shall be provided with a noncombustible moisture-resistant case or enclosure that will provide reasonable protection against the accidental insertion of foreign objects.

(c) Exposed Live Parts. Transformers shall be so installed that live parts are guarded in accordance with Sections 110-17 and 110-34.

(d) Voltage Warning. The operating voltage of exposed live parts of transformer installations shall be indicated by signs or visible markings on the equipment or structures.

450-9. Ventilation. The ventilation shall be adequate to dispose of the transformer full-load losses without creating temperature rise which is in excess of the transformer rating.

(FPN): See ANSI/IEEE C57.12.00-1980, General Requirements for Liquid-Immersed Distribution, Power, and Regulating Transformers and ANSI/IEEE C57.12.01-1979, General Requirements for Dry-Type Distribution and Power Transformers.

450-10. Grounding. Exposed noncurrent-carrying metal parts of transformer installations, including fences, guards, etc., shall be grounded where required under the conditions and in the manner specified for electric equipment and other exposed metal parts in Article 250.

450-11. Marking. Each transformer shall be provided with a nameplate giving the name of the manufacturer; rated kilovolt-amperes; frequency; primary and secondary voltage; impedance of transformers 25 kVA and larger; and the amount and kind of insulating liquid where used. In addition, the nameplate of each dry-type transformer shall include the temperature class for the insulation system.

The information given on a transformer nameplate is necessary for determining whether the transformer is capable of carrying the load it is supplying as calculated in accordance with Article 220.

450-12. Terminal Wiring Space. The minimum wire bending space at fixed, 600 volts and below terminals of transformer line and load connections shall be as required in Section 373-6. Wiring space for pigtail connections shall conform to Table 370-6(b).

This rule is to ensure adequate wire bending space at fixed terminals of transformer line and load connections, rated 600 V or less, as this is a point of maximum mechanical and electrical stress on the conductor insulation. See commentary following Section 370-6.

450-13. Location. Transformers and transformer vaults shall be readily accessible to qualified personnel for inspection and maintenance.

Exception No. 1: Dry-type transformers 600 volts, nominal, or less, located in the open on walls, columns, or structures, shall not be required to be readily accessible.

Exception No. 2: Dry-type transformers not exceeding 600 volts, nominal, and 50 kVA shall be permitted in fire-resistant hollow spaces of buildings not permanently closed in by structure and provided they meet the ventilation requirements of Section 450-9.

Unless specified otherwise in this article, the term "fire resistant" means a construction having a minimum fire rating of 1 hour.

(FPN): See ANSI/ASTM E119-83, and Fire Tests of Building Construction and Materials, NFPA 251-1985.

(FPN): The location of different types of transformers is covered in Part B of Article 450. The location of transformer vaults is covered in Section 450-41.

B. Specific Provisions Applicable to Different Types of Transformers

450-21. Dry-type Transformers Installed Indoors.

(a) Not Over 112½ kVA. Dry-type transformers installed indoors and rated 112½ kVA or less shall have a separation of at least 12 inches (305 mm) from combustible material unless separated therefrom by a fire-resistant, heat-insulating barrier, or unless of a rating not over 600 volts and completely enclosed except for ventilating openings.

(b) Over 112½ kVA. Individual dry-type transformers of more than 112½ kVA rating shall be installed in a transformer room of fire-resistant construction.

Exception No. 1 to (b): Transformers with 80°C rise or higher ratings and separated from combustible material by a fire-resistant, heat-insulating barrier or by not less than 6 feet (1.83 m) horizontally and 12 feet (3.66 m) vertically.

Exception No. 2 to (b): Transformers with 80°C rise or higher ratings and of completely enclosed and ventilated-type construction.

(c) Over 35,000 Volts. Dry-type transformers rated over 35,000 volts shall be installed in a vault complying with Part C of this article.

Dry-type transformers depend on the surrounding air for adequate ventilation and where rated 112½ kVA or less are not required to be installed in a fire-resistive transformer room.

ARTICLE 450—TRANSFORMERS AND VAULTS

Transformers of the dry type, gas-filled, or less-flammable liquid-insulated transformers (see Section 450-23) installed indoors with a primary voltage of not more than 35,000 volts are commonly used because a transformer vault is not required.

For the same reason, askarel-filled transformers have been extensively used indoors in the past. Askarel, which contains a polychlorinated biphenyl (PCB), is no longer being manufactured, but acceptable substitutes that comply with Section 450-23 are now available. See Figure 450-14.

Figure 450-10 shows a 1,500 kVA gas-filled dry-type transformer available in ratings through 5,000 kVA, 34½ kV for use indoors or outdoors. These units are built using the conventional ventilated dry-type core and coils, but sealed in a heavy welded steel tank and filled with fluorocarbon gas for dielectric strength as well as cooling. Since the transformers are completely hermetically sealed in a heavy-gage steel tank, they are considered safe indoors and outdoors, and there is little likelihood of flames or gases escaping in the event of a short circuit or transformer failure. These units can be used for any explosive, highly combustible, or dangerous area and offer high resistance to fire or explosion. See Sections 501-2, 502-2, and 503-2.

Figure 450-11 shows a dry-type transformer with the outside casing in place and with the latest core and coil design for a typical dry-type power transformer rated at 1,000 kVA, 13,800-V to 480-V, 3-phase, 60 Hz. This transformer has a high-voltage and low-voltage flange for connection to switchgear and a high-voltage, 2-position (double-throw), 3-pole load break-air switch which may be attached to the case and arranged as a selector switch for the connection of the transformer primary to either of two feeder sources.

Dry-type transformers rated 112½ kVA or less are required to be separated from combustible material or rated less than 600 V and completely enclosed, except for ventilating openings. Noncombustible insulations used in transformers, such as mica, porcelain, and glass, which can withstand high temperatures, have permitted the application of larger dry-type transformers. However, combustible materials, such as varnish, are used with those insulations, and under short-circuit conditions, flames can escape from the transformer enclosure. Hence, transformers rated 112½ kVA or less are required to be spaced 12 in. or separated by fire-resistive barriers from combustibles or be completely enclosed. Those rated over 112½ kVA are required to be located in fire-resistive transformer rooms or vaults.

450-22. Dry-type Transformers Installed Outdoors. Dry-type transformers installed outdoors shall have a weatherproof enclosure.

Transformers exceeding 112½ kVA shall not be located within 12 inches (305 mm) of combustible materials of buildings.

450-23. Less-Flammable Liquid-Insulated Transformers. Transformers insulated with listed less-flammable liquids shall be permitted to be installed without a vault in Type I and Type II buildings in areas in which no combustible materials are stored, provided there is a liquid confinement area, the liquid has a fire point of not less than 300°C, and the installation complies with all restrictions provided for in the listing of the liquid. Such indoor transformer installations not meeting the restrictions of the liquid listing, or installed in other than Type I or Type II buildings, or in areas where combustible materials are stored, shall (1) be provided with an automatic fire extinguishing system and a liquid confinement area, or (2) be installed in a vault complying with Part C of this article.

Transformers installed indoors and rated over 35,000 volts shall be installed in a vault.

Transformers installed outdoors shall comply with the safeguards of Section 450-27.

(FPN): As used in this section, "noncombustible" refers to Type I and Type II building construction and noncombustible materials as defined in Types of Building Construction, NFPA 220-1985 (ANSI).

Figure 450-10. 1,500-kVA gas-filled dry-type transformer available
in ratings through 5,000 kVA, 34½ kVA for use indoors or outdoors.
(*Westinghouse Electric Corp.*)

NFPA 220 defines Type I building construction as "that type in which the
structural members, including walls, columns, beams, floors, and roofs, are of
approved noncombustible or limited-combustible materials and have fire resistance ratings not less than those set forth in Table 3" of NFPA 220.

Type II building construction is defined as "that type not qualifying as Type I
construction in which the structural members including walls, columns, beams,
floors, and roofs are of approved noncombustible or limited-combustible materials
and have fire resistance ratings not less than those set forth in Table 3" of NFPA
220.

(FPN): See definition of "listed" in Article 100.

Two listing agencies, Factory Mutual Research Corp. and Underwriters Laboratories Inc., list less-flammable liquids for transformers. These liquids have a fire
point of at least 300°C. This type of transformer may be installed indoors without
a vault in buildings of Types I and II construction in areas where no combustible
materials are stored provided they are not rated over 35,000 V, there is a liquid
confinement area, and the installation complies with all of the limitations provided
for in the listing.

The Factory Mutual listing is based on a test in which the burning characteristics
of the fluid are measured. These characteristics, the radiative and convective heat,
may be found in the Factory Mutual Approval Guide. The radiative heat release is
the heat exposure to the walls (see Figure 450-12). The convective heat release is
the exposure to the ceiling (see Figure 450-13). Application of the heat release
criteria is based on the size of the liquid confinement area, the building
construction, the ceiling height, and the distance from the confinement area to the

Figure 450-11. A dry-type transformer with a core and coil design rated at 1,000 kVA, 13,800 V to 480 V, 3-phase, 60 Hz. (*Westinghouse Electric Corp.*)

walls. Further information on application may be found in Factory Mutual Loss Prevention Data Sheet 5-4/14-8.

The Underwriters Laboratories Inc. listing is based on primary side current-limiting fuses, a tank withstand strength of 12 PSIG, and pressure relief devices. UL currently limits the listing to three-phase transformers. Further information may be obtained from the Underwriters Laboratories Inc. Gas and Oil Equipment Directory under Dielectric Mediums (EOUV) or the manufacturer. See also commentary following Section 450-27.

450-24. Nonflammable Fluid-Insulated Transformers. Transformers insulated with a dielectric fluid identified as nonflammable shall be permitted to be installed indoors or outdoors. Such transformers installed indoors and rated over 35,000 volts shall be installed in a vault.

For the purposes of this section, a nonflammable dielectric fluid is one which does not have a flash point or fire point, and is not flammable in air.

450-25. Askarel-Insulated Transformers Installed Indoors. Askarel-insulated transformers installed indoors and rated over 25 kVA shall be furnished with a pressure-relief vent. Where installed in a poorly ventilated place, they shall be furnished with a means for absorbing any gases generated by arcing inside the case, or the pressure-relief vent shall be connected to a chimney or flue that will carry such gases outside the building. Askarel-insulated transformers rated over 35,000 volts shall be installed in a vault.

450-26. Oil-Insulated Transformers Installed Indoors. Oil-insulated transformers installed indoors shall be installed in a vault constructed as specified in Part C of this article.

Figure 450-12. The Factory Mutual Research Corp. listing restricts the distance from the liquid confinement area to the wall in which a given fluid may be used based on the radiative heat release rate of the fluid. Radiative heat release is considered as a fire exposure to the wall. See also Figure 450-13.

Figure 450-13. The Factory Mutual Research Corp. listing restricts the minimum ceiling height above the floor of the confinement area in which a given fluid may be used based on its convective heat release rate. Convective heat release is considered as a fire exposure to the ceiling. See also Figure 450-12.

Exception No. 1: Where the total capacity does not exceed 112½ kVA, the vault specified in Part C of this article shall be permitted to be constructed of reinforced concrete not less than 4 inches (102 mm) thick.

Exception No. 2: Where the nominal voltage does not exceed 600, a vault shall not be required if suitable arrangements are made to prevent a transformer oil fire from igniting other materials, and the total capacity in one location does not exceed 10 kVA in a section of the building classified as combustible, or 75 kVA where the surrounding structure is classified as fire-resistant construction.

Exception No. 3: Electric furnace transformers having a total rating not exceeding 75 kVA shall be permitted to be installed without a vault in a building or room of fire-resistant construction, provided suitable arrangements are made to prevent a transformer oil fire from spreading to other combustible material.

645

Figure 450-14. A liquid-insulated transformer filled with a listed, less-flammable liquid with a fire point of at least 300°C (572°F). (*Square D Co.*)

Exception No. 4: Transformers shall be permitted to be installed in a detached building that does not comply with Part C of this article if neither the building nor its contents presents a fire hazard to any other building or property, and if the building is used only in supplying electric service and the interior is accessible only to qualified persons.

Exception No. 5: Oil-insulated transformers shall be permitted to be used without a vault in portable and mobile surface mining equipment (such as electric excavators) if each of the following conditions is met:

a. Provision is made for draining leaking fluid to the ground.

b. Safe egress is provided for personnel.

c. A minimum ¼-inch (6.35-mm) steel barrier is provided for personnel protection.

450-27. Oil-Insulated Transformers Installed Outdoors. Combustible material, combustible buildings, and parts of buildings, fire escapes, and door and window openings shall be safeguarded from fires originating in oil-insulated transformers installed on roofs, attached to, or adjacent to a building or combustible material.

Space separations, fire-resistant barriers, automatic water spray systems, and enclosures that confine the oil of a ruptured transformer tank are recognized safeguards. One or more of these safeguards shall be applied according to the degree of hazard involved in cases where the transformer installation presents a fire hazard.

Oil enclosures shall be permitted to consist of fire-resistant dikes, curbed areas or basins, or trenches filled with coarse crushed stone. Oil enclosures shall be provided with trapped drains where the exposure and the quantity of oil involved are such that removal of oil is important.

(FPN): For additional information on transformers installed on poles or structures or underground, see National Electrical Safety Code, ANSI C2-1984.

646

The following Formal Interpretation No. 81-2 was issued in June, 1981. The words "high fire point liquid" in Section 450-23 of the 1981 *NEC* were changed to "less-flammable liquid" in the 1984 *NEC*.

Question 1:	Is it the intent of the 1981 *National Electrical Code* to consider a high fire point liquid as described in Section 450-23 a substitute for any of the fire safeguards described in Section 450-27?
Answer:	No.
Question 2:	Is it the intent of the 1981 *National Electrical Code* that a high fire point liquid-insulated transformer have one or more of the fire safeguards described in Section 450-27 if the installation (e.g. location) of the transformer presents a fire hazard?
Answer:	Yes.

450-28. Modification of Transformers. When modifications are made to a transformer in an existing installation which changes the type of the transformer with respect to Part B of this article, such transformer shall be marked to show the type of insulating liquid installed and the modified transformer installation shall comply with the applicable requirements for that type of transformer.

Many askarel-insulated transformers are being modified by replacing the askarel with either oil or a less-flammable liquid. When such a modification takes place, the completed installation is required to have the same degree of safety as a new installation. For example, replacement of askarel with oil in an indoor installation without a vault may not be acceptable. See Section 450-26 and exceptions. If the replacement liquid is a less-flammable liquid, see Section 450-23.

C. Transformer Vaults

450-41. Location. Vaults shall be located where they can be ventilated to the outside air without using flues or ducts wherever such an arrangement is practicable.

450-42. Walls, Roof and Floor. The walls and roofs of vaults shall be constructed of materials which have adequate structural strength for the conditions with a minimum fire resistance of 3 hours. The floors of vaults in contact with the earth shall be of concrete not less than 4 inches (102 mm) thick, but when the vault is constructed with a vacant space or other stories below it, the floor shall have adequate structural strength for the load imposed thereon and a minimum fire resistance of 3 hours.

Vaults are intended primarily as passive fire protection. The need is dictated by the combustibility of the dielectric media and the size of the transformer. Transformers insulated with mineral oil have the greatest need for passive protection to prevent the spread of burning oil to other combustible materials.

There is less of a need for a vault around a dry-type transformer of less than 35,000 V. If the transformer has adequate clearance from combustible construction and storage, a fire would be confined to the transformer. Askarel-insulated transformers of less than 35,000 V do not require vaults since askarel is considered a non-combustible fluid. Transformers with a listed less-flammable liquid insulation may be installed without a vault where all of the restrictions of the listing have been complied with. See commentary following Section 450-23.

(FPN): For additional information, see ANSI/ASTM E119-83, and Fire Tests of Building Construction and Materials, NFPA 251-1985.

ARTICLE 450—TRANSFORMERS AND VAULTS

(FPN): Six-inch (152-mm) thick reinforced concrete is a typical 3-hour construction.

Exception: Where transformers are protected with automatic sprinkler, water spray, carbon dioxide, or halon, construction of 1-hour rating shall be permitted.

450-43. Doorways. Vault doorways shall be protected as follows:

(a) Type of Door. Each doorway leading into a vault from the building interior shall be provided with a tight-fitting door having a minimum fire rating of 3 hours. The authority having jurisdiction shall be permitted to require such a door for an exterior wall opening where conditions warrant.

Exception: Where transformers are protected with automatic sprinkler, water spray, carbon dioxide, or halon, construction of 1-hour rating shall be permitted.

(FPN): For additional information, see Standard for Fire Doors and Windows, NFPA 80-1983 (ANSI).

(b) Sills. A door sill or curb of sufficient height to confine within the vault the oil from the largest transformer shall be provided, and in no case shall the height be less than 4 inches (102 mm).

(c) Locks. Entrance doors shall be equipped with locks, and doors shall be kept locked, access being allowed only to qualified persons. Locks and latches shall be so arranged that the door can be readily and quickly opened from the inside.

450-45. Ventilation Openings. Where required by Section 450-9, openings for ventilation shall be provided in accordance with (a) through (f) below.

(a) Location. Ventilation openings shall be located as far away as possible from doors, windows, fire escapes, and combustible material.

(b) Arrangement. A vault ventilated by natural circulation of air shall be permitted to have roughly half of the total area of openings required for ventilation in one or more openings near the floor and the remainder in one or more openings in the roof or in the sidewalls near the roof, or all of the area required for ventilation shall be permitted in one or more openings in or near the roof.

(c) Size. For a vault ventilated by natural circulation of air to an outdoor area, the combined net area of all ventilating openings, after deducting the area occupied by screens, gratings, or louvers, shall not be less than 3 square inches (1936 sq mm) per kVA of transformer capacity in service, and in no case shall the net area be less than 1 square foot (0.093 sq m) for any capacity under 50 kVA.

(d) Covering. Ventilation openings shall be covered with durable gratings, screens, or louvers, according to the treatment required in order to avoid unsafe conditions.

(e) Dampers. All ventilation openings to the indoors shall be provided with automatic closing fire dampers that operate in response to a vault fire. Such dampers shall possess a standard fire rating of not less than 1½ hours.

(FPN): See Standard for Fire Dampers, ANSI/UL 555-1972.

(f) Ducts. Ventilating ducts shall be constructed of fire-resistant material.

450-46. Drainage. Where practicable, vaults containing more than 100 kVA transformer capacity shall be provided with a drain or other means that will carry off any accumulation of oil

648

or water in the vault unless local conditions make this impracticable. The floor shall be pitched to the drain where provided.

450-47. Water Pipes and Accessories.   Any pipe or duct system foreign to the electrical installation shall not enter or pass through a transformer vault. Piping or other facilities provided for vault fire protection, or for transformer cooling, shall not be considered foreign to the electrical installation.

450-48. Storage in Vaults.   Materials shall not be stored in transformer vaults.

ARTICLE 460 — CAPACITORS

Contents

460-1. Scope.   This article covers the installation of capacitors on electric circuits.

Surge capacitors or capacitors included as a component part of other apparatus and conforming with the requirements of such apparatus are excluded from these requirements.

This article also covers the installation of capacitors in hazardous (classified) locations as modified by Articles 501 through 503.

460-2. Enclosing and Guarding.

(a) Containing More than 3 Gallons (11.36 L) of Flammable Liquid.   Capacitors containing more than 3 gallons (11.36 L) of flammable liquid shall be enclosed in vaults or outdoor fenced enclosures complying with Article 710.

(b) Accidental Contact.   Capacitors shall be enclosed, located, or guarded so that persons cannot come into accidental contact or bring conducting materials into accidental contact with exposed energized parts, terminals, or buses associated with them.

Exception: No additional guarding is required for enclosures accessible only to authorized and qualified persons.

A. 600 Volts, Nominal, and Under

460-6. Drainage of Stored Charge. Capacitors shall be provided with a means of draining the stored charge.

(a) Time of Discharge. The residual voltage of a capacitor shall be reduced to 50 volts, nominal, or less, within 1 minute after the capacitor is disconnected from the source of supply.

(b) Means of Discharge. The discharge circuit shall be either permanently connected to the terminals of the capacitor or capacitor bank, or provided with automatic means of connecting it to the terminals of the capacitor bank on removal of voltage from the line. Manual means of switching or connecting the discharge circuit shall not be used.

Figure 460-1. Power factor correction capacitors with discharge resistors. (*Square D Co.*)

Means are required to be provided to drain off the stored charge in a capacitor after the supply circuit has been opened. Otherwise, a person servicing the equipment could receive a severe shock or damage may occur to the equipment.

Figure 460-2, parts (a) and (b), show the method in which capacitors are connected in a motor circuit so that they may be switched with the motor. In either arrangement the stored charge will drain off through the windings when the circuit is opened. Figure 460-2, part (c), shows a third arrangement where the capacitor is connected to the line side of the motor starter contacts.

Capacitors are often equipped with built-in resistors to drain off the stored charge, although this type is not needed when connected as shown in Figure 460-2, parts (a) and (b).

460-8. Conductors.

(a) Ampacity. The ampacity of capacitor circuit conductors shall not be less than 135 percent of the rated current of the capacitor. The ampacity of conductors that connect a capacitor to the terminals of a motor or to motor circuit conductors shall not be less than one third the

Figure 460-2. Methods of connecting capacitors in induction motor circuit for power factor correction.

ampacity of the motor circuit conductors and in no case less than 135 percent of the rated current of the capacitor.

(b) Overcurrent Protection.

(1) An overcurrent device shall be provided in each ungrounded conductor for each capacitor bank.

Except as permitted in the following exception, it is intended that the overcurrent device be separate from the overcurrent device protecting any other equipment or conductor.

Exception: A separate overcurrent device shall not be required for a capacitor connected on the load side of a motor overload protective device.

(2) The rating or setting of the overcurrent device shall be as low as practicable.

(c) Disconnecting Means.

(1) A disconnecting means shall be provided in each ungrounded conductor for each capacitor bank.

Except as permitted in the following exception, it is intended that the disconnecting means be separate from the disconnecting means for any other equipment.

Exception: Where a capacitor is connected on the load side of a motor overload protective device.

(2) The disconnecting means shall open all ungrounded conductors simultaneously.

(3) The disconnecting means shall be permitted to disconnect the capacitor from the line as a regular operating procedure.

(4) The rating of the disconnecting means shall not be less than 135 percent of the rated current of the capacitor.

ARTICLE 460—CAPACITORS

Capacitors are rated in kilovars, which is abbreviated kvar and means reactive kilovolt-amperes. The kvar rating shows how many reactive kilovolt-amperes the capacitor will supply in order to cancel out the reactive kilovolt-amperes caused by inductance. For example, a 20-kvar capacitor will cancel out 20 kVA of inductive reactive kilovolt-amperes.

The basic unit is 3-phase and delta-connected internally, but single-phase and 2-phase units are also available. They are constructed with built-in fuses for short-circuit protection and discharge resistors that reduce the voltage to 50-V crest or less when disconnected from the power supply. This will occur within one minute on 600-V units and within 5 minutes for 2,400- and 4,160-V units.

The capacitor circuit conductors and disconnecting means are required to have an ampacity not less than 135 percent of the rated current of the capacitor. This is because all capacitors are manufactured with a tolerance of −0 percent to +15 percent, so that a 100-kvar capacitor may actually draw a current equivalent to a 115-kvar capacitor. In addition, the current drawn by a capacitor varies directly with the line voltage, and any variation in the line voltage from a pure sine wave form causes the capacitor to draw an increased current. Considering these several factors, the increased current can amount to 135 percent of the rated current of the capacitor.

The current corresponding to the kvar rating of a 3-phase capacitor is computed from the formula

$$Ic = \frac{kVAr \times 1{,}000}{1.73 \times volts}.$$

The ampacity of the conductors and the switching device is then determined by multiplying $Ic \times 1.35$. The most effective power factor correction is obtained when the individual capacitors are connected directly to the terminals of the motors, transformers, and other inductive machinery.

When connected together and operated as a unit, no complicated calculations are needed to determine the proper size capacitor to use. Capacitor manufacturers publish tables in which the required capacitor value is indicated by referring to the speed and hp of the motor. These values will improve the motor power factor to approximately 95 percent. To improve a plant power factor, capacitor manufacturers also publish tables to assist in calculating the total kvar rating of capacitors required to improve the power factor to any desired value.

460-9. Rating or Setting of Motor Overload Device. Where a motor installation includes a capacitor connected on the load side of the motor overload device, the rating or setting of the motor overload device shall be determined in accordance with Section 430-32.

Exception: Instead of using the full-load rated current of the motor as provided in Section 430-32, a lower value corresponding with the improved power factor of the motor circuit shall be used. Section 430-22 applies with respect to the rating of the motor circuit conductors.

Where a capacitor is connected on the load side of the overload relays, as shown in Figure 460-2, part (a), consideration is required to be given to the reduction in line current due to the improved power factor when selecting the rating or setting of the motor running overcurrent device. A value lower than indicated in Section 430-32 should be used for proper protection of the motor.

460-10. Grounding. Capacitor cases shall be grounded in accordance with Article 250.

Exception: Where the capacitor units are supported on a structure which is designed to operate at other than ground potential.

460-12. Marking. Each capacitor shall be provided with a nameplate giving the name of the manufacturer, rated voltage, frequency, kilovar or amperes, number of phases, and, if filled with a combustible liquid, the amount of liquid in gallons. When filled with a nonflammable liquid, the nameplate shall so state. The nameplate shall also indicate if a capacitor has a discharge device inside the case.

B. Over 600 Volts, Nominal

460-24. Switching.

(a) Load Current. Group-operated switches shall be used for capacitor switching and shall be capable of (1) carrying continuously not less than 135 percent of the rated current of the capacitor installation; (2) interrupting the maximum continuous load current of each capacitor, capacitor bank, or capacitor installation that will be switched as a unit; (3) withstanding the maximum inrush current, including contributions from adjacent capacitor installations; (4) carrying currents due to faults on capacitor side of switch.

(b) Isolation.

(1) A means shall be installed to isolate from all sources of voltage each capacitor, capacitor bank, or capacitor installation that will be removed from service as a unit.

(2) The isolating means shall provide a visible gap in the electrical circuit adequate for the operating voltage.

(3) Isolating or disconnecting switches (with no interrupting rating) shall be interlocked with the load interrupting device or shall be provided with prominently displayed caution signs in accordance with Section 710-22 to prevent switching load current.

(c) Additional Requirements for Series Capacitors. The proper switching sequence shall be assured by use of one of the following: (1) mechanically sequenced isolating and bypass switches; (2) interlocks; or (3) switching procedure prominently displayed at the switching location.

460-25. Overcurrent Protection.

(a) Provided to Detect and Interrupt Fault-Current. A means shall be provided to detect and interrupt fault current likely to cause dangerous pressure within an individual capacitor.

(b) Single-Phase or Multiphase Devices. Single-phase or multiphase devices shall be permitted for this purpose.

(c) Protected Individually or in Groups. Capacitors shall be permitted to be protected individually or in groups.

(d) Protective Devices Rated or Adjusted. Protective devices for capacitors or capacitor equipment shall be rated or adjusted to operate within the limits of the Safe Zone for individual capacitors.

Exception: If the protective devices are rated or adjusted to operate within the limits for Zone 1 or Zone 2, the capacitors shall be enclosed or isolated.

In no event shall the rating or adjustment of the protective devices exceed the maximum limit of Zone 2.

(FPN): For definitions of the Safe Zone, Zone 1, and Zone 2, see the Standard for Shunt Power Capacitors, ANSI/IEEE 18-1980.

The reference to Zones 1 and 2 of ANSI/IEEE 18-1980 pertains to the performance of the capacitors under fault conditions. If a fault current exceeds the limit established for Zone 2, the capacitor tank may burst.

ARTICLE 470—RESISTORS AND REACTORS

460-26. Identification. Each capacitor shall be provided with a permanent nameplate giving the maker's name, rated voltage, frequency, kilovar or amperes, number of phases, and the amount of liquid in gallons identified as flammable, if such is the case.

460-27. Grounding. Capacitor neutrals and cases, if grounded, shall be grounded in accordance with Article 250.

Exception: Where the capacitor units are supported on a structure which is designed to operate at other than ground potential.

460-28. Means for Discharge.

(a) Means to Reduce the Residual Voltage. A means shall be provided to reduce the residual voltage of a capacitor to 50 volts or less within 5 minutes after the capacitor is disconnected from the source of supply.

(b) Connection to Terminals. A discharge circuit shall be either permanently connected to the terminals of the capacitor or provided with automatic means of connecting it to the terminals of the capacitor bank after disconnection of the capacitor from the source of supply. The windings of motors, or transformers, or of other equipment directly connected to capacitors without a switch or overcurrent device interposed shall meet the requirements of (a) above.

ARTICLE 470 — RESISTORS AND REACTORS

For Rheostats, see Section 430-82.

Contents

A. 600 Volts, Nominal, and Under

470-1. Scope. This article covers the installation of separate resistors and reactors on electric circuits.

Exception: Resistors and reactors that are component parts of other apparatus.

This article also covers the installation of resistors and reactors in hazardous (classified) locations as modified by Articles 501 through 503.

470-2. Location. Resistors and reactors shall not be placed where exposed to physical damage.

470-3. Space Separation. A thermal barrier shall be required if the space between the resistors and reactors and any combustible material is less than 12 inches (305 mm).

470-4. Conductor Insulation. Insulated conductors used for connections between resistance elements and controllers shall be suitable for an operating temperature of not less than 90°C (194°F).

Exception: Other conductor insulations shall be permitted for motor starting service.

Resistors are made in many different sizes and shapes and for different purposes. They may be wire or ribbon wound, form wound, edgewise wound, cast grid, punched steel grid, or box resistors. They may be mounted in the open or in ventilated metal boxes or cabinets depending upon their use and location. Since they give off heat, they are required to be guarded and located at safe distances from combustible materials. When mounted on switchboards or installed in control panels, they are not required to have additional guards.

Reactors are installed in a circuit to introduce inductance for motor starting, controlling the current, and paralleling of transformers. Current-limiting reactors are installed to limit the amount of current that can flow in a circuit when a short circuit occurs. Reactors can be divided into two classes, those with iron cores and those that use no magnetic materials in the windings. Both types may be air cooled or oil immersed.

Mechanical stresses due to their external fields exist between air core reactors, and the manufacturer's recommendations should be followed in spacing and bracing between units and fastening of supporting insulators.

Saturable reactors are used for theater dimming. See Section 520-25 and commentary. These have, in addition to the ac winding, an auxiliary winding connected line-to-line or line-to-ground in order to neutralize charging current and prevent a voltage rise. Those used on high-voltage systems are usually oil immersed.

B. Over 600 Volts, Nominal

470-18. General.

(a) Protected Against Physical Damage. Resistors and reactors shall be protected against physical damage.

(b) Isolated by Enclosure or Elevation. Resistors and reactors shall be isolated by enclosure or elevation to protect personnel from accidental contact with energized parts.

(c) Combustible Materials. Resistors and reactors shall not be installed in close enough proximity to combustible materials to constitute a fire hazard and in no case closer than within 1 foot (305 mm) of combustible materials.

(d) Clearances. Clearances from resistors and reactors to grounded surfaces shall be adequate for the voltage involved.

(FPN): See Article 710.

(e) Temperature Rise from Induced Circulating Currents. Metallic enclosures of reactors and adjacent metal parts shall be installed so that the temperature rise from induced circulating currents will not be hazardous to personnel or constitute a fire hazard.

470-19. Grounding. Resistor and reactor cases or enclosures shall be grounded in accordance with Article 250.

470-20. Oil-Filled Reactors. Installation of oil-filled reactors, in addition to the above requirements, shall comply with applicable requirements of Article 450.

ARTICLE 480 — STORAGE BATTERIES

Contents

480-1. Scope. The provisions of this article shall apply to all stationary installations of storage batteries.

There are two general types of storage cells, the lead-acid type and the alkali type.

Basically, a lead-acid cell consists of a positive plate, usually lead peroxide (a semisolid compound) mounted on a framework or grid for support, and a negative plate made of sponge lead mounted on a grid. Grids are generally made of a lead-antimony alloy and the electrolyte is usually sulfuric acid and distilled water.

In the alkali-type cell (or Edison cell), the positive plate material is nickel oxide and the negative plate material is iron oxide. The electrolyte is a solution consisting mostly of potassium hydroxide (an alkaline).

480-2. Definitions.

Storage Battery: A battery comprised of one or more rechargeable cells of the lead-acid, nickel-cadmium, or other rechargeable electrochemical types.

Sealed Cell or Battery: A sealed cell or battery is one which has no provision for the addition of water or electrolyte or for external measurement of electrolyte specific gravity. The individual cells shall be permitted to contain a venting arrangement as described in Section 480-9(b).

Nominal Battery Voltage: The voltage computed on the basis of 2.0 volts per cell for the lead-acid type and 1.2 volts per cell for the alkali type.

480-3. Wiring and Equipment Supplied from Batteries. Wiring and equipment supplied from storage batteries shall be subject to the requirements of this Code applying to wiring and equipment operating at the same voltage.

Exception: As otherwise provided for communication systems in Article 800.

480-4. Grounding. The requirements of Article 250 shall apply.

480-5. Insulation of Batteries of Not Over 250 Volts. This section shall apply to storage batteries having cells so connected as to operate at a nominal battery voltage of not over 250 volts.

(a) Vented Lead-Acid Batteries. Cells and multicompartment batteries with covers sealed to containers of nonconductive, heat-resistant material shall not require additional insulating support.

(b) Vented Alkaline-type Batteries. Cells with covers sealed to jars of nonconductive, heat-resistant material shall require no additional insulation support. Cells in jars of conductive material shall be installed in trays of nonconductive material with not more than 20 cells (24 volts, nominal) in the series circuit in any one tray.

(c) Rubber Jars. Cells in rubber or composition containers shall require no additional insulating support where the total nominal voltage of all cells in series does not exceed 150 volts. Where the total voltage exceeds 150 volts, batteries shall be sectionalized into groups of 150 volts or less and each group shall have the individual cells installed in trays or on racks.

(d) Sealed Cells or Batteries. Sealed cells and multicompartment sealed batteries constructed of nonconductive, heat-resistant material shall not require additional insulating support. Batteries constructed of a conducting container shall have insulating support if a voltage is present between the container and ground.

480-6. Insulation of Batteries of Over 250 Volts. The provisions of Section 480-5 shall apply to storage batteries having the cells so connected as to operate at a nominal voltage exceeding 250 volts, and, in addition, the provisions of this section shall also apply to such batteries. Cells shall be installed in groups having a total nominal voltage of not over 250 volts on any one rack. Insulation, which can be air, shall be provided between racks and shall have a minimum separation between live battery parts of opposite polarity of 2 inches (50.8 mm) for battery voltages not exceeding 600 volts. Maximum protection can be secured by sectionalizing high-voltage batteries into groups.

480-7. Racks and Trays. Racks and trays shall comply with (a) and (b) below.

(a) Racks. Racks, as required in this article, are rigid frames designed to support cells or trays. They shall be substantial and made of:

(1) Metal, so treated as to be resistant to deteriorating action by the electrolyte and provided with nonconducting members directly supporting the cells or with continuous insulating material other than paint or conducting members; or

(2) Other construction such as fiberglass or other suitable nonconductive materials.

(b) Trays. Trays are frames, such as crates or shallow boxes usually of wood or other nonconductive material, so constructed or treated as to be resistant to deteriorating action by the electrolyte.

480-8. Battery Locations. Battery locations shall conform to (a) and (b) below.

(a) Ventilation. Provisions shall be made for sufficient diffusion and ventilation of the gases from the battery to prevent the accumulation of an explosive mixture.

Compliance with this section is necessary to prevent classification of a battery location as a hazardous (classified) location in accordance with Article 500.

It is not the intent of Section 480-8(a) to mandate mechanical ventilation. Hydrogen disperses rapidly and requires very little air movement to prevent accumulation. Unrestricted natural air movement in the vicinity of the battery, together with normal air changes for occupied spaces or heat removal, will normally be sufficient. If the space is confined, mechanical ventilation may be required in the vicinity of the battery.

Ventilation can be a fan, roof ridge vent, or louvered areas.

(b) Live Parts. Guarding of live parts shall comply with Section 110-17.

Batteries are required to be located in a clean, dry room and arranged to provide sufficient work space for inspection and maintenance. Provision is required to be made for adequate ventilation to prevent an accumulation of an explosive mixture of the gases from the batteries.

The fumes given off by storage batteries are very corrosive; therefore, wiring and its insulation is required to be of a type that will withstand corrosive action. See Section 310-9. Special precautions are necessary to ensure that all metalwork (metal raceways, metal racks, etc.) is designed or treated so as to be corrosion resistant. Manufacturers suggest that aluminum conduit be used to withstand the corrosive battery fumes, or, if steel conduits are used, it is recommended that they be zinc-coated and corrosion protected with a coating of an asphaltum-type paint. See Section 300-6.

Overcharging heats a battery and causes gassing and loss of water. A battery should not be allowed to reach temperatures over 110°F because heat causes a shedding of active materials from the plates that will eventually form a sediment buildup in the bottom of the case and short-circuit the plates and the cell. Because mixtures of oxygen and hydrogen are highly explosive, flame or sparks should never be allowed near a cell, especially if the filler cap is removed.

480-9. Vents.

(a) Vented Cells. Each vented cell shall be equipped with a flame arrestor designed to prevent destruction of the cell due to ignition of gases within the cell by an external spark or flame under normal operating conditions.

(b) Sealed Cells. Sealed battery/cells shall be equipped with a pressure-release vent to prevent excessive accumulation of gas pressure or the battery/cell shall be designed to prevent scatter of cell parts in event of a cell explosion.

5 Special Occupancies

ARTICLE 500 — HAZARDOUS (CLASSIFIED) LOCATIONS

Contents

500-1. Scope — Articles 500 Through 503. Articles 500 through 503 cover the requirements for electrical equipment and wiring for all voltages in locations where fire or explosion hazards may exist due to flammable gases or vapors, flammable liquids, combustible dust, or ignitible fibers or flyings.

The *National Electrical Code* does not classify areas for the manufacture, transportation, storage and use of explosive materials such as ammunition, dynamite, blasting powder, etc. Areas where such materials are present are not considered hazardous (classified) locations in accordance with Article 500. However, many organizations responsible for the safety of such areas require equipment and wiring methods suitable for hazardous locations as one of many safety precautions, even though the equipment has not been investigated for such locations. The logic is that use of hazardous location equipment and wiring methods is safer than ordinary location equipment and wiring methods.

Further information on these locations can be found in NFPA 495-1985, *Code for the Manufacture, Transportation, Storage, and Use of Explosive Materials.*

500-2. Location and General Requirements. Locations are classified depending on the properties of the flammable vapors, liquids or gases, or combustible dusts or fibers which may be present and the likelihood that a flammable or combustible concentration or quantity is present. Where pyrophoric materials are the only materials used or handled, these locations shall not be classified.

Pyrophoric materials ignite spontaneously upon contact with the air. The use of electrical equipment suitable for a hazardous (classified) location will not prevent ignition of the material. Material handling methods should be designed to prevent contact between the pyrophoric material and the air.

Each room, section, or area shall be considered individually in determining its classification.

Exception: Except as modified in Articles 500 through 503, all other applicable rules contained in this Code shall apply to electric equipment and wiring installed in hazardous (classified) locations.

ARTICLE 500—HAZARDOUS (CLASSIFIED) LOCATIONS

(FPN No. 1): For definitions of "approved" and "explosionproof" as used in these articles, see Article 100; "dust-ignition-proof" is defined in Section 502-1.

Equipment and associated wiring approved as intrinsically safe shall be permitted in any hazardous (classified) location for which it is approved, and the provisions of Articles 500 through 517 shall not be considered applicable to such installations. Wiring of intrinsically safe circuits shall be physically separated from wiring of all other circuits that are not intrinsically safe. Means shall be provided to prevent the passage of gases and vapors. Intrinsically safe equipment and wiring shall not be capable of releasing sufficient electrical or thermal energy under normal or abnormal conditions to cause ignition of a specific flammable or combustible atmospheric mixture in its most easily ignitible concentration.

Abnormal conditions shall include accidental damage to any field-installed wiring, failure of electrical components, application of overvoltage, adjustment and maintenance operations, and other similar conditions.

(FPN No. 2): For further information, see Intrinsically Safe Apparatus and Associated Apparatus for Use in Class I, II, and III, Division 1 Hazardous Locations, NFPA 493-1978 (ANSI) and Installation of Intrinsically Safe Instrument Systems in Class I Hazardous Locations (ANSI/ISA RP 12.6-1976).

The purpose of NFPA 493, *Standard for Intrinsically Safe Apparatus and Associated Apparatus for Use in Class I, II, and III, Division 1 Hazardous Locations*, is to provide requirements for the construction and testing of electrical apparatus, or parts of such apparatus, in which the circuits themselves are incapable of causing ignition in Class I, II, or III, Division 1 locations, in accordance with Articles 500, 501, 502, and 503 of the *NEC*.

NFPA 493 applies not only to apparatus or parts of apparatus in the hazardous (classified) location, but also to any parts, such as power supplies and recorders, located outside of the hazardous (classified) location, where the intrinsic safety of the electrical circuits in the hazardous (classified) location may be influenced by the design and construction of such parts. The detailed requirements apply only to apparatus for use in, or associated with, a location made hazardous by the presence of flammable gas or vapor, combustible dust, or easily ignitible fibers or flyings in air under normal atmospheric conditions. If other-than-normal atmospheric conditions exist, equipment approved as intrinsically safe may not be intrinsically safe. This is especially true if the atmosphere is oxygen-enriched.

In evaluating safety, all interconnected apparatus and circuits are required to be considered, even if located in a Division 2 hazardous (classified) location, a nonhazardous location, or protected by other means, such as an explosionproof or purged and pressurized enclosure. They are required to be examined to be sure that, under normal or fault conditions, they cannot provide a source of ignition-capable energy to the apparatus in the Divison 1 hazardous (classified) location. Associated apparatus and circuits are required to conform to the requirements of the location in which the apparatus and circuits are installed.

An intrinsically safe circuit is one in which any spark or thermal effect produced either normally or in specified fault conditions is, under the test conditions prescribed in NFPA 493, incapable of causing ignition of a specified mixture of gas or vapor in air in its most easily ignited concentration. Intrinsically safe circuits are required to be identified as intrinsically safe.

Although the scope of ANSI/RP 12.6, Installation of Intrinsically Safe Instrument Systems in Class I Hazardous Locations, is limited to instrument systems, the principles are applicable to other types of intrinsically safe systems. Precautions must be taken to ensure against intrusion of unsafe energy from nonintrinsically safe circuits, particularly in nonhazardous locations where there are fewer restrictions on the wiring methods used. Separation of intrinsically safe and nonintrinsically safe circuits is usually necessary to ensure that the circuits in the hazardous (classified) locations remain intrinsically safe.

660

The requirement that means be provided to prevent the passage of gases and vapors will necessitate, in Class I locations, some type of sealing or ventilation for raceways and cables capable of transmitting gases or vapors, if these cables or raceways provide communication between a Division 1 and Division 2 or nonhazardous location, or between a Division 2 and a nonhazardous location. Raceways and some cables can act to transmit gases. This requirement is intended to provide the same degree of safety for intrinsically safe wiring as provided for in Section 501-5(a)(4), for example. However, for intrinsically safe wiring, an explosionproof seal is not required. The seal can be similiar to that required in Section 300-7(a).

(FPN No. 3): Through the exercise of ingenuity in the layout of electrical installations for hazardous (classified) locations, it is frequently possible to locate much of the equipment in less hazardous or in nonhazardous locations and thus to reduce the amount of special equipment required. In some cases, hazards may be reduced or hazardous (classified) locations limited or eliminated by adequate positive-pressure ventilation from a source of clean air in conjunction with effective safeguards against ventilation failure. For further information, see Purged and Pressurized Enclosures for Electrical Equipment in Hazardous Locations, NFPA 496-1982 (ANSI).

NFPA 496, *Standard for Purged and Pressurized Enclosures for Electrical Equipment in Hazardous (Classified) Locations*, covers purged enclosures for electrical equipment in Class I hazardous (classified) locations, and pressurized enclosures for electrical equipment in Class II hazardous (classified) locations.

Class I Hazardous (Classified) Locations: The object of NFPA 496 for Class I hazardous (classified) locations is to provide information for the design of purged and pressurized enclosures to eliminate or reduce within the enclosure a Class I hazardous (classified) location classification, as defined in Article 500 of the *Code*. By this means, equipment that is not otherwise acceptable for hazardous (classified) locations may be utilized in accordance with the *Code*.

Purging is defined as the process of supplying an enclosure with clean air or an inert gas, at sufficient flow and positive pressure to reduce to an acceptably safe level the concentration of any flammable gases or vapors initially present, and to maintain this safe level by positive pressure with or without continuous flow.

Type X purging reduces the classification within an enclosure from Division 1 to nonhazardous.

Type Y purging reduces the classification within an enclosure from Division 1 to Division 2.

Type Z purging reduces the classification within an enclosure from Division 2 to nonhazardous.

Class II Hazardous (Classified) Locations: The object of NFPA 496 for Class II locations is to provide information for the design of pressurized enclosures which prevents the entrance of dusts into an enclosure. By this means, equipment that is not otherwise acceptable for hazardous (classified) locations may be utilized in accordance with the *Code*. Pressurization, for the purposes of NFPA 496, may be defined as the process of supplying an enclosure with clean air or an inert gas, with or without continuous flow, at sufficient pressure to prevent the entrance of combustible dust.

It should be noted that an atmosphere made hazardous by combustible dust inside an enclosure cannot be reduced to a safe level by supplying a flow of clean air in the same manner as gases or vapors. The enclosure must be opened and the dust removed. Visual inspection can determine if the dust has been removed. Positive pressure will prevent entrance of a dust into a clean enclosure.

(FPN No. 4): It is important that the authority having jurisdiction be familiar with such recorded industrial experience as well as with such standards of the National Fire Protection Association as may be of use in the classification of various areas with respect to hazard.

(FPN No. 5): For further information, see Flammable and Combustible Liquids Code, NFPA 30-1984; Drycleaning Plants, NFPA 32-1985; Manufacture of Organic Coatings, NFPA 35-1982 (ANSI); Solvent

ARTICLE 500—HAZARDOUS (CLASSIFIED) LOCATIONS

Extraction Plants, NFPA 36-1985 (ANSI); Storage and Handling of Liquefied Petroleum Gases, NFPA 58-1986; Storage and Handling of Liquefied Petroleum Gases at Utility Gas Plants, NFPA 59-1984; and Classification of Class I Hazardous Locations for Electrical Installations in Chemical Plants, NFPA 497A-1986 (ANSI).

(FPN No. 6): For protection against static electricity hazards, see Recommended Practice on Static Electricity, NFPA 77-1983 (ANSI).

(FPN No. 7): For electrical classification of laboratory areas, see Standard for Fire Protection of Laboratories Using Chemicals, NFPA 45-1982.

All conduit referred to herein shall be threaded with a NPT standard conduit cutting die that provides ¾-inch taper per foot. Such conduit shall be made up wrenchtight to minimize sparking when fault current flows through the conduit system. Where it is impractical to make a threaded joint tight, a bonding jumper shall be utilized.

Care should be exercised if intermediate metal conduit is used, since other than National Pipe Threads may be used on the intermediate metal conduit.

500-3. Special Precaution. Articles 500 through 503 require equipment construction and installation that will ensure safe performance under conditions of proper use and maintenance.

(FPN No. 1): It is important that inspection authorities and users exercise more than ordinary care with regard to installation and maintenance.

(FPN No. 2): The explosion characteristics of air mixtures of gases, vapors, or dusts vary with the specific material involved. For Class I locations, Groups A, B, C, and D, the classification involves determinations of maximum explosion pressure, maximum safe clearance between parts of a clamped joint in an enclosure, and the minimum ignition temperature of the atmospheric mixture. For Class II locations, Groups E, F, and G, the classification involves the tightness of the joints of assembly and shaft openings, to prevent entrance of dust in the dust-ignition-proof enclosure, the blanketing effect of layers of dust on the equipment that may cause overheating, electrical conductivity of the dust, and the ignition temperature of the dust. It is necessary, therefore, that equipment be approved not only for the class, but also for the specific group of the gas, vapor, or dust that will be present.

(FPN No. 3): Low ambient conditions require special consideration. Explosionproof or dust-ignition-proof equipment may not be suitable for use at temperatures lower than -25°C (-13°F) unless they are approved for low-temperature service. However at low ambient temperatures flammable concentrations of vapors may not exist in a location classified Class I, Division 1 at normal ambient temperature.

At low ambient temperatures, such as those encountered in the Arctic, the strengths of materials change. This is particularly true for some sealing materials. In addition, explosion pressures increase at very low temperatures. However, the extent of the hazardous (classified) location may also change at low ambient conditions, depending on the flash point of the material involved.

(FPN No. 4): For purposes of testing, approval, and area classification, various air mixtures (not oxygen-enriched) have been grouped on the basis of their characteristics and facilities have been made available for testing and approving equipment for use in the following atmospheric groups:

Determining the proper group classification for flammable gases and vapors involves a determination of explosion pressures and maximum safe clearance between parts of a clamped joint under several conditions, and comparison of the values obtained with those obtained for presently classified materials under the same test conditions. Although some work has been done on the classification of flammable materials on the basis of chemical structure, the method is not sufficiently refined or accurate to ensure proper classification of all flammable materials.

For additional information on the rationale for classification, reference may be made to the following: (1) "Rationale for Classification of Combustible Gases, Vapors, and Dusts with Reference to the National Electrical Code," Publication

NMAB 353-6, 1982, a report of the Committee on Evaluation of Industrial Hazards, The National Materials Advisory Board, Commission on Engineering and Technical Systems, National Research Council. This publication is available from the National Technical Information Service (NTIS), Springfield, VA 22151. (2) "An Investigation of Fifteen Flammable Gases or Vapors with Respect to Explosion-Proof Electrical Equipment," Bulletin of Research No. 58 by Underwriters Laboratories Inc., August 1969 (also Bulletin of Research Nos. 58A and 58B, which supplement No. 58). These are available from Underwriters Laboratories Inc., Publications Stock, 333 Pfingsten Rd., Northbrook, IL 60062.

(FPN No. 5): Group A: Atmospheres containing acetylene.

(FPN No. 6): Group B: Atmospheres such as butadiene,* ethylene oxide,** propylene oxide,** acrolein,** or hydrogen (or gases or vapors equivalent in hazard to hydrogen, such as manufactured gas).

(FPN No. 7): Group C: Atmospheres such as cyclopropane, ethyl ether, ethylene, or gases or vapors of equivalent hazard.

(FPN No. 8): Group D: Atmospheres such as acetone, alcohol, ammonia,*** benzene, benzol, butane, gasoline, hexane, lacquer solvent vapors, naphtha, natural gas, propane, or gases or vapors of equivalent hazard.

(FPN No. 9): *Group D equipment may be used for this atmosphere if such equipment is isolated in accordance with Section 501-5(a) by sealing all conduit ½-inch size or larger.

(FPN No. 10): **Group C equipment may be used for this atmosphere if such equipment is isolated in accordance with Section 501-5(a) by sealing all conduit ½-inch size or larger.

(FPN No. 11): ***For classification of areas involving ammonia atmosphere, see Safety Code for Mechanical Refrigeration (ANSI/ASHRAE 15-1978) and Safety Requirements for the Storage and Handling of Anhydrous Ammonia (ANSI/CGA G2.1-1981).

(FPN No. 12): For properties of flammable liquids, gases, and solids, see Classification of Gases, Vapors and Dusts for Electrical Equipment in Hazardous (Classified) Locations, NFPA 497M-1986, and Fire Hazard Properties of Flammable Liquids, Gases, and Volatile Solids, NFPA 325M-1984.

The following table is reprinted from NFPA 497M-1986. Additional tables in NFPA 497M cover materials with flash points 37.8°C (100°F) and higher.

Group Classification and Autoignition Temperature (AIT) of Selected Flammable Gases and Vapors of Liquids having Flash Points below 100°F (37.8°C).

| | | AIT | |
Material	Group	°F	(°C)
Acetaldehyde	C*	347	175
Acetone	D*	869	465
Acetonitrile	D	975	524
Acetylene	A*	581	305
Acrolein (inhibited)	B(C)*¹	455	235
Acrylonitrile	D*	898	481
Allyl Alcohol	C*	713	378
Allyl Chloride	D	905	485
Ammonia	D*²	928	498
n-Amyl Acetate	D	680	360
sec-Amyl Acetate	D	—	—
Benzene	D*	928	498
1,3-Butadiene	B(D)*¹	788	420
Butane	D*	550	288
1-Butanol	D*	650	343
2-Butanol	D*	761	405
n-Butyl Acetate	D*	790	421
iso-Butyl Acetate	D*	790	421
sec-Butyl Acetate	D	—	—

Group Classification and Autoignition Temperature (AIT) (Continued)

Material	Group	AIT °F	AIT (°C)
Butylamine	D	594	312
Butylene	D	725	385
Butyl Mercaptan	C	—	—
n-Butyraldehyde	C*	425	218
Carbon Disulfide	-*3	194	90
Carbon Monoxide	C*	1128	609
Chlorobenzene	D	1099	593
Chloroprene	D	—	—
Crotonaldehyde	C*	450	232
Cumene	D	795	424
Cyclohexane	D	473	245
Cyclohexene	D	471	244
Cyclopropane	D*	938	503
1,1-Dichloroethane	D	820	438
1,2-Dichloroethylene	D	860	460
1,3-Dichloropropene	D	—	—
Dicyclopentadiene	C	937	503
Diethyl Ether	C*	320	160
Diethylamine	C*	594	312
Di-isobutylene	D*	736	391
Di-isopropylamine	C	600	316
Dimethylamine	C	752	400
1,4-Dioxane	C	356	180
Di-n-propylamine	C	570	299
Epichlorohydrin	C*	772	411
Ethane	D*	882	472
Ethanol	D*	685	363
Ethyl Acetate	D*	800	427
Ethyl Acrylate (inhibited)	D*	702	372
Ethylamine	D*	725	385
Ethyl Benzene	D	810	432
Ethyl Chloride	D	966	519
Ethylene	C*	842	450
Ethylenediamine	D*	725	385
Ethylene Dichloride	D*	775	413
Ethylenimine	C*	608	320
Ethylene Oxide	B(C)*1	804	429
Ethyl Formate	D	851	455
Ethyl Mercaptan	C*	572	300
n-Ethyl Morpholine	C	—	—
Formaldehyde (Gas)	B	795	429
Gasoline	D*	536-880	280-471
Heptane	D*	399	204
Heptene	D	500	260
Hexane	D*	437	225
2-Hexanone	D	795	424
Hexenes	D	473	245
Hydrogen	B*	968	520
Hydrogen Cyanide	C*	1000	538
Hydrogen Selenide	C	—	—
Hydrogen Sulfide	C*	500	260
Isoamyl Acetate	D	680	360
Isobutyl Acrylate	D	800	427
Isobutyraldehyde	C	385	196
Isoprene	D*	428	220
Isopropyl Acetate	D	860	460
Isopropylamine	D	756	402
Isopropyl Ether	D*	830	443
Isopropyl Glycidyl Ether	C	—	—
Liquefied Petroleum Gas	D	761-842	405-450
Manufactured Gas (containing more than 30% H_2 by volume)	B*	—	—
Mesityl Oxide	D*	652	344
Methane	D*	999	630

Group Classification and Autoignition Temperature (AIT) (Continued)

Material	Group	AIT °F	AIT (°C)
Methanol	D*	725	385
Methyl Acetate	D	850	454
Methylacetylene	C*	—	—
Methylacetylene-Propadiene (stabilized)	C	—	—
Methyl Acrylate	D	875	468
Methylamine	D	806	430
Methylcyclohexane	D	482	250
Methyl Ether	C*	662	350
Methyl Ethyl Ketone	D*	759	404
Methyl Formal	C*	460	238
Methyl Formate	D	840	449
Methyl Isobutyl Ketone	D*	840	440
Methyl Isocyanate	D	994	534
Methyl Mercaptan	C	—	—
Methyl Methacrylate	D	792	422
2-Methyl-1-Propanol	D*	780	416
2-Methyl-2-Propanol	D*	892	478
Monomethyl Hydrazine	C	382	194
Naphtha (Petroleum)	D*[4]	550	288
Nitroethane	C	778	414
Nitromethane	C	785	418
1-Nitropropane	C	789	421
2-Nitropropane	C*	802	428
Nonane	D	401	205
Nonene	D	—	—
Octane	D*	403	206
Octene	D	446	230
Pentane	D*	470	243
1-Pentanol	D*	572	300
2-Pentanone	D	846	452
1-Pentene	D	527	275
Propane	D*	842	450
1-Propanol	D*	775	413
2-Propanol	D*	750	399
Propionaldehyde	C	405	207
n-Propyl Acetate	D	842	450
Propylene	D*	851	455
Propylene Dichloride	D	1035	557
Propylene Oxide	B(C)*[1]	840	449
n-Propyl Ether	C*	419	215
Propyl Nitrate	B*	347	175
Pyridine	D*	900	482
Styrene	D*	914	490
Tetrahydrofuran	C*	610	321
Toluene	D*	896	480
Triethylamine	C*	—	—
Turpentine	D	488	253
Unsymmetrical Dimethyl Hydrazine (UDMH)	C*	480	249
Valeraldehyde	C	432	222
Vinyl Acetate	D*	756	402
Vinyl Chloride	D*	882	472
Vinylidene Chloride	D	1058	570
Xylenes	D*	867-984	464-529

Notes to Table

*Material has been classified by test.

[1]If equipment is isolated by sealing all conduit ½ in. (12.7 mm) or larger, in accordance with Article 501-5(a) of NFPA 70, *National Electrical Code*, equipment for the group classification shown in parentheses is permitted.

ARTICLE 500—HAZARDOUS (CLASSIFIED) LOCATIONS

[2]For classification of areas involving ammonia, see *Safety Code for Mechanical Refrigeration*, ANSI/ASHRAE 15, and *Safety Requirements for the Storage and Handling of Anhydrous Ammonia*, ANSI/CGA G2.1.

[3]Certain chemicals may have characteristics that require safeguards beyond those required for any of the above groups. Carbon Disulfide is one of these chemicals because of its low autoignition temperature and small joint clearance to arrest flame propagation.

[4]Petroleum naphtha is a saturated hydrocarbon mixture whose boiling range is 20° to 135°C. It is also known as benzine, ligroin, petroleum ether, and naphtha.

References: Autoignition temperatures listed above are the lowest value for each material as listed in NFPA 325M, *Fire Hazard Properties of Flammable Liquids, Gases, and Volatile Solids*, or as reported in an article by Hilado, C. J. and Clark, S. W., in *Chemical Engineering*, September 4, 1972.

(FPN No. 13): Group E: Atmospheres containing combustible metal dusts regardless of resistivity, or other combustible dusts of similarly hazardous characteristics having resistivity of less than 10^5 ohm-centimeter.

(FPN No. 14): Group F: Atmospheres containing carbon black, charcoal, coal or coke dusts which have more than 8 percent total volatile material (carbon black per ASTM D1620; charcoal, coal and coke dusts per ASTM D271) or atmospheres containing these dusts sensitized by other materials so that they present an explosion hazard, and having resistivity greater than 10^2 ohm-centimeter but equal to or less than 10^8 ohm-centimeter.

See commentary following Section 500-3(d).

(FPN No. 15): Group G: Atmospheres containing combustible dusts having resistivity of 10^5 ohm-centimeter or greater.

The following table is part of Table 3-5 in NFPA 497M-1986. For the complete table and information on Group E dusts, see NFPA 497M.

Selected Nonconductive Dusts Classified as Group G — Ignition Sensitivity Equal to or Greater than 0.2; Explosion Severity Equal to or Greater than 0.5.

Material	°F	Minimum Cloud or Layer Ignition Temp.[1]	°C
AGRICULTURAL DUSTS			
Alfalfa Meal	392		200
Almond Shell	392		200
Apricot Pit	446		230
Cellulose	500		260
Cherry Pit	428		220
Cinnamon	446		230
Citrus Peel	518		270
Cocoa Bean Shell	698		370
Cocoa, natural, 19% fat	464		240
Coconut Shell	428		220
Corn	482		250
Corncob Grit	464		240
Corn Dextrine	698		370
Cornstarch, commercial	626		330
Cornstarch, modified	392		200
Cork	410		210
Cottonseed Meal	392		200
Cube Root, South Amer.	446		230
Flax Shive	446		230
Garlic, dehydrated	680	NL	360
Guar Seed	932	NL	500
Gum, Arabic	500		260
Gum, Karaya	464		240
Gum, Manila (copal)	680	Cl	360
Gum, Tragacanth	500		260
Hemp Hurd	428		220
Lycopodium	590		310

666

Selected Nonconductive Dusts Classified as Group G (Continued)

Material	Minimum Cloud or Layer Ignition Temp.[1]		
	°F		°C
Malt Barley	482		250
Milk, Skimmed	392		200
Pea Flour	500		260
Peach Pit Shell	410		210
Peanut Hull	410		210
Peat, Sphagnum	464		240
Pecan Nut Shell	410		210
Pectin	392		200
Potato Starch, Dextrinated	824	NL	440
Pyrethrum	410		210
Rauwolfia Vomitoria Root	446		230
Rice	428		220
Rice Bran	914	NL	490
Rice Hull	428		220
Safflower Meal	410		210
Soy Flour	374		190
Soy Protein	500		260
Sucrose	662	Cl	350
Sugar, Powdered	698	Cl	370
Tung, Kernels, Oil-free	464		240
Walnut Shell, Black	428		220
Wheat	428		220
Wheat Flour	680		360
Wheat Gluten, gum	968	NL	520
Wheat Starch	716	NL	380
Wheat Straw	428		220
Woodbark, Ground	482		250
Wood Flour	500		260
Yeast, Torula	500		260
CHEMICALS			
Acetoacetanilide	824	M	440
Acetoacet-p-phenetidide	1040	NL	560
Adipic Acid	1022	M	550
Anthranilic Acid	1076	M	580
Aryl-nitrosomethylamide	914	NL	490
Azelaic Acid	1130	M	610
2,2-Azo-bis-butyronitrile	662		350
Benzoic Acid	824	M	440
Benzotriazole	824	M	440
Bisphenol-A	1058	M	570
Chloroacetoacetanilide	1184	M	640
Diallyl Phthalate	896	M	480
Dicumyl Peroxide (suspended on CaCO₃), 40-60	356		180
Dicyclopentadiene Dioxide	788	NL	420
Dihydroacetic Acid	806	NL	430
Dimethyl Isophthalate	1076	M	580
Dimethyl Terephthalate	1058	M	570
3,5 - Dinitrobenzoic Acid	860	NL	460
Dinitrotoluamide	932	NL	500
Diphenyl	1166	M	630
Ditertiary Butyl Paracresol	878	NL	470
Ethyl Hydroxyethyl Cellulose	734	NL	390
Fumaric Acid	968	M	520
Hexamethylene Tetramine	770	S	410
Hydroxyethyl Cellulose	770	NL	410
Isotoic Anhydride	1292	NL	700
Methionine	680		360
Nitrosoamine	518	NL	270
Para-oxy-benzaldehyde	716	Cl	380
Paraphenylene Diamine	1148	M	620
Paratertiary Butyl Benzoic Acid	1040	M	560
Pentaerythritol	752	M	400

Selected Nonconductive Dusts Classified as Group G (Continued)

Material	°F	Minimum Cloud or Layer Ignition Temp.[1]	°C
Phenylbetanaph-thylamine	1256	NL	680
Phthalic Anydride	1202	M	650
Phthalimide	1166	M	630
Salicylanilide	1130	M	610
Sorbic Acid	860		460
Stearic Acid, Aluminum Salt	572		300
Stearic Acid, Zinc Salt	950	M	510
Sulfur	428		220
Terephthalic Acid	1256	NL	680
DRUGS			
2-Acetylamino-5-nitrothiazole	842		450
2-Amino-5-nitrothiazole	860		460
Aspirin	1220	M	660
Gulasonic Acid, Diacetone	788	NL	420
Mannitol	860	M	460
Nitropyridone	806	M	430
l-Sorbose	698	M	370
Vitamin B1, mononitrate	680	NL	360
Vitamin C (Ascorbic Acid)	536		280
DYES, PIGMENTS, INTERMEDIATES			
Beta-napthalene-azo-Dimethylaniline	347		175
Green Base Harmon Dye	347		175
Red Dye Intermediate	347		175
Violet 200 Dye	347		175
PESTICIDES			
Benzethonium Chloride	716	Cl	380
Bis (2-Hydroxy-5-chlorophenyl) methane	1058	NL	570
Crag No. 974	590	Cl	310
Dieldrin (20%)	1022	NL	550
2,6-Ditertiary-butyl-paracresol	788	NL	420
Dithane	356		180
Ferbam	302		150
Manganese Vancide	248		120
Sevin	284		140
a, a - Trithiobis (N, N-Dimethylthioformamide)	446		230
THERMOPLASTIC RESINS AND MOLDING COMPOUNDS			
Acetal Resins			
Acetal, Linear (Polyformaldehyde)	824	NL	440
Acrylic Resins			
Acrylamide Polymer	464		240
Acrylonitrile Polymer	860		460
Acrylonitrile-Vinyl Pyridine Copolymer	464		240
Acrylonitrile-Vinyl Chloride-Vinylidene Chloride Copolymer (70-20-10)	410		210
Methyl Methacrylate-Polymer	824	NL	440
Methyl Methacrylate-Ethyl Acrylate Copolymer	896	NL	480
Methyl Methacrylate-Ethyl Acrylate-Styrene Copolymer	824	NL	440
Methyl Methacrylate-Styrene-Butadierne-Acrylonitrile Copolymer	896	NL	480
Methacrylic Acid Polymer	554		290
Cellulosic Resins			
Cellulose Acetate	644		340
Cellulose Triacetate	806	NL	430
Cellulose Acetate Butyrate	698	NL	370
Cellulose Propionate	860	NL	460
Ethyl Cellulose	608	Cl	320
Methyl Cellulose	644		340
Carboxymethyl Cellulose	554		290
Hydroxyethyl Cellulose	644		340

Selected Nonconductive Dusts Classified as Group G (Continued)

Material	°F	Minimum Cloud or Layer Ignition Temp.[1]	°C
Chlorinated Polyether Resins			
Chlorinated Polyether Alcohol	860		460
Nylon (Polyamide) Resins			
Nylon Polymer (Polyhexamethylene Adipamide)	806		430
Polycarbonate Resins			
Polycarbonate	1310	NL	710
Polyethylene Resins			
Polyethylene, High Pressure Process	716		380
Polyethylene, Low Pressure Process	788	NL	420
Polyethylene Wax	752	NL	400
Polymethylene Resins			
Carboxypolymethylene	968	NL	520
Polypropylene Resins			
Polypropylene (No Antioxidant)	788	NL	420
Rayon Resins			
Rayon (Viscose) Flock	482		250
Styrene Resins			
Polystyrene Molding Compound	1040	NL	560
Polystyrene Latex	932		500
Styrene-Acrylonitrile (70-30)	932	NL	500
Styrene-Butadiene Latex (>75% Styrene; Alum Coagulated)	824	NL	440
Vinyl Resins			
Polyvinyl Acetate	1022	NL	550
Polyvinyl Acetate/Alcohol	824		440
Polyvinyl Butyral	734	NL	390
Vinyl Chloride - Acrylonitrile Copolymer	878		470
Polyvinyl Chloride - Dioctyl Phthalate Mixture	608	NL	320
Vinyl Toluene - Acrylonitrile Butadiene Copolymer	936	NL	530
THERMOSETTING RESINS AND MOLDING COMPOUNDS			
Allyl Resins			
Allyl Alcohol Derivative (CR-39)	932	NL	500
Amino Resins			
Urea Formaldehyde Molding Compound	860	NL	460
Urea Formaldehyde - Phenol Formeldehyde Molding Compound (Wood Flour Filler)	464		240
Epoxy Resins			
Epoxy	1004	NL	540
Epoxy - Bisphenol A	950	NL	510
Phenol Furfural	590		310
Phenolic Resins			
Phenol Formaldehyde	1076	NL	580
Phenol Formaldehyde Molding Compound (Wood Flour Filler)	932	NL	500
Phenol Formaldehyde, Polyalkylene-Polyamine Modified	554		290
Polyester Resins			
Polyethylene Terephthalate	932	NL	500
Styrene Modified Polyester-Glass Fiber Mixture	680		360
Polyurethane Resins			
Polyurethane Foam, No Fire Retardant	824		440
Polyurethane Foam, Fire Retardant	734		390
SPECIAL RESINS AND MOLDING COMPOUNDS			
Alkyl Ketone Dimer Sizing Compound	320		160

Selected Nonconductive Dusts Classified as Group G (Continued)

Material	Minimum Cloud or Layer Ignition Temp.[1]		
	°F		°C
Cashew Oil, Phenolic, Hard	356		180
Chlorinated Phenol	1058	NL	570
Coumarone-Indene, Hard	968	NL	520
Ethylene Oxide Polymer	662	NL	350
Ethylene-Maleic Anhydride Copolymer	1004	NL	540
Lignin, Hydrolized, Wood-Type, Fines	842	NL	450
Petin Acrylate Monomer	428	NL	220
Petroleum Resin (Blown Asphalt)	932		500
Rosin, DK	734	NL	390
Rubber, Crude, Hard	662	NL	350
Rubber, Synthetic, Hard (33% S)	608	NL	320
Shellac	752	NL	400
Sodium Resinate	428		220
Styrene - Maleic Anhydride Copolymer	878	Cl	470

Notes to Table

[1]Normally, the minimum ignition temperature of a layer of a specific dust is lower than the minimum ignition temperature of a cloud of that dust. Since this is not universally true, the lower of the two minimum ignition temperatures is listed. If no symbol appears between the two temperature columns, then the layer ignition temperature is shown. "Cl" means the cloud ignition temperature is shown. "NL" means that no layer ignition temperature is available and the cloud ignition temperature is shown. "M" signifies that the dust layer melts before it ignites; the cloud ignition temperature is shown. "S" signifies that the dust layer sublimes before it ignites; the cloud ignition temperature is shown.

[2]These materials may be classified in Group E, depending on their resistivity.

(FPN No. 16): Certain chemical atmospheres may have characteristics that require safeguards beyond those required for any of the above groups. Carbon disulfide is one of these chemicals because of its low ignition temperature, 100°C (212°F), and the small joint clearance to arrest its flame.

(FPN No. 17): Certain metal dusts may have characteristics that require safeguards beyond those required for atmospheres containing the dusts of aluminum, magnesium, and their commercial alloys. For example, zirconium, thorium and uranium dusts have extremely low ignition temperatures [as low as 20°C (68°F)], and minimum ignition energies lower than any material classified in any of the Class I or Class II Groups.

(FPN No. 18): Certain dusts may require additional precautions due to chemical phenomena that can result in the generation of ignitible gases. See National Electrical Safety Code (ANSI C2-1984), Section 127A-Coal Handling Areas.

Publication NMAB 353-4, "Classifications of Dusts Relative to Electrical Equipment in Class II Hazardous Locations," published in 1982 by the Committee on Evaluation of Industrial Hazards, National Materials Advisory Board, Commission on Engineering and Technical Systems, National Research Council, National Academy of Sciences, includes a description of test methods to determine the ignition temperatures and electrical resistivity of combustible dusts. The publication is available from the National Technical Information Service (NTIS), Springfield, VA 22151.

(a) Approval for Class and Properties. Equipment shall be approved not only for the class of location but also for the explosive, combustible, or ignitible properties of the specific gas, vapor, dust, fiber, or flyings that will be present. In addition, Class I equipment shall not have any exposed surface that operates at a temperature in excess of the ignition temperature of the specific gas or vapor. Class II equipment shall not have an external temperature higher than that specified in Section 500-3(d). Class III equipment shall not exceed the maximum surface temperatures specified in Section 503-1.

Equipment that has been approved for a Division 1 location shall be permitted in a Division 2 location of the same class and group.

Where specifically permitted in Articles 501 through 503, general-purpose equipment or equipment in general-purpose enclosures shall be permitted to be installed in Division 2 locations if the equipment does not constitute a source of ignition under normal operating conditions.

Unless otherwise specified, normal operating conditions for motors shall be assumed to be rated full-load steady conditions.

It is not intended that locked-rotor or other motor overload conditions be considered when evaluating motor operating temperatures in Class I, Division 2 locations. However, abnormal load conditions are considered when evaluating explosionproof motors for Class I, Division 1 locations and motors for Class II locations, such as dust-ignitionproof motors.

Where flammable gases or combustible dusts are or may be present at the same time, the simultaneous presence of both shall be considered when determining the safe operating temperature of the electrical equipment.

Coal-handling facilities are an example of a location where methane gas and coal dust may be present at the same time.

(FPN): The characteristics of various atmospheric mixtures of gases, vapors, and dusts depend on the specific material involved.

(b) Marking. Approved equipment shall be marked to show the Class, Group, and operating temperature or temperature range referenced to a 40°C ambient.

It should be noted that the marked operating temperature or temperature range is referenced to a 40°C (104°F) ambient. Unless the equipment is provided with thermally actuated sensors which limit the temperature to that marked on the equipment, operation in ambient temperatures higher than 40°C (104°F) will probably increase the operating temperature of the equipment. Many explosionproof and dust-ignitionproof motors are equipped with thermal protectors. In a like manner, operation in ambient temperatures lower than 40°C (104°F) will usually reduce the operating temperature.

The temperature range, if provided, shall be indicated in identification numbers, as shown in Table 500-3(b).

Identification numbers marked on equipment nameplates shall be in accordance with Table 500-3(b).

Equipment which is approved for Class I and Class II shall be marked with the maximum safe operating temperature, as determined by simultaneous exposure to the combinations of Class I and Class II conditions.

Exception No. 1: Equipment of the nonheat-producing type, such as junction boxes, conduit, and fittings and equipment of the heat-producing type having a maximum temperature not more than 100°C (212°F), shall not be required to have a marked operating temperature or temperature range.

Exception No. 2: Fixed lighting fixtures marked for use in Class I, Division 2 or Class II, Division 2 locations only shall not be required to be marked to indicate the group.

Exception No. 3: Fixed general-purpose equipment in Class I locations, other than fixed lighting fixtures, which is acceptable for use in Class I, Division 2 locations shall not be required to be marked with the Class, Group, Division or operating temperature.

ARTICLE 500—HAZARDOUS (CLASSIFIED) LOCATIONS

An example of such equipment is a squirrel-cage induction motor without brushes, switching mechanisms, or similar arc-producing devices. See the second paragraph of Section 501-8(b).

Exception No. 4: Fixed dusttight equipment other than fixed lighting fixtures which are acceptable for use in Class II, Division 2 and Class III locations shall not be required to be marked with the Class, Group, Division or operating temperature.

Table 500-3(b). Identification Numbers

| Maximum Temperature | | Identification |
Degrees C	Degrees F	Number
450	842	T1
300	572	T2
280	536	T2A
260	500	T2B
230	446	T2C
215	419	T2D
200	392	T3
180	356	T3A
165	329	T3B
160	320	T3C
135	275	T4
120	248	T4A
100	212	T5
85	185	T6

(FPN): For purposes of testing and approval, various atmospheric mixtures (not oxygen-enriched) have been grouped on the basis of their characteristics, and facilities have been made available for testing and approving equipment for use in the atmospheric groups listed in Classification of Gases, Vapors, and Dusts for Electrical Equipment in Hazardous (Classified) Locations, NFPA 497M-1986. Since there is no consistent relationship between explosion properties and ignition temperature, the two are independent requirements.

(c) Class I Temperature. The temperature marking specified in (b) above shall not exceed the ignition temperature of the specific gas or vapor to be encountered.

The ignition temperature of a solid, liquid, or gaseous substance is the minimum temperature required to initiate or cause self-sustained combustion independent of the heating or heated element.

(FPN): For information regarding ignition temperatures of gases and vapors, see Classification of Gases, Vapors, and Dusts for Electrical Equipment in Hazardous (Classified) Locations, NFPA 497M-1986, and Fire Hazard Properties of Flammable Liquids, Gases, and Volatile Solids, NFPA 325M-1986.

Formerly the temperature limit of each Group was assumed to be the lowest ignition temperature of any material in the Group, i.e., 280°C for Group D, 180°C for Group C.

(FPN): To avoid revising this limit as new gases are added (see hexane in Group D and acetaldehyde in Group C), temperature will be specified in future markings.

The ignition temperature for which equipment was approved prior to this requirement shall be assumed to be as follows:

Group A—280°C (536°F)   Group C—180°C (356°F)
Group B—280°C (536°F)   Group D—280°C (536°F)

The preceding information on ignition temperatures for Class I materials was added as a Tentative Interim Amendment to the 1968 edition of the *NEC* and has been part of the *Code* since the 1971 edition. Listed or labeled heat-producing equipment, such as lighting fixtures and motors, manufactured before circa 1975 may not be marked with the operating temperature or temperature range. Unless the actual operating temperatures are marked on the equipment or are otherwise known, the intent is that the operating temperatures noted above be assumed. For multiple rated equipment (e.g., Class I, Groups C and D), the lowest operating temperature [180°C (356°F)] may be assumed.

Flammable gases or vapors are separated into four different atmospheric groups: Groups A, B, C, and D. It is to be noted that *Code* requirements for Class I locations do not vary for different kinds of gas or vapor contained in the atmosphere except in those cases where seals may be used in all conduits to change the group classification. See fine print notes nos. 6, 9 and 10 to Section 500-3 on materials such as butadiene and ethylene oxide. It is necessary to select equipment that is designed for use in the particular group involved; however, equipment may be listed for use in Class I, Group D or use in Class I, Group C, etc. The reason for designating the groups in this way is that explosive mixtures have different explosion pressures and maximum safe clearances between parts of a joint in an enclosure.

Underwriters Laboratories Inc. and Factory Mutual Research Corp. list or approve electrical equipment suitable for use in all groups of Class I locations and further information is available from the UL Hazardous Locations Equipment Directory and FM Approval Guide. It should be noted (from the UL Directory) that "only those products bearing the appropriate Listing Mark and the company's name, trade name, trademark, or other recognized identification should be considered as covered by UL's Listing and Follow-Up Service."

(d) Class II Temperature.   The surface temperature marking specified in (b) above shall be less than the ignition temperature of the specific dust and in no case shall it be greater than the temperature given below for Groups E, F, and G. (See Classification of Gases, Vapors, and Dusts for Electrical Equipment in Hazardous (Classified) Locations, NFPA 497M-1986 for minimum ignition temperatures of specific dusts.)

Exception: Equipment subject to overloads shall not exceed 150°C (302°F) in normal operation and shall not exceed the ignition temperature of the specific dust or 200°C (392°F), whichever is lower, when installed in locations which are classified due to carbonaceous dusts.

The maximum surface temperature for which equipment was approved prior to this requirement shall be assumed to be as follows:

| | Equipment that Is Not Subject to Overloading | | Equipment (such as Motors or Power Transformers) that May Be Overloaded | | | |
| | | | Normal Operation | | Abnormal Operation | |
Class II Group	Degrees C	Degrees F	Degrees C	Degrees F	Degrees C	Degrees F
E	200	392	200	392	200	392
F	200	392	150	302	200	392
G	165	329	120	248	165	329

Class II locations are hazardous because of the presence of combustible dust. Prior to the 1984 *National Electrical Code*, the Class II groups were defined as follows:

Group E: Atmospheres containing metal dust, including aluminum, magnesium, and their commercial alloys, and materials of similarly hazardous characteristics having resistivity of 10^2 ohm-centimeter or less.

Group F: Atmospheres containing carbon black, charcoal, coal or coke dusts which have more than 8 percent total volatile material (carbon black per ASTM D1620; charcoal, coal and coke dusts per ASTM D271), or atmospheres containing these dusts sensitized by other materials so that they present an explosion hazard, and having resistivity of greater than 10^2 ohm-centimeter but equal to or less than 10^8 ohm-centimeter.

Group G: Atmospheres containing flour, starch, grain or combustible plastics or chemical dusts having resistivity greater than 10^8 ohm-centimeter.

In the 1984 *NEC*, the groups were redefined. Group F was eliminated, and the resistivity limits of Groups E and G were revised to include the carbonaceous dusts. The new definitions for Groups E and G are shown in Section 500-3, fine print notes nos. 13 and 15, of the 1987 edition.

Although most carbonaceous dusts were classified as Group G in the 1984 *NEC*, the use of coal dusts with a resistivity lower than 10^5 ohm-centimeter required the use of equipment suitable for Class II Division 1 Group E. Motors in particular require special construction in order to prevent penetration of fine metal dusts through the shaft openings. In addition, if the dust could vary between Group E and Group G, the equipment would be required to meet Group E construction and Group G maximum temperature requirements, which are much lower than Group F.

Group F was reintroduced into the 1987 *NEC* to allow the use of less restrictive Group F temperatures and equipment construction in locations which are hazardous due to the presence of carbonaceous dusts with resistivity of greater than 10^2 ohm-centimeter but equal to or less than 10^8-ohm centimeter. Dusts other than carbonaceous dusts with resistivities in the range of 10^2 ohm-centimeter to 10^5 ohm-centimeter would continue to be classified as Group E or Group G. See commentary and tables following Section 500-3, and commentary to Section 502-1.

As in Class I locations, equipment must be approved not only for the class but also for the specific group. It is important that, in addition to the proper selection of equipment, high standards of installation be maintained for subsequent additions or alterations.

The NFPA and ANSI standards referenced in Articles 500 through 517 should be obtained for more information on specific hazardous (classified) locations.

The following NFPA standards and recommended practices include information on the extent of hazardous (classified) locations in specific occupancies or industries.

NFPA No.	Title of Standard
30	Flammable and Combustible Liquids Code
30A	Automotive and Marine Service Station Code
32	Drycleaning Plants
33	Spray Application Using Flammable and Combustible Materials
34	Dipping and Coating Processes Using Flammable or Combustible Liquids
35	Manufacture of Organic Coatings
36	Solvent Extraction Plants
40	Cellulose Nitrate Motion Picture Film, Storage and Handling of
50A	Gaseous Hydrogen Systems at Consumer Sites
50B	Liquefied Hydrogen Systems at Consumer Sites
51	Welding, Cutting and Allied Processes, Oxygen-Fuel Gas Systems for
51A	Acetylene Cylinder Charging Plants
58	Liquefied Petroleum Gases, Storage and Handling of
59	Liquefied Petroleum Gases at Utility Gas Plants, Storage and Handling of
59A	Liquefied Natural Gas (LNG), Production, Storage and Handling of
61A	Manufacturing and Handling Starch, Prevention of Fire and Dust Explosions in Facilities
61B	Grain Elevators and Facilities Handling Bulk Raw Agricultural Commodities, Prevention of Fires and Explosions in
61C	Feed Mills, Prevention of Fire and Dust Explosions in
61D	Milling of Agricultural Commodities for Human Consumption, Prevention of Fire and Dust Explosions in
65	Aluminum, Processing and Finishing
81	Fur Storage, Fumigation and Cleaning

NFPA No.	Title of Standard
85D	Fuel Oil-Fired Multiple Burner Boiler-Furnaces, Prevention of Furnace Explosions in
88A	Parking Structures
88B	Repair Garages
99	Health Care Facilities
407	Aircraft Fuel Servicing
409	Aircraft Hangars
480	Magnesium Storage, Handling and Processing
481	Titanium, Production, Processing, Handling, and Storage
493	Intrinsically Safe Apparatus and Associated Apparatus for Use in Class I, II, and III, Division 1 Hazardous Locations
495	Explosive Materials, Manufacture, Transportation, Storage, and Use of
496	Purged and Pressurized Enclosures for Electrical Equipment
497A	Classification of Class I Hazardous (Classified) Locations for Electrical Installations in Chemical Process Areas
651	Aluminum and Magnesium Powder, Manufacture of
654	Chemical, Dye, Pharmaceutical, and Plastics Industries, Prevention of Fire and Dust Explosions in
655	Sulfur Fires and Explosions, Prevention of

500-4. Specific Occupancies. Articles 510 through 517 cover garages, aircraft hangars, gasoline dispensing and service stations, bulk storage plants, spray application, dipping and coating processes, and health care facilities.

500-5. Class I Locations. Class I locations are those in which flammable gases or vapors are or may be present in the air in quantities sufficient to produce explosive or ignitible mixtures. Class I locations shall include those specified in (a) and (b) below.

(a) Class I, Division 1. A Class I, Division 1 location is a location: (1) in which ignitible concentrations of flammable gases or vapors can exist under normal operating conditions; or (2) in which ignitible concentrations of such gases or vapors may exist frequently because of repair or maintenance operations or because of leakage; or (3) in which breakdown or faulty operation of equipment or processes might release ignitible concentrations of flammable gases or vapors, and might also cause simultaneous failure of electric equipment.

(FPN): This classification usually includes locations where volatile flammable liquids or liquefied flammable gases are transferred from one container to another; interiors of spray booths and areas in the vicinity of spraying and painting operations where volatile flammable solvents are used; locations containing open tanks or vats of volatile flammable liquids; drying rooms or compartments for the evaporation of flammable solvents; locations containing fat and oil extraction equipment using volatile flammable solvents; portions of cleaning and dyeing plants where flammable liquids are used; gas generator rooms and other portions of gas manufacturing plants where flammable gas may escape; inadequately ventilated pump rooms for flammable gas or for volatile flammable liquids; the interiors of refrigerators and freezers in which volatile flammable materials are stored in open, lightly stoppered, or easily ruptured containers; and all other locations where ignitible concentrations of flammable vapors or gases are likely to occur in the course of normal operations.

(b) Class I, Division 2. A Class I, Division 2 location is a location: (1) in which volatile flammable liquids or flammable gases are handled, processed, or used, but in which the liquids, vapors, or gases will normally be confined within closed containers or closed systems from which they can escape only in case of accidental rupture or breakdown of such containers or systems, or in case of abnormal operation of equipment; or (2) in which ignitible concentrations of gases or vapors are normally prevented by positive mechanical ventilation, and which might become hazardous through failure or abnormal operation of the ventilating equipment; or (3) that is adjacent to a Class I, Division 1 location, and to which ignitible concentrations of gases or vapors might occasionally be communicated unless such communication is prevented by adequate positive-pressure ventilation from a source of clean air, and effective safeguards against ventilation failure are provided.

(FPN): This classification usually includes locations where volatile flammable liquids or flammable gases or vapors are used, but which, in the judgment of the authority having jurisdiction, would become hazardous only in case of an accident or of some unusual operating condition. The quantity of flammable material that might escape in case of accident, the adequacy of ventilating equipment, the total area involved, and the record of the industry or business with respect to explosions or fires are all factors that merit consideration in determining the classification and extent of each location.

(FPN): Piping without valves, checks, meters, and similar devices would not ordinarily introduce a hazardous condition even though used for flammable liquids or gases. Locations used for the storage of flammable liquids or of liquefied or compressed gases in sealed containers would not normally be considered hazardous unless subject to other hazardous conditions also.

Electrical conduits and their associated enclosures separated from process fluids by a single seal or barrier shall be classed as a Division 2 location if the outside of the conduit and enclosures is a nonhazardous location.

500-6. Class II Locations. Class II locations are those that are hazardous because of the presence of combustible dust. Class II locations shall include those specified in (a) and (b) below.

(a) Class II, Division 1. A Class II, Division 1 location is a location: (1) in which combustible dust is in the air under normal operating conditions in quantities sufficient to produce explosive or ignitible mixtures; or (2) where mechanical failure or abnormal operation of machinery or equipment might cause such explosive or ignitible mixtures to be produced, and might also provide a source of ignition through simultaneous failure of electric equipment, operation of protection devices, or from other causes; or (3) in which combustible dusts of an electrically conductive nature may be present in hazardous quantities.

(FPN): Combustible dusts which are electrically nonconductive include dusts produced in the handling and processing of grain and grain products, pulverized sugar and cocoa, dried egg and milk powders, pulverized spices, starch and pastes, potato and woodflour, oil meal from beans and seed, dried hay, and other organic materials which may produce combustible dusts when processed or handled. Electrically conductive dusts are dusts with a resistivity less than 10^5 ohm-centimeter. Dusts containing magnesium or aluminum are particularly hazardous and the use of extreme precaution will be necessary to avoid ignition and explosion.

(b) Class II, Division 2. A Class II Division 2 location is a location where combustible dust is not normally in the air in quantities sufficient to produce explosive or ignitible mixtures, and dust accumulations are normally insufficient to interfere with the normal operation of electrical equipment or other apparatus, but combustible dust may be in suspension in the air as a result of infrequent malfunctioning of handling or processing equipment and where combustible dust accumulations on, in, or in the vicinity of the electrical equipment may be sufficient to interfere with the safe dissipation of heat from electrical equipment or may be ignitible by abnormal operation or failure of electrical equipment.

(FPN): The quantity of combustible dust that may be present and the adequacy of dust removal systems are factors that merit consideration in determining the classification and may result in an unclassified area.

(FPN): Where products such as seed are handled in a manner which produces low quantities of dust, the amount of dust deposited may not warrant classification.

500-7. Class III Locations. Class III locations are those that are hazardous because of the presence of easily ignitible fibers or flyings, but in which such fibers or flyings are not likely to be in suspension in the air in quantities sufficient to produce ignitible mixtures. Class III locations shall include those specified in (a) and (b) below.

(a) Class III, Division 1. A Class III, Division 1 location is a location in which easily ignitible fibers or materials producing combustible flyings are handled, manufactured, or used.

(FPN): Such locations usually include some parts of rayon, cotton, and other textile mills; combustible fiber manufacturing and processing plants; cotton gins and cotton-seed mills; flax-processing plants; clothing manufacturing plants; woodworking plants; and establishments and industries involving similar hazardous processes or conditions.

(FPN): Easily ignitible fibers and flyings include rayon, cotton (including cotton linters and cotton waste), sisal or henequen, istle, jute, hemp, tow, cocoa fiber, oakum, baled waste kapok, Spanish moss, excelsior, and other materials of similar nature.

(b) Class III, Division 2. A Class III, Division 2 location is a location in which easily ignitible fibers are stored or handled.

Exception: In process of manufacture.

Sections 500-5, 500-6, and 500-7 recognize three classes of hazardous (classified) locations with varying degrees of hazards, and each class is then subdivided into two divisions. The requirements for Division 1 of each class are more stringent than those for Division 2.

Briefly, the hazards of the three classes are defined as follows: Class I, flammable gases or vapors; Class II, combustible dust; and Class III, combustible fibers or flyings.

When a given location is classified as hazardous, it should not be difficult to determine in which of the three classes it belongs; however, when it is unknown whether a location is definitely hazardous, it would be difficult to apply rules to an area that may, because of a change in process or material, become hazardous. In this case, common sense and good judgment must prevail in classifying an area that is likely to become hazardous and in determining those portions of the premises to be classed Division 1 or Division 2.

ARTICLE 501 — CLASS I LOCATIONS

Contents

501-1. General. The general rules of this Code shall apply to the electric wiring and equipment in locations classified as Class I in Section 500-5.

Exception: As modified by this article.

The more common Class I locations are those areas involved in the handling or processing of volatile flammable liquids such as gasoline, naphtha, benzene, diethyl ether, and acetone, or flammable gases such as hydrogen, methane, and propane.

Where ignitible concentrations (concentrations within the flammable or explosive limits) of flammable gases or vapors are present, atmospheres that are explosive when ignited by an arc, a spark, or high temperature exist. NFPA 325M, *Fire Hazard Properties of Flammable Liquids, Gases, and Volatile Solids*, includes information on the explosive limits of flammable liquids, gases, and volatile solids. All electrical equipment that may cause ignition-capable arcs or sparks should be kept out of Class I locations where practicable. If this is not practicable, such apparatus must be approved for the purpose and installed properly. The arc produced at the contacts of listed or labeled intrinsically safe equipment is not ignition-capable because the energy available is insufficient to cause ignition.

Hermetic sealing of all electric equipment is impractical because equipment such as motors, conventional switches, and circuit breakers have movable parts that must be operated through the enclosing case, that is, the lever of a switch or the shaft of a motor must have sufficient clearance to operate freely. In addition, in many cases it is necessary to have access to the inside of enclosures for installation, servicing, or alterations.

It is practically impossible to make threaded conduit joints gastight. The conduit system and apparatus enclosure "breathe" due to temperature changes, and any flammable gases or vapors in the room may slowly enter the conduit or enclosure creating an explosive mixture. Should an arc occur, an explosion could take place.

When an explosion occurs within the enclosure or conduit system, the burning mixture, or hot gases, must be sufficiently confined within the system to prevent ignition of any explosive mixture that might be present in the room. An apparatus enclosure must be designed with sufficient strength to withstand the maximum pressure that can be generated by an internal explosion in order to prevent rupture and the release of burning or hot gases. Enclosures have been designed to withstand such internal explosions. Such enclosures are "explosionproof."

It has been found that during an explosion within an enclosure gases will escape through any paths or openings that exist, but that the gases will be sufficiently cooled where carried out through an opening that is long in proportion to its width; that is, the spiral path of at least five fully engaged threads of a screwed-on junction box cover, as illustrated in Figure 501-1. This principle is also applied in the design of explosionproof enclosures for apparatus by providing a wide machined flange on the body of the enclosure and a similar machined flange on the cover. These machined flanges are so ground that, when the cover is seated in place, the clearance between the two surfaces will at no point exceed, for example, 0.0015 in. If an explosion occurs within the enclosure, escaping gas travels a considerable distance through a very small opening. It is, therefore, sufficiently cooled when it enters and mixes with the surrounding atmosphere that ignition of the external explosive mixture cannot occur.

The clearance between flat surfaces may increase somewhat under explosion conditions because the internal pressures created by the explosion tend to force the surfaces apart. The amount of increase in the joint clearance depends on the "stiffness" of the enclosure parts, the size, strength, and spacing of the bolts, and the explosion pressure. See Figure 501-3. Simply measuring the joint width and clearance when there are no internal pressures will not indicate what the clearances will be under the dynamic conditions of an explosion. Actual explosion tests are usually needed to demonstrate the acceptability of the design.

Figure 501-1. Hot gases are cooled as they pass through the threads of a screw-type cover of an explosionproof junction box.

Figure 501-2. Hot gases are cooled as they pass across a machined flanged joint. The clearance between the machined surfaces is kept very small.

Figure 501-3. Effect of internal explosion on cover-to-body joint clearance in explosionproof enclosure. (*Underwriters Laboratories Inc.*)

679

ARTICLE 501—CLASS I LOCATIONS

501-2. Transformers and Capacitors.

(a) Class I, Division 1. In Class I, Division 1 locations, transformers and capacitors shall comply with the following:

(1) Containing Liquid that Will Burn. Transformers and capacitors containing a liquid that will burn shall be installed only in approved vaults that comply with Sections 450-41 through 450-48, and in addition: (1) there shall be no door or other communicating opening between the vault and the Division 1 location; and (2) ample ventilation shall be provided for the continuous removal of flammable gases or vapors; and (3) vent openings or ducts shall lead to a safe location outside of buildings; and (4) vent ducts and openings shall be of sufficient area to relieve explosion pressures within the vault, and all portions of vent ducts within the buildings shall be of reinforced concrete construction.

(2) Not Containing Liquid that Will Burn. Transformers and capacitors that do not contain a liquid that will burn shall: (1) be installed in vaults complying with (a)(1) above, or (2) be approved for Class I locations.

(b) Class I, Division 2. In Class I, Division 2 locations, transformers and capacitors shall comply with Sections 450-21 through 450-27.

501-3. Meters, Instruments, and Relays.

(a) Class I, Division 1. In Class I, Division 1 locations, meters, instruments, and relays, including kilowatt-hour meters, instrument transformers, resistors, rectifiers, and thermionic tubes, shall be provided with enclosures approved for Class I, Division 1 locations.

> See the comments on purged and pressurized enclosures for electrical equipment in hazardous (classified) locations following the fine print notes in Section 500-2 and the comments on explosionproof enclosures following the exception to Section 501-1.

Enclosures approved for Class I, Division 1 locations include: (1) explosionproof enclosures, and (2) purged and pressurized enclosures.

(FPN): See NFPA 496-1982 (ANSI), Purged and Pressurized Enclosures for Electrical Equipment in Hazardous Locations.

(b) Class I, Division 2. In Class I, Division 2 locations, meters, instruments, and relays shall comply with the following:

(1) Contacts. Switches, circuit breakers, and make-and-break contacts of pushbuttons, relays, alarm bells, and horns shall have enclosures approved for Class I, Division 1 locations in accordance with (a) above.

Exception: General-purpose enclosures shall be permitted, if current-interrupting contacts are:

a. Immersed in oil; or,

b. Enclosed within a chamber hermetically sealed against the entrance of gases or vapors; or,

> There are several types of "hermetic" seals, including fusion seals such as the glass-to-metal seals in mercury tube switches and some "reed" switches, welded seals, soldered seals, and seals made with gaskets. Seals of the glass-to-metal fusion type are usually the most reliable. Soft solder seals can be relatively porous, and their effectiveness is highly dependent on workmanship. Although gasketed seals

can be very effective, depending on the gasket material used, gasket materials are easily damaged and can deteriorate rapidly when exposed to atmospheres containing solvent vapors.

c. In circuits that under normal conditions do not release sufficient energy to ignite a specific ignitible atmospheric mixture; i.e., are nonincendive.

The word "nonincendive" as used here originated in publications of the Instrument Society of America (ISA), such as ISA Monogram No. 1110. It first appeared in this section and Section 501-14(b)(1) in the 1975 edition of the *Code*. It means that, under the conditions specified, there is insufficient energy available to cause ignition. "Nonincendive" is similar to "intrinsically safe," which is defined in Section 500-2 and NFPA 493, but does not include consideration of fault and all of the abnormal conditions inherent in the definition of "intrinsically safe." A circuit may be "nonincendive" in a Group D atmosphere, but not in a Group C atmosphere, as the minimum ignition energies for the various flammable materials differ.

(2) Resistors and Similar Equipment. Resistors, resistance devices, thermionic tubes, rectifiers, and similar equipment that is used in or in connection with meters, instruments, and relays shall comply with (a) above.

Exception: General-purpose-type enclosures shall be permitted if such equipment is without make-and-break or sliding contacts (other than as provided in (b)(1) above) and if the maximum operating temperature of any exposed surface will not exceed 80 percent of the ignition temperature in degrees Celsius of the gas or vapor involved or has been tested and found incapable of igniting the gas or vapor.

The intent of "or has been tested and found incapable of igniting the gas or vapor" is to permit approved equipment with operating temperatures higher than 80 percent of the ignition temperature. If the equipment has been tested, the safety factor inherent in this "80 percent rule" is not needed. The system of temperature measurement must be specified, as 80 percent of a temperature in degrees Celsius is not the same temperature as 80 percent of that temperature in degrees Fahrenheit.

(3) Without Make-or-Break Contacts. Transformer windings, impedance coils, solenoids, and other windings that do not incorporate sliding or make-or-break contacts shall be provided with enclosures. General-purpose type enclosures shall be permitted.

(4) General-Purpose Assemblies. Where an assembly is made up of components for which general-purpose enclosures are acceptable as provided in (b)(1), (b)(2), and (b)(3) above, a single general-purpose enclosure shall be acceptable for the assembly. Where such an assembly includes any of the equipment described in (b)(2) above, the maximum obtainable surface temperature of any component of the assembly shall be clearly and permanently indicated on the outside of the enclosure. Alternatively, approved equipment shall be permitted to be marked to indicate the temperature range for which it is suitable, using the identification numbers of Table 500-3(b).

(5) Fuses. Where general-purpose enclosures are permitted in (b)(1), (b)(2), (b)(3) and (b)(4) above, fuses for overcurrent protection of instrument circuits not subject to overloading in normal use shall be permitted to be mounted in general-purpose enclosures if each such fuse is preceded by a switch complying with (b)(1) above.

(6) Connections. To facilitate replacements, process control instruments shall be permitted to be connected through flexible cord, attachment plug, and receptacle, provided: (1) a switch complying with (b)(1) above is provided so that the attachment plug is not depended on to interrupt current; and (2) the current does not exceed 3 amperes at 120 volts, nominal; and (3) the power-supply cord does not exceed 3 feet (914 mm), is of a type approved for extra-hard usage or for hard usage if protected by location, and is supplied through an attachment plug and receptacle of the locking and grounding type; and (4) only necessary receptacles are provided; and (5) the receptacle carries a label warning against unplugging under load.

501-4. Wiring Methods. Wiring methods shall comply with (a) and (b) below.

(a) Class I, Division 1. In Class I, Division 1 locations, threaded rigid metal conduit, threaded steel intermediate metal conduit, or Type MI cable with termination fittings approved for the location shall be the wiring method employed. All boxes, fittings, and joints shall be threaded for connection to conduit or cable terminations, and shall be explosionproof. Threaded joints shall be made up with at least five threads fully engaged. Type MI cable shall be installed and supported in a manner to avoid tensile stress at the termination fittings. Where necessary to employ flexible connections, as at motor terminals, flexible fittings approved for Class I locations shall be used.

This section indicates that termination fittings used with Type MI cable are required to be approved for the specific purpose. It is intended that Type MI cable fittings approved and marked {see Section 500-3(b)} for the hazardous (classified) location class and group be used. Type MI cable fittings have a clamp-type joint, which must be investigated to determine that it is explosionproof. Type MI cable fittings suitable for nonhazardous locations may not be suitable for Class I, Division 1 hazardous (classified) locations. Rigid metal conduit and intermediate metal conduit are required to be threaded with a (NPT) standard conduit cutting die that provides ¾-in. taper per ft, and five full threads must be engaged. Each joint is required to be made up tight at couplings, unions, and threaded hubs of junction boxes, device boxes, conduit bodies, etc.

Figure 501-4 shows an explosionproof junction box having three hubs and a threaded opening for the screw-type cover. Unused openings must be effectively closed by inserting threaded metal plugs engaging at least five full threads and affording protection equivalent to that of the wall of the box. Figure 501-5 shows a larger type explosionproof junction box with a bolted flanged cover.

Figure 501-6 shows a flexible fitting, which is available in lengths up to 3 ft, for use in Class I, Division 1 locations. The fitting consists of a deeply corrugated bronze tube with an internal fibrous tubular protective liner and an outer cover of braided fine bronze wires. A threaded fitting is securely attached to each end of the flexible tube. The flexible fitting is commonly used at motor connections, can withstand continuous vibration for long periods of time, is explosionproof, and affords maximum protection to any enclosed conductors.

(b) Class I, Division 2. In Class I, Division 2 locations, threaded rigid metal conduit, threaded steel intermediate metal conduit, enclosed gasketed busways, enclosed gasketed wireways, or Type PLTC cable in accordance with the provisions of Article 725, Type MI, MC, MV, TC, or SNM cable with approved termination fittings shall be the wiring method employed. Type PLTC, MI, MC, MV, TC, or SNM cable shall be permitted to be installed in cable tray systems and shall be installed in a manner to avoid tensile stress at the termination fittings. Boxes, fittings, and joints shall not be required to be explosionproof except as required by Sections 501-3(b)(1), 501-6(b)(1), and 501-14(b)(1). Where provision must be made for limited flexibility, as at motor terminals, flexible metal fittings, flexible metal conduit with approved fittings, liquidtight flexible metal conduit with approved fittings, or flexible cord approved for extra-hard usage and provided with approved bushed fittings shall be used. An additional conductor for grounding shall be included in the flexible cord unless other acceptable means of grounding are provided.

In Class I, Division 2 locations, boxes, fittings, and joints are not required to be explosionproof at lighting outlets or at enclosures containing no arcing devices.

Figure 501-4. An explosionproof junction box with a screw-type cover. (*Crouse-Hinds*)

Figure 501-5. Cutaway view of explosionproof junction box and bolted flanged cover. (*Appleton Electric Co.*)

Figure 501-6. A flexible explosionproof fitting. (*Crouse-Hinds*)

Where general-purpose enclosures are permitted by this section, rigid or intermediate metal conduit may be used with locknuts and bushings; however, a bonding jumper with proper fittings is required to be used between the enclosure and the raceway to ensure adequate bonding from the hazardous area to the point of grounding for the service equipment. See Section 501-16(a).

Where limited flexibility is necessary and approved fittings are required for use with flexible metal conduit, liquidtight flexible metal conduit, and extra-hard usage flexible cord, the fittings are not required to be specifically approved for Class I locations. Also, where flexible conduit is used, internal or external bonding jumpers with proper fittings are required to be provided as per Section 501-16(b).

This section also permits a variety of cables, cable tray systems in accordance with Section 318-3(d), enclosed gasketed wireways, and enclosed gasketed busways. The cable and cable fittings, cable trays, wireways, and busways are not required to be specifically listed or labeled for Class I locations. For example, if Type MC cable is used, neither the cable nor the fittings need to be listed for use in hazardous (classified) locations.

Exception: Wiring, which under normal conditions cannot release sufficient energy to ignite a specific ignitible atmospheric mixture by opening, shorting or grounding, shall be permitted using any of the methods suitable for wiring in ordinary locations.

This exception is intended to permit what have been termed "nonincendive field circuits" [see comments on "nonincendive" following Item c. of the exception to Section 501-3(b)(1)]. Many low-voltage, low-energy circuits are of this type. However, a Class 2 circuit as defined in Article 725 is not necessarily "nonincendive." There is considerable equipment listed by such testing laboratories as Factory Mutual Research Corp. and Underwriters Laboratories Inc. that have "nonincendive" circuits intended for field wiring in the various groups in Class I, Division 2 locations. Some common telephone circuits and thermocouple circuits are also "nonincendive."

501-5. Sealing and Drainage. Seals in conduit and cable systems shall comply with (a) through (f) below. Sealing compound shall be of a type approved for the conditions and use. Sealing compound shall be used in Type MI cable termination fittings to exclude moisture and other fluids from the cable insulation.

(FPN): Seals are provided in conduit and cable systems to minimize the passage of gases and vapors and prevent the passage of flames from one portion of the electrical installation to another through the conduit. Such communication through Type MI cable is inherently prevented by construction of the cable. Unless specifically designed and tested for the purpose, conduit and cable seals are not intended to prevent the passage of liquids, gases or vapors at a continuous pressure differential across the seal. Even at differences in pressure across the seal equivalent to a few inches of water, there may be a slow passage of gas or vapor through a seal, and through conductors passing through the seal. See Section 501-5(e)(2). Temperature extremes and highly corrosive liquids and vapors can affect the ability of seals to perform their intended function. See Section 501-5(c)(2).

The sealing compound used in conduit fittings for sealing is somewhat porous, so that gases, particularly those under slight pressure and gases with small molecules, such as hydrogen, can pass slowly through the sealing compound. Also, the seal is around the insulation on the conductor, and gases can be transmitted slowly through the air spaces (the interstices) between strands of stranded conductors. See the second fine print note to Section 501-5(e)(2). However, experience has shown that under normal conditions, and with only normal atmospheric pressure differentials across the seal, the passage of gas through a seal is not sufficient to result in a hazard. Sealing fittings are usually listed for use only with the same manufacturer's sealing compound.

The use of teflon types or joint compounds on conduit threads may weaken the seal fitting. Cracks have occurred during hydraulic testing of fittings with these materials. See Section 110-3(b) and commentary following the section.

(a) Conduit Seals, Class I, Division 1.   In Class I, Division 1 locations, conduit seals shall be located as follows:

(1) In each conduit run entering an enclosure for switches, circuit breakers, fuses, relays, resistors, or other apparatus which may produce arcs, sparks, or high temperatures. Seals shall be placed as close as practicable and in no case more than 18 inches (457 mm) from such enclosures. Explosionproof unions, couplings, elbows, capped elbows and conduit bodies similar to "L," "T," and "Cross" type shall be the only enclosures or fittings permitted between the sealing fitting and the enclosure. The conduit bodies shall not be larger than the largest trade size of the conduits.

Exception: Conduit 1½ inches and smaller entering an explosionproof enclosure for switches, circuit breakers, fuses, relays, or other apparatus which may produce arcs or sparks shall not be required to be sealed if the current-interrupting contacts are:

   a. Enclosed within a chamber hermetically sealed against the entrance of gases or vapors; or,

   b. Immersed in oil in accordance with Section 501-6(b)(1)(2).

(2) In each conduit of 2-inch size or larger entering the enclosure or fitting housing terminals, splices, or taps and within 18 inches (457 mm) of such enclosure or fitting.

(FPN): See notes under Group B in sixth Fine Print Note to Section 500-3.

(3) Where two or more enclosures for which seals are required under (a)(1) and (a)(2) above are connected by nipples or by runs of conduit not more than 36 inches (914 mm) long, a single seal in each such nipple connection or run of conduit shall be considered sufficient if located not more than 18 inches (457 mm) from either enclosure.

(4) In each conduit run leaving the Class I, Division 1 location. The sealing fitting shall be permitted on either side of the boundary of such location but shall be so designed and installed to minimize the amount of gas or vapor which may have entered the conduit system within the Division 1 location from being communicated to the conduit beyond the seal. There shall be no union, coupling, box, or fitting in the conduit between the sealing fitting and the point at which the conduit leaves the Division 1 location.

Exception: Metal conduit containing no unions, couplings, boxes, or fittings that passes completely through a Class I, Division 1 location with no fittings less than 12 inches (305 mm) beyond each boundary shall not be required to be sealed if the termination points of the unbroken conduit are in nonhazardous locations.

(b) Conduit Seals, Class I, Division 2.   In Class I, Division 2 locations, conduit seals shall be located as follows:

(1) For connections to explosionproof enclosures that are required to be approved for Class I locations, seals shall be provided in accordance with (a)(1), (a)(2) and (a)(3) above. All portions of the conduit run or nipple between the seal and such enclosure shall comply with Section 501-4(a).

(2) In each conduit run passing from a Class I, Division 2 location into a nonhazardous location. The sealing fitting shall be permitted on either side of the boundary of such location but shall be so designed and installed to minimize the amount of gas or vapor which may have entered the conduit system within the Division 2 location from being communicated to the conduit beyond the seal. Rigid metal conduit or threaded steel intermediate metal conduit shall be used between the sealing fitting and the point at which the conduit leaves the Division 2 location, and a threaded connection shall be used at the sealing fitting. There shall be no union, coupling, box, or fitting in the conduit between the sealing fitting and the point at which the conduit leaves the Division 2 location.

Exception: Metal conduit containing no unions, couplings, boxes or fittings that passes completely through a Class I, Division 2 location with no fittings less than 12 inches (305 mm) beyond each boundary shall not be required to be sealed if the termination points of the unbroken conduit are in nonhazardous locations.

(c) Class I, Divisions 1 and 2. Where required, seals in Class I, Division 1 and 2 locations shall comply with the following:

(1) Fittings. Enclosures for connections or equipment shall be provided with an approved integral means for sealing, or sealing fittings approved for Class I locations shall be used. Sealing fittings shall be accessible.

(2) Compound. Sealing compound shall be approved and shall provide a seal against passage of gas or vapors through the seal fitting, shall not be affected by the surrounding atmosphere or liquids, and shall not have a melting point of less than 93°C (200°F).

(3) Thickness of Compounds. In a completed seal, the minimum thickness of the sealing compound shall not be less than the trade size of the conduit, and in no case less than ⅝ inch (16 mm).

(4) Splices and Taps. Splices and taps shall not be made in fittings intended only for sealing with compound, nor shall other fittings in which splices or taps are made be filled with compound.

(5) Assemblies. In an assembly where equipment that may produce arcs, sparks, or high temperatures is located in a compartment separate from the compartment containing splices or taps, and an integral seal is provided where conductors pass from one compartment to the other, the entire assembly shall be approved for Class I locations. Seals in conduit connections to the compartment containing splices or taps shall be provided in Class I, Division 1 locations where required by (a)(2) above.

(d) Cable Seals, Class I, Division 1. In Class I, Division 1 locations each multiconductor cable in conduit shall be considered as a single conductor if the cable is incapable of transmitting gases or vapors through the cable core. These cables shall be sealed in accordance with (a) above.
Cables with a gas/vapor-tight continuous sheath capable of transmitting gases or vapors through the cable core shall be sealed in the Division 1 location after removing the jacket and any other coverings so that the sealing compound will surround each individual insulated conductor and the outer jacket.

(e) Cable Seals, Class I, Division 2. In Class I, Division 2 locations, cable seals shall be located as follows:

(1) Cables entering enclosures which are required to be approved for Class I locations shall be sealed at the point of entrance. The sealing fitting shall comply with (b)(1) above. Multiconductor cables with a gas/vapor-tight continuous sheath capable of transmitting gases or vapors through the cable core shall be sealed in an approved fitting in the Division 2 location after removing the jacket and any other coverings so that the sealing compound will surround each individual insulated conductor in such a manner as to minimize the passage of gases and vapors. Multiconductor cables in conduit shall be sealed as described in (d) above.

(2) Cables with a gas/vapor-tight continuous sheath and which will not transmit gases or vapors through the cable core in excess of the quantity permitted for seal fittings shall not be required to be sealed except as required in (e)(1) above. The minimum length of such cable run shall not be less than that length which limits gas or vapor flow through the cable core to the rate permitted for seal fittings [0.007 cubic feet per hour (198 cubic centimeters per hour) of air at a pressure of 6 inches of water (1493 pascals)].

The ability of a cable to transmit gases or vapors through the core (primarily between insulated conductors) depends not only on how tightly packed the conductors are within the outer sheaths, and the location and composition of fillers, but also on how the cable has been handled and the geometry of the cable run. If there is any question as to whether or not the cable run is capable of transmitting gases or vapors through the core, sealing is suggested.

(FPN): See Outlet Boxes and Fittings for Use in Hazardous Locations, ANSI/UL 886-1980.

(FPN): The cable core does not include the interstices of the conductor strands.

The intent is that the conductors themselves be individually sealed, such as by dipping the ends in wax, before measuring the rate of flow. However, if this is done, the wax should be removed before making electrical connections or putting the system into service.

(3) Cables with a gas/vapor-tight continuous sheath capable of transmitting gases or vapors through the cable core shall not be required to be sealed except as required in (e)(1) above, unless the cable is attached to process equipment or devices that may cause a pressure in excess of 6 inches (1493 pascals) of water to be exerted at a cable end, in which case a seal, barrier or other means shall be provided to prevent migration of flammables into an unclassified area.

Exception: Cables with an unbroken gas/vapor-tight continuous sheath shall be permitted to pass through a Class I, Division 2 location without seals.

(4) Cables which do not have gas/vapor-tight continuous sheath shall be sealed at the boundary of the Division 2 and nonhazardous location in such a manner as to minimize the passage of gases or vapors into a nonhazardous location.

(FPN): The sheath mentioned in (d) and (e) above may be either metal or a nonmetallic material.

(f) Drainage.

(1) Control Equipment. Where there is a probability that liquid or other condensed vapor may be trapped within enclosures for control equipment or at any point in the raceway system, approved means shall be provided to prevent accumulation or to permit periodic draining of such liquid or condensed vapor.

(2) Motors and Generators. Where the authority having jurisdiction judges that there is a probability that liquid or condensed vapor may accumulate within motors or generators, joints and conduit systems shall be arranged to minimize entrance of liquid. If means to prevent accumulation or to permit periodic draining are judged necessary, such means shall be provided at the time of manufacture and shall be considered an integral part of the machine.

(3) Canned Pumps, Process Connections, Etc. For canned pumps, process connections for flow, pressure, or analysis measurement, etc., that depend upon a single seal diaphragm or tube to prevent process fluids from entering the electrical conduit system, an additional approved seal, barrier or other means shall be provided to prevent the process fluid from entering the conduit system beyond the additional devices or means, if the primary seal fails.

The additional approved seal or barrier and the interconnecting enclosure shall meet the temperature and pressure conditions to which they will be subjected upon failure of the primary seal unless other approved means are provided to accomplish the purpose above.

Other means which are used in the liquefied natural gas industry consist of a vented enclosure containing busbars. The conduit from the canned pump terminates at the enclosure, and the conductors are connected to one end of the solid busbars. The circuit continues through the short busbar section to another set of conductors and a sealed conduit.

Drains, vents or other devices shall be provided so that primary seal leakage will be obvious.

(FPN): See also the last paragraph of Section 500-5(b) and Fine Print Note to Section 501-5.

Seals in conduits are used to prevent an explosion from traveling through the conduit to another enclosure, and to minimize the passage of gases or vapors from a hazardous (classified) location to a nonhazardous location. Sealing compound must be used as soon as possible on Type MI cable terminations to exclude moisture from cable insulation.

Where the conduit enters an enclosure containing arcing or high-temperature equipment, a sealing fitting is required to be placed within 18 in. (457 mm) of the enclosure it isolates; conduit bodies ("L," "T," etc.), couplings, unions, and elbows are the only enclosures or fittings permitted between the seal and the enclosure. See Figure 501-11 for an approved type of union. If two enclosures are spaced not more than 36 in. (914 mm) apart, a single seal may be placed between two connecting nipples if the seal is located not more than 18 in. (457 mm) from either enclosure.

In each 2-in. or larger conduit, a sealing fitting is required to be placed within 18 in. (457 mm) of the entrance to an explosionproof enclosure that houses terminals, splices, or taps.

A sealing fitting is required where the conduit leaves a Division 1 location or passes from a Division 2 location to a nonhazardous location. The sealing fitting is permitted on either side of the boundary, and there is to be no union, coupling, box, etc., between the seal and the boundary. It is preferable to locate the fitting on the nonhazardous location side. This sealing fitting serves two purposes. It completes the explosionproof wiring and enclosure system. Note that a ½-in. conduit connected to an explosionproof box containing only splices, even in a Division 1 location, is not required to be sealed within 18 in. (457 mm) of the box. The seal at the boundary of the Division 1 location serves to complete the explosionproof system. The sealing fitting at the boundary also prevents the conduit system from serving as a pipe to transmit flammable mixtures from a Division 1 or Division 2 location to a less hazardous (classified) location.

In Class I, Division 2 locations, a seal is required in each conduit entering an enclosure that is required to be explosionproof in order to complete the explosionproof enclosure.

Figure 501-7 illustrates the sealing of a fitting. A dam must be provided to prevent the sealing material from running out of the fitting while it is still in the liquid state. All conductors must be separated to permit the sealing material to run between them. The sealing compound is required to have a minimum thickness of not less than the trade size of the conduit and in no case less than ⅝ in. Conduit fittings for sealing are for use only with sealing compound supplied with the fitting and specified by the manufacturer in instructions furnished with the fitting.

Unless the additional seal or barrier, described in Section 501-5(f)(3), and interconnecting enclosures meet the performance requirements of the primary seal, the application of pressure or exposure to extreme temperatures must be prevented at the additional seal or barrier, so that the process fluid will not enter the conduit system if the primary seal fails. If the process fluid is a gas or can become a gas under ordinary atmospheric conditions (liquefied natural gas, for example), the drain mentioned in Section 501-5(f)(3) should be a vent. See commentary following Section 501-5(f)(3).

The necessary sealing may be accomplished by a sealing fitting and compound. To eliminate the time-consuming task of field-poured seals, a factory-sealed device with the seal designed into the device is permissible. A wide selection of factory-sealed devices is available for a variety of installations in hazardous (classified) locations. Factory-sealed devices are usually marked as such. Explosionproof motors are normally factory sealed, and no other seal is required. Where a conduit terminates in a motor, however, and if the conduit is 2 in. or larger, a seal is required to be placed within 18 in. (457 mm) of the motor terminal housing.

Figure 501-9 shows a sealing fitting designed for use in a vertical run of conduit to provide drainage for any condensation of moisture trapped by the seal above an enclosure. Any accumulation of water runs over the surface of the sealing compound down to an explosionproof drain, through which it automatically drains. Figure 501-8 shows a sealing fitting designed for either a horizontal or vertical conduit run. Figure 501-10 shows a combination drain and breather fitting. These fittings are specially designed to serve as a water drain and an air vent while providing positive explosionproof protection. The fitting permits the escape of accumulated water through its drain, and the breather allows the continuous circulation of air, preventing condensation of any moisture that may be present. Individual drain or breather fittings are also available. It is good practice to consider the installation of drain, breather, or combination fittings in order to guard against water accumulation with subsequent insulation failures, even though prevalent conditions may not indicate a need.

Figure 501-12 illustrates a Class I, Division 1 location using threaded rigid metal conduit or threaded intermediate metal conduit and explosionproof fittings and equipment including motors, motor controllers, pushbutton stations, lighting outlets, and junction boxes. The enclosures for the disconnecting means and motor controller for the motor (right part of the drawing) are placed in a nonhazardous location and are thus not required to be explosionproof.

Each of the three conduits is sealed on the nonhazardous side before passing into the hazardous (classified) location. The pigtail leads of both motors are factory sealed at the motor-terminal housing, and, unless the size of the flexible fitting entering the motor-terminal housing is 2 in. (50.8 mm) or larger, no other seals are needed at this point. Because the pushbutton control station and the motor controller and disconnect (left part of the drawing) are considered arc-producing devices, conduits are sealed within 18 in. (457 mm) of the entrance to these enclosures. Seals are required even though the contacts may be immersed in oil.

A seal is provided within 18 in. (457 mm) of the lighting switch. The design of the lighting fixture, as required by Underwriters Laboratories Inc., is such that the explosionproof chamber for the wiring must be separated or sealed from the lamp compartment, hence a separate seal is not required adjacent to UL-listed lighting fixtures. The lighting fixture is suspended on a conduit stem threaded into the cover of an explosionproof ceiling box. See Section 501-9.

501-6. Switches, Circuit Breakers, Motor Controllers, and Fuses.

(a) Class I, Division 1. In Class I, Division 1 locations, switches, circuit breakers, motor controllers, and fuses, including pushbuttons, relays, and similar devices, shall be provided with enclosures and the enclosure in each case, together with the enclosed apparatus, shall be approved as a complete assembly for use in Class I locations.

(b) Class I, Division 2. Switches, circuit breakers, motor controllers, and fuses in Class I, Division 2 locations shall comply with the following:

(1) Type Required. Circuit breakers, motor controllers, and switches intended to inter-rupt current in the normal performance of the function for which they are installed shall be provided with enclosures approved for Class I, Division 1 locations in accordance with Section 501-3(a), unless general-purpose enclosures are provided and (1) the interruption of current occurs within a chamber hermetically sealed against the entrance of gases and vapors, or (2) the current make-and-break contacts are oil-immersed, and of the general-purpose type having a 2-inch (50.8-mm) minimum immersion for power and a 1-inch (25.4-mm) minimum immersion for control.

689

Figure 501-7. A sealing fitting placed in a run of conduit to minimize the passage of gases from one portion of the electrical installation to another. (*Crouse-Hinds*)

Figure 501-8. A sealing fitting for a horizontal or vertical conduit run with a removable screw-type fitting for draining purposes. (*Appleton Electric Co.*)

(2) Isolating Switches. Fused or unfused disconnect and isolating switches for transformers or capacitor banks that are not intended to interrupt current in the normal performance of the function for which they are installed, shall be permitted to be installed in general-purpose enclosures.

(3) Fuses. For the protection of motors, appliances, and lamps, other than as provided in (b)(4) below, standard plug or cartridge fuses shall be permitted, provided they are placed within enclosures approved for the location; or fuses shall be permitted if they are within general-purpose enclosures, and if they are of a type in which the operating element is immersed in oil or other approved liquid or the operating element is enclosed within a chamber hermetically sealed against the entrance of gases and vapors.

(4) Fuses or Circuit Breakers for Overcurrent Protection. Where not more than ten sets of approved enclosed fuses or not more than ten circuit breakers that are not intended to be used as switches for the interruption of current are installed for branch-circuit or feeder protection in any one room, area, or section of the Class I, Division 2 location, general-purpose-type enclosures for such fuses or circuit breakers shall be permitted if the fuses or circuit breakers are for the protection of circuits or feeders supplying lamps in fixed positions only.

690

Figure 501-9. A sealing fitting with an automatic drain plug. (*Appleton Electric Co.*)

Figure 501-10. A combination breather-drainage fitting. (*Appleton Electric Co.*)

Figure 501-11. An explosionproof union. (*Appleton Electric Co.*)

(FPN): A set of fuses is all the fuses required to protect all the ungrounded conductors of a circuit. For example, a group of three fuses protecting an ungrounded 3-phase circuit and a single fuse protecting the ungrounded conductor of an identified 2-wire single-phase circuit is a set of fuses in each instance.

Fuses complying with (b)(3) above shall not be required to be included in counting the ten sets of fuses permitted in general-purpose enclosures.

(5) Fuses Internal to Lighting Fixtures. Approved cartridge fuses shall be permitted as supplementary protection within lighting fixtures.

Figure 501-13 shows an explosionproof panelboard consisting of an assembly of branch-circuit devices enclosed in a cast-metal explosionproof housing. These panelboards are provided with bolted access covers and threaded conduit-entry hubs designed to withstand the force of any internal explosion.

Figure 501-14 shows an open and closed view of a cylindrical-type ("spin-top") combination motor controller, a motor control starter, and circuit breaker in an explosionproof enclosure. The top and bottom covers are threaded on for quick removal for installation and servicing. Figure 501-15 shows the same type of equipment in a rectangular enclosure with a hinged, bolted-on cover. These types of housings are designed to accomodate a wide variety of either manually or magnetically operated across-the-line types of motor starters in a variety of ratings.

Figure 501-16 illustrates a standard toggle switch in an explosionproof enclosure.

Figure 501-12. A Class I, Division 1 location where threaded metal conduits, sealing fittings, explosionproof fittings, and equipment for power and lights are used.

In Class I, Division 2 locations, it is assumed that fuses or circuit breakers will seldom open the circuit when used to protect feeders or branch circuits supplying lamps in fixed positions only. Division 2 locations are not normally hazardous but may become so [see Section 500-5(b)], and since it is unlikely that the fuse or circuit breaker in such a circuit will operate simultaneously with the occurrence of an explosive mixture inside the enclosure, general-purpose enclosures are permitted for such overcurrent devices.

Section 501-6(b)(5) permits fuses, often used for ballast protection in high-intensity-discharge and outdoor fluorescent fixtures.

501-7. Control Transformers and Resistors. Transformers, impedance coils, and resistors used as, or in conjunction with, control equipment for motors, generators, and appliances shall comply with (a) and (b) below.

(a) Class I, Division 1. In Class I, Division 1 locations, transformers, impedance coils, and resistors, together with any switching mechanism associated with them, shall be provided with enclosures approved for Class I, Division 1 locations in accordance with Section 501-3(a).

(b) Class I, Division 2. In Class I, Division 2 locations, control transformers and resistors shall comply with the following:

(1) Switching Mechanisms. Switching mechanisms used in conjunction with transformers, impedance coils, and resistors shall comply with Section 501-6(b).

(2) Coils and Windings. Enclosures for windings of transformers, solenoids, or impedance coils shall be permitted to be of the general-purpose type.

(3) Resistors. Resistors shall be provided with enclosures; and the assembly shall be approved for Class I locations, unless resistance is nonvariable and maximum operating temperature, in degrees Celsius, will not exceed 80 percent of the ignition temperature of the gas or vapor involved, or has been tested and found incapable of igniting the gas or vapor.

692

Figure 501-13. An explosionproof panelboard with provisions for twelve circuits. (*Appleton Electric Co.*)

Figure 501-14. An explosionproof enclosure for a motor control starter and circuit breaker (open and closed views). (*Appleton Electric Co.*)

501-8. Motors and Generators.

(a) **Class I, Division 1.** In Class I, Division 1 locations, motors, generators, and other rotating electric machinery shall be: (1) approved for Class I, Division 1 locations; or (2) of the

Figure 501-15. A magnetic motor starter for use in a Class I, Group D location. Note the number of securing bolts and the width of the flange. (*General Electric Co.*)

Single-pole
single-throw
toggle switch

Figure 501-16. A standard toggle switch in an explosionproof enclosure.

totally enclosed type supplied with positive-pressure ventilation from a source of clean air with discharge to a safe area, so arranged to prevent energizing of the machine until ventilation has been established and the enclosure has been purged with at least 10 volumes of air, and also arranged to automatically de-energize the equipment when the air supply fails; or (3) of the totally enclosed inert gas-filled type supplied with a suitable reliable source of inert gas for pressuring the enclosure, with devices provided to ensure a positive pressure in the enclosure and arranged to automatically de-energize the equipment when the gas supply fails; or (4) of a type designed to be submerged in a liquid which is flammable only when vaporized and mixed with air, or in a gas or vapor at a pressure greater than atmospheric and which is flammable only when mixed with air; and the machine is so arranged to prevent energizing it until it has been purged with the liquid or gas to exclude air, and also arranged to automatically de-energize the equipment when the supply of liquid, or gas or vapor fails or the pressure is reduced to atmospheric.

Totally enclosed motors of Types (2) or (3) shall have no external surface with an operating temperature in degrees Celsius in excess of 80 percent of the ignition temperature of the gas or vapor involved. Appropriate devices shall be provided to detect and automatically de-energize the motor or provide an adequate alarm if there is any increase in temperature of the motor beyond designed limits. Auxiliary equipment shall be of a type approved for the location in which it is installed.

(FPN): See ASTM Test Procedure (Designation D 2155-69).

The intent of Section 501-8(a)(4) is to permit nonexplosionproof motors submerged in liquefied natural gas (LNG), liquefied petroleum gas (LPG), etc. It does not permit nonexplosionproof motors under water, such as in wet pits, unless the motors are provided with some other system of explosion protection, e.g., purged and pressurized per NFPA 496, *Standard for Purged and Pressurized Enclosures for Electrical Equipment in Hazardous (Classified) Locations.*

The ASTM Test Procedure is used to determine the ignition temperature of some flammable and combustible liquids.

(b) Class I, Division 2. In Class I, Division 2 locations, motors, generators, and other rotating electric machinery in which are employed sliding contacts, centrifugal or other types of switching mechanism (including motor overcurrent, overloading and overtemperature devices), or integral resistance devices, either while starting or while running, shall be approved for Class I, Division 1 locations, unless such sliding contacts, switching mechanisms, and resistance devices are provided with enclosures approved for Class I, Division 2 locations in accordance with Section 501-3(b). When operated at rated voltage, the exposed surface of space heaters used to prevent condensation of moisture during shut-down periods shall not exceed 80 percent of the ignition temperature in degrees Celsius of the gas or vapor involved.

Many motor heaters are deenergized automatically when the motor is running. However, the heater ratings are usually low when compared to the normal heat generated during motor operation. Unless otherwise indicated on the motor wiring diagram or in instructions provided with the motor, there is no need to deenergize the heater except to save energy.

In Class I, Division 2 locations, the installation of open or nonexplosionproof enclosed motors, such as squirrel-cage induction motors without brushes, switching mechanisms, or similar arc-producing devices shall be permitted.

(FPN): It is important to consider the temperature of internal and external surfaces which may be exposed to the flammable atmosphere.

It is intended that the phrase "other rotating electric machinery" include electric brakes. Listed and labeled electric brakes are available for Class I, Division 1, Group C and D locations.

Figures 501-17 and 501-18 show closed and opened views of a totally enclosed fan-cooled motor approved for use in explosive atmospheres. The main frame and end-bells are designed with sufficient strength to withstand an internal explosion, and flames or hot gases are cooled while escaping because of the wide metal-to-metal joints between the frame and the end-bells and the long, close-tolerance clearance provided for the free-turn of the shaft. Air circulation outside the motor is maintained by a nonsparking (aluminum, bronze, or a nonstatic-generating-type

Figure 501-17. Terminal housing of a motor approved for use in specific hazardous locations. Note integral sealing of the motor. (*General Electric Co.*)

Figure 501-18. View showing internal fan of motor in Figure 501-17.

plastic) fan on the end opposite the shaft end of the motor. A sheet metal housing surrounds this fan to reduce the likelihood of a person or object contacting the moving blades and to direct the flow of air. Internal fans on the shaft circulate air around the windings.

Motors that have arcing or sparking devices, such as commutators, internal switches, or other control devices, must be explosionproof. General-purpose squirrel-cage induction motors may be used in Division 2 locations.

Since some open-type motors are permitted in Class I, Division 2 locations, care should be exercised in selecting the motor types when flammable gases or vapors with very low ignition temperatures may be present. Modern motors with high-temperature insulation systems, such as Class H [180°C (356°F)], may operate close to or above the ignition temperature of the flammable mixture.

501-9. Lighting Fixtures. Lighting fixtures shall comply with (a) or (b) below.

(a) Class I, Division 1. In Class I, Division 1 locations, lighting fixtures shall comply with the following:

(1) Approved Fixtures. Each fixture shall be approved as a complete assembly for the Class I, Division 1 location and shall be clearly marked to indicate the maximum wattage of lamps for which it is approved. Fixtures intended for portable use shall be specifically approved as a complete assembly for that use.

(2) Physical Damage. Each fixture shall be protected against physical damage by a suitable guard or by location.

(3) Pendant Fixtures. Pendant fixtures shall be suspended by and supplied through threaded rigid metal conduit stems or threaded steel intermediate conduit stems, and threaded joints shall be provided with set-screws or other effective means to prevent loosening. For stems longer than 12 inches (305 mm), permanent and effective bracing against lateral displacement shall be provided at a level not more than 12 inches (305 mm) above the lower end of the stem, or flexibility in the form of a fitting or flexible connector approved for the Class I, Division 1 location shall be provided not more than 12 inches (305 mm) from the point of attachment to the supporting box or fitting.

(4) Supports. Boxes, box assemblies, or fittings used for the support of lighting fixtures shall be approved for Class I locations.

(b) Class I, Division 2. In Class I, Division 2 locations, lighting fixtures shall comply with the following:

(1) Portable Lighting Equipment. Portable lighting equipment shall comply with (a)(1) above.

Exception: Where portable lighting equipment are mounted on movable stands and are connected by flexible cords, as covered in Section 501-11, they shall be permitted, when mounted in any position, provided that they conform to Section 501-9(b)(2) below.

(2) Fixed Lighting. Lighting fixtures for fixed lighting shall be protected from physical damage by suitable guards or by location. Where there is danger that falling sparks or hot metal from lamps or fixtures might ignite localized concentrations of flammable vapors or gases, suitable enclosures or other effective protective means shall be provided. Where lamps are of a size or type that may, under normal operating conditions, reach surface temperatures exceeding 80 percent of the ignition temperature in degrees Celsius of the gas or vapor involved, fixtures shall comply with (a)(1) above or shall be of a type which has been tested and found incapable of igniting the gas or vapor if the ignition temperature is not exceeded.

(3) Pendant Fixtures. Pendant fixtures shall be suspended by threaded rigid metal conduit stems, threaded steel intermediate metal conduit stems or by other approved means. For rigid stems longer than 12 inches (305 mm), permanent and effective bracing against lateral displacement shall be provided at a level not more than 12 inches (305 mm) above the lower end of the stem, or flexibility in the form of an approved fitting or flexible connector shall be provided not more than 12 inches (305 mm) from the point of attachment to the supporting box or fitting.

(4) Switches. Switches that are a part of an assembled fixture or of an individual lampholder shall comply with Section 501-6(b)(1).

(5) Starting Equipment. Starting and control equipment for electric-discharge lamps shall comply with Section 501-7(b).

Exception: A thermal protector potted into a thermally protected fluorescent lamp ballast if the lighting fixture is approved for locations of this Class and Division.

Figures 501-19 and 501-20 show typical lighting fixtures for Class I, Group C and D locations and a variety of parts of a complete lighting fixture assembly. The outlet boxes have an internally threaded opening designed to receive the cover. A pendant fixture is attached to the cover by threaded rigid metal conduit or threaded intermediate metal conduit. To prevent loosening from vibration or lamp changing, threaded joints are required to be provided with set-screws. The set-screws should not interrupt the explosionproof joint. Rigid metal conduit or intermediate metal conduit stems longer than 12 in. (305 mm) require effective bracing or a flexible fitting approved for the purpose and placed not more than 12 in. (305 mm) from the point of attachment to the supporting box, cover, or fitting.

A globeholder is threaded onto the body of the fixture housing and supports a heavy glass globe, guard, and reflector. It is available in sizes suitable for lamps from 40 W through 500 W. In designing any hazardous (classified) location lighting system, operating temperatures must be considered. Therefore, if the area is Class I, Division 1, fixtures approved for this location, and properly marked, must be used. Generally, enclosed and gasketed fixtures (previously called vaportight fixtures) without guards, if breakage is unlikely, or fixtures approved for Class I, Division 2 locations, are required in Division 2 locations. Fixtures listed by Underwriters Laboratories Inc. for use in any of the groups under Class I, either Division 1 or 2 locations, or both, are designed to operate without causing ignition of surrounding flammable gas or vapor atmospheres, and are marked with the operating temperature or temperature range code [see Table 500-3(b)].

Figure 501-21 shows an explosionproof handlamp. It is required that lamp compartments be sealed from the terminal compartment. Provisions are required to be made for the connection of 3-conductor (one, a grounding conductor), flexible, extra-hard usage cord. See Section 501-11.

501-10. Utilization Equipment.

(a) Class I, Division 1. In Class I, Division 1 locations, all utilization equipment shall be approved for Class I, Division 1 locations.

(b) Class I, Division 2. In Class I, Division 2 locations, all utilization equipment shall comply with the following:

(1) Heaters. Electrically heated utilization equipment shall conform with either a. or b. below.

a. The heater shall not exceed 80 percent of the ignition temperature in degrees Celsius of the gas or vapor involved on any surface which is exposed to the gas or vapor when continuously

Figure 501-19. A typical lighting fixture for use in Class I, Group C and D locations. (*Crouse-Hinds*)

energized at the maximum rated ambient temperature. If a temperature controller is not provided, these conditions shall apply when the heater is operated at 120 percent of rated voltage.

Exception: For motor-mounted anti-condensation space heaters see Section 501-8(b).

   b. The heater shall be approved for Class I, Division 1 locations.

(2) Motors. Motors of motor-driven utilization equipment shall comply with Section 501-8(b).

(3) Switches, Circuit Breakers, and Fuses. Switches, circuit breakers, and fuses shall comply with Section 501-6(b).

   The requirements for utilization equipment in Class I locations are virtually identical for Division 1 and 2 locations, except for heaters. Electric pipe tracing systems listed for Class I, Division 2 locations and complying with Section 501-10(b)(1)a. are available.

501-11. Flexible Cords, Class I, Divisions 1 and 2. A flexible cord shall be permitted only for connection between portable lighting equipment or other portable utilization equipment and the fixed portion of its supply circuit; and where used shall: (1) be of a type approved for extra-hard usage; (2) contain, in addition to the conductors of the circuit, a grounding conductor complying with Section 400-23; (3) be connected to terminals or to supply conductors in an approved manner; (4) be supported by clamps or by other suitable means in such a manner that there will be no tension on the terminal connections; and (5) be provided with suitable seals where the flexible cord enters boxes, fittings, or enclosures of the explosionproof type.

Exception: As provided in Sections 501-3(b)(6) and 501-4(b).

Electric submersible pumps with means for removal without entering the wet-pit shall be considered portable utilization equipment.

(FPN): See Section 501-13 for flexible cords exposed to liquids having a deleterious effect on the conductor insulation.

   The second paragraph recognizes a wet-pit type of installation that is finding increasing acceptance for waste-water systems. Listed equipment for this use is available. See commentary following Section 501-8(a).

699

CLASS I, DIVISION 1 — FIXTURE HANGING METHODS.

GRC   GRFC   GRJS   CPST   GRT   EFHC

HUB COVER   UNION HUB COVER   GRK CANOPY COVER   HUB COVER   HUB COVER   LC COUPLINGS

RIGID CONDUIT 12" MAXIMUM LENGTH   ESD SWIVEL   EXHF FLEXIBLE COUPLINGS   EXGF FLEXIBLE COUPLINGS

AA51 PENDANT FIXTURE

Figure 501-20. Various components used in an explosionproof lighting fixture installation. (*Appleton Electric Co.*)

Figure 501-21. An explosionproof handlamp for use in Class I locations. (*Appleton Electric Co.*)

501-12. Receptacles and Attachment Plugs, Class I, Divisions 1 and 2. Receptacles and attachment plugs shall be of the type providing for connection to the grounding conductor of a flexible cord and shall be approved for Class I locations.

Exception: As provided in Section 501-3(b)(6).

Figure 501-22 shows an explosionproof receptacle and attachment plug with an interlocking switch. The design of this device is such that when the switch is in the "on" position, the plug cannot be removed, and also the switch cannot be placed in the "on" position when the plug has been removed; that is, the plug cannot be inserted or removed unless the switch is in the "off" position. The receptacle is factory sealed with a provision for threaded-conduit entry to the switch compartment; the plug is for use with Type S or equivalent extra-hard-service flexible cord having a grounding conductor.

Figure 501-23 shows a 30-A, 4-pole receptacle and attachment plug assembly that is suitable for use without a switch. The design is such that the mating parts of the receptacle and plug are enclosed in a chamber that seals the arc and, by delayed-action construction, prevents complete removal of the plug until the arc or hot metal has cooled. The receptacle is factory sealed and the attachment plug is designed for use with a 4-conductor cord (3-conductor, 3-phase circuit with one grounding conductor) or a 3-conductor cord (two circuit conductors and one grounding conductor).

Figure 501-22. A receptacle and attachment plug of the explosionproof type with an interlocking switch. The switch must be in the "off" position to remove the attachment plug. (*Appleton Electric Co.*)

Figure 501-23. A four-pole (delayed action) explosionproof receptacle and attachment plug suitable for use without a switch. (*Appleton Electric Co.*)

501-13. Conductor Insulation, Class I, Divisions 1 and 2. Where condensed vapors or liquids may collect on, or come in contact with, the insulation on conductors, such insulation shall be of a type approved for use under such conditions; or the insulation shall be protected by a sheath of lead or by other approved means.

Nylon-jacketed conductors, such as Types THWN and TW that are suitable for use where exposed to gasoline, have gained widespread acceptance because of their ease of handling, application, and economics.

An excerpt from Underwriters Laboratories Inc. Electrical Construction Materials Directory states the following: Wires, Thermoplastic

Gasoline Resistant TW — Indicates a TW conductor with a jacket of extruded nylon suitable for use in wet locations, and for exposure to mineral oil, and to liquid gasoline and gasoline vapors at ordinary ambient temperature. It is identified by tag marking and by printing on the insulation or nylon jacket with the designation "Type TW Gasoline and Oil Resistant I."

Also listed for the above use is "Gasoline Resistant THWN" with the designation "Type THWN Gasoline and Oil Resistant II."

It should be noted that other thermoplastic wires may be suitable for exposure to mineral oil; but with the exception of those marked "Gasoline and Oil Resistant," reference to mineral oil does not include gasoline or similar light-petroleum solvents.

The conductor itself must bear the marking legend designating its use as suitable for gasoline exposure; such designation on the tag alone is not sufficient.

501-14. Signaling, Alarm, Remote-Control, and Communication Systems.

(a) Class I, Division 1. In Class I, Division 1 locations, all apparatus and equipment of signaling, alarm, remote-control, and communication systems, regardless of voltage, shall be approved for Class I, Division 1 locations, and all wiring shall comply with Sections 501-4(a) and 501-5(a) and (c).

(b) Class I, Division 2. In Class I, Division 2 locations, signaling, alarm, remote-control, and communication systems shall comply with the following:

(1) Contacts. Switches, circuit breakers, and make-and-break contacts of pushbuttons, relays, alarm bells, and horns shall have enclosures approved for Class I, Division 1 locations in accordance with Section 501-3(a).

Exception: General-purpose enclosures shall be permitted if current interrupting contacts are:

a. Immersed in oil; or

b. Enclosed within a chamber hermetically sealed against the entrance of gases or vapors; or

c. In circuits that under normal conditions do not release sufficient energy to ignite a specific ignitible atmospheric mixture, i.e., are nonincendive.

See commentary following Item c. of Section 501-3(b)(1), Exception.

(2) Resistors and Similar Equipment. Resistors, resistance devices, thermionic tubes, rectifiers, and similar equipment shall comply with Section 501-3(b)(2).

(3) Protectors. Enclosures shall be provided for lightning protective devices and for fuses. Such enclosures shall be permitted to be of the general-purpose type.

(4) Wiring and Sealing. All wiring shall comply with Sections 501-4(b) and 501-5(b) and (c).

Audible signaling devices, such as bells, sirens, and horns, other than the newer electronic types, usually involve make-and-break contacts that are capable of producing a spark of sufficient energy to cause ignition of a hazardous atmospheric mixture. Therefore, when used in Class I locations, this type of equipment is required to be contained in explosionproof enclosures and wiring methods are required to comply with Section 501-4 and sealing fittings are required to be provided in accordance with Section 501-5. Figure 501-24 shows a signal siren for use in Class I locations.

Explosionproof devices or explosionproof enclosures may prove more practical than oil-immersed contacts because maintaining the condition and level of the oil can be a problem. Hermetically sealed enclosures, such as float-operated mercury-tube switches, are available for some applications. Electronic signal devices without make-and-break contacts will usually not require explosionproof enclosures in Division 2 locations.

Figure 501-24. A signal siren mounted on an explosionproof enclosure for use in hazardous areas. (*Crouse-Hinds*)

501-15. Live Parts, Class I, Divisions 1 and 2.   There shall be no exposed live parts.

Contact with the circuit could produce sparks that could cause an explosion in a hazardous (classified) location.

501-16. Grounding, Class I, Divisions 1 and 2.   Wiring and equipment in Class I, Division 1 and 2 locations shall be grounded as specified in Article 250 and with the following additional requirements:

(a) Bonding.   The locknut-bushing and double-locknut types of contacts shall not be depended upon for bonding purposes but bonding jumpers with proper fittings or other approved means of bonding shall be used. Such means of bonding shall apply to all intervening raceways, fittings, boxes, enclosures, etc. between Class I locations and the point of grounding for service equipment.

(b) Types of Equipment Grounding Conductors.   Where flexible metal conduit or liquidtight flexible metal conduit is used as permitted in Section 501-4(b), and is to be relied upon to complete a sole equipment grounding path, it shall be installed with internal or external bonding jumpers in parallel with each conduit and complying with Section 250-79.

Special consideration is necessary in the grounding and bonding of exposed noncurrent-carrying metal parts of equipment, such as the frames or metal exteriors of motors, fixed or portable lamps, lighting fixtures, enclosures, and conduits to ensure permanent and effective mechanical and electrical connections to prevent the possibility of arcs or sparks caused by ineffective or poor grounding methods. To be effective, proper grounding and bonding applies to all interconnected raceways, fittings, enclosures, etc., between hazardous (classified) locations and the point of grounding for service equipment. Where conduit is used in hazardous (classified) locations, it is preferable that threaded connections also be employed in the nonhazardous location.

Figure 501-25. A fitting for the connection of an external bonding jumper used with liquidtight flexible metal conduit.

501-17. Surge Protection, Class I, Divisions 1 and 2. Surge arresters, including their installation and connection, shall comply with Article 280. In addition, surge arresters if installed in a Class I, Division 1 location shall be in suitable enclosures.

Some surge arresters, such as the older style lightning arresters, are spark-producing devices. Others, such as solid-state types, are not. Surge arresters should be connected to the service conductors outside the building and be bonded to the service-entrance raceway system. For services less than 1,000 V, the arrester grounding conductor is connected as provided in Section 280-21.

Where the service voltage is less than 600 V, the supply system is a secondary system; thus the grounded service conductor should always be bonded to the equipment grounding conductor as required by the provisions of Article 250.

In Class I, Division 1 locations, all surge arresters are required to be installed in explosionproof or purged and pressurized enclosures. In Class I, Division 2 locations, only the spark-producing types of surge arresters need such protection. They can also be installed in oil-filled enclosures or have the arcing or sparking contacts in hermetically sealed chambers. The nonsparking type of surge arrester needs no special enclosure in a Class I, Division 2 location.

ARTICLE 502 — CLASS II LOCATIONS

Contents

502-1. General. The general rules of this Code shall apply to the electric wiring and equipment in locations classified as Class II locations in Section 500-6.

Exception: As modified by this article.

"Dust-ignitionproof," as used in this article, shall mean enclosed in a manner that will exclude ignitible amounts of dusts or amounts that might affect performance or rating and that, where installed and protected in accordance with this Code, will not permit arcs, sparks, or heat otherwise generated or liberated inside of the enclosure to cause ignition of exterior accumulations or atmospheric suspensions of a specified dust on or in the vicinity of the enclosure.

Equipment installed in Class II locations shall be able to function at full rating without developing surface temperatures high enough to cause excessive dehydration or gradual carbonization of any organic dust deposits that may occur.

(FPN): Dust that is carbonized or excessively dry is highly susceptible to spontaneous ignition.

Equipment and wiring of the type defined in Article 100 as explosionproof shall not be required and shall not be acceptable in Class II locations unless approved for such locations.

See Figure 502-3.

Where Class II, Groups E and F dusts having a resistivity less than 10^5 ohm-centimeter are present in hazardous quantities, there are only Division 1 locations.

Class II, Division 1 and 2 locations are defined in Section 500-6 as hazardous due to the presence of combustible dust. These locations are separated into three groups:

Group E: atmospheres containing metal dusts, regardless of resistivity, such as aluminum and magnesium, and dusts of similarly hazardous characteristics having a resistivity of less than 100,000 ohm-centimeter;

Group F: atmospheres containing carbon black, charcoal, coal, or coke dusts which have more than 8 percent total volatile material (carbon black per ASTM D1620; charcoal, coal, and coke dusts per ASTM D271) or atmospheres containing these dusts sensitized by other materials so that they present an explosion hazard, and having a resistivity greater than 10^2 ohm-centimeter but equal to or less than 10^8 ohm-centimeter; and

Group G: atmospheres containing nonconductive dusts, such as flour, starch, grain, or combustible plastics or chemical dusts having a resistivity of 100,000 ohm-centimeter or greater.

Note that the last paragraph specifically indicates that there are no Division 2 locations (only Division 1) if electrically conductive Group E and F dusts are present (i.e., dusts with a resistivity less than 100,000 ohm-centimeter). The Instrument Society of America Standard ISA-S12.10-1973, Area Classification in Hazardous Dust Locations, provides some measurements of electrical resistivity of dusts.

It should be noted that equipment suitable for one class and group is not necessarily suitable for any other class and group. To protect against explosion in hazardous (classified) locations, all electrical equipment exposed to the hazardous atmospheres is required to be suitable for such locations. Look for the Underwriters Laboratories Inc. Listing Mark or Factory Mutual (FM) approval. Do not take for granted that equipment suitable for Class I use is also suitable for Class II use. Grain dust, for example, will ignite at a temperature lower than that of many flammable vapors.

Any one, or more, of the following four hazards may be present in a Class II location:

1. An explosive mixture of air and dust;
2. Accumulations of dust that interfere with the safe dissipation of heat from electrical equipment;
3. Accumulation of electrically conductive dust lodging on live parts; and
4. Deposits of dust that could be ignited by arcs or sparks.

In the layout of electrical installations for hazardous (classified) locations, it is preferable to locate service equipment, switchboards, panelboards, and much of the electrical equipment in less hazardous areas, usually in a separate room.

502-2. Transformers and Capacitors.

(a) Class II, Division 1. In Class II, Division 1 locations, transformers and capacitors shall comply with the following:

(1) Containing Liquid that Will Burn. Transformers and capacitors containing a liquid that will burn shall be installed only in approved vaults complying with Sections 450-41 through 450-48, and in addition: (1) doors or other openings communicating with the Division 1 location shall have self-closing fire doors on both sides of the wall, and the doors shall be carefully fitted and provided with suitable seals (such as weather stripping) to minimize the entrance of dust into the vault; (2) vent openings and ducts shall communicate only with the outside air; and (3) suitable pressure-relief openings communicating with the outside air shall be provided.

(2) Not Containing Liquid that Will Burn. Transformers and capacitors that do not contain a liquid that will burn shall: (1) be installed in vaults complying with Sections 450-41 through 450-48, or (2) be approved as a complete assembly, including terminal connections for Class II locations.

(3) Metal Dusts. No transformer or capacitor shall be installed in a location where dust from magnesium, aluminum, aluminum bronze powders, or other metals of similarly hazardous characteristics may be present.

(b) Class II, Division 2. In Class II, Division 2 locations, transformers and capacitors shall comply with the following:

(1) Containing Liquid that Will Burn. Transformers and capacitors containing a liquid that will burn shall be installed in vaults complying with Sections 450-41 through 450-48.

(2) Containing Askarel. Transformers containing askarel and rated in excess of 25 kVA shall: (1) be provided with pressure-relief vents; (2) be provided with a means for absorbing any gases generated by arcing inside the case, or the pressure-relief vents shall be connected to a chimney or flue that will carry such gases outside the building; and (3) have an air space of not less than 6 inches (152 mm) between the transformer cases and any adjacent combustible material.

(3) Dry-type Transformers. Dry-type transformers shall be installed in vaults or shall: (1) have their windings and terminal connections enclosed in tight metal housings without ventilating or other openings, and (2) operate at not over 600 volts, nominal.

At this time no UL-listed dry-type or less-flammable liquid-insulated transformers that are dusttight and suitable for use in a Class II location are available. It may be possible to construct a small, low-voltage, dusttight (without ventilating openings) dry-type transformer, but transformers having a primary voltage rating of over 600 V are required to be either less-flammable liquid-insulated or installed in a vault. In almost all cases, transformers can be located remote from dust atmospheres.

Capacitors used for power-factor correction of individual motors are of sealed construction but, if installed in Class II, Division 1 locations, are also required to be approved as a complete assembly including dusttight terminal enclosures. The only special requirement for capacitors in Division 2 locations is that they are not permitted to contain oil or any other liquid that will burn; otherwise they are to be installed in vaults.

Capacitor and transformer oils (such as askarel) that do not burn have, in the past, contained PCBs, and production of such oil has been stopped.

Figure 502-1 illustrates suitable protection for wiring systems in Class II locations supplied from overhead transmission lines. This protection includes surge (lightning) arresters on the primary side of the transformers (within 1,000 ft of the service entrance), surge-protective capacitors connected to the supply side of the main service disconnecting means, and interconnection of all grounds. Arresters should be of the proper voltage rating for the system to which they are connected and where protecting the primary supply should be located within 300 ft of the transformers. Surge capacitors are to protect against abrupt increases in voltage and should be provided with automatic means for dissipating any stored charge.

502-4. Wiring Methods. Wiring methods shall comply with (a) and (b) below.

(a) Class II, Division 1. In Class II, Division 1 locations, threaded rigid metal conduit, threaded steel intermediate metal conduit or Type MI cable with termination fittings approved for the location shall be the wiring method employed. Type MI cable shall be installed and supported in a manner to avoid tensile stress at the termination fittings.

(1) Fittings and Boxes. Fittings and boxes shall be provided with threaded bosses for connection to conduit or cable terminations, shall have close-fitting covers, and shall have no

Figure 502-1. Lightning protection: arrester, interconnected grounding, and surge capacitors.

openings (such as holes for attachment screws) through which dust might enter or through which sparks or burning material might escape. Fittings and boxes in which taps, joints, or terminal connections are made, or that are used in locations where dusts are of a combustible electrically conductive nature, shall be approved for Class II locations.

(2) Flexible Connections. Where necessary to employ flexible connections, dusttight flexible connectors, liquidtight flexible metal conduit with approved fittings, or flexible cord approved for extra-hard usage and provided with bushed fittings shall be used. Where flexible cords are used and electrically conducting dusts are encountered, they shall be provided with dusttight seals at both ends. An additional conductor for grounding shall be provided in the flexible cord unless other acceptable means of grounding is provided. Where flexible connections are subject to oil or other corrosive conditions, the insulation of the conductors shall be of a type approved for the condition or shall be protected by means of a suitable sheath.

(b) Class II, Division 2. In Class II, Division 2 locations, rigid metal conduit, intermediate metal conduit, electrical metallic tubing, dusttight wireways, or Type MI, MC, or SNM cable with approved termination fittings, or Type PLTC or TC cable installed in ventilated channel-type cable trays in a single layer with a space not less than the larger cable diameter between the two adjacent cables shall be the wiring method employed.

Exception: Wiring, which under normal conditions cannot release sufficient energy to ignite a specific combustible dust mixture by opening, shorting or grounding, shall be permitted using any of the methods suitable for wiring in ordinary locations.

(1) Wireways, Fittings, and Boxes. Wireways, fittings, and boxes in which taps, joints, or terminal connections are made shall be designed to minimize the entrance of dust, and: (1) shall be provided with telescoping or close-fitting covers or other effective means to prevent the escape of sparks or burning material, and (2) shall have no openings (such as holes for attachment screws) through which, after installation, sparks or burning material might escape or through which adjacent combustible material might be ignited.

(2) Flexible Connections. Where flexible connections are necessary, (a)(2) above shall apply.

708

Where it is necessary to use flexible connections, liquidtight flexible metal conduit or extra-hard usage flexible cord is permitted. The preferred method, however, would be to use a flexible fitting as shown in Figure 501-6. Where liquidtight flexible metal conduit is used, a bonding jumper (internal or external) is required to be provided around such conduit. See Section 502-16(b). An additional conductor for grounding is required to be provided where flexible cord is used.

In Division 1 locations, boxes containing taps, joints, or terminal connections and boxes that are used where electrically-conductive dusts (dusts with resistivities less than 100,000 ohm-centimeter) are present must be dust-ignitionproof and must be provided with threaded hubs, as shown in Figure 502-2.

To provide adequate bonding in Division 2 locations, threaded hubs, as shown in Figure 502-2, should be used. Figure 502-2 also shows a close-fitting cover as required for Class II locations. Standard pressed steel boxes are permitted where they do not contain taps, joints, or terminal connections and a bonding jumper is provided around the box.

Figure 502-2. Junction boxes with threaded hubs suitable for use in Class II, Group E hazardous atmospheres. (*Appleton Electric Co.*)

502-5. Sealing, Class II, Divisions 1 and 2. Where a raceway provides communication between an enclosure that is required to be dust-ignition-proof and one that is not, suitable means shall be provided to prevent the entrance of dust into the dust-ignition-proof enclosure through the raceway. One of the following means shall be permitted: (1) a permanent and effective seal; (2) a horizontal raceway not less than 10 feet (3.05 m) long; or (3) a vertical raceway not less than 5 feet (1.52 m) long and extending downward from the dust-ignition-proof enclosure.

Where a raceway provides communication between an enclosure that is required to be dust-ignition-proof and an enclosure in an unclassified location, seals will not be required.

Sealing fittings shall be accessible.

This section provides three suitable ways to prevent dust from entering the dust-ignitionproof enclosure through the raceway where a raceway connects an enclosure that is required to be dust-ignitionproof to one that is not. If sealing fittings are used, any of the fittings designed for use in Class I locations can be used. No sealing method is needed in the special, but not unusual, situation in which no dust can enter the raceway in the hazardous (classified) location. See Figure 502-4.

502-6. Switches, Circuit Breakers, Motor Controllers, and Fuses.

(a) Class II, Division 1. In Class II, Division 1 locations, switches, circuit breakers, motor controllers, and fuses shall comply with the following:

(1) Type Required. Switches, circuit breakers, motor controllers, and fuses, including pushbuttons, relays, and similar devices that are intended to interrupt current during normal operation or that are installed where combustible dusts of an electrically conductive nature may be present, shall be provided with dust-ignition-proof enclosures, which, together with the enclosed equipment in each case, shall be approved as a complete assembly for Class II locations.

(2) Isolating Switches. Disconnecting and isolating switches containing no fuses and not intended to interrupt current and not installed where dusts may be of an electrically conductive nature shall be provided with tight metal enclosures that shall be designed to minimize the entrance of dust, and that shall: (1) be equipped with telescoping or close-fitting covers or with other effective means to prevent the escape of sparks or burning material, and (2) have no openings (such as holes for attachment screws) through which, after installation, sparks or burning material might escape or through which exterior accumulations of dust or adjacent combustible material might be ignited.

(3) Metal Dusts. In locations where dust from magnesium, aluminum, aluminum bronze powders, or other metals of similarly hazardous characteristics may be present, fuses, switches, motor controllers, and circuit breakers shall have enclosures specifically approved for such locations.

(b) Class II, Division 2. In Class II, Division 2 locations, enclosures for fuses, switches, circuit breakers, and motor controllers, including pushbuttons, relays, and similar devices, shall be dusttight.

Figure 502-3 shows a pushbutton station with pilot light suitable for both Class I and Class II hazardous (classified) locations. Figure 502-5 shows a panelboard suitable for use in Class II locations only. Many, but not necessarily all, of the switches or circuit breakers approved for Class I, Division 1 locations are also approved for Class II locations. It is important to always look for the listing and identification of the hazardous (classified) locations for which the listing has been given.

502-7. Control Transformers and Resistors.

(a) Class II, Division 1. In Class II, Division 1 locations, control transformers, solenoids, impedance coils, resistors, and any overcurrent devices or switching mechanisms associated with them shall have dust-ignition-proof enclosures approved for Class II locations. No control transformer, impedance coil, or resistor shall be installed in a location where dust from magnesium, aluminum, aluminum bronze powders, or other metals of similarly hazardous characteristics may be present unless provided with an enclosure approved for the specific location.

(b) Class II, Division 2. In Class II, Division 2 locations, transformers and resistors shall comply with the following:

(1) Switching Mechanisms. Switching mechanisms (including overcurrent devices) associated with control transformers, solenoids, impedance coils, and resistors shall be provided with dusttight enclosures.

(2) Coils and Windings. Where not located in the same enclosure with switching mechanisms, control transformers, solenoids, and impedance coils shall be provided with tight metal housings without ventilating openings.

(3) Resistors. Resistors and resistance devices shall have dust-ignition-proof enclosures approved for Class II locations.

Exception: Where the maximum normal operating temperature of the resistor will not exceed 120°C (248°F), nonadjustable resistors or resistors that are part of an automatically timed starting sequence shall be permitted to have enclosures complying with (b)(2) above.

Figure 502-3. An explosionproof and dust-tight pushbutton control station that is suitable for use in Class I, Group C and D and Class II, Group E, F, and G locations. (*Appleton Electric Co.*)

502-8. Motors and Generators.

(a) Class II, Division 1. In Class II, Division 1 locations, motors, generators, and other rotating electrical machinery shall be:

(1) Approved for Class II, Division 1 locations, or

(2) Totally enclosed pipe-ventilated, meeting temperature limitations in Section 502-1.

It is intended that the phrase "other rotating electrical machinery" include electric brakes. Listed and labeled electric brakes are available for Class I, Group E, F, and G locations.

Although some explosionproof (Class I, Division 1) motors are also dust-ignitionproof, and approved for both Class I and II locations, this is by no means true of all motors. Always look for the marking to be sure the motor is designed and tested for the Class II location involved. If control wiring to the motor is necessary (see motor installation instruction), be sure the control circuit is properly installed and connected. Most motors for Class II locations require internal thermal protection to comply with the temperature limitations in Section 500-3(d), and integral horsepower Class II motors may require both power and control circuit wiring from the motor controller to the motor.

Figure 502-4. Illustrated are four methods permitted for preventing the entrance of dust into the dust-ignitionproof enclosure through the raceway.

Figure 502-5. A dust-ignitionproof panelboard for use in Class II, Group E, F, and G locations. (*Appleton Electric Co.*)

(b) Class II, Division 2. In Class II, Division 2 locations, motors, generators, and other rotating electrical equipment shall be totally enclosed nonventilated, totally enclosed pipe ventilated, totally enclosed fan cooled or dust-ignition-proof for which maximum full-load external temperature shall be in accordance with Section 500-3(d) for normal operation when operating in free air (not dust blanketed) and shall have no external openings.

Exception: If the authority having jurisdiction believes accumulations of nonconductive nonabrasive dust will be moderate, and if machines can be easily reached for routine cleaning and maintenance, the following shall be permitted to be installed:

a. Standard open-type machines without sliding contacts, centrifugal or other types of switching mechanism (including motor overcurrent, overloading and overtemperature devices), or integral resistance devices.

b. Standard open-type machines with such contacts, switching mechanisms, or resistance devices enclosed within dusttight housings without ventilating or other openings.

c. Self-cleaning textile motors of the squirrel-cage type.

Section 502-8(b) permits all types of totally enclosed motors in Class II, Division 2 locations if the external surface temperatures without a dust blanket do not exceed the temperatures indicated under maximum full load (normal operation) conditions in Section 500-3(d). Totally enclosed fan-cooled (TEFC) motors are specifically mentioned. The motor should be examined carefully to be sure there are no external openings, even though the motor may be marked "TEFC."

Figure 502-6 shows a totally enclosed pipe-ventilated motor showing intake piping through which cool, clean air is delivered to the motor from a fan or blower. The exhaust opening is connected to a pipe discharging to the outside of the building in order to prevent dust accumulation inside the motor.

Totally enclosed motors that have no special provision for cooling may be used in Class II, Division 2 locations, but to deliver the same horsepower, they must be considerably larger than an open-type, fan-cooled, or pipe-ventilated motor.

Figure 502-6. A pipe-ventilated motor that meets temperature limitations of Section 502-1. (*General Electric Co.*)

502-9. Ventilating Piping. Ventilating pipes for motors, generators, or other rotating electric machinery, or for enclosures for electric equipment, shall be of metal not lighter than No. 24 MSG, or of equally substantial noncombustible material, and shall comply with the following: (1) lead directly to a source of clean air outside of buildings; (2) be screened at the outer ends to

ARTICLE 502—CLASS II LOCATIONS

prevent the entrance of small animals or birds; and (3) be protected against physical damage and against rusting or other corrosive influences.

Ventilating pipes shall also comply with (a) and (b) below.

(a) Class II, Division 1. In Class II, Division 1 locations, ventilating pipes, including their connections to motors or to the dust-ignition-proof enclosures for other equipment, shall be dusttight throughout their length. For metal pipes, seams and joints shall comply with one of the following: (1) be riveted and soldered; (2) be bolted and soldered; (3) be welded; or (4) be rendered dusttight by some other equally effective means.

(b) Class II, Division 2. In Class II, Division 2 locations, ventilating pipes and their connections shall be sufficiently tight to prevent the entrance of appreciable quantities of dust into the ventilated equipment or enclosure, and to prevent the escape of sparks, flame, or burning material that might ignite dust accumulations or combustible material in the vicinity. For metal pipes, lock seams and riveted or welded joints shall be permitted; and tight-fitting slip joints shall be permitted where some flexibility is necessary, as at connections to motors.

502-10. Utilization Equipment.

(a) Class II, Division 1. In Class II, Division 1 locations, all utilization equipment shall be approved for Class II locations. Where dust from magnesium, aluminum, aluminum bronze powders, or other metals of similarly hazardous characteristics may be present, such equipment shall be approved for the specific location.

(b) Class II, Division 2. In Class II, Division 2 locations, all utilization equipment shall comply with the following:

(1) Heaters. Electrically heated utilization equipment shall be approved for Class II locations.

Exception: Metal-enclosed radiant heating panel equipment shall be dusttight and marked in accordance with Section 500-3(d).

(2) Motors. Motors of motor-driven utilization equipment shall comply with Section 502-8(b).

(3) Switches, Circuit Breakers, and Fuses. Enclosures for switches, circuit breakers, and fuses shall be dusttight.

(4) Transformers, Impedance Coils, and Resistors. Transformers, solenoids, impedance coils, and resistors shall comply with Section 502-7(b).

502-11. Lighting Fixtures. Lighting fixtures shall comply with (a) and (b) below.

(a) Class II, Division 1. In Class II, Division 1 locations, lighting fixtures for fixed and portable lighting shall comply with the following:

(1) Approved Fixtures. Each fixture shall be approved for Class II locations and shall be clearly marked to indicate the maximum wattage of the lamp for which it is approved. In locations where dust from magnesium, aluminum, aluminum bronze powders, or other metals of similarly hazardous characteristics may be present, fixtures for fixed or portable lighting and all auxiliary equipment shall be approved for the specific location.

(2) Physical Damage. Each fixture shall be protected against physical damage by a suitable guard or by location.

(3) Pendant Fixtures. Pendant fixtures shall be suspended by threaded rigid metal conduit stems, threaded steel intermediate metal conduit stems, by chains with approved fittings, or by other approved means. For rigid stems longer than 12 inches (305 mm), permanent and effective bracing against lateral displacement shall be provided at a level not more than 12 inches (305 mm) above the lower end of the stem, or flexibility in the form of a fitting or a flexible connector approved for the location shall be provided not more than 12 inches (305 mm) from the point of attachment to the supporting box or fitting. Threaded joints shall be provided with set-screws or other effective means to prevent loosening. Where wiring between an outlet box or fitting and a pendant fixture is not enclosed in conduit, flexible cord approved for hard usage shall be used, and suitable seals shall be provided where the cord enters the fixture and the outlet box or fitting. Flexible cord shall not serve as the supporting means for a fixture.

(4) Supports. Boxes, box assemblies, or fittings used for the support of lighting fixtures shall be approved for Class II locations.

(b) Class II, Division 2. In Class II, Division 2 locations, lighting fixtures shall comply with the following:

(1) Portable Lighting Equipment. Portable lighting equipment shall be approved for Class II locations. They shall be clearly marked to indicate the maximum wattage of lamps for which they are approved.

(2) Fixed Lighting. Lighting fixtures for fixed lighting, where not of a type approved for Class II locations, shall provide enclosures for lamps and lampholders that shall be designed to minimize the deposit of dust on lamps and to prevent the escape of sparks, burning material, or hot metal. Each fixture shall be clearly marked to indicate the maximum wattage of the lamp that shall be permitted without exceeding an exposed surface temperature in accordance with Section 500-3(d) under normal conditions of use.

(3) Physical Damage. Lighting fixtures for fixed lighting shall be protected from physical damage by suitable guards or by location.

(4) Pendant Fixtures. Pendant fixtures shall be suspended by threaded rigid metal conduit stems, threaded steel intermediate metal conduit stems, by chains with approved fittings, or by other approved means. For rigid stems longer than 12 inches (305 mm), permanent and effective bracing against lateral displacement shall be provided at a level not more than 12 inches (305 mm) above the lower end of the stem, or flexibility in the form of an approved fitting or a flexible connector shall be provided not more than 12 inches (305 mm) from the point of attachment to the supporting box or fitting. Where wiring between an outlet box or fitting and a pendant fixture is not enclosed in conduit, flexible cord approved for hard usage shall be used. Flexible cord shall not serve as the supporting means for a fixture.

(5) Electric-Discharge Lamps. Starting and control equipment for electric-discharge lamps shall comply with the requirements of Section 502-7(b).

Figure 502-7 shows a fixture listed by Underwriters Laboratories Inc. as suitable for use in Groups E, F, and G of Class II locations. Lighting fixtures, fixed or portable, and auxiliary equipment (such as ballasts) are required to be approved for use in Group E atmospheres where metal dusts are present.

Other than the requirement that the fixture is to be marked to indicate maximum lamp wattage, the only requirements for fixtures in Division 2 locations are that the lamps be enclosed in suitable glass globes to minimize dust deposits on the lamps and to prevent the escape of sparks or burning material. Guards are required to be provided unless, of course, globe breakage is unlikely.

Flexible cord of the hard-usage type is permitted with approved sealed connections for the wiring of chain-suspended or hook-and-eye suspended fixtures. Flexible cords are not intended to be used as a cord pendant or drop cord.

ARTICLE 502—CLASS II LOCATIONS

The portable handlamp shown in Figure 501-21 is approved as a complete assembly for use in Class I locations and also in any Class II, Group F or G location.

Figure 502-7. A typical lighting fixture for use in Class II, Division 1 locations. Where breakage is unlikely, a metal guard is not required.

502-12. Flexible Cords, Class II, Divisions 1 and 2. Flexible cords used in Class II locations shall comply with the following: (1) be of a type approved for extra-hard usage; (2) contain, in addition to the conductors of the circuit, a grounding conductor complying with Section 400-23; (3) be connected to terminals or to supply conductors in an approved manner; (4) be supported by clamps or by other suitable means in such a manner that there will be no tension on the terminal connections; and (5) be provided with suitable seals to prevent the entrance of dust where the flexible cord enters boxes or fittings that are required to be dust-ignition-proof.

502-13. Receptacles and Attachment Plugs.

(a) Class II, Division 1. In Class II, Division 1 locations, receptacles and attachment plugs shall be of the type providing for connection to the grounding conductor of the flexible cord and shall be approved for Class II locations.

(b) Class II, Division 2. In Class II, Division 2 locations, receptacles and attachment plugs shall be of the type providing for connection to the grounding conductor of the flexible cord and shall be so designed that connection to the supply circuit cannot be made or broken while live parts are exposed.

502-14. Signaling, Alarm, Remote-Control, and Communication Systems, Meters, Instruments, and Relays.

(FPN): See Article 800 for rules governing the installation of communication circuits.

(a) Class II, Division 1. In Class II, Division 1 locations, signaling, alarm, remote-control, and communication systems; and meters, instruments, and relays shall comply with the following:

(1) Wiring Methods. Where accidental damage or breakdown of insulation might cause arcs, sparks, or high temperatures, the wiring method shall be rigid metal conduit, intermediate metal conduit, electrical metallic tubing, or Type MI cable with approved termination fittings.

For rigid conduit, intermediate metal conduit, or electrical metallic tubing, the number of conductors shall be limited only by the requirement that the cross-sectional area of all conductors shall not exceed 40 percent of the area of the raceway. Where limited flexibility is desirable or where exposure to physical damage is not severe, flexible cord approved for extra-hard usage shall be permitted.

(2) Contacts. Switches, circuit breakers, relays, contactors, fuses and current-breaking contacts for bells, horns, howlers, sirens, and other devices in which sparks or arcs may be produced shall be provided with enclosures approved for a Class II location.

Exception: Where current-breaking contacts are immersed in oil, or where the interruption of current occurs within a chamber sealed against the entrance of dust, enclosures shall be permitted to be of the general-purpose type.

(3) Resistors and Similar Equipment. Resistors, transformers, choke coils, rectifiers, thermionic tubes, and other heat-generating equipment shall be provided with enclosures approved for Class II locations.

Exception: Where resistors or similar equipment are immersed in oil, or enclosed in a chamber sealed against the entrance of dust, enclosures shall be permitted to be of the general-purpose type.

(4) Rotating Machinery. Motors, generators, and other rotating electric machinery shall comply with Section 502-8(a).

(5) Combustible Electrically Conductive Dusts. Where dusts are of a combustible electrically conductive nature, all wiring and equipment shall be approved for Class II locations.

(6) Metal Dusts. Where dust from magnesium, aluminum, aluminum bronze powders, or other metals of similarly hazardous characteristics may be present, all apparatus and equipment shall be approved for the specific conditions.

(b) Class II, Division 2. In Class II, Division 2 locations, signaling, alarm, remote-control, and communication systems; and meters, instruments, and relays shall comply with the following:

(1) Contacts. Enclosures shall comply with (a)(2) above; or contacts shall have tight metal enclosures designed to minimize the entrance of dust, and shall have telescoping or tight-fitting covers and no openings through which, after installation, sparks or burning material might escape.

Exception: In circuits that under normal conditions do not release sufficient energy to ignite a dust layer, enclosures shall be permitted to be of the general-purpose type.

(2) Transformers and Similar Equipment. The windings and terminal connections of transformers, choke coils, and similar equipment shall be provided with tight metal enclosures without ventilating openings.

(3) Resistors and Similar Equipment. Resistors, resistance devices, thermionic tubes, rectifiers, and similar equipment shall comply with (a)(3) above.

Exception: Enclosures for thermionic tubes, nonadjustable resistors, or rectifiers for which maximum operating temperature will not exceed 120°C (248°F) shall be permitted to be of the general-purpose type.

(4) Rotating Machinery. Motors, generators, and other rotating electric machinery shall comply with Section 502-8(b).

(5) Wiring Methods. The wiring method shall comply with Section 502-4(b).

502-15. Live Parts, Class II, Divisions 1 and 2. Live parts shall not be exposed.

502-16. Grounding, Class II, Divisions 1 and 2. Wiring and equipment in Class II, Division 1 and 2 locations shall be grounded as specified in Article 250 and with the following additional requirements:

(a) Bonding. The locknut-bushing and double-locknut types of contact shall not be depended upon for bonding purposes but bonding jumpers with proper fittings or other approved means of bonding shall be used. Such means of bonding shall apply to all intervening raceways, fittings, boxes, enclosures, etc. between Class II locations and the point of grounding for service equipment.

(b) Types of Equipment Grounding Conductors. Where flexible conduit is used as permitted in Section 502-4 it shall be installed with internal or external bonding jumpers in parallel with each conduit and complying with Section 250-79.

Single locknuts or double locknuts and bushings are not to be depended upon for bonding purposes. Bonding jumpers or other approved means with proper fittings are required for the interconnection of all raceways, junction boxes, fittings, enclosures, etc., between the hazardous area and all the way to the grounding electrode conductor connection point at the service equipment. Where installed outside the raceway or enclosure, the grounding conductor is not to exceed 6 ft (1.83 m) and is to be routed with the raceway or enclosure. See Section 250-79.

Exception: In Class II, Division 2 areas where approved liquidtight flexible metal conduit 6 feet (1.83 m) or less in length and fittings are used and overcurrent protection in the circuit is limited to 10 amperes or less and is not a power utilization load, the additional ground jumper shall be permitted to be deleted.

502-17. Surge Protection, Class II, Divisions 1 and 2. Surge arresters, including their installation and connection shall comply with Article 280. In addition, surge arresters if installed in a Class II, Division 1 location shall be in suitable enclosures.

Surge-protective capacitors shall be of a type designed for specific duty.

ARTICLE 503 — CLASS III LOCATIONS

Contents

503-10. Flexible Cords, Class III, Divisions 1 and 2.

503-11. Receptacles and Attachment Plugs, Class III, Divisions 1 and 2.

503-12. Signaling, Alarm, Remote-Control, and Local Loudspeaker Intercommunication Systems, Class III, Divisions 1 and 2.

503-13. Electric Cranes, Hoists, and Similar Equipment, Class III, Divisions 1 and 2.

(a) Power Supply.

(b) Contact Conductors.

(c) Current Collectors.

(d) Control Equipment.

503-14. Storage-Battery Charging Equipment, Class III, Divisions 1 and 2.

503-15. Live Parts, Class III, Divisions 1 and 2.

503-16. Grounding, Class III, Divisions 1 and 2.

(a) Bonding.

(b) Types of Equipment Grounding Conductors.

503-1. General.   The general rules of this Code shall apply to electric wiring and equipment in locations classified as Class III locations in Section 500-7.

Exception: As modified by this article.

Equipment installed in Class III locations shall be able to function at full rating without developing surface temperatures high enough to cause excessive dehydration or gradual carbonization of accumulated fibers or flyings. Organic material that is carbonized or excessively dry is highly susceptible to spontaneous ignition. The maximum surface temperatures under operating conditions shall not exceed 165°C (329°F) for equipment that is not subject to overloading, and 120°C (248°F) for equipment (such as motors or power transformers) that may be overloaded.

(FPN): For electric trucks, see Powered Industrial Trucks Including Type Designations, Areas of Use, Maintenance and Operation, NFPA 505-1982 (ANSI).

Class III locations usually include textile mills (cotton, rayon, etc.) where easily ignitible fibers or combustible flyings are present in the manufacturing process. Sawmills and other woodworking plants, where sawdust, wood shavings, and combustible fibers or flyings are present, may also become hazardous. If wood flour (dust) is present, the location is a Class II, Group G location, not a Class III location.

Fibers or flyings are hazardous not only because they are easily ignited, but also because flames spread through them quickly. Such fires travel with a rapidity approaching an explosion and are commonly called flash fires.

Division 1 of Class III applies to locations where material is handled, manufactured, or used. Division 2 applies to locations where material is stored or handled, but where no manufacturing processes are performed. There are no group designations in Class III locations.

503-2. Transformers and Capacitors, Class III, Divisions 1 and 2.   Transformers and capacitors shall comply with Section 502-2(b).

503-3. Wiring Methods.   Wiring methods shall comply with (a) and (b) below.

(a) Class III, Division 1.   In Class III, Division 1 locations, the wiring method shall be rigid metal conduit, rigid nonmetallic conduit, intermediate metal conduit, electrical metallic tubing, dusttight wireways, or Type MI, MC, or SNM cable with approved termination fittings.

(1) Boxes and Fittings.   All boxes and fittings shall be dusttight.

This section was revised for the 1987 *Code*. The requirements formerly required fittings and boxes with close-fitting or telescoping-type covers for taps, joints, or terminal connections. This section now requires dusttight enclosures as defined in Article 100.

(2) Flexible Connections. Where necessary to employ flexible connections, dusttight flexible connectors, liquidtight flexible metal conduit with approved fittings, or flexible cord approved for extra-hard usage and provided with bushed fittings shall be used. An additional conductor for equipment grounding shall be provided in the flexible cord unless other approved means of equipment grounding is provided.

(b) Class III, Division 2. In Class III, Division 2 locations, the wiring method shall comply with (a) above.

Exception: In sections, compartments, or areas used solely for storage and containing no machinery, open wiring on insulators shall be permitted where installed in accordance with Article 320, but only on condition that protection as required by Section 320-14 be provided where conductors are not run in roof spaces and are well out of reach of sources of physical damage.

503-4. Switches, Circuit Breakers, Motor Controllers, and Fuses, Class III, Divisions 1 and 2. Switches, circuit breakers, motor controllers, and fuses, including pushbuttons, relays, and similar devices, shall be provided with dusttight enclosures.

See definition of "dusttight" in Article 100.

503-5. Control Transformers and Resistors, Class III, Divisions 1 and 2. Transformers, impedance coils, and resistors used as or in conjunction with control equipment for motors, generators, and appliances shall be provided with dusttight enclosures complying with the temperature limitations in Section 503-1.

See definition of "dusttight" in Article 100.

503-6. Motors and Generators, Class III, Divisions 1 and 2. In Class III, Division 1 and 2 locations, motors, generators, and other rotating machinery shall be totally enclosed nonventilated, totally enclosed pipe-ventilated, or totally enclosed fan-cooled.

Exception: In locations where, in the judgment of the authority having jurisdiction, only moderate accumulations of lint or flyings will be likely to collect on, in, or in the vicinity of a rotating electric machine, and where such machine is readily accessible for routine cleaning and maintenance, one of the following shall be permitted:

a. Self-cleaning textile motors of the squirrel-cage types;

b. Standard open-type machines without sliding contacts, centrifugal or other types of switching mechanism, including motor overload devices; or

c. Standard open-type machines having such contacts, switching mechanisms, or resistance devices enclosed within tight housings without ventilating or other openings.

It is intended that the phrase "other rotating machinery" include electric brakes. Listed and labeled electric brakes are available for Class II, Group G locations, and according to Underwriters Laboratories Inc. Hazardous Location Equipment Directory, such brakes are suitable for Class III locations.

503-7. Ventilating Piping, Class III, Divisions 1 and 2. Ventilating pipes for motors, generators, or other rotating electric machinery, or for enclosures for electric equipment shall be of metal not lighter than No. 24 MSG, or of equally substantial noncombustible material, and shall comply with the following: (1) lead directly to a source of clean air outside of buildings; (2)

be screened at the outer ends to prevent the entrance of small animals or birds; and (3) be protected against physical damage and against rusting or other corrosive influences.

Ventilating pipes shall be sufficiently tight, including their connections, to prevent the entrance of appreciable quantities of fibers or flyings into the ventilated equipment or enclosure and to prevent the escape of sparks, flame, or burning material that might ignite accumulations of fibers or flyings or combustible material in the vicinity. For metal pipes, lock seams and riveted or welded joints shall be permitted; and tight-fitting slip joints shall be permitted where some flexibility is necessary, as at connections to motors.

503-8. Utilization Equipment, Class III, Divisions 1 and 2.

(a) Heaters. Electrically heated utilization equipment shall be approved for Class III locations.

(b) Motors. Motors of motor-driven utilization equipment shall comply with Section 503-6.

(c) Switches, Circuit Breakers, Motor Controllers, and Fuses. Switches, circuit breakers, motor controllers, and fuses shall comply with Section 503-4.

503-9. Lighting Fixtures, Class III, Divisions 1 and 2.

(a) Fixed Lighting. Lighting fixtures for fixed lighting shall provide enclosures for lamps and lampholders that are designed to minimize entrance of fibers and flyings and to prevent the escape of sparks, burning material, or hot metal. Each fixture shall be clearly marked to show the maximum wattage of the lamps that shall be permitted without exceeding an exposed surface temperature of 165°C (329°F) under normal conditions of use.

(b) Physical Damage. A fixture that may be exposed to physical damage shall be protected by a suitable guard.

(c) Pendant Fixtures. Pendant fixtures shall be suspended by stems of threaded rigid metal conduit, threaded intermediate metal conduit, threaded metal tubing of equivalent thickness, or by chains with approved fittings. For stems longer than 12 inches (305 mm), permanent and effective bracing against lateral displacement shall be provided at a level not more than 12 inches (305 mm) above the lower end of the stem, or flexibility in the form of an approved fitting or a flexible connector shall be provided not more than 12 inches (305 mm) from the point of attachment to the supporting box or fitting.

(d) Portable Lighting Equipment. Portable lighting equipment shall be equipped with handles and protected with substantial guards. Lampholders shall be of the unswitched type with no provision for receiving attachment plugs. There shall be no exposed current-carrying metal parts and all exposed noncurrent-carrying metal parts shall be grounded. In all other respects, portable lighting equipment shall comply with (a) above.

503-10. Flexible Cords, Class III, Divisions 1 and 2.
Flexible cords shall comply with the following: (1) be of a type approved for extra-hard usage; (2) contain, in addition to the conductors of the circuit, a grounding conductor complying with Section 400-23; (3) be connected to terminals or to supply conductors in an approved manner; (4) be supported by clamps or other suitable means in such a manner that there will be no tension on the terminal connections; and (5) be provided with suitable means to prevent the entrance of fibers or flyings where the cord enters boxes or fittings.

503-11. Receptacles and Attachment Plugs, Class III, Divisions 1 and 2.
Receptacles and attachment plugs shall be of the grounding type and shall be so designed to minimize the accumulation or the entry of fibers or flyings, and shall prevent the escape of sparks or molten particles.

Exception: In locations where, in the judgment of the authority having jurisdiction, only moderate accumulations of lint or flyings will be likely to collect in the vicinity of a receptacle, and where such receptacle is readily accessible for routine cleaning, general-purpose grounding-type receptacles mounted so as to minimize the entry of fibers or flyings shall be permitted.

503-12. Signaling, Alarm, Remote-Control, and Local Loudspeaker Intercommunication Systems, Class III, Divisions 1 and 2.
Signaling, alarm, remote-control, and local loudspeaker intercommunication systems shall comply with the requirements of Article 503 regarding wiring methods, switches, transformers, resistors, motors, lighting fixtures, and related components.

503-13. Electric Cranes, Hoists, and Similar Equipment, Class III, Divisions 1 and 2.
Where installed for operation over combustible fibers or accumulations of flyings, traveling cranes and hoists for material handling, traveling cleaners for textile machinery, and similar equipment shall comply with (a) through (d) below.

(a) Power Supply. Power supply to contact conductors shall be isolated from all other systems and shall be equipped with an acceptable ground detector that will give an alarm and automatically de-energize the contact conductors in case of a fault to ground or will give a visual and audible alarm as long as power is supplied to the contact conductors and the ground fault remains.

(b) Contact Conductors. Contact conductors shall be so located or guarded as to be inaccessible to other than authorized persons and shall be protected against accidental contact with foreign objects.

(c) Current Collectors. Current collectors shall be so arranged or guarded as to confine normal sparking and prevent escape of sparks or hot particles. To reduce sparking, two or more separate surfaces of contact shall be provided for each contact conductor. Reliable means shall be provided to keep contact conductors and current collectors free of accumulations of lint or flyings.

(d) Control Equipment. Control equipment shall comply with Sections 503-4 and 503-5.

In a Class III location, cranes installed over accumulations of fibers or flyings and equipped with rolling or sliding collectors making contact with bare conductors introduce two hazards:

1. Any arcing between a conductor and a collector rail may ignite combustible fibers or lint accumulated on or near the bare conductor. This hazard may be prevented by maintaining the proper alignment of the bare conductor, by using a collector designed so that proper contact is always maintained, and by using guards or shields to confine hot metal particles that may be caused by arcing.

2. If enough moisture is present, fibers and flyings accumulating on the insulating supports of the bare conductors may form a conductive path between the conductors, or from one conductor to ground, thereby permitting enough current to flow to ignite the fibers. Where the system is ungrounded, a current flow to ground is unlikely to start a fire. A suitable recording ground detector will give an alarm and automatically deenergize contact conductors when the insulation resistance is lowered by an accumulation of fibers on the insulators or in case of a fault to ground. A ground-fault indicator is permitted that will maintain an alarm until the system is deenergized or the ground fault is cleared.

503-14. Storage-Battery Charging Equipment, Class III, Divisions 1 and 2.
Storage-battery charging equipment shall be located in separate rooms built or lined with substantial noncombustible materials so constructed as to adequately exclude flyings or lint and shall be well ventilated.

503-15. Live Parts, Class III, Divisions 1 and 2.
Live parts shall not be exposed.

Exception: As provided in Section 503-13.

503-16. Grounding, Class III, Divisions 1 and 2. Wiring and equipment in Class III, Divisions 1 and 2 shall be grounded as specified in Article 250 and with the following additional requirements:

(a) Bonding. The locknut-bushing and double-locknut types of contacts shall not be depended upon for bonding purposes but bonding jumpers with proper fittings or other approved means of bonding shall be used. Such means of bonding shall apply to all intervening raceways, fittings, boxes, enclosures, etc. between Class III locations and the point of grounding for service equipment.

(b) Types of Equipment Grounding Conductors. Where flexible conduit is used as permitted in Section 503-3, it shall be installed with internal or external bonding jumpers in parallel with each conduit and complying with Section 250-79.

ARTICLE 510 — HAZARDOUS (CLASSIFIED)
LOCATIONS — SPECIFIC

Contents

510-1. Scope.   510-2. General.

510-1. Scope. Articles 511 through 517 cover occupancies or parts of occupancies that are or may be hazardous because of atmospheric concentrations of flammable liquids, gases, or vapors, or because of deposits or accumulations of materials that may be readily ignitible.

510-2. General. The general rules of this Code shall apply to electric wiring and equipment in occupancies within the scope of Articles 511 through 517, except as such rules are modified in those articles. Where unusual conditions exist in a specific occupancy, the authority having jurisdiction shall judge with respect to the application of specific rules.

Information and copies of standards may be obtained from the National Fire Protection Association (NFPA), Batterymarch Park, Quincy, MA 02269.

ARTICLE 511 — COMMERCIAL GARAGES,
REPAIR AND STORAGE

Contents

723

511-5. Sealing.
511-6. Wiring in Spaces Above Class I
  Locations.
  (a) Fixed Wiring Above Class I
    Locations.
  (b) Pendants.
  (c) Grounded Conductor.
  (d) Attachment Plug Receptacles.
511-7. Equipment Above Class I
  Locations.
  (a) Arcing Equipment.

  (b) Fixed Lighting.
511-8. Battery Charging Equipment.
511-9. Electric Vehicle Charging.
  (a) Connections.
  (b) Connector Design and
    Location.
  (c) Plug Connections to Vehicles.
511-10. Ground-Fault Circuit-Inter-
    rupter Protection for
    Personnel.

511-1. Scope. These occupancies shall include locations used for service and repair operations in connection with self-propelled vehicles (including passenger automobiles, buses, trucks, tractors, etc.) in which volatile flammable liquids are used for fuel or power.

Article 100 defines a garage as "a building or portion of a building in which one or more self-propelled vehicles carrying volatile flammable liquid for fuel or power are kept for use, sale, storage, rental, repair, exhibition, or demonstrating purposes, and all that portion of a building which is on or below the floor or floors in which such vehicles are kept and which is not separated therefrom by suitable cutoffs."

A mechanical ventilating system capable of continuously providing at least six air changes per hour is required for all enclosed, basement, and underground parking garages.

Operations involving open flame or electric arcs, including fusion gas and electric welding, are required to be restricted to areas specifically provided for such purposes.

Approved suspended unit heaters may be used provided they are located not less than 8 ft (2.4 m) above the floor and are installed in accordance with the conditions of their approval. See NFPA 88B-1985, *Standard for Repair Garages*.

511-2. Locations. Areas in which flammable fuel is transferred to vehicle fuel tanks shall conform to Article 514. Parking garages used for parking or storage and where no repair work is done except exchange of parts and routine maintenance requiring no use of electrical equipment, open flame, welding, or the use of volatile flammable liquids are not classified, but they shall be adequately ventilated to carry off the exhaust fumes of the engines.

(FPN): For further information, see Parking Structures, NFPA 88A-1985, and Repair Garages, NFPA 88B-1985.

511-3. Class I Locations. Classification under Article 500.

(a) Up to a Level of 18 Inches (457 mm) Above the Floor. For each floor the entire area up to a level of 18 inches (457 mm) above the floor shall be considered to be a Class I, Division 2 location except where the enforcing agency determines that there is mechanical ventilation providing a minimum of four air changes per hour.

(b) Any Pit or Depression Below Floor Level. Any pit or depression below floor level shall be considered to be a Class I, Division 1 location which shall extend up to said floor level, except that any pit or depression in which six air changes per hour are exhausted at the floor level of the pit shall be permitted to be judged by the enforcing agency to be a Class I, Division 2 location.

(c) Areas Adjacent to Defined Locations with Positive Pressure Ventilation. Areas adjacent to defined locations in which flammable vapors are not likely to be released such as stock rooms, switchboard rooms, and other similar locations shall not be classified when mechanically ventilated at a rate of four or more air changes per hour or when effectively cut off by walls or partitions.

(d) Adjacent Areas by Special Permission. Adjacent areas which by reason of ventilation, air pressure differentials, or physical spacing are such that, in the opinion of the authority enforcing this Code, no ignition hazard exists shall be classified as nonhazardous.

(e) Fuel Dispensing Units. When fuel dispensing units (other than liquid petroleum gas which is prohibited) are located within buildings, the requirements of Article 514 shall govern.

When mechanical ventilation is provided in the dispensing area, the controls shall be interlocked so that the dispenser cannot operate without ventilation as prescribed in Section 500-5(b).

See Figures 514-1 and 514-2.

(f) Portable Lighting Equipment. Portable lighting equipment shall be equipped with handle, lampholder, hook and substantial guard attached to the lampholder or handle. All exterior surfaces which might come in contact with battery terminals, wiring terminals, or other objects shall be of nonconducting material or shall be effectively protected with insulation. Lampholders shall be of unswitched type and shall not provide means for plug-in of attachment plugs. Outer shell shall be of molded composition or other suitable material. Unless the lamp and its cord are supported or arranged in such a manner that they cannot be used in the locations classified in Section 511-3 they shall be of a type approved for Class I, Division 1 locations.

Figure 511-1. This cord, which is part of a portable lamp assembly, is required to be arranged so that the lamp cannot be used in a Class I location; otherwise, the lamp must be of a type approved for Class I, Division 1 hazardous locations (explosionproof). (*Appleton Electric Co.*)

Sections 511-3(a) and (b) classify Class I, Divisions 1 and 2 locations of commercial garages. Fuel dispensing units located within the garage are required to be governed by the requirements of Article 514.

The Class I, Division 2 location above grade within a commercial garage extends 18 in. (457 mm) above the floor level unless the authority having jurisdiction determines otherwise because there is mechanical ventilation providing at least four air changes per hour.

The Class I, Division 1 location below grade extends from the floor of the pit or depression to floor level, unless the authority having jurisdiction permits the pit or depression to be classified Class I, Division 2 because ventilation providing at least six air changes per hour exhausts air at the floor level of the pit or depression.

Figure 511-2. Classification of locations in commercial garages.

511-4. Wiring and Equipment in Class I Locations. Within Class I locations as defined in Section 511-3, wiring and equipment shall conform to applicable provisions of Article 501. Raceways embedded in a masonry wall or buried beneath a floor shall be considered to be within the Class I location above the floor if any connections or extensions lead into or through such areas.

This section applies to raceways in walls and below floors of Class I locations in commercial garages. A raceway that is in a masonry wall or buried beneath a floor may not have any connections or extensions leading into or through a Class I, Division 1 or 2 location if it is to be considered in a nonhazardous location and not subject to the provisions of Article 501. Article 501 applies to the raceway if any part of it is not imbedded in the wall, or the wall is not masonry. Article 501 applies to the raceway if any part of it is not buried beneath the floor. The floor material is not specified.

511-5. Sealing. Approved seals conforming to the requirements of Section 501-5 shall be provided, and Section 501-5(b)(2) shall apply to horizontal as well as vertical boundaries of the defined Class I locations.

Seals are required if any part of the raceway is in, or passes through, a Class I, Division 2 location. See commentary on seals with Section 501-5.

This raceway <u>is</u> considered
to be in the Class I area

These raceways are <u>not</u> considered
to be in the Class I area
(seals not required)

Figure 511-3. Raceways embedded in a masonry wall or buried beneath the floor are not considered to be in the Class I location — only if there are no extensions into the Class I location.

511-6. Wiring in Spaces Above Class I Locations.

(a) Fixed Wiring Above Class I Locations. All fixed wiring above Class I locations shall be in metallic raceways, rigid nonmetallic conduit, electrical nonmetallic tubing, or shall be Type MI, TC, SNM, or Type MC cable. Cellular metal floor raceways or cellular concrete floor raceways shall be permitted to be used only for supplying ceiling outlets or extensions to the area below the floor, but such raceways shall have no connections leading into or through any Class I location above the floor.

(b) Pendants. For pendants, flexible cord suitable for the type of service and approved for hard usage shall be used.

(c) Grounded Conductor. When a circuit which supplies portables or pendants includes a grounded conductor as provided in Article 200, receptacles, attachment plugs, connectors, and similar devices shall be of polarized type, and the grounded conductor of the flexible cord shall be connected to the screw shell of any lampholder or to the grounded terminal of any utilization equipment supplied.

(d) Attachment Plug Receptacles. Attachment plug receptacles in fixed position shall be located above the level of any defined Class I location, or be approved for the location.

511-7. Equipment Above Class I Locations.

(a) Arcing Equipment. Equipment that is less than 12 feet (3.66 m) above the floor level and that may produce arcs, sparks, or particles of hot metal, such as cutouts, switches, charging panels, generators, motors, or other equipment (excluding receptacles, lamps and lampholders) having make-and-break or sliding contacts, shall be of the totally enclosed type or so constructed as to prevent escape of sparks or hot metal particles.

(b) Fixed Lighting. Lamps and lampholders for fixed lighting that is located over lanes through which vehicles are commonly driven or that may otherwise be exposed to physical damage shall be located not less than 12 feet (3.66 m) above floor level, unless of the totally enclosed type or so constructed as to prevent escape of sparks or hot metal particles.

511-8. Battery Charging Equipment. Battery chargers and their control equipment, and batteries being charged shall not be located within locations classified in Section 511-3.

511-9. Electric Vehicle Charging.

(a) Connections. Flexible cords and connectors used for charging shall be suitable for the type of service and approved for extra-hard usage. Their ampacity shall be adequate for the charging current.

(b) Connector Design and Location. Connectors shall be so designed and installed that they will disconnect readily at any position of the charging cable, and live parts shall be guarded from accidental contact. No connector shall be located within a Class I location as defined in Section 511-3.

(c) Plug Connections to Vehicles. Where plugs are provided for direct connection to vehicles, the point of connection shall not be within a Class I location as defined in Section 511-3, and where the cord is suspended from overhead, it shall be so arranged that the lowest point of sag is at least 6 inches (152 mm) above the floor. Where the vehicle is equipped with an approved plug that will disconnect readily, and where an automatic arrangement is provided to pull both cord and plug beyond the range of physical damage, no additional connector shall be required in the cable or at the outlet.

511-10. Ground-Fault Circuit-Interrupter Protection for Personnel. All 125-volt single-phase, 15- and 20-ampere receptacles, where electrical automotive diagnostic equipment, electrical hand tools and portable lighting devices are used, shall have ground-fault circuit-interrupter protection for personnel.

> This requirement is new in the 1987 *Code*. Ground-fault circuit-interrupters (GFCIs) intended to protect personnel from shock hazards are designed to trip when a ground fault current of 5 milliamperes (±1ma) or greater is detected. Ground-fault protectors intended to protect equipment and prevent fires may trip at a much higher level. See the definition of ground-fault circuit-interrupter in Article 100 and Figures 210-14 and 210-15.
>
> The GFCI necessary to comply with this requirement may be contained within the receptacle or may be a circuit-breaker type GFCI.

ARTICLE 513 — AIRCRAFT HANGARS

Contents

(b) Lampholders.
(c) Portable Lighting Equipment.
(d) Portable Equipment.
513-6. Stanchions, Rostrums, and Docks.
(a) In Class I Location.
(b) Not in Class I Location.
(c) Mobile Type.
513-7. Sealing.
513-8. Aircraft Electrical Systems.
513-9. Aircraft Battery — Charging and Equipment.

513-10. External Power Sources for Energizing Aircraft.
(a) Not Less than 18 Inches (457 mm) Above Floor.
(b) Marking for Mobile Units.
(c) Cords.
513-11. Mobile Servicing Equipment with Electric Components.
(a) General.
(b) Cords and Connectors.
(c) Restricted Use.
513-12. Grounding.

513-1. Definition.   An aircraft hangar is a location used for storage or servicing of aircraft in which gasoline, jet fuels, or other volatile flammable liquids or flammable gases are used. It shall not include locations used exclusively for aircraft that have never contained such liquids or gases, or that have been drained and properly purged.

For further information, see NFPA 409-1985, Standard on Aircraft Hangars.

513-2. Classification of Locations.

(a) Below Floor Level.   Any pit or depression below the level of the hangar floor shall be classified as a Class I, Division 1 location that shall extend up to said floor level.

(b) Areas Not Cut Off or Ventilated.   The entire area of the hangar, including any adjacent and communicating areas not suitably cut off from the hangar, shall be classified as a Class I, Division 2 location up to a level 18 inches (457 mm) above the floor.

(c) Vicinity of Aircraft.   The area within 5 feet (1.52 m) horizontally from aircraft power plants or aircraft fuel tanks shall be classified as a Class I, Division 2 location that shall extend upward from the floor to a level 5 feet (1.52 m) above the upper surface of wings and of engine enclosures.

In order to properly classify the area in accordance with this section, it is necessary to obtain information on the aircraft parking patterns, the types of aircraft, and the operations to be performed in the hangar. See Figure 513-1.

Consideration of future changes in aircraft types and locations is appropriate to avoid the need for costly wiring and equipment changes as a result of changes in the area classification.

(d) Areas Suitably Cut Off and Ventilated.   Adjacent areas in which flammable liquids or vapors are not likely to be released, such as stock rooms, electrical control rooms, and other similar locations, shall not be classified where adequately ventilated and where effectively cut off from the hangar itself by walls or partitions.

513-3. Wiring and Equipment in Class I Locations.   All wiring and equipment that is or may be installed or operated within any of the Class I locations defined in Section 513-2 shall comply with the applicable provisions of Article 501. All wiring installed in or under the hangar floor shall comply with the requirements for Class I, Division 1 locations. Where such wiring is located in vaults, pits, or ducts, adequate drainage shall be provided; and the wiring shall not be placed within the same compartment with any service other than piped compressed air.

Attachment plugs and receptacles in Class I locations shall be approved for Class I locations or

Figure 513-1. Area classification in aircraft hangars.

shall be so designed that they cannot be energized while the connections are being made or broken.

513-4. Wiring Not Within Class I Locations.

(a) **Fixed Wiring.** All fixed wiring in a hangar, but not within a Class I location as defined in Section 513-2, shall be installed in metallic raceways or shall be Type MI, TC, SNM or Type MC cable.

Exception: Wiring in nonhazardous locations as defined in Section 513-2(d) shall be of a type recognized in Chapter 3.

(b) **Pendants.** For pendants, flexible cord suitable for the type of service and approved for hard usage shall be used. Each such cord shall include a separate grounding conductor.

(c) **Portable Equipment.** For portable utilization equipment and lamps, flexible cord suitable for the type of service and approved for extra-hard usage shall be used. Each such cord shall include a separate grounding conductor.

(d) Grounded and Grounding Conductors. Where a circuit supplies portables or pendants and includes a grounded conductor as provided in Article 200, receptacles, attachment plugs, connectors, and similar devices shall be of the polarized type, and the grounded conductor of the flexible cord shall be connected to the screw shell of any lampholder or to the grounded terminal of any utilization equipment supplied. Approved means shall be provided for maintaining continuity of the grounding conductor between the fixed raceway system and the noncurrent-carrying metal portions of pendant fixtures, portable lamps, and portable utilization equipment.

513-5. Equipment Not Within Class I Locations.

(a) Arcing Equipment. In locations other than those described in Section 513-2, equipment that is less than 10 feet (3.05 m) above wings and engine enclosures of aircraft and that may produce arcs, sparks, or particles of hot metal, such as lamps and lampholders for fixed lighting, cutouts, switches, receptacles, charging panels, generators, motors, or other equipment having make-and-break or sliding contacts, shall be of the totally enclosed type or so constructed as to prevent escape of sparks or hot metal particles.

Exception: Equipment in areas described in Section 513-2(d) shall be permitted to be of the general-purpose type.

(b) Lampholders. Lampholders of metal-shell, fiber-lined types shall not be used for fixed incandescent lighting.

(c) Portable Lighting Equipment. Portable lighting equipment that are used within a hangar shall be approved for the location in which they are used.

(d) Portable Equipment. Portable utilization equipment that is or may be used within a hangar shall be of a type suitable for use in Class I, Division 2 locations.

513-6. Stanchions, Rostrums, and Docks.

(a) In Class I Location. Electric wiring, outlets, and equipment (including lamps) on or attached to stanchions, rostrums, or docks that are located or likely to be located in a Class I location as defined in Section 513-2(c) shall comply with the requirements for Class I, Division 2 locations.

(b) Not in Class I Location. Where stanchions, rostrums, or docks are not located or likely to be located in a Class I location as defined in Section 513-2(c), wiring and equipment shall comply with Sections 513-4 and 513-5, except that such wiring and equipment not more than 18 inches (457 mm) above the floor in any position shall comply with (a) above. Receptacles and attachment plugs shall be of a locking type that will not readily disconnect.

(c) Mobile Type. Mobile stanchions with electric equipment complying with (b) above shall carry at least one permanently affixed warning sign to read: "WARNING — KEEP 5 FEET CLEAR OF AIRCRAFT ENGINES AND FUEL TANK AREAS."

513-7. Sealing.
Approved seals shall be provided in accordance with Section 501-5. Sealing requirements specified in Section 501-5(a)(4) and (b)(2) shall apply to horizontal as well as to vertical boundaries of the defined Class I locations. Raceways embedded in a masonry floor or buried beneath a floor shall be considered to be within the Class I location above the floor where any connections or extensions lead into or through such location.

513-8. Aircraft Electrical Systems.
Aircraft electrical systems shall be de-energized when the aircraft is stored in a hangar, and, whenever possible, while the aircraft is undergoing maintenance.

513-9. Aircraft Battery — Charging and Equipment. Aircraft batteries shall not be charged when installed in an aircraft located inside or partially inside a hangar.

Battery chargers and their control equipment shall not be located or operated within any of the Class I locations defined in Section 513-2, and shall preferably be located in a separate building or in an area such as defined in Section 513-2(d). Mobile chargers shall carry at least one permanently affixed warning sign to read: "WARNING — KEEP 5 FEET CLEAR OF AIRCRAFT ENGINES AND FUEL TANK AREAS." Tables, racks, trays, and wiring shall not be located within a Class I location, and, in addition, shall comply with Article 480.

513-10. External Power Sources for Energizing Aircraft.

(a) Not Less than 18 Inches (457 mm) Above Floor. Aircraft energizers shall be so designed and mounted that all electric equipment and fixed wiring will be at least 18 inches (457 mm) above floor level and shall not be operated in a Class I location as defined in Section 513-2(c).

(b) Marking for Mobile Units. Mobile energizers shall carry at least one permanently affixed warning sign to read: "WARNING — KEEP 5 FEET CLEAR OF AIRCRAFT ENGINES AND FUEL TANK AREAS."

(c) Cords. Flexible cords for aircraft energizers and ground support equipment shall be approved for the type of service and extra-hard usage and shall include an equipment grounding conductor.

513-11. Mobile Servicing Equipment with Electric Components.

(a) General. Mobile servicing equipment (such as vacuum cleaners, air compressors, air movers, etc.) having electric wiring and equipment not suitable for Class I, Division 2 locations shall be so designed and mounted that all such fixed wiring and equipment will be at least 18 inches (457 mm) above the floor. Such mobile equipment shall not be operated within the Class I location defined in Section 513-2(c) and shall carry at least one permanently affixed warning sign to read: "WARNING — KEEP 5 FEET CLEAR OF AIRCRAFT ENGINES AND FUEL TANK AREAS."

(b) Cords and Connectors. Flexible cords for mobile equipment shall be suitable for the type of service and approved for extra-hard usage, and shall include an equipment grounding conductor. Attachment plugs and receptacles shall be approved for the location in which they are installed, and shall provide for connection of the equipment grounding conductor to the raceway system.

(c) Restricted Use. Equipment that is not identified as suitable for Class I, Division 2 locations shall not be operated in locations where maintenance operations likely to release flammable liquids or vapors are in progress.

513-12. Grounding. All metal raceways and all noncurrent-carrying metal portions of fixed or portable equipment, regardless of voltage, shall be grounded as provided in Article 250.

ARTICLE 514 — GASOLINE DISPENSING
AND SERVICE STATIONS

Contents

514-1. Definition.
514-2. Class I Locations.
514-3. Wiring and Equipment Within
Class I Locations.
514-4. Wiring and Equipment Above
Class I Locations.

514-5. Circuit Disconnects.
514-6. Sealing.
  (a) At Dispenser.
  (b) At Boundary.
514-7. Grounding.
514-8. Underground Wiring.

514-1. Definition. A gasoline dispensing and service station is a location where gasoline or other volatile flammable liquids or liquefied flammable gases are transferred to the fuel tanks (including auxiliary fuel tanks) of self-propelled vehicles.

Other areas used as lubritoriums, service rooms, repair rooms, offices, salesrooms, compressor rooms, and similar locations shall comply with Articles 510 and 511 with respect to electric wiring and equipment.

Where the authority having jurisdiction can satisfactorily determine that flammable liquids having a flash point below 38°C (100°F), such as gasoline, will not be handled, such authority may classify that location as nonhazardous.

(FPN): For further information regarding safeguards for gasoline dispensing and service stations, see *Automotive and Marine Service Station Code*, NFPA 30A-1984.

514-2.[x] Class I Locations. Table 514-2 shall be applied where Class I liquids are stored, handled, or dispensed and shall be used to delineate and classify service stations. A Class I location shall not extend beyond an unpierced wall, roof, or other solid partition.

Table 514-2 is essentially the same as Table 6 in NFPA 30A-1984, *Automotive and Marine Service Station Code.*

Table 514-2[x]. Class I Locations—Service Stations

Location	Class I, Group D Division	Extent of Class I Location
Underground Tank		
Fill Opening	1	Any pit, box, or space below grade level, any part of which is within the Division 1 or 2 location.
	2	Up to 18 inches above grade level within a horizontal radius of 10 feet from a loose fill connection and within a horizontal radius of 5 feet from a tight fill connection.
Vent—Discharging Upward	1	Within 3 feet of open end of vent, extending in all directions.
	2	Space between 3 feet and 5 feet of open end of vent, extending in all directions.

Table 514-2   (Continued)

Location	Class I, Group D Division	Extent of Class I Location
Dispensing Units (except overhead type) Pits	1	Any pit, box, or space below grade level, any part of which is within the Division 1 or 2 location.
Dispenser	1	The space within a dispenser enclosure up to 4 feet vertically above the base except that space defined as Division 2. Any space within a nozzle boot.
	2	Spaces within a dispenser enclosure above the Division 1 location. Spaces within a dispenser enclosure isolated from Division 1 by a solid partition or a solid nozzle boot but not completely surrounded by Division 1 location. Within 18 inches horizontally in all directions from the Division I location located within the dispenser enclosure. Within 18 inches horizontally in all directions from the opening of a nozzle boot not isolated by a vapor-tight partition, except that the classified location need not be extended around a 90 degree or greater corner.
Outdoor	2	Up to 18 inches above grade level within 20 feet horizontally of any edge of enclosure.
Indoor with Mechanical Ventilation	2	Up to 18 inches above grade or floor level within 20 feet horizontally of any edge of enclosure.
with Gravity Ventilation	2	Up to 18 inches above grade or floor level within 25 feet horizontally of any edge of enclosure.
Dispensing Units, Overhead Type	1	Within the dispenser enclosure and 18 inches in all directions from the enclosure where not suitably cut off by ceiling or wall. All electrical equipment integral with the dispensing hose or nozzle.
	2	A space extending 2 feet horizontally in all directions beyond the Division 1 location and extending to grade below this classified location.
	2	Up to 18 inches above grade level within 20 feet horizontally measured from a point vertically below the edge of any dispenser enclosure.
Remote Pump—Outdoor	1	Any pit, box, or space below grade level if any part is within a horizontal distance of 10 feet from any edge of pump.
	2	Within 3 feet of any edge of pump, extending in all directions. Also up to 18 inches above grade level within 10 feet horizontally from any edge of pump.
Remote Pump—Indoor	1	Entire space within any pit.
	2	Within 5 feet of any edge of pump, extending in all directions. Also up to 3 feet above floor or grade level within 25 feet horizontally from any edge of pump.
Lubrication or Service Room— with Dispensing	1	Any pit within any unventilated area.
	2	Any pit with ventilation.
	2	Space up to 18 inches above floor or grade level and 3 feet horizontally from a lubrication pit.
Dispenser for Class I Liquids	2	Within 3 feet of any fill or dispensing point, extending in all directions.

Table 514-2   (Continued)

Location	Class I, Group D Division	Extent of Class I Location
Lubrication or Service Room— without Dispensing	2	Entire space within any pit used for lubrication or similar services where Class I liquids may be released.
	2	Space up to 18 inches above any such pit, and extending a distance of 3 feet horizontally from any edge of the pit.
Special Enclosure Inside Building (See NFPA 30A-1984, Automotive and Marine Service Station Code, Section 2-2)	1	Entire enclosure.
Sales, Storage and Rest Rooms	Ordinary	If there is any opening to these rooms within the extent of a Division 1 location, the entire room shall be classified as Division 1.
Vapor Processing Systems Pits	1	Any pit, box, or space below grade level, any part of which is within a Division 1 or 2 location or which houses any equipment used to transport or process vapors.
Vapor Processing Equipment Located Within Protective Enclosures	2	Within any protective enclosure housing vapor processing equipment.
Vapor Processing Equipment Not Within Protective Enclosures (excluding piping and combustion devices)	2	The space within 18 inches in all directions of equipment containing flammable vapor or liquid extending to grade level. Up to 18 inches above grade level within 10 feet horizontally of the vapor processing equipment.
Equipment Enclosures	1	Any space within the enclosure where vapor or liquid is present under normal operating conditions.
	2	The entire space within the enclosure other than Division 1.
Vacuum Assist Blowers	2	The space within 18 inches in all directions extending to grade level. Up to 18 inches above grade level within 10 feet horizontally.

For SI units: one inch = 25.4 millimeters; one foot = 0.3048 meter.

514-3. Wiring and Equipment Within Class I Locations.   All electric equipment and wiring within Class I locations defined in Section 514-2 shall comply with the applicable provisions of Article 501.

Exception: As permitted in Section 514-8.

(FPN): For special requirements for conductor insulation, see Section 501-13.

For gasoline and oil-resistant insulated conductors, see the commentary following Section 501-13.

514-4. Wiring and Equipment Above Class I Locations.   Wiring and equipment above the Class I locations defined in Section 514-2 shall comply with Sections 511-6 and 511-7.

514-5. Circuit Disconnects.   Each circuit leading to or through a dispensing pump shall be provided with a switch or other acceptable means to disconnect simultaneously from the source of supply all conductors of the circuit, including the grounded neutral, if any.

TOP VIEW

SIDE VIEW

Division 1   Division 2

Figure 514-1. Extent of Class I location around gasoline dispensing units (except overhead type).

It is important to note that all conductors of a circuit, including the grounded conductor, that may be present within a dispensing device are required to be provided with a switch or special-type circuit breaker that will simultaneously disconnect all conductors. The intent is that no energized conductors be in the dispenser vicinity during maintenance or alteration. Considering possible accidental reversal of the polarities of conductors at panelboards, the grounded conductor must be able to be switched to the open or off position. Grounded conductors may be present in old-style pump motors, or they may pass through a dispenser as part of a circuit for the island lighting.

Since a fire or large gasoline spill at the dispensing island may make it impossible to operate the switches on the dispensing island that shut off the flow of gasoline, paragraph 4-1.2 of NFPA 30A, *Automotive and Marine Service Station Code*, requires an easily accessible and clearly identified emergency power cutoff to be provided at a location remote from the dispensing device. The term "clearly identified" means that a sign is to be posted indicating where the cutoff switch is located. This emergency power cutoff should be readily accessible and not blocked

TOP VIEW

SIDE VIEW

Division 1   Division 2

Figure 514-2. Extent of Class I location around overhead gasoline dispensing units.

by the storage of such things as tires or cases of lubricating oil. All service station operators as well as responding fire fighters should know the location of the emergency power cutoff.

Figure 514-3. A gasoline dispensing installation indicating locations for sealing fittings.

Figure 514-4. Seals are required at points marked "S." Seals are not required at the sign and two lights because conduit runs do not pass through a hazardous location.

514-6. Sealing.

(a) At Dispenser. An approved seal shall be provided in each conduit run entering or leaving a dispenser or any cavities or enclosures in direct communication therewith. The sealing fitting shall be the first fitting after the conduit emerges from the earth or concrete.

(b) At Boundary. Additional seals shall be provided in accordance with Section 501-5. Section 501-5(a)(4) and (b)(2) shall apply to horizontal as well as to vertical boundaries of the defined Class I locations.

Sealing fittings are required in all conduits leaving a Class I location. All conduits passing under the boundaries of the hazardous (classified) locations [20-ft (6.1-m)

Figure 514-5. Location and permitted
use of rigid nonmetallic conduit.

radius from dispenser] or the tank fill-pipe [10-ft (3.05-m) radius from a loose fill connection and 5-ft (1.52-m) radius from a tight-fill connection] are considered as being in a Class I, Division 1 location (see Section 514-8), and the seal is to be the first fitting at the point of emergence. A seal is required to be provided in each conduit run entering or leaving a dispenser, so even though a conduit runs from dispenser to dispenser and does not leave the hazardous (classified) location, a seal is necessary when leaving and again when entering the dispenser. Panelboards are generally located in a room classified as a nonhazardous location; however, any conduit coming from the dispenser, or passing under the hazardous (classified) location boundaries from the dispenser or tank fill-pipe, would require a seal at the panelboard location. Where the panelboard is located in the lube or repair room, all conduits emerging into the 18-in. (457-mm) hazardous (classified) location would require seals. See Figures 514-3 and 514-4.

514-7. Grounding.   Metal portions of dispensing pumps, metal raceways, and all noncurrent-carrying metal parts of electric equipment, regardless of voltage, shall be grounded as provided in Article 250.

514-8. Underground Wiring.   Underground wiring shall be installed in threaded rigid metal conduit or threaded steel intermediate metal conduit. Any portion of electrical wiring or equipment which is below the surface of a Class I, Division 1 or Division 2 location (as defined in Table 514-2) shall be considered to be in a Class I, Division 1 location, which shall extend at least to the point of emergence above grade. Refer to Exception No. 3 of Section 300-5(a).

Experience has shown that the fuel spilled in the vicinity of gasoline pumps in service stations tends to accumulate underground where it can enter electrical conduits and accumulate in voids. This section, therefore, classifies the space below surface areas subject to fuel spills as Class I, Division 1 locations.

Exception No. 1: Type MI cable shall be permitted where it is installed in accordance with Article 330.

Exception No. 2: Rigid nonmetallic conduit complying with Article 347 shall be permitted when buried under not less than 2 feet (610 mm) of earth. Where rigid nonmetallic conduit is used, threaded rigid metal conduit or threaded steel intermediate metal conduit shall be used for the last 2 feet (610 mm) of the underground run to emergence or to the point of connection to the aboveground raceway; an equipment grounding conductor shall be included to provide electrical continuity of the raceway system and for grounding of noncurrent-carrying metal parts.

Exception No. 2 to Section 514-8 makes it clear that, if rigid nonmetallic conduit is used for underground wiring, threaded rigid metal conduit or threaded steel intermediate metal conduit must be used for the last 2 ft (610 mm) of the underground run to emergence or to the point of connection to the aboveground raceway. The rigid nonmetallic conduit, including rigid nonmetallic conduit elbows and fittings, is required to be located not less than 2 ft (610 mm) below grade. See Figure 514-5.

If rigid nonmetallic conduit is used, an equipment grounding conductor must be included and bonded to the explosionproof raceway system inside the dispenser. This may be accomplished by terminating the equipment grounding conductor on the ground screw provided in the junction box.

ARTICLE 515 — BULK STORAGE PLANTS

Contents

515-1. Definition. A bulk storage plant is a location where gasoline or other volatile flammable liquids are stored in tanks having an aggregate capacity of one carload or more, and from which such products are distributed (usually by tank truck).

515-2.ˣ Class I Locations. Table 515-2 shall be applied where Class I liquids are stored, handled, or dispensed and shall be used to delineate and classify bulk storage plants. The Class I location shall not extend beyond an unpierced wall, roof, or other solid partition.

> Table 515-2 is essentially the same as Table 6-5.3 in NFPA 30-1984, *Flammable and Combustible Liquids Code.*

515-3. Wiring and Equipment Within Class I Locations. All electric wiring and equipment within the Class I locations defined in Section 515-2 shall comply with the applicable provisions of Article 501.

> *Exception: As permitted in Section 515-5.*

515-4. Wiring and Equipment Above Class I Locations. All fixed wiring above Class I locations shall be in metallic raceways or be Type MI, TC, SNM, or Type MC cable. Fixed equipment that may produce arcs, sparks, or particles of hot metal, such as lamps and lampholders for fixed lighting, cutouts, switches, receptacles, motors, or other equipment having make-and-break or sliding contacts, shall be of the totally enclosed type or be so constructed as to prevent escape of sparks or hot metal particles. Portable lamps or other utilization equipment and their flexible cords shall comply with the provisions of Article 501 for the class of location above which they are connected or used.

515-5. Underground Wiring.

(a) Wiring Method. Underground wiring shall be installed in threaded rigid metal conduit, threaded steel intermediate metal conduit, or where buried under not less than 2 feet (610 mm) of earth shall be permitted in rigid nonmetallic conduit or an approved cable. Where rigid nonmetallic conduit is used, threaded rigid metal conduit or threaded steel intermediate metal conduit shall be used for the last 2 feet (610 mm) of the conduit run to emergence or to the point of connection to the aboveground raceway. Where cable is used, it shall be enclosed in rigid or threaded steel intermediate metal conduit from the point of lowest buried cable level to the point of connection to the aboveground raceway.

See commentary following Section 514-8.

Table 515-2^x. Class I Locations—Bulk Plants

Location	Class I, Group D Division	Extent of Class I Location
Tank Vehicle and Tank Car		
Loading Through Open Dome When classifying extent of space, consideration shall be given to fact that tank cars or tank vehicles may be spotted at varying points. Therefore, the extremities of the loading or unloading positions shall be used.	1	Within 3 feet of edge of dome, extending in all directions.
	2	Space between 3 feet and 15 feet from edge of dome, extending in all directions.
Loading Through Bottom Connections with Atmospheric Venting	1	Within 3 feet of point of venting to atmosphere, extending in all directions.
	2	Space between 3 feet and 15 feet from point of venting to atmosphere, extending in all directions. Also up to 18 inches above grade within a horizontal radius of 10 feet from point of loading connection.
Loading Through Closed Dome with Atmospheric Venting	1	Within 3 feet of open end of vent, extending in all directions.
	2	Space between 3 feet and 15 feet from open end of vent, extending in all directions. Also within 3 feet of edge of dome, extending in all directions.
Loading Through Closed Dome with Vapor Recovery	2	Within 3 feet of point of connection of both fill and vapor lines, extending in all directions.
Bottom Loading with Vapor Recovery or Any Bottom Unloading	2	Within 3 feet of point of connections, extending in all directions. Also up to 18 inches above grade within a horizontal radius of 10 feet from point of connection.
Pumps, Bleeders, Withdrawal Fittings, Meters and Similar Devices		
Indoors	2	Within 5 feet of any edge of such devices, extending in all directions. Also up to 3 feet above floor or grade level within 25 feet horizontally from any edge of such devices.
Outdoors	2	Within 3 feet of any edge of such devices, extending in all directions. Also up to 18 inches above grade level within 10 feet horizontally from any edge of such devices.
Storage and Repair Garage for Tank Vehicles	1	All pits or spaces below floor level.
	2	Space up to 18 inches above floor or grade level for entire storage or repair garage.
Drainage Ditches, Separators, Impounding Basins	2	Space up to 18 inches above ditch, separator, or basin. Also up to 18 inches above grade within 15 feet horizontally from any edge.

Table 515-2 (Continued)

Location	Class I, Group D Division	Extent of Class I Location
Garages for Other than Tank Vehicles	Ordinary	If there is any opening to these rooms within the extent of an outdoor Division 1 or 2 location, the entire room shall be classified the same as the area classification at the point of the opening.
Outdoor Drum Storage	Ordinary	
Indoor Warehousing Where There Is No Flammable Liquid Transfer	Ordinary	If there is any opening to these rooms within the extent of an indoor Division 1 or 2 location, the room shall be classified the same as if the wall, curb or partition did not exist.
Office and Rest Rooms	Ordinary	
Drum and Container Filling		
Outdoors, or Indoors with Adequate Ventilation	1	Within 3 feet of vent and fill opening, extending in all directions.
	2	Space between 3 feet and 5 feet from vent or fill opening, extending in all directions. Also up to 18 inches above floor or grade level within a horizontal radius of 10 feet from vent or fill opening.
Tank—Aboveground*		
Shell, Ends, or Roof and Dike Area	2	Within 10 feet from shell, ends, or roof of tank. Space inside dikes to level of top of dike.
Vent	1	Within 5 feet of open end of vent, extending in all directions.
	2	Space between 5 feet and 10 feet from open end of vent, extending in all directions.
Floating Roof	1	Space above the roof and within the shell.
Pits		
Without Mechanical Ventilation	1	Entire space within pit if any part is within a Division 1 or 2 location.
With Mechanical Ventilation	2	Entire space within pit if any part is within a Division 1 or 2 location.
Containing Valves, Fittings or Piping, and Not Within a Division 1 or 2 Location	2	Entire pit.

For SI units: one inch = 25.4 millimeters; one foot = 0.3048 meter.
* For Tanks—Underground, see Section 514-2.

(b) Insulation. Conductor insulation shall comply with Section 501-13.

(c) Nonmetallic Wiring. Where rigid nonmetallic conduit or cable with a nonmetallic sheath is used, an equipment grounding conductor shall be included to provide for electrical continuity of the raceway system and for grounding of noncurrent-carrying metal parts.

515-6. Sealing. Approved seals shall be provided in accordance with Section 501-5. Sealing requirements in Section 501-5(a)(4) and (b)(2) shall apply to horizontal as well as to vertical boundaries of the defined Class I locations. Buried raceways under defined Class I locations shall be considered to be within such locations.

Material: Flammable Liquid

Figure 515-1. Tank car/tank truck loading and unloading via closed system. Transfer through dome only.

Material: Flammable Liquid

Figure 515-2. Tank car/tank truck loading and unloading via closed system. Bottom product transfer only.

Liquid transfer line

15 ft radius

3 ft radius

Grade

Below grade location such as sump

Division 1   Division 2

Material: Flammable Liquid

Figure 515-3. Tank car/tank truck loading and unloading via open system. Top or bottom product transfer.

515-7. Gasoline Dispensing.   Where gasoline dispensing is carried on in conjunction with bulk station operations, the applicable provisions of Article 514 shall apply.

515-8. Grounding.   All metal raceways and all noncurrent-carrying metal parts of electric equipment shall be grounded as provided in Article 250.

Figure 515-4. Tank car/tank truck loading and unloading via closed system. Transfer through dome only.

Figure 515-5. Drum filling station, outdoors or indoors with adequate ventilation.

Dike height less than the distance from container to dike (H less than X)

Dike height greater than the distance from container to dike (H greater than X)

Figure 515-6. Storage tanks for cryogenic liquids. [From NFPA 59A, *Standard for the Production, Storage and Handling of Liquefied Natural Gas* (LNG)]

Material: Flammable Liquid

Figure 515-7. Storage tanks, outdoors at grade. (From API Recommended Practice 500A).

ARTICLE 516 — SPRAY APPLICATION, DIPPING AND COATING PROCESSES

Contents

ARTICLE 516—SPRAY APPLICATION, DIPPING, COATING

516-1. Scope. This article covers the regular or frequent application of flammable liquids, combustible liquids and combustible powders by spray operations and the application of flammable liquids, or combustible liquids at temperatures above their flashpoint, by dipping, coating, or other means.

(FPN): For further information regarding safeguards for these processes, such as fire protection, posting of warning signs, and maintenance, see Standard for Spray Application Using Flammable and Combustible Materials, NFPA 33-1985 (ANSI), and Standard for Dipping and Coating Processes Using Flammable or Combustible Liquids, NFPA 34-1982 (ANSI). For additional information regarding ventilation, see Blower and Exhaust Systems, Dust, Stock and Vapor Removal or Conveying, NFPA 91-1983.

516-2. Classification of Locations. Classification is based on dangerous quantities of flammable vapors, combustible mists, residues, dusts or deposits.

(a) Class I or Class II, Division 1 Locations. The following spaces shall be considered Class I or Class II, Division 1 locations as applicable.

(1)[x] The interiors of spray booths and rooms except as specifically provided in Section 516-3(d).

(2)[x] The interior of exhaust ducts.

(3)[x] Any area in the direct path of spray operations.

(4)[x] For dipping and coating operations, all space within 5 feet (1.52 m) in any direction from the vapor sources extending from these surfaces to the floor. The vapor source shall be the liquid surface in the dip tank, the wetted surface of the drain board and the surface of the dipped object over either the liquid surface or the wetted surface of the drain board and extending from these surfaces to the floor.

(5)[x] Pits within 25 feet (7.62 m) horizontally of the vapor source. If pits are in the classified area and extend beyond 25 feet (7.62 m) the Class I, Division 1 area shall include the entire pit unless a vapor stop is provided.

(b) Class I or Class II, Division 2 Locations. The following spaces shall be considered Class I or Class II, Division 2 as applicable.

(1)[x] For open spraying, all space outside of but within 20 feet (6.10 m) horizontally and 10 feet (3.05 m) vertically of the Class I, Division 1 location as defined in Section 516-2(a), and not separated from it by partitions. See Figure 1.

(2)[x] For spraying operations conducted within a closed top, open face, or front spray booth, the space shown in Figure 2, and the space within 3 feet (914 mm) in all directions from openings other than the open face or front.

The Class I or Class II, Division 2 location shown in Figure 2 shall extend from the open face or front of the spray booth in accordance with the following:

a. If the ventilation system is interlocked with the spraying equipment so as to make the spraying equipment inoperable when the ventilation system is not in operation, the space shall extend 5 feet (1.52 m) from the open face or front of the spray booth, and as otherwise shown in Figure 2A.

b. If the ventilation system is not interlocked with the spraying equipment so as to make the spraying equipment inoperable when the ventilation system is not in operation, the space

For SI units: one inch = 25.4 millimeters; one foot = 0.3048 meter.

Figure 1.ˣ Class I or Class II, Division 2 Locations Adjacent to an Unenclosed Spray Operation.

shall extend 10 feet (3.05 m) from the open face or front of the spray booth, and as otherwise shown in Figure 2B.

(3)ˣ For spraying operations conducted within an open top spray booth, the space 3 feet (914 mm) above the booth and within 3 feet (914 mm) of other booth openings shall be considered Class I or Class II, Division 2.

(4)ˣ For spraying operations confined to an enclosed spray booth or room, the space within 3 feet (914 mm) in all directions from any openings shall be considered Class I or Class II, Division 2 as shown in Figure 3.

(5)ˣ For dip tanks and drain boards, and for other hazardous operations, all space beyond the limits for Class I, Division 1 and within 8 feet (2.44 m) of the vapor source as defined in (a)(4). In addition, all space from the floor to 3 feet (914 mm) above the floor, and extending 25 feet (7.62 m) horizontally from the vapor source as defined in (a)(4) as shown in Figure 4.

(c) Adjacent Locations. Adjacent locations that are cut off from the defined Class I or Class II locations by tight partitions without communicating openings, and within which hazardous vapors or combustible powders are not likely to be released, shall be classified as nonhazardous.

(d) Nonhazardous Locations. Locations utilizing drying, curing, or fusion apparatus and provided with positive mechanical ventilation adequate to prevent accumulation of flammable concentrations of vapors, and provided with effective interlocks to de-energize all electric equipment (other than equipment approved for Class I locations) in case the ventilating

For SI units: one inch = 25.4 millimeters; one foot = 0.3048 meter.

A. When ventilation system is interlocked with spray equipment.

B. When ventilation system is not interlocked with spray equipment.

Figure 2.ˣ Class I or Class II, Division 2 Locations Adjacent to a Closed Top, Open Faced or Open Front Spray Booth.

equipment is inoperative, shall be permitted to be classified as nonhazardous where the authority having jurisdiction so judges.

(FPN): For further information regarding safeguards, see Ovens and Furnaces, Design, Location and Equipment, NFPA 86-1985 (ANSI).

516-3. Wiring and Equipment in Class I Locations.

(a) Wiring and Equipment — Vapors. All electric wiring and equipment within the Class I location (containing vapor only—not residues) defined in Section 516-2 shall comply with the applicable provisions of Article 501.

(b)ˣ Wiring and Equipment — Vapors and Residues. Unless approved for both readily ignitible deposits and the flammable vapor location, no electric equipment shall be installed or used where it may be subject to hazardous accumulations of readily ignitible deposits or residues,

Plan View

Elevation

For SI units: one inch = 25.4 millimeters; one foot = 0.3048 meter.

Figure 3.ˣ Class I or Class II, Division 2 Locations Adjacent to Openings in an Enclosed Spray Booth or Room

as the susceptibility to spontaneous heating and ignition of some residues may be greatly increased with rise in temperature. Type MI cable and wiring in threaded rigid metal conduit or threaded steel intermediate metal conduit shall be permitted to be installed in such locations.

Where readily ignitible vapors and residues are present, the only wiring methods permitted are threaded rigid metal conduit, threaded steel intermediate metal conduit, and Type MI cable.

Electric equipment and lighting fixtures approved for Class I, Division 1 locations may be installed where not subjected to readily ignitible deposits or residues.

(c) Illumination. Illumination of readily ignitible areas through panels of glass or other transparent or translucent material shall be permitted only if it complies with the following: (1) fixed lighting units are used as the source of illumination; (2) the panel effectively isolates the

For SI units: one inch = 25.4 millimeters; one foot = 0.3048 meter.

Figure 4.ˣ The Extent of Class I, Division 1 and Class I, Division 2 Hazardous (Classified) Locations for a Paint Dipping Operation.

Class I location from the area in which the lighting unit is located; (3) the lighting unit is approved for its specific location; (4) the panel is of a material or is so protected that breakage will be unlikely; and (5) the arrangement is such that normal accumulations of hazardous residue on the surface of the panel will not be raised to a dangerous temperature by radiation or conduction from the source of illumination.

Underwriters Laboratories Inc. Hazardous Locations Equipment Directory indicates that UL-listed fixtures suitable for use in hazardous (classified) locations having deposits of readily combustible paint residue are so marked.

(d)ˣ Portable Equipment. Portable electric lamps or other utilization equipment shall not be used in a spray area during spray operations.

Exception No. 1: Where portable electric lamps are required for operations in spaces not readily illuminated by fixed lighting within the spraying area, they shall be of the type approved for Class I, Division 1 locations where readily ignitible residues may be present.

Exception No. 2: Where portable electric drying apparatus are used in automobile refinishing spray booths and the following requirements are met: (1) the apparatus and its electrical connections are not located within the spray enclosure during spray operations; (2) electrical equipment within 18 inches (45.7 cm) of the floor is approved for Class I, Division 2 locations; (3) all metallic parts of the drying apparatus are electrically bonded and grounded; and (4) interlocks are provided to prevent the operation of spray equipment while drying apparatus is within the spray enclosure, to allow for a 3-minute purge of the enclosure before energizing the drying apparatus and to shut off drying apparatus on failure of ventilation system.

(e) Electrostatic Equipment. Electrostatic spraying or detearing equipment shall be installed and used only as provided in Section 516-4.

(FPN): For further information, see Standard for Spray Application Using Flammable and Combustible Materials, NFPA 33-1985 (ANSI).

516-4.ˣ Fixed Electrostatic Equipment. This section shall apply to any equipment using electrostatically charged elements for the atomization, charging, and/or precipitation of hazardous materials for coatings on articles or for other similar purposes in which the charging or atomizing device is attached to a mechanical support and is not hand held or manipulated. Where fixed electrostatic spraying and detearing equipment is installed, such equipment shall be of an approved type and shall comply with (a) through (h) below.

(a) Power and Control Equipment. Transformers, power packs, control apparatus, and all other electric portions of the equipment shall be installed outside of the Class I location as defined in Section 516-2 or be of a type approved for the location.

Exception: High-voltage grids, electrodes, electrostatic atomizing heads, and their connections shall be permitted within the Class I location.

(b) Electrostatic Equipment. Electrodes and electrostatic atomizing heads shall be: (1) located in suitable areas provided with adequate mechanical ventilation; (2) adequately supported in permanent locations; and (3) effectively insulated from ground. Electrodes and electrostatic atomizing heads that are permanently attached to their bases, supports, or reciprocators shall be considered as complying with this section. Insulators shall be nonporous.

Fine-wire elements, where used, shall be under tension at all times and be of unkinked hardened steel or material of comparable strength.

(c) High-Voltage Leads. High-voltage leads shall be properly insulated and protected from mechanical injury or exposure to destructive chemicals. Any exposed element at high voltage shall be effectively and permanently supported on suitable insulators and shall be effectively guarded against accidental contact or grounding. An automatic means shall be provided for grounding the electrode system when the primary of its high-voltage supply is electrically de-energized for any reason.

(d) Separation of Goods from Electrostatic Equipment. A safe distance of at least twice the sparking distance shall be maintained between goods being painted and electrodes or electrostatic atomizing heads or conductors. A suitable sign indicating this safe distance shall be conspicuously posted near the assembly.

(e) Support of Goods. Goods being coated or deteared shall be supported on conveyors or hangers. The conveyors or hangers shall be so arranged as to assure that the parts being coated or deteared are electrically connected to ground with a resistance of 1 megohm or less, and to maintain safe distances between goods and the electrodes or electrostatic atomizing heads at all times. Goods shall be supported to prevent such swinging or movement which would reduce the clearance to less than that specified in (d) above.

(f) Automatic Controls. Electrostatic apparatus shall be equipped with automatic means which will rapidly de-energize the high-voltage elements under any of the following conditions: (1) stoppage of ventilating fans or failure of ventilating equipment from any cause; (2) stoppage of the conveyor carrying goods through the high-voltage field; (3) occurrence of a ground or excessive current leakage at any point in the high-voltage system; (4) de-energizing of the high voltage supply; (5) reduction of clearances below that specified in (d) above.

(g) Grounding. All electrically conductive objects within the charging influence of the electrodes except those required by the process to be at high voltage shall be adequately grounded. This requirement shall apply to paint containers, wash cans, guards, and any other electrically conductive objects or devices in the area. The equipment shall carry a prominent permanently installed warning regarding the necessity for grounding these objects.

(h) Isolation. Safeguards such as adequate booths, fencing, railings or other means shall be placed about the equipment so that they, either by their location or character, or both, assure that a safe isolation of the process is maintained from plant storage or personnel.

516-5.ˣ Electrostatic Hand-Spraying Equipment. This section shall apply to any equipment using electrostatically charged elements for the atomization, charging, and/or precipitation of materials for coatings on articles, or for other similar purposes in which the atomizing device is hand held or manipulated during the spraying operation. Electrostatic hand-spraying equipment and devices used in connection with paint-spraying operations shall be of approved types and shall comply with (a) through (e) below.

(a) General. The high-voltage circuits shall be designed so as not to produce a spark of sufficient intensity to ignite the most readily ignitible of those vapor-air mixtures likely to be encountered, nor result in appreciable shock hazard upon coming in contact with a grounded object under all normal operating conditions. The electrostatically charged exposed elements of the hand gun shall be capable of being energized only by an actuator which also controls the coating material supply.

(b) Power Equipment. Transformers, power packs, control apparatus, and all other electric portions of the equipment shall be located outside of the Class I location or be approved for the location.

Exception: The hand gun itself and its connections to the power supply shall be permitted within the Class I location.

(c) Handle. The handle of the spraying gun shall be electrically connected to ground by a metallic connection and be so constructed that the operator in normal operating position is in intimate electrical contact with the grounded handle to prevent buildup of a static charge on the operator's body. Signs indicating the necessity for grounding other persons entering the spray area shall be conspicuously posted.

(d) Electrostatic Equipment. All electrically conductive objects in the spraying area shall be adequately grounded. This requirement shall apply to paint containers, wash cans, and any other electrically conductive objects or devices in the area. The equipment shall carry a prominent, permanently installed warning regarding the necessity for this grounding feature.

(e) Support of Objects. Objects being painted shall be maintained in metallic contact with the conveyor or other grounded support. Hooks shall be regularly cleaned to ensure adequate grounding of 1 megohm or less. Areas of contact shall be sharp points or knife edges where possible. Points of support of the object shall be concealed from random spray where feasible; and where the objects being sprayed are supported from a conveyor, the point of attachment to the conveyor shall be so located as to not collect spray material during normal operation.

516-6.ˣ Powder Coating. This section shall apply to processes in which combustible dry powders are applied. The hazards associated with combustible dusts are present in such a process to a degree, depending upon the chemical composition of the material, particle size, shape, and distribution.

(FPN): The hazards associated with combustible dusts are inherent in this process. Generally speaking, the hazard rating of the powders employed is dependent upon the chemical composition of the material, particle size, shape, and distribution.

(a) Electric Equipment and Sources of Ignition. Electric equipment and other sources of ignition shall comply with the requirements of Article 502. Portable electric lamps and other utilization equipment shall not be used within a Class II location during operation of the finishing processes. When such lamps or utilization equipment are used during cleaning or repairing operations, they shall be of a type approved for Class II, Division 1 locations, and all exposed metal parts shall be effectively grounded.

Exception: Where portable electric lamps are required for operations in spaces not readily illuminated by fixed lighting within the spraying area, they shall be of the type approved for Class II, Division 1 locations where readily ignitible residues may be present.

(b) Fixed Electrostatic Spraying Equipment. The provisions of Sections 516-4 and (a) above shall apply to fixed electrostatic spraying equipment.

(c) Electrostatic Hand-Spraying Equipment. The provisions of Sections 516-5 and (a) above shall apply to electrostatic hand-spraying equipment.

(d) Electrostatic Fluidized Beds. Electrostatic fluidized beds and associated equipment shall be of approved types. The high-voltage circuits shall be so designed that any discharge produced when the charging electrodes of the bed are approached or contacted by a grounded object shall not be of sufficient intensity to ignite any powder-air mixture likely to be encountered nor to result in an appreciable shock hazard.

(1) Transformers, power packs, control apparatus, and all other electric portions of the equipment shall be located outside the powder-coating area or shall otherwise comply with the requirements of (a) above.

Exception: The charging electrodes and their connections to the power supply shall be permitted within the powder-coating area.

(2) All electrically conductive objects within the powder-coating area shall be adequately grounded. The powder-coating equipment shall carry a prominent, permanently installed warning regarding the necessity for grounding these objects.

(3) Objects being coated shall be maintained in electrical contact (less than 1 megohm) with the conveyor or other support in order to ensure proper grounding. Hangers shall be regularly cleaned to ensure effective electrical contact. Areas of electrical contact shall be sharp points or knife edges where possible.

(4) The electric equipment and compressed-air supplies shall be interlocked with a ventilation system so that the equipment cannot be operated unless the ventilating fans are in operation.

516-7. Wiring and Equipment Above Class I and II Locations.

(a) Wiring. All fixed wiring above the Class I and II locations shall be in metal raceways, rigid nonmetallic conduit, electrical nonmetallic tubing, or shall be Type MI, TC, SNM, or Type MC cable. Cellular metal floor raceways shall be permitted only for supplying ceiling outlets or extensions to the area below the floor of a Class I or II location, but such raceways shall have no connections leading into or through the Class I or II location above the floor unless suitable seals are provided.

(b) Equipment. Equipment that may produce arcs, sparks, or particles of hot metal, such as lamps and lampholders for fixed lighting, cutouts, switches, receptacles, motors, or other equipment having make-and-break or sliding contacts, where installed above a Class I or II location or above a location where freshly finished goods are handled, shall be of the totally enclosed type or be so constructed as to prevent escape of sparks or hot metal particles.

516-8. Grounding. All metal raceways and all noncurrent-carrying metal parts of fixed or portable equipment, regardless of voltage, shall be grounded as provided in Article 250.

> NFPA 33-1985, *Standard for Spray Application Using Flammable and Combustible Materials*, covers the application of flammable or combustible materials as a spray by compressed air, "airless" or "hydraulic atomization," or by steam, electrostatic methods, or any other means in continuous or intermittent processes. It also covers the application of combustible powders when applied by powder spray guns, electrostatic powder spray guns, and fluidized beds or electrostatic fluidized beds.
>
> NFPA 33 outlines the requirements for the maintenance of safe conditions.
>
> The proper maintenance and operation of processes and process areas where flammable and combustible materials are handled and applied is critical with respect to the protection of life and property from fire or explosion.
>
> It has been shown that the largest fire losses and frequency of fires have occurred where the proper application of codes and standards has not been used.
>
> *Spray Area*: Any area in which dangerous quantities of flammable or combustible vapors, mists, residues, dusts, or deposits are present due to the operation of spray processes.
>
> A spray area shall include:
>
> (a) The interior of spray booths and rooms (with certain exceptions).
>
> (b) The interior of ducts exhausting from spraying processes.
>
> (c) Any area in the direct path of spraying operations.
>
> The authority having jurisdiction may, for the purpose of NFPA 33, define the limits of the spray area in any specific case. The "spray area" in the vicinity of spraying operations will necessarily vary with the design and arrangement of equipment and method of operation. When spraying operations are strictly confined to predetermined spaces which are provided with adequate and reliable ventilation, such as a properly constructed spray booth, the "spray area" will ordinarily not extend beyond the booth enclosure. When, however, spraying operations are not confined to adequately ventilated spaces, the "spray area" may extend throughout the entire room containing spraying operations.

Spray Booth: A power-ventilated structure provided to enclose or accommodate a spraying operation, to confine and limit the escape of spray, vapor, and residue, and to safely conduct or direct them to an exhaust system. Spray booths are manufactured in a variety of forms, including automotive refinishing, downdraft, open-face, traveling, tunnel, and updraft booths.

Spray Room: A power-ventilated, fully enclosed room used exclusively for open spraying of flammable or combustible materials. The entire spray room is a spray area. A spray booth is not a spray room.

Waterwash Spray Booth: A spray booth equipped with a water washing system designed to minimize dusts or residues entering exhaust ducts and to permit the recovery of overspray finishing material.

Dry Spray Booth: A spray booth not equipped with a water washing system. A dry spray booth may be equipped with (1) distribution or baffle plates to promote an even flow of air through the booth or cause deposit of overspray before it enters exhaust duct; (2) overspray dry filters to minimize dusts or residues entering exhaust ducts; (3) overspray dry filter rolls designed to minimize dusts or residues entering exhaust ducts; or (4) where dry powders are being sprayed, with powder collection systems so arranged in the exhaust to capture oversprayed material.

Notes on Electrical Installations:

The safety of life and property from fire or explosion as a result of spray applications of flammable and combustible paints and finishes varies depending upon the arrangement and operation of a particular installation.

The principal hazards of spray application operations originate from flammable or combustible liquids or powders and their vapors or mists as well as from highly combustible residues or powders.

Properly constructed spray booths, with adequate mechanical ventilation, may be used to discharge vapors or powder to a safe location and reduce the possibility of an explosion. In like manner, the accumulation of overspray residues, many of which are not only highly combustible but also subject to spontaneous ignition, can be controlled.

The elimination of all sources of ignition in areas where flammable or combustible liquids, vapors, mists, or combustible residues are present, together with constant supervision and maintenance, is essential to the safe operation of spraying.

The human element necessitates careful consideration of the location of the operation and the installation of extinguishing equipment in order to reduce the possibility of fire spreading to other property and minimize the probability of damage to other property.

It is obvious that there should be no open flames or spark-producing equipment in any area where, because of inadequate ventilation, explosive vapor-air mixtures or mists are present. It is equally obvious that no open flames or spark-producing equipment should be located where highly combustible spray residues will be deposited on them. Because some residues may be ignited at very low temperatures, additional consideration must be given to operating temperatures of equipment subject to residue deposits. Many deposits may be ignited at temperatures produced by low-pressure steam pipes or by incandescent light globes, even those of explosionproof types.

It should be noted that electrical equipment is generally not permitted inside any spray booth, in the exhaust duct from a spray booth, in the entrained air of an exhaust system from a spraying operation, or in the direct path of spray, unless such equipment is specifically listed for both readily ignitible deposits and flammable vapor.

The determination of the extent of hazardous areas involved in spray application requires an understanding of the dual hazards of flammable vapors, mists, or powders, and highly combustible deposits applied to each individual installation.

757

When electrical equipment is installed in locations not subject to deposits of combustible residues but, due to inadequate ventilation, is subject to explosive concentrations of flammable vapors or mists, only approved explosionproof or other types of equipment approved for Class I, Division 1 locations (for example, purged and pressurized or intrinsically safe equipment or systems) are permitted.

When spraying areas containing dangerous quantities of flammable or combustible vapors, mists, residues, dusts, or deposits under normal operation have been determined, the adjacent unpartitioned areas, which are safe under normal operating conditions, but which may become dangerous due to accident or careless operation, should be given consideration. Equipment known to produce sparks or flames under normal operating conditions should not be installed in these adjacent unpartitioned areas.

When spraying operations are confined to adequately ventilated spray booths or rooms, there should be no deposits of combustible residues or dangerous concentrations of flammable vapors, mists, or dusts outside the spray booth under normal operating conditions.

In the interest of safety, however, it should be noted that, unless separated by partitions, an area within a certain distance [see Section 516-2(b)] of the Class I (or II), Division 1 spraying area, depending upon the arrangement, is classified as Division 2; that is, it should contain no equipment that produces ignition-capable sparks under normal operation. Furthermore, within this distance, electric lamps are required to be enclosed to prevent hot particles from falling on freshly painted stock or other readily ignitible material and, if subject to physical damage, are required to be properly guarded. See Section 516-7(b).

Even though it is contemplated that areas adjacent to spray booths (particularly where coating material stocks are located) will be provided with ventilation sufficient to prevent the presence of flammable vapors or deposits, it is nevertheless advisable that electric lamps be totally enclosed to prevent the falling of hot particles in any area where there may be freshly painted stock, accidentally spilled flammable or combustible materials, readily ignitible refuse, or flammable or combustible liquid containers accidentally left open. See Section 516-7(b).

Where electric lamps are in areas subject to atmospheres of flammable vapor, lamps should be replaced when electricity is off; otherwise there may be a spark from this source.

Sufficient lighting for coating operations, booth cleaning, and booth repair work should be provided at the time the equipment is installed in order to avoid the use of "temporary" or "emergency" lamps connected to ordinary extension cords in this area. See Section 516-3(d). A satisfactory and practical method of lighting is the use of ¼-in. thick wired or tempered glass panels in the top or sides of the spray booth with electrical light fixtures outside the booth, hence not in the direct path of the spray. See Section 516-3(c).

In order to prevent sparks from the accumulation of static electricity, all electrically conductive objects, including metal parts of spray booths, exhaust ducts, piping systems conveying flammable or combustible liquids or paint, solvent tanks, and canisters should be properly grounded. See paragraph 4-9.1 of NFPA 33.

Automobile undercoating operations in garages, conducted in areas having adequate natural or mechanical ventilation, are exempt from the requirements pertaining to spray-coating operations when (1) undercoating materials not more hazardous than kerosene (as classified by Underwriters Laboratories Inc. with respect to fire hazard rating 30-40) are used, or (2) undercoating materials using only solvents having a flash point in excess of 38°C (100°F) are used, and (3) no open flames are within 20 ft (6.1 m) while such operations are conducted.

ARTICLE 517 — HEALTH CARE FACILITIES

Contents

A. General

517-1. Scope.

The provisions of this article shall apply to electrical construction and installation criteria in health care facilities.

(FPN): This article is not intended to apply to veterinary facilities.

(FPN): For information concerning performance, maintenance and testing criteria refer to the appropriate health care facilities documents.

The requirements of this article are intended to apply to all types of health care facilities. The requirements for each type of health care facility are nevertheless intended to be applied in a very specific manner. An example of the application of this article could be a suite of doctors' offices within a hospital. The doctor's business office would be treated as an ordinary occupancy and would be required to meet the applicable portion of the balance of this *Code*, including the requirement in Section 328-5(4). The examining rooms attached to the doctor's business office would be required to meet the provisions of Part C of Article 517, and a nearby X-ray unit, whether operated by a group of doctors or the hospital itself, would be required to meet the provisions of Part K of Article 517.

The scope also includes health care facilities that may be mobile or supply very limited outpatient services. However, the scope does not include animal hospitals.

Other standards referenced in this article are *Standard for Health Care Facilities*, NFPA 99-1984; *Life Safety Code®*, NFPA 101®-1985; *Standard for the Installation of Centrifugal Fire Pumps*, NFPA 20-1983; and *Standard for Nonflammable Medical Gas Systems*, NFPA 56F-1983.

517-2. Definitions.

Alternate Power Source. One or more generator sets, or battery systems where permitted, intended to provide power during the interruption of the normal electrical services or the public utility electrical service intended to provide power during interruption of service normally provided by the generating facilities on the premises.

Anesthetizing Location. Any area of a health care facility which has been designated to be used for the administration of any flammable or nonflammable inhalation anesthetic agent in the course of examination or treatment including the use of such agents for relative analgesia.

This definition recognizes that in an emergency it may be necessary to administer an anesthetic almost anywhere in a health care facility; however, only those areas in a health care facility set aside by intent for the induction of anesthetics are required to meet the provisions of Part G of Article 517. This definition, as well as the provisions of Part G, is not intended to apply to the administration of analgesic anesthetics such as might be employed in a dental office.

Critical Branch. A subsystem of the emergency system consisting of feeders and branch circuits supplying energy to task illumination, special power circuits, and selected receptacles serving areas and functions related to patient care, and which are connected to alternate power sources by one or more transfer switches during interruption of the normal power source.

Electrical Life Support Equipment. Electrically powered equipment whose continuous operation is necessary to maintain a patient's life.

Emergency System. A system of feeders and branch circuits meeting the requirements of Article 700, and intended to supply alternate power to a limited number of prescribed functions

761

vital to the protection of life and patient safety, with automatic restoration of electrical power within 10 seconds of power interruption.

Equipment System. A system of feeders and branch circuits arranged for delayed, automatic or manual connection to the alternate power source and which serves primarily 3-phase power equipment.

Essential Electrical System. A system comprised of alternate sources of power and all connected distribution systems and ancillary equipment, designed to assure continuity of electrical power to designated areas and functions of a health care facility during disruption of normal power sources, and also designed to minimize disruption within the internal wiring system.

Exposed Conductive Surfaces. Those surfaces which are capable of carrying electric current and which are unprotected, unenclosed, or unguarded, permitting personal contact. Paint, anodizing, and similar coatings are not considered suitable insulation, unless they are listed for the use.

This definition is intended to clarify the requirements of Section 517-81. Specifically, it points out that the mere application of paint or similar coatings does not necessarily render a metallic surface nonconductive. Under the terms of this definition, the coating material must be listed as an electrical insulating medium. See definition of "listed" in Article 100.

Flammable Anesthetics. Gases or vapors such as fluroxene, cyclopropane, divinyl ether, ethyl chloride, ethyl ether, and ethylene, which may form flammable or explosive mixtures with air, oxygen, or reducing gases such as nitrous oxide.

Flammable Anesthetizing Location. Any area of the facility which has been designated to be used for the administration of any flammable inhalation anesthetic agents in the normal course of examination or treatment.

Hazard Current. For a given set of connections in an isolated power system, the total current that would flow through a low impedance if it were connected between either isolated conductor and ground.
    FAULT HAZARD CURRENT: The hazard current of a given isolated system with all devices connected except the line isolation monitor.
    MONITOR HAZARD CURRENT: The hazard current of the line isolation monitor alone.
    TOTAL HAZARD CURRENT: The hazard current of a given isolated system with all devices, including the line isolation monitor, connected.

Health Care Facilities. Buildings or parts of buildings that contain but are not limited to occupancies such as: hospitals, nursing homes, residential custodial care facilities, supervisory care facilities, clinics, medical and dental offices, and ambulatory health care facilities, whether fixed or mobile.

Hospital. A building or part thereof used for the medical, psychiatric, obstetrical or surgical care, on a 24-hour basis, of four or more inpatients. Hospital, wherever used in this Code, shall include general hospitals, mental hospitals, tuberculosis hospitals, children's hospitals, and any such facilities providing inpatient care.

Isolated Power System. A system comprising an isolating transformer or its equivalent, a line isolation monitor, and its ungrounded circuit conductors.

Isolation Transformer. A transformer of the multiple-winding type, with the primary and secondary windings physically separated, which inductively couples its secondary winding to the grounded feeder systems that energize its primary winding.

Life Safety Branch. A subsystem of the emergency system consisting of feeders and branch circuits, meeting the requirements of Article 700 and intended to provide adequate power needs to ensure safety to patients and personnel, and which are automatically connected to alternate power sources during interruption of the normal power source.

Line Isolation Monitor. A test instrument designed to continually check the balanced and unbalanced impedance from each line of an isolated circuit to ground and equipped with a built-in test circuit to exercise the alarm without adding to the leakage current hazard.

(FPN): "Line isolation monitor" was formerly known as "ground contact indicator."

Nursing Home. A building or part thereof used for the lodging, boarding and nursing care, on a 24-hour basis, of four or more persons who, because of mental or physical incapacity, may be unable to provide for their own needs and safety without the assistance of another person. Nursing home, wherever used in this Code, shall include nursing and convalescent homes, skilled nursing facilities, intermediate care facilities, and infirmaries of homes for the aged.

Nurses' Stations. Areas intended to provide a center of nursing activity for a group of nurses serving bed patients, where the patient calls are received, nurses are dispatched, nurses' notes written, inpatient charts prepared, and medications prepared for distribution to patients. Where such activities are carried on in more than one location within a nursing unit, all such separate areas are considered a part of the nurses' station.

Patient Equipment Grounding Point. A jack or terminal bus which serves as the collection point for redundant grounding of electric appliances serving a patient vicinity or for grounding other items in order to eliminate electromagnetic interference problems.

Patient Vicinity. In an area in which patients are normally cared for, the patient vicinity is the space with surfaces likely to be contacted by the patient or an attendant who can touch the patient. Typically in a patient room, this encloses a space within the room not less than 6 feet (1.83 m) beyond the perimeter of the bed in its nominal location, and extending vertically not less than 7½ feet (2.29 m) above the floor.

> This area is limited to patients in bed. It is also limited to the bed in its nominal position, that is, the position of the bed as called for in the architect's plans, rather than the position of the bed as it may be found in daily use subject to movement by housekeeping staff or the convenience of the medical staff. It is not intended that a "halo" of electrical hazard follow the bed as it is moved about the room or the health care facility.
>
> Definitions for hospital, nursing home, and residential custodial care facility are all identical to the same definitions as employed in NFPA *101, Life Safety Code.*

Psychiatric Hospital. A building used exclusively for the psychiatric care, on a 24-hour basis, of four or more inpatients.

Reference Grounding Point. A terminal bus which is the equipment grounding bus or an extension of the equipment grounding bus and is a convenient collection point for installed grounding wires or other bonding wires where used.

Residential Custodial Care Facility. A building, or part thereof, used for the lodging or boarding of four or more persons who may be incapable of self-preservation because of age, or physical or mental limitation. This includes facilities such as homes for the aged, nurseries (custodial care for children under 6 years of age), and mentally retarded care institutions. Day care facilities that do not provide lodging or boarding for institutional occupants are not classified as residential custodial care facilities.

Room Bonding Point. A grounding terminal or group of terminals which serves as a collection point for grounding exposed metal or conductive building surfaces in a room.

Selected Receptacles. A minimum number of electrical receptacles to accommodate appliances ordinarily required for local tasks or likely to be used in patient care emergencies.

Task Illumination. Provision for the minimum lighting required to carry out necessary tasks in the described areas, including safe access to supplies and equipment, and access to exits.

Therapeutic High-Frequency Diathermy Equipment. Therapeutic high-frequency diathermy equipment is therapeutic induction and dielectric heating equipment.

Wet Location, Health Care Facility. A patient care area that is normally subject to wet conditions, including standing water on the floor, or routine dousing or drenching of the work area. Routine housekeeping procedures and incidental spillage of liquids do not define a wet location.

This definition excludes such areas as laundry rooms, boiler rooms, and utility areas which, although routinely wet, are not patient care areas. The governing body of the health care facility may elect to include under this definition such areas as hydrotherapy areas, dialysis laboratories, and certain wet laboratories. Lavatories or bathrooms within a health care facility are not intended to be classified as a wet location.

517-3. General. The requirements in Parts C, D, and E apply not only to single-function buildings, but are also intended to be individually applied to their respective forms of occupancy within a multifunction building (i.e., a doctor's examining room located within a residential custodial care facility would be required to meet the provisions of Part C).

B. Wiring Systems — General

517-6. Applicability. Part B shall apply to all health care facilities. Installations in facilities which provide patient care, equipment or services identified in other parts of this article shall also comply with the requirements of that part.

517-10. Wiring Methods. Except as modified in this article, wiring methods shall comply with the applicable requirements of Chapters 1 through 4 of this Code.

517-11. Grounding of Receptacles and Fixed Electrical Equipment. In areas used for patient care, the grounding terminals of all receptacles and all noncurrent-carrying conductive surfaces of fixed electrical equipment likely to become energized that are subject to personal contact, operating at over 100 volts, shall be grounded by an insulated copper conductor. The grounding conductor shall be sized in accordance with Table 250-95 and installed in metal raceways with the branch-circuit conductors supplying these receptacles or fixed equipment.

Exception No. 1: Metal raceways are not required where Type MC cable, Type MI cable, or Type AC cable with an insulated grounding conductor is used.

Exception No. 2: Metal faceplates shall be permitted to be grounded by means of a metal mounting screw(s) securing the faceplate to a grounded outlet box or grounded wiring device.

Exception No. 3: An equipment grounding conductor enclosed in the sheath of a nonmetallic-sheathed cable assembly installed in accordance with the limitations of Sections 336-2, 336-3, and 336-4 shall be permitted to be used in accordance with Parts C and D of this article.

This rule applies to any area used for patient care and is not limited to patient rooms. Additional areas, such as therapy areas, recreational areas, solaria, and certain patient corridors, would also be included. It should be clearly understood that this section requires grounding by means of a copper conductor, usually insulated, installed with the branch-circuit conductors. The conductor can be either solid or stranded. A separate insulated equipment grounding conductor is not required to be run upstream from the branch-circuit panelboard with the feeder conductors in a metal raceway.

Exception No. 1 permits metal-sheathed cables with an insulated grounding conductor.

Exception No. 2 permits metal faceplates to be grounded by means of the metal mounting screws rather than having a separate equipment grounding conductor run to the metal plate.

Exception No. 3 recognizes that a copper equipment grounding conductor (covered or bare) enclosed in the sheath of Type NM or NMC cable in accordance with the provisions of this exception is permitted in lieu of a separate insulated grounding conductor. However, Section 517-81 does not permit nonmetallic-sheathed cable in patient care areas, so the exception has little, if any, application. See Section 517-43, Exception.

This rule differs from the general grounding rule for such equipment under Section 250-45 in that not just specific items, but all cord- and plug-connected equipment (over 100 V) is covered.

517-13. Receptacles with Insulated Grounding Terminals. Receptacles with insulated grounding terminals as permitted in Section 250-74, Exception No. 4, shall be identified; such identification shall be visible after installation.

(FPN): Care is important in specifying such a system with receptacle insulated grounds since the grounding impedance is controlled only by the grounding wires and does not benefit functionally from any parallel grounding paths.

This section prevents the indiscriminate use of such devices, and the compromising of the potential difference requirements within critical care areas.

Proper identification may be by color-coding the receptacle orange or by other approved means.

517-14. Ground-Fault Protection.

(a) Feeders. When ground-fault protection is provided for operation of the service disconnecting means, an additional step of ground-fault protection shall be provided in the next level of feeder downstream toward the load. Such protection shall consist of overcurrent devices and current transformers or other equivalent protective equipment which shall cause the feeder disconnecting devices to open.

(b) Selectivity. Ground-fault protection for operation of the service and feeder disconnecting means shall be fully selective such that the feeder device and not the service device shall open on ground faults on the load side of the feeder device. A six-cycle minimum separation between the service and feeder ground-fault tripping bands shall be provided. Operating time of the disconnecting devices shall be considered in selecting the time spread between these two bands to achieve 100 percent selectivity.

(FPN): See Section 230-95, Fine Print Note, for transfer of alternate source where ground-fault protection is applied.

Wherever ground-fault protective (GFP) equipment is applied to the service providing power to a health care facility, whether by design or by reason of the requirements of Section 230-95, an additional level of ground-fault protection is required downstream. Under this rule, ground-fault protection is required to be applied to every feeder, and additional ground-fault protective devices may be applied farther downstream at the option of the governing body of the health care facility. With proper coordination, this additional ground-fault protection is intended to limit a ground fault to a single feeder and thereby prevent a total outage of the entire health care system. Coordination includes consideration of the trip setting, the time setting, and the time required for operation (opening time) of each level of the GFP system.

However, when a health care installation, such as a doctor's office, is a part of a larger general-use facility (for example, a business office building) that has service ground-fault protection in accordance with Section 230-95, it is not intended that ground-fault protection be required on the health care facility (doctor's office) feeder since no additional protection will be achieved insofar as the doctor's office is concerned.

The last fine print note to Section 230-95(b) calls attention to problems that may arise when ground-fault protected systems are transferred to another supply system.

(c) Testing. When equipment ground-fault protection is first installed, each level shall be performance tested to ensure compliance with (b) above.

See Section 230-95(c) and its commentary.

C. Clinics, Medical and Dental Offices, Outpatient Facilities, and Other Health Care Facilities Not Covered in Parts D and E

517-30. Applicability. Part C shall apply to those portions of clinics, medical and dental offices, and outpatient facilities wherein patients are intended to be examined or treated. It shall not apply to business offices, corridors, waiting rooms, and the like.

517-31. Wiring, Grounding and Receptacles. Wiring, grounding and receptacle installations shall be in accordance with Sections 517-10 and 517-11.

517-32.ˣ Essential Electrical System.

(a) General. The requirements of this section shall apply to those health care facilities described in Section 517-30, in which:

(1) Inhalation anesthetics are administered in any concentration to patients, or

(2) Patients require electrically operated or mechanical life support devices.

(b) Scope. The essential electrical system for these facilities shall comprise a system capable of supplying a limited amount of lighting and power service which is considered essential for life safety and orderly cessation of procedures during the time normal electrical service is interrupted for any reason.

(c) Connections. The essential electrical system shall supply power for:

(1) Task illumination which is related to the safety of life and which is necessary for the safe cessation of procedures in progress.

(2) All anesthesia and resuscitative equipment used in areas where inhalation anesthetics are administered to patients including alarm and alerting devices.

(FPN): See Nonflammable Medical Gas Systems, NFPA 56F-1983 (ANSI), Chapters 3 and 6.

(3) All electrically operated and mechanical equipment in areas where procedures are performed that require such equipment for the support of the patient's life.

(d) Alternate Source of Power.

(1) Power Source. The alternate source of power for the system shall be specifically designed for this purpose and shall be either a generator, battery system or self-contained battery integral with the equipment.

(2) System Capacity. The alternate source of power shall be separate and independent of the normal source and shall have a capacity to sustain its connected loads for a minimum of $1\frac{1}{2}$ hours after loss of the normal source.

(3) System Operation. The system shall be so arranged that, in the event of a failure of the normal power source, the alternate source of power shall be automatically connected to the load within 10 seconds.

(FPN): See Health Care Facilities, NFPA 99-1984 (ANSI), Sections 8-5.5.2, Description of Transfer Switch Operation with Engine Generator Sets, and 8-5.5.3, Description of Transfer Switch Operation with Battery Systems.

Section 517-32 and NFPA 99, *Standard for Health Care Facilities*, require an alternate source of power for those types of health care facilities where patients are treated in essentially the same manner as in hospitals, even though the facility may not be called a "hospital."

D. Nursing Homes and Residential Custodial Care Facilities

(FPN): For performance, maintenance and testing requirements of essential electrical systems in nursing homes and residential custodial care facilities, see Health Care Facilities, NFPA 99-1984 (ANSI).

517-40.ˣ Applicability. The requirements of Part D, Sections 517-42 through 517-47, shall apply to nursing homes and residential custodial care facilities.

Exception: Any free-standing building used for health care other than those described in Parts C and E of this article shall be exempted from the requirements of Sections 517-44 through 517-47 provided:

a. It maintains admitting and discharge policies that preclude the provision of care for any patient or resident who may need to be sustained by electrical life support equipment, and

b. Offers no surgical treatment requiring general anesthesia, and

c. Provides an automatic battery-operated system(s) or equipment that shall be effective for at least $1\frac{1}{2}$ hours and is otherwise in accordance with Section 700-12, and that shall be capable of supplying lighting for exit lights, exit corridors, stairways, nursing stations, medical preparation areas, boiler rooms and communication areas. This system shall also supply battery power to operate all alarm systems.

(FPN): See Life Safety Code, NFPA 101-1985 (ANSI).

NFPA 99, *Standard for Health Care Facilities*, recognizes two classes of nursing homes or residential custodial care facilities. For the smaller, less complex facility, only a minimum alternate service need be furnished.

Where treatment of patients is of a more complex nature, the requirements of Sections 517-44 through 517-47 are required to be applied. The branches of the emergency system for this class of occupancy bear identical titles to their counterparts for hospital-type occupancies.

517-41. Inpatient Hospital Care Facilities. Nursing homes and residential custodial care facilities which provide inpatient hospital care shall comply with the requirements of Part E, Hospitals.

ARTICLE 517—HEALTH CARE FACILITIES

Regardless of the name applied to the facility, the type of electrical system is dependent upon the type of patient care provided. Where such care is clearly inpatient hospital care, a hospital-type electrical system is required to be installed.

517-42. Facilities Contiguous with Hospitals. Nursing homes and residential custodial care facilities which are contiguous with a hospital shall be permitted to have their essential electrical systems supplied by that of the hospital.

When a hospital, nursing home, or residential custodial care facility share what is essentially the same building, the nursing home is not required to have its own essential electrical system but may derive its supply from the hospital. It should be noted, however, that this rule applies only to the electrical supply and does not permit the sharing of transfer devices and the like.

517-43. Wiring, Grounding, and Receptacles. Wiring, grounding, and receptacle installation shall be in accordance with Sections 517-10 and 517-11.

Exception: Patient sleeping areas wired in accordance with the requirements of Chapters 1 through 4 of this Code.

The exception recognizes that sleeping rooms in nursing homes are usually not patient care areas.

517-44. Essential Electrical Systems.

(a)ˣ General. Essential electrical systems for nursing homes and residential custodial care facilities shall be comprised of two separate branches capable of supplying a limited amount of lighting and power service which is considered essential for the protection of life safety and effective operation of the institution during the time normal electrical service is interrupted for any reason. These two separate branches shall be the life safety branch and the critical branch.

(b)ˣ Transfer Switches. The number of transfer switches to be used shall be based upon reliability, design, and load considerations. Each branch of the essential electrical system shall be served by one or more transfer switches as shown in Diagrams 517-44(1) and 517-44(2). One transfer switch shall be permitted to serve one or more branches in a facility with a maximum demand on the essential electrical system of 150 kVA.

The 150 kVA limit in the last sentence is not an extract from NFPA 99-1984.

(FPN): See Health Care Facilities, NFPA 99-1984 (ANSI): Section 8-4.5.2, Description of Transfer Switch Operation; Section 8-2.2.4, Automatic Transfer Switch Features; and Section 8-2.2.4, Nonautomatic Transfer Device Features.

(c) Capacity of System. The essential electrical system shall have adequate capacity to meet the demand for the operation of all functions and equipment to be served by each branch at one time.

(d) Separation from Other Circuits. The life safety branch shall be kept entirely independent of all other wiring and equipment and shall not enter the same raceways, boxes or cabinets with other wiring except as follows:

(1) In transfer switches,

(2) In exit or emergency lighting fixtures supplied from two sources, or

(3) In a common junction box attached to exit or emergency lighting fixtures supplied from two sources.

768

SMALL ELECTRICAL SYSTEM – NURSING HOMES
AND RESIDENTIAL CUSTODIAL
CARE FACILITIES

NORMAL SOURCES

ALTERNATE SOURCE

SE

NON-ESSENTIAL LOADS

LIFE SAFETY
BRANCH

CRITICAL
BRANCH

ESSENTIAL ELECTRICAL SYSTEM

SE — SERVICE ENTRANCE

☐ — OVERCURRENT PROTECTION

— AUTOMATIC SWITCHING EQUIPMENT

— DELAYED AUTOMATIC SWITCHING EQUIPMENT

— TRANSFORMER

G — GENERATOR

Diagram 517-44(1)

The wiring of the critical branch shall be permitted to occupy the same raceways, boxes or cabinets of other circuits that are not part of the life safety branch.

517-45ˣ. Automatic Connection to Life Safety Branch. The life safety branch shall be so installed and connected to the alternate source of power that all functions specified herein shall be automatically restored to operation within 10 seconds after the interruption of the normal source. The life safety branch shall supply power for the following lighting, receptacles, and equipment:

Diagram 517-44(2)

SMALL ELECTRICAL SYSTEM--- NURSING HOMES
AND RESIDENTIAL CUSTODIAL
CARE FACILITIES
(SINGLE TRANSFER SWITCH)

NORMAL SOURCES   ALTERNATE SOURCE

NONESSENTIAL
LOADS

ESSENTIAL ELECTRICAL SYSTEM

SE	SERVICE ENTRANCE
□	OVERCURRENT PROTECTION
[automatic switching symbol]	AUTOMATIC SWITCHING EQUIPMENT
[transformer symbol]	TRANSFORMER
G	GENERATOR

Diagram 517-44(3)

(FPN): The life safety branch is called the emergency system in Health Care Facilities, NFPA 99-1984 (ANSI).

(a) Illumination of Means of Egress. Illumination of means of egress as is necessary for corridors, passageways, stairways, landings and exit doors and all ways of approach to exits. Switching arrangement to transfer patient corridor lighting from general illumination circuits shall be permitted providing only one of two circuits can be selected, and both circuits cannot be extinguished at the same time.

(FPN): See Life Safety Code, NFPA 101-1985 (ANSI), Section 5-10.

(b) Exit Signs. Exit signs and exit directional signs.

(FPN): See Life Safety Code, NFPA 101-1985 (ANSI), Section 5-11.

(c) Alarm and Alerting Systems. Alarm and alerting systems, including:

(1) Fire alarms activated at manual stations, electric water flow alarm devices in connection with sprinkler systems, and automatic fire or smoke or products of combustion detection devices.

(FPN): See Life Safety Code, NFPA 101-1985 (ANSI), Sections 7-6, 12-3.4, and 12-3.5.

(2) Alarms required for systems used for the piping of nonflammable medical gases.

(FPN): See Standard for Nonflammable Medical Gas Systems, NFPA 56F-1983 (ANSI).

(d) Communication Systems. Communication systems, where used for issuing instructions during emergency conditions.

(e) Dining and Recreation Areas. Sufficient lighting in dining and recreation areas to provide illumination to exit ways.

(f) Generator Set Location. Task illumination and selected receptacles in the generator set location.

(g) Elevator Cab Lighting, Control and Communication Systems. No function other than those listed in (a) through (g) shall be connected to the life safety branch.

517-46^x. Connection to Critical Branch. The critical branch shall be so installed and connected to the alternate power source that the equipment listed in Section 517-46(a) shall be automatically restored to operation at appropriate time-lag intervals following the restoration of the life safety branch to operation. Its arrangement shall also provide for the additional connection of equipment listed in Section 517-46(b) by either delayed automatic or manual operation.

(a) Delayed Automatic Connection. The following equipment shall be connected to the critical branch and shall be arranged for delayed automatic connection to the alternate power source:

(1) Patient care areas — task illumination and selected receptacles in:

    a. Medication preparation areas.

    b. Pharmacy dispensing areas.

    c. Nurses' stations (unless adequately lighted by corridor luminaires).

(2) Sump pumps and other equipment required to operate for the safety of major apparatus and associated control systems and alarms.

(b) Delayed Automatic or Manual Connection. The following equipment shall be connected to the critical branch and shall be arranged for either delayed automatic or manual connection to the alternate power source:

(1) Heating equipment to provide heating for patient rooms.

Exception: Heating of general patient rooms during disruption of the normal source shall not be required under any of the following conditions:

a. The outside design temperature is higher than -6.7°C (+20°F), or

b. The outside design temperature is lower than -6.7°C (+20°F) and where a selected room(s) is provided for the needs of all confined patients, then only such room(s) need be heated, or

It has become common practice in some areas of the country to install individual room heating/air conditioners rather than have a central heating/air conditioning plant. When these individual units are electrically powered, it may not be practical to apply this high-demand load to the generator. When the governing body of the nursing home has full-time skilled attendants who can move people to one room(s) which will be heated when this smaller load is picked up by the generator, then the intent of the *Code* is satisfied. The provisions for limited heating during emergency conditions are based on consideration of "outside" design temperature.

c. The facility is served by a dual source of normal power as described in Section 517-47(c), Fine Print Note.

(FPN): The outside design temperature is based on the 97½ percent design values as shown in Chapter 4 of the ASHRAE Handbook of Fundamentals (1981).

(2) Elevator Service. In instances where disruption of power would result in elevators stopping between floors, throw-over facilities shall be provided to allow the temporary operation of any elevator for the release of passengers. For elevator cab lighting, control and signal system requirements, see Section 517-45(g).

(3) Additional illumination, receptacles, and equipment shall be permitted to be connected only to the critical branch.

517-47. Sources of Power.

(a) Two Independent Sources of Power. Essential electrical systems shall have a minimum of two independent sources of power: a normal source generally supplying the entire electrical system, and one or more alternate sources for use when the normal source is interrupted.

(b)ˣ Alternate Source of Power. The alternate source of power shall be a generator(s) driven by some form of prime mover(s), and located on the premises.

Exception No. 1: Where the normal source consists of generating units on the premises, the alternate source shall be either another generator set, or an external utility service.

Exception No. 2: Nursing homes or residential custodial care facilities meeting the requirements of the Exception to Section 517-40 shall be permitted to use a battery system or self-contained battery integral with the equipment.

(c) Location of Essential Electrical System Components. Careful consideration shall be given to the location of the spaces housing the components of the essential electrical system to minimize interruptions caused by natural forces common to the area (e.g., storms, floods, earthquakes, or hazards created by adjoining structures or activities). Consideration shall also be given to the possible interruption of normal electrical services resulting from similar causes as well as possible disruption of normal electrical service due to internal wiring and equipment failures.

(FPN): Facilities whose normal source of power is supplied by two or more separate central station-fed services experience greater than normal electrical service reliability than those with only a single feed. Such a dual source of normal power consists of two or more electrical services fed from separate generator sets or a utility distribution network having multiple power input sources and arranged to provide mechanical and electrical separation so that a fault between the facility and the generating sources will not likely cause an interruption of more than one of the facility service feeders.

ARTICLE 517—HEALTH CARE FACILITIES

E. Hospitals

(FPN): For performance, maintenance and testing requirements of essential electrical systems in hospitals, see Health Care Facilities, NFPA 99-1984 (ANSI). For installation of centrifugal fire pumps, see Standard for the Installation of Centrifugal Fire Pumps, NFPA 20-1983 (ANSI).

(FPN): For additional information, see Health Care Facilities, NFPA 99-1984 (ANSI).

517-58. Applicability. The requirements of Part E, Sections 517-60 through 517-65, shall apply to hospitals where an essential electrical system is required.

Exception: Those facilities covered by Parts C and D.

(FPN): For information as to the need for an essential electrical system, see Health Care Facilities, NFPA 99-1984 (ANSI).

517-60. Essential Electrical Systems.

(a) General.

(1)[x] Essential electrical systems for hospitals shall be comprised of two separate systems capable of supplying a limited amount of lighting and power service which is considered essential for life safety and effective hospital operation during the time the normal electrical service is interrupted for any reason. These two systems shall be the emergency system and the equipment system.

(2)[x] The emergency system shall be limited to circuits essential to life safety and critical patient care. These are designated the life safety branch and the critical branch.

(3)[x] The equipment system shall supply major electrical equipment necessary for patient care and basic hospital operation.

(4)[x] The number of transfer switches to be used shall be based upon reliability, design, and load considerations. Each branch of the essential electrical system shall be served by one or more transfer switches as shown in Diagrams 517-60(1) and 517-60(2). One transfer switch shall be permitted to serve one or more branches in a facility with a maximum demand on the essential electrical system of 150 kVA.

The 150 kVA limit in the last sentence is not an extract from NFPA 99-1984.

(FPN): See Health Care Facilities, NFPA 99-1984 (ANSI): Section 8-2.2.4, Automatic Transfer Switch Features; Section 8-4.5.2, Description of Transfer Switch Operation; and Section 8-2.2.4, Nonautomatic Transfer Device Features.

Diagrams 517-60(1), 517-60(2), and 517-60(3) indicate possible electrical system connections for hospitals. Diagram 517-60(2) illustrates a common situation where the expansion of the facility necessitates the addition of a normal source to that already in place. As shown in the diagram, this would not necessarily require the addition of another alternate source. Provided the alternate source has a capacity for all of the intended load, it may serve multiple services.

For a small electrical system having a maximum demand on the essential electrical system of 150 kVA, see Diagram 517-60(3). A small load can be served by a single transfer switch that would handle the loads associated with both the emergency system and the equipment system. This, of course, is on the assumption that the transfer switch has sufficient capacity to handle the combined loads, and the alternate source of power is sufficiently large to withstand the impact of the simultaneous transfer of both systems in the event of a normal power loss.

Diagram 517-60(1)

(b) Wiring Requirements.

(1) Separation from Other Circuits. The life safety branch and critical branch of the emergency system shall be kept entirely independent of all other wiring and equipment and shall not enter the same raceways, boxes or cabinets with each other or other wiring, except as follows:

    a. In transfer switches,

    b. In exit or emergency lighting fixtures supplied from two sources, or

    c. In a common junction box attached to exit or emergency lighting fixtures supplied from two sources.

The wiring of the equipment system shall be permitted to occupy the same raceways, boxes or cabinets of other circuits that are not part of the emergency system.

(2) Isolated Power Systems. Where isolated power systems are installed in any of the areas in Section 517-63(a)(1) and (a)(2), each system shall be supplied by an individual circuit serving no other load.

(3) Mechanical Protection of the Emergency System. The wiring of the emergency system of a hospital shall be mechanically protected by installation in metallic raceways.

Exception No. 1: Flexible power cords of appliances, or other utilization equipment, connected to the emergency system shall not be required to be enclosed in raceways.

Exception No. 2: Secondary circuits of transformer-powered communication or signaling systems shall not be required to be enclosed in raceways unless otherwise specified by Chapter 7 or 8.

TYPICAL LARGE ELECTRICAL SYSTEM - HOSPITALS

Diagram 517-60(2)

SMALL ELECTRICAL SYSTEM---HOSPITALS
(SINGLE TRANSFER SWITCH)

NORMAL SOURCES   ALTERNATE SOURCES

SE

NONESSENTIAL
LOADS

ESSENTIAL ELECTRICAL SYSTEM

SE	SERVICE ENTRANCE
□	OVERCURRENT PROTECTION
	AUTOMATIC SWITCHING EQUIPMENT
	TRANSFORMER
G	GENERATOR

Diagram 517-60(3)

Exception No. 3: Branch-circuit wiring as permitted in Sections 517-101(b)(1) and (c)(1).

Exception No. 2 exempts nurses' call, telephone, and alarm circuits from being run in metal raceways, provided they comply with their applicable articles elsewhere in the *Code*. Although this provides substantial latitude in the wiring method, it should be noted that the restrictions of Section 300-22 (ducts, plenums and other air-handling spaces) still apply unless conductors listed as having adequate fire-resistant and low smoke-producing characteristics are used as required by the exceptions under Sections 725-38(b)(3), 760-28(c)(3), and 800-3(b)(3). Also, see other restrictions under Sections 725-38, 760-29, and 800-3.

(c) Capacity of Systems. The essential electrical system shall have adequate capacity to meet the demand for the operation of all functions and equipment to be served by each system and branch.

ARTICLE 517—HEALTH CARE FACILITIES

517-61ˣ. Emergency System. Those functions of patient care depending on lighting or appliances that are connected to the emergency system shall be divided into two mandatory branches: the life safety branch and the critical branch, described in Sections 517-62 and 517-63.

The branches of the emergency system shall be installed and connected to the alternate power source so that all functions specified herein for the emergency system shall be automatically restored to operation within 10 seconds after interruption of the normal source.

517-62ˣ. Life Safety Branch. The life safety branch of the emergency system shall supply power for the following lighting, receptacles, and equipment:

(a) Illumination of Means of Egress. Illumination of means of egress, such as lighting required for corridors, passageways, stairways and landings at exit doors, and all necessary ways of approach to exits. Switching arrangements to transfer patient corridor lighting in hospitals from general illumination circuits to night illumination circuits shall be permitted provided only one of two circuits can be selected, and both circuits cannot be extinguished at the same time.

(FPN): See Life Safety Code, NFPA 101-1985 (ANSI), Section 5-10.

(b) Exit Signs. Exit signs and exit directional signs.

(FPN): See Life Safety Code, NFPA 101-1985 (ANSI), Section 5-11.

(c) Alarm and Alerting Systems. Alarm and alerting systems including:

(1) Fire alarms, actuated at manual stations.

(2) Electric water-flow alarm devices in connection with sprinkler systems.

(3) Automatic fire or smoke or products of combustion detection devices.

(FPN): See Life Safety Code, NFPA 101-1985 (ANSI), Sections 12-1 and 12-2.

(4) Alarms required for systems used for the piping of nonflammable medical gases.

(FPN): See Nonflammable Medical Gas Systems, NFPA 56F-1983 (ANSI).

(d) Communication Systems. Hospital communication systems, where used for issuing instructions during emergency conditions.

(e) Generator Set Location. Task illumination and selected receptacles at the generator set location.

(f) Elevator Cab Lighting, Control and Signal Systems. No function other than those listed in (a) through (f) shall be connected to the life safety branch.

517-63ˣ. Critical Branch.

(a) Task Illumination and Selected Receptacles. The critical branch of the emergency system shall supply power for task illumination, fixed equipment, selected receptacles, and special power circuits serving the following areas and functions related to patient care.

The critical branch is intended to serve a limited number of receptacles and locations to reduce the load and to minimize the chances of a fault condition. Receptacles in general patient care area corridors are permitted on the critical branch, but they are required to be identified in some manner (color coded or labeled) as part of the critical branch.

(1) Anesthetizing locations — task illumination, all receptacles and fixed equipment.

(2) The isolated power systems in special environments.

(3) Patient care areas — task illumination and selected receptacles in:

a. Infant nurseries,

b. Medication preparation areas,

c. Pharmacy dispensing areas,

d. Selected acute nursing areas,

e. Psychiatric bed areas (omit receptacles),

f. Ward treatment rooms, and

g. Nurses' stations (unless adequately lighted by corridor luminaires).

(4) Additional specialized patient care task illumination and receptacles, where needed.

(5) Nurse call systems.

(6) Blood, bone and tissue banks.

(7) Telephone equipment room and closets.

(8) Task illumination, receptacles, and special power circuits for:

a. Acute care beds (selected),

b. Angiographic labs,

c. Cardiac catheterization labs,

d. Coronary care units,

e. Hemodialysis rooms or areas,

f. Emergency room treatment areas (selected),

g. Human physiology labs,

h. Intensive care units, and

i. Postoperative recovery rooms (selected).

(9) Additional task illumination, receptacles and special power circuits needed for effective hospital operation. Single-phase fractional horsepower exhaust fan motors which are interlocked with three-phase motors on the equipment shall be permitted to be connected to the critical branch.

(b) Subdivision of the Critical Branch. It shall be permitted to subdivide the critical branch into two or more branches.

(FPN): It is important to analyze the consequences of supplying an area with only critical care branch power when failure occurs between the area and the transfer switch. Some proportion of normal and critical power, or critical power from separate transfer switches, may be appropriate.

517-64.ˣ Equipment System Connection to Alternate Power Source. The equipment system shall be installed and connected to the alternate source, such that the equipment described in Section 517-64(a) is automatically restored to operation at appropriate time-lag intervals following the energizing of the emergency system. Its arrangement shall also provide for the subsequent connection of equipment described in Section 517-64(b).

(a) Equipment for Delayed Automatic Connection. The following equipment shall be arranged for delayed automatic connection to the alternate power source:

(1) Central suction systems serving medical and surgical functions, including controls. Such suction systems shall be permitted on the critical branch.

(2) Sump pumps and other equipment required to operate for the safety of major apparatus, including associated control systems and alarms.

(3) Compressed air systems serving medical and surgical functions, including controls.

(FPN): The above equipment may be arranged for sequential delayed automatic action to the alternate power source to prevent overloading the generator where engineering studies indicate it is necessary.

(b) Equipment for Delayed Automatic or Manual Connection. The following equipment shall be arranged for either delayed automatic or manual connection to the alternate power source:

(1) Heating equipment to provide heating for operating, delivery, labor, recovery, intensive care, coronary care, nurseries, and general patient rooms.

Exception: Heating of general patient rooms and infection isolation rooms during disruption of the normal source shall not be required under any of the following conditions:

a. The outside design temperature is higher than -6.7°C (+20°F), or

b. The outside design temperature is lower than -6.7°C (+20°F) and where a selected room(s) is provided for the needs of all confined patients then only such room(s) need be heated, or

See commentary following Section 517-46(b)(1), Exception b.

c. The facility is served by a dual source of normal power as described in Section 517-65(c), Fine Print Note.

(FPN): The design temperature is based on the 97½ percent design value as shown in Chapter 4 of the ASHRAE Handbook of Fundamentals (1981).

(2) Elevator(s) selected to provide service to patient, surgical, obstetrical and ground floors during interruption of normal power.

In instances where interruption of normal power would result in other elevators stopping between floors, throw-over facilities shall be provided to allow the temporary operation of any elevator for the release of patients or other persons who may be confined between floors.

(3) Supply and exhaust ventilating systems for surgical and obstetrical delivery suites, special and intensive care units, isolation rooms constructed specifically for infection control, emergency treatment spaces, and laboratory fume hoods.

(4) Hyperbaric facilities.

(5) Hypobaric facilities.

(6) Automatically operated doors.

(7) Minimal electrically heated autoclaving equipment shall be permitted to be arranged for either automatic or manual connection to the alternate source.

(8) Other selected equipment shall be permitted to be served by the equipment system.

Careful consideration should be given to the effect of placing fire pumps on the equipment system. In spite of the fact that manual connection of fire pumps is permitted, future additions of other equipment to the equipment system may eventually compromise its ability to handle the fire-pump load. For this reason, a separate alternate source may provide the best assurance of continued capacity for the fire-pump load.

517-65. Sources of Power.

(a)ˣ Two Independent Sources of Power. Essential electrical systems shall have a minimum of two independent sources of power: a normal source generally supplying the entire electrical system, and one or more alternate sources for use when the normal source is interrupted.

(b)ˣ Alternate Source of Power. The alternate source of power shall be a generator(s) driven by some form of prime mover(s), and located on the premises.

Exception: Where the normal source consists of generating units on the premises, the alternate source shall be either another generating set, or an external utility service.

(c) Location of Essential Electrical System Components. Careful consideration shall be given to the location of the spaces housing the components of the essential electrical system to minimize interruptions caused by natural forces common to the area (e.g., storms, floods, earthquakes, or hazards created by adjoining structures or activities). Consideration shall also be given to the possible interruption of normal electrical services resulting from similar causes as well as possible disruption of normal electrical service due to internal wiring and equipment failures.

(FPN): Facilities whose normal source of power is supplied by two or more separate central station-fed services experience greater than normal electrical service reliability than those with only a single feed. Such a dual source of normal power consists of two or more electrical services fed from separate generator sets or a utility distribution network having multiple power input sources and arranged to provide mechanical and electrical separation so that a fault between the facility and the generating sources will not likely cause an interruption of more than one of the facility service feeders.

F. Patient Care Areas

The provisions of Part F apply to hospitals, nursing homes, and residential custodial care facilities that are not limited to specific services. Nursing homes and residential custodial care facilities that provide limited service may not be required to be provided with an essential electrical system, and are not covered by this part. See Sections 517-32 and 517-40, Exception.

(FPN): See Health Care Facilities, NFPA 99-1984 (ANSI).

517-80. General.

(a) Installation/Construction Criteria. It is the purpose of Part F to specify the installation criteria and/or wiring methods which will minimize electrical hazards by the maintenance of adequately low-potential differences only between exposed conductive surfaces which are likely to become energized and could be contacted by a patient.

(FPN): In a health care facility, it is difficult to prevent the occurrence of a conductive or capacitive path from the patient's body to some grounded object, because that path may be established accidentally or through instrumentation directly connected to the patient. Other electrically conductive surfaces which may make an additional contact with the patient, or instruments which may be connected to the patient, then become possible sources of electric currents which can traverse the patient's body. The hazard is increased as more apparatus is associated with the patient, and therefore more intensive precautions must be taken. Control of electric shock hazard requires the limitation of electric current that might flow in an electric circuit involving the patient's body, by raising the resistance of the conductive circuit which includes the patient, or by insulating exposed surfaces which might become energized, in addition to reducing the potential difference which can appear between exposed conductive surfaces in the patient vicinity, or by combinations of these methods. A special problem is presented by the patient with an externalized direct conductive path to the heart muscle. The patient may be electrocuted at current levels so low that additional protection in the design of appliances, insulation of the catheter, and control of medical practice are required.

The fine print note recognizes the possibility of increased sensitivity to electric shock by patients whose body resistance may be compromised either accidentally or by a necessary medical procedure. Such diverse situations as incontinence or the insertion of a catheter may render a patient much more vulnerable to the effects of an electric current. For these reasons, it is essential that those responsible for the design, installation, and maintenance of the electrical system in patient care areas be well acquainted with at least the rudiments of the hazard as explained in this note.

Since the original recognition of this hazard in the 1971 *Code*, continued clinical evaluation of the problem has provided a better understanding of the limits of the hazard, bringing about the changes in both value and wiring methods in the *Code*.

The *Code* clearly assigns designation of the types of patient care areas to the governing body of the health care facility. Both the design and inspection of a patient care area must therefore be based on the governing body's designation rather than the superficial appearance of the area.

(b)ˣ Patient Care Areas.   Areas of a health care facility in which patient care is administered are classified as general care areas, critical care areas, and wet locations. The governing body of the facility shall designate these areas in accordance with the type of patient care anticipated, and with the following definitions of the three types of areas.

(1) General care areas are patient bedrooms, examining rooms, treatment rooms, clinics, and similar areas in which it is intended that the patient shall come in contact with ordinary appliances such as a nurse call system, electrical beds, examining lamps, telephone, and entertainment devices. In such areas, it may also be intended that patients be connected to electromedical devices (such as heating pads, electrocardiographs, drainage pumps, monitors, otoscopes, ophthalmoscopes, peripheral intravenous lines).

(2) Critical care areas are those special care units, intensive care units, coronary care units, angiography laboratories, cardiac catheterization laboratories, delivery rooms, operating rooms, and similar areas in which patients are intended to be subjected to invasive procedures and connected to line-operated, electromedical devices.

(3) A wet location is a patient care area that is normally subject to wet conditions including standing water on the floor or routine dousing or drenching of the work area. Routine housekeeping procedures and incidental spillage of liquids do not define a wet location.

517-81. Grounding.

(a) Methods.   In addition to the requirements of Section 517-11, all branch circuits serving patient care areas shall be provided with a ground path for fault current by installation in rigid metal conduit, intermediate metal conduit, electrical metallic tubing, Type MI cable, Type MC cable, or Type AC cable where the outer metal jacket is an approved grounding means. Integrity of this ground path shall be verified.

It is intended by this section that a redundant ground path through the raceway be provided. This path is in addition to the path through the insulated grounding conductor required in Section 517-11. See commentary following Section 517-11.

Patient care areas are not limited to hospitals. They are also found in the facilities covered under Parts C and D of Article 517.

(b) Performance. Any two exposed conductive surfaces in the patient vicinity shall not exceed the following potential differences at frequencies of 1000 hertz or less measured across a 1000-ohm resistance.

(1) General Care Areas. 500 mV under normal operation.

(2) Critical Care Areas. 40 mV under normal operation.

Only exposed conductive surfaces (defined in Section 517-2) within the patient vicinity are required to meet the limitations of this section. The patient vicinity does not apply to ambulatory patients, only to the nominal location of the patient bed. The 1000-ohm resistance is intended to represent the patient in his or her nominal worst-case condition.

Voltage limitations for general-care areas will ordinarily be met by a reasonable level of electrical installation and maintenance. The voltage levels required for critical care areas may necessitate an additional degree of inspection and maintenance, but much of the problem can be eliminated by the use of electrical insulating or insulation-coated surfaces utilizing approved materials within the patient vicinity.

Figure 517-1. A portable field probe used to detect leakage currents, static electricity, and improper grounds in patient care areas. (*Daniel Woodhead* Co.)

517-82. Panelboard Bonding. The equipment grounding terminal bars of the normal and essential electrical system panelboards shall be bonded together with an insulated continuous copper conductor not smaller than No. 10.

517-83. General Care Areas.

(a) Patient Bed Location Branch Circuits. Each patient bed location where inpatient care is provided shall be supplied by at least two branch circuits, at least one of which originated in

Figure 517-2. A "Hospital Grade" attachment plug that is designed for maximum performance in hospital environments. The plastic construction contributes to visible check of connections and toward preventing accidental energization of exposed conductive parts. (*Daniel Woodhead Co.*)

Figure 517-3. A battery-operated precision instrument for use on all hospital electrical equipment. This instrument measures and detects line voltage and leakage current between the grounding pole of a receptacle and the exposed conductive surfaces of nonelectrical equipment, and/or between the grounding pole and conductive surfaces of fixed or portable electrical equipment. (*Neurodyne-Dempsey, Inc.*)

a normal system panelboard; all branch circuits from the normal system shall originate in the same panelboard.

Patient bed locations in this type of area are prohibited from deriving all of their branch circuits from the emergency system. At least one branch circuit for each patient bed location is required to originate in a normal system panelboard. This is a reflection of the requirements stated in Section 517-63.

Exception No. 1: Branch circuits serving only special-purpose outlets or receptacles, such as portable X-ray outlets, need not be served from the same distribution panel or panels.

Exception No. 2: Clinics, medical and dental offices, and outpatient facilities; psychiatric, substance abuse, and rehabilitation hospitals; nursing homes and residential custodial care facilities meeting the requirements of the Exception to Section 517-40.

(b) Patient Bed Location Receptacles.   Each patient bed location shall be provided with a minimum of four single or two duplex receptacles; each receptacle shall be grounded by means of an insulated copper conductor sized in accordance with Table 250-95.

Exception No. 1: Psychiatric, substance abuse, and rehabilitation hospitals meeting the requirements of the Exception to Section 517-40.

Exception No. 2: Psychiatric security rooms shall not be required to have receptacle outlets installed in the room.

517-84. Critical Care Areas.

(a) Patient Bed Location Branch Circuits.   Each patient bed location shall be supplied by at least two branch circuits, one or more from the emergency system and one or more circuits from the normal system. At least one branch circuit from the emergency system shall supply an outlet(s) only at that bed location. All branch circuits from the normal system shall be from a single panelboard; all branch circuits from the emergency system shall be from a single panelboard. Emergency system receptacles shall be identified, and shall also indicate the panelboard and circuit number supplying them.

Exception: Branch circuits serving only special-purpose receptacles or equipment in critical care areas shall be permitted to be served by other panelboards.

Conversely to Section 517-83(a), patient bed locations in critical care areas are required to have at least one branch circuit derived from the emergency system. Additionally, at least one branch circuit that supplies no other location is required at each bed location, and this branch circuit may not have any other receptacle outlets serving any other bed location. It is required that this branch circuit be supplied by the emergency system. Furthermore, each emergency system receptacle is required to bear some form of identification indicating that it is part of the emergency system, and a label or other appropriate means is required to specify the panelboard and circuit number from which it is derived. These requirements are intended to ensure that critical care patients will not be without electrical power regardless of whether the equipment, the branch circuits, or the normal system itself is at fault.

(b) Patient Bed Location Receptacles.   Each patient bed location shall be provided with a minimum of six single or three duplex receptacles listed "Hospital Grade" and so identified; each receptacle shall be grounded to the reference grounding point by means of an insulated copper equipment grounding conductor.

"Hospital Grade" receptacles have special requirements, particularly with regard to the grounding circuit. They are identified by the marking "Hospital Only" or by the marking "Hospital Grade" and a green dot on the face of the receptacle. See Figure 517-2 for a "Hospital Grade" attachment plug.

(c) Grounding and Bonding, Patient Vicinity.

(1) A patient bed location shall be permitted to have a patient equipment grounding point, grounded to the reference grounding point by means of an insulated continuous copper conductor, not smaller than No. 10, running directly to the reference grounding point or by means of a conductor permanently connected to the grounding conductor of a nearby power receptacle. The patient equipment grounding point, where supplied, shall be permitted to contain one or more jacks listed for the purpose.

(2) Fixed exposed conductive surfaces in the patient vicinity likely to become energized shall be connected to the room bonding point(s) or the reference grounding point by continuous copper conductors, or conductive building structural members having conductance at least equal to AWG No. 10 copper wire. The bonding conductors, if installed, shall be permitted to be arranged centrically or looped as convenient.

Exception: Small wall-mounted conductive surfaces not likely to become energized, such as surface-mounted towel and soap dispensers, mirrors, and so forth, need not be connected to the room bonding point. Similarly, large metal surfaces not likely to become energized (such as window and door frames) need not be intentionally grounded by connection to the room bonding point.

(3) The requirements in Section 517-84(c)(2) shall not apply to bedside stands, over-bed tables, chairs, portable IV poles, and small portable nonelectrical devices such as trays, pitchers, bedpans and the like. The requirements in Section 517-84(c)(2) shall not apply to portable appliances or furniture.

(4) Any of the grounding and bonding points in Section 517-84(c)(1) and (c)(2) shall be permitted to be combined into a single point.

(d) Panelboard Grounding. When a grounded electrical distribution system is used, and metallic feeder raceway or Type MC or MI cables are installed, grounding of a panelboard or switchboard shall be assured by one of the following means at each termination or junction point of the raceway or Type MC or MI cable:

(1) A grounding bushing and a continuous copper bonding jumper, sized in accordance with Section 250-95, where a locknut-bushing connection is provided.

(2) Connection of feeder raceways or Type MC or MI cables to threaded hubs or bosses on terminating enclosures.

(3) Other approved devices, such as bonding-type locknuts or bushings.

(e) Isolated Power System Grounding. Where an isolated ungrounded power source is used and limits the first-fault current to a low magnitude, the grounding conductor associated with the secondary circuit shall be permitted to be run outside of the enclosure of the power conductors in the same circuit.

(FPN): Although it is permitted to run the grounding conductor outside of the conduit, it is safer to run it with the power conductors to provide better protection in case of a second ground fault.

Running the conductor inside the raceway reduces the impedance of the grounding path.

(f) Special Purpose Receptacle Grounding. The equipment grounding conductor for special purpose receptacles such as the operation of mobile X-ray equipment shall be extended to the reference grounding points of branch circuits for all locations likely to be served from such receptacles. When such a circuit is served from an isolated ungrounded system, the grounding conductor need not be run with the power conductors; however, the equipment grounding terminal of the special purpose receptacle shall be connected to the reference grounding point.

517-90. Additional Protective Techniques.

(a) Critical Care Areas.

(1) Isolated power systems shall be permitted to be used for critical care areas.

(2) Isolated power system equipment shall be listed for the purpose and the system so designed and installed that it meets the provisions and is in accordance with Section 517-104.

Exception: The audible and visual indicators of the line isolation monitor shall be permitted to be located at the nursing station for the area being served.

(b) Pediatric and Psychiatric Locations. Fifteen- and 20-ampere, 125-volt receptacles intended to supply patient care areas of pediatric or psychiatric wards, rooms, or areas shall be tamperproof. For the purpose of this section, a tamperproof receptacle is a receptacle which by its construction limits improper access to its energized contacts.

(c) Wet Locations. Fifteen- and 20-ampere, 125-volt, single-phase receptacles supplying wet locations shall be provided with ground-fault circuit-interrupters if interruption of power under fault conditions can be tolerated, or an isolated power system if such interruption cannot be tolerated.

In areas that the governing body of the facility designates a wet location, ground-fault circuit-interrupters are required to be provided for the protection of receptacles, if a circuit interruption can be tolerated. Otherwise, an isolated power system would be required. This rule applies only to 15- and 20-ampere, 125-volt single-phase receptacles and not to fixed, permanently wired equipment.

(FPN): For requirements for installation of therapeutic pools and tubs, see Part F of Article 680.

G. Inhalation Anesthetizing Locations

(FPN): For further information regarding safeguards for anesthetizing locations, see Health Care Facilities, NFPA 99-1984, Chapters 3 and 4 (ANSI).

517-100. Anesthetizing Location Classifications.

(a) Hazardous (Classified) Location.

(1)ˣ In a location where flammable anesthetics are employed, the entire area shall be considered to be a Class I, Division 1 location which shall extend upward to a level 5 feet (1.52 m) above the floor. The remaining volume up to the structural ceiling is considered to be above a hazardous (classified) location.

(2) Any room or location in which flammable anesthetics or volatile flammable disinfecting agents are stored shall be considered to be a Class I, Division 1 location from floor to ceiling.

(b) Other-than-Hazardous (Classified) Location. Any inhalation anesthetizing location designated for the exclusive use of nonflammable anesthetizing agents shall be considered to be an other-than-hazardous (classified) location.

This section divides anesthetizing locations into either a hazardous (classified) location, where flammable or nonflammable anesthetics may be interchangeably employed, or an other-than-hazardous location, where only nonflammable anesthetics may be employed. In the case of the flammable anesthetizing location, the entire volume of the room extending upward from a level 5 ft (1.52 m) above the floor to the surface of the structural ceiling of the room, and including the space between a drop ceiling and the structural ceiling, is considered to be above a "hazardous (classified) location."

517-101. Wiring and Equipment.

(a) Within Hazardous Anesthetizing Locations.

(1)ˣ In hazardous (classified) location(s) referred to in Section 517-100, all fixed wiring and equipment, and all portable equipment, including lamps and other utilization equipment,

787

operating at more than 10 volts between conductors shall comply with the requirements of Sections 501-1 through 501-15 and Section 501-16(a) and (b) for Class I, Division 1 locations. All such equipment shall be specifically approved for the hazardous atmospheres involved.

(2) Where a box, fitting, or enclosure is partially, but not entirely, within a hazardous (classified) location(s), the hazardous (classified) location(s) shall be considered to be extended to include the entire box, fitting, or enclosure.

(3) Receptacles and attachment plugs in hazardous (classified) location(s) shall be listed for use in Class I, Group C hazardous (classified) locations, and shall have provision for the connection of a grounding conductor.

(4) Flexible cords used in hazardous areas for connection to portable utilization equipment, including lamps operating at more than 8 volts between conductors, shall be of a type approved for extra-hard usage in accordance with Table 400-4, and shall include an additional conductor for grounding.

(5) A storage device for the flexible cord shall be provided, and shall not subject the cord to bending at a radius of less than 3 inches (76 mm).

(b) Above Hazardous Anesthetizing Locations.

(1) Wiring above a hazardous area referred to in Section 517-100 shall be installed in rigid metal conduit, electrical metallic tubing, intermediate metal conduit, Type MI cable, or Type MC cable which employs a continuous, gas/vapor-tight metallic sheath.

(2) Installed equipment which may produce arcs, sparks, or particles of hot metal, such as lamps and lampholders for fixed lighting, cutouts, switches, generators, motors, or other equipment having make-and-break or sliding contacts, shall be of the totally enclosed type or so constructed as to prevent escape of sparks or hot metal particles.

Exception: Wall-mounted receptacles installed above the hazardous area in flammable anesthetizing locations shall not be required to be totally enclosed or have openings guarded or screened to prevent dispersion of particles.

(3) Surgical and other lighting fixtures shall conform to Section 501-9(b).

Exception No. 1: The surface temperature limitations set forth in Section 501-9(b)(2) shall not apply.

Exception No. 2: Integral or pendant switches which are located above and cannot be lowered into the hazardous (classified) location(s) shall not be required to be explosionproof.

(4) Approved seals shall be provided in conformance with Section 501-5, and Section 501-5(a)(4) shall apply to horizontal as well as to vertical boundaries of the defined hazardous (classified) locations.

Exception: Seals shall be permitted within 18 inches (457 mm) of the point at which a conduit emerges from a wall forming the boundary of an anesthetizing location if all of the following conditions are met:

a. The junction box, switch or receptacle contains a seal-off device between the arcing contacts and the conduit.

b. The conduit is continuous (without coupling or fitting) between the junction box and the sealing fitting within 18 inches (457 mm) of the point where the conduit emerges from the wall.

(5) Receptacles and attachment plugs located above hazardous anesthetizing locations shall be listed for hospital use for services of prescribed voltage, frequency, rating, and number of conductors with provision for the connection of the grounding conductor. This requirement shall apply to attachment plugs and receptacles of the 2-pole, 3-wire grounding type for single-phase 120-volt, nominal, ac service.

See commentary following Section 517-84(b).

(6) Plugs and receptacles for connection of 250-volt, 50-ampere and 60-ampere ac medical equipment for use above hazardous (classified) locations shall be so arranged that the 60-ampere receptacle will accept either the 50-ampere or the 60-ampere plug. Fifty-ampere receptacles shall be designed so as not to accept the 60-ampere attachment plug. The plugs shall be of the 2-pole, 3-wire design with a third contact connecting to the insulated (green or green with yellow stripe) equipment grounding conductor of the electrical system.

(c) Other-than-Hazardous Anesthetizing Locations.

(1) Wiring serving other-than-hazardous (classified) locations as defined in Section 517-100 shall be installed in rigid metal conduit, intermediate metal conduit, or electrical metallic tubing or shall be in Type MI cable, Type MC cable, or Type AC cable with an insulated equipment grounding conductor.

Exception: Pendant receptacle constructions employing at least SJO or equivalent flexible cords suspended not less than 6 feet (1.83 m) from the floor.

(2) Receptacles and attachment plugs installed and used in other-than-hazardous (classified) locations shall be listed for hospital use for services of prescribed voltage, frequency, rating, and number of conductors with provision for connection of the grounding conductor. This requirement shall apply to attachment plugs and receptacles of the 2-pole, 3-wire grounding type for single-phase 120-, 208-, or 240-volt, nominal, ac service.

See commentary following Section 517-84(b).

(3) Plugs and receptacles for connection of 250-volt, 50-ampere, and 60-ampere ac medical equipment for use in other-than-hazardous (classified) locations shall be so arranged that the 60-ampere receptacle will accept either the 50-ampere or the 60-ampere plug. The 50-ampere receptacle shall be designed so as not to accept the 60-ampere attachment plug. The plug shall be of the 2-pole, 3-wire design with a third contact connecting to the insulated (green or green with yellow stripe) equipment grounding conductor of the electrical system.

517-103[x]. Grounding. In any anesthetizing area, all metallic raceways and metal-sheathed cables, and all noncurrent-carrying conductive portions of fixed or portable electric equipment shall be grounded.

Exception: Equipment operating at not more than 10 volts between conductors shall not be required to be grounded.

It should be noted that the grounding requirements for anesthetizing locations apply only to metal raceways and electric equipment. Carts, tables, and other nonelectrical items are not required to be grounded. However, in flammable anesthetizing locations, portable carts and tables usually have a resistance to ground of not over 1,000,000 ohms, through use of conductive tires and wheels and conductive flooring, to avoid the build-up of static electrical charges. Such requirements will be found in NFPA 99-1984, *Standard for Health Care Facilities,* Chapter 3.

517-104. Circuits in Anesthetizing Locations.

(a) Isolated Power Systems.

(1)[x] Except as permitted in Section 517-104(c), each power circuit within, or partially within, a flammable anesthetizing location as referred to in Section 517-100 shall be isolated from any distribution system supplying other-than-flammable anesthetizing locations. Each isolated power circuit shall be controlled by a switch having a disconnecting pole in each isolated circuit conductor. Such isolation shall be accomplished by means of one or more transformers having no electrical connection between primary and secondary windings, by means of motor generator sets, or by means of suitably isolated batteries.

(2) Circuits supplying primaries of isolating transformers shall operate at not more than 600 volts between conductors and shall be provided with proper overcurrent protection. The secondary voltage of such transformers shall not exceed 600 volts between conductors of each circuit. All circuits supplied from such secondaries shall be ungrounded, and shall have an approved overcurrent device of proper ratings in each conductor. Circuits supplied directly from batteries or from motor generator sets shall be ungrounded, and shall be protected against overcurrent in the same manner as transformer-fed secondary circuits. If an electrostatic shield is present, it shall be connected to the reference grounding point.

(3) The isolating transformers, motor generator sets, or batteries and battery chargers, together with their primary and/or secondary overcurrent devices, shall not be installed in hazardous (classified) locations. The isolated secondary circuit wiring extending into a hazardous anesthetizing location shall be installed in accordance with Section 501-4.

(4) An isolated branch circuit supplying an anesthetizing location shall supply no other location. The insulation of the branch-circuit conductors on the secondary side of the isolated power supply shall have a dielectric constant of 3.5 or less. Wire pulling compounds that increase the dielectric constant shall not be used on the secondary conductors of the isolated power supply.

(5) The isolated circuit conductors shall be identified as follows:
Isolated Conductor No. 1 — Orange
Isolated Conductor No. 2 — Brown

For three-phase systems, the third conductor shall be identified as yellow.

(b)ˣ Line Isolation Monitor.

(1) In addition to the usual control and overcurrent protective devices, each isolated power system shall be provided with a continually operating line isolation monitor that indicates possible leakage or fault currents from either isolated conductor to ground. The monitor shall be designed so that a green signal lamp, conspicuously visible to persons in the anesthetizing location, remains lighted when the system is adequately isolated from ground; an adjacent red signal lamp and an audible warning signal (remote if desired) shall be energized when the total hazard current (consisting of possible resistive and capacitive leakage currents) from either isolated conductor to ground reaches a threshold value of 5 milliamperes under nominal line voltage conditions. The line isolation monitor is not to alarm for a fault hazard current of less than 3.7 milliamperes. The line isolation monitor is not to alarm for a total hazard current of less than 5.0 milliamperes.

Exception: A system shall be permitted to be designed to operate at a lower threshold value of total hazard current. A line isolation monitor for such a system shall be permitted to be approved with the provision that the fault hazard current shall be permitted to be reduced but not to less than 35 percent of the corresponding threshold value of the total hazard current, and the monitor hazard current is to be correspondingly reduced to no more than 50 percent of the alarm threshold value of the total hazard current.

(FPN): Such systems contribute little additional electrical safety and are used for special applications.

(2) The line isolation monitor shall be designed to have sufficient internal impedance such that when properly connected to the isolated system the maximum internal current that can flow through the line isolation monitor, when any point of the isolated system is grounded, shall be 1 milliampere.

Exception: The line isolation monitor shall be permitted to be of the low impedance type such that the current through the line isolation monitor, when any point of the isolated system is grounded, will not exceed twice the alarm threshold value for a period not exceeding 5 milliseconds.

(FPN): Reduction of the monitor hazard current, provided this reduction results in an increased "not alarm" threshold value for the fault hazard current, will increase circuit capacity.

(3) An ammeter calibrated in the total hazard current of the system (contribution of the fault hazard current plus monitor hazard current) shall be mounted in a plainly visible place on the line isolation monitor with the "alarm on" zone at approximately the center of the scale. It is desirable to locate the ammeter so that it is conspicuously visible to persons in the anesthetizing location.

Exception: The line isolation monitor may be a composite unit, with a sensing section cabled to a separate display panel section on which the alarm and/or test functions are located.

See Figure 517-4.

Figure 517-4. Line isolation monitor (right) for use with isolated power systems, remote indicator alarm (top left), and multiple annunciator panel (bottom left), which can monitor several operating rooms from a central location such as a nurses' station. (*Square D Co.*)

(c) Grounded Power Systems.

(1) A general-purpose lighting circuit connected to the normal grounded service shall be installed in each operating room.

Exception: Where connected to any alternate source permitted in Section 700-12 which is separate from the source serving the emergency system.

The failure of the emergency circuit feeder that supplies the operating room will ordinarily plunge the room into darkness. By requiring a general-purpose lighting circuit supplied by a normal source feeder, the effect of this kind of failure is minimized.

(2) Branch circuits supplying only listed, fixed, therapeutic and diagnostic equipment, permanently installed above the hazardous (classified) location and in other-than-hazardous (classified) locations, shall be permitted to be supplied from a normal grounded service, single- or three-phase system, provided:

a. Wiring for grounded and isolated circuits does not occupy the same raceway,

b. All conductive surfaces of the equipment are grounded,

c. Equipment (except enclosed X-ray tubes and the leads to the tubes) are located at least 8 feet (2.44 m) above the floor or outside the anesthetizing location, and

d. Switches for the grounded branch circuit are located outside the hazardous (classified) location.

Exception: Parts c. and d. shall not apply in other-than-hazardous (classified) locations.

(3) Branch circuits supplying only fixed lighting shall be permitted to be supplied by a normal grounded service provided.

a. Such fixtures are located at least 8 feet (2.44 m) above the floor,

b. All conductive surfaces of fixtures are grounded,

c. Wiring for circuits supplying power to fixtures does not occupy the same raceway for circuits supplying isolated power, and

d. Switches are wall-mounted and located above hazardous (classified) locations.

(4) Wall-mounted remote control stations for remote control switches operating at 24 volts or less shall be permitted to be installed in any anesthetizing location.

(5) An isolated power center listed for the purpose and its grounded primary feeder shall be permitted to be located in an anesthetizing location provided it is installed above a hazardous (classified) location, or in an other-than-hazardous (classified) location.

517-105^x. Low-Voltage Equipment and Instruments.

(a) **Equipment Requirements.** Low-voltage equipment which is frequently in contact with the bodies of persons or has exposed current-carrying elements shall:

(1) Operate on an electrical potential of 10 volts or less, or

(2) Be approved as intrinsically safe or double-insulated equipment.

(3) Be moisture-resistant.

(b) **Power Supplies.** Power shall be supplied to low-voltage equipment from:

(1) An individual portable isolating transformer (autotransformers shall not be used) connected to an isolated power circuit receptacle by means of an appropriate cord and attachment plug, or

(2) A common low-voltage isolating transformer installed in a nonhazardous location, or

(3) Individual dry-cell batteries, or

(4) Common batteries made up of storage cells located in a nonhazardous location.

(c) Isolated Circuits. Isolating-type transformers for supplying low-voltage circuits shall:

(1) Have approved means for insulating the secondary circuit from the primary circuit, and

(2) Have the core and case grounded.

(d) Controls. Resistance or impedance devices shall be permitted to control low-voltage equipment but shall not be used to limit the maximum available voltage to the equipment.

(e) Battery-Powered Appliances. Battery-powered appliances shall not be capable of being charged while in operation unless their charging circuitry incorporates an integral isolating-type transformer.

(f) Receptacles or Attachment Plugs. Any receptacle or attachment plug used on low-voltage circuits shall be of a type which does not permit interchangeable connection with circuits of higher voltage.

(FPN): Any interruption of the circuit, even circuits as low as 8 volts, either by any switch, or loose or defective connections anywhere in the circuit, may produce a spark sufficient to ignite flammable anesthetic agents. [See Section 3-2.5.2 of Health Care Facilities, NFPA 99-1984 (ANSI)].

H. Communications, Signaling Systems, Data Systems, Fire Protective Signaling Systems, and Low-Voltage Systems

Part H calls attention to the fact that certain wiring methods, although appropriate to a nonhealth care facility installation, could be inappropriate in a patient care area. See commentary following Section 517-81(a). This part recognizes a common necessity for connecting appliances within the patient vicinity to other appliances that may be located some distance away.

517-120. Patient Care Areas. Equivalent insulation, isolation, and grounding to that required for the electrical distribution systems in patient care areas shall be provided for communications, signaling systems, data system circuits, fire protective signaling systems, and low-voltage systems.

(FPN): An acceptable alternate means of providing isolation for patient/nurse call systems is by the use of nonelectrified signaling, communication or control devices held by the patient, or within reach of the patient.

(FPN): For grounding requirements, see Section 250-95.

517-121. Other-than-Patient-Care Areas. See Articles 725, 760, and 800.

517-122. Signal Transmission Between Appliances.

(a) General. Permanently installed signal cabling from an appliance in a patient location to remote appliances shall employ a signal transmission system which prevents hazardous grounding interconnection of the appliances. See Section 517-81.

(b) Common Signal Grounding Wire. Common signal grounding wires (i.e., the chassis ground for single-ended transmission) shall be permitted to be used between appliances all located within the patient vicinity, provided the appliances are served from the same reference grounding point.

K. X-ray Installations

Nothing in this part shall be construed as specifying safeguards against the useful beam or stray X-ray radiation.

(FPN): Radiation safety and performance requirements of several classes of X-ray equipment are regulated under Public Law 90-602 and are enforced by the Department of Health and Human Services.

(FPN): In addition, information on radiation protection by the National Council on Radiation Protection and Measurements is published as Reports of the National Council on Radiation Protection and Measurement. These reports are obtainable from NCRP Publications, P. O. Box 30175, Washington, D.C. 20014.

517-140. Definitions.

Long-Time Rating. A rating based on an operating interval of 5 minutes or longer.

Mobile. X-ray equipment mounted on a permanent base with wheels and/or casters for moving while completely assembled.

Momentary Rating. A rating based on an operating interval that does not exceed 5 seconds.

Portable. X-ray equipment designed to be hand carried.

Transportable. X-ray equipment to be installed in a vehicle or that may be readily disassembled for transport in a vehicle.

517-141. Connection to Supply Circuit.

(a) Fixed and Stationary Equipment. Fixed and stationary X-ray equipment shall be connected to the power supply by means of a wiring method meeting the general requirements of this Code.

Exception: Equipment properly supplied by a branch circuit rated at not over 30 amperes shall be permitted to be supplied through a suitable attachment plug and hard-service cable or cord.

(b) Portable, Mobile, and Transportable Equipment. Individual branch circuits shall not be required for portable, mobile, and transportable medical X-ray equipment requiring a capacity of not over 60 amperes.

(c) Over 600-Volt Supply. Circuits and equipment operated on a supply circuit of over 600 volts shall comply with Article 710.

517-142. Disconnecting Means.

(a) Capacity. A disconnecting means of adequate capacity for at least 50 percent of the input required for the momentary rating or 100 percent of the input required for the long-time rating of the X-ray equipment, whichever is greater, shall be provided in the supply circuit.

(b) Location. The disconnecting means shall be operable from a location readily accessible from the X-ray control.

(c) Portable Equipment. For equipment connected to a 120-volt branch circuit of 30 amperes or less, a grounding-type attachment plug and receptacle of proper rating shall be permitted to serve as a disconnecting means.

517-143. Rating of Supply Conductors and Overcurrent Protection.

(a) Diagnostic Equipment.

(1) The ampacity of supply branch-circuit conductors and the current rating of overcurrent protective devices shall not be less than 50 percent of the momentary rating or 100 percent of the long-time rating whichever is greater.

(2) The ampacity of supply feeder and the current rating of overcurrent protective devices supplying two or more branch circuits supplying X-ray units shall not be less than 50 percent of the momentary demand rating of each of the two largest diagnostic X-ray units plus 20 percent of the momentary ratings of each of the additional diagnostic X-ray units. Where simultaneous bi-plane examinations are undertaken with the X-ray units the supply conductors and overcurrent protective devices shall be 100 percent of the momentary rating of each X-ray unit.

(FPN): The minimum conductor size for branch and feeder circuits is also governed by voltage regulation requirements. For a specific installation, the manufacturer usually specifies: minimum distribution transformer and conductor sizes, rating of disconnecting means, and overcurrent protection.

(b) Therapeutic Equipment. The ampacity of conductors and rating of overcurrent protective devices shall not be less than 100 percent of the current rating of medical X-ray therapy equipment.

(FPN): The ampacity of the branch-circuit conductors and the ratings of disconnecting means and overcurrent protection for X-ray equipment are usually designated by the manufacturer for the specific installation.

517-145. Control Circuit Conductors.

(a) Number of Conductors In Raceway. The number of control circuit conductors installed in a raceway shall be determined in accordance with Section 300-17.

(b) Minimum Size of Conductors. Sizes No. 18 or No. 16 fixture wires as specified in Section 725-16 and flexible cords shall be permitted for the control and operating circuits of X-ray and auxiliary equipment where protected by not larger than 20-ampere overcurrent devices.

517-146. Equipment Installations. All equipment for new X-ray installations and all used or reconditioned X-ray equipment moved to and reinstalled at a new location shall be of an approved type.

517-148. Transformers and Capacitors. Transformers and capacitors that are part of an X-ray equipment shall not be required to comply with Articles 450 and 460.
Capacitors shall be mounted within enclosures of insulating material or grounded metal.

517-151. Guarding and Grounding.

(a) High-Voltage Parts. All high-voltage parts, including X-ray tubes, shall be mounted within grounded enclosures. Air, oil, gas, or other suitable insulating media shall be used to insulate the high voltage from the grounded enclosure. The connection from the high-voltage equipment to X-ray tubes and other high-voltage components shall be made with high-voltage shielded cables.

(b) Low-Voltage Cables. Low-voltage cables connecting to oil-filled units that are not completely sealed, such as transformers, condensers, oil coolers, and high-voltage switches, shall have insulation of the oil-resistant type.

(c) Noncurrent-Carrying Metal Parts. Noncurrent-carrying metal parts of X-ray and associated equipment (controls, tables, X-ray tube supports, transformer tanks, shielded cables, X-ray tube heads, etc.) shall be grounded in the manner specified in Article 250, as modified by Section 517-11 under the criteria set forth in Section 517-81 for critical care areas.

Exception: Battery-operated equipment.

ARTICLE 518 — PLACES OF ASSEMBLY

Contents

518-1. Scope. This article covers all buildings or portions of buildings or structures designed or intended for the assembly of 100 or more persons.

518-2. General Classifications. Places of Assembly shall include, but are not limited to:

Assembly Halls	Pool Room
Exhibition Halls	Club Rooms
Armories	Places of Awaiting
Dining Facilities	Transportation
Restaurants	Court Rooms
Church Chapels	Conference Rooms
Dance Halls	Auditoriums
Mortuary Chapels	Auditoriums within:
Museums	Schools
Skating Rinks	Mercantile Establishments
Gymnasiums	Business Establishments
Multipurpose Rooms	Other Occupancies.
Bowling Lanes	

Occupancy of any room or space for assembly purposes by less than 100 persons in a building of other occupancy, and incidental to such other occupancy, shall be classed as part of the other occupancy and subject to the provisions applicable thereto.

Where any such building structure, or portion thereof, contains a projection booth or stage platform or area for the presentation of theatrical or musical productions, either fixed or portable, the wiring for that area and all equipment that is used in the referenced area, and portable equipment and wiring for use in the production that will not be connected to permanently installed wiring shall comply with Article 520.

See commentary following Section 520-1.

(FPN): For methods of determining population capacity, see local building code or in its absence Life Safety Code, NFPA 101-1985 (ANSI).

This article applies to places of assembly designed or intended for the assembly of 100 or more persons. It would apply, for example, to a church chapel or auditorium for occupancy by 100 or more persons, determined by the methods for occupancy population capacity appearing in NFPA *101—1985, Life Safety Code.* But the article does not apply to a supermarket, even though it may contain 100 or more persons, because a supermarket is not specifically designed or intended for the assembly of persons; nor is it considered to be an auditorium.

The following information for determining occupancy capacity is contained in NFPA *101—1985, Life Safety Code.*

8-1.7 Occupant Load

8-1.7.1 The occupant load permitted in any assembly building, structure, or portion thereof shall be determined by dividing the net floor area or space assigned to that use by the square foot (square meter) per occupant as follows:

(a) An assembly area of concentrated use without fixed seats such as an auditorium, church, chapel, dance floor, discotheque or lodge room — 7 sq ft (.65 sq m) per person.

(b) An assembly area of less concentrated use such as a conference room, dining room, drinking establishment, exhibit room, gymnasium, or lounge — 15 sq ft (1.4 sq m) per person.

(c) Bleachers, pews, and similar bench-type seating — 18 linear in. (45.7 linear cm) per person.

(d) Fixed seating. The occupant load of an area having fixed seats shall be determined by the number of fixed seats installed. Required aisle space serving the fixed seats shall not be used to increase the occupant load.

(e) Libraries. In stack areas — 100 sq ft (9.3 sq m) per person; in reading rooms — 50 sq ft (4.6 sq m) per person.

8-1.7.2 The occupant load permitted in a building or portion thereof may be increased above that specified in 8-1.7.1 if the necessary aisles and exits are provided but shall not exceed a density of 1 person per 5 sq ft (.46 sq m). To increase the occupant load, a diagram indicating placement of equipment, aisles, exits, and seating shall be provided to and approved by the authority having jurisdiction prior to any increase in occupant load.

518-3. Other Articles.

(a) Hazardous (Classified) Areas. Hazardous (classified) areas located in any assemblage occupancy shall be installed in accordance with Article 500 — Hazardous (Classified) Locations.

(b) Temporary Wiring. In exhibition halls used for display booths, as in trade shows, the temporary wiring shall be installed in accordance with Article 305 — Temporary Wiring, except that approved flexible cables and cords shall be permitted to be laid on floors where protected from contact by the general public.

See Figure 518-1.

Figure 518-1. A treadle, such as this one, can be used to protect cords from abuse where they are laid across pedestrian ways, for instance, as part of a temporary wiring scheme such as may be used in exhibition halls. (*Daniel Woodhead Co.*)

(c) Emergency Systems. Control of emergency systems shall comply with Article 700 — Emergency Systems.

518-4. Wiring Methods. The fixed wiring methods shall be metal raceways, nonmetallic raceways encased in not less than 2 inches (50.8 mm) of concrete, Type MI cable, or Type MC cable.

Exception No. 1: Nonmetallic-sheathed cable, Type AC cable, and rigid nonmetallic conduit shall be permitted to be installed in those buildings or portions thereof that are not required to be fire-rated construction by the applicable building code.

Exception No. 2: As provided in Article 640 — Sound Reproduction and Similar Equipment, in Article 800 — Communication Circuits, and in Article 725 for Class 2 and Class 3 remote-control and signaling circuits, and in Article 760 for fire protective signaling circuits.

(FPN): Fire-rated construction is the fire-resistive classification used in building codes.

Refer to Figure 518-2. The washrooms and office area of this single-story facility are not places of assembly as defined in Section 518-2, and therefore require no special wiring methods. On the inside surface of the storage area walls, and on or in the partitions between storage areas, ordinary wiring methods can be used as these, too, are not places of assembly. However, inside any hollow spaces of the fire-rated storage area walls, the main requirements of Section 518-4 and Exception No. 2 are applicable as the serving corridors are part of the places of assembly as a result of this particular building design.

In a like manner, wiring in ceilings or floors, required to be of fire-rated construction in a place of assembly as defined in Section 518-2, is also required to comply with the main rule of Section 518-4, except as noted in Exception No. 2.

Although the partitions between the places of assembly and the central serving corridors, the partitions between the reception area and adjacent place of assembly, and the partitions between the food preparation area and the adjacent places of assembly are not required to be fire-rated by the local building code (in this case), they are part of the place of assembly. The wiring in or on these partitions still comes under the main rule of Section 518-4, and Exception No. 1 is not applicable.

The intent is that, within a place of assembly as defined in Section 518-2, the main rule of Section 518-4 and Exception No. 2 apply to any wall, floor, or ceiling. Exception No. 1 applies to those portions of the building and those places of assembly not required to be fire-rated.

Figure 518-2. The heavy lines represent walls required by the local building code to be of fire-rated construction. See the commentary text for discussion. The light lines represent walls not required by the local building code to be of fire-rated construction.

ARTICLE 520 — THEATERS AND SIMILAR LOCATIONS

Contents

A. General

520-1. Scope. This article covers all buildings or that part of a building or structure designed or intended to be used for dramatic, musical, motion picture projection, or similar purposes and to areas of motion picture and television studios which incorporate assembly areas.

These special requirements apply only to that part of a building used as a theater or for a similar purpose and do not necessarily apply to the entire building. For example, they would apply to an auditorium in a school building used for dramatic or other performances. The special requirements of this chapter would be applicable to the stage, auditorium, dressing rooms, and main corridors leading to the auditorium, but not to other parts of the building that are not involved in the use of the auditorium for performances or entertainment.

520-2. Motion Picture Projectors. Motion picture equipment and its installation and use shall comply with Article 540.

520-3. Sound Reproduction. Sound-reproducing equipment and its installation shall comply with Article 640.

520-4. Wiring Methods. The fixed wiring method shall be metal raceways, nonmetallic raceways encased in at least 2 inches (50.8 mm) of concrete, Type MI cable, or Type MC cable.

Exception No. 1: As provided in Article 640 for sound reproduction, in Article 800 for communication circuits, in Article 725 for Class 2 and Class 3 remote-control and signaling circuits, and in Article 760 for fire protective signaling circuits.

Exception No. 2: The wiring for portable switchboards, stage set lighting, stage effects, and other wiring not fixed as to location shall be permitted with approved flexible cords and cables as provided elsewhere in Article 520. Fastening such cables and cords by uninsulated staples or nailing shall not be permitted.

Theaters and similar buildings are usually required to be of fire-rated construction as determined by applicable building codes; therefore, the fixed wiring methods are limited to metal raceways such as rigid metal conduit, intermediate metal conduit, electrical metallic tubing, nonmetallic raceways encased in 2 in. (50.8 mm) of concrete, or Type MI or MC cable.

Exceptions to the wiring rules for metal- (or concrete-) enclosed wiring are permitted for the installation of communication circuits, Class 2 and 3 remote-control and signaling circuits, and fire-protective signaling circuits. Where portability, flexibility, and adjustments are necessary for portable switchboards, stage lighting, and special effects, suitable cords and cables are permitted.

520-5. Number of Conductors in Raceway. The number of conductors permitted in any metal conduit, rigid nonmetallic conduit as permitted in this article, or electrical metallic tubing for border or stage pocket circuits or for remote-control conductors shall not exceed the percentage fill shown in Table 1 of Chapter 9. Where contained within an auxiliary gutter or a wireway, the sum of the cross-sectional areas of all contained conductors at any cross section shall not exceed 20 percent of the interior cross-sectional area of the auxiliary gutter or wireway. The thirty-conductor limitation of Sections 362-5 and 374-5 shall not apply.

520-6. Enclosing and Guarding Live Parts.   Live parts shall be enclosed or guarded to prevent accidental contact by persons and objects. All switches shall be of the externally operable type. Dimmers, including rheostats, shall be placed in cases or cabinets that enclose all live parts.

Figure 520-1. An electronic dimmer board for stage lighting. (*Packaged Lighting Systems, Inc.*)

520-7. Emergency Systems.   Control of emergency systems shall comply with Article 700 — Emergency Systems.

B. Fixed Stage Switchboard

520-21. Dead Front.   Stage switchboards shall be of the dead-front type and shall comply with Part C of Article 384 unless approved based on suitability as a stage switchboard as determined by a qualified testing laboratory and recognized test standards and principles.

520-22. Guarding Back of Switchboard.   Stage switchboards having exposed live parts on the back of such boards shall be enclosed by the building walls, wire mesh grills, or by other approved methods. The entrance to this enclosure shall be by means of a self-closing door.

520-23. Control and Overcurrent Protection of Receptacle Circuits.   Means shall be provided at a stage lighting switchboard to which load circuits are connected for individual overcurrent protection of stage lighting branch circuits and stage and gallery receptacles used for cord- and plug-connected stage equipment. Where the stage switchboard contains dimmers to control nonstage lighting, the locating of the overcurrent protective devices for these branch circuits at the stage switchboard shall be permitted.

Any receptacles intended for the connection of stage lighting equipment, no matter where located, are covered by the term "gallery receptacles." The circuits supplying such receptacles are required to be controlled from the same location as the other stage lighting circuits.

520-24. Metal Hood.   A stage switchboard that is not completely enclosed dead-front and dead-rear or recessed into a wall shall be provided with a metal hood extending the full length of the board to protect all equipment on the board from falling objects.

Because stages are usually crowded and a great deal of flammable material is often present, a stage switchboard is not permitted to have exposed live parts on its front. Moreover, the space at the rear of a stage switchboard is required to be guarded in order to prevent entrance or contact by unqualified and unauthorized persons. One accepted method of accomplishing this is by enclosing the space between the rear of the switchboard and the wall in a sheet-steel housing with a door at one end.

Major stage switchboards are usually of the remote-control type. Pilot switches on the stage switchboard control the operation of remote contactors, which are installed in a convenient location such as below the stage. In turn, these contactors control the lighting circuits.

The front view of a small stage switchboard of the partial remote-control type is shown in Figure 520-2. Dimmers for individual circuits are operated by the egg-shaped handles. The usual location of a stage switchboard is in a recess in the proscenium wall. After passing through switches and dimmers, many of the main circuits are required to be subdivided into branch circuits so that no branch circuit will be loaded to more than 20 A (see Section 520-41). In a switchboard of the remote-control type, the branch-circuit fuses are located on the same panel as the contactors. In a direct-control-type switchboard, and sometimes in a remote-control-type switchboard, branch-circuit fuses are located on special panelboards, called "magazine panels," placed in the space behind the switchboard, usually in the location of the junction box.

520-25. Dimmers.   Dimmers shall comply with (a) through (d) below.

(a) Disconnection and Overcurrent Protection.   Where dimmers are installed in ungrounded conductors, each dimmer shall have overcurrent protection not greater than 125 percent of the dimmer rating, and shall be disconnected from all ungrounded conductors when the master or individual switch or circuit breaker supplying such dimmer is in the open position.

(b) Resistance- or Reactor-type Dimmers.   Resistance- or series reactor-type dimmers shall be permitted to be placed in either the grounded or the ungrounded conductor of the circuit. Where designed to open either the supply circuit to the dimmer or the circuit controlled by it, the dimmer shall then comply with Section 380-1. Resistance- or reactor-type dimmers placed in the grounded neutral conductor of the circuit shall not open the circuit.

(c) Autotransformer-type Dimmers.   The circuit supplying an autotransformer-type dimmer shall not exceed 150 volts between conductors. The grounded conductor shall be common to the input and output circuits.

(d) Solid-State-type Dimmers.   The circuit supplying a solid-state dimmer shall not exceed 150 volts between conductors unless the dimmer is specifically approved for higher voltage operation. When a grounded conductor supplies a dimmer, it shall be common to the input and output circuits. Dimmer chassis shall be connected to the equipment grounding conductor.

(FPN): See Section 210-9 for circuits derived from autotransformers.

Figure 520-3 illustrates three branch circuits arranged to be controlled by a single switch and a single dimmer plate. A single-pole switch on the stage

Figure 520-2. An autotransformer-type dimmer switchboard. (*Kliegl Bros.*)

switchboard feeds a short bus on the magazine panel. The magazine panel is like an ordinary panelboard, but branch circuits are directly connected to the bus (without switches), and the circuits are divided into several sections which contain separate feeder buses. One side of the variable resistor or dimmer plate is connected to the neutral bus at the switchboard, and the other side is connected to the neutral bus in the magazine panel. In order to avoid shunting of the dimmer, causing it to lose its control of the brightness of the lamps, the neutral bus in the magazine is required to be effectively insulated from ground and separate from other neutral buses in the panel.

The dimmer is permanently connected to the neutral of the wiring system, which is required to be effectively grounded; hence, the dimmer is essentially at ground potential.

Circuits supplying autotransformer-type dimmers are not permitted to exceed 150 V between conductors and, by means of a movable contact, any desired voltage may be applied to the lamps from full-line voltage to such a low voltage that the lamps provide no illumination. See Figure 520-4. This type of dimmer produces very little heat, operates at a high efficiency, and, within its maximum rating, its dimming effect is independent of the wattage of the load. See commentary under Section 470-4 where saturable reactors are used for dimmers on stage switchboards.

520-26. Type of Switchboard. Stage switchboard shall be either one or a combination of the following types:

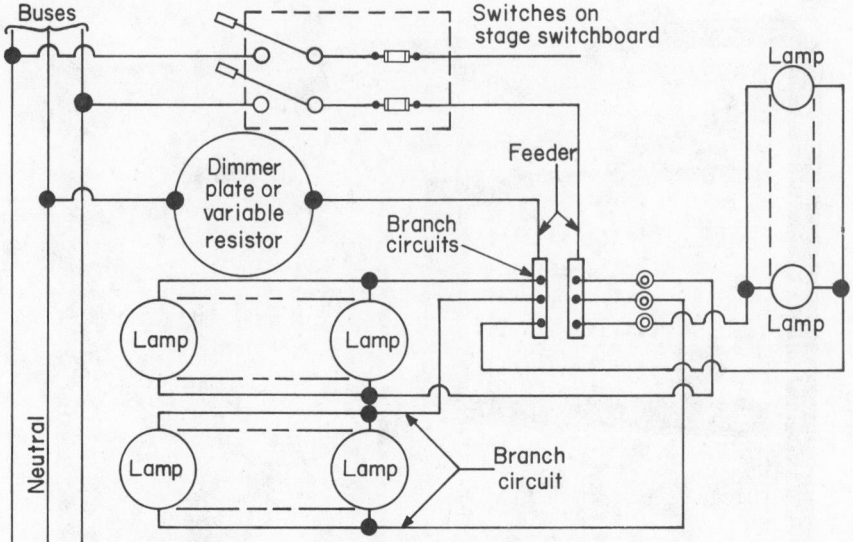

Figure 520-3. A schematic diagram of a typical stage switchboard showing connections for control switches, dimmer plate, and one section of a magazine panel showing feeder and branch-circuit connections for control of three lighting circuits.

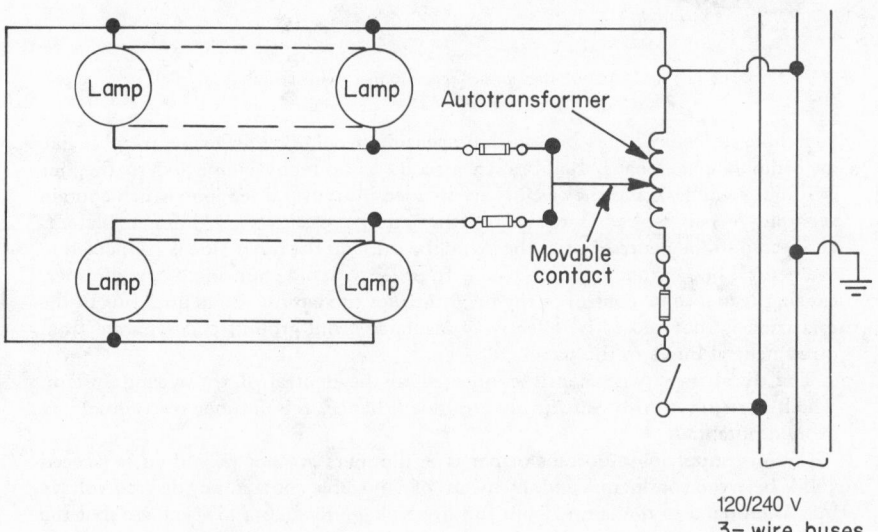

Figure 520-4. Typical connections for an autotransformer-type dimmer.

(a) Manual. Dimmers and switches are operated by handles mechanically linked to the control devices.

(b) Remotely Controlled. Devices are operated electrically from a pilot-type control console or panel. Pilot control panels shall either be part of the switchboard or shall be permitted to be at another location.

(c) Intermediate. A stage switchboard with circuit interconnections is a secondary switchboard (patch panel) or panelboard remote to the primary stage switchboard. It shall contain overcurrent protection. Where the required branch circuit overcurrent protection is provided in the dimmer panel, it shall be permitted to be omitted from the intermediate switchboard.

520-27. Stage Switchboard Feeders. Feeders supplying stage switchboards shall be one of the following:

(a) Single Feeder. A single feeder disconnected by a single disconnect device.

(b) Multiple Feeders to Intermediate Stage Switchboard (Patch Panel). Multiple feeders of unlimited quantity shall be permitted, provided that all multiple feeders are part of a single system. When combined, neutral conductors in a given raceway shall be of sufficient ampacity to carry the maximum unbalanced current supplied by multiple feeder conductors in the same raceway, but need not be greater than the ampacity of the neutral supplying the primary stage switchboard. Parallel neutral conductors shall comply with Section 310-4. The neutral of feeders supplying solid-state, 3-phase, 4-wire dimming systems shall be considered a current-carrying conductor.

> The feeders to this device are often dimmer-controlled circuits at 100 amperes or less, single phase, so they can be distributed to different combinations of the same size or smaller branch curcuits. Many installations use a common neutral. Therefore, the neutral must be capable of carrying the maximum unbalanced current supplied by multiple feeder conductors in the same raceway.

(c) Separate Feeders to Single Primary Stage Switchboard (Dimmer Bank). Installations with separate feeders to a single primary stage switchboard shall have a disconnecting means for each feeder. The primary stage switchboard shall have a permanent and obvious label stating the number and location of disconnecting means. If the disconnecting means are located in more than one distribution switchboard, the primary stage switchboard shall be provided with barriers to correspond with these multiple locations.

> This section permits several separate feeders to a stage switchboard rather than one very large feeder.

C. Stage Equipment — Fixed

520-41. Circuit Loads. Footlights, border lights, and proscenium side lights shall be so arranged that no branch circuit supplying such equipment will carry a load exceeding 20 amperes.

Exception: Where heavy-duty lampholders only are used, such circuits shall be permitted to comply with Article 210 for circuits supplying heavy-duty lampholders.

> Sections 210-23(b) and (c) permit 30-A, 40-A, or 50-A branch circuits if heavy-duty lampholders, such as admedium or mogul-base Edison screw-shell types, are used for fixed lighting.

520-42. Conductor Insulation. Foot, border, proscenium, or portable strip light fixtures and connector strips shall be wired with conductors having insulation suitable for the temperatures at which the conductors will be operated and not less than 125°C (257°F).

(FPN): See Table 310-13 for conductor types.

520-43. Footlights.

(a) Metal Trough Construction. Where metal trough construction is employed for footlights, the trough containing the circuit conductors shall be made of sheet metal not lighter than No. 20 MSG treated to prevent oxidation. Lampholder terminals shall be kept at least ½ inch (12.7 mm) from the metal of the trough. The circuit conductors shall be soldered to the lampholder terminals.

(b) Other-than-Metal-Trough Construction. Where the metal trough construction specified in Section 520-43(a) is not used, footlights shall consist of individual outlets with lampholders, wired with rigid metal conduit, intermediate metal conduit, or flexible metal conduit, Type MC cable, or mineral-insulated, metal-sheathed cable. The circuit conductors shall be soldered to the lampholder terminals. Disappearing footlights shall be so arranged that the current supply will be automatically disconnected when the footlights are replaced in the recess designed for them.

Metal troughs are commonly employed for footlights because the installation costs are less than individual outlets. Figure 520-5 illustrates a view of footlights in a typical installation.

Disappearing footlights are arranged so as to automatically disconnect the current supply when the footlights are in the closed position, thereby preventing heat-entrapment that could cause a fire.

Figure 520-5. Disappearing footlights arranged to automatically disconnect the current supply when in the closed position to prevent heat-entrapment.

520-44. Borders and Proscenium Sidelights.

(a) General. Borders and proscenium sidelights shall be: (1) constructed as specified in Section 520-43; (2) suitably stayed and supported; and (3) so designed that the flanges of the reflectors or other adequate guards will protect the lamps from mechanical injury and from accidental contact with scenery or other combustible material.

(b) Cables for Border Lights. Cables for supply to border lights shall be Type G, S, SO, ST, STO, or W flexible cable as provided in Table 400-4. The cables shall be suitably supported. Such cables shall be employed only where flexible conductors are necessary.

Figure 520-6 shows a modern border light installed over a stage. Figure 520-7 is a cross-sectional view giving construction details. This particular border light is designed for 200-W lamps. Each lamp is provided with its own reflector to obtain the highest illumination efficiency. Fitted to each reflector is a glass roundel available in any color. Commonly, red, white, and blue are used for three-color equipment, and red, white, blue, and amber for four-color equipment. A splice box is provided on top of the housing for enclosing connections between the cable supplying the border light and the border light's internal wiring which consists of wiring from the splice box to the lamp sockets in a trough extending the length of the border.

To facilitate height adjustment for cleaning and lamp replacement, border lights are usually supported by steel cables. Therefore, the circuit conductors supplying the border lights are required to be carried to the border in a flexible cable. The size of the individual conductor of the cable may be No. 14, though No. 12 is more commonly used.

Figure 520-6. A suspended border-light assembly for installation over a stage. (*Kliegl Bros.*)

520-45. Receptacles. Receptacles for electrical equipment or fixtures on stages shall be rated in amperes.

(1) A continuous load shall not exceed 80 percent of the receptacle rating.

(2) A noncontinuous load shall not exceed 100 percent of the receptacle rating.

Conductors supplying receptacles shall be in accordance with Article 310.

520-46. Connector Strips, Drop Boxes, and Stage Pockets. Receptacles for the connection of portable stage lighting equipment shall be pendant or mounted in suitable pockets or enclosures and comply with Section 520-45.

Figure 520-8 shows a single-receptacle stage floor pocket desighed for flush mounting, and Figure 520-9 shows a three-gang floor pocket designed for flush mounting. The standard-type plug which is used with either floor pockets or wall pockets of these types is also shown.

520-47. Lamps in Scene Docks. Lamps installed in scene docks shall be so located and guarded as to be free from physical damage and shall provide an air space of not less than 2 inches (50.8 mm) between such lamps and any combustible material.

520-48. Curtain Motors. Curtain motors having brushes or sliding contacts shall comply with one of the conditions in (a) through (f) below.

(a) Types. Be of the totally enclosed, enclosed-fan-cooled, or enclosed-pipe-ventilated type.

9"

8"

7"

|←6"→|←6"→|←6"→|←6"→|←6"→|←6"→|

Spacing of lights

Figure 520-7. A cross-sectional view of a typical light in the border assembly shown in Figure 520-6. (*Kliegl Bros.*)

Figure 520-8. A single receptacle in a stage floor pocket. (*Kliegl Bros.*)

(b) Separate Rooms or Housings. Be enclosed in separate rooms or housings built of noncombustible material so constructed as to exclude flyings or lint, and properly ventilated from a source of clean air.

(c) Solid Metal Covers. Have the brush or sliding-contact end of motor enclosed by solid metal covers.

(d) Tight Metal Housings. Have brushes or sliding contacts enclosed in substantial, tight metal housings.

808

Figure 520-9. A three-gang, three-receptacle stage floor pocket designed for flush mounting. (*Kliegl Bros.*)

(e) Upper and Lower Half Enclosures.   Have the upper half of the brush or sliding-contact end of the motor enclosed by a wire screen or perforated metal and the lower half enclosed by solid metal covers.

(f) Wire Screens or Perforated Metal.   Have wire screens or perforated metal placed at the commutator of brush ends. No dimension of any opening in the wire screen or perforated metal shall exceed .05 inch (1.27 mm), regardless of the shape of the opening and of the material used.

520-49. Flue Damper Control.   Where stage flue dampers are released by an electrical device, the circuit operating the device shall be normally closed and shall be controlled by at least two externally operable switches, one switch being placed at the electrician's station and the other where designated by the authority having jurisdiction. The device shall be designed for the full voltage of the circuit to which it is connected, no resistance being inserted. The device shall be located in the loft above the scenery and shall be enclosed in a suitable metal box having a tight, self-closing door.

In addition to the flue dampers being controlled from two externally operable switches at different locations, the design of a normally closed circuit ensures that the flue dampers will operate when the circuit opens for any reason, such as a circuit breaker tripping or a fuse blowing.

D. Portable Switchboards on Stage

520-50. Road-Show Connection Panel (A Type of Patch Panel).   A panel designed to allow for road show connection of portable stage switchboards to fixed lighting outlets by means of permanently installed supplementary circuits. The panel, supplementary circuits, and outlets shall comply with (a) through (d) below.

(a) Load Circuits.   Circuits shall terminate in grounded polarized inlets of current and voltage rating which matches the fixed load receptacle.

(b) Circuit Transfer.   Circuits which are transferred between fixed and portable switchboards shall have both the line and neutral transferred simultaneously.

(c) Overcurrent Protection.   The supply devices of these supplementary circuits shall be protected by branch-circuit overcurrent protective devices. The individual supplementary circuit, within the road show connection panel and theatre, shall be protected by branch-circuit overcurrent protective devices of suitable ampacity installed within the road show connection panel.

(d) Enclosure.   Panel construction shall be as per Article 384.

Road-show connection panels facilitate the connection of portable switchboards to permanently installed wiring. The requirements in Section 520-50 (c) are intended to prevent damage to the permanently installed wiring from overloads occurring in the portable switchboards.

520-51. Supply. Portable switchboards shall be supplied only from outlets of sufficient voltage and ampere rating. Such outlets shall include only externally operable, enclosed fused switches or circuit breakers mounted on stage or at the permanent switchboard in locations readily accessible from the stage floor. Provisions for connection of an equipment grounding conductor shall be provided. The neutral of feeders supplying solid-state, 3-phase, 4-wire dimmer systems shall be considered a current-carrying conductor.

520-52. Overcurrent Protection. Circuits from portable switchboards directly supplying equipment containing incandescent lamps of not over 300 watts shall be protected by overcurrent protective devices having a rating or setting of not over 20 amperes. Circuits for lampholders over 300 watts shall be permitted where overcurrent protection complies with Article 210.

520-53. Construction and Feeders. Portable switchboards and feeders for use on stages shall comply with (a) through (n) below.

(a) Enclosure. Portable switchboards shall be placed within an enclosure of substantial construction, which shall be permitted to be so arranged that the enclosure is open during operation. Enclosures of wood shall be completely lined with sheet metal of not less than No. 24 MSG and shall be well galvanized, enameled, or otherwise properly coated to prevent corrosion or be of a corrosion-resistant material.

(b) Live Parts. There shall be no exposed live parts within the enclosure.

Exception: For dimmer faceplates as provided in (e) below.

(c) Switches and Circuit Breakers. All switches and circuit breakers shall be of the externally operable, enclosed type.

(d) Circuit Protection. Overcurrent devices shall be provided in each ungrounded conductor of every circuit supplied through the switchboard. Enclosures shall be provided for all overcurrent devices in addition to the switchboard enclosure.

(e) Dimmers. The terminals of dimmers shall be provided with enclosures, and dimmer faceplates shall be so arranged that accidental contact cannot be readily made with the faceplate contacts.

(f) Interior Conductors. All conductors other than busbars within the switchboard enclosure shall be stranded. Conductors shall be approved for an operating temperature at least equal to the approved operating temperature of the dimming devices used in the switchboard and in no case less than the following: (1) resistance-type dimmers: 200°C (392°F); or (2) reactor-type, autotransformer, and solid-state dimmers: 125°C (257°F). All control wiring shall comply with Article 725.

Each conductor shall have an ampacity at least equal to the rating of the circuit breaker, switch, or fuse which it supplies. Circuit interrupting and bus bracing shall be in accordance with Sections 110-9 and 110-10. Switchboards with inadequate short-circuit withstand rating shall be protected on the line side by current-limiting devices. The short-circuit withstand rating shall be marked on the switchboard.

Exception: Conductors for pilot light circuits having overcurrent protection of not over 20 amperes.

Conductors shall be enclosed in metal wireways or be securely fastened in position and shall be bushed where they pass through metal.

(g) Pilot Light. A pilot light shall be provided within the enclosure and shall be so connected to the circuit supplying the board that the opening of the master switch will not cut off the supply to the lamp. This lamp shall be on an individual branch circuit having overcurrent protection rated or set at not over 15 amperes.

(h) Supply Conductors. The supply to a portable switchboard shall be by means of Type S, SO, ST, or STO cords, or G or W cable. The supply cords or cable shall terminate within the switchboard enclosure, in an externally operable fused master switch or circuit breaker, or in a connector assembly identified for the purpose. The supply cords or cable (and connector assembly) shall have sufficient ampacity to carry the total load connected to the switchboard and shall be protected by overcurrent devices.

Single-conductor cables shall be minimum No. 1 AWG in size. The single-conductor cables for a supply shall be of the same length, type, size, and be grouped together, but not bundled. The equipment grounding conductor shall be permitted to be of a different type, provided it meets the other requirements of this section, and it shall be permitted to be reduced in size as permitted by Section 250-95. Neutral and equipment grounding conductors shall be identified as per Section 310-12.

Exception No. 1: Supply Conductors Not Over 10 Feet (3.05 m) Long. In cases where supply conductors do not exceed 10 feet (3.05 m) in length between supply and switchboard or supply and a subsequent overcurrent device, the ampacity of the supply conductors shall be at least one-quarter of the ampacity of the supply overcurrent protection device where all of the following conditions are met:

a. The supply conductors shall terminate in a single overcurrent protection device that will limit the load to the ampacity of the supply conductors. This single overcurrent device shall be permitted to supply additional overcurrent devices on its load side.

b. The supply conductors shall not penetrate walls, floors, or ceilings, or be run through doors or traffic areas. The supply conductors shall be adequately protected from physical damage.

c. The supply conductors shall be suitably terminated in an approved manner.

d. Conductors shall be continuous without splices or connectors.

e. Conductors shall not be bundled.

f. Conductors shall be supported above the floor in an approved manner.

Exception No. 2: Supply Conductors Not Over 20 Feet (6.1 m) Long. In cases where supply conductors do not exceed 20 feet (6.1 m) in length between supply and switchboard or supply and a subsequent overcurrent protection device, the ampacity of the supply conductors shall be at least one-half the rating of the supply overcurrent protection device where all of the following conditions are met:

a. The supply conductors shall terminate in a single overcurrent protection device that will limit the load to the ampacity of the supply conductors. This single overcurrent device shall be permitted to supply additional overcurrent devices on its load side.

b. The supply conductors shall not penetrate walls, floors, or ceilings, or be run through doors or traffic areas. The supply conductors shall be adequately protected from physical damage.

c. The supply conductors shall be suitably terminated in an approved manner.

d. The supply conductors shall be supported in an approved manner at least 7 feet (2.13 m) above the floor except at terminations.

e. The supply conductors shall not be bundled.

f. Tap conductors shall be in unbroken lengths.

Loads of 144 kVA and greater are not uncommon, even on portable switchboard equipment. Installations in the field include lighting for theatrical-type productions with large numbers of lighting fixtures. However, only a fraction of the many fixtures installed are used at any one time. The intent is that the supply conductors are required to be sized according to their overcurrent protection, and not by the total connected load. These exceptions are similar to those found in Section 240-21 for taps.

(i) Cable Arrangement. Cables shall be protected by bushings where they pass through enclosures and shall be so arranged that tension on the cable will not be transmitted to the connections. Where power conductors pass through metal, the requirements of Section 300-20 shall apply.

(j) Number of Supply Interconnections. Where connectors are used in a supply conductor, there shall be a maximum number of three interconnections (mated connector pairs) when the total length from supply to switchboard does not exceed 100 feet (30.5 m). In cases where the total length from supply to switchboard exceeds 100 feet (30.5 m), one additional interconnection shall be permitted for each additional 100 feet (30.5 m) of supply conductor.

Addition of excessive numbers of interconnects could jeopardize the mechanical and electrical integrity of the supply conductors.

(k) Protection of Supply Conductors and Connectors. All supply conductors and connectors shall be protected against physical damage by an approved means. This protection shall not be required to be raceways.

(l) Flanged Surface Inlets. Flanged surface inlets (recessed plugs) that are used to accept the power shall be rated in amperes.

(m) Terminals. Terminals to which stage cables are connected shall be so located as to permit convenient access to the terminals.

(n) Supply Neutral Terminal. In portable switchboard equipment designed for use with 3-phase, 4-wire with ground supply, the supply neutral terminal and its associated busbar and/or equivalent wiring shall have an ampacity equal to twice the ampacity of the largest ungrounded supply terminal. The power supply lines for portable switchboards shall be sized considering the neutral as a current-carrying conductor.

Exception: Where portable switchboard equipment is specifically constructed to be internally converted in the field, in an approved manner, from use with a balanced 3-phase, 4-wire with ground supply to a balanced single-phase, 3-wire with ground supply, the supply neutral terminal and its associated busbar, equivalent wiring, or both shall have an ampacity equal to that of the largest ungrounded single-phase supply terminal.

This exception was changed in the 1987 *Code*. The 1984 *Code* required the supply neutral terminal and its associated busbar and/or equivalent wiring to have an ampacity equal to 200 percent of the largest ungrounded single-phase supply terminal. The requirement was changed to 100 percent because the usual neutral current that can occur in a 3-phase solid-state switchboard due to SCR phase control is at worst case 26 percent above the maximum load current. A neutral conductor of a convertible switchboard will usually be rated at least 50 percent larger than the largest ungrounded supply conductor.

E. Stage Equipment — Portable

520-61. Arc Lamps. Arc lamps shall be listed.

520-62. Portable Plugging Boxes. Portable plugging boxes shall comply with (a) through (e) below.

(a) Enclosure. The construction shall be such that no current-carrying part will be exposed.

(b) Receptacles and Overcurrent Protection. Receptacles shall comply with Section 520-45 and shall have branch-circuit overcurrent protection in the box. Fuses and circuit breakers shall be protected against physical damage. Cords or cables supplying pendant receptacles shall be Type S, SO, ST, or STO cords, or G or W cables.

(c) Busbars and Terminals. Busbars shall have an ampacity equal to the sum of the ampere ratings of all the circuits connected to the busbar. Lugs shall be provided for the connection of the master cable.

(d) Flanged Surface Inlets. Flanged surface inlets (recessed plugs) that are used to accept the power shall be rated in amperes.

(e) Cable Arrangement. Cables shall be adequately protected where they pass through enclosures and be so arranged that tension on the cable will not be transmitted to the terminations.

520-63. Bracket Fixture Wiring.

(a) Bracket Wiring. Brackets for use on scenery shall be wired internally, and the fixture stem shall be carried through to the back of the scenery where a bushing shall be placed on the end of the stem.

Exception: Externally wired brackets or other fixtures shall be permitted where wired with cords designed for hard usage that extend through scenery and without joint or splice in canopy of fixture back and terminate in an approved-type stage connector located, where practical, within 18 inches (457 mm) of the fixture.

(b) Mounting. Fixtures shall be securely fastened in place.

520-64. Portable Strips. Portable strips shall be constructed in accordance with the requirements for border lights and proscenium side lights in Section 520-44(a). The supply cable shall be protected by bushings where it passes through metal and shall be so arranged that tension on the cable will not be transmitted to the connections.

(FPN): See Section 520-42 for wiring of portable strips.

(FPN): See Section 520-68, Exception No. 2, for insulation types required on single conductors.

520-65. Festoons. Joints in festoon wiring shall be staggered. Lamps enclosed in lanterns or similar devices of combustible material shall be equipped with guards.

Festoon wiring is a string of lights which is suspended between two points more than 15 ft apart. Joints in festoon wiring are required to be staggered and properly insulated. This ensures that connections will not be opposite one another, which could cause sparking due to improper insulation or unraveling of insulation which, in turn, could ignite lanterns or other combustible material enclosing lamps. It should also be noted that when lampholders have terminals of a type that puncture the conductor insulation and make contact with the conductors, stranded-type conductors should be used.

520-66. Special Effects. Electrical devices used for simulating lightning, waterfalls, and the like shall be so constructed and located that flames, sparks, or hot particles cannot come in contact with combustible material.

ARTICLE 520—THEATERS AND SIMILAR LOCATIONS

520-67. Cable Connectors. Cable connectors, male and female, for flexible conductors shall be constructed so that tension on the cord or cable will not be transmitted to the connections. The female half shall be attached to the load end of the power supply cord or cable. The connector shall be rated in amperes and designed so that differently rated devices cannot be connected together. AC multipole connectors shall be polarized and comply with Section 410-56(e) and Section 410-58.

(FPN): See Section 400-10 for pull at terminals.

520-68. Conductors for Portables. Flexible conductors used to supply portable stage equipment shall be Type S, SO, ST, STO, G, or W.

Exception No. 1: Reinforced cord shall be permitted to supply stand lamps where the cord is not subject to severe physical damage and is protected by an overcurrent device rated at not over 20 amperes.

Exception No. 2: A special assembly of conductors in sleeving no longer than 3.3 feet (1.0 m) shall be permitted to be employed in lieu of flexible cord if the individual wires are stranded and rated over 125°C (257°F) and the outer sleeve is glass fiber with a wall thickness of at least 0.025 inches (635 micrometers).

Exception No. 3: Portable stage equipment requiring flexible supply conductors with a higher temperature rating where one end is permanently attached to the equipment shall be permitted to employ alternate suitable conductors as determined by a qualified testing laboratory and recognized test standards.

520-69. Adapters. Adapters, two-fers, and other single and multiple circuit outlet devices shall comply with (a) and (b) below.

See Figure 520-10.

Molded splice

Figure 520-10. A two-fer consists of two cord connectors on separate cords connected together to a single supply cord.

(a) No Reduction in Current Rating. Each receptacle and its corresponding cable shall have the same current and voltage rating as the plug supplying it. It shall not be utilized in a stage circuit with a greater current rating.

(b) Connectors. All connectors shall be wired in accordance with Sections 520-67 and 520-68.

814

Adapters are available which would permit the use of undersized cords on portable switchboards for connection to larger-sized receptacles. For example, a No 12 AWG wire, with an ampacity of 20 amperes, could be connected to a 100-ampere circuit. An overload could result in a fire since the circuit breaker or fuse would not provide adequate protection.

F. Dressing Rooms

520-71. Pendant Lampholders. Pendant lampholders shall not be installed in dressing rooms.

520-72. Lamp Guards. All exposed incandescent lamps in dressing rooms, where less than 8 feet (2.44 m) from the floor, shall be equipped with open-end guards riveted to the outlet box cover or otherwise sealed or locked in place.

Because of the many different types of flammable materials, such as costumes, wigs, etc., present in dressing rooms, pendant lampholders are not permitted. Lamps are required to be provided with suitable open-end guards (to permit relamping) that are not easily removed. This makes it difficult to circumvent their intended purpose of preventing contact between the lamps and flammable material.

520-73. Switches Required. All lights and receptacles in dressing rooms shall be controlled by wall switches installed in the dressing rooms. Each switch controlling receptacles shall be provided with a pilot light to indicate when the receptacles are energized.

G. Grounding

520-81. Grounding. All metal raceways and metal-sheathed cables shall be grounded. The metal frames and enclosures of all equipment, including border lights and portable lighting fixtures, shall be grounded. Grounding, where employed, shall be in accordance with Article 250.

ARTICLE 530 — MOTION PICTURE AND TELEVISION STUDIOS AND SIMILAR LOCATIONS

Contents

A. General

530-1. Scope. The requirements of this article shall apply to television studios and motion picture studios using either film or electronic cameras, except as provided in Section 520-1, and exchanges, factories, laboratories, stages, or a portion of the building in which film or tape more than ⅞ inch (22 mm) in width is exposed, developed, printed, cut, edited, rewound, repaired, or stored.

(FPN): For methods of protecting against cellulose nitrate film hazards, see Standard for the Storage and Handling of Cellulose Nitrate Motion Picture Film, NFPA 40-1982.

The requirements for motion picture studios and television studios are virtually the same, and are intended to apply only to those locations presenting special hazards. Otherwise, the conditions are similar to theater stages; therefore, the applicable provisions of Article 520 should be observed, such as for stages, dressing rooms, etc.

The special hazards are temporary structures constructed of wood or other combustible material.

B. Stage or Set

530-11. Permanent Wiring. The permanent wiring shall be Type MC cable, Type MI cable, or in approved raceways.

Exception: Communication circuits, and sound recording and reproducing equipment shall be permitted to be wired as permitted by Articles 640 and 800.

530-12. Portable Wiring. The wiring for stage set lighting, stage effects, electric equipment used as stage properties, and other wiring not fixed as to location shall be done with approved flexible cords and cables. Splices or taps shall be permitted in flexible cords used to supply stage properties when such are made with approved devices and the circuit is protected at not more than 20 amperes. Such cables and cords shall not be fastened by staples or nailing.

530-13. Stage Lighting and Effects Control. Switches used for studio stage set lighting and effects (on the stages and lots and on location) shall be of the externally operable type. Where contactors are used as the disconnecting means for fuses, an individual externally operable switch, such as a tumbler switch, for the control of each contactor shall be located at a distance of not more than 6 feet (1.83 m) from the contactor, in addition to remote-control switches.

Exception: A single externally operable switch shall be permitted to simultaneously disconnect all the contactors on any one location board, where located at a distance of not more than 6 feet (1.83 m) from the location board.

530-14. Plugging Boxes. Each receptacle of dc plugging boxes shall be rated at not less than 30 amperes.

530-15. Enclosing and Guarding Live Parts.

(a) Live Parts. Live parts shall be enclosed or guarded to prevent accidental contact by persons and objects.

(b) Switches. All switches shall be of the externally operable type.

(c) Rheostats. Rheostats shall be placed in approved cases or cabinets that enclose all live parts, having only the operating handles exposed.

(d) Current-Carrying Parts. Current-carrying parts of bull-switches, location boards, spiders, and plugging boxes shall be so enclosed, guarded, or located that persons cannot accidentally come into contact with them or bring conductive material into contact with them.

530-16. Portable Lamps. Portable lamps and work lights shall be equipped with flexible cords, composition or metal-sheathed porcelain sockets, and substantial guards.

Exception: Portable lamps used as properties in a motion picture set or television stage set, on a studio stage or lot, or on location.

530-17. Portable Arc Lamps. Portable arc lamps shall be substantially constructed. The arc shall be provided with an enclosure designed to retain sparks and carbons and to prevent persons or materials from coming into contact with the arc or bare live parts. The enclosures shall be ventilated. All switches shall be of the externally operable type.

530-18. Overcurrent Protection — Short-Time Rating.*

General. Automatic overcurrent protective devices (circuit breakers or fuses) for motion picture studio stage set lighting and the stage cables for such stage set lighting shall be as given in (a) through (e) below.

(FPN): Note: *Special consideration is given to motion picture studios and similar locations because filming periods are of short duration of 20 minutes.

(a) Stage Cables. Stage cables for stage set lighting shall be protected by means of overcurrent devices set at not more than 400 percent of the ampacity given in applicable tables of Articles 310 and 400.

(b) Feeders. In buildings used primarily for motion picture production, the feeders from the substations to the stages shall be protected by means of overcurrent devices (generally located in the substation) having suitable ampere rating. The overcurrent devices shall be permitted to be multipole or single-pole gang-operated. No pole or overcurrent device shall be required in the neutral conductor. The overcurrent device setting for each feeder shall not exceed 400 percent of the ampacity of the feeder, as given in applicable tables of Article 310. Short-term ratings shall not be permitted when equipment is operated for periods in excess of 20 minutes.

An overcurrent device setting of up to 400 percent is permissible when the loads are of short duration. This section permits the use of short-term ratings when the equipment operates for 20 minutes or less. A longer period of operation may be a fire hazard.

(c) Location Boards. Overcurrent protection (fuses or circuit breakers) shall be provided at the "location boards." Fuses in the "location boards" shall have an ampere rating of not over 400 percent of the ampacity of the cables between the "location boards" and the plugging boxes.

(d) Plugging Boxes. Cables and cords supplied through plugging boxes shall be of copper. Cables and cords smaller than No. 8 shall be attached to the plugging box by means of a plug containing two cartridge fuses or a 2-pole circuit breaker. The rating of the fuses or the setting of the circuit breaker shall not be over 400 percent of the rated ampacity of the cables or cords as given in applicable tables of Articles 310 and 400. Plugging boxes shall not be permitted on ac systems.

(e) Lighting. Work lights, stand lamps, and fixtures shall be connected to plugging boxes by means of plugs containing two cartridge fuses not larger than 20 amperes, or they shall be permitted to be connected to special outlets on circuits protected by fuses or circuit breakers rated at not over 20 amperes. Plug fuses shall not be used unless they are on the load side of the fuse or circuit breakers on the "location boards."

530-19. Sizing of Feeder Conductors for Television Studio Sets.

(a) General. It shall be permissible to apply the demand factors listed in Table 530-19(a) to that portion of the maximum possible connected load for studio or stage set lighting for all permanently installed feeders between substations and stages and to all permanently installed feeders between the main stage switchboard and stage distribution centers or location boards.

Table 530-19(a).   Demand Factors for Stage Set Lighting

Total Stage Set Lighting Load (Volt-amperes)	Feeder Demand Factor
First 50,000 or less at	100%
More than 50,000 to 100,000	75%
More than 100,000 to 200,000	60%
All over 200,000	50%

(b) Portable Feeders. A demand factor of 50 percent of maximum possible connected load shall be permitted for all portable feeders.

530-20. Grounding.
Type MC cable, Type MI cable, metal raceways, and all noncurrent-carrying metal parts of appliances, devices, and equipment shall be grounded as specified in Article 250. This shall not apply to pendant and portable lamps, to stage lighting and stage sound equipment, nor to other portable and special stage equipment operating at not over 150 volts dc to ground.

530-21. Plugs and Receptacles.
Plugs and receptacles shall be rated in amperes. All ac plugs and receptacles shall be grounded and polarized.

C. Dressing Rooms

530-31. Dressing Rooms.
Fixed wiring in dressing rooms shall be installed in accordance with wiring methods covered in Chapter 3. Wiring for portable dressing rooms shall be approved.

D. Viewing, Cutting, and Patching Tables

530-41. Lamps at Tables.
Only composition or metal-sheathed, porcelain, keyless lampholders equipped with suitable means to guard lamps from physical damage and from film and film scrap shall be used at patching, viewing, and cutting tables.

E. Cellulose Nitrate Film Storage Vaults

530-51. Lamps in Cellulose Nitrate Film Storage Vaults. Lamps in cellulose nitrate film storage vaults shall be installed in rigid fixtures of the glass enclosed and gasketed type. Lamps shall be controlled by a switch having a pole in each ungrounded conductor. This switch shall be located outside of the vault and provided with a pilot light to indicate whether the switch is on or off. This switch shall disconnect from all sources of supply all ungrounded conductors terminating in any outlet in the vault.

530-52. Motors and Other Equipment in Cellulose Nitrate Film Storage Vaults. No receptacles, outlets, electric motors, heaters, portable lights, or other portable electric equipment shall be located in cellulose nitrate film storage vaults.

F. Substations

530-61. Substations. Wiring and equipment of over 600 volts, nominal, shall comply with Article 710.

530-62. Low-Voltage Switchboards. On 600 volts, nominal, or less, switchboards shall comply with Article 384.

530-63. Overcurrent Protection of DC Generators. Three-wire dc generators shall have protection consisting of overcurrent devices having an ampere rating or setting in accordance with the generator ampere rating. Single-pole or double-pole overcurrent devices shall be permitted, and no pole or overcurrent coil shall be required in the neutral lead (whether it is grounded or ungrounded).

530-64. Working Space and Guarding. Working space and guarding in permanent fixed substations shall comply with Sections 110-16 and 110-17.

(FPN): For guarding of live parts on motors and generators, see Sections 430-11 and 430-14.

Exception: Switchboards of not over 250 volts dc between conductors, when located in substations or switchboard rooms accessible to qualified persons only, shall not be required to be dead-front.

530-65. Portable Substations. Wiring and equipment in portable substations shall conform to the sections applying to installations in permanently fixed substations, but, due to the limited space available, the working spaces shall be permitted to be reduced, provided that the equipment shall be so arranged that the operator can work safely, and so that other persons in the vicinity cannot accidentally come into contact with current-carrying parts or bring conducting objects into contact with them while they are energized.

530-66. Grounding at Substations. Noncurrent-carrying metal parts shall be grounded in accordance with Article 250.

Exception: Frames of dc circuit breakers installed on switchboards.

ARTICLE 540 — MOTION PICTURE PROJECTORS

Contents

A. General
540-1. Scope.

B. Definitions
540-2. Professional Projector.
540-3. Nonprofessional Projector.

C. Equipment and Projectors of the Professional Type
540-10. Motion Picture Projection Room Required.
540-11. Location of Associated Electrical Equipment.
  (a) Motor Generator Sets, Transformers, Rectifiers, Rheostats, and Similar Equipment.
  (b) Switches, Overcurrent Devices, or Other Equipment.

  (c) Emergency Systems.
540-12. Work Space.
540-13. Conductor Size.
540-14. Conductors on Lamps and Hot Equipment.
540-15. Flexible Cords.
540-20. Approval.
540-21. Marking.

D. Nonprofessional Projectors
540-31. Motion Picture Projection Room Not Required.
540-32. Approval.

E. Sound Recording and Reproduction
540-50. Sound Recording and Reproduction.

A. General

540-1. Scope. The provisions of this article apply to motion picture projection rooms, motion picture projectors, and associated equipment of the professional and nonprofessional types using incandescent, carbon arc, Xenon, or other light source equipment which develops hazardous gases, dust, or radiation.

(FPN): For further information, see Storage and Handling of Cellulose Nitrate Motion Picture Film, NFPA 40-1982.

The definitions of hazardous (classified) locations in Article 500 do not include a motion picture projection room as a hazardous (classified) location, even though some of the older types of film, such as cellulose nitrate film, rarely used now, are highly flammable. In comparison, cellulose acetate film, called "safety film," a much safer film, is in wide use today. Since film is not volatile at ordinary temperatures and no flammable gases are present, the wiring installation is not required to be suitable for hazardous (classified) locations as defined in Article 500, but should be done with special care to protect against the hazards of fire.

B. Definitions

540-2. Professional Projector: The professional projector is a type using 35- or 70-millimeter film which has a minimum width of 1⅜ inches (35 mm) and has on each edge 5.4 perforations per inch, or a type using carbon arc, Xenon, or other light source equipment which develops hazardous gases, dust, or radiation.

540-3. Nonprofessional Projector: Nonprofessional projectors are those types other than described in Section 540-2.

C. Equipment and Projectors of the Professional Type

540-10. Motion Picture Projection Room Required. Every professional-type projector shall be located within a projection room. Every projection room shall be of permanent construction, approved for the type of building in which the projection room is located. All projection ports, spotlight ports, viewing ports, and similar openings shall be provided with glass or other approved material so as to completely close the opening. Such rooms shall not be considered as hazardous (classified) locations as defined in Article 500.

(FPN): For further information on protecting openings in projection rooms handling cellulose nitrate motion picture film, see Life Safety Code, NFPA 101-1985 (ANSI).

540-11. Location of Associated Electrical Equipment.

(a) Motor Generator Sets, Transformers, Rectifiers, Rheostats, and Similar Equipment. Motor generator sets, transformers, rectifiers, rheostats, and similar equipment for the supply or control of current to projection or spotlight equipment shall, if practicable, be located in a separate room. Where placed in the projection room, they shall be so located or guarded that arcs or sparks cannot come in contact with film, and motor generator sets shall have the commutator end or ends protected as provided in Section 520-48.

(b) Switches, Overcurrent Devices, or Other Equipment. Switches, overcurrent devices, or other equipment not normally required or used for projectors, sound reproduction, flood or other special effect lamps, or other equipment shall not be installed in projection rooms.

Exception No. 1: Remote control switches for the control of auditorium lights or switches for the control of motors operating curtains and masking of the motion picture screen.

Exception No. 2: In projection rooms approved for use only with cellulose acetate (safety) film, the installation of appurtenant electrical equipment used in conjunction with the operation of the projection equipment and the control of lights, curtains, and audio equipment, etc., shall be permitted. In such projection rooms, a sign reading "Safety Film Only Permitted in This Room" shall be posted on the outside of each projection room door and within the projection room itself in a conspicuous location.

(c) Emergency Systems. Control of emergency systems shall comply with Article 700 — Emergency Systems.

The plan of a projection room of a motion picture theater is illustrated in Figure 540-1. This plan shows one stereopticon or "effect machine" (L), two spot machines (S), and three motion picture projectors (P).

A dc arc lamp is the light source in each of the six machines. The dc supply is furnished by two motor generator sets that are usually installed in soundproof areas so as not to interfere with the sound-reproducing equipment and are controlled from the generator panel in the projection room or booth. Two 500 MCM feeder cables are run from each generator to the dc panelboard.

A branch circuit consisting of two No. 2/0 cables runs from the dc panelboard to each projector (P) and to each spot machine (S). One of the two branch-circuit conductors runs directly to projector (P); the other passes through an auxiliary gutter to the bank of resistors in the rheostat room and then to the projector. The resistors are equipped with short-circuiting switches so that the total resistance in series with each arc may be preset to a desired value.

Since the stereopticon or effect machine (L) contains two arc lamps, two circuits with No. 1 AWG conductors are routed to this machine.

Section 540-13 requires that the conductors supplying outlets for arc and Xenon projectors of the professional type are not to be smaller than No. 8 AWG and are required to be of sufficient size for the projector employed. Hence, in each case the maximum current drawn by the lamps should be determined. In this example, when the arc lamps are adjusted for a large picture, the arc in each projector draws nearly 150 A. Four outlets, in addition to the main outlet for supplying the arc, are located at each projector for the following auxiliary circuits:

(1) Foot switches operating the shutters in front of the lenses for changing from one projector to another are supplied by Outlets F.

(2) Outlets G are for the No. 8 AWG equipment grounding conductor, which is connected to the projector frames and to a metal water pipe.

(3) Outlets C supply a small incandescent lamp inside the lamphouse and a lamp illuminating the turntable.

(4) Motors used to operate the projectors are supplied from Outlets M.

Two exhaust fans and two duct systems, one exhausting from the ceiling of the projection room and one connected to the arc-lamp housing of each machine, provide ventilation.

Figure 540-1. A typical layout of a projection room including associated generator equipment. Modern projectors contain rectifiers as an integral part of their equipment, thereby eliminating generators and other associated equipment.

540-12. Work Space. Each motion picture projector, floodlight, spotlight, or similar equipment shall have clear working space not less than 30 inches (762 mm) wide on each side and at the rear thereof.

Exception: One such space shall be permitted between adjacent pieces of equipment.

540-13. Conductor Size. Conductors supplying outlets for arc and Xenon projectors of the professional type shall not be smaller than No. 8 and shall be of sufficient size for the projector employed. Conductors for incandescent-type projectors shall conform to normal wiring standards as provided in Section 210-24.

540-14. Conductors on Lamps and Hot Equipment. Asbestos-covered conductors Type AA or other types of insulated conductors having a maximum operating temperature of 200°C (392°F) shall be used on all lamps or other equipment where the ambient temperature at the conductors as installed will exceed 50°C (122°F).

540-15. Flexible Cords. Cords approved for hard usage as provided in Table 400-4 shall be used on portable equipment.

540-20. Approval. Projectors and enclosures for arc, Xenon and incandescent lamps and rectifiers, transformers, rheostats and similar equipment shall be approved.

540-21. Marking. Projectors and other equipment shall be marked with the maker's name or trademark and with the voltage and current for which they are designed in accordance with Section 110-21.

D. Nonprofessional Projectors

540-31. Motion Picture Projection Room Not Required. Projectors of the nonprofessional or miniature type, when employing cellulose acetate (safety) film, shall be permitted to be operated without a projection room.

540-32. Approval. Projection equipment shall be listed.

E. Sound Recording and Reproduction

540-50. Sound Recording and Reproduction. Sound recording and reproduction equipment shall be installed as provided in Article 640.

ARTICLE 545 — MANUFACTURED BUILDING

Contents

A. General

545-1. Scope. This article covers requirements for a manufactured building and/or building components as herein defined.

545-2. Other Articles. Wherever the requirements of other articles of this Code and Article 545 differ, the requirements of Article 545 shall apply.

545-3. Definitions.

Manufactured Building: "Manufactured Building" means any building which is of closed construction and which is made or assembled in manufacturing facilities on or off the building site for installation, or assembly and installation on the building site, other than mobile homes or recreational vehicles.

823

ARTICLE 545—MANUFACTURED BUILDING

Building Component: "Building Component" means any subsystem, subassembly, or other system designed for use in or integral with or as part of a structure, which can include structural, electrical, mechanical, plumbing, and fire protection systems, and other systems affecting health and safety.

Building System: "Building System" means plans, specifications, and documentation for a system of manufactured building or for a type or a system of building components, which can include structural, electrical, mechanical, plumbing, and fire protection systems, and other systems affecting health and safety, and including such variations thereof as are specifically permitted by regulation, and which variations are submitted as part of the building system or amendment thereto.

Closed Construction: "Closed Construction" means any building, building component, assembly, or system manufactured in such a manner that all concealed parts of processes of manufacture cannot be inspected before installation at the building site without disassembly, damage, or destruction.

545-4. Wiring Methods.

(a) Methods Permitted. All raceway and cable wiring methods included in this Code and such other wiring systems specifically intended and listed for use in manufactured buildings shall be permitted with listed fittings and with fittings listed and identified for manufactured buildings.

(b) Securing Cables. In closed construction, cables shall be permitted to be secured only at cabinets, boxes, or fittings where No. 10 AWG or smaller conductors are used and protection against physical damage is provided as required by Section 300-4.

545-5. Service-Entrance Conductors. Service-entrance conductors shall meet the requirements of Article 230. Provisions shall be made to route the service-entrance conductors from the service equipment to the point of attachment of the service.

(FPN): See Section 310-10 for temperature limitation of conductors.

545-6. Installation of Service-Entrance Conductors. Service-entrance conductors shall be installed after erection at the building site.

Exception: Where point of attachment is known prior to manufacture.

545-7. Service Equipment Location. The service equipment shall be located at a readily accessible point nearest to the entrance of the conductors either inside or outside the building.

545-8. Protection of Conductors and Equipment. Protection shall be provided for exposed conductors and equipment during processes of manufacturing, packaging, in transit, and erection at the building site.

545-9. Boxes.

(a) Other Dimensions. Boxes of dimensions other than those required in Table 370-6(a) shall be permitted to be installed when tested, identified, and listed to applicable standards.

(b) Not Over 100 Cubic Inches. Any box not over 100 cubic inches in size, intended for mounting in closed construction, shall be affixed with anchors or clamps so as to provide a rigid and secure installation.

545-10. Receptacle or Switch with Integral Enclosure. A receptacle or switch with integral enclosure and mounting means, when tested, identified, and listed to applicable standards, shall be permitted to be installed.

See Figure 545-1 and the commentary following Section 300-15, Exception No. 5.

Figure 545-1. A special type of tool that is used to connect nonmetallic-sheathed cable to an approved boxless switch or receptacle. (*Amp Inc.*)

545-11. Bonding and Grounding. Prewired panels and/or building components shall provide for the bonding and/or grounding of all exposed metals likely to become energized, in accordance with Article 250, Parts E, F, and G.

545-12. Grounding Electrode Conductor. The grounding electrode conductor shall meet the requirements of Article 250, Part J. Provisions shall be made to route the grounding electrode conductor from the service equipment to the point of attachment to the grounding electrode.

545-13. Component Interconnections. Fittings and connectors which are intended to be concealed at the time of on-site assembly, when tested, identified, and listed to applicable standards, shall be permitted for on-site interconnection of modules or other building components. Such fittings and connectors shall be equal to the wiring method employed in insulation, temperature rise, fault-current withstand and shall be capable of enduring the vibration and minor relative motions occurring in the components of manufactured building.

Structural components or modules are usually constructed in manufacturing facilities and then transported over the road to a building site for complete assembly of, for instance, a dwelling unit, a motel, an office building, etc. At the on-site location, approved wiring methods are employed to interconnect two or more modules. Figures 545-2 and 545-3 show types of nonmetallic-sheathed cable connectors permitted for such interconnections.

Figure 545-2. A type of nonmetallic-sheathed cable connector used for interconnecting modules in a manufacturing building. The parts are shown before mating together. (*Amp Inc.*)

Figure 545-3. The nonmetallic-sheathed cable connector shown in Figure 545-2 after being joined together. (*Amp Inc.*)

ARTICLE 547 — AGRICULTURAL BUILDINGS

Contents

547-1. Scope. The provisions of this article shall apply to the following agricultural buildings or that part of a building as specified in (a) and (b) below.

(a) Excessive Dust and Dust with Water. Agricultural buildings where excessive dust and dust with water may accumulate. Such buildings include all areas of totally enclosed and environmentally controlled poultry and livestock confinement systems, where litter dust, feed dust, including mineral feed particles, may accumulate and enclosed areas of similar or like nature.

(b) Corrosive Atmosphere. Agricultural buildings where a corrosive atmosphere exists. Such buildings include totally enclosed and environmentally controlled areas where (1) poultry and animal excrement may cause corrosive vapors in the confinement area; (2) corrosive particles may combine with water; (3) the area is damp and wet by reason of periodic washing for cleaning and sanitizing with water and cleansing agents; (4) similar conditions exist.

547-2. Other Articles. For agricultural buildings not having conditions as specified in Section 547-1, the electrical installations shall be made in accordance with the applicable articles in this Code.

547-3. General. Electrical equipment or devices installed in accordance with the provisions of this article shall be installed in a manner such that they will function at full rating without developing surface temperatures in excess of the specified normal safe operating range of the equipment or device.

547-4. Wiring Methods. In agricultural buildings as described in Section 547-1(a) and (b), Types UF, NMC, SNM, copper SE, or other cables or raceways suitable for the location, with approved termination fittings, shall be the wiring methods employed. Article 320 wiring methods shall be permitted for Section 547-1(a). Buildings wired in accordance with the provisions of Article 502 shall be permitted. All cables shall be secured within 8 inches (203 mm) of each cabinet, box, or fitting.

> Where cables are installed in agricultural buildings, they are required to be secured within 8 in. (20.3 mm) of cabinets, boxes, or fittings. This distance is less than that required for cables in other types of occupancies.

(FPN): See Sections 300-7 and 347-9 for installation of raceway systems exposed to widely different temperatures.

(a) Boxes, Fittings, and Wiring Devices. All boxes and fittings shall comply with Section 547-5.

(b) Flexible Connections. Where necessary to employ flexible connections, dusttight flexible connectors, liquidtight flexible metal conduit, or flexible cord listed and identified for hard usage shall be used. All shall be used with listed and identified fittings.

547-5. Switches, Circuit Breakers, Controllers, and Fuses. Switches, circuit breakers, controllers, and fuses, including pushbuttons, relays and similar devices, used in buildings described in Section 547-1(a) and (b), shall be provided with a weatherproof, corrosion-resistant enclosure designed to minimize the entrance of dust, water, and corrosive elements, and shall be equipped with a telescoping or close-fitting cover.

547-6. Motors. Motors and other rotating electrical machinery shall be totally enclosed or so designed as to minimize the entrance of dust, moisture, or corrosive particles.

547-7. Lighting Fixtures. Lighting fixtures installed in agricultural buildings described in Section 547-1 shall comply with the following:

(a) Minimize the Entrance of Dust. Lighting fixtures shall be installed to minimize the entrance of dust, foreign matter, moisture, and corrosive material.

(b) Exposed to Physical Damage. Any lighting fixture that may be exposed to physical damage shall be protected by a suitable guard.

(c) Exposed to Water. A fixture that may be exposed to water from condensation and/or building cleansing water or solution shall be watertight.

547-8. Grounding, Bonding, and Equipotential Plane.

(a) Grounding and Bonding. Grounding and bonding shall comply with Article 250.

(FPN): See Section 250-21 for objectionable current over grounding conductors.

Neutral-to-earth potentials can be increased [see commentary following Sections 547-8(b) and 547-8(c)] when services (to different farms, for example) are tied together. Where neutral-to-earth potentials are a problem, separation of the service supplying the building where the problem exists from other services may be part of the solution. The utility may also provide a primary-to-secondary neutral isolator at or near its power transformer to isolate a farm from other electrical system impacts.

Exception: The main bonding jumper shall not be required at the distribution panelboard in or on buildings housing livestock or poultry where all the following conditions are met:

a. All buildings and premises wiring are under the same ownership.

b. An equipment grounding conductor of the same size as the circuit conductors is run with the supply conductors.

c. Service disconnecting means is provided at the distribution point for supply to those buildings.

d. The equipment grounding conductor is bonded to the grounded circuit conductor at the service equipment.

e. A grounding electrode is provided and connected to the equipment grounding conductor in the distribution panelboard.

(b) Concrete Embedded Elements. Wire mesh or other conductive elements where provided in the concrete floor of animal confinement areas to provide an equipotential plane shall be bonded to the building grounding electrode system. The bonding conductor shall be copper, insulated, covered or bare, not smaller than No. 8. The means of bonding to wire mesh or conductive elements shall be by pressure connectors or clamps of brass, copper, copper alloy or an equally substantial approved means.

Equipotential Plane: An equipotential plane is an area where a wire mesh or other conductive elements are embedded in concrete, bonded to all adjacent conductive equipment, structures, or surfaces and connected to the electrical grounding system to prevent a difference in voltage from developing within the plane.

(FPN): If a wire mesh or other conductive grid is embedded in a concrete floor or platform, and if this grid is bonded to the electrical system grounding bus, livestock making contact between the concrete floor or platform and the equipment or metal structure will be less likely to be exposed to a level of voltage that may alter animal behavior or productivity.

The requirements in the Exception to Section 547-8(a) and in Section 547-8(b) address the so-called "stray voltage" problem resulting from the neutral-to-earth potentials common in electrical systems. In most occupancies this neutral-to-earth potential does not result in a problem because, under normal conditions, it involves only a fraction of a volt up to a few volts, steady-state. However, livestock (dairy cows in particular) are very sensitive to voltage differences, and a potential difference of only ½ volt or so may affect their behavior and milk production. Dairy cows may be exposed to these neutral-to-earth potentials when they are standing on wet concrete and touch a metal water or feeder trough, for example. The concrete is at approximately earth potential, and the metal trough may be connected to the building service neutral by the equipment grounding conductor for the water-pump motor or feeder motor.

The neutral-to-earth potential on any system is a function of the neutral circuit impedances, the ground resistances of the many grounding electrodes in the typical system where transformer primary and secondary neutral conductors are connected together, the current in the primary and secondary neutral conductors, and other variables. The neutral-to-earth potential usually increases momentarily when 120-volt motors start because of the larger current, and therefore larger voltage drop in the branch-circuit and feeder neutral conductors.

The Exception to Section 547-8(a) maintains the low-impedance path in the grounding conductor circuit needed to rapidly clear ground faults. However, since it permits separation of the grounded (neutral) and equipment grounding conductors at the livestock building disconnect, the voltage drop on the feeder neutral does not appear as a voltage differential on grounded equipment in the building. See Figure 547-1.

Where the equipment grounding conductor with the supply (feeder) conductors to the livestock or poultry building is run underground, it is required to be copper, insulated or covered. See Sections 250-24 and 547-7(c).

(c) Separate Equipment Grounding Conductor. In agricultural buildings as described in Sections 547-1(a) and (b), noncurrent-carrying metal parts of equipment, raceways, and other enclosures where required to be grounded, shall be grounded by a copper equipment grounding conductor installed between the equipment and the building disconnecting means. If installed underground, the equipment grounding conductor shall be insulated or covered.

The intent of Section 547-8(c) is to improve the longevity of equipment grounding conductors in the highly corrosive locations typical of many farm buildings.

(FPN): Grounding electrode system resistances lower than required by Article 250, Part H, may reduce potential differences in livestock facilities.

The minimum system grounding requirements achieved by the grounding electrode systems covered in Article 250, Part H are adequate for electrical safety,

829

Figure 547-1. A main bonding jumper is not required at livestock or poultry buildings in accordance with Section 547-8(a), Exception. Overcurrent devices for other circuits are not shown in order to simplify drawing. Note that there may be distribution points (panelboards) between the service and the livestock or poultry building.

but may not be adequate where neutral-to-earth potentials are a problem. See commentary following Section 547-8(b). Resistances to ground in the order of 0.5 to 4 ohms may be needed.

ARTICLE 550 — MOBILE HOMES
AND MOBILE HOME PARKS

Contents

550-1. Scope. The provisions of this article cover the electrical conductors and equipment installed within or on mobile homes, the conductors that connect mobile homes to a supply of electricity, and the installation of electrical wiring, fixtures, equipment, and appurtenances related to electrical installations within a mobile home park up to the mobile home service-entrance conductors or, if none, the mobile home service equipment.

The Federal Mobile Home Construction and Safety Standard, issued by the Federal Housing and Urban Development Administration (HUD), has incorporated many of the provisions of Article 550 of the *NEC*. The federal standard contains the requirements for electrical systems, conductors, and equipment installed within or on mobile homes and the conductors that connect mobile homes to a supply of electricity.

The regulations pertaining to electrical systems are located in the Code of Federal Regulations, Title 24, Sections 3280.801 through 3280.816. It is required that new mobile homes comply with the federal standard. In some cases, HUD has delegated the enforcement of this standard to state and private inspection agencies and to qualified testing laboratories.

See Article 545 for the requirements for manufactured buildings.

550-2. Definitions.

Appliance, Fixed: An appliance which is fastened or otherwise secured at a specific location.

Appliance, Portable: An appliance which is actually moved or can easily be moved from one place to another in normal use.

(FPN): For the purpose of this article, the following major appliances other than built-in are considered portable if cord-connected: refrigerators, gas range equipment, clothes washers, dishwashers without booster heaters, or other similar appliances.

Appliance, Stationary: An appliance which is not easily moved from one place to another in normal use.

Distribution Panelboard: See definition of panelboard in Article 100.

Feeder Assembly: The overhead or under-chassis feeder conductors, including the grounding conductor, together with the necessary fittings and equipment or a power-supply cord listed for mobile home use, designed for the purpose of delivering energy from the source of electrical supply to the distribution panelboard within the mobile home.

Laundry Area: An area containing or designed to contain either a laundry tray, clothes washer, and/or a clothes dryer.

Mobile Home: A factory-assembled structure or structures equipped with the necessary service connections and made so as to be readily movable as a unit or units on its own running gear and designed to be used as a dwelling unit(s) without a permanent foundation.

(FPN): The phrase "without a permanent foundation" indicates that the support system is constructed with the intent that the mobile home placed thereon will be moved from time to time at the convenience of the owner.

See commentary following Section 550-4(b).

Mobile Home Accessory Building or Structure: Any awning, cabana, ramada, storage cabinet, carport, fence, windbreak, or porch established for the use of the occupant of the mobile home upon a mobile home lot.

Mobile Home Lot: A designated portion of a mobile home park designed for the accommodation of one mobile home and its accessory buildings or structures for the exclusive use of its occupants.

Mobile Home Park: A contiguous parcel of land which is used for the accommodation of occupied mobile homes.

Mobile Home Service Equipment: The equipment containing the disconnecting means, overcurrent protective devices, and receptacles or other means for connecting a mobile home feeder assembly.

Park Electrical Wiring Systems: All of the electrical wiring, fixtures, equipment, and appurtenances related to electrical installations within a mobile home park, including the mobile home service equipment.

550-3. Other Articles. Wherever the requirements of other articles of this Code and Article 550 differ, the requirements of Article 550 shall apply.

550-4. General Requirements.

(a) Mobile Home Not Intended as a Dwelling Unit. A mobile home not intended as a dwelling unit, as for example equipped for sleeping purposes only, contractor's on-site offices, construction job dormitories, mobile studio dressing rooms, banks, clinics, mobile stores, or intended for the display or demonstration of merchandise or machinery, shall not be required to meet the provisions of this article pertaining to the number or capacity of circuits required. It shall, however, meet all other applicable requirements of this article if provided with an electrical installation intended to be energized from a 120-volt or 120/240-volt ac power supply system. Where different voltage is required by either design or available power supply system, adjustment shall be made in accordance with other articles and sections for the voltage used.

(b) In Other than Mobile Home Parks. Mobile homes installed in other than mobile home parks shall comply with the provisions of this article.

It is intended that a mobile home constructed under the requirements of Article 550 be installed in accordance with the requirements of Article 550, including the requirement of Section 550-5(a), even though the mobile home may be installed on a permanent foundation.

(c) Connection to Wiring System. The provisions of this article apply to mobile homes intended for connection to a wiring system rated 120/240 volts, nominal, 3-wire ac, with grounded neutral.

(d) Listed or Labeled. All electrical materials, devices, appliances, fittings, and other equipment shall be listed or labeled by a qualified testing agency and shall be connected in an approved manner when installed.

A. Mobile Homes

550-5. Power Supply.

(a) Service Equipment. The mobile home service equipment shall be located adjacent to the mobile home and not mounted in or on the mobile home. The power supply to the mobile home shall be a feeder assembly consisting of not more than one listed 50-ampere mobile home power-supply cord with integral molded cap, or a permanently installed circuit.

Exception: A mobile home that is factory-equipped with gas or oil-fired central heating equipment and cooking appliances shall be permitted to be provided with a listed mobile home power-supply cord rated 40 amperes.

(b) Power-Supply Cord. If the mobile home has a power-supply cord, it shall be permanently attached to the distribution panelboard or to a junction box permanently connected to the distribution panelboard, with the free end terminating in an attachment plug cap.

Cords with adapters and pigtail ends, extension cords, and similar items shall not be attached to, or shipped with, a mobile home.

A suitable clamp or the equivalent shall be provided at the distribution panelboard knockout to afford strain relief for the cord to prevent strain from being transmitted to the terminals when the power-supply cord is handled in its intended manner.

The cord shall be a listed type with four conductors, one of which shall be identified by a continuous green color or a continuous green color with one or more yellow stripes for use as the grounding conductor.

(c) Attachment Plug Cap. The attachment plug cap shall be a 3-pole, 4-wire, grounding type, rated 50 amperes, 125/250 volts with a configuration as shown in Figure 550-5(c) and intended for use with the 50-ampere, 125/250 receptacle configuration shown in Figure 550-5(c). It shall be molded of butyl rubber, neoprene, or other materials which have been found suitable for the purpose, and shall be molded to the flexible cord so that it adheres tightly to the cord at the point where the cord enters the attachment plug cap. If a right-angle cap is used, the configuration shall be so oriented that the grounding member is farthest from the cord.

(FPN): Complete details of the 50-ampere plug and receptacle shown in Figure 550-5(c) can be found in ANSI Standard Dimensions of Caps, Plugs and Receptacles, C73.17-1972.

Receptacle   Cap

125 / 250-volt, 50-amp,
3-pole, 4-wire, grounding type

Figure 550-5(c). 50-ampere, 125/250 volt receptacle and attachment-plug-cap configurations, 3-pole, 4-wire, grounding types, used for mobile home supply cords and mobile home parks.

(d) Overall Length of a Power-Supply Cord. The overall length of a power-supply cord, measured from the end of the cord, including bared leads, to the face of the attachment plug cap shall not be less than 21 feet (6.4 m) and shall not exceed 36½ feet (11.13 m). The length of the cord from the face of the attachment plug cap to the point where the cord enters the mobile home shall not be less than 20 feet (6.1 m).

(e) Marking. The power-supply cord shall bear the following marking: "For use with mobile homes — 40 amperes" or "For use with mobile homes — 50 amperes."

(f) Point of Entrance. The point of entrance of the feeder assembly to the mobile home shall be in the exterior wall, floor, or roof.

(FPN): For location of distribution panelboard, see Section 550-6(a).

(FPN): For location of attachment of feeder assembly, see Section 550-23(d).

(g) Protected. Where the cord passes through walls or floors, it shall be protected by means of conduits and bushings or equivalent. The cord shall be permitted to be installed within the mobile home walls, provided a continuous raceway having a maximum size of 1¼ inches (31.8 mm) is installed from the branch-circuit panelboard to the underside of the mobile home floor.

(h) Protection Against Corrosion and Mechanical Damage. Permanent provisions shall be made for the protection of the attachment plug cap of the power-supply cord and any connector cord assembly or receptacle against corrosion and mechanical damage if such devices are in an exterior location while the mobile home is in transit.

(i) Mast Weatherhead or Raceway. Where the calculated load exceeds 50 amperes or where a permanent feeder is used, the supply shall be by means of:

(1) One mast weatherhead installation installed in accordance with Article 230 containing four continuous, insulated, color-coded, feeder conductors, one of which shall be an equipment grounding conductor; or,

(2) A metal raceway or rigid nonmetallic conduit from the disconnecting means in the mobile home to the underside of the mobile home with provisions for the attachment to a suitable junction box or fitting to the raceway on the underside of the mobile home [with or without conductors as in Section 550-5(i)(1)].

In some localities, mobile homes are permanently connected, as permitted in Section 550-5(i). In this regard, local requirements must be checked for the approved method of installing overhead and underground feeder assemblies.

A raceway is required from the distribution panelboard in the mobile home to the underside of the mobile home. Whether the feeder conductors in this raceway are pulled in by the mobile home manufacturer or by installers in the field is optional. No matter who installs the conductors, they should comprise four continuous, insulated, color-coded conductors, as indicated in Section 550-5(i)(1).

550-6. Disconnecting Means and Branch-Circuit Protective Equipment. The branch-circuit equipment shall be permitted to be combined with the disconnecting means as a single assembly. Such a combination shall be permitted to be designated as a distribution panelboard. If a fused distribution panelboard is used, the maximum fuse size for the mains shall be plainly marked, with lettering at least ¼ inch (6.4 mm) high and visible when fuses are changed.

When plug fuses and fuseholders are used, they shall be tamper-resistant, Type S enclosed in dead-front fuse panelboards. Electrical distribution panelboards containing circuit breakers shall also be dead-front type.

(FPN): See Section 110-22 concerning identification of each disconnecting means and each service, feeder, or branch circuit at the point where it originated and the type marking needed.

(a) Disconnecting Means. A single disconnecting means shall be provided in each mobile home consisting of a circuit breaker, or a switch and fuses and its accessories installed in a readily accessible location near the point of entrance of the supply cord or conductors into the mobile home. The main circuit breakers or fuses shall be plainly marked "Main." This equipment shall contain a solderless type of grounding connector or bar for the purposes of grounding with sufficient terminals for all grounding conductors. The neutral bar termination of the grounded circuit conductors shall be insulated in accordance with Section 550-11(a). The disconnecting equipment shall have a rating suitable for the connected load. The distribution equipment, either circuit breaker or fused type, shall be located a minimum of 24 inches (610 mm) from the bottom of such equipment to the floor level of the mobile home.

ARTICLE 550—MOBILE HOMES AND PARKS

(FPN): See Section 550-15(b) for information on disconnecting means for branch circuits designed to energize heating and/or air-conditioning equipment located outside the mobile home, other than room air conditioners.

A distribution panelboard main circuit breaker shall be rated 50 amperes and employ a 2-pole circuit breaker rated 40 amperes for a 40-ampere supply cord, or 50 amperes for a 50-ampere supply cord. A distribution panelboard employing a disconnect switch and fuses shall be rated 60 amperes and shall employ a single 2-pole, 60-ampere fuseholder with 40- or 50-ampere main fuses for 40- or 50-ampere supply cords, respectively. The outside of the distribution panelboard shall be plainly marked with the fuse size.

The distribution panelboard shall be located in an accessible location, shall not be located in a bathroom, and shall be permitted to be located just inside a closet entry if the location is such that a clear space of 6 inches (152 mm) to easily ignitible materials is maintained in front of the distribution panelboard, and the distribution panelboard door can be extended to its full open position (at least 90 degrees). A clear working space at least 30 inches (762 mm) wide and 30 inches (762 mm) in front of the distribution panelboard shall be provided. This space shall extend from floor to the top of the distribution panelboard.

(b) Branch-Circuit Protective Equipment. Branch-circuit distribution equipment shall be installed in each mobile home and shall include overcurrent protection for each branch circuit consisting of either circuit breakers or fuses.

The branch-circuit overcurrent devices shall be rated: (1) not more than the circuit conductors; and (2) not more than 150 percent of the rating of a single appliance rated 13.3 amperes or more which is supplied by an individual branch circuit; but (3) not more than the fuse size marked on the air conditioner or other motor-operated appliance.

A 15-ampere multiple receptacle shall be permitted when connected to a 20-ampere laundry circuit.

(c) Two-Pole Circuit Breakers. When circuit breakers are provided for branch-circuit protection, 240-volt circuits shall be protected by a 2-pole common or companion trip, or handle-tied paired circuit breakers.

(d) Electrical Nameplates. A metal nameplate on the outside adjacent to the feeder assembly entrance shall read: "This Connection for 120/240-Volt, 3-Pole, 4-Wire, 60 Hertz, . . . Ampere Supply." The correct ampere rating shall be marked in the blank space.

550-7. Branch Circuits. The number of branch circuits required shall be determined in accordance with (a) through (c) below.

(a) Lighting. Based on 3 volt-amperes per square foot (0.093 sq m) times outside dimensions of the mobile home (coupler excluded) divided by 120 volts to determine the number of 15- or 20-ampere lighting area circuits, e.g.,

$$\frac{3 \times \text{Length} \times \text{Width}}{120 \times 15 \text{ (or 20)}} = \text{No. of 15- (or 20-) ampere circuits.}$$

The lighting circuits shall be permitted to serve built-in gas ovens with electric service only for lights, clocks or timers, or listed cord-connected garbage disposal units.

(b) Small Appliances. For the small appliance load in kitchen, pantry, family room, dining room, and breakfast rooms of mobile homes, two or more 20-ampere appliance branch circuits in addition to the branch circuits specified in Section 550-7(a) shall be provided for all receptacle outlets in these rooms, and such circuits shall have no other outlets. Receptacle outlets supplied by at least two appliance receptacle branch circuits shall be installed in the kitchen.

(c) General Appliances. (Including furnace, water heater, range, and central or room air conditioner, etc.) There shall be one or more circuits of adequate rating in accordance with the following:

(1) Ampere rating of fixed appliances not over 50 percent of circuit rating if lighting outlets (receptacles, other than kitchen, dining area, and laundry, considered as lighting outlets) are on the same circuit;

(2) For fixed appliances on a circuit without lighting outlets, the sum of rated amperes shall not exceed the branch-circuit rating. Motor loads or other continuous duty loads shall not exceed 80 percent of the branch-circuit rating;

(3) The rating of a single cord- and plug-connected appliance on a circuit having no other outlets shall not exceed 80 percent of the circuit rating;

(4) The rating of a range branch circuit shall be based on the range demand as specified for ranges in Section 550-13(b)(5).

(FPN): For the laundry branch circuit, see Section 220-4(c).

(FPN): For central air conditioning, see Article 440.

550-8. Receptacle Outlets.

(a) Grounding-type Receptacle Outlets. All receptacle outlets: (1) shall be of grounding type; (2) shall be installed according to Section 210-7; and (3) except when supplying specific appliances, receptacles shall be 15- or 20-ampere, 125-volt, either single or duplex and shall accept parallel-blade attachment plugs.

(b) Ground-Fault Circuit-Interrupters. All 120-volt, single-phase, 15- and 20-ampere receptacle outlets installed outdoors and in bathrooms, including receptacles in light fixtures, shall have ground-fault circuit protection for personnel. Ground-fault circuit protection for personnel shall be provided for receptacle outlets located adjacent to any lavatory. Feeders supplying branch circuits shall be permitted to be protected by a ground-fault circuit-interrupter in lieu of the provision for such interrupters specified herein.

No receptacle shall be required in the area occupied by a toilet, toilet and/or shower, or toilet and tub/shower enclosure area. If a receptacle is installed in such an area, it shall have ground-fault circuit protection for personnel.

(c) Cord-Connected Fixed Appliance. A grounding-type receptacle outlet shall be provided for each cord-connected fixed appliance installed.

(d) Required Receptacle Outlets. Receptacle outlets required in all rooms other than the bath, closet, and hall areas shall be installed so that no point along the floor line is more than 6 feet (1.83 m) measured horizontally from an outlet in that space. Countertops shall have receptacles located every 6 feet (1.83 m). The contiguous measurement of countertop and floor line shall be permitted when measured from the required receptacle in rooms requiring small appliance circuits. Receptacle outlets on small appliance circuits shall not be included in determining the spacing for receptacle outlets of other circuits.

Exception No. 1: Where the measured distance is interrupted by an interior doorway, sink, refrigerator, range, oven, or cooktop, an additional receptacle outlet shall be provided when the interrupted space is at least 2 feet (610 mm) wide at the floor line and at least 12 inches (305 mm) wide at the countertop.

Exception No. 2: Receptacles concealed by stationary appliances shall not be considered as the required outlets.

Exception No. 3: The distance along a floor line occupied by a door opened fully against that space need not be included in establishing the horizontal measurement if the door swing is limited to 90 degrees nominal by that wall space.

ARTICLE 550—MOBILE HOMES AND PARKS

Exception No. 4: Receptacle requirements for bar-type counters and for fixed room dividers no more than 8 feet (2.44 m) in length shall be permitted to be provided by a receptacle outlet in the wall at the nearest point where the counter or room divider attaches to the wall.

(FPN): To qualify as a "fixed room divider" the divider cannot be more than 8 feet (2.44 m) in length nor more than 4 feet (1.22 m) in height and may be attached to a wall at one end only.

(e) Outdoor Receptacle Outlets. At least one receptacle outlet shall be installed outdoors. A receptacle outlet located in a compartment accessible from the outside of the mobile home shall be considered an outdoor receptacle. Outdoor receptacle outlets shall be protected as required in Section 550-8(b).

(f) Receptacle Outlets Not Permitted. Receptacle outlets shall not be installed in or within reach [30 inches (762 mm)] of a shower or bathtub space.

(g) Heat Tape Outlet. A heat tape outlet, if installed, and if located on the underside of the mobile home at least 3 feet (914 mm) from the outside edge, shall not be considered an outdoor receptacle outlet. A heat tape outlet, if installed, shall be located within 2 feet (610 mm) of the cold water inlet.

550-9. Fixtures and Appliances.

(a) Fasten Appliances in Transit. Facilities shall be provided to securely fasten appliances when the mobile home is in transit. (See Section 550-11 for provisions on grounding.)

(1) Pendant-type fixtures or pendant cords shall be listed and identified for the interconnection of building components.

(2) Where a lighting fixture is installed over a bathtub or in a shower stall, it shall be of the enclosed and gasketed type listed for wet locations.

(3) The switch for shower lighting fixtures and exhaust fans located over a tub or in a shower stall shall be located outside the tub or shower space.

(b) Accessibility. Every appliance shall be accessible for inspection, service, repair, or replacement without removal of permanent construction.

550-10. Wiring Methods and Materials.
Except as specifically limited in this section, the wiring methods and materials included in this Code shall be used in mobile homes.

(a) Nonmetallic Boxes. Nonmetallic boxes shall be permitted only with nonmetallic cable or nonmetallic conduit.

(b) Nonmetallic Cable Protection. Nonmetallic cable located 15 inches (381 mm) or less above the floor, if exposed, shall be protected from physical damage by covering boards, guard strips, or raceways. Cable likely to be damaged by stowage shall be so protected in all cases.

(c) Metal-Covered and Nonmetallic Cable Protection. Metal-covered and nonmetallic cables shall be permitted to pass through the centers of the wide side of 2-inch by 4-inch studs. However, they shall be protected where they pass through 2-inch by 2-inch studs or at other studs or frames where the cable or armor would be less than 1½ inches (38 mm) from the inside or outside surface of the studs where the wall covering materials are in contact with the studs. Steel plates on each side of the cable, or a tube, with not less than No. 16 MSG wall thickness shall be required to protect the cable. These plates or tubes shall be securely held in place.

(d) Metal Faceplates. Where metal faceplates are used, they shall be effectively grounded.

(e) Installation Requirements. If a range, clothes dryer, or similar appliance is connected by metal-covered cable or flexible metal conduit, a length of free cable or conduit shall be provided to permit moving the appliance. The cable or flexible metal conduit shall be secured to the wall. A length of not less than 3 feet (914 mm) of free cable or conduit shall be provided to permit moving the appliance. Type NM or Type SE cable shall not be used to connect a range or dryer. This shall not prohibit the use of Type NM or Type SE cable between the branch-circuit overcurrent protective device and a junction box or range or dryer receptacle.

(f) Conduit. Where rigid metal conduit or intermediate metal conduit is terminated at an enclosure with a locknut and bushing connection, two locknuts shall be provided, one inside and one outside of the enclosure. Rigid nonmetallic conduit shall be permitted. All cut ends of conduit shall be reamed or otherwise finished to remove rough edges.

(g) Switches. Switches shall be rated as follows:

(1) For lighting circuits, switches shall have a 10-ampere, 120- 125-volt rating, or higher, if needed for the connected load.

(2) For motors or other loads, switches shall have ampere or horsepower ratings, or both, adequate for loads controlled. (An "ac general-use" snap switch shall be permitted to control a motor 2 horsepower or less with full-load current not over 80 percent of the switch ampere rating.)

(h) Free Conductor at Each Box. At least 4 inches (102 mm) of free conductor shall be left at each box except where conductors are intended to loop without joints.

(i) Under-Chassis Wiring. (Exposed to weather.)

(1) Where outdoor or under-chassis line-voltage wiring is exposed to moisture or physical damage, it shall be protected by rigid metal conduit or intermediate metal conduit. The conductors shall be suitable for wet locations.

Exception: Electrical metallic tubing or rigid nonmetallic conduit shall be permitted where closely routed against frames and equipment enclosures.

(2) The cables or conductors shall be Type NMC, TW, or equivalent.

(j) Boxes, Fittings, and Cabinets. Boxes, fittings, and cabinets shall be securely fastened in place and shall be supported from a structural member of the home, either directly or by using a substantial brace.

Exception: Snap-in type boxes. Boxes provided with special wall or ceiling brackets and wiring devices with integral enclosures, which securely fasten to walls or ceilings and are identified for the use, shall be permitted without support from a structural member or brace. The testing and approval shall include the wall and ceiling construction systems for which the boxes and devices are intended to be used.

(k) Appliance Terminal Connections. Appliances having branch-circuit terminal connections which operate at temperatures higher than 60°C (140°F) shall have circuit conductors as described in (1) or (2) below.

(1) Branch-circuit conductors having an insulation suitable for the temperature encountered shall be permitted to be run directly to the appliance.

(2) Conductors having an insulation suitable for the temperature encountered shall be run from the appliance terminal connection to a readily accessible outlet box placed at least 1 foot (305 mm) from the appliance. These conductors shall be in a suitable raceway which shall extend for at least 4 feet (1.22 m).

(l) Component Interconnections. Fittings and connectors which are intended to be concealed at the time of assembly shall be listed and identified for the interconnection of building components. Such fittings and connectors shall be equal to the wiring method employed in insulation, temperature rise, fault-current withstanding, and shall be capable of enduring the vibration and shock occurring in mobile home transportation.

550-11. Grounding. Grounding of both electrical and nonelectrical metal parts in a mobile home shall be through connection to a grounding bus in the mobile home distribution panelboard. The grounding bus shall be grounded through the green-colored insulated conductor in the supply cord or the feeder wiring to the service ground in the service-entrance equipment located adjacent to the mobile home location. Neither the frame of the mobile home nor the frame of any appliance shall be connected to the neutral conductor in the mobile home.

(a) Insulated Neutral.

(1) The grounded circuit conductor (neutral) shall be insulated from the grounding conductors and from equipment enclosures and other grounded parts. The grounded (neutral) circuit terminals in the distribution panelboard and in ranges, clothes dryers, counter-mounted cooking units, and wall-mounted ovens shall be insulated from the equipment enclosure. Bonding screws, straps, or buses in the distribution panelboard or in appliances shall be removed and discarded.

(2) Connections of ranges and clothes dryers with 120/240-volt, 3-wire ratings shall be made with 4-conductor cord and 3-pole, 4-wire, grounding-type plugs, or by Type AC cable, Type MC cable, or conductors enclosed in flexible metal conduit.

(b) Equipment Grounding Means.

(1) The green-colored insulated grounding wire in the supply cord or permanent feeder wiring shall be connected to the grounding bus in the distribution panelboard or disconnecting means.

(2) In the electrical system, all exposed metal parts, enclosures, frames, lamp fixture canopies, etc., shall be effectively bonded to the grounding terminal or enclosure of the distribution panelboard.

(3) Cord-connected appliances, such as washing machines, clothes dryers, refrigerators, and the electrical system of gas ranges, etc., shall be grounded by means of a cord with grounding conductor and grounding-type attachment plug.

(c) Bonding of Noncurrent-Carrying Metal Parts.

(1) All exposed noncurrent-carrying metal parts that may become energized shall be effectively bonded to the grounding terminal or enclosure of the distribution panelboard. A bonding conductor shall be connected between the distribution panelboard and accessible terminal on the chassis.

(2) Grounding terminals shall be of the solderless type and listed as pressure-terminal connectors recognized for the wire size used. The bonding conductor shall be solid or stranded, insulated or bare, and shall be No. 8 copper minimum, or equal. The bonding conductor shall be routed so as not to be exposed to physical damage.

(3) Metallic gas, water, and waste pipes and metallic air-circulating ducts shall be considered bonded if they are connected to the terminal on the chassis [see Section 550-11(c)(1)] by clamps, solderless connectors, or by suitable grounding-type straps.

(4) Any metallic roof and exterior covering shall be considered bonded if (a) the metal panels overlap one another and are securely attached to the wood or metal frame parts by metallic fasteners, and (b) if the lower panel of the metallic exterior covering is secured by metallic fasteners at a cross member of the chassis by two metal straps per mobile home unit or section at opposite ends.

The bonding strap material shall be a minimum of 4 inches (102 mm) in width of material equivalent to the skin or a material of equal or better electrical conductivity. The straps shall be fastened with paint-penetrating fittings, such as screws and starwashers or equivalent.

The provisions of Section 550-5 require that the feeder assembly for a mobile home consist of four color-coded insulated conductors, one of which is the grounded conductor (white) and one of which is used for grounding purposes (green). Thus, the "grounded" and "grounding" conductors are kept independent of each other and are connected only at the service equipment (at the point of connection of the grounding electrode conductor). Grounding of both electrical and nonelectrical metal parts, including the frame of the mobile home or the frame of any appliance, is accomplished by connection to the equipment grounding bus [never to the grounded conductor (neutral bus)].

Bonding screws, straps, or buses, which bond the grounded (neutral) circuit conductors to the noncurrent-carrying metal parts in the mobile home panelboard or in appliances (ranges, clothes dryers, etc.), are required to be removed and discarded.

550-12. Testing.

(a) Dielectric Strength Test. The wiring of each mobile home shall be subjected to a 1-minute, 900-volt, dielectric strength test (with all switches closed) between live parts (including neutral) and the mobile home ground. Alternatively, the test shall be permitted to be performed at 1,080 volts for 1 second. This test shall be performed after branch circuits are complete and after fixtures or appliances are installed.

Exception: Listed fixtures or appliances shall not be required to withstand the dielectric strength test.

(b) Continuity and Operational Tests and Polarity Checks. Each mobile home shall be subjected to:

(1) An electrical continuity test to assure that all exposed electrically conductive parts are properly bonded;

(2) An electrical operational test to demonstrate that all equipment, except water heaters and electric furnaces, is connected and in working order; and

(3) Electrical polarity checks of permanently wired equipment and receptacle outlets to determine that connections have been properly made.

550-13. Calculations.
The following method shall be employed in computing the supply-cord and distribution-panelboard load for each feeder assembly for each mobile home in lieu of the procedure shown in Article 220 and shall be based on a 3-wire, 120/240-volt supply with 120-volt loads balanced between the two legs of the 3-wire system.

ARTICLE 550—MOBILE HOMES AND PARKS

(a) Lighting and Small Appliance Load:

Lighting Volt-Amperes: Length times width of mobile home floor (outside dimensions) times 3 volt-amperes per square foot; e.g.,

Length × width × 3 = ...lighting volt-amperes.

Small Appliance Volt-Amperes: Number of circuits times 1,500 volt-amperes for each 20-ampere appliance receptacle circuit (see definition of Appliance, Portable with note) including 1,500 volt-amperes for laundry circuit; e.g.,

Number of circuits × 1,500 = ...small appliance volt-amperes.

Total: Lighting volt-amperes plus small appliance = ...total volt-amperes.

First 3,000 total volt-amperes at 100 percent plus remainder at 35 percent = ...
volt-amperes to be divided by 240 volts to obtain current (amperes) per leg.

(b) Total Load for Determining Power Supply. Total load for determining power supply is the summation of:

(1) Lighting and small appliance load as calculated in Section 550-13(a).

(2) Nameplate amperes for motors and heater loads (exhaust fans, air conditioners, electric, gas, or oil heating).

Omit smaller of the heating and cooling loads, except include blower motor if used as air-conditioner evaporator motor. Where an air conditioner is not installed and a 40-ampere power supply cord is provided, allow 15 amperes per leg for air conditioning.

(3) 25 percent of current of largest motor in (2).

(4) Total of nameplate amperes for: disposal, dishwasher, water heater, clothes dryer, wall-mounted oven, cooking units.

Where number of these appliances exceeds three, use 75 percent of total.

(5) Derive amperes for free-standing range (as distinguished from separate ovens and cooking units) by dividing values below by 240 volts.

Nameplate Rating	Use
0 thru 10,000 watts	80 percent of rating
over 10,000 thru 12,500 watts	8,000 volt-amperes
over 12,500 thru 13,500 watts	8,400 volt-amperes
over 13,500 thru 14,500 watts	8,800 volt-amperes
over 14,500 thru 15,500 watts	9,200 volt-amperes
over 15,500 thru 16,500 watts	9,600 volt-amperes
over 16,500 thru 17,500 watts	10,000 volt-amperes

(6) If outlets or circuits are provided for other than factory-installed appliances, include the anticipated load.

See following Example for illustration of application of this calculation.

Example

A mobile home floor is 70 feet × 10 feet and has two small appliance circuits, a 1000-volt-ampere, 240-volt heater, a 200-volt-ampere, 120-volt exhaust fan, a 400-volt-ampere, 120-volt dishwasher, and a 7000-volt-ampere electric range.

Lighting and small appliance load

Lighting 70 × 10 × 3 VA/sq ft =		2100 volt-amperes
Small appliance 1500 × 2 =		3000 volt-amperes
Laundry 1500 × 1 =		1500 volt-amperes
		6600 volt-amperes

1st 3000 volt-amperes at 100 percent .... 3000 volt-amperes
Remainder (6600–3000) at 35 percent .... 1260 volt-amperes

$$\frac{4260 \text{ volt-amperes}}{240 \text{ volts}} = 17.75 \text{ amperes per leg}$$

4260 volt-amperes

	Amperes per leg	
	A	B
Lighting and appliances	17.75	17.75
Heater, 1000 VA ÷ 240 volt =	4.2	4.2
Fan, 200VA ÷ 120 volt =	1.7	
Dishwasher, 400VA ÷ 120 =		3.3
Range, 7000 VA × .8 ÷ 240 =	23.3	23.3
Totals	46.95	48.55

Based on the higher current calculated for either leg, a minimum 50-ampere supply cord is required.

For SI units: one square foot = 0.093 square meter; one foot = 0.3048 meter.

(c) Optional Method of Calculation for Lighting and Appliance Load. For mobile homes, the optional method for calculating lighting and appliance load shown in Section 220-30 and Table 220-30 shall be permitted.

550-14. Interconnection of Multiple Section Mobile Home Units.

(a) Fixed-type Wiring. Approved and listed fixed-type wiring methods shall be used to join portions of a circuit which must be electrically joined which are located in adjacent sections of mobile homes after the home is installed on its support foundation. The circuit's junction shall be accessible for disassembly when the home is prepared for relocation.

(b) Disconnecting Means. Multiple section mobile homes not having permanently installed feeders, and which are to be moved from one location to another, shall be permitted to have disconnecting means with branch-circuit protective equipment in each unit when so located that after assembly or joining together of units, they shall not be interconnected on either the line side or the load side, except that the grounding means shall be electrically interconnected.

(FPN): Subsection (b) above applies to connection of previously constructed mobile homes where multiple feeder assemblies were allowed. The present Code does not permit more than one cord or feeder to a mobile home.

550-15. Outdoor Outlets, Fixtures, Air-Cooling Equipment, Etc.

(a) Listed for Outdoor Use. Outdoor fixtures and equipment shall be listed for outdoor use. Outdoor receptacle or convenience outlets shall be of a gasketed-cover type for use in wet locations.

(b) Outside Heating and/or Air-Conditioning Equipment. A mobile home provided with a branch circuit designed to energize heating and/or air-conditioning equipment located outside the mobile home, other than room air conditioners, shall have such branch-circuit conductors terminate in a listed outlet box, or disconnecting means, located on the outside of the mobile home. A label shall be permanently affixed adjacent to the outlet box and contain the following information:

> This connection is for heating and/or air-conditioning equipment. The branch circuit is rated at not more than _____ amperes, at _____ volts, 60-Hertz, _____ conductor ampacity. A disconnecting means shall be located within sight of the equipment.

The correct voltage and ampere rating shall be given. The tag shall be not less than 0.020 inch (508 micrometers), etched brass, stainless steel, anodized or alclad aluminum or equivalent. The tag shall not be less than 3 inches (76 mm) by 1¾ inches (44.5 mm) minimum size.

ARTICLE 550—MOBILE HOMES AND PARKS

B. Mobile Home Parks

550-21. Distribution System. The mobile home park secondary electrical distribution system to mobile home lots shall be single-phase, 120/240 volts, nominal. For the purpose of Part B, where the park service exceeds 240 volts, nominal, transformers and secondary distribution panelboards shall be treated as services.

(FPN): See Table 550-22 for calculation of load.

Section 550-4(c) applies to mobile homes intended for connection to a wiring system nominally rated 120/240 V, 3-wire ac, with a grounded neutral; therefore, distribution systems at mobile home parks must supply 120/240 V to the mobile home lot. Because appliances and other equipment are usually installed during the manufacturing process of mobile homes and are rated 120/240 V, a 120/208-V supply derived from a 4-wire, 120/208-V wye system is unsuitable.

Section 550-22(a) requires park electrical wiring systems to be calculated on the basis of not less than 16,000 VA (at 120/240 V) for each mobile home service; however, the ampacity of the feeder circuit conductors to each mobile home lot is not to be less than 100 A (at 120/240 V) according to Section 550-22(b).

550-22. Calculated Load.

(a) Minimum Allowable Demand Factors. Park electrical wiring systems shall be calculated (at 120/240 volts) on the larger of: (1) 16,000 volt-amperes for each mobile home lot, or (2) the load calculated in accordance with Section 550-13 for the largest typical mobile home that each lot will accept. It shall be permissible to compute the feeder or service load in accordance with Table 550-22. No demand factor shall be allowed for any other load, except as provided in this Code.

Table 550-22
Demand Factors for Feeders and Service-Entrance Conductors

Number of Mobile Home	Demand Factor (Percent)
1	100
2	55
3	44
4	39
5	33
6	29
7–9	28
10–12	27
13–15	26
16–21	25
22–40	24
41–60	23
61 and over	22

(b) Adequate Feeder Capacity. Mobile home lot feeder circuit conductors shall have adequate capacity for the loads supplied, and shall be rated at not less than 100 amperes at 120/240 volts.

See commentary following Section 550-21.

550-23. Mobile Home Service Equipment.

(a) Rating. Mobile home service equipment shall be rated at not less than 100 amperes, and provision shall be made for connecting a mobile home feeder assembly by a permanent wiring method. Power outlets used as mobile home service equipment shall also be permitted to contain receptacles rated up to 50 amperes with appropriate overcurrent protection. Fifty-ampere receptacles shall conform to the configuration shown in Figure 550-5(c).

(FPN): Complete details on the 50-ampere attachment plug cap configuration can be found in American National Standard Dimensions of Caps, Plugs and Receptacles, ANSI C73.17-1972.

(b) Additional Outside Electrical Equipment. Mobile home service equipment shall also contain a means for connecting a mobile home accessory building or structure or additional electrical equipment located outside a mobile home by a fixed wiring method.

(c) Additional Receptacles. Additional receptacles shall be permitted for connection of electrical equipment located outside the mobile home, and all such 125-volt, single-phase, 15- and 20-ampere receptacles shall be protected by a listed ground-fault circuit-interrupter protection.

(d) Location. Mobile home service equipment shall be readily accessible and shall be located in sight from and not more than 30 feet (9.14 m) from the exterior wall of the mobile home it serves.

(e) Mounting Height. Mobile home disconnecting means shall be located not less than 2 feet (610 mm) above finished grade or working platform. The disconnecting means shall be so installed that the center of the grip of the operating handle, when in its highest position, will not be more than 6½ feet (1.98 m) above the finished grade or working platform.

Mobile home service equipment is required to be located in sight from the mobile home, but the equipment can be up to 30 ft from any point on the exterior wall of the mobile home. This recognizes use of feeder raceways external to the mobile home.

(f) Grounded. Each mobile home service equipment shall be grounded in accordance with Article 250 for service equipment.

550-24. Feeder. Mobile home feeder conductors shall consist of a listed cord, factory-installed in accordance with Section 550-5(b), or a permanently installed feeder containing four continuous, insulated, color-coded conductors which shall be identified by the factory or field marking of the conductors in compliance with Section 310-12.

Figure 550-1. Mobile home service equipment and power outlet assembly showing metering, disconnecting means, overcurrent protective devices, and receptacle. (*Midwest*)

ARTICLE 551 — RECREATIONAL VEHICLES
AND RECREATIONAL VEHICLE PARKS

Contents

551-1. Scope. The provisions of this article cover the electrical conductors and equipment installed within or on recreational vehicles, the conductors that connect recreational vehicles to a supply of electricity, and the installation of equipment and devices related to electrical installations within a recreational vehicle park.

(FPN): For requirements on the installation of plumbing and heating systems in recreational vehicles, refer to Standard for Recreational Vehicles, NFPA 501C-1982 (ANSI).

Laws in many states require a factory inspection by state electrical inspectors. The requirements of such laws follow closely the requirements of NFPA 501C, Standard on Firesafety Criteria for Recreational Vehicles. Section 1-5 in NFPA 501C specifies that electrical installations in recreational vehicles shall comply with Part A of Article 551 and other applicable sections of the *Code*.

551-2. Definitions. (See Article 100 for other definitions.)

Air-Conditioning or Comfort-Cooling Equipment: All of that equipment intended or installed for the purpose of processing the treatment of air so as to control simultaneously its temperature, humidity, cleanliness, and distribution to meet the requirements of the conditioned space.

Appliance, Fixed: An appliance which is fastened or otherwise secured at a specific location.

Appliance, Portable: An appliance which is actually moved or can easily be moved from one place to another in normal use.

(FPN): For the purpose of this article, the following major appliances other than built-in are considered portable if cord-connected: refrigerators, gas range equipment, clothes washers, dishwashers without booster heaters, or other similar appliances.

Appliance, Stationary: An appliance which is not easily moved from one place to another in normal use.

Camping Trailer: A vehicular portable unit mounted on wheels and constructed with collapsible partial side walls which fold for towing by another vehicle and unfold at the campsite to provide temporary living quarters for recreational, camping, or travel use. (See "Recreational Vehicle.")

Converter: A device which changes electrical energy from one form to another, as from alternating current to direct current.

Dead Front: (As applied to switches, circuit breakers, switchboards, and distribution panelboards.) So designed, constructed, and installed that no current-carrying parts are normally exposed on the front.

Disconnecting Means: The necessary equipment usually consisting of a circuit breaker or switch and fuses, and their accessories, located near the point of entrance of supply conductors in a recreational vehicle and intended to constitute the means of cutoff for the supply to that recreational vehicle.

Receptacles used as disconnecting means shall be accessible (as applied to wiring methods) and capable of interrupting their rated current without hazard to the operator.

Distribution Panelboard: A single panel or group of panel units designed for assembly in the form of a single panel; including buses, and with or without switches and/or automatic overcurrent protective devices for the control of light, heat, or power circuits of small individual as well as aggregate capacity; designed to be placed in a cabinet or cutout box placed in or against a wall or partition and accessible only from the front.

Frame: Chassis rail and any welded addition thereto of metal thickness of 16 MSG or greater.

Low-Voltage: An electromotive force rated nominal 24 volts, nominal, or less, supplied from a transformer, converter, or battery.

Motor Home: A vehicular unit designed to provide temporary living quarters for recreational, camping, or travel use built on or permanently attached to a self-propelled motor vehicle chassis or on a chassis cab or van which is an integral part of the completed vehicle. (See "Recreational Vehicle.")

Power-Supply Assembly: The conductors, including the grounding conductors, insulated from one another, the connectors, attachment plug caps, and all other fittings, grommets, or devices installed for the purpose of delivering energy from the source of electrical supply to the distribution panel within the recreational vehicle.

ARTICLE 551—RECREATIONAL VEHICLES, PARKS

Recreational Vehicle: A vehicular-type unit primarily designed as temporary living quarters for recreational, camping, or travel use, which either has its own motive power or is mounted on or drawn by another vehicle. The basic entities are: travel trailer, camping trailer, truck camper, and motor home.

Transformer: A device, which when used, will raise or lower the voltage of alternating current of the original source.

Travel Trailer: A vehicular unit mounted on wheels, designed to provide temporary living quarters for recreational, camping, or travel use, of such size or weight as not to require special highway movement permits when drawn by a motorized vehicle, and with a living area of less than 220 square feet (20.44 sq m), excluding built-in equipment (such as wardrobes, closets, cabinets, kitchen units or fixtures) and bath and toilet rooms. (See "Recreational Vehicle.")

Truck Camper: A portable unit constructed to provide temporary living quarters for recreational, travel, or camping use, consisting of a roof, floor, and sides, designed to be loaded onto and unloaded from the bed of a pick-up truck. (See "Recreational Vehicle.")

A. Recreational Vehicles

551-3. Other Articles. Whenever the requirements of other articles of this Code and Article 551 differ, the requirements of Article 551 shall apply.

551-4. General Requirements.

(a) Not Covered. A recreational vehicle not used for the purposes as defined in Section 551-2 shall not be required to meet the provisions of Part A pertaining to the number or capacity of circuits required. It shall, however, meet all other applicable requirements of this article if the recreational vehicle is provided with an electrical installation intended to be energized from a 120- or 120/240-volt, nominal, ac power-supply system.

(b) Systems. This article covers battery and direct-current power (12-volt or less) systems, combination electrical systems, generator installations, and 120- or 120/240-volt, nominal, systems.

551-5. Low-Voltage Systems.

(a) Low-Voltage Circuits. Low-voltage circuits furnished and installed by the recreational vehicle manufacturer, other than those related to braking, are subject to this Code. Circuits supplying lights subject to federal or state regulations shall comply with applicable government regulations and this Code.

(b) Low-Voltage Wiring.

(1) Copper conductors shall be used for low-voltage circuits.

Exception: Metal chassis or frame shall be permitted as the return path to the source of supply. Connections to the chassis or frame shall be made (1) in an accessible location, (2) by means of copper conductors and copper or copper alloy terminals of the solderless type identified for the size of wire used, and (3) mechanically secure.

It is not the intent of this section to permit the use of the sidewalls or the roof to serve as the ground return path. See definition of "frame" in Section 551-2.

(2) Conductors shall conform to the requirements for Type HDT, SGT, SGR, or Type SXL, or shall have insulation in accordance with Table 310-13 or the equivalent. Conductor sizes No. 6 through 18 AWG or SAE shall be listed.

(FPN): See SAE Standard J1128-1975 for Types HDT and SXL, and SAE Standard J1127-1980 for Types SGT and SGR.

(3) Single-wire, low-voltage conductors shall be of the stranded type.

(4) All insulated low-voltage conductors shall be surface marked at intervals no greater than 4 feet (1.22 m) as follows:

a. Listed conductors shall be marked as required by the listing agency.

b. SAE conductors shall be marked with the name or logo of the manufacturer, specification designation, and wire gage.

c. Other conductors shall be marked with the name or logo of the manufacturer, temperature rating, wire gage, conductor material, and insulation thickness.

(c) Low-Voltage Wiring Methods.

(1) Conductors shall be protected against physical damage and shall be secured. Where insulated conductors are clamped to the structure, the conductor insulation shall be supplemented by an additional wrap or layer of equivalent material, except that jacketed cables need not be so protected. Wiring shall be routed away from sharp edges, moving parts, or heat sources.

(2) Conductors shall be spliced or joined with splicing devices that provide a secure connection or by brazing, welding, or soldering with a fusible metal or alloy. Soldered splices shall first be so spliced or joined as to be mechanically and electrically secure without solder and then soldered. All splices, joints, and free ends of conductors shall be covered with an insulation equivalent to that on the conductors.

(3) Battery and direct-current circuits shall be physically separated by at least a ½-inch (12.7-mm) gap or other approved means from circuits of a different power source. Acceptable methods shall be by clamping, routing, or equivalent means which ensure permanent total separation. Where circuits of different power sources cross, the external jacket of the nonmetallic-sheathed cables shall be deemed adequate separation.

(4) Ground terminals shall be accessible for service. The surface on which ground terminals make contact shall be cleaned and free from oxide or paint, or shall be electrically connected through use of a cadmium, tin, or zinc plated internal-external toothed lockwasher or lockring terminals. Ground terminal attaching screws, rivets or bolts, nuts and lockwashers shall be cadmium, tin or zinc plated, except rivets shall be permitted to be unanodized aluminum when attaching to aluminum structures.

(5) The chassis-grounding terminal of the battery shall be bonded to the vehicle chassis with a minimum No. 8 AWG copper conductor or equivalent. In the event the power lead from the battery exceeds No. 8 AWG, then the bonding conductor shall be of an equal size.

> Section 551-5(c)(5) requires that the chassis-grounding terminal of the battery is to be bonded to the vehicle chassis with a No. 8 AWG copper conductor minimum or equivalent. This minimizes the possibility of low-voltage circuit-fault current paths through the ac panelboard bonding conductor and the equipment grounding conductor of the combination ac/dc appliance and then through the negative dc conductor feeding the appliance which may be also bonded to the external metal cover of the appliance. The ac equipment grounding conductor of the appliance may not have sufficient ampacity to safely conduct the dc fault current. This will necessitate installation of the battery bonding conductor. Some recreational vehicles have one side of the battery circuit already bonded to the frame by a No. 8 AWG or larger copper conductor.

ARTICLE 551—RECREATIONAL VEHICLES, PARKS

(d) Battery Installations. Storage batteries subject to the provisions of this Code shall be securely attached to the vehicle and installed in an area vaportight to the interior and ventilated directly to the exterior of the vehicle. When batteries are installed in a compartment, the compartment shall be ventilated with openings having a minimum area of 1.7 square inches (1100 sq mm) at both the top and at the bottom. When compartment doors are equipped for ventilation the openings shall be within 1 inch (25.4 mm) of the top and bottom. Batteries shall not be installed in a compartment containing spark or flame producing equipment except that they shall be permitted to be installed in the engine generator compartment if the only charging source is from the engine generator.

(e) Overcurrent Protection.

(1) Low-voltage circuit wiring shall be protected by overcurrent protective devices rated not in excess of the ampacity of copper conductors, as follows:

Wire Size	Ampacity	Wire Type
18	6	Stranded only
16	8	Stranded only
14	15	Stranded or Solid
12	20	Stranded or Solid
10	30	Stranded or Solid

(2) Circuit breakers or fuses shall be of an approved type, including automotive types. Fuseholders shall be clearly marked with maximum fuse size and shall be protected against shorting and physical damage by a cover or equivalent means.

The requirement for protection of fuseholders by a cover or equivalent means is intended to reduce the possibility of the low-voltage system shorting to ground.

(FPN): For further information, see Society of Automotive Engineers (SAE) Standard for Electric Fuses (Cartridge Type), ANSI/SAE J554(b)-1981; Standard for Blade Type Electric Fuses, SAE J1284; and Underwriters Laboratories Inc. Standard for Automotive Glass Tube Fuses, UL 275-1978.

(3) Higher current-consuming, direct-current appliances such as pumps, compressors, heater blowers, and similar motor-driven appliances shall be installed in accordance with the manufacturer's instructions.

Motors which are controlled by automatic switching or by latching-type manual switches shall be protected in accordance with Section 430-32(c).

(4) The overcurrent protective device shall be installed in an accessible location on the vehicle within 18 inches (457 mm) of the point where the power supply connects to the vehicle circuits. If located outside the recreational vehicle, the device shall be protected against weather and physical damage.

Exception: External low-voltage supply shall be permitted to be fused within 18 inches (457 mm) after entering the vehicle or after leaving a metal raceway.

(f) Switches. Switches shall have a direct-current rating not less than the connected load.

(g) Lighting Fixtures. All low-voltage interior lighting fixtures shall be listed.

(h) Cigarette Lighter Receptacles. Twelve-volt receptacles that will accept and energize cigarette lighters shall be installed in a noncombustible outlet box or the assembly shall be identified by the manufacturer of the product as thermally protected.

852

Twelve-volt systems for running and signal lights, similar to those in a conventional automobile, are covered in Sections 551-5, 551-6, and 551-7. In many recreational vehicles, 12-V systems are also used for interior lighting and other small loads. The 12-V system is often supplied from an onboard battery or through a transfer switch from a 120/12-V transformer in conjunction with a full-wave rectifier.

551-6. Combination Electrical Systems.

(a) General. Vehicle wiring suitable for connection to a battery or direct-current supply source shall be permitted to be connected to a 120-volt source provided that the entire wiring system and equipment are rated and installed in full conformity with Part A requirements covering 120-volt electrical systems. Circuits fed from alternating-current transformers shall not supply direct-current appliances.

(b) Voltage Converters (120-Volt Alternating Current to Low-Voltage Direct Current). The 120-volt alternating current side of the voltage converter shall be wired in full conformity with Part A requirements for 120-volt electrical systems.

Exception: Converters supplied as an integral part of a listed appliance shall not be subject to the above.

All converters and transformers shall be listed for use in recreation vehicles and designed or equipped to provide over-temperature protection. To determine the converter rating the following formula shall be applied to the total connected load, including average battery charging rate, of all 12-volt equipment:
The first 20 amperes of load at 100 percent; plus
The second 20 amperes of load at 50 percent; plus
All load above 40 amperes at 25 percent.

Exception: A low-voltage appliance which is controlled by a momentary switch (normally "open") which has no means for holding in the "closed" position shall not be considered as a "connected load" when determining the required converter rating. Momentarily energized appliances shall be limited to those used to prepare the vehicle for occupancy or travel.

(c) Bonding Voltage Converter Enclosures. The noncurrent-carrying metal enclosure of the voltage converter shall be bonded to the frame of the vehicle with a No. 8 AWG copper conductor minimum or equivalent. The grounding conductor for the battery and the metal enclosure shall be permitted to be the same conductor.

The intent of this section is to reduce the possibility of damage to the power-supply cord by large dc fault currents which may find their way back to the vehicle frame or the battery through the ac grounding conductor of the converter. Metal enclosures of UL-listed converters are provided with an external pressure terminal connector for this purpose. See commentary following Section 551-5(c)(5).

(d) Dual-Voltage Fixtures or Appliances. Fixtures or appliances having both 120-volt and low-voltage connections shall be listed for dual voltage.

In such fixtures, barriers are used to separate the 120-V and the 12-V wiring connections.

(e) Autotransformers. Autotransformers shall not be used.

(f) Receptacles and Plug Caps. Where a recreational vehicle is equipped with a 120-volt or 120/240-volt alternating-current system and/or a low-voltage system, receptacles and plug caps of the low-voltage system shall differ in configuration from those of the 120- or 120/240-volt system. When a vehicle equipped with a battery or direct-current system has an external connection for low-voltage power, the receptacle shall have a configuration that will not accept 120-volt power.

551-7. Generator Installations.

(a) Mounting. Generators shall be mounted in such a manner as to be effectively bonded to the recreational vehicle chassis.

(b) Generator Protection. Equipment shall be installed to ensure that the current-carrying conductors from the engine generator and from an outside source are not connected to a vehicle circuit at the same time.

(c) Installation of Storage Batteries and Generators. Storage batteries and internal-combustion-driven generator units (subject to the provisions of this Code) shall be secured in place to avoid displacement from vibration and road shock.

(d) Ventilation of Generator Compartments. Compartments accommodating internal-combustion-driven generator units shall be provided with ventilation in accordance with instructions provided by the manufacturer of the generator unit.

(e) Supply Conductors. The supply conductors from the engine generator to the first termination on the vehicle shall be of the stranded type and be installed in listed flexible metal conduit. The point of first termination shall be in a (1) panelboard, (2) junction box with a blank cover, (3) junction box with a receptacle, or (4) receptacle assembly listed in conjunction with the generator.

The panelboard or junction box with a receptacle shall be installed within the vehicle's interior and within 18 inches (457 mm) of the compartment wall but not inside the compartment. A junction box with a blank cover shall be mounted on the compartment wall, and shall be permitted inside or outside the compartment. A receptacle assembly listed in conjunction with the generator shall be mounted in accordance with its listing. Overcurrent protection in accordance with Section 240-3 shall be provided for supply conductors as an integral part of a listed generator or shall be located within 18 inches (457 mm) of their point of entry into the vehicle.

(f) Compartment Construction. Generator compartments shall be lined with galvanized steel, not less than 26 MSG thick. Seams and joints shall be lapped, mechanically secured and made vaportight to the interior of the vehicle. Alternate materials and methods of construction shall be permitted to be used if they provide equivalent quality, strength, effectiveness, fire resistance, durability and safety. Fuel lines and exhaust systems shall not penetrate into the living area. Holes for electrical conduit, conductors or cables into the living area shall be sealed vaportight.

> This section was included in order to provide protection from fire or carbon monoxide which could enter the vehicle.

551-8. 120- or 120/240-Volt, Nominal, Systems.

(a) General Requirements. The electrical equipment and material of recreational vehicles indicated for connection to a wiring system rated 120 volts, nominal, 2-wire with ground, or a wiring system rated 120/240 volts, nominal, 3-wire with ground, shall be listed and installed in accordance with the requirements of Part A.

(b) Materials and Equipment. Electrical materials, devices, appliances, fittings, and other equipment installed, intended for use in, or attached to the recreational vehicle shall be listed. All products shall be used only in the manner in which they have been tested and found suitable for the intended use.

(c) Other Sources. Other sources of ac power such as inverters or motor generators shall be listed for use in recreational vehicles and shall be installed in accordance with the terms of the listing. Other sources of ac power shall be wired in full conformity with the requirements in Part A of this article covering 120-volt electrical systems.

(d) Alternate Source Restriction. Transfer equipment, if not integral with the listed power source, shall be installed to ensure that the current-carrying conductors from other sources of ac power and from an outside source are not connected to the vehicle circuit at the same time.

(e) Ground-Fault Circuit-Interrupter Protection. The internal wiring of a recreational vehicle having only one 15- or 20-ampere branch circuit as permitted in Sections 551-10(a) and (b) shall have ground-fault circuit-interrupter protection for personnel. The ground-fault circuit-interrupter shall be installed at the point where the power supply assembly terminates within the recreational vehicle. Where a separable cord set is not employed, the ground-fault circuit-interrupter shall be permitted to be an integral part of the attachment plug of the power supply assembly. The ground-fault circuit-interrupter shall provide protection also under the conditions of an open grounded circuit conductor or interchanged circuit conductors.

551-9. Receptacle Outlets Required.

(a) Spacing. Receptacle outlets shall be installed at wall spaces 2 feet (610 mm) wide or more so that no point along the floor line is more than 6 feet (1.83 m), measured horizontally, from an outlet in that space.

Exception No. 1: Bath and hall areas.

Exception No. 2: Wall spaces occupied by kitchen cabinets, wardrobe cabinets, built-in furniture, behind doors which may open fully against a wall surface, or similar facilities.

(b) Location. Receptacle outlets shall be installed:

(1) Adjacent to counter tops in the kitchen [at least one on each side of the sink if counter tops are on each side and are 12 inches (305 mm) or over in width].

(2) Adjacent to the refrigerator and gas range space, except when a gas-fired refrigerator or cooking appliance, requiring no external electrical connection, is factory-installed.

(3) Adjacent to counter top spaces of 12 inches (305 mm) or more in width which cannot be reached from a receptacle required in Section 551-9(b)(1) by a cord of 6 feet (1.83 m) without crossing a traffic area, cooking appliance, or sink.

(c) Ground-Fault Circuit Protection. Where provided, each 120-volt, single-phase, 15- or 20-ampere receptacle outlet shall have ground-fault circuit protection for personnel in the following locations:

(1) Adjacent to a bathroom lavatory. [The receptacle outlet shall be a minimum of 24 inches (610 mm) from the compartment floor.]

This section permits mounting of a bathroom receptacle in the side of a lavatory cabinet when installation of a receptacle is not possible in a thin wall.

(2) Adjacent to any lavatory.

(3) In the area occupied by a toilet, toilet and/or shower, or toilet and tub-shower enclosure.

(4) On the exterior of the vehicle.

The receptacle outlet shall be permitted in a listed lighting fixture. A receptacle outlet shall not be installed in a tub or combination tub-shower compartment.

Exception: Where ground-fault circuit-interrupter protection is provided in accordance with Section 551-8(e).

(d) Face-Up Position. A receptacle shall not be installed in a face-up position in any counter top or similar horizontal surfaces within the living area.

551-10. Branch Circuits Required. Each recreational vehicle containing a 120-volt electrical system shall contain one of the following:

(a) One 15-Ampere Circuit. One 15-ampere circuit to supply lights, receptacles outlets and fixed appliances. Such recreational vehicles shall be equipped with one 15-ampere switch and fuse, or 15-ampere circuit breaker.

(b) One 20-Ampere Circuit. One 20-ampere circuit to supply lights, receptacle outlets and fixed appliances. Such recreational vehicles shall be equipped with one 20-ampere switch and fuse, or 20-ampere circuit breaker.

(c) Two or More 15- or 20-Ampere Circuits. Two or more 15- or 20-ampere circuits to supply lights, receptacle outlets and fixed appliances. Such recreational vehicles shall be equipped with a 30-ampere rated main power supply assembly.

(FPN): See Section 210-23(a) for permissible loads. See Section 551-13(c) for main disconnect and overcurrent protection requirements.

(d) Power Supply Assembly. A 40- or 50-ampere power supply assembly which shall be calculated in accordance with the following method:

(1) Lighting. If electric lighting is provided either directly or indirectly (through a voltage converter) by the 120-volt or 120/240-volt system, calculate lighting wattage at 3 volt-amperes per square foot using exterior dimensions (exclusive of hitch and cab) as follows:

Length (feet) × width (feet) × 3 = _____ lighting volt-amperes.

(2) Small Appliance. Number of circuits times 1,500 volt-amperes for each 20-ampere appliance receptacle circuit, e.g.,

Number of Circuits × 1,500 = _____ small appliance volt-amperes.

(3) Total. Lighting volt-amperes plus small appliance volt-amperes = _____ total volt-amperes.

(4) First 3,000 total volt-amperes at 100 percent plus remainder at 35 percent = _____ volt-amperes to be divided by voltage to obtain current (amperes) per leg.

	Amperes per Leg	
	A	B
Lighting and small appliance current (amperes) per leg (from D above) =		

(5) Add nameplate amperes for motors and heater loads (exhaust fans, air conditioners*, electric, gas, or oil heating*). Also include anticipated loads in above categories when prewired outlets or circuits are installed for other than factory-installed major appliances.
*Omit smaller of heating or air conditioning load, except include any motor common to both functions.

(6) Add 25 percent of amperes of largest motor in E =

(7) Add nameplate amperes of the following appliances. Include anticipated loads when prewired outlets or circuits are installed for other than factory-installed major appliances. When number of appliances is four or more, use 75 percent of total.

Disposal   _____ _____
Water Heater   _____ _____
Wall-Mounted Ovens   _____ _____
Cooking Units   _____ _____
                                  _____
TOTAL   _____ _____   = _____

(8) Add amperes for free-standing range as distinguished from separate ovens and cooking units. Derive from following table by dividing volt-amperes by 240 volts.

Range	Nameplate Rating (watts)	Use (volt-amperes)
(Freestanding range as	0 thru 10,000	80 percent of rating
distinguished from	over 10,000 thru 12,500	8,000
separate oven and	over 12,500 thru 13,500	8,400
cooking units)	over 13,500 thru 14,500	8,800
	over 14,500 thru 15,500	9,200
	over 15,500 thru 16,500	9,600
	over 16,500 thru 17,500	10,000

551-11. Branch-Circuit Protection.

(a) Rating. The branch-circuit overcurrent devices shall be rated:

(1) Not more than the circuit conductors; and

(2) Not more than 150 percent of the rating of a single appliance rated 13.3 amperes or more and supplied by an individual branch circuit; but

(3) Not more than the overcurrent protection size marked on an air conditioner or other motor-operated appliances.

(b) Protection for Smaller Conductors. A 20-ampere fuse or circuit breaker shall be permitted for protection for fixture leads, cords, or small appliances, and No. 14 tap conductors, not over 6 feet (1.83 m) long for recessed lighting fixtures.

(c) 15-Ampere Receptacle Considered Protected by 20 Amperes. If more than one outlet or load is on a branch circuit, a 15-ampere receptacle shall be permitted to be protected by a 20-ampere fuse or circuit breaker.

551-12. Power-Supply Assembly.

(a) 15-Ampere Main Power-Supply Assembly. Recreational vehicles wired in accordance with Section 551-10(a) shall use a listed 15-ampere, or larger, main power-supply assembly.

(b) 20-Ampere Main Power-Supply Assembly. Recreational vehicles wired in accordance with Section 551-10(b) shall use a listed 20-ampere, or larger, main power-supply assembly.

(c) 30-Ampere Main Power-Supply Assembly. Recreational vehicles wired in accordance with Section 551-10(c) shall use a listed 30-ampere, or larger, main power-supply assembly.

(d) 40- or 50-Ampere Power-Supply Assembly. In accordance with Section 551-10(d), any recreational vehicle with a rating in excess of 30 amperes, 120 volts, shall use a listed 40-ampere or 50-ampere, 120/240-volt power-supply assembly.

Exception No. 1: When the calculated load of the recreational vehicle exceeds 30 amperes, 120 volts, a second power-supply cord shall be permitted. Where a two-cord supply system is installed, they shall not be interconnected on either the line side or the load side. The grounding circuits and grounding means shall be electrically interconnected.

Exception No. 2: For a dual-supply source consisting of a generator and a power-supply cord, see Section 551-14.

551-13. Distribution Panelboard.

(a) Listed and Appropriately Rated. A listed and appropriately rated distribution panelboard or other equipment specifically listed for the purpose shall be used. The grounded conductor termination bar shall be insulated as provided in Section 551-23(c); the grounding bar shall be attached to the metal enclosure of the panelboard or other approved grounding means.

(b) Location. The distribution panelboard shall be installed in a readily accessible location. Working clearance for the panelboard shall be no less than 24 inches (610 mm) wide and 30 inches (762 mm) deep.

Exception: Where the panelboard cover is exposed to the inside aisle space, then one of the working clearance dimensions shall be permitted to be reduced to a minimum of 22 inches (559 mm). A panelboard is considered exposed where the panelboard cover is within 2 inches (50.8 mm) of the aisle's finished surface.

(c) Dead-Front Type. The distribution panelboard shall be of the dead-front type and shall consist of one or more circuit breakers or Type S fuseholders. A main disconnecting means shall be provided where fuses are used or where more than two circuit breakers are employed. A main overcurrent protective device not exceeding the power-supply assembly rating shall be provided where more than two branch circuits are employed.

551-14. Multiple Supply Source.

(a) Multiple Supply Sources. Where a multiple supply system consisting of an alternate power source and a power supply cord is installed, the feeder from the generator shall be protected by an overcurrent protective device. Installation shall be in accordance with Sections 551-7(a) and (b) and 551-8.

(b) Calculation of Loads. Calculation of loads shall be in accordance with Section 551-10.

(c) Multiple Supply Sources Capacity. The multiple supply sources shall not be required to be of the same capacity.

(d) Alternate Power Sources Exceeding 30 Amperes. If an alternate power source exceeds 30 amperes, 120 volts, nominal, it shall be permissible to wire it as a 120-volt, nominal, system or a 120/240-volt, nominal, system, providing an overcurrent protective device of the proper rating is installed in the feeder.

(e) Power-Supply Assembly Not Less than 30 Amperes. The external power-supply assembly shall be permitted to be less than the calculated load but not less than 30 amperes and shall have overcurrent protection not greater than the capacity of the external power-supply assembly.

551-15. Means for Connecting to Power Supply.

(a) Assembly. The power-supply assembly or assemblies shall be factory-supplied or factory-installed when of the permanently connected type as specified herein:

(1) Separable. Where a separable power-supply assembly consisting of a cord with a female connector and molded attachment plug cap is provided, the vehicle shall be equipped with a permanently mounted, flanged surface inlet (male-recessed-type motor-base receptacle) wired directly to the distribution panelboard by an approved wiring method. The attachment plug cap shall be of a listed type.

(2) Permanently Connected. Each power-supply assembly shall be connected directly to the terminals of the distribution panelboard or conductors within a junction box and provided with means to prevent strain from being transmitted to the terminals. The ampacity of the conductors between each junction box and the terminals of each distribution panelboard shall be at least equal to the ampacity of the power-supply cord. The supply end of the assembly shall be equipped with an attachment plug of the type described in Section 551-15(c). Where the cord passes through the walls or floors, it shall be protected by means of conduit and bushings or equivalent.

(b) Cord. The cord exposed usable length shall be measured from the point of entrance to the recreational vehicle or the face of the flanged surface inlet (motor-base attachment plug) to the face of the attachment plug at the supply end.

The cord exposed usable length, measured to the point of entry on the vehicle exterior, shall be a minimum of 23 feet (7.0 m) when the point of entrance is at the side of the vehicle, or shall be a minimum 28 feet (8.5 m) when the point of entrance is at the rear of the vehicle.

When the cord entrance into the vehicle is more than 3 feet (0.9 m) above the ground, the minimum cord lengths above shall be increased by the vertical distance of the cord entrance heights above 3 feet (0.9 m).

(FPN): See Section 551-15(e).

(c) Attachment Plugs.

(1) Recreational vehicles having only one 15-ampere branch circuit as permitted by Section 551-10(a) shall have an attachment plug which shall be 2-pole, 3-wire, grounding type, rated 15 amperes, 125 volts, conforming to the configuration shown in Figure 551-15(c).

(FPN): Complete details of this configuration can be found in American National Standard ANSI C73.11-1972.

(2) Recreational vehicles having only one 20-ampere branch circuit as permitted in Section 551-10(b) shall have an attachment plug which shall be 2-pole, 3-wire, grounding type, rated 20 amperes, 125 volts, conforming to the configuration shown in Figure 551-15(c).

(FPN): Complete details of this configuration can be found in American National Standard ANSI C73.12-1972.

(3) Recreational vehicles wired in accordance with Section 551-10(c) shall have an attachment plug which shall be 2-pole, 3-wire, grounding type, rated 30 amperes, 125 volts, conforming to the configuration shown in Figure 551-15(c) intended for use with units rated at 30 amperes, 125 volts.

(FPN): Complete details of this configuration can be found in American National Standard Dimensions of Caps, Plugs and Receptacles, ANSI C73.13-1972.

(4) Recreational vehicles having a power-supply assembly rated 40 amperes or 50 amperes as permitted by Section 551-10(d) shall have a 3-pole, 4-wire, grounding-type attachment plug rated 50 amperes, 125/250 volts, conforming to the configuration shown in Figure 551-15(c).

(FPN): Complete details of this configuration can be found in American National Standard Dimensions of Caps, Plugs and Receptacles, ANSI C73.17-1972.

(d) Labeling at Electrical Entrance. Each recreational vehicle shall have permanently affixed to the exterior skin at or near the point of entrance of the power-supply cord(s) a label 3 inches (76 mm) by 1¾ inches (44.5 mm) minimum size, made of etched, metal-stamped or embossed brass, stainless steel, anodized or alclad aluminum not less than 0.020 inch (508

ARTICLE 551—RECREATIONAL VEHICLES, PARKS

Receptacles   Caps

20 amp

125-volt,
2-pole,
3-wire,
grounding type

125-volt, 20-amp,
2-pole, 3-wire, grounding type

125-volt, 15-amp,
2-pole, 3-wire, grounding type

30 amp

125-volt, 2-pole, 3-wire, grounding type

50 amp

125 / 250-volt, 3-pole, 4-wire, grounding type

Figure 551-15(c). Configurations for grounding-type receptacles and attachment plug caps used for recreational vehicle supply cords and recreational vehicle lots.

micrometers) thick, or other suitable material [e.g., 0.005-inch (127-micrometers) plastic laminates], which reads, as appropriate, either:

"This connection is for 110-125 volt ac, 60 Hz _____ ampere supply," or
"This connection is for 120/240 volt ac, 3-pole, 4-wire 60 Hz _____ ampere supply."
The correct ampere rating shall be marked in the blank space.

(e) Location. The point of entrance of a power-supply assembly shall be located within 15 feet (4.57 m) of the rear, on the left (road) side or at the rear, left of the longitudinal center of the vehicle, within 18 inches (457 mm) of the outside wall.

Exception: A recreational vehicle equipped with only a listed flexible drain system or a side-vent drain system shall be permitted to have the electrical point of entrance located on either side provided the drain(s) for the plumbing system is (are) located on the same side.

551-16. Wiring Methods.

(a) Wiring Systems. Rigid metal conduit, intermediate metal conduit, electrical metallic tubing, rigid nonmetallic conduit, flexible metal conduit, metal-clad cable, Type AC cable, and nonmetallic-sheathed cable shall be permitted. An equipment grounding means shall be provided in accordance with Section 250-91.

See commentary following Section 350-5.

(b) Conduit. Where rigid metal conduit or intermediate metal conduit is terminated at an enclosure with a locknut and bushing connection, two locknuts shall be provided, one inside and one outside of the enclosure. All cut ends of conduit shall be reamed or otherwise finished to remove rough edges.

See commentary following Sections 348-11 and 373-6(c).

(c) Nonmetallic Boxes. Nonmetallic boxes shall be acceptable only with nonmetallic-sheathed cable or rigid and nonmetallic conduit.

(d) Boxes. In walls and ceilings constructed of wood or other combustible material, boxes and fittings shall be flush with the finished surface or project therefrom.

(e) Mounting. Wall and ceiling boxes shall be mounted in accordance with Article 370.

Exception No. 1: Snap-in type boxes or boxes provided with special wall or ceiling brackets that securely fasten boxes in walls or ceilings shall be permitted.

Exception No. 2: A wooden plate providing a 1½-inch (38-mm) minimum width backing around the box and of a thickness of ½-inch (12.7 mm) or greater (actual) glued to the wall panel shall be considered as approved means for mounting outlet boxes.

This exception permits mounting of outlet boxes by screws to a wooden plate secured by adhesive to the back of the wall panel. This wooden plate is required to be not less than ½ in. (12.7 mm) thick, and is required to extend at least 1½ in. (38 mm) around the box. This recognizes the special construction of recreational vehicle walls which often makes it quite difficult or impossible to attach an outlet box to a structural member as required by Section 370-13(b).

(f) Sheath Armor. The sheath of nonmetallic-sheathed cable, metal-clad cable and Type AC cable shall be continuous between outlet boxes and other enclosures.

(g) Protected. Metal-clad, Type AC, or nonmetallic-sheathed cables shall be permitted to pass through the centers of the wide side of 2-inch by 4-inch studs. However, they shall be protected where they pass through 2-inch by 2-inch studs or at other studs or frames where the cable would be less than 1½ inches (38 mm) from the inside or outside surface. Steel plates on each side of the cable, or a steel tube, with not less than No. 16 MSG wall thickness, shall be installed to protect the cable. These plates or tubes shall be securely held in place.

(h) Bends. No bend shall have a radius of less than five times the cable diameter.

(i) Cable Supports. When connected with cable connectors or clamps, cables shall be supported within 12 inches (305 mm) of outlet boxes, distribution panelboards, and splice boxes on appliances. Supports shall be provided every 4½ feet (1.37 m) at other places.

(j) Nonmetallic Box Without Cable Clamps. Nonmetallic-sheathed cables shall be supported within 8 inches (203 mm) of a nonmetallic outlet box without cable clamps.

Exception: Where wiring devices with integral enclosures are employed with a loop of extra cable to permit future replacement of the device, the cable loop shall be considered as an integral portion of the device.

(k) Physical Damage. Where subject to physical damage, exposed nonmetallic cable shall be protected by covering boards, guard strips, or raceways.

(l) Metal Faceplates. Metal faceplates shall be of ferrous metal not less than 0.030 inch (762 micrometers) in thickness or of nonferrous metal not less than 0.040 inch (1.02 mm) in thickness. Nonmetallic faceplates shall be listed.

(m) Metal Faceplates Effectively Grounded. Where metal faceplates are used, they shall be effectively grounded.

(n) Moisture or Physical Damage. Where outdoor or underchassis wiring is 120 volts, nominal, or over and is exposed to moisture or physical damage, the wiring shall be protected by rigid metal conduit, intermediate metal conduit, or by electrical metallic tubing or rigid nonmetallic conduit that is closely routed against frames and equipment enclosures.

(o) Component Interconnections. Fittings and connectors which are intended to be concealed at the time of assembly shall be listed and identified for the interconnection of building components. Such fittings and connectors shall be equal to the wiring method employed in insulation, temperature rise, fault-current withstanding, and shall be capable of enduring the vibration and shock occurring in recreational vehicles.

(p) Method of Connecting Expandable Units.

(1) That portion of a branch circuit that is installed in an expandable unit shall be permitted to be connected to the portion of the branch circuit in the main body of the vehicle by means of an attachment plug and cord listed for hard usage. The cord and its connections shall conform to all provisions of Article 400 and shall be considered as a permitted use under Section 400-7.

Exception: Where the attachment plug and cord are located within the vehicle's interior, use of plastic thermoset or elastomer parallel cords Type SPT-3, SP-3 or SPE shall be permitted.

(2) If the receptacle provided for connection of the cord to the main circuit is located on the outside of the vehicle it shall be protected with a ground-fault circuit-interrupter for personnel and be listed for wet locations. A cord located on the outside of a vehicle shall be identified for outdoor use.

(3) Unless removable or stored within the vehicle interior, the cord assembly shall have permanent provisions for protection against corrosion and mechanical damage while the vehicle is in transit.

(4) The cord shall be installed so as not to permit exposed live attachment plug pins.

(q) Prewiring for Air Conditioning Installation. Prewiring installed for the purpose of facilitating future air-conditioning installation shall conform to the following and other applicable portions of this article. The circuit shall serve no other purpose.

(1) An overcurrent protective device with a rating compatible with the circuit conductors shall be installed in the distribution panelboard and wiring connections completed.

(2) The load end of the circuit shall terminate in a junction box with a blank cover. The free ends of the conductors shall be adequately capped or taped.

(3) A label conforming to Section 551-15(d) shall be placed on or adjacent to the junction box and shall read:

AIR-CONDITIONING CIRCUIT. THIS
CONNECTION IS FOR AIR CONDITIONERS
RATED 110-125 VOLT AC, 60 HZ _____
AMPERES MAXIMUM. DO NOT EXCEED
CIRCUIT RATING.

An ampere rating, not to exceed 80 percent of the circuit rating, shall be legibly marked in the blank space.

(r) Prewiring for Generator Installation. Prewiring installed for the purpose of facilitating future generator installation shall conform to the following and other applicable portions of this article.

(1) Circuit conductors shall be appropriately sized in relation to the anticipated load and shall be protected by an overcurrent device in accordance with their ampacities.

(2) Where junction boxes are utilized at the circuit originating and/or terminus points, free ends of the conductors shall be adequately capped or taped.

(3) When devices such as receptacle outlet, transfer switch, etc., are installed, the installation shall be complete including circuit conductor connections. All devices shall be listed and appropriately rated.

(4) A label conforming to Section 551-15(d) shall be placed on the cover of each junction box containing incomplete circuitry and shall read, as appropriate, either:

GENERATOR CIRCUIT. THIS CONNECTION
IS FOR GENERATORS RATED 110-125 VOLT
AC, 60 HZ AMPERES MAXIMUM.
OR
GENERATOR CIRCUIT. THIS CONNECTION
IS FOR GENERATORS RATED 120/240 VOLT
AC, 60 HZ AMPERES MAXIMUM.

The correct ampere rating shall be legibly marked in the blank space.

551-17. Conductors and Boxes.

(a) Maximum Number of Conductors. The maximum number of conductors permitted in boxes shall be in accordance with Section 370-6.

(b) Free Conductor at Each Box. At least 4 inches (102 mm) of free conductor shall be left at each box except where conductors are intended to loop without joints.

551-18. Grounded Conductors. The identification of grounded conductors shall be in accordance with Section 200-6.

551-19. Connection of Terminals and Splices. Conductor splices and connections at terminals shall be in accordance with Section 110-14. If splices of the equipment grounding conductor in nonmetallic-sheathed cable are made in boxes containing devices, the splices shall be insulated.

551-20. Switches. Switches shall be rated as follows:

(a) Lighting Circuits. For lighting circuits, switches shall be rated not less than 10 amperes, 120-125 volts and in no case less than the connected load.

(b) Motors or Other Loads. For motors or other loads, switches shall have ampere or horsepower ratings, or both, adequate for loads controlled. (An ac general-use snap switch shall be permitted to control a motor 2 horsepower or less with full-load current not over 80 percent of the switch ampere rating.)

551-21. Receptacles. All receptacle outlets shall be: (1) of the grounding type, and (2) installed in accordance with Sections 210-7 and 210-21.

551-22. Lighting Fixtures.

(a) General. Any combustible wall or ceiling finish exposed between the edge of a fixture canopy, or pan and the outlet box, shall be covered with noncombustible material or a material identified for the purpose.

(b) Shower Fixtures. If a lighting fixture is provided over a bathtub or in a shower stall, it shall be of the enclosed and gasketed type and listed for the type of installation, and shall be ground-fault circuit-interrupter protected if rated at 120 volts, nominal.

The switch for shower lighting fixtures and exhaust fans, located over a tub or in a shower stall, shall be located outside the tub or shower space.

> Many shower lights have a metal base and, due to low ceilings in recreational vehicles, may be easily reached by most persons under a shower or standing in a bathtub. This section will permit lighting fixtures to be installed above a tub or shower enclosure if shock-hazard protection is provided by a ground-fault circuit-interrupter.

(c) Outdoor Outlets, Fixtures, Air-Cooling Equipment, Etc. Outdoor fixtures and other equipment shall be listed for outdoor use.

551-23. Grounding. (See also Section 551-25 on bonding of noncurrent-carrying metal parts.)

(a) Power-Supply Grounding. The grounding conductor in the supply cord or feeder shall be connected to the grounding bus or other approved grounding means in the distribution panelboard.

(b) Distribution Panelboard. The distribution panelboard shall have a grounding bus with sufficient terminals for all grounding conductors or other approved grounding means.

(c) Insulated Neutral.

(1) The grounded circuit conductor (neutral) shall be insulated from the equipment grounding conductors and from equipment enclosures and other grounded parts. The grounded (neutral) circuit terminals in the distribution panelboard and in ranges, clothes dryers, counter-mounted cooking units, and wall-mounted ovens shall be insulated from the equipment enclosure. Bonding screws, straps, or buses in the distribution panel board or in appliances shall be removed and discarded.

(2) Connection of electric ranges and electric clothes dryers utilizing a grounded (neutral) conductor, if cord-connected, shall be made with 4-conductor cord and 3-pole, 4-wire, grounding-type plug caps and receptacles.

551-24. Interior Equipment Grounding.

(a) Exposed Metal Parts. In the electrical system, all exposed metal parts, enclosures, frames, lighting fixture canopies, etc., shall be effectively bonded to the grounding terminals or enclosure of the distribution panelboard.

(b) Equipment Grounding Conductors. Bare wires, green-colored wires, or green wires with yellow stripe(s) shall be used for equipment grounding conductors only.

(c) Grounding of Electrical Equipment. Where grounding of electrical equipment is specified, it shall be permitted as follows:

(1) Connection of metal raceway (conduit or electrical metallic tubing), the sheath of metal-clad cable, or the armor of Type AC cable to metallic outlet boxes.

(2) A connection between the one or more equipment grounding conductors and a metal box by means of a grounding screw, which shall be used for no other purpose, or a listed grounding device.

(3) The equipment grounding conductor in nonmetallic-sheathed cable shall be permitted to be secured under a screw threaded into the fixture canopy other than a mounting screw or cover screw, or attached to a listed grounding means (plate) in a nonmetallic outlet box for fixture mounting (grounding means shall also be permitted for fixture attachment screws).

(d) Grounding Connection in Nonmetallic Box. A connection between the one or more grounding conductors brought into a nonmetallic outlet box shall be so arranged that a connection can be made to any fitting or device in that box that requires grounding.

(e) Grounding Continuity. Where more than one equipment grounding conductor of a branch circuit enters a box, all such conductors shall be in good electrical contact with each other, and the arrangement shall be such that the disconnection or removal of a receptacle, fixture, or other device fed from the box will not interfere with or interrupt the grounding continuity.

(f) Cord-Connected Appliances. Cord-connected appliances, such as washing machines, clothes dryers, refrigerators, and the electrical system of gas ranges, etc., shall be grounded by means of an approved cord with equipment grounding conductor and grounding-type attachment plug.

551-25. Bonding of Noncurrent-Carrying Metal Parts.

(a) Required Bonding. All exposed noncurrent-carrying metal parts that may become energized shall be effectively bonded to the grounding terminal or enclosure of the distribution panelboard.

(b) Bonding Chassis. A bonding conductor shall be connected between any distribution panelboard and an accessible terminal on the chassis. Aluminum or copper-clad aluminum conductors shall not be used for bonding if such conductors or their terminals are exposed to corrosive elements.

Exception: Any recreational vehicle which employs a unitized metal chassis-frame construction to which the distribution panelboard is securely fastened with a bolt(s) and nut(s) or by welding or riveting shall be considered to be bonded.

(c) Bonding Conductor Requirements. Grounding terminals shall be of the solderless type and listed as pressure terminal connectors recognized for the wire size used. The bonding conductor shall be solid or stranded, insulated or bare, and shall be No. 8 copper minimum, or equal.

(d) Metallic Roof and Exterior Bonding. The metal roof and exterior covering shall be considered bonded where:

(1) The metal panels overlap one another and are securely attached to the wood or metal frame parts by metal fasteners, and

(2) The lower panel of the metal exterior covering is secured by metal fasteners at each cross member of the chassis, or the lower panel is bonded to the chassis by a metal strap.

(e) Gas, Water, and Waste Pipe Bonding. The gas, water, and waste pipes shall be considered grounded if they are bonded to the chassis.

(FPN): See Section 551-25(b) for chassis bonding.

(f) Furnace and Metal Air Duct Bonding. Furnace and metal circulating air ducts shall be bonded.

551-26. Appliance Accessibility and Fastening. Every appliance shall be accessible for inspection, service, repair, and replacement without removal of permanent construction. Means shall be provided to securely fasten appliances in place when the recreational vehicle is in transit.

551-27. Factory Tests (Electrical). Each recreational vehicle shall be subjected to the following tests:

(a) Circuits of 120 Volts or 120/240 Volts. Each recreational vehicle designed with a 120-volt or a 120/240-volt electrical system shall withstand the applied potential without electrical breakdown of a 1-minute, 900-volt dielectric strength test, or a 1-second, 1080-volt dielectric strength test, with all switches closed, between current-carrying conductors, including neutral, and the recreational vehicle ground. During the test, all switches and other controls shall be in the "on" position. Fixtures and permanently installed appliances shall not be required to withstand this test.

Each recreational vehicle shall be subjected to: (1) a continuity test to assure that all metallic parts are properly bonded; (2) operational tests to demonstrate that all equipment is properly connected and in working order; and (3) polarity checks to determine that connections have been properly made.

(b) Low-Voltage Circuits. Low-voltage circuit conductors in each recreational vehicle shall withstand the applied potential without electrical breakdown of a 1-minute, 500-volt or a 1-second, 600-volt dielectric strength test. The potential shall be applied between live and grounded conductors.

The test shall be permitted on running light circuits before the lights are installed provided the vehicle's outer covering and interior cabinetry has been secured. The braking circuit shall be permitted to be tested before being connected to the brakes, provided the wiring has been completely secured.

B. Recreational Vehicle Parks

551-41. Definitions.

Power-Supply Assembly. The conductors, including the grounding conductors, insulated from one another, the connectors, attachment plug caps, and all other fittings, grommets, or devices installed for the purpose of delivering energy from the source of electrical supply to the distribution panelboard within the recreational vehicle.

Recreational Vehicle Park. A plot of land upon which two or more recreational vehicle sites are located, established, or maintained for occupancy by recreational vehicles of the general public as temporary living quarters for recreation or vacation purposes.

Recreational Vehicle Site. A plot of ground within a recreational vehicle park intended for the accommodation of either a recreational vehicle, tent, or other individual camping unit on a temporary basis.

Recreational Vehicle Site Feeder Circuit Conductors. The conductors from the park service equipment to the recreational vehicle site supply equipment.

Recreational Vehicle Site Supply Equipment. The necessary equipment, usually a power outlet, consisting of a circuit breaker or switch and fuse and their accessories, located near the point of entrance of supply conductors to a recreational vehicle site and intended to constitute the disconnecting means for the supply to that site.

Recreational Vehicle Stand. That area of a recreational vehicle site intended for the placement of a recreational vehicle.

551-42. Type Receptacles Provided. Every recreational vehicle site with electrical supply shall be equipped with at least one 15- or 20-ampere, 125-volt receptacle. A minimum of 75 percent of all recreational vehicle sites with electrical supply shall each be equipped with a 30-ampere, 125-volt receptacle conforming to Figure 551-15(c). This supply shall be permitted to include additional receptacle configurations conforming to Section 551-52. The remainder of all recreational vehicle sites with electrical supply shall be equipped with one or more of the receptacle configurations conforming to Section 551-52.

All 15- and 20-ampere, 125-volt receptacles shall have listed ground-fault circuit-interrupter protection for personnel. Additional receptacles shall be permitted, for the connection of electrical equipment outside the recreational vehicle within the recreational vehicle park, and all such 125-volt, single-phase, 15- and 20-ampere receptacles shall have ground-fault circuit-interrupter protection for personnel.

This section requires at least one 15- or 20-ampere 125-volt receptacle at each recreational vehicle campsite. Existing recreational vehicle campgrounds may have some sites that are equipped with 30-ampere receptacles only. Adapter plugs or "cheater" cords are often used to connect a recreational vehicle with 15- or 20-ampere supply cord to a 30-ampere receptacle outlet. This practice does not provide adequate overload protection for the cord or the connected load. This section will help assure the availability of the proper receptacle.

551-43. Distribution System. The recreational vehicle park secondary electrical distribution system to recreational vehicle sites shall be derived from a single-phase 120/240-volt, 3-wire system.

551-44. Calculated Load.

(a) Basis of Calculations. Electrical service and feeders shall be calculated on the basis of not less than 3,600 volt-amperes per site equipped with both 20-ampere and 30-ampere supply facilities and 2,400 volt-amperes per site equipped with only 20-ampere supply facilities. The demand factors set forth in Table 551-44 shall be the minimum allowable demand factors that shall be permitted in calculating load for service and feeders.

Table 551-44
Demand Factors for Feeders and Service-Entrance Conductors for Park Sites

Number of Recreational Vehicle Sites	Demand Factor (percent)	Number of Recreational Vehicle Sites	Demand Factor (percent)
1	100	10–12	47
2	100	13–15	45
3	100	16–18	44
4	89	19–21	42
5	71	22–40	40
6	63	41–100	39
7–9	53	101 plus	37

(b) Transformers and Secondary Distribution Panelboards. For the purpose of this Code, where the park service exceeds 240 volts, transformers and secondary distribution panelboards shall be treated as services.

(c) Demand Factors. The demand factor for a given number of sites shall apply to all sites indicated. For example: twenty sites calculated at 42 percent of 3,600 volt-amperes result in a permissible demand of 1512 volt-amperes per site or a total of 30,240 volt-amperes for twenty sites.

(FPN): These demand factors may be inadequate in areas of extreme hot or cold temperature with loaded circuits for heating or air conditioning.

(d) Feeder Circuit Capacity. Recreational vehicle site feeder circuit conductors shall have adequate ampacity for the loads supplied, and shall be rated at not less than 30 amperes.

(FPN): Due to the long circuit lengths typical in most recreational vehicle parks, feeder conductor sizes found in ampacity tables of Article 310 may be inadequate to maintain the voltage regulation suggested in the Fine Print Note to Section 210-19. Total circuit voltage drop is a summation of the voltage drops of each serial circuit segment, where the load for each segment is calculated using the load that segment sees and the demand factors of Section 551-44(a).

551-45. Overcurrent Protection.   Overcurrent protection shall be provided in accordance with Article 240.

551-46. Grounding.   All electrical equipment and installations in recreational vehicle parks shall be grounded as required by Article 250.

551-47. Recreational Vehicle Site Supply Equipment.

(a) Location.   Where provided, the recreational vehicle site electrical supply equipment shall be located on the left (road) side of the parked vehicle, on a line which is 9 feet (2.74 m), ± 1 foot (0.3 m), from the longitudinal centerline of the stand and shall be located at any point on this line from the rear of the stand to 15 feet (4.57 m) forward of the rear of the stand.

(b) Disconnecting Means.   A disconnecting switch or circuit breaker shall be provided in the site supply equipment for disconnecting the power supply to the recreational vehicle.

(c) Access.   All site supply equipment shall be accessible by an unobstructed entrance or passageway not less than 2 feet (610 mm) wide and 6½ feet (1.98 m) high.

(d) Mounting Height.   Site supply equipment shall be located not less than 2 feet (610 mm) nor more than 6½ feet (1.98 m) above the ground.

(e) Working Space.   Sufficient space shall be provided and maintained about all electric equipment to permit ready and safe operation, in accordance with Section 110-16.

551-48. Grounding, Recreational Vehicle Site Supply Equipment.

(a) Exposed Noncurrent-Carrying Metal Parts.   Exposed noncurrent-carrying metal parts of fixed equipment, metal boxes, cabinets, and fittings, which are not electrically connected to grounded equipment, shall be grounded by a continuous equipment grounding conductor run with the circuit conductors from the service equipment or from the transformer of a secondary distribution system. Equipment grounding conductors shall be sized in accordance with Section 250-95.

(b) Secondary Distribution System.   Each secondary distribution system shall be grounded at the transformer.

(c) Neutral Conductor Not to Be Used as an Equipment Ground.   The neutral conductor shall not be used as an equipment ground for recreational vehicles or equipment within the recreational vehicle park.

(d) No Connection on the Load Side.   No connection to a grounding electrode shall be made to the neutral conductor on the load side of the service disconnecting means or transformer distribution panelboard.

551-49. Protection of Outdoor Equipment.

(a) Wet Locations.   All switches, circuit breakers, receptacles, control equipment, and metering devices located in wet locations or outside of a building shall be rainproof equipment.

(b) Meters. If secondary meters are installed, meter sockets without meters installed shall be blanked-off with an approved blanking plate.

Figure 551-1. Recreational vehicle site supply equipment with receptacles per Section 551-52 and ground-fault circuit-interrupter protection for the 20-A 125-volt receptacle outlet.

551-50. Clearance for Overhead Conductors. Open conductors of not over 600 volts, nominal, shall have a vertical clearance of not less than 18 feet (5.49 m) and a horizontal clearance of not less than 3 feet (914 mm) in all areas subject to recreational vehicle movement. In all other areas, clearances shall conform to Sections 225-18 and 225-19.

(FPN): For clearances of conductors over 600 volts, nominal, see National Electrical Safety Code, ANSI C2-1984.

551-51. Underground Service, Feeder, Branch-Circuit and Recreational Vehicle Site Feeder Circuit Conductors.

(a) General. All direct-burial conductors, including the equipment grounding conductor if of aluminum, shall be insulated and identified for the use. All conductors shall be continuous from fitting to fitting. All splices and taps shall be made in approved junction boxes or by use of material listed and identified for the purpose.

(b) Protection Against Physical Damage. Where underground conductors enter or leave a building or trench, they shall be protected against physical damage by rigid metal conduit, intermediate metal conduit, rigid nonmetallic conduit Schedule 80, electrical metallic tubing, or other approved mechanical means, extending a minimum of 18 inches (457 mm) into the trench from the finished grade.

(FPN): See Section 300-5 and Article 339 for conductors or Type UF cable used underground or in direct burial in earth.

551-52. Receptacles. A receptacle to supply electric power to a recreational vehicle shall be one of the configurations shown in Figure 551-15(c) in the following ratings:

(a) 50 Ampere. 125/250 volts, 50-ampere, 3-pole, 4-wire, grounding type for 120/240-volt systems.

(b) 30 Ampere. 125-volt, 30-ampere, 2-pole, 3-wire, grounding type for 120-volt systems.

(c) 20 Ampere. 125-volt, 20-ampere, 2-pole, 3-wire, grounding type for 120-volt systems.

(FPN): Complete details of these configurations can be found in American National Standard Dimensions of Caps, Plugs and Receptacles, ANSI C73.17-1972; ANSI C73.13-1972; and C73.12-1972.

ARTICLE 553 — FLOATING BUILDINGS

Contents

A. General

553-1. Scope. This article covers wiring, services, feeders, and grounding for floating buildings.

553-2. Definition.

Floating Building. A building unit as defined in Article 100, which floats on water, is moored in a permanent location, and has a premises wiring system served through connection by permanent wiring to an electricity supply system not located on the premises.

553-3. Application of Other Articles. Wiring for floating buildings shall comply with the applicable provisions of other articles of this Code, except as modified by this article.

B. Services and Feeders

553-4. Location of Service Equipment. The service equipment for a floating building shall be located adjacent to, but not in or on, the building.

The intent here is to ensure that supply conductors to a floating building can be disconnected in an emergency, such as during a storm, where the floating dwelling unit has to be moved quickly.

Overcurrent protection for supply conductors is also provided where these conductors may develop excessive leakage when underwater or where a short circuit or fault may occur.

553-5. Service Conductors. One set of service conductors shall be permitted to serve more than one set of service equipment.

553-6. Feeder Conductors. Each floating building shall be supplied by a single set of feeder conductors from its service equipment.

Exception: Where the floating building has multiple occupancy, each occupant shall be permitted to be supplied by a single set of feeder conductors extended from the occupant's service equipment to the occupant's panelboard.

553-7. Installation of Services and Feeders.

(a) Flexibility. Flexibility of the wiring system shall be maintained between floating buildings and the supply conductors. All wiring shall be so installed that motion of the water surface and changes in the water level will not result in unsafe conditions.

(b) Wiring Methods. Liquidtight flexible metal conduit with approved fittings shall be permitted for feeders and where flexible connections are required for services.

(FPN): See Sections 555-1 and 555-6.

C. Grounding

553-8. General Requirements. Grounding of both electrical and nonelectrical parts in a floating building shall be through connection to a grounding bus in the building panelboard. The grounding bus shall be grounded through a green-colored insulated equipment grounding conductor run with the feeder conductors and connected to a grounding terminal in the service equipment. The grounding terminal in the service equipment shall be grounded by connection through a green insulated grounding electrode conductor to a grounding electrode on shore.

553-9. Insulated Neutral. The grounded circuit conductor (neutral) shall be a white insulated conductor. The neutral conductor shall be connected to the equipment grounding terminal in the service equipment and, except for that connection, it shall be insulated from the equipment grounding conductors, equipment enclosures, and all other grounded parts. The neutral circuit terminals in the panelboard and in ranges, clothes dryers, counter-mounted cooking units, and the like, shall be insulated from the enclosures.

553-10. Equipment Grounding.

(a) Electrical Systems. All enclosures and exposed metal parts of electrical systems shall be bonded to the grounding bus.

(b) Cord-Connected Appliances. Where required to be grounded, cord-connected appliances shall be grounded by means of an equipment grounding conductor in the cord and a grounding-type attachment plug.

553-11. Bonding of Noncurrent-Carrying Metal Parts. All metal parts in contact with the water, all metal piping, and all noncurrent-carrying metal parts that may become energized, shall be bonded to the grounding bus in the panelboard.

ARTICLE 555 — MARINAS AND BOATYARDS

Contents

555-1. Scope. This article covers the installation of wiring and equipment in the areas comprising fixed or floating piers, wharfs, docks, and other areas in marinas, boatyards, boat basins, and similar establishments that are used, or intended for use, for the purpose of repair, berthing, launching, storage, or fueling of small craft and the moorage of floating buildings.

See Article 553 for requirements for floating buildings, including floating dwelling units.

555-2. Application of Other Articles. Wiring and equipment for marinas and boatyards shall comply with this article and also with the applicable provisions of other articles of this Code.

(FPN): See fine print notes following Sections 210-19(a) and 215-2(b) for voltage drop on branch circuits and feeders respectively.

(FPN): For disconnection of auxiliary power from boats, see Pleasure and Commerical Motor Craft, NFPA 302-1984 (ANSI).

555-3. Receptacles. Where shore power is supplied, those accommodations for boats 20 feet (6.1 m) or less in length shall be equipped with shore-power receptacles of a locking and grounding type rated at not less than 20 amperes.

Where shore power is supplied to accommodations for boats longer than 20 feet (6.1 m) in length, shore-power receptacles of a locking and grounding type rated at 30 amperes or more shall be provided.

Fifteen- and 20-ampere, single-phase, 125-volt receptacles other than those supplying shore power to boats located at piers, wharfs, and other locations shall be protected by ground-fault circuit-interrupters.

(FPN): For various configurations and ratings of locking- and grounding-type receptacles and caps, see Dimensions of Caps, Plugs, and Receptacles, ANSI C73-1972, and Supplement ANSI C73a-1980.

(FPN): For locking- and grounding-type receptacles for auxiliary power to boats, see Marinas and Boatyards, NFPA 303-1984 (ANSI).

(FPN): In locating receptacles consideration should be given to the maximum tide level and wave action.

Receptacles that provide shore power for boats are required to be single and of the locking- and grounding-types. See Figure 555-1 and also Figure 210-7 for a complete chart of grounding-type locking plug and receptacle configurations. See Figure 555-2 for a power outlet assembly used at marinas and boatyards.

Each single receptacle that supplies shore power to boats is required to be supplied from an individual branch circuit. Locking- and grounding-type receptacles and attachment caps are required to ensure proper connections to prevent unintentional disconnection of onboard equipment such as bilge pumps, refrigerators, etc. Fifteen- and 20-A, single-phase, 125-V receptacles, other than those supplying shore power to boats, that are used for maintenance or other purposes at piers, wharves, etc., may be of the general-purpose, nonlocking types, and are required to be protected by ground-fault circuit-interrupters. See Figure 210-14.

The third fine print note calls attention to the possibility of high waves (4 to 5 ft) which are often created by large cruisers and freighter traffic. This condition causes outlets and boxes to become filled with water which results in loss of power and corrosion of the receptacle and attachment plugs.

555-4. Branch Circuits. Each single receptacle that supplies shore power to boats shall be supplied from a power outlet or panelboard by an individual or multiwire branch circuit of the voltage class and rating corresponding to the rating of the receptacle.

Either an individual or a multiwire branch circuit may be used with a common neutral. See commentary following Section 300-13.

555-5. Feeders and Services. The load for each ungrounded feeder and service conductor supplying receptacles that supply shore power for boats shall be calculated as follows:

For 1–4 receptacles	100%	of the sum of the rating of the receptacles
For 5–8	90%	" " " " " "
For 9–14	80%	" " " " " "
For 15–30	70%	" " " " " "
For 31–40	60%	" " " " " "
For 41–50	50%	" " " " " "
For 51–70	40%	" " " " " "
For 71–100	30%	" " " " " "
For 101 plus	20%	" " " " " "

(FPN): These demand factors may be inadequate in areas of extreme hot or cold temperature with loaded circuits for heating, air-conditioning, or refrigerating equipment.

555-6. Wiring Methods. The wiring method shall be one or more of the following identified as suitable for use where exposed to the weather or water: (1) rigid nonmetallic conduit; (2) mineral-insulated, metal-sheathed cable; (3) nonmetallic cable; (4) corrosion-resistant rigid metal conduit; (5) corrosion-resistant intermediate metal conduit; (6) underground wiring that complies with the requirements of Chapter 3 of this Code; (7) Type MC cable.

Exception No. 1: Where flexibility is required, other types identified for the purpose.

Exception No. 2: Open wiring shall be permitted by special permission.

(FPN): In granting special permission, major factors include possible contact of open wires with masts, cranes, or similar structures or equipment.

(FPN): For further information on wiring methods for various locations, see Marinas and Boatyards, NFPA 303-1984 (ANSI).

555-7. Grounding.

(a) Equipment to Be Grounded. The following items shall be connected to an equipment grounding conductor run with the circuit conductors in a raceway or cable:

(1) Boxes, cabinets, and all other metal enclosures.

(2) Metal frames of utilization equipment.

(3) Grounding terminals of grounding-type receptacles.

(b) Type of Equipment Grounding Conductor. The equipment grounding conductor shall be an insulated copper conductor with a continuous outer finish that is either green or green with one or more yellow stripes.

(c) Size of Equipment Grounding Conductor. The insulated copper equipment grounding conductor shall be sized in accordance with Section 250-95 but not smaller than No. 12.

Figure 555-1. Typical configurations for single, locking- and grounding-type receptacles and attachment plug caps used to provide shore power for boats in marinas and boatyards.

Figure 555-2. Power outlet assembly suitable for use at docks, wharves, piers, and other locations that provide shore power to boats. (*Hubbell*)

(d) Branch-Circuit Equipment Grounding Conductor. The insulated equipment grounding conductor for branch circuits shall terminate at a grounding terminal in a remote panelboard or the grounding terminal in the main service equipment.

(e) Feeder Equipment Grounding Conductors. Where a feeder supplies a remote panelboard, an insulated equipment grounding conductor shall extend from a grounding terminal in the service equipment to a grounding terminal in the remote panelboard.

The purpose of Section 555-7 is to provide an insulated equipment grounding conductor that will ensure a grounding circuit of high integrity. Because of corrosive conditions present in marinas and boatyards, metal raceways and boxes are not permitted to serve as equipment grounding conductors.

555-8. Wiring Over and Under Navigable Water. Wiring over and under navigable water shall be subject to approval by the authority having jurisdiction.

Some federal and local agencies have specific authority over navigable waterways; therefore, their approval of any proposed installation over or under such a waterway should be obtained.

555-9. Gasoline Dispensing Stations — Hazardous (Classified) Locations.

(a) Class I, Division 1 Location. The following spaces shall be considered a Class I, Division 1 location:

(1) The space within the dispenser from its base to a level measured 4 feet (1.22 m) vertically from its base.

(2) The space outside the dispenser for a distance measured 4 feet (1.22 m) horizontally from all points of the dispenser and measured vertically upwards for a distance of 18 inches (457 mm) from the base of the dispenser.

(3) The entire space between the base of the dispenser and the lowest water surface for a distance of 4 feet (1.22 m) measured horizontally from any point on the outside of the dispenser.

(b) Class I, Division 2 Location. In an outside location, the following space shall be considered a Class I, Division 2 location (spaces which are Class I, Division 1 as defined above are excluded. Buildings within the following space which are not suitably cut off shall be included.) This space shall include the entire volume enveloped within the following limits:

(1) A horizontal limit of 20 feet (6.1 m) from all points on the exterior enclosure of a dispenser.

(2) An upper limit of 18 inches (457 mm) measured vertically from the base of the dispenser.

(3) A lower limit which shall be the lowest water surface.

(FPN): For further information, see Marinas and Boatyards, NFPA 303-1984 (ANSI).

Section 4-3 in NFPA 303, *Fire Protection Standard for Marinas and Boatyards*, and NFPA 30A, *Automotive and Marine Service Station Code*, include requirements pertaining to gasoline dispensing stations. See also Chapter 5 of NFPA 303 for electrical wiring and equipment requirements for marinas and boatyards.

555-11. Sealing.

(a) At Dispenser. An approved seal shall be provided in each conduit run entering or leaving a dispenser or any cavities or enclosures in direct communication therewith.

(b) At Boundary. Additional seals shall be provided in accordance with Section 501-5. Section 501-5(a)(4) and (b)(2) shall apply to horizontal as well as to vertical boundaries of the defined hazardous (classified) locations.

6 Special Equipment

ARTICLE 600 — ELECTRIC SIGNS AND OUTLINE LIGHTING

Contents

(b) Tube Connections Other than with Receptacles.

(c) Receptacles.

(d) Bushings.

(e) Show Windows.

(f) Receptacles and Bushing Seals.

(g) Enclosures of Metal.

(h) Enclosures of Insulating Material.

(i) Live Parts.

600-35. Switches on Doors.

600-36. Fixed Outline Lighting and Skeleton-type Signs for Interior Use.

(a) Tube Support.

(b) Transformers.

(c) Supply Conductors.

(d) High-Tension Conductors.

600-37. Portable Gas Tube Signs for Show Windows and Interior Use.

(a) Location.

(b) Transformer.

(c) Supply Conductors.

(d) High-Voltage Conductors.

(e) Grounding.

(f) Support.

A. General

600-1. Scope. This article covers the installation of conductors and equipment for electric signs and outline lighting as defined in Article 100.

600-2. Disconnect Required. Each outline lighting installation, and each sign of other than the portable type, shall be controlled by an externally operable switch or breaker which will open all ungrounded conductors.

(a) In Sight of Sign. The disconnecting means shall be within sight of the sign or outline lighting which it controls.

Exception: Signs operated by electronic or electromechanical controllers located external to the sign shall have a disconnecting means located within sight from the controller location. The disconnecting means shall disconnect the sign and the controller from all ungrounded supply conductors and shall be so designed that no pole can be operated independently. The disconnecting means shall be permitted to be in the same enclosure with the controller. The disconnecting means shall be capable of being locked in the open position.

The disconnecting means is required to be located in a direct line of sight from the sign or outline lighting which it controls. This requirement is for the protection of a worker who can keep the disconnecting means within view while working on the sign. The exception permits disconnecting means capable of being locked in the open position to be located elsewhere.

See Figure 600-1.

(b) Control Switch Rating. Switches, flashers, and similar devices controlling transformers shall be either rated for controlling inductive load(s) or have an ampere rating not less than twice the ampere rating of the transformer.

Exception: For other than motors, ac general-use snap switches shall be permitted to be used on alternating-current circuits to control inductive loads not exceeding the ampere rating of the switch.

(FPN): See Section 380-14 for rating of snap switches.

A switching device that controls the primary circuit of a transformer supplying a luminous gas tube encounters unusually severe arcing of its contacts. Therefore, the switch or flasher is required to be a general-use ac snap switch or have a current rating of at least twice the rating of the transformer it controls.

600-3. Enclosures as Pull Boxes. The wiring method used to supply signs and outline lighting shall terminate in the sign or transformer enclosures.

Figure 600-1. Example 1 depicts the disconnecting means placement which satisfies the requirements of Section 600-2(a). Example 2 illustrates the location of a disconnecting means as permitted by the Exception to Section 600-2(a).

Exception: Such signs and transformer boxes shall be permitted to be used as pull or junction boxes for conductors supplying other adjacent signs, outline lighting systems and floodlights that are part of signs provided the conductors extending from the equipment are protected by an overcurrent device rated 20 amperes or less.

600-4. Listing Required. Every electric sign of any type, fixed or portable, shall be listed and installed in conformance with that listing, unless otherwise permitted by special permission.

Section 600-4 requires every electric sign of any type to be listed, unless otherwise permitted by special permission (i.e., the written consent of the authority having jurisdiction). Large signs are often transported in several parts from the factory to the location where they are assembled. It is at this time that an inspection authority should be present to ensure that the components are assembled in conformance with their listing.

600-5. Grounding. Signs, troughs, tube terminal boxes, and other metal frames shall be grounded in the manner specified in Article 250.

Exception No. 1: Insulated and Inaccessible. Where they are insulated from ground and from other conducting surfaces and are inaccessible to unauthorized persons.

Exception No. 2: Isolated Parts. Isolated noncurrent-carrying metal parts of outline lighting may be bonded by No. 14 conductors, protected from physical damage, and grounded in accordance with Article 250.

600-6. Branch Circuits.

(a) Rating. Circuits which supply lamps, ballasts, and transformers, or combinations, shall be rated not to exceed 20 amperes. Circuits containing electric-discharge lighting transformers exclusively shall not be rated in excess of 30 amperes.

(b) Required Branch Circuit. Each commercial building and each commercial occupancy with ground floor footage accessible to pedestrians shall be provided at an accessible location outside the occupancy, with at least one outlet for sign or outline lighting use. The outlet(s) shall be supplied by a 20-ampere branch circuit which supplies no other load.

Exception: Interior hallways or corridors shall not be considered outside the occupancy.

A commercial occupancy with ground-floor footage and with an entrance for pedestrians from a sidewalk, street, enclosed mall, etc., is required to have at least one outlet for sign or outline lighting use supplied by an individual 20-A branch circuit.

Signs for commercial occupancies are usually in use for three hours or longer and are therefore considered continuous loads and are not permitted to exceed 80 percent of the rating of the branch circuit (16 A).

(c) Computed Load. The load for the required branch circuit installed for the supply of exterior signs or outline lighting shall be computed at a minimum of 1200 volt-amperes.

600-7. Marking.

(a) Signs. Signs shall be marked with the maker's name; and, for incandescent lamp signs, with the number of lampholders; and, for electric-discharge-lamp signs, with input amperes at full load and input voltage. The marking of the sign shall be visible after installation.

(b) Transformers. Transformers shall be marked with the maker's name; and transformers for electric-discharge-lamp signs shall be marked with the input rating in amperes or volt-amperes, the input voltage, and the open-circuit output voltage.

600-8. Enclosures.

(a) Conductors and Terminals. Conductors and terminals in sign boxes, cabinets, and outline troughs shall be enclosed in metal or other noncombustible material.

Exception: The supply leads shall not be required to be enclosed.

(b) Cutouts, Flashers, etc. Cutouts, flashers, and similar devices shall be enclosed in metal boxes, the doors of which shall be arranged so they can be opened without removing obstructions or finished parts of the enclosure.

(c) Strength. Enclosures shall have ample strength and rigidity.

(d) Material. Signs and outline lighting shall be constructed of metal or other noncombustible material. Wood shall be permitted for external decoration if placed not less than 2 inches (50.8 mm) from the nearest lampholder or current-carrying part.

Exception: Portable signs of the indoor type shall not be required to meet this requirement.

(e) Minimum Thickness — Enclosure Metal. Sheet copper shall be at least 20 ounce [0.028 inch (711 micrometers)]. Sheet steel shall be of No. 28 MSG.

Exception: For outline lighting and for electric-discharge signs, sheet steel shall be of No. 24 MSG if not ribbed, corrugated, or embossed over its entire surface and of No. 26 MSG if it is so ribbed, corrugated, or embossed.

(f) Protection of Metal. All steel parts of enclosures shall be galvanized or otherwise protected from corrosion.

(g) Enclosures Exposed to Weather. Enclosures for outdoor use shall be weatherproof and shall have at least two drain holes, each not larger than ½ inch (12.7 mm) or smaller than ¼ inch (6.35 mm).

600-9. Portable Signs. Portable signs, letters, fixtures, symbols, and similar displays used in conjunction with fixed outdoor signs shall only be used when in compliance with all applicable provisions of this Code and, in addition, shall meet all of the following requirements:

(a) Weatherproof Receptacle and Attachment Plug. A weatherproof receptacle and attachment plug having one pole for grounding shall be provided for each individual letter, fixture, or sign.

(b) Cords. All cords shall be Type S, SJ, SJO, SJT, SJTO, SO, or ST, 3-conductor, with one conductor grounded as provided in the foregoing.

(c) Cord from Ground Level. No cord shall be less than 10 feet (3.05 m) from the ground level directly underneath.

Section 600-9 is not intended to apply to portable outdoor electric signs, such as those mounted on trailers. It is intended to apply only to portable parts used in conjunction with fixed outdoor signs.

600-10. Clearances.

(a) Vertical and Horizontal. Signs and outline system enclosures shall have not less than the vertical and horizontal clearances from open conductors specified in Article 225.

(b) Elevation. The bottom of sign and outline lighting enclosures shall not be less than 16 feet (4.88 m) above areas accessible to vehicles.

Exception: The bottom of such enclosures shall be permitted to be less than 16 feet (4.88 m) above areas accessible to vehicles where such enclosures are protected from physical damage.

600-11. Outdoor Portable Signs. The internal wiring of an outdoor sign that is portable or mobile and is readily accessible shall be supplied from, and protected by, ground-fault circuit-interrupters identified for use with portable electric signs, thereby providing protection for personnel. The required ground-fault circuit-interrupter shall be permitted on or within the sign or as an integral part of the attachment plug of the supply cord connected to the sign. Conductive supports of a sign covered by this section shall be considered part of the sign.

A ground-fault circuit-interrupter in or on the sign will not provide protection for faults on the line (supply) side of the ground-fault circuit-interrupter, so inspection of the cord used for supplying portable outdoor signs protected in this manner is desirable. See Figure 600-2 for a ground-fault circuit-interrupter designed to serve as an attachment plug, and therefore capable of protecting both the sign and the supply cord.

It is the intent that a ground-fault circuit-interrupter identified for use with portable electric signs be provided with open neutral protection, so that the ground-fault circuit-interrupter will provide protection even if the neutral conductor supplying the sign and ground-fault circuit-interrupter opens.

B. 600 Volts, Nominal, or Less

600-21. Installation of Conductors.

(a) Wiring Method. Conductors shall be installed in rigid metal conduit, intermediate metal conduit, rigid nonmetallic conduit, flexible metal conduit, liquidtight flexible metal conduit, liquidtight flexible nonmetallic conduit, electrical metallic tubing, metal-clad cable, Type AC cable, metal troughing, mineral-insulated metal-sheathed cable, and metal poles complying with all requirements of Section 410-15(b).

Figure 600-2. Raintight ground-fault circuit-interrupter with open neutral protection. This unit is designed for use on the line end of a flexible cord. (*Pass & Seymour, Inc.*)

(b) Insulation and Size. Conductors shall be of a type listed for general use and shall not be smaller than No. 14.

Exception No. 1: Conductors not smaller than No. 18 of a type listed in Table 402-3 shall be permitted:

a. In portable signs.

b. As short leads permanently attached to lampholders or electric-discharge ballasts.

c. As leads not more than 8 feet (2.44 m) long permanently attached to electric-discharge lampholders or electric-discharge ballasts if the leads are enclosed in wiring channels.

d. For signs with multiple incandescent lamps requiring one conductor from a control to one or more lamps whose total load does not exceed 250 watts, if in an approved cable assembly of two or more conductors.

Exception No. 2: Conductors not smaller than No. 20 shall be permitted as short leads permanently attached to synchronous motors.

(c) Exposed to Weather. Conductors in raceways, metal-clad cable, or enclosures exposed to the weather shall be of the lead-covered type or other type specially listed for the conditions.

Exception: This shall not apply when rigid metal conduit, intermediate metal conduit, rigid nonmetallic conduit, electrical metallic tubing, or enclosures are made raintight and arranged to drain.

(d) Number of Conductors in Raceway. The number of conductors in a raceway for sign fixtures shall be in accordance with Table 1 of Chapter 9.

(e) Conductors Soldered to Terminals. Where the conductors are fastened to lampholders other than of the pin type, they shall be soldered to the terminals or made with wire connectors, and the exposed parts of conductors and terminals shall be treated to prevent corrosion. Where the conductors are fastened to pin-type lampholders that protect the terminals from the entrance of water, and that have been found acceptable for sign use, the conductors shall be of the stranded type but shall not be required to be soldered to the terminals.

Conductors are required to be sized No. 14 or larger (note exceptions) and installed in the specified raceways or metal-clad cables. Unless raceways or enclosures exposed to the weather are made raintight and arranged to drain, conductors are required to be lead-covered or approved for wet locations. See Table 310-13.

600-22. Lampholders. Lampholders shall be of the unswitched type having bodies of suitable insulating material and shall be so constructed and installed as to prevent turning. Miniature

882

lampholders shall not be employed for outdoor signs and outline lighting. The screw-shell contact of all sign lampholders in grounded circuits shall be connected to the grounded conductor of the circuit.

600-23. Conductors Within Signs and Troughs. Wires within the sign and outline lighting troughs shall be installed as to be mechanically secure.

600-24. Protection of Leads. Bushings shall be employed to protect wires feeding through enclosures.

C. Over 600 Volts, Nominal

600-31. Installation of Conductors.

(a) Wiring Method. Conductors shall be installed as concealed conductors on insulators, in rigid metal conduit, in intermediate metal conduit, in rigid nonmetallic conduit, in flexible metal conduit, in liquidtight flexible metal conduit, or in electrical metallic tubing, or as Type MC cable.

(b) Insulation and Size. Conductors shall be of a type identified for voltage not less than the voltage of the circuit and shall not be smaller than No. 14.

Exception: Conductors not smaller than No. 18 shall be permitted:

a. As leads not more than 8 feet (2.44 m) long permanently attached to electric-discharge lampholders or electric-discharge ballasts if the leads are enclosed in wiring channels.

b. In show window displays or small portable signs, as leads not more than 8 feet (2.44 m) long that run from the line ends of the tubing to the secondary windings of transformers if the leads are permanently attached within the transformer enclosure.

(c) Bends in Conductors. Sharp bends in the conductors shall be avoided.

(d) Concealed Conductors on Insulators — Indoors. Concealed conductors on insulators shall be separated from each other and from all objects other than the insulators on which they are mounted by a spacing of not less than 1½ inches (38 mm) for voltages above 10,000 and not less than 1 inch (25.4 mm) for voltages of 10,000 or less. They shall be installed in channels lined with noncombustible material and used for no other purpose, except that the primary circuit conductors shall be permitted to be in the same channel. The insulators shall be of noncombustible, nonabsorbent material. Concealed conductors on insulators shall not be allowed outside the sign enclosure.

(e) Conductors in Raceways. Where the conductors are covered with lead or other metal sheathing, the covering shall extend beyond the end of the raceway, and the surface of the cable shall not be injured where the covering terminates.

(1) In damp or wet locations, the insulation on all conductors shall extend beyond the metal covering or raceway not less than 4 inches (102 mm) for voltages over 10,000, 3 inches (76 mm) for voltages over 5000 but not exceeding 10,000, and 2 inches (50.8 mm) for voltages of 5000 or less.

(2) In dry locations the insulation shall extend beyond the end of the metal covering or raceways not less than 2½ inches (64 mm) for voltages over 10,000, 2 inches (50.8 mm) for voltages over 5000 but not exceeding 10,000, and 1½ inches (38 mm) for voltages of 5000 or less.

(3) For conductors at grounded midpoint terminals, no spacing shall be required.

ARTICLE 600—ELECTRIC SIGNS

(4) A metal raceway containing a single conductor from one secondary terminal of a transformer shall not exceed 20 feet (6.1 m) in length.

(f) Show Windows and Similar Locations. Conductors that hang freely in the air, away from combustible material, and where not subject to physical damage, as in some show window displays, shall not be required to be otherwise protected.

(g) Between Tubing and Grounded Midpoint. Conductors shall be permitted to be run from the ends of tubing to the grounded midpoint of transformers specifically designed for the purpose and provided with terminals at the midpoint. Where such connections are made to the transformer grounded midpoint, the connections between the high-voltage terminals of the transformer and the line ends of the tubing shall be as short as possible.

600-32. Transformers.

(a) Voltage. The transformer secondary open-circuit voltage shall not exceed 15,000 volts with an allowance on test of 1000 volts additional. For end-grounded transformers, the secondary open-circuit voltage shall not exceed 7500 volts with an allowance on test of 500 volts additional.

(b) Type. Transformers shall be of a type identified for use with electrical-discharge tubing and shall be limited in rating to a maximum of 4500 volt-amperes.

Open core-and-coil-type transformers shall be limited to 5000 volts with an allowance on test of 500 volts and to indoor applications in small portable signs.

Transformers for outline lighting installations shall have secondary current ratings not more than 30 milliamperes.

Exception: Where the transformers and all wiring connected to them are installed in accordance with Article 410 for electric-discharge lighting of the same voltage.

(c) Exposed to Weather. Transformers used outdoors shall be of the weatherproof type or shall be protected from the weather by enclosure in the sign body or in a separate metal box.

(d) Transformer Secondary Connections. The high-voltage windings of transformers shall not be connected in parallel or in series.

Exception No. 1: Two transformers each having one end of its high-voltage winding connected to the metal enclosure shall be permitted to have their high-voltage windings connected in series to form the equivalent of a midpoint-grounded transformer. The grounded ends shall be connected by insulated conductors not smaller than No. 14.

Exception No. 2: Transformers for small portable signs, show windows, and similar locations that are equipped with leads permanently attached to the secondary winding within the transformer enclosure and that do not extend more than 8 feet (2.44 m) beyond the enclosure for attaching to the line ends of the tubing shall not be smaller than No. 18.

(e) Accessibility. Transformers shall be located where accessible and shall be securely fastened in place.

(f) Working Space. A work space at least 3 feet (914 mm) high and measuring at least 3 feet (914 mm) by 3 feet (914 mm) horizontally shall be provided about each transformer or its enclosure where not installed in a sign.

(g) Attic Locations. Transformers shall be permitted to be located in attics provided there is a passageway at least 3 feet (914 mm) in height and at least 2 feet (610 mm) in width, provided with a suitable permanent fixed walkway or catwalk at least 12 inches (305 mm) in width extending from the point of entry into the attic to each transformer.

It is intended that Article 600 provide the necessary safeguards for personnel who are required to perform maintenance on signs and outline lighting by requiring a disconnecting means, by requiring that the use of open wiring be permitted only as concealed wiring on insulators within a sign enclosure, and by further requiring that transformers be located in a safe, accessible location.

600-33. Electric-Discharge Tubing.

(a) Design. The tubing shall be of such length and design as not to cause a continuous overvoltage on the transformer.

(b) Support. Tubing shall be adequately supported on noncombustible, nonabsorbent supports. Tubing supports shall, where practicable, be adjustable.

(c) Contact with Flammable Material and Other Surfaces. The tubing shall be free from contact with flammable material and shall be located where not normally exposed to physical damage. Where operating at over 7500 volts, the tubing shall be supported on noncombustible, nonabsorbent insulating supports that maintain a spacing of not less than ¼ inch (6.35 mm) between the tubing and the nearest surface.

600-34. Terminals and Electrode Receptacles for Electric-Discharge Tubing.

(a) Terminals. Terminals of the tubing shall be inaccessible to unqualified persons and isolated from combustible material and grounded metal or shall be enclosed. Where enclosed, they shall be separated from grounded metal and combustible material by noncombustible, nonabsorbent insulating material or by not less than 1½ inches (38 mm) of air. Terminals shall be relieved from stress by the independent support of the tubing.

(b) Tube Connections Other than with Receptacles. Where tubes do not terminate in receptacles designed for the purpose, all live parts of tube terminals and conductors shall be supported so as to maintain a separation of not less than 1½ inches (38 mm) between conductors or between conductors and any grounded metal.

(c) Receptacles. Electrode receptacles for the tubing shall be of noncombustible, nonabsorbent insulating material.

(d) Bushings. Where electrodes enter the enclosure of outdoor signs or of an indoor sign operating at a voltage in excess of 7500 volts, bushings shall be used unless receptacles are provided. Electrode terminal assemblies shall be supported not more than 6 inches (152 mm) from the electrode terminals.

(e) Show Windows. In the exposed type of show-window signs, terminals shall be enclosed by receptacles.

(f) Receptacles and Bushing Seals. A flexible, nonconducting seal shall be permitted to close the opening between the tubing and the receptacle or bushing against the entrance of dust or moisture. This seal shall not be in contact with grounded conductive material and shall not be depended upon for the insulation of the tubing.

(g) Enclosures of Metal. Enclosures of metal for electrodes shall not be less than No. 24 MSG sheet metal.

(h) Enclosures of Insulating Material. Enclosures of insulating material shall be noncombustible, nonabsorbent, and suitable for the voltage of the circuit.

(i) Live Parts. Live parts shall be enclosed or suitably guarded to prevent contact.

Electric-discharge tubing is required to be of such length and design that it will not cause a continuous overload on the transformer. A tube too long or too small in diameter increases the impedance of the load and, thus, would burden the transformer. Generally, primary voltages of transformers are 120 V, and proper installation and maintenance of transformers and high-voltage secondary conductors will minimize the possibility of injury or fire. Precautions should be taken to ensure that secondary conductors are properly terminated to the tube electrodes, and that these connections are protected from contact by unauthorized persons or by any flammable or combustible material. Broken tubes should be replaced or de-energized.

600-35. Switches on Doors. Doors or covers giving access to uninsulated parts of indoor signs or outline lighting exceeding 600 volts, nominal, and accessible to unqualified persons shall either be provided with interlock switches that on the opening of the doors or covers disconnect the primary circuit, or shall be so fastened that the use of other than ordinary tools will be necessary to open them.

600-36. Fixed Outline Lighting and Skeleton-type Signs for Interior Use.

(a) Tube Support. Gas tubing shall be supported independently of the conductors by means of insulators of noncombustible, nonabsorptive materials such as glass or porcelain or by suspension from suitable wires or chains.

(b) Transformers. Transformers shall be installed in metal enclosures and as near as practicable to the gas tubing system.

(c) Supply Conductors. The supply conductors for the transformers shall be enclosed in grounded metal raceway or rigid nonmetallic conduit where installed in accordance with the requirements of Article 347.

(d) High-Tension Conductors. High-tension conductors shall be insulated for the voltage of the circuit and shall be enclosed in grounded metal raceway.

Exception: Conductors not exceeding 4 feet (1.22 m) in length between gas tubing and adjacent metal enclosures shall be permitted to be enclosed in continuous glass or other insulating sleeves.

600-37. Portable Gas Tube Signs for Show Windows and Interior Use. This section shall apply to the installation and use of portable gas tube signs.

(a) Location. Portable gas tube signs shall be for indoor use only.

(b) Transformer. The transformer shall be of the window type or shall be within a metal enclosure.

(c) Supply Conductors. Supply conductors shall consist of hard or extra-hard usage-type cord containing an equipment grounding conductor. The cord shall not exceed 10 feet (3.05 m) in length.

(d) High-Voltage Conductors. High-voltage conductors shall not be more than 6 feet (1.83 m) long and shall be located where not subject to mechanical injury, and shall be insulated for the voltage of the circuit and be protected by continuous glass or other insulating sleeves or tubing.

(e) Grounding. Transformers and attached noncurrent-carrying metal parts shall be grounded in accordance with Article 250.

(f) Support. Portable indoor signs shall be held in place by not more than two open hooks attached to the transformer case.

ARTICLE 604 — MANUFACTURED WIRING SYSTEMS

Contents

604-1. Scope.
604-2. Definition.
604-3. Uses Permitted.
604-4. Uses Not Permitted.
604-5. Other Articles.

604-6. Construction.
   (a) Cable or Conduit Types.
   (b) Receptacles and Connectors.
   (c) Other Component Parts.
604-7. Unused Outlets.

604-1. Scope. The provisions of this article apply to field-installed wiring using off-site manufactured subassemblies for branch circuits, remote-control circuits, signaling circuits, and communication circuits in accessible areas.

604-2. Definition.

Manufactured Wiring System: A system containing component parts that are assembled in the process of manufacture and cannot be inspected at the building site without damage or destruction to the assembly.

604-3. Uses Permitted. The manufactured wiring systems shall be permitted in accessible and dry locations and in plenums and spaces used for environmental air, when listed for this application, and installed in accordance with Section 300-22.

Exception: In concealed spaces, one end of tapped cable shall be permitted to extend into hollow walls for direct termination at switch and outlet points.

604-4. Uses Not Permitted. Where conductors or cables are limited by the provisions in Articles 333 and 334.

604-5. Other Articles. Installations shall conform with, but not be limited only to, applicable sections of the following articles: 110, 200, 210, 220, 250, 300, 310, 333, 334, 350, 410, 545, 640, 700, 725 and 800.

604-6. Construction.

(a) Cable or Conduit Types.

(1) Cable shall be listed armored cable or metal-clad cable containing nominal 600-volt No. 12 AWG copper insulated conductors with a bare No. 12 AWG copper equipment grounding conductor.

(2) Conduit shall be listed flexible metal conduit containing nominal 600-volt No. 12 AWG copper insulated conductors with an insulated or bare No. 12 AWG copper equipment grounding conductor.

(3) Each section shall be marked to identify the type of cable or conduit.

(b) Receptacles and Connectors. Receptacles and connectors shall be locking type, uniquely polarized and identified for the purpose and shall be part of a listed assembly for the appropriate system.

See Figure 604-1.

Figure 604-1. Components of a manufactured wiring system. (*RELOC — a Div. of Lithonia Lighting*)

(c) Other Component Parts. Other component parts shall be listed for the appropriate system.

604-7. Unused Outlets. All unused outlets shall be capped to effectively close the connector openings.

ARTICLE 605 — OFFICE FURNISHINGS

(Consisting of Lighting Accessories and Wired Partitions)

Contents

605-1. Scope. This article covers electrical equipment, lighting accessories and wiring systems used to connect, or contained within, or installed on relocatable wired partitions.

605-2. General. Wiring systems shall be identified as suitable for providing power for lighting accessories and appliances in wired partitions. These partitions shall not extend from floor to ceiling.

(a) Use.   These assemblies shall be installed and used only as provided for by this article.

(b) Other Articles.   Except as modified by the requirements of this article, all other articles of this Code shall apply.

(c) Hazardous (Classified) Locations.   Where used in hazardous (classified) locations, these assemblies shall conform with Articles 500 through 517 in addition to this article.

605-3. Wireways.   All conductors and connections shall be contained within wiring channels of metal or other material identified as suitable for the conditions of use. Wiring channels shall be free of projections or other conditions that may damage conductor insulation.

(FPN): Conductors as used in this section do not include flexible cord.

605-4. Partition Interconnections.   The electrical connection between partitions shall be a flexible assembly identified for use with wired partitions.

Exception: Flexible cord shall be permitted for the connection between partitions provided all of the following conditions are met:

a. The cord is extra-hard usage type.

b. The partitions are mechanically contiguous.

c. The cord is not longer than necessary for maximum positioning of the partitions but in no case to exceed 2 feet (610 mm).

d. The cord is terminated at an attachment plug and cord-connector with strain relief.

605-5. Lighting Accessories.   Lighting equipment listed and identified for use with wired partitions shall comply with all of the following:

(a) Support.   A means for secure attachment or support shall be provided.

(b) Connection.   Where cord- and plug-connection is provided, the cord length shall be suitable for the intended application, but shall not exceed 9 feet (2.74 m) in length. The cord shall not be smaller than 18 AWG, shall contain an equipment grounding conductor, and shall be of the hard usage type. Connection by other means shall be identified as suitable for the condition of use.

(c) Receptacle Outlet.   Convenience receptacles shall not be permitted in lighting accessories.

605-6. Fixed-type Partitions.   Wired partitions that are fixed (secured to building surfaces) shall be permanently connected to the building electrical system by one of the wiring methods of Chapter 3.

605-7. Free-Standing Type Partitions.   Partitions of the free-standing type (not fixed) shall be permitted to be permanently connected to the building electrical system by one of the wiring methods of Chapter 3.

605-8. Free-Standing Type Partitions, Cord- and Plug-Connected.   Individual partitions of the free-standing type, or groups of individual partitions which are electrically connected, mechanically contiguous and do not exceed 30 feet (9.14 m) when assembled shall be permitted to be connected to the building electrical system by a single flexible cord and plug provided all of the following conditions are met:

(a) Flexible Power Supply Cord. The flexible power-supply cord shall be extra-hard usage type with No. 12 AWG or larger conductors with an insulated grounding conductor and not exceeding 2 feet (610 mm) in length.

(b) Receptacle Supplying Power. The receptacle(s) supplying power shall be on a separate circuit serving only panels and no other loads and shall be located not more than 12 inches (305 mm) from the partition which is connected to it.

(c) Receptacle Outlets, Maximum. Individual partitions or groups of interconnected individual partitions shall not contain more than thirteen 15-ampere, 125-volt receptacle outlets.

(d) Multiwire Circuits, Not Permitted. Individual partitions or groups of interconnected individual partitions shall not contain multiwire circuits.

(FPN): See Section 210-4 for circuits supplying partitions in Sections 605-6 and 605-7.

ARTICLE 610 — CRANES AND HOISTS

Contents

890

A. General

610-1. Scope. This article covers the installation of electric equipment and wiring used in connection with cranes, monorail hoists, hoists, and all runways.

(FPN): For further information, see Safety Code for Cranes, Derricks, Hoists, Jacks, and Slings (ANSI B-30).

610-2. Special Requirements for Particular Locations.

(a) Hazardous (Classified) Locations. All equipment which operates in a hazardous (classified) location shall conform to Article 500.

(1) Equipment used in locations which are hazardous because of the presence of flammable gases or vapors shall conform to Article 501.

(2) Equipment used in locations which are hazardous because of combustible dust shall conform to Article 502.

(3) Equipment used in locations which are hazardous because of the presence of easily ignitible fibers or flyings shall conform to Article 503.

See commentary following Section 503-13(d).

(b) Combustible Materials. Where a crane, hoist, or monorail hoist operates over readily combustible material, the resistors shall be placed in a well-ventilated cabinet composed of noncombustible material so constructed that it will not emit flames or molten metal.

Exception: Resistors shall be permitted to be located in a cage or cab constructed of noncombustible material which encloses the sides of the cage or cab from the floor to a point at least 6 inches (152 mm) above the top of the resistors.

(c) Electrolytic Cell Lines. See Section 668-32.

Special precautions are necessary on electrolytic cell lines to prevent introduction of exposed grounded parts, as described in Section 668-32.

B. Wiring

610-11. Wiring Method. Conductors shall be enclosed in raceways or be Type MC cable, or Type MI cable.

Exception No. 1: Contact conductors.

Exception No. 2: Short lengths of open conductors at resistors, collectors, and other equipment.

Exception No. 3: Where flexible connections are necessary to motors and similar equipment, flexible stranded conductors shall be installed in flexible metal conduit, liquidtight flexible metal conduit, multiconductor cable, or an approved nonmetallic enclosure.

Exception No. 4: Where multiconductor cable is used with a suspended pushbutton station, the station shall be supported in some satisfactory manner that protects the electric conductors against strain.

Use of short lengths of "open" wiring is a permitted wiring method on cranes and hoists where a separately bushed hole from a box or fitting is provided for each conductor, and the method is used for the connection of resistors, collectors, or

Figure 610-1. A suitable grip for strain relief with a suspended pushbutton station. (*Hubbell, Kellems Div.*)

similar equipment. In addition to other types of raceways, flexible metal conduit, liquidtight flexible metal conduit, multiconductor cable, or an approved nonmetallic enclosure (tubing) is permissible where flexibility is necessary.

610-12. Raceway Terminal Fittings.   Conductors leaving raceways shall comply with one of the following:

(a) Separately Bushed Hole.   A box or terminal fitting having a separately bushed hole for each conductor shall be used wherever a change is made from rigid metal conduit, intermediate metal conduit, electrical metallic tubing, metal-clad cable, mineral-insulated cable, or surface raceway wiring to open wiring. A fitting used for this purpose shall not contain taps or splices and shall not be used at fixture outlets.

(b) Bushing in Lieu of a Box.   A bushing shall be permitted to be used in lieu of a box at the end of a rigid metal conduit, intermediate metal conduit or electrical metallic tubing where the raceway terminates at unenclosed controls or similar equipment including contact conductors, collectors, resistors, brakes, power circuit limit switches, and dc split frame motors.

610-13. Types of Conductors.   Conductors shall comply with Table 310-13.

Exception No. 1: Conductor(s) exposed to external heat or connected to resistors shall have a flame-resistant outer covering or be covered with flame-resistant tape individually or as a group.

Exception No. 2: Contact conductors along runways, crane bridges, and monorails shall be permitted to be bare, and shall be copper, aluminum, steel, or other alloys or combinations thereof in the form of hard drawn wire, tees, angles, tee rails, or other stiff shapes.

Exception No. 3: Flexible conductors shall be permitted to be used to convey current and, where practicable, cable reels or take-up devices shall be employed.

610-14. Rating and Size of Conductors.

(a) Ampacity.   The allowable ampacities of conductors shall be as shown in Table 610-14(a).

(FPN): For the ampacities of conductors between controllers and resistors, see Section 430-23.

(b) Secondary Resistor Conductors. Where the secondary resistor is separate from the controller, the minimum size of the conductors between controller and resistor shall be calculated by multiplying the motor secondary current by the appropriate factor from Table 610-14(b) and selecting a wire from Table 610-14(a).

Table 610-14(b). Secondary Conductor Rating Factors

Time in Seconds		Ampacity of Wire in Percent of Full-Load Secondary Current
On	Off	
5	75	35
10	70	45
15	75	55
15	45	65
15	30	75
15	15	85
Continuous Duty		110

(c) Minimum Size. Conductors external to motors and controls shall not be smaller than No. 16.

Exception No. 1: No. 18 wire in multiple conductor cord shall be permitted for control circuits at not over 7 amperes.

Exception No. 2: Wires not smaller than No. 20 shall be permitted for electronic circuits.

(d) Contact Conductors. Contact wires shall have an ampacity not less than that required by Table 610-14(a) for 75°C wire, and in no case shall they be smaller than the following:

Distance Between End Strain Insulators or Clamp-type Intermediate Supports	Size of Wire
0–30 feet	No. 6
30–60 feet	No. 4
Over 60 feet	No. 2

For SI units: one foot = 0.3048 meter.

(e) Calculation of Motor Load.

(1) For one motor, use 100 percent of motor nameplate full-load ampere rating.

(2) For multiple motors on a single crane or hoist, the minimum circuit ampacity of the power supply conductors shall be the nameplate full-load ampere rating of the largest motor or group of motors for any single crane motion, plus 50 percent of the nameplate full-load ampere rating of the next largest motor or group of motors, using that column of Table 610-14(a) which applies to the longest time-rated motor.

(3) For multiple cranes and/or hoists supplied by a common conductor system, compute the motor minimum ampacity for each crane as defined in Section 610-14(e), add them together, and multiply the sum by the appropriate demand factor from Table 610-14(e).

(f) Other Loads. Additional loads, such as heating, lighting, and air conditioning, shall be provided for by application of the appropriate sections of this Code.

Table 610-14(a). Ampacities of Insulated Conductors up to Four Conductors in Raceway or Cable**
Used with Short-Time Rated Crane and Hoist Motors

Max. Operating Temp.	75°C		90°C		110°C	
	Type MTW, RH, RHW, THW, THWN, XHHW		Type AVB, FEP, FEPB, PFA, PFAH, RHH, SA, TA, THHN, XHHW*, Z		Type AVA	
Size AWG MCM	60 min	30 min	60 min	30 min	60 min	30 min
16	10	12	..	..	..	..
14	25	26	31	32	38	40
12	30	33	36	40	45	50
10	40	43	49	52	60	65
8	55	60	63	69	73	80
6	76	86	83	94	93	105
5	85	95	95	106	109	121
4	100	117	111	130	126	147
3	120	141	131	153	145	168
2	137	160	148	173	163	190
1	143	175	158	192	177	215
0	190	233	211	259	239	294
00	222	267	245	294	275	331
000	280	341	305	372	339	413
0000	300	369	319	399	352	440
250	364	420	400	461	447	516
300	455	582	497	636	554	707
350	486	646	542	716	616	809
400	538	688	593	760	666	856
450	600	765	660	836	740	930
500	660	847	726	914	815	1004

Other insulations shown in Table 310-13 and approved for the temperatures and location shall be permitted to be substituted for those shown in Table 610-14(a). The allowable ampacities of conductors used with 15-minute motors shall be the 30-minute ratings increased by 12 percent. * For dry locations only. See Table 310-13. ** For 5 or more simultaneously energized power conductors in raceway or cable, the ampacity of each power conductor shall be reduced to a value of 80 percent of that shown in the table.

Table 610-14(e). Demand Factors

Number of Cranes or Hoists	Demand Factor
2	0.95
3	0.91
4	0.87
5	0.84
6	0.81
7	0.78

(g) Nameplate. Each crane, monorail, or hoist shall be provided with a visible nameplate marked with the maker's name, the rating in volts, frequency, number of phases, and circuit amperes as calculated in Section 610-14(e) and (f).

610-15. Common Return. Where a crane or hoist is operated by more than one motor, a common-return conductor of proper ampacity shall be permitted.

C. Contact Conductors

610-21. Installation of Contact Conductors. Contact conductors shall comply with (a) through (h) below.

(a) Locating or Guarding Contact Conductors. Runway contact conductors shall be guarded and bridge contact conductors shall be located or guarded in a manner that persons cannot inadvertently touch energized current-carrying parts.

(b) Contact Wires. Wires that are used as contact conductors shall be secured at the ends by means of approved strain insulators and shall be so mounted on approved insulators that the extreme limit of displacement of the wire will not bring the latter within less than 1½ inches (38 mm) from the surface wired over.

(c) Supports Along Runways. Main contact conductors carried along runways shall be supported on insulating supports placed at intervals not exceeding 20 feet (6.1 m).

Exception: Supports for grounded rail conductors as provided in (f) below shall not be required to be of the insulating type.

Such conductors shall be separated not less than 6 inches (152 mm) other than for monorail hoists where a spacing of not less than 3 inches (76 mm) shall be permitted. Where necessary, intervals between insulating supports shall be permitted to be increased up to 40 feet (12.2 m), the separation between conductors being increased proportionately.

(d) Supports on Bridges. Bridge wire contact conductors shall be kept at least 2½ inches (64 mm) apart, and where the span exceeds 80 feet (24.4 m), insulating saddles shall be placed at intervals not exceeding 50 feet (15.2 m).

(e) Supports for Rigid Conductors. Conductors along runways and crane bridges, which are of the rigid type specified in Section 610-13, Exception No. 2, and not contained within an approved enclosed assembly, shall be carried on insulating supports spaced at intervals of not more than eighty times the vertical dimension of the conductor, but in no case greater than 15 feet (4.57 m), and spaced apart sufficiently to give a clear electrical separation of conductors or adjacent collectors of not less than 1 inch (25.4 mm).

(f) Track as Circuit Conductor. Monorail, tramrail, or crane-runway tracks shall be permitted as a conductor of current for one phase of a 3-phase, alternating-current system furnishing power to the carrier, crane, or trolley, provided all of the following conditions are met:

895

(1) The conductors supplying the other two phases of the power supply are insulated.

(2) The power for all phases is obtained from an insulating transformer.

(3) The voltage does not exceed 300 volts.

(4) The rail serving as a conductor is effectively grounded at the transformer and also shall be permitted to be grounded by the fittings used for the suspension or attachment of the rail to a building or structure.

Crane-runway tracks are permitted as a current-carrying conductor where part of a 3-phase system is furnishing power to the crane. Figure 610-2 illustrates a 3-phase isolated-delta secondary with one phase grounded at the transformer. It is also permitted to be grounded through the metal supporting means attached to the metal frame of a building.

To power supply disconnecting means and overcurrent protection

To collector conductors

To track

Figure 610-2. Three-phase delta-isolating transformer.

(g) Electrical Continuity of Contact Conductors. All sections of contact conductors shall be mechanically joined to provide a continuous electrical connection.

(h) Not to Supply Other Equipment. Contact conductors shall not be used as feeders for any equipment other than the crane or cranes which they are primarily designed to serve.

610-22. Collectors. Collectors shall be so designed as to reduce to a minimum sparking between them and the contact conductor; and where operated in rooms used for the storage of easily ignitible combustible fibers and materials, they shall comply with Section 503-13.

D. Disconnecting Means

610-31. Runway Conductor Disconnecting Means. A disconnecting means having a continuous ampere rating not less than that computed in Section 610-14(e) and (f) shall be provided between the runway contact conductors and the power supply. Such disconnecting means shall consist of a motor circuit switch or circuit breaker. This disconnecting means shall be readily accessible and operable from the ground or floor level, shall be arranged to be locked in the open position, shall open all ungrounded conductors simultaneously, and shall be placed within view of the crane or hoist and the runway contact conductors.

610-32. Disconnecting Means for Cranes and Monorail Hoists. A motor circuit switch or circuit breaker arranged to be locked in the open position shall be provided in the leads from the runway contact conductors or other power supply on all cranes and monorail hoists.

Exception: Where a monorail hoist or hand-propelled crane bridge installation meets all of the following, the disconnect shall be permitted to be omitted.

a. The unit is floor controlled.

b. The unit is within view of the power supply disconnecting means.

c. No fixed work platform has been provided for servicing the unit.

Where the disconnecting means is not readily accessible from the crane or monorail hoist operating station, means shall be provided at the operating station to open the power circuit to all motors of the crane or monorail hoist.

Many crane installations are not arranged so that the unit is within view of the power supply disconnecting means, hence the requirement that a disconnecting means (lock-open type) be provided in the contact conductors. However, personnel should be aware that, while servicing one crane, another unit on the same system could remain energized and could be run into the person performing maintenance on the locked-out unit.

610-33. Rating of Disconnecting Means. The continuous ampere rating of the switch or circuit breaker required by Section 610-32 shall not be less than 50 percent of the combined short-time ampere rating of the motors, nor less than 75 percent of the sum of the short-time ampere rating of the motors required for any single motion.

E. Overcurrent Protection

610-41. Feeders, Runway Conductors. The runway supply conductors and main contact conductors of a crane or monorail shall be protected by an overcurrent device(s) which shall not be greater than the largest rating or setting of any branch-circuit protective device, plus the sum of the nameplate ratings of all the other loads with application of the demand factors from Table 610-14(e).

610-42. Branch-Circuit Short-Circuit and Ground-Fault Protection. Branch circuits shall be protected as follows:

(a) Fuse or Circuit Breaker Rating. Crane, hoist, and monorail hoist motor branch circuits shall be protected by fuses or inverse-time circuit breakers having a rating in accordance with Table 430-152. Taps to control circuits shall be permitted to be taken from the load side of a branch-circuit protective device, provided each tap and piece of equipment is properly protected.

Exception No. 1: When two or more motors operate a single motion, the sum of their nameplate current ratings shall be considered as a single motor current in the above calculations.

Exception No. 2: Two or more motors shall be permitted to be connected to the same branch circuit if no tap to an individual motor has an ampacity less than one-third that of the branch circuit and if each motor is protected for overload according to Section 610-43.

(b) Taps to Brake Coils. Taps to brake coils do not require separate overcurrent protection.

610-43. Motor and Branch-Circuit Overload Protection. Each motor, motor control, and branch-circuit conductor shall be protected from overload by one of the following means:

(1) A single motor shall be considered as protected when the branch-circuit overcurrent device meets the rating requirements of Section 610-42.

(2) Overload relay elements in each ungrounded circuit conductor, with all relay elements protected from short circuit by the branch-circuit protection.

(3) Thermal sensing device(s), sensitive to motor temperature or to temperature and current which are thermally in contact with the motor winding(s). A hoist or trolley is considered to be protected if the sensing device is connected in the hoist's upper limit switch circuit so as to prevent further hoisting during an overload condition of either motor.

ARTICLE 610—CRANES AND HOISTS

Exception No. 1: If the motor is manually controlled, with spring return controls, the overload protective device need not protect the motor against stalled rotor conditions.

Exception No. 2: Where two or more motors drive a single trolley, truck, or bridge and are controlled as a unit by a single set of overload devices with a rating equal to the sum of their rated full-load currents. A hoist or trolley is considered to be protected if the sensing device is connected in the hoist's upper limit switch circuit so as to prevent further hoisting during an overtemperature condition of either motor.

Exception No. 3: Hoists and monorail hoists and their trolleys which are not used as part of an overhead traveling crane do not require individual motor overload protection provided the largest motor does not exceed 7½ horsepower and all motors are under manual control of the operator.

F. Control

610-51. Separate Controllers. Each motor shall be provided with an individual controller.

Exception No. 1: Where two or more motors drive a single hoist, carriage, truck, or bridge, they shall be permitted to be controlled by a single controller.

Exception No. 2: One controller shall be permitted to be switched between motors provided,

a. The controller shall have a horsepower rating which shall not be lower than the horsepower rating of the largest motor.

b. Only one motor is operated at one time.

610-53. Overcurrent Protection. Conductors of control circuits shall be protected against overcurrent. Control circuits shall be considered as protected by overcurrent devices that are rated or set at not more than 300 percent of the ampacity of the control conductors.

Exception No. 1: Taps to control transformers shall be considered as protected when the secondary circuit is protected by a device rated or set at not more than 200 percent of the rated secondary current of the transformer and not more than 200 percent of the ampacity of the control circuit conductors.

Exception No. 2: Such conductors shall be considered as being properly protected by the branch-circuit overcurrent devices where the opening of the control circuit would create a hazard, as for example, the control circuit of a hot metal crane.

610-55. Limit Switch. A limit switch or other device shall be provided to prevent the load block from passing the safe upper limit of travel of all hoisting mechanisms.

610-57. Clearance. The dimension of the working space in the direction of access to live parts which are likely to require examination, adjustment, servicing, or maintenance while alive shall be a minimum of 2½ feet (762 mm). Where controls are enclosed in cabinets, the door(s) shall either open at least 90 degrees or be removable.

G. Grounding

610-61. Grounding. All exposed metal parts of cranes, monorail hoists, hoists and accessories including pendant controls shall be metallically joined together into a continuous electrical conductor so that the entire crane or hoist will be grounded in accordance with Article 250. Moving parts, other than removable accessories or attachments, having metal-to-metal bearing surfaces shall be considered to be electrically connected to each other through the bearing surfaces for grounding purposes. The trolley frame and bridge frame shall be considered as electrically grounded through the bridge and trolley wheels and its respective tracks unless local conditions, such as paint or other insulating material, prevent reliable metal-to-metal contact. In this case a separate bonding conductor shall be provided.

It is not the intent that the trolley frame or bridge frame serve as the equipment grounding conductor for electric equipment (such as motors, motor controllers, etc.) on a crane. Electric equipment is required to be grounded in accordance with Article 250. See Section 250-91(b) for acceptable types of equipment grounding conductors. However, it is intended that the trolley frame and bridge frame be bonded together and grounded. The bonding and grounding of these nonelectrical structural parts can be through the bridge and trolley wheels and the respective tracks, unless local conditions prevent reliable metal-to-metal contact.

ARTICLE 620 — ELEVATORS, DUMBWAITERS, ESCALATORS, AND MOVING WALKS

Contents

899

A. General

620-1. Scope. This article covers the installation of electric equipment and wiring used in connection with elevators, dumbwaiters, escalators, and moving walks.

(FPN): For further information, see Safety Code for Elevators and Escalators (ANSI/ASME A17.1-1984).

This article is also applicable to similar equipment, such as moving theater stages. The fine print note is necessary to provide for lighting requirements for and about the equipment, including workspace areas.

620-2. Voltage Limitations. The nominal voltage used for elevator, dumbwaiter, escalator, and moving walk operating control and signaling circuits, operating equipment, driving machine motors, machine brakes, and motor-generator sets shall not exceed the following:

(a) 300 Volts. For operating control and signaling circuits and related equipment, including door operator motors.

Exception: Higher voltages shall be permitted for frequencies of 25- through 60-hertz alternating current or for direct current provided the current in the system cannot, under any conditions, exceed 8 milliamperes for alternating current or 30 milliamperes for direct current.

(b) 600 Volts. Driving machine motors, machine brakes, and motor-generator sets.

Exception: Higher voltages shall be permitted for driving motors of motor-generator sets.

620-3. Live Parts Enclosed. All live parts of electric apparatus in the hoistways, at the landings, or in or on the cars of elevators and dumbwaiters or in the wellways or the landings of escalators or moving walks shall be enclosed to protect against accidental contact.

B. Conductors

620-11. Insulation of Conductors. The insulation of conductors installed in connection with elevators, dumbwaiters, escalators, and moving walks shall comply with (a) through (d) below.

(a) Hoistway Door Interlock Wiring. The conductors to the hoistway door interlocks from the hoistway riser shall be flame-retardant and suitable for a temperature of not less than 200°C (392°F). Conductors shall be Type SF or equivalent.

(b) Traveling Cables. Traveling cables used as flexible connections between the elevator or dumbwaiter car and the raceway shall be of the types of elevator cable listed in Table 400-4 or other approved types.

(c) Other Wiring. All conductors in raceways; in or on the cars of elevators and dumbwaiters; in the wellways of escalators and moving walks; and in the machine room of elevators, dumbwaiters, escalators, and moving walks shall have flame-retardant insulation.

(d) Insulation. All conductors shall have an insulation voltage rating equal to at least the maximum nominal circuit voltage rating of any conductor within the enclosure, cable or raceway.

Conductors shall be Type MTW, T, TF, TFF, TFN, TFFN, THHN, THW, THWN, TW, XHHW, AWM or any other conductor with insulation designated as flame retardant. Shielded conductors shall be permitted providing such conductors are insulated for the maximum voltage found in the cable or raceway system.

Hoistway door interlock wiring is required to be suitable for 200°C (392°F). See Table 310-13 for conductor application and insulation. See also Table 310-18.

See Table 400-4 for approved types of elevator cables to be used in hazardous (classified) and nonhazardous locations. See also Note 6 to Table 400-4. A characteristic equally important with respect to safety is the prevention of twisting of cables during their rise and fall with the elevator or dumbwaiter.

620-12. Minimum Size of Conductors. The minimum size of conductors used for elevator, dumbwaiter, escalator, and moving walk wiring, other than conductors that form an integral part of control equipment, shall be as follows:

(a) Traveling Cables.

(1) For lighting circuits: No. 14.

Exception: No. 20 or larger conductors shall be permitted in parallel provided the ampacity is equivalent to at least that of No. 14 wire.

(2) Operating control and signaling circuits: No. 20.

(b) Other Wiring. All operating control and signaling circuits: No. 24.

Extensive use of electronics with the correspondingly lower currents permits the use of smaller wire sizes; hence, conductors of elevator cables may be sized as small as No. 20 AWG conforming to the description in Table 400-4. Operating control and signal circuits in other-than-traveling cables may be as small as No. 24 AWG. They should, of course, have the necessary strength and durability for the conditions to which they will be exposed.

620-13. Motor Circuit Conductors. Conductors supplying elevator, dumbwaiter, escalator or moving walk motors shall have an ampacity in accordance with (a), (b), and (c) below based on the nameplate current rating of the motors. With generator field control, the ampacity shall be based on the nameplate current rating of the driving motor of the motor-generator set which supplies power to the elevator motor.

(FPN): The heating of conductors depends on root-mean-square current values which, with generator field control, are reflected by the nameplate current rating of the motor-generator set driving motor rather than by the rating of the elevator motor, which represents actual but short-time and intermittent full-load current values.

(a) Conductors Supplying Single Motor. Conductors supplying a single motor shall have an ampacity in conformance with Section 430-22, and Table 430-22(a) Exception.

(b) Conductors Supplying Several Motors. Conductors supplying two or more motors shall have an ampacity of not less than 125 percent of the nameplate current rating of the highest rated motor in the group plus the sum of the nameplate current ratings of the remainder of the motors in the group.

(c) Feeder Demand Factor. Feeder conductors of less ampacity than required by (b) above shall be permitted subject to the requirements of Section 430-26.

ARTICLE 620—ELEVATORS, DUMBWAITERS

C. Wiring

620-21. Wiring Methods. Conductors located in hoistways, in escalator and moving walk wellways, in or on cars, and in machine and control rooms, not including the traveling cables connecting the car and hoistway wiring, shall be installed in rigid metal conduit, intermediate metal conduit, electrical metallic tubing, rigid nonmetallic conduit, wireways, or be Type MC cable or Type MI cable.

Exception No. 1: Flexible metal conduit or Type AC cable shall be permitted in hoistways and in escalator and moving walk wellways between risers and limit switches, interlocks, operating buttons, and similar devices. Low-voltage cables (24 volts or less) shall be permitted to be installed between risers and signal fixtures and within escalators and moving walkways where supported and protected from physical abuse.

Exception No. 2: Short runs of flexible metal conduit or Type AC cable shall be permitted on cars where so located as to be free from oil and if securely fastened in place.

Exception No. 3: Hard service cords and junior hard service cords conforming to the requirements of Article 400 (Table 400-4) shall be permitted as flexible connections between the fixed wiring on the car and devices on the car doors or gates. Hard service cords only shall be permitted as flexible connections for the top-of-car operating device or the car-top work light. Devices or fixtures shall be grounded by means of an equipment grounding conductor run with the circuit conductors. Cables with smaller conductors and other types and thicknesses of insulation and jackets shall be permitted as flexible connections between the fixed wiring on the car and devices on the car doors or gates, if listed for this use.

Exception No. 4: Flexible metal conduit or Type AC cable, not exceeding 6 feet (1.83 m) in length, shall be permitted between control panels and machine motors, machine brakes, motor-generator sets, and pumping unit motors and valves. Conductors shall also be permitted to be grouped together and taped or corded without being installed in a raceway. Such cable groups shall be supported at intervals not over 3 feet (914 mm) and so located as to be free from physical damage.

Exception No. 5: Flexible metal conduit of ⅜ inch nominal trade size shall be permitted in lengths not in excess of 6 feet (1.83 m).

Exception No. 6: Hard service cords conforming to the requirements of Article 400 (Table 400-4) shall be permitted as flexible connections on escalators or moving walk control panels and disconnecting means where the entire control panel and disconnecting means are arranged for removal from machine spaces as permitted in Section 620-72, Exception.

Where motor-generators, machine motors, or pumping unit motors and valves are located adjacent to or underneath control equipment and are provided with extra length terminal leads not exceeding 6 feet (1.83 m) in length, such leads shall be permitted to be extended to connect directly to controller terminal studs without regard to the carrying-capacity requirements of Articles 430 and 445. Auxiliary gutters shall be permitted in machine and control rooms between controllers, starters, and similar apparatus.

620-22. Car Light Source. A separate branch circuit shall supply the car lights for each elevator.

D. Installation of Conductors

620-31. Raceway Terminal Fittings. Conductors shall comply with Section 300-16(b). In locations where raceways project from the floor and terminate in other than a wiring enclosure, they shall extend at least 6 inches (152 mm) above the floor.

620-32. Wireways. Section 362-5 shall not apply to wireways. The sum of the cross-sectional area of the individual conductors in a wireway shall not be more than 50 percent of the interior cross-sectional area of the wireway.

Vertical runs of wireways shall be securely supported at intervals not exceeding 15 feet (4.57 m) and shall have not more than one joint between supports. Adjoining wireway sections shall be securely fastened together to provide a rigid joint.

620-33. Number of Conductors in Raceways. The sum of the cross-sectional area of the operating and control circuit conductors in raceways shall not exceed 40 percent of the interior cross-sectional area of the raceway.

Exception: In wireways as permitted in Section 620-32.

620-34. Supports. Supports for cables or raceways in a hoistway or in an escalator or moving walk wellway shall be securely fastened to the guide rail or to the hoistway or wellway construction.

620-35. Auxiliary Gutters (Wiring Troughs). Auxiliary gutters shall not be subject to the restrictions of Section 374-2 as to length or of Section 374-5 as to number of conductors.

620-36. Different Systems in One Raceway or Traveling Cable. Conductors for operating, control, power, signaling, and lighting circuits of 600 volts or less shall be permitted to be run in the same traveling cable or raceway system if all conductors are insulated for the maximum voltage found in the cables or raceway system and if all live parts of the equipment are insulated from ground for this maximum voltage. Such a traveling cable or raceway shall also be permitted to include shielded conductors and/or one or more coaxial cables, if such conductors are insulated for the maximum voltage found in the cable or raceway system. Conductors shall be permitted to be covered with suitable shielding for telephone, audio, video or higher frequency communication circuits.

With the use of greater numbers of individual cables and the use of much longer cables in tall buildings, there is a possibility of intertwisting cable loops. In order to eliminate the practice of tying a cable to the traveling cable, one elevator cable or raceway is permitted to enclose all the conductors of power, control, lighting, video, and communication circuits, where all conductors are insulated for the maximum voltage of any conductor within the cable or raceway.

620-37. Wiring in Hoistways. Main feeders for supplying power to elevators and dumbwaiters shall be installed outside the hoistway. Only such electric wiring, raceways, and cables used directly in connection with the elevator or dumbwaiter, including wiring for signals, for communication with the car, for lighting, heating, air conditioning and ventilating the car, for fire detecting systems, for pit sump pumps, and for heating and lighting the hoistway, shall be permitted inside the hoistway.

Exception: By special permission, feeders for elevators shall be permitted within an existing hoistway, if no conductors are spliced within the hoistway.

620-38. Electric Equipment in Garages and Similar Occupancies. Electric equipment and wiring used for elevators, dumbwaiters, escalators, and moving walks in garages shall comply with the requirements of Article 511. Wiring and equipment located on the underside of the car platform shall be considered as being located in the hazardous area.

620-39. Sidewalk Elevators. Sidewalk elevators with sidewalk doors located exterior to the building shall have all electric wiring in rigid metal conduit, intermediate metal conduit, liquidtight flexible metal conduit or electrical metallic tubing and all electrical outlets, switches, junction boxes, and fittings shall be weatherproof.

E. Traveling Cables

620-41. Suspension of Traveling Cables. Traveling cables shall be so suspended at the car and hoistways' ends as to reduce the strain on the individual copper conductors to a minimum.

ARTICLE 620—ELEVATORS, DUMBWAITERS

Traveling cables shall be supported by one of the following means: (1) by its steel supporting member(s); (2) by looping the cables around supports for unsupported lengths less than 100 feet (30.5 m); (3) by suspending from the supports by a means that automatically tightens around the cable when tension is increased for unsupported lengths up to 200 feet (61 m).

620-42. Hazardous (Classified) Locations. In hazardous (classified) locations, traveling cables shall be of a type approved for hazardous (classified) locations and shall be secured to explosionproof cabinets as provided in Section 501-11.

620-43. Location of and Protection for Cables. Traveling cable supports shall be so located as to reduce to a minimum the possibility of damage due to the cables coming in contact with the hoistway construction or equipment in the hoistway. Where necessary, suitable guards shall be provided to protect the cables against damage.

620-44. Installation of Traveling Cables. Traveling cable shall be permitted to be run without the use of raceway or conduit for a distance not exceeding 6 feet (1.83 m) in length as measured from the first point of support on the elevator car or hoistway wall, providing the conductors are grouped together and taped or corded, or in the original sheath.

Traveling cables shall be permitted to be continued to elevator control panels and to elevator car and machine room connections, as fixed wiring, providing they are suitably supported and protected from damage.

F. Disconnecting Means and Control

620-51. Disconnecting Means. Elevators, dumbwaiters, escalators, and moving walks shall have a single means for disconnecting all ungrounded main power supply conductors for each unit. Where multiple driving machines are connected to a single elevator, escalator, moving walk, or pumping unit, there shall be one disconnecting means to disconnect the motor(s) and control valve operating magnets.

Where there is more than one driving machine in a machine room, disconnecting means shall be numbered to correspond to the number of the driving machine which they control.

(a) Type. The disconnecting means shall be an enclosed externally operable fused motor circuit switch or circuit breaker arranged to be locked in the open position. No provision shall be made to close this disconnecting means from any other part of the premises, nor shall circuit breakers be opened automatically by a fire alarm system.

(b) Location. The disconnecting means shall be located where it is readily accessible to qualified persons.

(1) On elevators without generator field control the disconnecting means shall be located within sight of the power converter or motor starter. When the disconnecting means is not within sight of the hoist machine or control panel, an additional manually operated switch shall be installed adjacent to the remote equipment, connected in the control circuit to prevent starting.

(2) On elevators with generator field control, the disconnecting means shall be located within sight of the motor starter for the driver motor of the motor-generator set. When the disconnecting means is not within sight of the hoist machine, the control panel, or the motor-generator set, an additional manually operated switch shall be installed adjacent to the remote equipment, connected in the control circuit to prevent starting.

(3) On escalators and moving walks, the disconnecting means shall be installed in the space where the controller is located.

620-52. Power from More than One Source.

(a) Single- and Multi-Car Installations. On single- and multi-car installations, equipment receiving electrical power from more than one source shall be provided with a disconnecting means from each source of electrical power within sight of the equipment served.

904

(b) Warning Sign for Multiple Disconnecting Means. Where multiple disconnecting means are used and parts of the control panel remain energized from a source other than the one disconnected, a warning sign shall be mounted on or adjacent to the disconnecting means. The sign shall be clearly legible and shall read "Warning — Parts of the control panel are not de-energized by this switch."

(c) Interconnection Multicar Control Panels. Where interconnections between control panels are necessary for the operation of the system on multicar installations that remain energized from a source other than the one disconnected, a warning sign in accordance with Section 620-52(b) shall be mounted on or adjacent to the disconnecting means.

620-53. Phase Protection.

(a) Electric Elevators. Electric elevators driven by polyphase alternating-current motors shall be provided with a means to prevent starting of the elevator motor when: (1) the phase rotation is in the wrong direction, or (2) there is a failure in any phase.

If the motor rotation were in the wrong direction, the elevator car would also travel in the wrong direction, hence the use of a reverse-phase relay which would prevent the controller from energizing the motor. This condition is possible when a worker unintentionally reverses two conductor leads of the motor circuit during maintenance or replacement.

(b) Hydraulic Elevators. Hydraulic elevators powered by a polyphase alternating-current motor shall be provided with the means to prevent overheating of the drive system (pump and motor) due to phase rotation reversals or failure.

Although phase reversal will not result in the car traveling in the wrong direction if the elevator is hydraulically operated, phase reversal can cause overheating of the drive system because the pump will run backwards.

G. Overcurrent Protection

620-61. Overcurrent Protection. Overcurrent protection shall be provided as follows:

(a) Control and Operating Circuits. Control and operating circuits and signaling circuits shall be protected against overcurrent in accordance with the requirements of Section 725-12.

(b) Motors.

(1) Duty on elevator and dumbwaiter driving machine motors and driving motors of motor-generators used with generator field control shall be classed as intermittent. Such motors shall be protected against overcurrent in accordance with Section 430-33.

(2) Duty on escalator and moving walk driving machine motors shall be classed as continuous. Such motors shall be protected against overcurrent in accordance with Section 430-32.

(3) Escalator and moving walk driving machine motors and driving motors of motor-generator sets shall be protected against running overcurrent as provided in Table 430-37.

H. Machine Room

620-71. Guarding Equipment. Elevator, dumbwaiter, escalator, and moving walk driving machines, motor-generator sets, motor controllers, and disconnecting means shall be installed in a room or enclosure set aside for that purpose. The room or enclosure shall be secured against unauthorized access.

ARTICLE 620—ELEVATORS, DUMBWAITERS

Exception: Dumbwaiter, escalator, or moving walk motor controllers shall be permitted outside the spaces herein specified, provided they are enclosed in cabinets with doors or removable panels capable of being locked in the closed position and the disconnecting means is located adjacent to the motor controller. Such cabinets shall be permitted in the balustrading on the side away from the moving steps or moving treadway.

620-72. Clearance Around Control Panels and Disconnecting Means. Sufficient clear working space shall be provided around control panels and disconnecting means to provide safe and convenient access to all live parts of the equipment necessary for maintenance and adjustment. The minimum clear working space about live parts on control panels and disconnecting means shall not be less than specified in Section 110-16.

Exception: Where an escalator or moving walk control panel and disconnecting means are mounted in the same space as the escalator or moving walk drive machine and the clearances specified cannot be provided, the clearance requirements of Section 110-16 shall be permitted to be waived where the entire panel and disconnecting means are arranged so that they can be readily removed from the machine space and are provided with flexible leads to all external connections.

Where control panels are not located in the same space as the drive machine, they shall be located in cabinets with doors or removable panels capable of being locked in the closed position. Such cabinets shall be permitted in the balustrading on the side away from the moving steps or moving treadway.

J. Grounding

620-81. Metal Raceways Attached to Cars. Metal raceways, Type MC cable, Type MI cable, or Type AC cable attached to elevator cars shall be bonded to grounded metal parts of the car which they contact.

620-82. Electric Elevators. For electric elevators, the frames of all motors, elevator machines, controllers, and the metal enclosures for all electric devices in or on the car or in the hoistway shall be grounded in accordance with Article 250.

620-83. Nonelectric Elevators. For elevators other than electric having any electric conductors attached to the car, the metal frame of the car, where normally accessible to persons, shall be grounded in accordance with Article 250.

K. Overspeed

620-91. Overspeed Protection for Elevators. Under overhauling load conditions a means shall be provided on the load side of each elevator power disconnecting means to prevent the elevator from attaining a speed equal to the governor tripping speed or a speed in excess of 125 percent of the elevator rated speed, whichever is the lesser.

Overhauling load conditions shall include all loads up to rated elevator loads for freight elevators and all loads up to 125 percent of rated elevator loads for passenger elevators.

620-92. Motor-Generator Overspeed Device. Motor-generators driven by direct-current motors and used to supply direct current for the operation of elevator machine motors shall be provided with speed-limiting devices as required by Section 430-89(c) that will prevent the elevator from attaining at any time a speed of more than 125 percent of its rated speed.

620-101. Emergency Power. An elevator can be powered by an emergency power system provided that when operating on such emergency power there is conformance with Section 620-91.

Exception: Where the emergency power system is designed to operate only one elevator at a time, the energy absorption means, if required, shall be permitted on the line side of the disconnecting means, provided all other requirements of Section 620-91 are conformed to when operating any of the elevators the system might serve.

(a) Other Building Loads. Other building loads, such as power and light that can be supplied by the emergency power system, shall not be considered as means of absorbing the regenerated energy for the purpose of conforming to Section 620-91 unless such loads are using their normal power from the emergency power system when it is activated.

(b) Disconnecting Means. The disconnecting means required by Section 620-51 shall disconnect the emergency power service and the normal power service.

ARTICLE 630 — ELECTRIC WELDERS

Contents

A. General

630-1. Scope. This article covers electric arc welding, resistance welding apparatus, and other similar welding equipment that is connected to an electric supply system.

The two general types of electric welding are resistance welding and arc welding. Resistance welding or "spot" welding is the process of joining or fusing together electrically two or more metal sheets or parts without any preparation of stock. The metal parts are placed between two electrodes, or welding points, and a heavy current at a low voltage is passed through the electrodes. The metal parts offer a great resistance to the flow of current so that they heat to a molten state and a weld is made.

Arc welding is the "butting" of two metal parts to be welded and striking an arc at this joint with a metal electrode (a flux-coated wire rod). The electrode, itself, is melted and supplies the extra metal necessary for joining the metal parts.

A transformer supplies current for one ac arc welder, and a generator or rectifier supplies current for one or more dc arc welders.

907

B. AC Transformer and DC Rectifier Arc Welders

630-11. Ampacity of Supply Conductors. The ampacity of conductors for ac transformer and dc rectifier arc welders shall be as follows:

(a) Individual Welders. The rated ampacity of the supply conductors shall not be less than the current values determined by multiplying the rated primary current in amperes given on the welder nameplate and the following factor based upon the duty cycle or time rating of the welder.

Duty Cycle (percent)	100	90	80	70	60	50	40	30	20 or less
Multiplier	1.00	.95	.89	.84	.78	.71	.63	.55	.45

For a welder having a time rating of 1 hour, the multiplying factor shall be 0.75.

(b) Group of Welders. The rated ampacity of conductors that supply a group of welders shall be permitted to be less than the sum of the currents, as determined in accordance with (a) above, of the welders supplied. The conductor rating shall be determined in each case according to the welder loading based on the use to be made of each welder and the allowance permissible in the event that all the welders supplied by the conductors will not be in use at the same time. The load value used for each welder shall take into account both the magnitude and the duration of the load while the welder is in use.

(FPN): Conductor ratings based on 100 percent of the current, as determined in accordance with (a) above, of the two largest welders, 85 percent for the third largest welder, 70 percent for the fourth largest welder, and 60 percent for all the remaining welders, can be assumed to provide an ample margin of safety under high-production conditions with respect to the maximum permissible temperature of the conductors. Percentage values lower than those given are permissible in cases where the work is such that a high-operating duty cycle for individual welders is impossible.

Even under high-production conditions, the loads on transformer arc welders are considered intermittent; therefore, it is permissible to reduce the ampacity of feeder conductors supplying several transformers (three or more) to the allowable percentages described in the fine print note. It is obvious that intermittent transformer arc welder loads would be considerably less than a continuous load equal to the sum of the full-load current ratings of all the transformers. See also Section 630-31(b).

630-12. Overcurrent Protection. Overcurrent protection for ac transformer and dc rectifier arc welders shall be as provided in (a) and (b) below. Where the nearest standard rating of the overcurrent device used is under the value specified in this section, or where the rating or setting specified results in unnecessary opening of the overcurrent device, the next higher standard rating or setting shall be permitted.

(a) For Welders. Each welder shall have overcurrent protection rated or set at not more than 200 percent of the rated primary current of the welder.

Exception: An overcurrent device shall not be required for a welder having supply conductors protected by an overcurrent device rated or set at not more than 200 percent of the rated primary current of the welder.

(b) For Conductors. Conductors that supply one or more welders shall be protected by an overcurrent device rated or set at not more than 200 percent of the conductor rating.

Some arc-welding machines have a welding range involving an excess secondary-current output capacity beyond that indicated by the marked secondary rating on the machines. This excess capacity (generally not more than 150 percent of the marked output capacity) is usually supplied by means of one or more secondary taps in addition to the tap, or taps, intended for normal output current; and the higher currents thus available are intended to provide for heavier welding work, including the use of larger-size electrodes. This excess capacity is somewhat analogous to the inherent overload capacity of motors and transformers, and it is not covered at present by any definite requirements and is not investigated by Underwriters Laboratories Inc. However, the abuse of this excess current capacity, and overloading of a welding machine, except for relatively short periods of time, may be hazardous and should receive careful consideration by all those concerned.

630-13. Disconnecting Means. A disconnecting means shall be provided in the supply for each ac transformer and dc rectifier arc welder which is not equipped with a disconnect mounted as an integral part of the welder.

The disconnecting means shall be a switch or circuit breaker, and its rating shall not be less than that necessary to accommodate overcurrent protection as specified under Section 630-12.

630-14. Marking. A nameplate shall be provided for ac transformer and dc rectifier arc welders giving the following information: name of manufacturer; frequency; number of phases; primary voltage; rated primary current; maximum open-circuit voltage; rated secondary current; basis of rating, such as the duty cycle or time rating.

C. Motor-Generator Arc Welders

630-21. Ampacity of Supply Conductors. The ampacity of conductors for motor-generator arc welders shall be as follows:

(a) Individual Welders. The rated ampacity of the supply conductors shall not be less than the current values determined by multiplying the rated primary current in amperes given on the welder nameplate and the following factor based upon the duty cycle or time rating of the welder.

Duty Cycle (percent)....	100	90	80	70	60	50	40	30	20 or less
Multiplier.....	1.00	.96	.91	.86	.81	.75	.69	.62	.55

For a welder having a time rating of 1 hour, the multiplying factor shall be 0.80.

(b) Group of Welders. The rated ampacity of conductors that supply a group of welders shall be permitted to be less than the sum of the currents, as determined in accordance with (a) above, of the welders supplied. The conductor rating shall be determined in each case according to the welder loading based on the use to be made of each welder and the allowance permissible in the event that all the welders supplied by the conductors will not be in use at the same time. The load value used for each welder shall take into account both the magnitude and the duration of the load while the welder is in use.

(FPN): Conductor ratings based on 100 percent of the current, as determined in accordance with (a) above, of the two largest welders, 85 percent for the third largest welder, 70 percent for the fourth largest welder, and 60 percent for all the remaining welders, can be assumed to provide an ample margin of safety under high-production conditions with respect to the maximum permissible temperature of the conductors. Percentage values lower than those given are permissible in cases where the work is such that a high-operating duty cycle for individual welders is impossible.

The ampacity of supply conductors for a welder that is not wired for a specific function, that is, one operated at varying intervals for different applications such as dissimilar metals or thicknesses, is permitted to be 70 percent of the rated primary current for automatically fed welders and 50 percent of the rated primary current for manually operated welders.

Rated primary current = kVA × 1,000 ÷ rated primary voltage (using values given on nameplate).

Where the actual primary current and duty cycle are known, such as for a welder wired for a specific operation, the ampacity of the supply conductors is not permitted to be less than the product of the actual primary current (current drawn during weld operation) and the multiplier [as given in Section 630-31(a)(2)] for the duty cycle at which the welder will be operated. For example, a spot welder is specifically set to perform 300 welds per hour on a 60-Hz system. Each weld draws current for 16 cycles. During the one-hour period, the welder draws current for 4,800 cycles (300 × 16). There are 216,000 cycles per hour (60 × 60 × 60).

$$\frac{4,800}{216,000} \times 100 \text{ percent} = 2.2 \text{ percent (duty cycle)}$$

or, a seam welder draws current for 3 cycles and is off for 4 cycles during every 7-cycle period.

$$\frac{3}{7} \times 100 \text{ percent} = 42.9 \text{ percent (duty cycle)}$$

An ammeter or equivalent capable of measuring current impulses for 3 cycles (1/20th of a second), as per the example, is required to measure the actual primary current. The duty cycle is set for a specific operation by adjusting the controller for the welder. When sizing supply conductors, voltage drop should be limited to a value permissible for the satisfactory performance of the welder.

630-22. Overcurrent Protection. Overcurrent protection for motor-generator arc welders shall be as provided in (a) and (b) below. Where the nearest standard rating of the overcurrent device used is under the value specified in this section, or where the rating or setting specified results in unnecessary opening of the overcurrent device, the next higher standard rating or setting shall be permitted.

(a) For Welders. Each welder shall have overcurrent protection rated or set at not more than 200 percent of the rated primary current of the welder.

Exception: An overcurrent device shall not be required for a welder having supply conductors protected by an overcurrent device rated or set at not more than 200 percent of the rated primary current of the welder.

(b) For Conductors. Conductors that supply one or more welders shall be protected by an overcurrent device rated or set at not more than 200 percent of the conductor rating.

630-23. Disconnecting Means. A disconnecting means shall be provided in the supply connection of each motor-generator arc welder.

The disconnecting means shall be a circuit breaker or motor-circuit switch, and its rating shall not be less than that necessary to accommodate overcurrent protection as specified under Section 630-22.

630-24. Marking. A nameplate shall be provided for each motor-generator arc welder giving the following information: name of manufacturer; rated frequency; number of phases; input voltage; input current; maximum open-circuit voltage; rated output current; basis of rating, such as duty cycle or time rating.

D. Resistance Welders

630-31. Ampacity of Supply Conductors. The ampacity of the supply conductors for resistance welders necessary to limit the voltage drop to a value permissible for the satisfactory performance of the welder is usually greater than that required to prevent overheating as prescribed in (a) and (b) below.

(a) Individual Welders. The rated ampacity for conductors for individual welders shall comply with the following:

(1) The rated ampacity of the supply conductors for a welder that may be operated at different times at different values of primary current or duty cycle shall not be less than 70 percent of the rated primary current for seam and automatically fed welders, and 50 percent of the rated primary current for manually operated nonautomatic welders.

(2) The rated ampacity of the supply conductors for a welder wired for a specific operation for which the actual primary current and duty cycle are known and remain unchanged shall not be less than the product of the actual primary current and the multiplier given below for the duty cycle at which the welder will be operated.

Duty Cycle (percent)....	50	40	30	25	20	15	10	7.5	5.0 or less
Multiplier.....	.71	.63	.55	.50	.45	.39	.32	.27	.22

(b) Groups of Welders. The rated ampacity of conductors that supply two or more welders shall not be less than the sum of the value obtained in accordance with (a) above for the largest welder supplied, and 60 percent of the values obtained for all the other welders supplied.

(FPN): Explanation of Terms. (1) The rated primary current is the rated kVA multiplied by 1000 and divided by the rated primary voltage, using values given on the nameplate. (2) The actual primary current is the current drawn from the supply circuit during each welder operation at the particular heat tap and control setting used. (3) The duty cycle is the percentage of the time during which the welder is loaded. For instance, a spot welder supplied by a 60-hertz system (216,000 cycles per hour) making four hundred 15-cycle welds per hour would have a duty cycle of 2.8 percent (400 multiplied by 15, divided by 216,000, multiplied by 100). A seam welder operating 2 cycles "on" and 2 cycles "off" would have a duty cycle of 50 percent.

630-32. Overcurrent Protection. Overcurrent protection for resistance welders shall be as provided in (a) and (b) below. Where the nearest standard rating of the overcurrent device used is under the value specified in this section, or where the rating or setting specified results in unnecessary opening of the overcurrent device, the next higher standard rating or setting shall be permitted.

(a) For Welders. Each welder shall have an overcurrent device rated or set at not more than 300 percent of the rated primary current of the welder.

Exception: An overcurrent device shall not be required for a welder having a supply circuit protected by an overcurrent device rated or set at not more than 300 percent of the rated primary current of the welder.

(b) For Conductors. Conductors that supply one or more welders shall be protected by an overcurrent device rated or set at not more than 300 percent of the conductor rating.

Conductors of resistance welders and arc welders are provided with overcurrent protection against short circuits. Proper application and operation of the welder will safeguard against overload conditions. See commentary following Section 630-12(b).

630-33. Disconnecting Means. A switch or circuit breaker shall be provided by which each resistance welder and its control equipment can be isolated from the supply circuit. The ampere rating of this disconnecting means shall not be less than the supply conductor ampacity determined in accordance with Section 630-31. The supply circuit switch shall be permitted as the welder disconnecting means where the circuit supplies only one welder.

630-34. Marking. A nameplate shall be provided for each resistance welder giving the following information: name of manufacturer; frequency; primary voltage rated kVA at 50 percent duty cycle; maximum and minimum open-circuit secondary voltage; short-circuit secondary current at maximum secondary voltage; and specified throat and gap setting.

E. Welding Cable

630-41. Conductors. Insulation of conductors intended for use in the secondary circuit of electric welders shall be flame retardant.

630-42. Installation. Cables shall be permitted to be installed in a dedicated cable tray as provided in (a), (b), and (c) below.

(a) Cable Support. The cable tray shall provide support at not greater than 6-inch (152-mm) intervals.

(b) Spread of Fire and Products of Combustion. The installation shall comply with Section 300-21.

(c) Signs. A permanent sign shall be attached to the cable tray at intervals not greater than 20 feet (6.1 m). The sign shall read "Cable tray for welding cables only."

See Section 318-3(b)(1), Exception.

ARTICLE 640 — SOUND-RECORDING AND SIMILAR EQUIPMENT

Contents

640-1. Scope. This article covers equipment and wiring for sound-recording and reproduction, centralized distribution of sound, public address, speech-input systems, and electronic organs.

Equipment covered by this article includes amplifiers, public address (PA) and centralized sound systems such as those utilized in schools, factories and similar

912

locations, intercommunication devices and systems, and devices used for recording and reproducing voice or music.

640-2. Application of Other Articles.

(a) Wiring to and Between Devices. Wiring and equipment from source of power to and between devices connected to the interior wiring systems shall comply with the requirements of Chapters 1 through 4, except as modified by this article.

(b) Wiring and Equipment. Wiring and equipment for public-address, speech-input, radio-frequency and audio-frequency systems, and amplifying equipment associated with radio receiving stations in centralized distribution systems shall comply with Article 725.

Chapters 1 through 4 apply generally to branch-circuit wiring that supplies power to sound systems and to wiring that supplies power between components of the system, unless modified by this article (see Sections 640-3 and 640-4, Exceptions).

Wiring and equipment with electrical power limitations that differentiate them from light and power circuits are required to comply with Article 725 (see Section 640-5).

Radio equipment is required to comply with Article 810 unless specifically referenced therein, such as in Section 810-2.

640-3. Number of Conductors in Conduit or Tubing.
The number of conductors in a conduit or tubing shall comply with Tables 1 through 7 of Chapter 9.

Exception No. 1: Special permission may be granted for the installation of two 2-conductor lead-covered cables in ¾-inch conduit or tubing, provided the cross-sectional area of each cable does not exceed .11 square inch.

Exception No. 2: Special permission may be granted for the installation of two 2-conductor No. 19 lead-covered cables in ½-inch conduit or tubing, provided the sum of the cross-sectional areas of the cables does not exceed 32 percent of the internal cross-sectional area of the conduit or tubing.

640-4. Wireways and Auxiliary Gutters.
Wireways shall comply with the requirements of Article 362, and auxiliary gutters shall comply with the requirements of Article 374.

Exception: Where used for sound-recording and reproduction, the following shall be complied with:

a. Conductors in wireways or gutters shall not fill the raceway to more than 75 percent of its depth.

b. Where the cover of auxiliary gutters is flush with the flooring and is subject to the moving of heavy objects, it shall be of steel at least ¼ inch (6.35 mm) in thickness; where not subject to moving of heavy objects, as in the rear of patch or other equipment panels, the cover shall be at least No. 10 MSG.

c. Wireways shall be permitted in concealed places provided they are run in a straight line between outlets or junction boxes. Covers of boxes shall be accessible. Edges of metal shall be rounded at outlet or junction boxes and all rough projections smoothed to prevent abrasion of insulation or conductors.

d. Wireways and auxiliary gutters shall be grounded and bonded in accordance with the requirements of Article 250. Where the wireway or auxiliary gutter does not contain power-supply wires, the equipment grounding conductor shall not be required to be larger than No. 14 copper or its equivalent. Where the wireway or auxiliary gutter contains power-supply wires, the equipment grounding conductor shall not be smaller than specified in Section 250-95.

640-5. Conductors.
Amplifier output circuits carrying audio-program signals of 70 volts or less and whose open-circuit voltage will not exceed 100 volts shall be permitted to employ Class 2 or Class 3 wiring as covered in Article 725.

913

(FPN): The above is based on amplifiers whose open-circuit voltage will not exceed 100 volts when driven with a signal at any frequency from 60 to 100 hertz sufficient to produce rated output (70.7 volts) into its rated load. This also accepts the known fact that the average program material is 12 db below the amplifier rating — thus the average rms voltage for an open-circuit 70-volt output would be only 25 volts.

640-6. Grouping of Conductors. Conductors of different systems grouped in the same raceway or other enclosure or in portable cords or cables shall comply with (a) through (c) below.

(a) Power-Supply Conductors. Power-supply conductors shall be properly identified and shall be used solely for supplying power to the equipment to which the other conductors are connected.

(b) Leads to Motor-Generator or Rotary Converter. Input leads to a motor-generator or rotary converter shall be run separately from the output leads.

(c) Conductor Insulation. The conductors shall be insulated individually, or collectively in groups, by insulation at least equivalent to that on the power supply and other conductors.

Exception: Where the power supply and other conductors are separated by a lead sheath or other continuous metallic covering.

640-7. Flexible Cords. Flexible cords and cables shall be of Type S, SJ, ST, SJO, or SJT or other approved types. The conductors of flexible cords, other than power-supply conductors, shall be permitted to be of a size not smaller than No. 26, provided such conductors are not in direct electrical connection with the power-supply conductors and are equipped with a current-limiting means so that the maximum power under any condition will not exceed 150 watts.

640-8. Terminals. Terminals shall be marked to show their proper connections. Terminals for conductors other than power-supply conductors shall be separated from the terminals of the power-supply conductors by a spacing at least as great as the spacing between power-supply terminals of opposite polarity.

Branch-circuit wiring that supplies power to sound systems and their components is usually a 120-V or 240-V power circuit and is not considered to be a part of the sound system and, therefore, is kept separate from sound system cables or conductors. It is permitted in the same enclosure, however, where terminals are spaced according to this section.

640-9. Storage Batteries. Storage batteries shall comply with (a) and (b) below.

(a) Installation. Storage batteries shall be installed in accordance with Article 480.

(b) Conductor Insulation. Storage-battery leads shall be rubber-covered or thermoplastic-covered.

640-10. Circuit Overcurrent Protection. Overcurrent protection shall be provided as follows:

(a) Heater or Filament (Cathode). Circuits to the heater or filament (cathode) of an electronic tube shall have overcurrent protection not exceeding 15 amperes where supplied by lighting branch circuits, or by storage batteries exceeding 20 ampere-hour capacity.

(b) Plate (Anode-Positive). Circuits to the plate (anode-positive) and to the screen grid of an electronic tube shall have overcurrent protection not exceeding 1.0 ampere.

(c) Control Grid. Circuits to the control grid of an electronic tube shall have overcurrent protection not exceeding 1.0 ampere where supplied by lighting branch circuits or by storage batteries exceeding 20 ampere-hour capacity.

(d) Location. Overcurrent devices shall be located as near as practicable to the source of power supply.

Overcurrent protection is required to be located at the point where the conductor to be protected receives its supply from a battery or other power source. The three circuits in subparagraphs (a), (b), and (c) are defined for clarity to assure proper application and value of overcurrent protective devices.

640-11. Amplifiers and Rectifiers — Type.

(a) Approved Type. Amplifiers and rectifiers shall be of an approved type and shall be suitably housed.

(b) Readily Accessible. Amplifiers and rectifiers shall be so located as to be readily accessible.

(c) Ventilation. Amplifiers and rectifiers shall be so located as to provide sufficient ventilation to prevent undue temperature rise within the housing.

640-12. Hazardous (Classified) Locations. Equipment used in hazardous (classified) locations shall comply with Article 500.

640-13. Protection Against Physical Damage. Amplifiers, rectifiers, loudspeakers, and other equipment shall be so located or protected as to guard against physical damage, such as might result in fire or personal hazard.

ARTICLE 645 — ELECTRONIC COMPUTER/DATA PROCESSING EQUIPMENT

Contents

645-1. Scope. This article covers equipment, power-supply wiring, equipment interconnecting wiring, and grounding of electronic computer/data processing equipment and systems, including electronic computer/data processing equipment and systems used as a terminal unit in an electronic computer/data processing room.

(FPN): For further information, see Standard for the Protection of Electronic Computer/Data Processing Equipment, NFPA 75-1981 (ANSI).

Article 645 includes only equipment and wiring *in the data processing room.* A data processing room is usually an enclosed area, with one or more means of entry, that contains data processing equipment. Small terminals, such as remote telephone terminal units, remote data terminals, personal computers, and cash registers in stores and supermarkets, are not covered by Article 645.

A data processing room is a room designed to comply with the special construction and fire protection provisions of NFPA 75, *Standard for the Protection of Electronic Computer/Data Processing Equipment.* Because of these special provisions, not all of the usual *Code* rules are applicable; for example, the wiring under the raised floor. See Section 300-22(c), Exception No. 6. The requirements in Article 645 are based on the assumption that the room will comply with NFPA 75.

645-2. Supply Circuits and Interconnecting Cables.

(a) Branch-Circuit Conductors.   The branch-circuit conductors to which one or more units of a data processing system are connected to a source of supply shall have an ampacity not less than 125 percent of the total connected load.

(b) Connecting Cables.   The data processing system shall be permitted to be connected by means of computer or data processing cable or flexible cord and an attachment plug cap or cord-set assembly specifically approved as a part of the data processing system. Separate units shall be permitted to be interconnected by means of flexible cords and cables specifically approved as part of the data processing system. When run on the surface of the floor, they shall be protected against physical damage.

(c) Under Raised Floors.   Power cables, communications cables and interconnecting cables associated with the data processing equipment shall be permitted under a raised floor provided:

(1) The raised floor is of suitable construction.

(FPN): See Standard for Electronic Computer/Data Processing Equipment, NFPA 75-1981 (ANSI).

(2) The branch-circuit supply conductors to receptacles are in rigid metal conduit, intermediate metal conduit, electrical metallic tubing, metal wireway, surface metal raceway with metal cover, flexible metal conduit, liquidtight flexible metal conduit, Type MI cable, Type MC cable, or Type AC cable.

(3) Ventilation in the underfloor area is used for the data processing equipment and data processing area only.

645-3. Disconnecting Means.   A disconnecting means shall be provided to disconnect the power to all electronic equipment in the data processing room. This disconnecting means shall be controlled from locations readily accessible to the operator at the principal exit doors. There shall also be a similar disconnecting means to disconnect the air-conditioning system serving this area. A single means to control both the electronic equipment and air-conditioning system disconnecting means shall be permitted.

This section requires two separate disconnecting means but permits a single control, such as one pushbutton, to operate both disconnecting means. The disconnecting means is required to disconnect the conductors of each circuit from their source of supply. See definition of "disconnecting means" in Article 100. The disconnecting means could be remotely controlled switching devices, such as relays, with pushbutton stations at the principal exit doors.

645-4. Grounding.   All exposed noncurrent-carrying metal parts of a data processing system shall be grounded in accordance with Article 250.

645-5. Marking.   Each unit of a data processing system that is intended to be supplied by a branch circuit shall be provided with a manufacturer's nameplate, which shall also include the rating in volts, the operating frequency, and the total load in amperes.

ARTICLE 650 — ORGANS

Contents

650-1. Scope. This article covers those electric circuits and parts of electrically operated organs which are employed for the control of the sounding apparatus and keyboards.

650-2. Other Articles. Electronic organs shall comply with the appropriate provisions of Article 640.

650-3. Source of Energy. The source of energy shall have a potential of not over 15 volts and shall be a self-excited generator, a two-coil transformer-type rectifier, or a battery.

650-4. Insulation — Grounding. The generator shall be effectively insulated from ground and from the motor driving it, or both the generator and the motor frames shall be grounded in the manner specified in Article 250.

> The energy source required to power electrically operated organs has a potential of less than 15 V and is generally supplied by a motor-driven generator, although a rectifier or a battery may be used.
>
> Usually the motor and generator are mounted on the same metal frame and are effectively grounded. However, if this is not the case, the generator is required to be effectively insulated from the motor and from ground. If the motor and generator were not grounded and the generator not effectively insulated, then a motor-winding fault could energize the motor housing and also the generator housing to a potential of 120 V or 240 V (depending on the motor branch-circuit), and damage to the generator windings or the organ circuit conductors could result.

650-5. Conductors. Conductors shall comply with (a) through (d) below.

(a) Size. No conductor shall be smaller than No. 26, and the common-return conductor shall not be smaller than No. 14.

(b) Insulation. Conductors shall have rubber, thermoplastic, asbestos, cotton, or silk insulation.

Exception: The common-return conductors shall be rubber-covered, thermoplastic, or asbestos-covered (Type AA, AI, or AIA).

The cotton or silk shall be permitted to be saturated with paraffin if desired.

(c) Conductors to Be Cabled. Except the common-return conductor and conductors inside the organ proper, the organ sections and the organ console conductors shall be cabled. The common-return conductor shall be permitted under an additional covering enclosing both cable and return conductor, or shall be permitted as a separate conductor and shall be permitted to be in contact with the cable.

(d) Cable Covering. The cable shall be provided with one or more braided outer coverings, or a tape shall be permitted in place of an inner braid. Where not installed in metal raceways, the outer braid shall be flame-retardant or shall be covered with a closely wound fireproof tape.

The common-return conductor carries the full voltage (usually about 10 V) of the control system and must be sized No. 14 AWG or larger. The other wires of the control system may be as small as No. 26 AWG and, being of the same polarity and potential, are not required to be overly protected from each other because they are required to be effectively insulated from the common-return conductor.

650-6. Installation of Conductors. Cables shall be securely fastened in place and shall be permitted to be attached directly to the organ structure without insulating supports. Cables shall not be placed in contact with other conductors.

Insulating supports are not required for such a low-voltage system; however, conductors that are required to be cabled are required to have a flame-retardant outer covering or are required to be run in metal raceways. Measures should be taken to prevent contact between cables and conductors of other systems.

650-7. Overcurrent Protection. Circuits shall be so arranged that all conductors shall be protected from overcurrent by an overcurrent device rated at not over 15 amperes.

Exception: The main supply conductors and the common-return conductor.

The two conductors that are run from the generator to the point of connection of the common-return conductor and to the many circuit conductors necessary for the system are the "main supply conductors" and do not require overcurrent protection. The common-return conductor also does not require overcurrent protection; however, the circuit conductors are required to be arranged to be protected by a 15-A overcurrent device at their connection point to the main supply conductor.

ARTICLE 660 — X-RAY EQUIPMENT

Contents

D. Guarding and Grounding
660-47. General.
  (a) High-Voltage Parts.

  (b) Low-Voltage Cables.
660-48. Grounding.

A. General

660-1. Scope. This article covers all X-ray equipment operating at any frequency or voltage for industrial or other nonmedical or nondental use.

(FPN): See Article 517 for medical and dental X-ray.

Nothing in this article shall be construed as specifying safeguards against the useful beam or stray X-ray radiation.

(FPN): Radiation safety and performance requirements of several classes of X-ray equipment are regulated under Public Law 90-602 and are enforced by the Department of Health and Human Services.

(FPN): In addition, information on radiation protection by the National Council on Radiation Protection and Measurements is published as Reports of the National Council on Radiation Protection and Measurement. These reports are obtainable from NCRP Publications, P.O. Box 30175, Washington, D.C. 20014.

660-2. Definitions.

  Long-Time Rating: A rating based on an operating interval of 5 minutes or longer.

  Mobile: X-ray equipment mounted on a permanent base with wheels and/or casters for moving while completely assembled.

  Momentary Rating: A rating based on an operating interval that does not exceed 5 seconds.

  Portable: X-ray equipment designed to be hand carried.

  Transportable: X-ray equipment to be installed in a vehicle or that may be readily disassembled for transport in a vehicle.

660-3. Hazardous (Classified) Locations. Unless approved for the location, X-ray and related equipment shall not be installed or operated in hazardous (classified) locations.

(FPN): See Article 517, Part G.

    X-ray equipment used in industrial establishments or similar locations is usually for the purpose of inspection of a process or product. This method permits testing without dismantling or applying stress to detect cracks, flaws, or structural defects. Welded joints are frequently inspected with X-ray equipment to detect hidden defects that may cause failure under stress.
    Among the industrial applications of X-rays, the most common is radiography where shadow pictures of the subject matter are produced on photographic film. The type and thickness of the material involved governs the voltage to be employed and may range from a few thousand volts (kilovolts) to millions of volts (megavolts). It is possible to X-ray metal objects that are 20 in. (508 mm) thick.
    Fluoroscopy is another X-ray technique that is used for industrial or commercial applications. This method is similar to radiography, but operates at a much lower voltage range (less than 250 kilovolts) and, instead of producing a film, a shadow picture is projected upon a screen such as is used for security checks of luggage at airport terminals. Fluoroscopy is capable of detecting extremely minute flaws or defects.

ARTICLE 660—X-RAY EQUIPMENT

660-4. Connection to Supply Circuit.

(a) Fixed and Stationary Equipment. Fixed and stationary X-ray equipment shall be connected to the power supply by means of a wiring method meeting the general requirements of this Code.

Exception: Equipment properly supplied by a branch circuit rated at not over 30 amperes shall be permitted to be supplied through a suitable attachment plug cap and hard-service cable or cord.

(b) Portable, Mobile, and Transportable Equipment. Individual branch circuits shall not be required for portable, mobile, and transportable X-ray equipment requiring a capacity of not over 60 amperes. Portable and mobile types of X-ray equipment of any capacity shall be supplied through a suitable hard-service cable or cord. Transportable X-ray equipment of any capacity shall be permitted to be connected to its power supply by suitable connections and hard-service cable or cord.

(c) Over 600 Volts, Nominal. Circuits and equipment operated at more than 600 volts, nominal, shall comply with Article 710.

660-5. Disconnecting Means.
A disconnecting means of adequate capacity for at least 50 percent of the input required for the momentary rating or 100 percent of the input required for the long-time rating of the X-ray equipment, whichever is greater, shall be provided in the supply circuit. The disconnecting means shall be operable from a location readily accessible from the X-ray control. For equipment connected to a 120-volt, nominal, branch circuit of 30 amperes or less, a grounding-type attachment plug cap and receptacle of proper rating shall be permitted to serve as a disconnecting means.

660-6. Rating of Supply Conductors and Overcurrent Protection.

(a) Branch-Circuit Conductors. The ampacity of supply branch-circuit conductors and the overcurrent protective devices shall not be less than 50 percent of the momentary rating or 100 percent of the long-time rating, whichever is the greater.

(b) Feeder Conductors. The rated ampacity of conductors and overcurrent devices of a feeder for two or more branch circuits supplying X-ray units shall not be less than 100 percent of the momentary demand rating [as determined by (a)] of the two largest X-ray apparatus plus 20 percent of the momentary ratings of other X-ray apparatus.

(FPN): The minimum conductor size for branch and feeder circuits is also governed by voltage regulation requirements. For a specific installation, the manufacturer usually specifies: minimum distribution transformer and conductor sizes, rating of disconnect means, and overcurrent protection.

660-7. Wiring Terminals.
X-ray equipment shall be provided with suitable wiring terminals or leads for the connection of power supply conductors of the size required by the rating of the branch circuit for the equipment.

Exception: Where provided with a permanently attached cord or a cord set.

660-8. Number of Conductors in Raceway.
The number of control circuit conductors installed in a raceway shall be determined in accordance with Section 300-17.

660-9. Minimum Size of Conductors.
Sizes No. 18 or 16 fixture wires as specified in Section 725-16 and flexible cords shall be permitted for the control and operating circuits of X-ray and auxiliary equipment where protected by not larger than 20-ampere overcurrent devices.

660-10. Equipment Installations.
All equipment for new X-ray installations and all used or reconditioned X-ray equipment moved to and reinstalled at a new location shall be of an approved type.

B. Control

660-20. Fixed and Stationary Equipment.

(a) Separate Control Device. A separate control device, in addition to the disconnecting means, shall be incorporated in the X-ray control supply or in the primary circuit to the high-voltage transformer. This device shall be a part of the X-ray equipment, but shall be permitted in a separate enclosure immediately adjacent to the X-ray control unit.

(b) Protective Device. A protective device, which shall be permitted to be incorporated into the separate control device, shall be provided to control the load resulting from failures in the high-voltage circuit.

660-21. Portable and Mobile Equipment.
Portable and mobile equipment shall comply with Section 660-20, but the manually controlled device shall be located in or on the equipment.

660-23. Industrial and Commercial Laboratory Equipment.

(a) Radiographic and Fluoroscopic Types. All radiographic- and fluoroscopic-type equipment shall be effectively enclosed or shall have interlocks that de-energize the equipment automatically to prevent ready access to live current-carrying parts.

(b) Diffraction and Irradiation Types. Diffraction- and irradiation-type equipment shall be provided with a positive means to indicate when it is energized. The indicator shall be a pilot light, readable meter deflection, or equivalent means.

Exception: Equipment or installations effectively enclosed or provided with interlocks to prevent access to live current-carrying parts during operation.

660-24. Independent Control.
Where more than one piece of equipment is operated from the same high-voltage circuit, each piece or each group of equipment as a unit shall be provided with a high-voltage switch or equivalent disconnecting means. This disconnecting means shall be constructed, enclosed, or located so as to avoid contact by persons with its live parts.

A control device provides means for initiating and terminating X-ray exposures and automatically times their duration.

C. Transformers and Capacitors

660-35. General.
Transformers and capacitors that are part of an X-ray equipment shall not be required to comply with Articles 450 and 460.

High-ratio step-up transformers that are an integral part of an X-ray are not required to comply with Article 450 and are generally used to provide the high voltage necessary for X-ray tubes. There is a lesser degree of fire hazard due to the low primary voltage; therefore, X-ray transformers are not required to be installed in fire-resistant vaults.

660-36. Capacitors.
Capacitors shall be mounted within enclosures of insulating material or grounded metal.

D. Guarding and Grounding

660-47. General.

(a) High-Voltage Parts. All high-voltage parts, including X-ray tubes, shall be mounted within grounded enclosures. Air, oil, gas, or other suitable insulating media shall be used to insulate the high voltage from the grounded enclosure. The connection from the high-voltage equipment to X-ray tubes and other high-voltage components shall be made with high-voltage shielded cables.

(b) Low-Voltage Cables. Low-voltage cables connecting to oil-filled units that are not completely sealed, such as transformers, condensers, oil coolers, and high-voltage switches, shall have insulation of the oil-resistant type.

Grounded enclosures are required to be provided for all high-voltage X-ray equipment, including X-ray tubes. High-voltage shielded cables are required to be used to connect high-voltage equipment to X-ray tubes, and the shield is required to be grounded as specified in Section 660-48.

660-48. Grounding. Noncurrent-carrying metal parts of X-ray and associated equipment (controls, tables, X-ray tube supports, transformer tanks, shielded cables, X-ray tube heads, etc.) shall be grounded in the manner specified in Article 250. Portable and mobile equipment shall be provided with an approved grounding-type attachment plug cap.

Exception: Battery-operated equipment.

ARTICLE 665 — INDUCTION AND DIELECTRIC HEATING EQUIPMENT

Contents

INDUCTION, DIELECTRIC HEATING EQUIPMENT—ARTICLE 665

A. General

665-1. Scope. This article covers the construction and installation of induction and dielectric heating equipment and accessories for industrial and scientific applications, but not for medical or dental applications, appliances, or line frequency pipelines and vessels heating.

(FPN): See Article 517 for medical and dental therapeutic equipment.

(FPN): See Article 422 for appliances.

(FPN): See Article 427, Part E for line frequency pipelines and vessels heating.

To prevent spurious radiation caused by induction and dielectric heating equipment and to ensure that the frequency spectrum is utilized equitably, the Federal Communications Commission (FCC) has established rules (Code of Federal Regulations, Title 47, Part 18) that govern the use of industrial heating equipment of this type operating above 10 kHz.

665-2. Definitions.

Dielectric Heating: Dielectric heating is the heating of a nominally insulating material due to its own dielectric losses when the material is placed in a varying electric field.

Heating Equipment: The term "heating equipment" as used in this article includes any equipment used for heating purposes whose heat is generated by induction or dielectric methods.

Induction Heating: Induction heating is the heating of a nominally conductive material due to its own I^2R losses when the material is placed in a varying electromagnetic field.

Induction and dielectric heating are used for ovens, furnaces, and industrial equipment where pieces of material are heated by a rapidly alternating magnetic or electric field. For further information on electric heating systems using an induction heater or a dielectric heater on ovens and furnaces, see NFPA 86, *Standard for Ovens and Furnaces;* and NFPA 86D, *Standard for Industrial Furnaces Using Vacuum as an Atmosphere.*

Theory of Operation — Solid-State Converter Power Circuit

The circuit consists of three sections: the rectifier section, the inverter section, and the tank circuit which includes the load coil located on the outside. The rectifier section input power is 480 V ac nominal, 3-phase, 60 Hz. See Figure 665-1. The output of the rectifier section is most generally a fixed 600-V dc, nominal. This feeds the inverter section which is a tuned variable frequency switching network that converts the dc power to single-phase, nominal, 180 Hz, 1 kHz, 3 kHz, or 10 kHz square wave or sinusoidal power. The operating frequency is determined by the control section. The single-phase output drives the tank circuit which consists of a load coil and tuning capacitors.

Variable output power is achieved by frequency variation of the inverter section. Since the tank circuit is a tuned load, as the output approaches the frequency of the tank circuit, the power into the load approaches the maximum output. At minimum frequency, the output power is very low. As the frequency increases, the power increases until a maximum is reached. This is the resonant frequency of the tank circuit.

Most induction heating loads exhibit a dynamic change as the work piece passes through the Curie temperature point (where the work load changes from the magnetic to the nonmagnetic state). The converter automatically adjusts to maintain a constant output power during this dynamic load change. If this maximum power is below the operator power setting, the converter unit will automatically limit to this maximum power point.

Figure 665-1. Simplified diagram of the components of a solid-state converter used for induction heating. (*Tocco Div. Park Ohio Industries*)

Induction Heating

Induction heating is accomplished with the aid of a current-carrying conductor that induces the transfer of electrical energy to the work by an eddy current. Induction heating, in general, involves frequencies ranging from 3 to about 500 kHz, and power outputs from a few hundred watts to several thousand kilowatts.

When induction heating is employed, a nominally conductive material is placed in an inductor coil. The effective intensity of inductance is caused by a current flow in the coil at a high frequency which produces a rapidly alternating magnetic field, thereby inducing a voltage in the material to be heated and causing a current to flow through the resistance of the material (I^2R loss), producing induction heating. See Figure 665-2.

Dielectric Heating

Dielectric heating equipment is similar to induction heating equipment; however, the frequencies are generally higher (in the order of 3 MHz or more) than those in induction heating. This type of heater is useful for heating materials that are commonly thought of as being nonconductive, for instance, heating plastic preforms before molding, curing glue and plywood, drying rayon cakes, and for many similar applications. Frequencies for this type of equipment range from 1 to 200 MHz, especially in the 1 to 50 MHz range. Vacuum-tube generators are used exclusively to supply dielectric heating power, and outputs range from a few hundred watts to several hundred kilowatts.

A typical wiring diagram of a vacuum-tube generator is shown in Figure 665-3. Whereas induction heating uses a varying magnetic field, dielectric heating employs a varying electric field. This is done by placing the material to be heated between a pair of metal plates, called electrodes, in the output circuit of the generator. When high-frequency voltage is applied to the electrodes, a rapidly alternating electric field is set up between them, passing through the material to be heated. Because of the electrical charges within the molecules of this material, the field causes the molecules to vibrate in proportion to its frequency. This internal molecular action generates the heat used for dielectric heating.

665-3. Other Articles. Wiring from the source of power to the heating equipment shall

Figure 665-2. Simplified diagram of the components of a vacuum-tube generator used for induction heating. (*Tocco Div. Park Ohio Industries*)

Figure 665-3. Simplified diagram of the components of a vacuum-tube generator used for dielectric heating. (*Tocco Div. Park Ohio Industries*)

comply with Chapters 1 through 4. Circuits and equipment operated at more than 600 volts, nominal, shall comply with Article 710.

665-4. Hazardous (Classified) Locations. Induction and dielectric heating equipment shall not be installed in hazardous (classified) locations as defined in Article 500.

Exception: Where the equipment and wiring are designed and approved for the hazardous (classified) locations.

B. Guarding, Grounding, and Labeling

665-20. Enclosures. The converting apparatus (including the dc line) and high-frequency electric circuits (excluding the output circuits and remote-control circuits) shall be completely contained within an enclosure or enclosures of noncombustible material.

665-21. Panel Controls. All panel controls shall be of dead-front construction.

665-22. Access to Internal Equipment. Doors or detachable panels shall be employed for internal access. Where doors are used giving access to voltages from 500 to 1000 volts ac or dc, either door locks shall be provided or interlocking shall be installed. Where doors are used giving access to voltages of over 1000 volts ac or dc, either mechanical lockouts with a disconnecting means to prevent access until voltage is removed from the cubicle, or both door interlocking and mechanical door locks shall be provided. Detachable panels not normally used for access to such parts shall be fastened in a manner that will make them inconvenient to remove.

665-23. Warning Labels. "Danger" labels shall be attached on the equipment, and shall be plainly visible even when doors are open or panels are removed from compartments containing voltages of over 250 volts ac or dc.

665-24. Capacitors. Where capacitors in excess of 0.1 microfarad are used in dc circuits, either as rectifier filter components or suppressors, etc., having circuit voltages of over 240 volts to ground, bleeder resistors or grounding switches shall be used as grounding devices. The time of discharge shall be in accordance with Section 460-6(a).

Where capacitors are individually switched out of a circuit, a bleeder resistor or automatic switch shall be used as a discharge means.

Where auxiliary rectifiers are used with filter capacitors in the output for bias supplies, tube keyers, etc., bleeder resistors shall be used even though the dc voltage may not exceed 240 volts.

665-25. Work Applicator Shielding. Protective cages or adequate shielding shall be used to guard work applicators other than induction heating coils. Induction heating coils shall be permitted to be protected by insulation and/or refractory materials. Interlock switches shall be used on all hinged access doors, sliding panels, or other easy means of access to the applicator. All interlock switches shall be connected in such a manner as to remove all power from the applicator when any one of the access doors or panels is open. Interlocks on access doors or panels shall not be required if the applicator is an induction heating coil at dc ground potential or operating at less than 150 volts ac.

665-26. Grounding and Bonding. Grounding and/or inter-unit bonding shall be used wherever required for circuit operation, for limiting to a safe value radio frequency potentials between all exposed noncurrent-carrying parts of the equipment and earth ground, between all equipment parts and surrounding objects, and between such objects and earth ground. Such grounding and bonding shall be installed in accordance with Article 250.

Bonding presents special problems at radio frequencies due to stray currents flowing between units of the equipment or to ground. These special bonding requirements are especially needed at dielectric heating frequencies (100 to 200 MHz) due to the differences in radio-frequency potential that can exist between the equipment and surrounding metal units or other units of the installation. Satisfactory bonding can be accomplished by placing all of the units of the equipment on a flooring or base consisting of a copper or aluminum sheet and thoroughly bonded where necessary by soldering, welding, or bolting.

By such special bonding, the radio-frequency resistance and reactance between units is held to a minimum, and any stray circulating currents flowing through this bonding will not cause a dangerous voltage drop.

It is necessary to provide operator protection from high radio-frequency potentials by shielding at dielectric heating frequencies. Interference with radio communication systems at such high frequencies may be eliminated by totally enclosing all components in a shielding of copper or aluminum.

665-27. Marking. Each heating equipment shall be provided with a nameplate giving the manufacturer's name and model identification and the following input data: line volts, frequency, number of phases, maximum current, full-load kVA, and full-load power factor.

665-28. Control Enclosures. Direct current or low-frequency ac shall be permitted in the control portion of the heating equipment. This shall be limited to not over 150 volts. Solid or stranded wire No. 18 or larger shall be used. A step-down transformer with proper overcurrent protection shall be permitted in the control enclosure to obtain an ac voltage of less than 150 volts. The higher-voltage terminals shall be guarded to prevent accidental contact. 60-hertz components shall be permitted to control high frequency where properly rated by the induction heating equipment manufacturer. Electronic circuits utilizing solid-state devices and tubes shall be permitted printed circuits or wires smaller than No. 18.

C. Motor-Generator Equipment

665-40. General. Motor-generator equipment shall include all rotating equipment designed to operate from an ac or dc motor or by mechanical drive from a prime mover, producing an alternating current of any frequency for induction and/or dielectric heating.

665-41. Ampacity of Supply Conductors. The ampacity of supply conductors shall be determined in accordance with Article 430.

665-42. Overcurrent Protection. Overcurrent protection shall be provided as specified in Article 430 for the electric supply circuit.

665-43. Disconnecting Means. The disconnecting means shall be provided as specified in Article 430.

A readily accessible disconnecting means shall be provided by which each heating equipment can be isolated from its supply circuit. The ampere rating of this disconnecting means shall not be less than the nameplate current rating of the equipment. The supply circuit disconnecting means shall be permitted as a heating equipment disconnecting means where the circuit supplies only one equipment.

665-44. Output Circuit. The output circuit shall include all output components external to the generator, including contactors, transformers, busbars, and other conductors, and shall comply with (a) and (b) below.

(a) Generator Output. The output circuit shall be isolated from ground.

Exception No. 1: Where the capacitive coupling inherent in the generator causes the generator terminals to have voltages from terminal to ground that are equal.

Exception No. 2: Where a vacuum or controlled atmosphere is used with a coil in a tank or chamber, the center point of the coil shall be grounded to maintain an equal potential between each terminal and ground.

Where rated at over 500 volts, the output circuit shall incorporate a dc ground protector unit. The dc impressed on the output circuit shall not exceed 30 volts and shall not exceed a current capability of 5 milliamperes.

An isolating transformer for matching the load and the source shall be permitted in the output circuit if the output secondary is not at dc ground potential.

(b) Component Interconnections. The various components required for a complete induction heating equipment installation shall be connected by properly protected multiconductor cable, busbar, or coaxial cable. Cables shall be installed in nonferrous raceways. Busbars shall be protected, where required, by nonferrous enclosures.

665-47. Remote Control.

(a) Selector Switch. Where remote controls are used for applying power, a selector switch shall be provided and interlocked to provide power from only one control point at a time.

(b) Foot Switches. Switches operated by foot pressure shall be provided with a shield over the contact button to avoid accidental closing of a switch.

D. Equipment Other than Motor-Generator

665-60. General.
Equipment other than motor-generators shall consist of all static multipliers and oscillator-type units utilizing vacuum tubes and/or solid-state devices. The equipment shall be capable of converting ac or dc to an ac frequency suitable for induction and/or dielectric heating.

665-61. Ampacity of Supply Conductors.
The ampacity of supply conductors shall be determined in accordance with (a) and (b) below.

(a) Nameplate Rating. The ampacity of the circuit conductors shall not be less than the nameplate current rating of the equipment.

(b) Two or More. The ampacity of conductors supplying two or more equipments shall not be less than the sum of the nameplate current ratings on all equipments.

Exception: If simultaneous operation of two or more equipments supplied from the same feeder is not possible, the ampacity of the feeder shall not be less than the sum of the nameplate ratings for the largest group of machines capable of simultaneous operation, plus 100 percent of the stand-by currents of the remaining machines supplied.

665-62. Overcurrent Protection.
Overcurrent protection shall be provided as specified in Article 240 for the equipment as a whole. This overcurrent protection shall be provided separately or as a part of the equipment.

665-63. Disconnecting Means.
A readily accessible disconnecting means shall be provided by which each heating equipment can be isolated from its supply circuit. The rating of this disconnecting means shall not be less than the nameplate rating of the equipment. The supply circuit disconnecting means shall be permitted for disconnecting the heating equipment where the circuit supplies only one equipment.

665-64. Output Circuit.
The output circuit shall include all output components external to the converting device, including contactors, transformers, busbars, and other conductors and shall comply with (a) and (b) below.

(a) Converter Output. The output circuit shall be isolated from ground.

Exception: Where a dc voltage can exist at the terminals because of an internal component failure, then the output circuit (direct or coupled) shall be at dc ground potential.

(b) Converter and Applicator Connection. Where the connections between the converter and the work applicator exceed 2 feet (610 mm) in length, the connections shall be enclosed or guarded with nonferrous, noncombustible material.

Figure 665-4. An 80-kW oscillator used to harden the exhaust valve seats of an automotive engine. (*Tocco Div. Park Ohio Industries*)

665-66. Line Frequency in Converter Equipment Output.   Commercial frequencies of 25- to 60-hertz alternating-current output shall be permitted to be coupled for control purposes, but shall be limited to not over 150 volts during periods of circuit operation.

665-67. Keying.   Where high-speed keying circuits dependent on the effect of "oscillator blocking" are employed, the peak radio-frequency output voltage during the blocked portion of the cycle shall not exceed 100 volts in units employing radio-frequency converters.

665-68. Remote Control.

(a) Selector Switch.   Where remote controls are used for applying power, a selector switch shall be provided and interlocked to provide power from only one control point at a time.

(b) Foot Switches.   Switches operated by foot pressure shall be provided with a shield over the contact button to avoid accidental closing of the switch.

ARTICLE 668 — ELECTROLYTIC CELLS

Contents

(b) Area Not Covered.
668-11. DC Cell Line Process Power Supply.
(a) Not Grounded.
(b) Metal Enclosures Grounded.
(c) Grounding Requirements.
668-12. Cell Line Conductors.
(a) Insulation and Material.
(b) Size.
(c) Connections.
668-13. Disconnecting Means.
(a) More than One Process Power Supply.
(b) Removable Links or Conductors.
668-14. Shunting Means.
(a) Partial or Total Shunting.
(b) Shunting One or More Cells.
668-15. Grounding.
668-20. Portable Electrical Equipment.
(a) Portable Electrical Equipment Not to Be Grounded.
(b) Isolating Transformers.
(c) Marking.

668-21. Power Supply Circuits and Receptacles for Portable Electrical Equipment.
(a) Isolated Circuits.
(b) Noninterchangeability.
(c) Marking.
668-30. Fixed and Portable Electrical Equipment.
(a) Electrical Equipment Not Required to Be Grounded.
(b) Exposed Conductive Surfaces Not Required to Be Grounded.
(c) Wiring Methods.
(d) Circuit Protection.
(e) Bonding.
668-31. Auxiliary Nonelectric Connections.
668-32. Cranes and Hoists.
(a) Conductive Surfaces to Be Insulated from Ground.
(b) Hazardous Electrical Conditions.
668-40. Enclosures.

668-1. Scope. The provisions of this article apply to the installation of the electrical components and accessory equipment of electrolytic cells, electrolytic cell lines and process power supply for the production of aluminum, cadmium, chlorine, copper, fluorine, hydrogen peroxide, magnesium, sodium, sodium chlorate and zinc.

Not covered by this article are cells used as a source of electric energy and for electroplating processes and cells used for the production of hydrogen.

(FPN): In general, any cell line or group of cell lines operated as a unit for the production of a particular metal, gas, or chemical compound may differ from any other cell lines producing the same product because of variations in the particular raw materials used, output capacity, use of proprietary methods or process practices, or other modifying factors to the extent that detailed Code requirements become overly restrictive and do not accomplish the stated purpose of this Code.

(FPN): For further information, see IEEE Standard for Electrical Safety Practices in Electrolytic Cell Line Working Zones: IEEE Std. 463-1977.

An electrolytic cell line and its dc process power supply circuit, both within a cell line working zone, constitute and are treated as an individual machine supplied from a single source, even though they may cover acres of space, have a load current in excess of 400,000 A dc, or a circuit voltage in excess of 1,000 V dc. The cell line process current passes through each cell in a series connection, and the load current cannot be subdivided, as it can, for example, in the heating circuit of a resistance-type electric furnace.

Because a cell line is supplied by its individual dc rectifier system, the rectifier or the entire cell line circuit is de-energized by removing its source of primary power.

In some electrolytic cell systems, the terminal voltage of the process supply can be appreciable. The voltage-to-ground of exposed live parts from one end of a cell line to the other is variable between the limits of the terminal voltage. Hence, operating and maintenance personnel and their tools are required to be insulated from ground.

Figure 668-1. A typical potroom in an aluminum reduction plant. (*Alcoa*)

668-2. Definitions.

Cell Line: An assembly of electrically interconnected electrolytic cells supplied by a source of direct-current power.

Cell Line Attachments and Auxiliary Equipment: As applied to Article 668, cell line attachments and auxiliary equipment include, but are not limited to: auxiliary tanks; process piping; duct work; structural supports; exposed cell line conductors; conduits and other raceways; pumps, positioning equipment and cell cutout or by-pass electrical devices. Auxiliary equipment includes tools, welding machines, crucibles, and other portable equipment used for operation and maintenance within the electrolytic cell line working zone.

In the cell line working zone, auxiliary equipment includes the exposed conductive surfaces of ungrounded cranes and crane-mounted cell-servicing equipment.

Electrolytic Cell: A receptacle or vessel in which electrochemical reactions are caused by applying electrical energy for the purpose of refining or producing usable materials.

Electrolytic Cell Line Working Zone: The cell line working zone is the space envelope wherein operation or maintenance is normally performed on or in the vicinity of exposed energized surfaces of electrolytic cell lines or their attachments.

668-3. Other Articles.

(a) Lighting, Ventilating, Material Handling. Chapters 1 through 4 shall apply to service feeders, branch circuits, and apparatus for supplying lighting, ventilating, material handling, and the like, which are outside the electrolytic cell line working zone.

(b) Systems Not Electrically Connected. Those elements of a cell line power-supply system that are not electrically connected to the cell supply system, such as the primary winding

931

of a two-winding transformer, the motor of a motor-generator set, feeders, branch circuits, disconnecting means, motor controllers, and overload protective equipment shall be required to comply with all applicable provisions of this Code.

(FPN): For the purpose of this section, "electrically connected" means connection capable of carrying current as distinguished from connection through electromagnetic induction.

(c) Electrolytic Cell Lines. Electrolytic cell lines shall comply with the provisions of Chapters 1, 2, 3, and 4.

Exception No. 1: The electrolytic cell line conductors shall not be required to comply with the provisions of Articles 110, 210, 215, 220, and 225. (See Section 668-11.)

Exception No. 2: Overcurrent protection of electrolytic cell dc process power circuits shall not be required to comply with the requirements of Article 240.

Exception No. 3: Equipment located or used within the electrolytic cell line working zone or associated with the cell line dc power circuits shall not be required to comply with the provisions of Article 250.

Exception No. 4: The electrolytic cells, cell line attachments and the wiring of auxiliary equipments and devices within the cell line working zone shall not be required to comply with the provisions of Articles 110, 210, 215, 220, and 225. (See Section 668-30.)

(FPN): See Section 668-15 on equipment, apparatus, and structural component grounding.

668-10. Cell Line Working Zone.

(a) Area Covered. The space envelope of the cell line working zone shall encompass any space:

(1) Within 96 inches (2.44 m) above energized surfaces of electrolytic cell lines or their energized attachments.

(2) Below energized surfaces of electrolytic cell lines or their energized attachments, provided the head room in the space beneath is less than 96 inches (2.44 m).

(3) Within 42 inches (1.07 m) horizontally from energized surfaces of electrolytic cell lines or their energized attachments or from the space envelope described in Section 668-10(a)(1) or (a)(2).

(b) Area Not Covered. The cell line working zone shall not be required to extend through or beyond walls, floors, roofs, partitions, barriers, or the like.

668-11. DC Cell Line Process Power Supply.

(a) Not Grounded. The dc cell line process power supply conductors shall not be required to be grounded.

(b) Metal Enclosures Grounded. All metal enclosures of dc cell line process power supply apparatus operating at a power supply potential between terminals of over 50 volts shall be grounded:

(1) Through protective relaying equipment, or

(2) By No. 2/0 AWG minimum copper grounding conductor or a conductor of equal ampacity.

(c) Grounding Requirements. The grounding connections required by Section 668-11(b) shall be installed in accordance with Sections 250-112, 250-113, 250-115, 250-117, and 250-118.

668-12. Cell Line Conductors.

(a) Insulation and Material. Cell line conductors shall be either bare, covered, or insulated and of copper, aluminum, copper-clad aluminum, steel, or other suitable material.

(b) Size. Cell line conductors shall be of such cross-sectional area that the temperature rise under maximum load conditions and at maximum ambient shall not exceed the safe operating temperature of the conductor insulation or the material of the conductor supports.

(c) Connections. Cell line conductors shall be joined by bolted, welded, clamped, or compression connectors.

668-13. Disconnecting Means.

(a) More than One Process Power Supply. Where more than one dc cell line process power supply serves the same cell line, a disconnecting means shall be provided on the cell line circuit side of each power supply to disconnect it from the cell line circuit.

(b) Removable Links or Conductors. Removable links or removable conductors shall be permitted to be used as the disconnecting means.

668-14. Shunting Means.

(a) Partial or Total Shunting. Partial or total shunting of cell line circuit current around one or more cells shall be permitted.

(b) Shunting One or More Cells. The conductors, switches, or combination of conductors and switches used for shunting one or more cells shall comply with the applicable requirements of Section 668-12.

668-15. Grounding. For equipment, apparatus, and structural components which are required to be grounded by provisions of Article 668, the provisions of Article 250 shall apply.

Exception No. 1: A water pipe electrode shall not be required to be used.

Exception No. 2: Any electrode or combination of electrodes described in Sections 250-81 and 250-83 shall be permitted.

668-20. Portable Electrical Equipment.

(a) Portable Electrical Equipment Not to Be Grounded. The frames and enclosures of portable electrical equipment used within the cell line working zone shall not be grounded.

Exception No. 1: Where the cell line circuit voltage does not exceed 200 volts dc these frames and enclosures shall be permitted to be grounded.

Exception No. 2: These frames and enclosures shall be permitted to be grounded where guarded.

(b) Isolating Transformers. Electrically powered, hand-held, cord-connected portable equipment with ungrounded frames or enclosures used within the cell line working zone shall be connected to receptacle circuits having only ungrounded conductors such as a branch circuit supplied by an isolating transformer with an ungrounded secondary.

ARTICLE 668—ELECTROLYTIC CELLS

Exception: Where frames and enclosures of such equipments are grounded as permitted in Section 668-20(a), Exception No. 1.

(c) Marking. Ungrounded portable electrical equipment shall be distinctively marked and shall employ plugs and receptacles of a configuration which prevents connection of this equipment to grounding receptacles and which prevents inadvertent interchange of ungrounded and grounded portable electrical equipments.

668-21. Power Supply Circuits and Receptacles for Portable Electrical Equipment.

(a) Isolated Circuits. Circuits supplying power to ungrounded receptacles for hand-held, cord-connected equipments shall be electrically isolated from any distribution system supplying areas other than the cell line working zone and shall be ungrounded. Power for these circuits shall be supplied through isolating transformers. Primaries of such transformers shall operate at not more than 600 volts between conductors and shall be provided with proper overcurrent protection. The secondary voltage of such transformers shall not exceed 300 volts between conductors, and all circuits supplied from such secondaries shall be ungrounded and shall have an approved overcurrent device of proper rating in each conductor.

(b) Noninterchangeability. Receptacles and their mating plugs for ungrounded equipment shall not have provision for a grounding conductor and shall be of a configuration which prevents their use for equipment required to be grounded.

(c) Marking. Receptacles on circuits supplied by an isolating transformer with an ungrounded secondary shall be a distinctive configuration, distinctively marked, and shall not be used in any other location in the plant.

668-30. Fixed and Portable Electrical Equipment.

(a) Electrical Equipment Not Required to Be Grounded. AC systems supplying fixed and portable electrical equipments within the cell line working zone shall not be required to be grounded.

(b) Exposed Conductive Surfaces Not Required to Be Grounded. Exposed conductive surfaces, such as electrical equipment housings, cabinets, boxes, motors, raceways, and the like that are within the cell line working zone shall not be required to be grounded.

(c) Wiring Methods. Auxiliary electrical devices such as motors, transducers, sensors, control devices, and alarms, mounted on an electrolytic cell or other energized surface, shall be connected to premises wiring systems by any of the following means:

(1) Multiconductor hard-usage cord;

(2) Wire or cable in suitable raceways, metal or nonmetallic cable trays. If metal conduit, cable tray, armored cable, or similar metallic systems are used, they shall be installed with insulating breaks such that they will not cause a potentially hazardous electrical condition.

(d) Circuit Protection. Circuit protection shall not be required for control and instrumentation that are totally within the cell line working zone.

(e) Bonding. Bonding of fixed electrical equipment to the energized conductive surfaces of the cell line, its attachments or auxiliaries shall be permitted. Where fixed electrical equipment is mounted on an energized conductive surface it shall be bonded to that surface.

668-31. Auxiliary Nonelectric Connections.
Auxiliary nonelectric connections, such as air hoses, water hoses, and the like, to an electrolytic cell, its attachments, or auxiliary equipments

shall not have continuous conductive reinforcing wire, armor, braids and the like. Hoses shall be of a nonconductive material.

668-32. Cranes and Hoists.

(a) Conductive Surfaces to Be Insulated from Ground. The conductive surfaces of cranes and hoists that enter the cell line working zone shall not be required to be grounded. The portion of an overhead crane or hoist which contacts an energized electrolytic cell or energized attachments shall be insulated from ground.

(b) Hazardous Electrical Conditions. Remote crane or hoist controls which may introduce hazardous electrical conditions into the cell line working zone shall employ one or more of the following systems:

(1) Insulated and ungrounded control circuit in accordance with Section 668-21(a);

(2) Nonconductive rope operator;

(3) Pendant pushbutton with nonconductive supporting means and having nonconductive surfaces or ungrounded exposed conductive surfaces;

(4) Radio.

668-40. Enclosures. General-purpose electrical equipment enclosures shall be permitted where a natural draft ventilation system prevents the accumulation of gases.

ARTICLE 669 — ELECTROPLATING

Contents

669-1. Scope. The provisions of this article apply to the installation of the electrical components and accessory equipment that supply the power and controls for electroplating, anodizing, electropolishing, and electrostripping. For purposes of this article the term electroplating shall be used to identify any or all of these processes.

Because of the extremely high currents and low voltages normally involved, conventional wiring methods cannot be used in electroplating, anodizing, electropolishing, and electrostripping processes. Note the permission to use bare conductors even in systems exceeding 50 V dc. See Figures 669-1 and 669-2. Some systems in the aluminum anodizing process have potentials up to 240 V. Warning signs are required to be posted to indicate the presence of bare conductors.

669-2. Other Articles. Except as modified by this article, wiring and equipment used for electroplating processes shall comply with the applicable requirements of Chapters 1 through 4.

669-3. General. Equipment for use in electroplating processes shall be identified for such service.

ARTICLE 669—ELECTROPLATING

669-5. Branch-Circuit Conductors. Branch-circuit conductors supplying one or more units of equipment shall have an ampacity of not less than 125 percent of the total connected load. The ampacities for busbars shall be in accordance with Section 374-6.

669-6. Wiring Methods. Conductors connecting the electrolyte tank equipment to the conversion equipment shall be as follows:

(a) Systems Not Exceeding 50 Volts DC. Insulated conductors shall be permitted to be run without insulated support provided they are protected from physical damage. Bare copper or aluminum conductors shall be permitted where supported on insulators.

(b) Systems Exceeding 50 Volts DC. Insulated conductors shall be permitted to be run on insulated supports provided they are protected from physical damage. Bare copper or aluminum conductors shall be permitted where supported on insulators and guarded against accidental contact in accordance with Section 110-17.

Exception: Unguarded bare conductors shall be permitted at the terminals.

Figure 669-1. A typical electroplating line.

669-7. Warning Signs. Warning signs shall be posted to indicate the presence of bare conductors.

669-8. Disconnecting Means.

(a) More than One Power Supply. Where more than one power supply serves the same dc system a disconnecting means shall be provided on the dc side of each power supply.

(b) Removable Links or Conductors. Removable links or removable conductors shall be permitted to be used as the disconnecting means.

Figure 669-2. Bare busbar to supply an electroplating tank.

669-9. Overcurrent Protection. DC conductors shall be protected from overcurrent by one or more of the following: (1) fuses or circuit breakers; (2) a current sensing device which operates a disconnecting means; or (3) other approved means.

ARTICLE 670 — INDUSTRIAL MACHINERY

Contents

670-1. Scope.
670-2. Definition of Industrial Machinery.
670-3. Machine Nameplate Data.
  (a) Permanent Nameplate.
  (b) Overcurrent Protection.
670-4. Supply Conductors.
  (a) Size.
  (b) Overcurrent Protection.

670-1. Scope. This article covers the definition of, the size and overcurrent protection of supply conductors to, and the nameplate data required on industrial metalworking machine tools, woodworking machinery, plastics machinery and mass production equipment, not portable by hand.

(FPN): For further information, see Electrical Standard for Industrial Machinery, NFPA 79-1985 (ANSI).

670-2. Definition of Industrial Machinery. For the purposes of this article, a machine tool is defined as a power-driven machine not portable by hand, used to shape or form metal or plastic by cutting, impact, pressure, electrical techniques, or a combination of these processes. Plastics machinery is defined as a power-driven machine not portable by hand, used to shape or form plastic by application of thermal and/or mechanical energy, by cutting, impact, pressure, or a combination of these processes.

Mass production industrial equipment is defined as a systematic array of one or more machine tools, plastics machinery, and/or assembly machines which is not portable by hand and which includes any associated material handling, manipulating, gaging, measuring, or inspection equipment.

The requirements of this article do not apply to any motor-driven machine not covered by this definition. Thus, these provisions do not apply to a machine or tool that can be carried from place to place by hand and is not normally used in a fixed location.

670-3. Machine Nameplate Data.

(a) Permanent Nameplate. A permanent nameplate listing supply voltage, phase, fre-

937

quency, full-load current, ampere rating of largest motor or load, short-circuit interrupting capacity of the machine overcurrent-protective device if furnished, and diagram number shall be attached to the control equipment enclosure or machine where plainly visible after installation.

The full-load current shown on the nameplate shall not be less than the sum of the full-load currents required for all motors and other equipment which may be in operation at the same time under normal conditions of use. Where unusual type loads, duty cycles, etc., require oversized conductors, the required capacity shall be included in the marked "full-load current."

Where more than one incoming supply circuit is to be provided, the nameplate shall state the above information for each circuit.

(b) Overcurrent Protection. Where overcurrent protection is provided in accordance with Section 670-4(b), the machine shall be marked "overcurrent protection provided at machine supply terminals."

670-4. Supply Conductors.

(a) Size. The size of the supply conductor shall be such as to have an ampacity not less than 125 percent of the full-load current rating of all resistance heating loads plus 125 percent of the full-load current rating of highest rated motor plus the sum of the full-load current ratings of all other connected motors and apparatus which may be in operation at the same time.

(FPN): For the protection of supply conductors to the machine, see Section 240-3.

(FPN): See Tables 310-16 through 310-31 for ampacity ratings of conductors rated 600 volts and below.

(b) Overcurrent Protection. A machine shall be considered as an individual unit and therefore shall be provided with a disconnecting means. The disconnecting means shall be permitted to be supplied by branch circuits protected by either fuses or circuit breakers. The disconnecting means shall not be required to incorporate overcurrent protection. When furnished as part of the machine, overcurrent protection shall consist of a single circuit breaker or set of fuses, the machine shall bear the marking required in Section 670-3, and the supply conductors shall be considered either as feeders or taps as covered by Section 240-21.

Section 5-10 in NFPA 79, *Electrical Standard for Industrial Machinery*, states: "The operating handle of the disconnecting means shall be readily accessible. The center of the grip of the operating handle of the disconnecting means, when in its highest position, shall not be more than 6½ ft (2 m) above the floor. A permanent operating platform, readily accessible by means of a permanent stair or ladder, shall be considered as the floor for the purpose of this requirement. The operating handle shall be capable of being locked only in the open (off) position. When the control enclosure door is closed, the operating handle shall positively indicate whether the disconnecting means is in the open (off) or closed position."

ARTICLE 675 — ELECTRICALLY DRIVEN OR CONTROLLED IRRIGATION MACHINES

Contents

A. General

675-1. Scope. The provisions of this article apply to electrically driven or controlled irrigation machines, and to the branch circuits and controllers for such equipment.

Electric pump motors used to supply water to irrigation machines are governed by the general requirements of the *Code*, not by Article 675.

675-2. Definitions.

Center Pivot Irrigation Machines: A center pivot irrigation machine is a multimotored irrigation machine which revolves around a central pivot and employs alignment switches or similar devices to control individual motors.

Collector Rings: A collector ring is an assembly of slip rings for transferring electrical energy from a stationary to a rotating member.

Irrigation Machines: An irrigation machine is an electrically driven or controlled machine, with one or more motors, not hand portable, and used primarily to transport and distribute water for agricultural purposes.

675-3. Other Articles. These provisions are in addition to, or amendatory of, the provisions of Article 430 and other articles in this Code which apply except as modified in this article.

The requirements of this article apply to special equipment for a particular condition, and supplement or modify the general rules. See Section 90-3, Code Arrangement.

675-4. Irrigation Cable.

(a) Construction. The cable used to interconnect enclosures on the structure of an irrigation machine shall be an assembly of stranded, insulated conductors with nonhygroscopic and nonwicking filler in a core of moisture- and flame-resistant, nonmetallic material overlaid with a metallic covering and jacketed with a moisture-, corrosion- and sunlight-resistant nonmetallic material.

The conductor insulation shall be of a type listed in Table 310-13 for an operating temperature of 75°C and for use in wet locations. The core insulating material thickness shall not be less than

30 mils and the metallic overlay thickness shall not be less than 8 mils. The jacketing material thickness shall not be less than 50 mils.

A composite of power, control, and grounding conductors in the cable shall be permitted.

(b) Alternate Wiring Methods. Other cables listed for the purpose.

(c) Supports. Irrigation cable shall be secured by straps, hangers or similar fittings identified for the purpose which shall be designed and installed as not to damage the cable. Cable shall be supported at intervals not exceeding 4 feet (1.22 m).

(d) Fittings. Fittings shall be used at all points where irrigation cable terminates. The fittings shall be designed for use with the cable and shall be suitable for the conditions of service.

675-5. More than Three Conductors in a Raceway or Cable. The signal and control conductors of a raceway or cable shall not be counted for the purpose of derating the conductors as required in Note 8 of Tables 310-16 through 310-31.

675-6. Marking on Main Control Panel. The main control panel shall be provided with a nameplate which shall give the following information: (1) the manufacturer's name, the rated voltage, the phase, and the frequency; (2) the current rating of the machine; and (3) the rating of the main disconnecting means and size of overcurrent protection required.

675-7. Equivalent Current Ratings. Where intermittent duty is not involved the provisions of Article 430 shall be used for determining ratings for controllers, disconnecting means, conductors, and the like. Where irrigation machines have inherent intermittent duty the following determinations of equivalent current ratings shall be used.

(a) Continuous-Current Rating. The equivalent continuous-current rating for the selection of branch-circuit conductors and branch-circuit devices shall be equal to 125 percent of the motor nameplate full-load current rating of the largest motor plus a quantity equal to the sum of each of the motor nameplate full-load current ratings of all remaining motors on the circuit multiplied by the maximum percent duty cycle at which they can continuously operate.

(b) Locked-Rotor Current. The equivalent locked-rotor current rating shall be equal to the numerical sum of the locked-rotor current of the two largest motors plus 100 percent of the sum of the motor nameplate full-load current ratings of all the remaining motors on the circuit.

675-8. Disconnecting Means.

(a) Main Controller. A controller which is used to start and stop the complete machine shall meet all of the following requirements:

(1) An equivalent continuous current rating not less than specified in Section 675-7(a) or 675-22(a).

(2) A horsepower rating not less than the value from Table 430-151 based on the equivalent locked-rotor current specified in Section 675-7(b) or 675-22(b).

(b) Main Disconnecting Means. The main disconnecting means for the machine shall be at the point of connection of electrical power to the machine or shall be visible and not more than 50 feet (15.2 m) from the machine and shall be readily accessible and capable of being locked in the open position. This disconnecting means shall have the same horsepower and current rating as required for the main controller.

This section permits the main disconnecting means to be up to 50 ft (15.2 m) from the machine if readily accessible and capable of being locked in the open position. This eliminates one set of overcurrent protective devices and one disconnecting means when the circuit originates at the motor control panel for the irrigation pump, and this panel is within 50 ft (15.2 m) of the center pivot machine. It also alleviates some potential problems with machines designed to be towed to a second site.

(c) Disconnecting Means for Individual Motors and Controllers. A disconnecting means shall be provided for each motor and controller and shall be located as required by Article 430, Part H. The disconnecting means shall not be required to be readily accessible.

Article 430, Part H, provides for safety during maintenance and inspection shutdown periods. See commentary following Section 430-103.

675-9. Branch-Circuit Conductors. The branch-circuit conductors shall have an ampacity not less than specified in Section 675-7(a) or 675-22(a).

675-10. Several Motors on One Branch Circuit.

Section 430-53 provides for motor branch-circuit short-circuit and ground-fault protection for several motors on one branch circuit. A combination of these requirements, which are more or less stringent for this special equipment application, is found in Section 675-10.

(a) Protection Required. Several motors, each not exceeding 2-horsepower rating, shall be permitted to be used on an irrigation machine circuit protected at not more than 30 amperes at 600 volts, nominal, or less, provided all of the following conditions are met:

(1) The full-load rating of any motor in the circuit shall not exceed 6 amperes.

(2) Each motor in the circuit shall have individual running overcurrent protection in accordance with Section 430-32.

(3) Taps to individual motors shall not be smaller than No. 14 copper and not more than 25 feet (7.62 m) in length.

(b) Individual Protection Not Required. Individual branch-circuit short-circuit protection for motors and motor controllers shall not be required where the requirements of Section 675-10(a) are met.

675-11. Collector Rings.

(a) Transmitting Current for Power Purposes. Collector rings shall have an ampacity not less than 125 percent of the full-load current of the largest device served plus the full-load current of all other devices served, or as determined from Section 675-7(a) or 675-22(a).

(b) Control and Signal Purposes. Collector rings for control and signal purposes shall have an ampacity not less than 125 percent of the full-load current of the largest device served plus the full-load current of all other devices served.

(c) Grounding. The collector ring used for grounding shall be of the same ampacity as the largest collector ring in the assembly.

(d) Protection. Collector rings shall be protected from the expected environment and from accidental contact by means of a suitable enclosure.

675-12. Grounding. The following equipment shall be grounded: (1) All electrical equipment on the irrigation machine; (2) all electrical equipment associated with the irrigation machine; (3)

ARTICLE 675—ELECTRICALLY DRIVEN IRRIGATION MACHINES

metallic junction boxes and enclosures; and (4) control panels or control equipment that supply or control electrical equipment to the irrigation machine.

Exception: Grounding shall not be required on machines where all of the following provisions are met:

a. The machine is electrically controlled but not electrically driven.

b. The control voltage is 30 volts or less.

c. The control or signal circuits are current-limited as specified in Section 725-31.

675-13. Methods of Grounding. Machines which require grounding shall have a noncurrent-carrying equipment grounding conductor provided as an integral part of each cord, cable, or raceway. This grounding conductor shall be equal in size to the supply conductors in each cord cable or raceway, but not smaller than No. 14 copper. Feeder circuits supplying power to irrigation machines shall have an equipment grounding conductor sized according to Table 250-95.

675-14. Bonding. Where electrical grounding is required on an irrigation machine, the metallic structure of the machine, metallic conduit, or metallic sheath of cable shall be bonded to the grounding conductor. Metal-to-metal contact with a part which is bonded to the grounding conductor and the noncurrent-carrying parts of the machine shall be considered as an acceptable bonding path.

675-15. Lightning Protection. If an irrigation machine has a stationary point, a driven ground rod shall be connected to the machine at the stationary point for lightning protection.

Where the electrical power supply to irrigation machine equipment is a service, provisions in Sections 250-81 and 250-83 would require a made grounding electrode, such as a driven ground rod. Consideration should be given to Section 250-86 and NFPA 78-1986, *Lightning Protection Code*, in areas where lightning protection is critical.

675-16. Energy from More than One Source. Equipment within an enclosure receiving electrical energy from more than one source shall not be required to have a disconnecting means for the additional source, provided that its voltage is 30 volts or less and meets the requirements of Section 725-31.

675-17. Connectors. External plugs and connectors on the equipment shall be of the weatherproof type.
Unless provided solely for the connection of circuits meeting the requirements of Section 725-31, external plugs and connectors shall be constructed as specified in Section 250-99(a).

B. Center Pivot Irrigation Machines

675-21. General. The provisions of Part B are intended to cover additional special requirements which are peculiar to center pivot irrigation machines. See Section 675-2 for definition of Center Pivot Irrigation Machines.

675-22. Equivalent Current Ratings. In order to establish ratings of controllers, disconnecting means, conductors, and the like, for the inherent intermittent duty of center pivot irrigation machines, the following determination shall be used:

Figure 675-1. A center pivot irrigation machine. (*Lockwood Corp.*)

The ratings of electrical components of any circuit should be selected so as to avoid extensive damage to the equipment during a short-circuit or a ground-fault condition. Section 675-22 gives the requirements for establishing ratings of components of special equipment for inherent intermittent duty. Also see commentary following Sections 110-10 and 430-52.

(a) Continuous-Current Rating. The equivalent continuous-current rating for the selection of branch-circuit conductors and branch-circuit devices shall be equal to 125 percent of the motor nameplate full-load current rating of the largest motor plus 60 percent of the sum of the motor nameplate full-load current ratings of all remaining motors on the circuit.

(b) Locked-Rotor Current. The equivalent locked-rotor current rating shall be equal to the numerical sum of two times the locked-rotor current of the largest motor plus 80 percent of the sum of the motor nameplate full-load current ratings of all the remaining motors on the circuit.

ARTICLE 680 — SWIMMING POOLS, FOUNTAINS, AND SIMILAR INSTALLATIONS

Contents

943

(c) Methods of Bonding.
(d) Grounding.
(e) Methods of Grounding.
(f) Receptacles.

680-63. Lighting Fixtures.

G. Hydromassage Bathtubs
680-70. Protection.
680-71. Other Electric Equipment.

A. General

680-1. Scope. The provisions of this article apply to the construction and installation of electric wiring for and equipment in or adjacent to all swimming, wading, therapeutic, and decorative pools, fountains, hot tubs, spas, and hydromassage bathtubs, whether permanently installed or storable, and to metallic auxiliary equipment, such as pumps, filters, and similar equipment.

(FPN): The term "pool" as used in the balance of this article includes swimming, wading, and permanently installed therapeutic pools. The term "fountain" as used in the balance of this article includes fountains, ornamental pools, display pools, and reflection pools.

This article applies to swimming pools and similar installations, indoors or outdoors, permanent or storable, whether or not served by any electrical circuits of any nature. Studies conducted by Underwriters Laboratories Inc., various manufacturers, and others indicate that a person in a swimming pool can receive a severe electric shock by reaching over and touching the energized casing of a faulty appliance, such as a radio, hair dryer, etc., as the person's body establishes a conductive path through the water and pool to earth. Also, a person not in contact with a faulty appliance or any grounded object may receive an electric shock and be rendered immobile by a potential gradient in the water itself. Accordingly, requirements of this article covering effective bonding and grounding, installation of receptacles and lighting fixtures, use of ground-fault circuit-interrupters, modified wiring methods, etc., apply not only to the installation of the pool, but also to installations and equipment adjacent to, or associated with, the pool.

680-2. Approval of Equipment. All electric equipment installed in the water, walls, or decks of pools, fountains, and similar installations shall comply with the provisions of this article.

680-3. Other Articles. Except as modified by this article, wiring and equipment in or adjacent to pools and fountains shall comply with the applicable requirements of Chapters 1 through 4.

(FPN): See Section 370-13 for junction boxes, Section 347-3 for rigid nonmetallic conduit, and Article 720 for low-voltage lighting.

Note that Section 370-13(d) specifies the requirements for the support of empty threaded boxes, and Section 347-3(b) does not permit equipment to be supported by rigid nonmetallic conduit. See Figure 680-1. See also commentary following Section 370-13(d).

680-4. Definitions.

Dry-Niche Lighting Fixture: A lighting fixture intended for installation in the wall of a pool or fountain in a niche that is sealed against the entry of pool water.

Forming Shell: A metal structure designed to support a wet-niche lighting fixture assembly and intended for mounting in a pool or fountain structure.

Hydromassage Bathtub: A permanently installed bathtub equipped with a recirculating piping system, pump and associated equipment. It is designed so it can accept, circulate, and discharge water upon each use.

945

Figure 680-1. Wet-niche fixture installation with J-box supported per Sections 370-13(d) and 347-3(b) above pool deck.

See commentary following Part G, heading.

Permanently Installed Decorative Fountains and Reflection Pools: Those that are constructed in the ground, on the ground, or in a building in such a manner that the fountain cannot be readily disassembled for storage and are served by electrical circuits of any nature. These units are primarily constructed for their aesthetic value and not intended for swimming or wading.

Permanently Installed Swimming, Wading, and Therapeutic Pools: Those that are constructed in the ground, on the ground, or in a building in such a manner that the pool cannot be readily disassembled for storage, whether or not served by electrical circuits of any nature.

See commentary following Part F, heading.

Pool Cover, Electrically Operated: Motor-driven equipment designed to cover and uncover the water surface of a pool by means of a flexible sheet or rigid frame.

See Section 680-26.

Spa or Hot Tub: A hydromassage pool, or tub for recreational or therapeutic use, not located in health care facilities, designed for immersion of users and usually having a filter, heater, and motor-driven blower. It may be installed indoors or outdoors, on the ground or supporting structure, or in the ground or supporting structure.

See commentary following Part D, heading.

Storable Swimming or Wading Pool: A pool with a maximum dimension of 18 feet (5.49 m) and a maximum wall height of 42 inches (1.07 m) and so constructed that it may be readily disassembled for storage and reassembled to its original integrity.

946

See commentary following Section 680-31 and Figure 680-10.

Wet-Niche Lighting Fixture: A lighting fixture intended for installation in a metal forming shell mounted in a pool or fountain structure where the fixture will be completely surrounded by water.

See Figures 680-1 and 680-5.

680-5. Transformers and Ground-Fault Circuit-Interrupters.

(a) Transformers. Transformers used for the supply of fixtures, together with the transformer enclosure, shall be identified for the purpose. The transformer shall be a two-winding type having a grounded metal barrier between the primary and secondary windings.

Unless marked otherwise, UL-listed swimming pool and spa transformers are not suitable for connection to a conduit that extends directly to an underwater pool light forming shell. Swimming pool and spa transformers are not permitted to be used outdoors unless they are marked "For Outdoor Use" or equivalent, in which case they have been found to be acceptable for both outdoor and indoor use. See Section 110-3(b).

(b) Ground-Fault Circuit-Interrupters. Ground-fault circuit-interrupters shall be self-contained units, circuit-breaker types, receptacle types, or other approved types.

See definition of "ground-fault circuit-interrupter" in Article 100.
A ground-fault circuit-interrupter is intended to be used only in a circuit that has a solidly grounded conductor. A Class A GFCI trips when the current to ground has a value in the range of 4 through 6 milliamperes and is suitable for use in swimming pool circuits. It should be noted, however, that swimming pool circuits installed before local adoption of the 1965 *National Electrical Code* may include sufficient leakage current to cause a Class A GFCI to trip. A Class B GFCI trips when the current to ground exceeds 20 milliamperes and is suitable for use with underwater swimming pool lighting fixtures only.

(c) Wiring. Conductors on the load side of a ground-fault circuit-interrupter or of a transformer, used to comply with provisions of Section 680-20(a)(1), shall not occupy conduit, boxes, or enclosures containing other conductors.

Exception No. 1: Ground-fault circuit-interrupters shall be permitted in a panelboard that contains circuits protected by other than ground-fault circuit-interrupters.

Exception No. 2: Supply conductors to a feed-through, receptacle-type, ground-fault circuit-interrupter shall be permitted in the same enclosure.

Exception No. 3: Conductors on the load side of a ground-fault circuit-interrupter shall be permitted to occupy conduit, boxes, or enclosures containing only conductors protected by ground-fault circuit-interrupters.

680-6. Receptacles, Lighting Fixtures, Lighting Outlets and Switching Devices.

(a) Receptacles.

(1) Receptacles on the property shall be located at least 10 feet (3.05 m) from the inside walls of a pool.

Exception: Receptacle(s) that provides power for water-pump motor(s) for a permanently installed pool, as permitted in Section 680-7, shall be permitted between 5 and 10 feet (1.52 and 3.05 m) from the inside walls of the pool, shall be single and of the locking and grounding types, and shall be protected by ground-fault circuit-interrupter(s).

(2) Where a permanently installed pool is installed at a dwelling unit(s), at least one 125-volt convenience receptacle shall be located a minimum of 10 feet (3.05 m) from and not more than 20 feet (6.08 m) from the inside wall of the pool.

(3) All 125-volt receptacles located within 20 feet (6.08 m) of the inside walls of a pool shall be protected by a ground-fault circuit-interrupter. See Section 210-8(a)(3).

Section 680-6(a) makes it clear that a locking- and grounding-type receptacle used for a recirculating pump motor is permitted where it will be not less than 5 ft (1.52 m) from the inside walls of the pool and is protected by a GFCI. This requirement also makes it clear that all receptacles located within 20 ft (6.1 m) of a permanently installed pool (outdoors or indoors, for dwelling unit or commerical use) are required to be protected by GFCIs. This distance of 20 ft (6.1 m) is intended to provide for location of receptacles beyond a pool deck. If located within the perimeter of a pool deck, the receptacle installation is likely to be a tripping hazard.

See Figure 680-2.

Figure 680-2. For permanently installed pools at dwelling unit(s), it is mandatory to install a 125-V receptacle between 10 and 20 ft from the inside wall of the pool.

(FPN): In determining the above dimensions, the distance to be measured is the shortest path the supply cord of an appliance connected to the receptacle would follow without piercing a floor, wall, ceiling, doorway with hinged or sliding door, window opening, or other effective permanent barrier.

See Figures 680-3 and 680-4.

(b) Lighting Fixtures and Lighting Outlets.

(1) Lighting fixtures and lighting outlets shall not be installed over the pool or over the area extending 5 feet (1.52 m) horizontally from the inside walls of a pool unless 12 feet (3.66 m) above the maximum water level.

Exception No. 1: Existing lighting fixtures and lighting outlets located less than 5 feet (1.52 m) measured horizontally from the inside walls of a pool shall be at least 5 feet (1.52 m) above the surface of the maximum water level and shall be rigidly attached to the existing structure.

Figure 680-3. This figure illustrates the shortest path a supply cord of an appliance connected to the receptacle would follow without piercing the wall.

Figure 680-4. This figure illustrates acceptable receptacle locations within 20 ft (6.1 m) of a swimming pool.

See Figure 680-5.

Exception No. 2: In indoor pool areas, the limitations of Section 680-6(b)(1) shall not apply if all of the following conditions are complied with: (1) fixtures are of totally enclosed type; (2) a ground-fault circuit-interrupter is installed in the branch circuit supplying the fixture(s); and (3) the distance from the bottom of the fixture to the maximum water level is not less than 7.5 feet (2.29 m).

(2) Lighting fixtures and lighting outlets installed in the area extending between 5 feet (1.52 m) and 10 feet (3.05 m) horizontally from the inside walls of a pool shall be protected by a ground-fault circuit-interrupter unless installed 5 feet (1.52 m) above the maximum water level and rigidly attached to the structure adjacent to or enclosing the pool.

Figure 680-5. The requirements for ground-fault circuit-interrupter protection for lighting fixtures and lighting outlets over pools.

(3) Cord-connected lighting fixtures shall meet the same specifications as other cord- and plug-connected equipment as set forth in Section 680-7 when installed within 16 feet (4.88 m) of any point on the water surface, measured radially.

(c) Switching Devices. Switching devices on the property shall be located at least 5 feet (1.52 m) from the inside walls of a pool unless separated from the pool by a solid fence, wall, or other permanent barrier.

Panelboards, time clocks, and pool light switches, etc., where located not less than 5 ft (1.52 m) from the inside walls of a pool, without a solid fence, wall or other permanent barrier, will be out of reach of persons who are in a pool, thereby preventing contact and possible shock hazards.

680-7. Cord- and Plug-Connected Equipment. Fixed or stationary equipment rated 20 amperes or less, other than an underwater lighting fixture for a permanently installed pool, shall be permitted to be connected with a flexible cord to facilitate the removal or disconnection for maintenance or repair. For other than storable pools, the flexible cord shall not exceed 3 feet (914 mm) in length and shall have a copper equipment grounding conductor not smaller than No. 12 with a grounding-type attachment plug.

(FPN): See Section 680-25(e) for connection with flexible cords.

In some geographic areas, it is preferable to disconnect the filter pump for a permanent pool during the cold weather months, and a 3-ft (914-mm) cord is permitted to facilitate the removal of fixed or stationary equipment for maintenance and storage.

The 3-ft (914-mm) cord limitation does not apply to cord- and plug-connected filter pumps used with storable-type pools, covered in Part C of this article, since these pumps are neither fixed nor stationary. Listed filter pumps for use with storable pools are considered portable and are permitted to be equipped with cords longer than 3 ft (914 mm).

680-8. Overhead Conductor Clearances. The following parts of pools shall not be placed under existing service-drop conductors or any other open overhead wiring; nor shall such wiring be installed above the following: (1) pools and the area extending 10 feet (3.05 m) horizontally from the inside of the walls of the pool; (2) diving structure; or (3) observation stands, towers, or platforms.

Exception No. 1: Structures listed in (1), (2), and (3) above shall be permitted under utility-owned, -operated and -maintained supply lines or service drops where such installations provide the following clearances:

	Insulated supply or service drop cables, 0–750 volts to ground, supported on and cabled together with an effectively grounded bare messenger	All other supply or service drop conductors	
		Voltage to Ground	
		0–15 kV	15–50 kV
A. Clearance in any direction to the water level, edge of water surface, base of diving platform or permanently-anchored raft	18 feet (5.49m)	25 feet (7.62m)	27 feet (8.23m)
B. Clearance in any direction to the diving platform or tower	14 feet (4.27m)	16 feet (4.88m)	18 feet (5.49m)
C. Horizontal limit of clearance measured from inside wall of the pool.	This limit shall extend to the outer edge of the structures listed in (1) and (2) above but not less than 10 feet (3.05m).		

Figure 680-8, Exception No. 1

Exception No. 2: Utility-owned, -operated, and -maintained communication conductors, community antenna system coaxial cables complying with Article 820, and the supporting messengers shall be permitted at a height of not less than 10 feet (3.05 m) above swimming and wading pools, diving structures and observation stands, towers or platforms.

(FPN): See Sections 225-18 and 225-19 for clearances for conductors not covered by this section.

680-9. Electric Pool Water Heaters. All electric pool water heaters shall have the heating elements subdivided into loads not exceeding 48 amperes and protected at not more than 60 amperes.

The ampacity of the branch-circuit conductors and the rating or setting of overcurrent protective devices shall not be less than 125 percent of the total load of the nameplate rating.

680-10. Underground Wiring Location.   Underground wiring shall not be permitted under the pool or under the area extending 5 feet (1.52 m) horizontally from the inside wall of the pool.

Exception No. 1: Wiring necessary to supply pool equipment permitted by this article shall be allowed within this area.

Exception No. 2: When space limitations prevent wiring from being routed 5 feet (1.52 m) or more from the pool, such wiring shall be permitted when installed in rigid metal conduit, intermediate metal conduit, or a nonmetallic raceway system. All metal conduit shall be corrosion-resistant and suitable for the location. The Exceptions to Section 300-5(a) shall not apply.

680-11. Equipment Rooms and Pits.   Electric equipment shall not be installed in rooms or pits which do not have adequate drainage to prevent water accumulation during normal operation or filter maintenance.

B. Permanently Installed Pools

680-20. Underwater Lighting Fixtures.

   (a) General.   Paragraphs (a) through (c) of this section apply to all lighting fixtures installed below the normal water level of the pool.

   (1) The design of an underwater lighting fixture supplied from a branch circuit either directly or by way of a transformer meeting the requirements of Section 680-5(a) shall be such that, when the fixture is properly installed without a ground-fault circuit-interrupter, there is no shock hazard with any likely combination of fault conditions during normal use (not relamping).

   In addition, a ground-fault circuit-interrupter shall be installed in the branch circuit supplying fixtures operating at more than 15 volts, so that there is no shock hazard during relamping. The installation of the ground-fault circuit-interrupter shall be such that there is no shock hazard with any likely fault-condition combination that involves a person in a conductive path from any ungrounded part of the branch circuit or the fixture to ground.

   Compliance with this requirement shall be obtained by the use of an approved underwater lighting fixture and by installation of an approved ground-fault circuit-interrupter in the branch circuit.

   (2) No lighting fixtures shall be installed for operation at over 150 volts between conductors.

   (3) Lighting fixtures mounted in walls shall be installed with the top of the fixture lens at least 18 inches (457 mm) below the normal water level of the pool. A lighting fixture facing upward shall have the lens adequately guarded to prevent contact by any person.

Exception: Lighting fixtures identified for use at a depth of not less than 4 inches (102 mm) below the normal water level of the pool shall be permitted.

   The reason for the 18-in. minimum submergence requirement is to reduce the likelihood that a person in the water and hanging on to the side of the pool directly over the fixture will have his or her chest cavity in line with the fixture. The exception covers fixtures that have been investigated and found acceptable for use where the chest cavity may be directly in front of the fixture. The highest level of leakage current in the pool from a wet-niche fixture with a broken lens and bulb is directly in front of the fixture.

   (4) Fixtures that depend on submersion for safe operation shall be inherently protected against the hazards of overheating when not submerged.

Fixtures that depend on submersion for safe operation are required to be inherently protected against the hazards of overheating when not submerged, for instance, during a relamping process. Protection against overheating is required to be built into or be a part of the fixture. A remotely located low-water cutoff switch would not provide the intended protection.

(b) Wet-Niche Fixtures.

(1) Approved metal forming shells shall be installed for the mounting of all wet-niche underwater fixtures and shall be equipped with provisions for threaded conduit entries.

Conduit shall extend from the forming shell to a suitable junction box or other enclosure located as provided in Section 680-21. Conduit shall be rigid metal, intermediate metal, or rigid nonmetallic.

Metal conduit shall be of brass or other approved corrosion-resistant metal.

Where rigid nonmetallic conduit is used, a No. 8 insulated copper conductor shall be installed in this conduit with provisions for terminating in the forming shell, junction box or transformer enclosure, or ground-fault circuit-interrupter enclosure. The termination of the No. 8 conductor in the forming shell shall be covered with, or encapsulated in, a listed potting compound to protect such connection from the possible deteriorating effect of pool water. Metal parts of the fixture and forming shell in contact with the pool water shall be of brass or other approved corrosion-resistant metal.

(2) The end of the flexible-cord jacket and the flexible-cord conductor terminations within a fixture shall be covered with, or encapsulated in, a suitable potting compound to prevent the entry of water into the fixture through the cord or its conductors. In addition, the grounding connection within a fixture shall be similarly treated to protect such connection from the deteriorating effect of pool water in the event of water entry into the fixture.

(3) The fixture shall be bonded to and secured to the forming shell by a positive locking device that assures a low-resistance contact and requires a tool to remove the fixture from the forming shell.

(c) Dry-Niche Fixtures.
A dry-niche lighting fixture shall be provided with: (1) provision for drainage of water, and (2) means for accommodating one equipment grounding conductor for each conduit entry.

Approved rigid metal conduit, intermediate metal conduit, or rigid nonmetallic conduit shall be installed from the fixture to the service equipment or panelboard. A junction box shall not be required, but if used shall not be required to be elevated or located as specified in Section 680-21(a)(4) if the fixture is specifically identified for the purpose.

Exception: Electrical metallic tubing shall be permitted to be used to protect conductors where installed on or within buildings.

Underwater lighting fixtures of either dry-niche or wet-niche types operating at more than 15 V require ground-fault circuit-interrupter protection. See commentary following Section 680-5(b).

Branch-circuit conductors for dry-niche fixtures are required to be installed in rigid metal conduit, intermediate metal conduit, or rigid nonmetallic conduit from the fixture to an approved panelboard or to the service equipment. Branch-circuit conductors for wet-niche fixtures leaving the pool junction box are required to be enclosed in rigid metal conduit, intermediate metal conduit, or rigid nonmetallic conduit, except in or on buildings where the conductors may be protected by electrical metallic tubing. However, unlike wet-niche fixtures, a junction box is not required for dry-niche fixtures. If one is used, it is not required to be elevated or located as specified in Section 680-21(a)(4). See Figures 680-1 and 680-5.

ARTICLE 680—SWIMMING POOLS, FOUNTAINS

Where rigid nonmetallic conduit is used between a forming shell for a wet-niche fixture and a junction box or other enclosure, a No. 8 insulated, copper bonding conductor is required to be installed within this conduit to provide electrical continuity between the forming shell and the junction box or other enclosure. This rigid nonmetallic conduit should be sized large enough to enclose both the No. 8 insulated copper bonding conductor and the approved flexible cord that supplies the wet-niche fixture to facilitate easy withdrawal and insertion of the bonding conductor and the cord.

** Not less than 8 in. above ground level, pool deck or max water level, whichever is greatest, to inside bottom of "J" box or enclosure.

*4 ft

Normal water level

Deck **

J

18-in. minimum to top of fixture lens. See Section 680-20 (a)(3) and Exception.

Brass or nonmetallic conduit or approved equivalent. See Section 680-20(b).

Threaded conduit entry

Metal-forming shell with wet-niche fixture

Threaded conduit entry

Rigid metal or nonmetallic conduit to panel. An insulated copper equipment ground conductor (unbroken) not less than No. 12 AWG, required.

*Unless junction box is separated from pool by a fence, wall, or other permanent barrier.

**Flush deck box for lighting systems, 15 V or less, filled with approved potting compound (680-21(a)(4) Exception).

Figure 680-6. Installation requirements for wet-niche forming shell and deck box.

680-21. Junction Boxes and Enclosures for Transformers or Ground-Fault Circuit-Interrupters.

(a) Junction Boxes. A junction box connected to a conduit that extends directly to a forming shell shall be:

(1) Equipped with threaded hubs or bosses; and

(2) Of copper, brass, suitable plastic, or other approved corrosion-resistant material; and

(3) Provided with electrical continuity between every connected metal conduit and the grounding terminals by means of copper, brass, or other approved corrosion-resistant metal that is integral with the box; and

(4) Located not less than 8 inches (203 mm), measured from the inside of the bottom of the box, above the ground level, pool deck, or maximum pool water level, whichever provides the greatest elevation, and located not less than 4 feet (1.22 m) from the inside wall of the pool unless separated from the pool by a solid fence, wall, or other permanent barrier.

Exception: On lighting systems of 15 volts or less, a flush deck box shall be permitted provided:

a. An approved potting compound is used to fill the box to prevent the entrance of moisture; and

Melted wax is often used to meet this requirement.

b. The flush deck box is located not less than 4 feet (1.22 m) from the inside wall of the pool.

954

(b) Other Enclosures. An enclosure for a transformer, ground-fault circuit-interrupter, or a similar device connected to a conduit that extends directly to a forming shell shall be:

(1) Equipped with threaded hubs or bosses; and

(2) Provided with an approved seal, such as duct seal at the conduit connection, that prevents circulation of air between the conduit and the enclosures; and

(3) Provided with electrical continuity between every connected metal conduit and the grounding terminals by means of copper, brass, or other approved corrosion-resistant metal that is integral with the enclosures; and

(4) Located not less than 8 inches (203 mm), measured from the inside bottom of the enclosure to the ground level, pool deck, or maximum pool water level, whichever provides the greatest elevation, and located not less than 4 feet (1.22 m) from the inside wall of the pool unless separated from the pool by a solid fence, wall, or other permanent barrier.

(c) Protection. Junction boxes and enclosures mounted above the grade of the finished walkway around the pool shall not be located in the walkway unless afforded additional protection, such as by location under diving boards, adjacent to fixed structures, and the like.

(d) Grounding Terminals. Junction boxes, transformer enclosures, and ground-fault circuit-interrupter enclosures connected to a conduit which extends directly to a forming shell shall be provided with a number of grounding terminals that shall be at least one more than the number of conduit entries.

(e) Strain Relief. The termination of a flexible cord of an underwater lighting fixture within a junction box, transformer enclosure, ground-fault circuit-interrupter, or other enclosure shall be provided with a strain relief.

680-22. Bonding.

(FPN): It is not the intent of this subsection to require that the No. 8 or larger solid copper bonding conductor be extended or attached to any remote panelboard, service equipment or any electrode, but only that it be employed to eliminate voltage gradients in the pool area as prescribed.

(a) Bonded Parts. The following parts shall be bonded together:

(1) All metallic parts of the pool structure, including the reinforcing metal of the pool shell, coping stones, and deck.

(2) All forming shells.

(3) All metal fittings within or attached to the pool structure.

(4) Metal parts of electric equipment associated with the pool water circulating system, including pump motors.

(5) Metal parts of equipment associated with pool covers including electric motors.

(6) Metal conduit, metal piping, and all fixed metal parts that are within 5 feet (1.52 m) of the inside walls of the pool and that are not separated from the pool by a permanent barrier.

This subsection would also include, for example, a metal door frame or metal window frame.

Exception No. 1: The usual steel tie wires shall be considered suitable for bonding the reinforcing steel together, and welding or special clamping shall not be required.

ARTICLE 680—SWIMMING POOLS, FOUNTAINS

Exception No. 2: Structural reinforcing steel or the walls of bolted or welded metal pool structures shall be permitted as a common bonding grid for nonelectrical parts where connections can be made in accordance with Section 250-113.

Section 250-113 requires that the connection be made by exothermic welding or listed clamps, connectors, etc.

Exception No. 3: Isolated parts which are no more than 4 inches (102 mm) in any dimension and do not penetrate into the pool structure more than 1 inch (25.4 mm) shall not require bonding.

(b) Common Bonding Grid. These parts shall be connected to a common bonding grid with a solid, copper conductor, insulated, covered, or bare, not smaller than No. 8. Connection shall be made by pressure connectors or clamps of brass, copper, or copper alloy. The common bonding grid may be any of the following:

(1) The structural reinforcing steel of a concrete pool where the reinforcing rods are bonded together by the usual steel tie wires or the equivalent; or,

(2) The wall of a bolted or welded metal pool; or,

(3) A solid, copper conductor, insulated, covered, or bare, not smaller than No. 8.

(c) Pool Water Heaters. For pool water heaters rated at more than 50 amperes which have specific instructions regarding bonding and grounding, only those parts designated to be bonded shall be bonded, and only those parts designated to be grounded shall be grounded.

It is important to know the difference between the terms "bonding" and "grounding" as they apply to this article. As defined in Article 100, bonding is "the permanent joining of metallic parts to form an electrically conductive path which will assure electrical continuity and the capacity to conduct safely any current likely to be imposed." See comments following Section 680-25(f).

This section indicates the metal parts that are required to be bonded together, including all metal parts of electric equipment associated with the pool water circulating system, all metal parts of the pool structure, and all fixed metal parts, which include conduit and piping, metal door frames, and metal window frames, etc., within 5 ft (1.52 m) of the inside walls of the pool and not separated by a permanent barrier. It should be understood that the bonding together of these parts does not mean that they are required to be connected to each other; it means that they are required to be connected to a common bonding grid with an insulated, covered, or bare solid copper conductor not smaller than No. 8. See Figures 680-7 and 680-8. Connections are required to be made by exothermic welds or by listed pressure connectors, clamps, or other listed means in accordance with Section 250-113. See fine print note following Section 680-22.

The reason for connecting metal parts (ladders, hand-rails, water-circulating equipment, forming shells, diving boards, etc.) to a common bonding grid (pool reinforcing steel, pool metal wall, or a No. 8 solid conductor) is to ensure that all such metal parts will be at the same electrical potential. This will reduce any possible shock hazard created by stray currents in the ground or piping connected to the swimming pool. This includes plastic piping as water containing salt or chemicals can have a low resistivity, thereby permitting dangerous currents to flow.

Since corrosion is normally associated with the wet conditions of swimming pool areas, wiring and connections should be checked periodically, especially bonding connections between the No. 8 copper conductor and, for instance, an aluminum (or other dissimilar metal) ladder.

Figure 680-7. Illustrated is a metal (i.e., steel, aluminum) perimeter pool with bolted (or welded) sections. The metal perimeter serves as the common bonding grid to which the metal ladder, the metal diving board, and pump motor are connected. Note that the pump motor is connected to a receptacle as per Sections 680-6 and 680-7.

Figure 680-8. Illustrated is a poured concrete pool. The structural reinforcing steel serves as the common bonding grid to which all metal appurtenances associated with the pool are connected. Safety rope hooks are not required to be bonded as per Section 680-22(a), Exception No. 3. The flush deck box meets the provisions of Section 680-21(a), Exception.

680-23. Underwater Audio Equipment. All underwater audio equipment shall be identified for the purpose.

(a) Speakers. Each speaker shall be mounted in an approved metal forming shell, the front of which is enclosed by a captive metal screen, or equivalent, that is bonded to and secured to the forming shell by a positive locking device that assures a low resistance contact and requires a tool to open for installation or servicing of the speaker. The forming shell shall be installed in a recess in the wall or floor of the pool.

(b) Wiring Methods. Rigid metal conduit or intermediate metal conduit of brass or other identified corrosion-resistant metal or rigid nonmetallic conduit shall extend from the forming shell to a suitable junction box or other enclosure as provided in Section 680-21. Where rigid nonmetallic conduit is used, a No. 8 insulated copper conductor shall be installed in this conduit with provisions for terminating in the forming shell and the junction box. The termination of the No. 8 conductor in the forming shell shall be covered with, or encapsulated in, a suitable potting compound to protect such connection from the possible deteriorating effect of pool water.

(c) Forming Shell and Metal Screen. The forming shell and metal screen shall be of brass or other approved corrosion-resistant metal.

680-24. Grounding. The following equipment shall be grounded: (1) wet-niche underwater lighting fixtures; (2) dry-niche underwater lighting fixtures; (3) all electric equipment located within 5 feet (1.52 m) of the inside wall of the pool; (4) all electric equipment associated with the recirculating system of the pool; (5) junction boxes; (6) transformer enclosures; (7) ground-fault circuit-interrupters; (8) panelboards that are not part of the service equipment and that supply any electric equipment associated with the pool.

680-25. Methods of Grounding.

(a) General. The following provisions shall apply to the grounding of underwater lighting fixtures, junction boxes, metal transformer enclosures, panelboards, motors and other electrical enclosures and equipment.

(b) Pool Lighting Fixtures and Related Equipment.

(1) Wet-niche lighting fixtures shall be connected to an equipment grounding conductor sized in accordance with Table 250-95 but not smaller than No. 12. It shall be an insulated copper conductor and shall be installed with the circuit conductors in rigid metal conduit, intermediate metal conduit, or rigid nonmetallic conduit.

Exception No. 1: Electrical metallic tubing shall be permitted to be used to protect conductors where installed on or within buildings.

Exception No. 2: The equipment grounding conductor between the wiring chamber of the secondary winding of a transformer and a junction box shall be sized in accordance with the overcurrent device in this circuit.

(2) The junction box, transformer enclosure, or other enclosure in the supply circuit to a wet-niche lighting fixture and the field-wiring chamber of a dry-niche lighting fixture shall be grounded to the equipment grounding terminal of the panelboard. This terminal shall be directly connected to the panelboard enclosure. The equipment grounding conductor shall be installed without joint or splice.

Exception No. 1: Where more than one underwater lighting fixture is supplied by the same branch circuit, the equipment grounding conductor, installed between the junction boxes, transformer enclosures, or other enclosures in the supply circuit to wet-niche fixtures or between the field-wiring compartments of dry-niche fixtures, shall be permitted to be terminated on grounding terminals.

Exception No. 2: Where the underwater lighting fixture is supplied from a transformer, ground-fault circuit-interrupter, clock-operated switch, or a manual snap switch which is located between the panelboard and a junction box connected to the conduit that extends directly to the underwater lighting fixture, the equipment grounding conductor shall be permitted to terminate on grounding terminals on the transformer, ground-fault circuit-interrupter, clock-operated switch enclosure, or an outlet box used to enclose a snap switch.

See commentary following Section 680-5(a).

(3) Wet-niche lighting fixtures that are supplied by a flexible cord or cable shall have all exposed noncurrent-carrying metal parts grounded by an insulated copper equipment grounding conductor that is an integral part of the cord or cable. This grounding conductor shall be connected to a grounding terminal in the supply junction box, transformer enclosure, or other enclosure. The grounding conductor shall not be smaller than the supply conductors and not smaller than No. 16.

(c) Motors.
Pool-associated motors shall be connected to an equipment grounding conductor sized in accordance with Table 250-95 but not smaller than No. 12. It shall be an insulated copper conductor and shall be installed with the circuit conductors in rigid metal conduit, intermediate metal conduit or rigid nonmetallic conduit.

Exception No. 1: Electrical metallic tubing shall be permitted to be used to protect conductors where installed on or within buildings.

Exception No. 2: Where necessary to employ flexible connections at or adjacent to the motor, liquidtight flexible metal conduit with approved fittings shall be permitted.

Exception No. 3: Any of the wiring methods recognized in Chapter 3 of this Code shall be permitted to be used in the interior of one-family dwelling units.

Although Exception No. 3 permits wiring methods such as nonmetallic-sheathed cable and armored cable in the interior of one-family dwelling units, it does not permit less than a No. 12 AWG insulated copper conductor for the equipment grounding conductor. Most existing installations will not have a grounding conductor meeting these requirements.

Exception No. 4: Flexible cord shall be permitted in accordance with Section 680-7.

See Figure 680-7.

(d) Panelboards. A panelboard, not part of the service equipment, shall have an equipment grounding conductor installed between its grounding terminal and the grounding terminal of the service equipment. This conductor shall be sized in accordance with Table 250-95 but not smaller than No. 12. It shall be an insulated conductor and shall be installed with the feeder conductors in rigid metal conduit, intermediate metal conduit, or rigid nonmetallic conduit. The equipment grounding conductor shall be connected to an equipment grounding terminal of the panelboard.

The insulated equipment grounding conductor may be aluminum or copper and installed in a raceway. It should be understood that, for an existing remote panelboard, Exception No. 1 permits an approved cable assembly with an insulated or covered aluminum or copper equipment grounding conductor. See Figure 680-9.

Exception No. 1: The equipment grounding conductor between an existing remote panelboard and the service equipment shall not be required to be in one of the conduits listed in paragraph (c) if the interconnection is by means of a flexible metal conduit or an approved cable assembly with an insulated or covered equipment grounding conductor.

Exception No. 2: Electrical metallic tubing shall be permitted to be used to protect conductors where installed on or within the building.

(FPN): See Section 348-1.

(e) Cord-Connected Equipment. Where fixed or stationary equipment is connected with a flexible cord to facilitate removal or disconnection for maintenance, repair, or storage as provided in Section 680-7, the equipment grounding conductors shall be connected to a fixed metal part of the assembly. The removable part shall be mounted on or bonded to the fixed metal part.

(f) Other Equipment. Other electrical equipment shall be grounded in accordance with Article 250 and connected by wiring methods of Chapter 3.

Equipment, other than underwater lighting fixtures and pool-associated motors, is required to be connected by wiring methods of Chapter 3 and grounded in accordance with Article 250. For example, an outdoor receptacle is permitted to be wired with Type UF cable containing an insulated or bare conductor for equipment grounding purposes. See Figure 680-9.

When the provisions of Sections 680-24 and 680-25 are considered, the difference between "bonding" and "grounding" becomes apparent. As required in these sections, "grounding" is the connection of noncurrent-carrying metal parts of electric equipment associated with the pool [or located within 5 ft (1.52 m) of the inside wall of the pool] to the grounding terminal bus of an approved panelboard [see Section 680-25(d)] or to the grounding terminal of the service equipment. This equipment grounding conductor provides a path of low impedance that limits the voltage to ground and facilitates the operation of the circuit overcurrent protective device(s). Furthermore, this grounding conductor is required to be an insulated

Figure 680-9. Circuits for pools may be derived from an existing remote panelboard that is supplied by an approved cable assembly as specified in Section 680-25(d), Exception No. 1. Section 680-25(f) permits Type UF cable to be used for the receptacle required by Section 680-6(a)(2), and other equipment; but circuit conductors for underwater lighting fixtures are required to be run in raceways. Circuit conductors for pool-associated motors other than flexible cord as permitted by Section 680-7 are required to be run in raceway. An exception is the interior of one-family dwelling units where any wiring method permitted by Chapter 3 is acceptable if the grounding conductor is at least No. 12 AWG copper, and insulated.

copper conductor not smaller than No. 12 AWG, and for underwater lighting it is required to be run with the circuit conductors in rigid metal conduit, intermediate metal conduit, rigid nonmetallic conduit (except where noted for motors), or, where installed in or on buildings, it may be protected by electrical metallic tubing. Also, all equipment grounding conductors are required to terminate at an equipment grounding terminal located within lighting fixtures, junction boxes, transformer enclosures, panelboards, service equipment, etc.

Bonding conductors, however, may be insulated, covered, or bare, and are required to be No. 8 copper or larger. They may be direct buried, and, where connected to metal parts of the pool structure or metal parts of electric equipment, they may be externally clamped or attached and are not required to be accessible. All of these parts form a common bonding grid that establishes an equipotential grounding system, and they do not have to be run to the equipment grounding terminals of panelboards or service equipment.

680-26. Electrically Operated Pool Covers.

(a) Motors and Controllers. The electric motors, controllers and wiring shall be located at least 5 feet (1.52 m) from the inside wall of the pool unless separated from the pool by a wall, cover or other permanent barrier. Electric motors installed below grade level shall be of the totally enclosed type.

(FPN): See Sections 373-2(a), 380-4 and 430-11.

(b) Wiring Methods. The electric motor and controller shall be connected to a circuit protected by a ground-fault circuit-interrupter.

680-27. Deck Area Heating. The provisions of this section apply to all pool deck areas, including a covered pool, where electrically operated comfort heating units are installed within 20 feet (6.1 m) of the inside wall of the pool.

(a) Unit Heaters. Unit heaters shall be rigidly mounted to the structure and shall be of the totally enclosed or guarded types. Unit heaters shall not be mounted over the pool or over the area extending 5 feet (1.52 m) horizontally from the inside walls of a pool.

(b) Permanently Wired Radiant Heaters. Radiant electric heaters shall be suitably guarded and securely fastened to their mounting device(s). Heaters shall not be installed over a pool or over the area extending 5 feet (1.52 m) horizontally from the inside walls of the pool and shall be mounted at least 12 feet (3.66 m) vertically above the pool deck unless otherwise approved.

(c) Radiant Heat Cables Not Permitted. Radiant heating cables embedded in or below the deck shall not be permitted.

Only unit heaters and permanently connected radiant heaters are permitted in the area extending 5 (1.52 m) to 20 ft (6.1 m) horizontally from the inside walls of a pool. Radiant heat cables embedded in the deck are not permitted.

C. Storable Pools

680-30. Pumps. A cord-connected pool filter pump shall incorporate an approved system of double insulation or its equivalent, and shall be provided with means for grounding only the internal and nonaccessible noncurrent-carrying metal parts of the appliance.

The means for grounding shall be an equipment grounding conductor run with the power-supply conductors in the flexible cord that is properly terminated in a grounding-type attachment plug having a fixed grounding contact member.

680-31. Ground-Fault Circuit-Interrupters Required. All electric equipment, including power supply cords, used with storable pools shall be protected by ground-fault circuit-interrupters.

A storable pool may be readily disassembled and has a maximum dimension of 18 ft (5.49 m) and a maximum wall height of 42 in. (1.07 m). See definition, Section 680-4. This type of pool, and its associated equipment, does not require bonding conductors. However, the filter pump is required to be double insulated or equivalent, and grounding means consisting of an equipment grounding conductor that is an integral part of the flexible cord is required to be provided. There are portable filter pumps for use with storable pools listed by Underwriters Laboratories Inc.

The storable pool is required to be located at least 10 ft (3.05 m) from any receptacle Section 680-6(a), and all electric equipment is required to have a ground-fault circuit-interrupter for personnel protection. See Figure 680-10.

(FPN): When flexible cords are used, see Section 400-4.

D. Spas and Hot Tubs

The requirements of this part are divided into two categories: outdoor installations and indoor installations. See Part G for hydromassage bathtub requirements.

Outdoor installations fall under the requirements of both Parts A and B of Article 680 with three exceptions:

1. Metal bands or hoops used to secure wooden staves are not required to be bonded.

2. Listed packaged units may be cord connected and are required to be protected by a GFCI.

3. Bonding by metal-to-metal mounting on a common frame or base is permitted.

Indoor installations are subject to basically the same requirements but take into consideration the more restricted confines of an indoor location.

Receptacles, wall switches, and electrical devices and controls not associated with a spa or hot tub are required to be located at least 5 ft (1.52 m) away. Receptacles within 20 ft (6.1 m), and those providing power to a spa or hot tub, are required to be protected by a GFCI.

Figure 680-10. Illustrated are the requirements for a storable-type pool. Metal appurtenances are not required to be bonded. The 3-wire cord may be longer than 3 ft. (Some listed filter pumps are equipped with cords 25 ft long.) The receptacle shown can be either a GFCI-type receptacle or one protected by a remote GFCI such as a GFCI-type circuit breaker.

Lighting fixtures located over a spa or hot tub or within 5 ft (1.52 m) horizontally are required to be protected by a GFCI.

Bonding and grounding requirements are similar to those in Parts A and B of Article 680, except that metal-to-metal mounting on a common frame or base is an acceptable bonding method.

Listed packaged units may be cord connected.

680-40. Outdoor Installations. A spa or hot tub installed outdoors shall comply with the provisions of Parts A and B.

Exception No. 1: Metal bands or hoops used to secure wooden staves are exempt from Section 680-22.

Exception No. 2: Listed packaged units shall be permitted to be cord- and plug-connected with a cord no longer than 15 feet (4.57 m) if protected by a ground-fault circuit-interrupter.

Exception No. 3: Bonding by metal-to-metal mounting on a common frame or base shall be permitted.

680-41. Indoor Installations. A spa or hot tub installed indoors shall conform to the requirements of this part and shall be connected by wiring methods of Chapter 3.

Exception: Listed packaged units rated 20 amperes or less shall be permitted to be cord- and plug-connected to facilitate the removal or disconnection for maintenance and repair.

(a) Receptacles.

(1) Receptacles on the property shall be located at least 5 feet (1.52 m) from the inside walls of the spa or hot tub.

(2) 125-volt receptacles located within 10 feet (3.05 m) of the inside walls of a spa or hot tub shall be protected by a ground-fault circuit-interrupter.

(FPN): In determining the above dimensions, the distance to be measured is the shortest path the supply cord of an appliance connected to the receptacle would follow without piercing a floor, wall, or ceiling of a building or other effective permanent barrier.

See also Section 680-6(a)(3), FPN, and Figure 680-4.

(3) Receptacles that provide power for a spa or hot tub shall be ground-fault circuit-interrupter protected.

(b) Lighting Fixtures and Lighting Outlets.

(1) Lighting fixtures and lighting outlets located over the spa or hot tub or within 5 feet (1.52 m) from the inside walls of the spa or hot tub shall be a minimum of 7 feet 6 inches (2.29 m) above the maximum water level and shall be protected by a ground-fault circuit-interrupter.

Exception No. 1: Lighting fixtures and lighting outlets located 12 feet (3.66 m) or more above the maximum water level shall not require protection by a ground-fault circuit-interrupter.

Exception No. 2: Lighting fixtures meeting the requirements of a. or b. below and protected by a ground-fault circuit-interrupter shall be permitted to be installed less than 7 feet 6 inches (2.29 m) over a spa or hot tub:

a. Recessed fixtures with a glass or plastic lens and nonmetallic trim suitable for use in wet locations.

b. Surface-mounted fixtures with a glass or plastic globe and a nonmetallic body suitable for use in wet locations.

(2) Underwater lighting fixtures shall comply with the provisions of Part B of this article.

(c) Wall Switches. Switches shall be located at least 5 feet (1.52 m), measured horizontally, from the inside walls of the spa or hot tub.

(d) Bonding. The following parts shall be bonded together:

(1) All metal fittings within or attached to the spa or hot tub structure.

(2) Metal parts of electric equipment associated with the spa or hot tub water circulating system, including pump motors.

(3) Metal conduit and metal piping within 5 feet (1.52 m) of the inside walls of the spa or hot tub and that are not separated from the spa or hot tub by a permanent barrier.

(4) All metal surfaces that are within 5 feet (1.52 m) of the inside walls of the spa or hot tub and not separated from the spa or hot tub area by a permanent barrier.

(5) Electrical devices and controls not associated with the spas or hot tubs shall be located a minimum of 5 feet (1.52 m) away from such units or be bonded to the spa or hot tub system.

(e) Methods of Bonding. All metal parts associated with the spa or hot tub shall be bonded by any of the following methods: the interconnection of threaded metal piping and fittings, metal-to-metal mounting on a common frame or base, or by the provisions of a copper bonding jumper, insulated, covered, or bare, not smaller than No. 8 solid.

(f) Grounding. The following equipment shall be grounded:

(1) All electric equipment located within 5 feet (1.52 m) of the inside wall of the spa or hot tub.

(2) All electric equipment associated with the circulating system of the spa or hot tub.

(g) Methods of Grounding.

(1) All electric equipment shall be grounded in accordance with Article 250 and connected by the wiring methods of Chapter 3.

963

(2) Where equipment is connected with a flexible cord, the equipment grounding conductor shall be connected to a fixed metal part of the assembly.

(h) Electric Water Heaters. All electric spa or hot tub water heaters shall be listed and have the heating elements subdivided into loads not exceeding 48 amperes and protected at not more than 60 amperes.

The ampacity of the branch-circuit conductors, and the rating or setting of overcurrent protective devices, shall not be less than 125 percent of the total load of the nameplate rating.

E. Fountains

680-50. General. The provisions of Part E shall apply to all fountains as defined in Section 680-4. Fountains which have water common to a pool shall comply with the pool requirements of this article.

Exception: Self-contained, portable fountains no larger than 5 feet (1.52 m) in any dimension are not covered by Part E.

680-51. Lighting Fixtures, Submersible Pumps, and Other Submersible Equipment.

(a) Ground-Fault Circuit-Interrupter. A ground-fault circuit-interrupter shall be installed in the branch circuit supplying fountain equipment.

Exception: Ground-fault circuit-interrupters shall not be required for equipment operating at 15 volts or less and supplied by a transformer complying with Section 680-5(a).

(b) Operating Voltage. All lighting fixtures shall be installed for operation at 150 volts or less between conductors. Submersible pumps and other submersible equipment shall operate at 300 volts or less between conductors.

(c) Lighting Fixture Lenses. Lighting fixtures shall be installed with the top of the fixture lens below the normal water level of the fountain unless approved for above water locations. A lighting fixture facing upward shall have the lens adequately guarded to prevent contact by any person.

(d) Overheating Protection. Electric equipment which depends on submersion for safe operation shall be protected against overheating by a low-water cut-off or other approved means when not submerged.

(e) Wiring. Equipment shall be equipped with provisions for threaded conduit entries or be provided with a suitable flexible cord. The maximum length of exposed cord in the fountain shall be limited to 10 feet (3.05 m). Cords extending beyond the fountain perimeter shall be enclosed in approved wiring enclosures. Metal parts of equipment in contact with water shall be of brass or other approved corrosion-resistant metal.

(f) Servicing. All equipment shall be removable from the water for relamping or normal maintenance. Fixtures shall not be permanently imbedded into the fountain structure so that the water level must be reduced or the fountain drained for relamping, maintenance, or inspection.

(g) Stability. Equipment shall be inherently stable or be securely fastened in place.

680-52. Junction Boxes and Other Enclosures.

(a) General. Junction boxes and other enclosures used for other than underwater installation shall comply with Section 680-21(a) (1), (2), (3); and (b), (c), and (d).

(b) Underwater Junction Boxes and Other Underwater Enclosures. Junction boxes and other underwater enclosures shall be submersible and (1) be equipped with provisions for threaded conduit entries or compression glands or seals for cord entry; (2) be of copper, brass, or other approved corrosion-resistant material; (3) be filled with an approved potting compound to prevent the entry of moisture; and (4) be firmly attached to the supports or directly to the fountain surface and bonded as required. When the junction box is supported only by the conduit the conduit shall be of copper, brass, or other approved corrosion-resistant metal. When the box is fed by nonmetallic conduit, it shall have additional supports and fasteners of copper, brass, or other approved corrosion-resistant material.

(FPN): See Section 370-13 for support of enclosures.

680-53. Bonding.   All metal piping systems associated with the fountain shall be bonded to the equipment grounding conductor of the branch circuit supplying the fountain.

(FPN): See Section 250-95 for sizing of these conductors.

680-54. Grounding.   The following equipment shall be grounded: (1) all electric equipment located within the fountain or within 5 feet (1.52 m) of the inside wall of the fountain; (2) all electric equipment associated with the recirculating system of the fountain; (3) panelboards that are not part of the service equipment and that supply any electric equipment associated with the fountain.

680-55. Methods of Grounding.

(a) Applied Provisions.   The provisions of Section 680-25 shall apply excluding paragraph (e).

(b) Supplied by a Flexible Cord.   Electric equipment that is supplied by a flexible cord shall have all exposed noncurrent-carrying metal parts grounded by an insulated copper equipment grounding conductor that is an integral part of this cord. This grounding conductor shall be connected to a grounding terminal in the supply junction box, transformer enclosure, or other enclosure.

680-56. Cord- and Plug-Connected Equipment.

(a) Ground-Fault Circuit-Interrupter.   All electric equipment, including power supply cords, shall be protected by ground-fault circuit-interrupters.

(b) Cord Type.   Flexible cord immersed in or exposed to water shall be a water-resistant Type SO or ST.

(c) Sealing.   The end of the flexible cord jacket and the flexible cord conductor termination within equipment shall be covered with or encapsulated in a suitable potting compound to prevent the entry of water into the equipment through the cord or its conductors. In addition, the ground connection within equipment shall be similarly treated to protect such connections from the deteriorating effect of water which may enter into the equipment.

(d) Terminations.   Connections with flexible cord shall be permanent, except that grounding-type attachment plugs and receptacles shall be permitted to facilitate removal or disconnection for maintenance, repair, or storage of fixed or stationary equipment not located in any water-containing part of a fountain.

F. Therapeutic Pools and Tubs in Health Care Facilities

Portable therapeutic appliances are covered by the provisions of Article 422. They are required to be protected by a GFCI unless protected by an approved system of double insulation.

Permanently installed therapeutic pools that cannot be readily disassembled are required to comply with Parts A and B of Article 680. The limitations regarding lighting fixtures over and around a swimming pool do not apply to therapeutic pools and tubs, if the lighting fixtures are totally enclosed.

Therapeutic tubs not easily moved are subject to basically the same requirements.

Bonding and grounding requirements are similar to those in Parts A and B of Article 680, except that metal-to-metal mounting on a common frame or base is permitted. Where equipment is connected by a flexible cord, the equipment grounding conductor is required to be connected to a fixed metal part of the assembly.

680-60. General. The provisions of Part F include therapeutic pools and tubs in health care facilities. See Section 517-2 for definition of health care facilities. Portable therapeutic appliances shall comply with Article 422.

680-61. Permanently Installed Therapeutic Pools. Therapeutic pools which are constructed in the ground, on the ground, or in a building in such a manner that the pool cannot be readily disassembled shall comply with Parts A and B of this article.

Exception: The limitations of Section 680-6(b)(1) and (2) shall not apply where all lighting fixtures are of the totally enclosed type.

680-62. Therapeutic Tubs (Hydrotherapeutic Tanks). Therapeutic tubs, used for the submersion and treatment of patients, which are not easily moved from one place to another in normal use or which are fastened or otherwise secured at a specific location including associated piping systems shall conform to this part.

(a) Ground-Fault Circuit-Interrupter. A ground-fault circuit-interrupter shall protect all therapeutic equipment.

Exception: Portable therapeutic appliances shall comply with Section 250-45.

(b) Bonding. The following parts shall be bonded together:

(1) All metal fittings within or attached to the tub structure.

(2) Metal parts of electric equipment associated with the tub water circulating system, including pump motors.

(3) Metal conduit and metal piping that are within 5 feet (1.52 m) of the inside walls of the tub and not separated from the tub by a permanent barrier.

(4) All metal surfaces that are within 5 feet (1.52 m) of the inside walls of the tub and not separated from the tub area by a permanent barrier.

(5) Electrical devices and controls not associated with the therapeutic tubs shall be located a minimum of 5 feet (1.52 m) away from such units or be bonded to the therapeutic tub system.

(c) Methods of Bonding. All metal parts associated with the tub shall be bonded by any of the following methods: the interconnection of threaded metal piping and fittings; metal-to-metal mounting on a common frame or base; connections by suitable metal clamps; or by the provisions of a solid copper bonding jumper, insulated, covered, or bare, not smaller than No. 8 AWG.

(d) Grounding. The following equipment shall be grounded:

(1) All electric equipment located within 5 feet (1.52 m) of the inside wall of the tub.

(2) All electric equipment associated with the circulating system of the tub.

(e) Methods of Grounding.

(1) All electric equipment shall be grounded in accordance with Article 250 and connected by wiring methods of Chapter 3.

(2) Where equipment is connected with a flexible cord, the equipment grounding conductor shall be connected to a fixed metal part of the assembly.

(f) Receptacles. All receptacles within 5 feet (1.52 m) of a therapeutic tub shall be protected by a ground-fault circuit-interrupter.

680-63. Lighting Fixtures. All lighting fixtures used in therapeutic pool areas shall be of the totally enclosed type.

G. Hydromassage Bathtubs

Hydromassage bathtubs (see definition in Section 680-4) are required to be protected by a GFCI. Except for this protection, they are treated the same as ordinary bathtubs. See Section 410-4(d) for special requirements relating to cord-connected fixtures, hanging fixtures, and pendants near bathtubs. Also see Sections 210-8(a)(1) and 210-8(b) for requirements for GFCI protection of bathroom receptacles.

680-70. Protection. Hydromassage bathtubs and their associated electric components shall be supplied by a circuit protected by a ground-fault circuit-interrupter.

680-71. Other Electric Equipment. Lighting fixtures, switches, receptacles, and other electric equipment located in the same room, and not directly associated with a hydromassage bathtub, shall be installed in accordance with the requirements of Chapters 1 through 4 in this Code covering the installation of that equipment in bathrooms.

ARTICLE 685 — INTEGRATED ELECTRICAL SYSTEMS

Contents

A. General

685-1. Scope. This article covers integrated electrical systems, other than unit equipment, in which orderly shutdown is necessary to ensure safe operation. An integrated electrical system as used in this article is a unitized segment of an industrial wiring system where all of the following conditions are met: (1) an orderly shutdown is required to minimize personnel hazard and equipment damage; (2) the conditions of maintenance and supervision assure that qualified persons will service the system; and (3) effective safeguards, acceptable to the authority having jurisdiction, are established and maintained.

Integrated electrical systems are commonly used in large industrial establishments where the electrical system and equipment are designed, installed, and operated by engineering workforces. The control equipment, including overcurrent devices, are located to be accessible to qualified personnel, but may not be readily accessible as defined in Article 100.

685-2. Application of Other Articles. In other articles applying to particular cases of installation of conductors and equipment, there are orderly shutdown requirements that are in addition to those of this article or are modifications of them:

	Section
More than One Building or Other Structure	230-84(a), Exception No. 2
Ground-Fault Protection of Equipment	230-95(a), Exception No. 1
Protection of Conductors	240-3, Exception No. 8
Electrical System Coordination	240-12
Grounding ac Systems of 50 to 1000 Volts	250-5(b), Exception No. 3
Orderly Shutdown	430-44
Disconnection	430-74, Exceptions No. 1 and 2
Disconnecting Means in Sight from Controller	430-102, Exception No. 2
Energy from More than One Source	430-113, Exceptions No. 1 and 2
Point of Connection	705-12, Exception No. 1

B. Orderly Shutdown

685-10. Location of Overcurrent Devices In or On Premises. Location of overcurrent devices which are critical to integrated electrical systems shall be permitted to be accessible with mounting heights allowed to assure security from operation by nonqualified personnel.

685-12. Direct-Current System Grounding. Two-wire direct-current circuits shall be permitted to be ungrounded.

685-14. Ungrounded Control Circuits. Where operational continuity is required, control circuits of 150 volts or less from separately derived systems shall be permitted to be ungrounded.

ARTICLE 690 — SOLAR PHOTOVOLTAIC SYSTEMS

Contents

(a) Circuits and Equipment.
(b) Power Transformers.
(c) Photovoltaic Source Circuits.

C. Disconnecting Means
690-13. All Conductors.
690-14. Additional Provisions.
690-15. Disconnection of Photovoltaic Equipment.
690-16. Fuses.
690-17. Switch or Circuit Breaker.
690-18. Disablement of an Array.

D. Wiring Methods
690-31. Methods Permitted.
(a) Wiring Systems.
(b) Single Conductor Cable.
690-32. Component Interconnections.
690-33. Connectors.
(a) Configuration.
(b) Guarding.
(c) Type.
(d) Grounding Member.
(e) Interruption of Circuit.
690-34. Access to Boxes.

E. Grounding
690-41. System Grounding.

690-42. Point of System Grounding Connection.
690-43. Size of Equipment Grounding Conductor.
690-44. Common Grounding Electrode.

F. Marking
690-51. Modules.
690-52. Photovoltaic Power Source.

G. Connection to Other Sources
690-61. Loss of System Voltage.
690-62. Ampacity of Neutral Conductor.
690-63. Unbalanced Interconnections.
(a) Single-Phase.
(b) Three-Phase.
690-64. Point of Connection.
(a) Supply Side.
(b) Load Side.

H. Storage Batteries
690-71. Installation.
(a) General.
(b) Dwellings.
690-72. State of Charge.
690-73. Grounding.

A. General

690-1. Scope. The provisions of this article apply to solar photovoltaic electrical energy systems including the array circuit(s), power conditioning unit(s) and controller(s) for such systems. Solar photovoltaic systems covered by this article may be interactive with other electric power production sources or stand alone, with or without electrical energy storage such as batteries. These systems may have alternating- or direct-current output for utilization.

In accordance with Section 705-3, Article 705 is also applicable to a solar photovoltaic system if it is interconnected with another power production source(s), which may be an electric utility, or an on-site generating system, such as a wind turbine, a hydroelectric generator, or the like.

A typical utility-interactive solar photovoltaic system at a dwelling is illustrated in Figure 690-1. Other circuit arrangements are permissible.

690-2. Definitions.

Array: A mechanically integrated assembly of modules or panels with a support structure and foundation, tracking, thermal control, and other components, as required, to form a direct-current power-producing unit.

Blocking Diode: A diode used to block reverse flow of current into a photovoltaic source circuit.

Interactive System: A solar photovoltaic system that operates in parallel with and may be designed to deliver power to another electric power production source connected to the same load. For the purpose of this definition, an energy storage subsystem of a solar photovoltaic system, such as a battery, is not another electric power production source.

%⧄—Overcurrent device and disconnecting means
F—Filter assembly
M—Meter
PCU—Power conditioning unit
SW—A visibly verifiable disconnecting device that may be required by the utility company. This device may be required to be capable of being locked in the open position. Reference: FPN under Section 705-22
TR—Transformer

Figure 690-1. Typical utility-interactive solar photovoltaic system at a dwelling. *Battery storage is more likely to be used with a stand-alone system.

Module: The smallest complete, environmentally protected assembly of solar cells, optics and other components, exclusive of tracking, designed to generate direct-current power under sunlight.

Panel: A collection of modules mechanically fastened together, wired, and designed to provide a field-installable unit.

Photovoltaic Output Circuit: Circuit conductors between the photovoltaic source circuit(s) and the power conditioning unit or direct-current utilization equipment. See Diagram 690-1.

Photovoltaic Power Source: An array or aggregate of arrays which generates direct-current power at system voltage and current.

Photovoltaic Source Circuit: Conductors between modules and from modules to the common connection point(s) of the direct-current system. See Diagram 690-1.

Power Conditioning Unit: Equipment which is used to change voltage level or waveform or both of electrical energy. Commonly a power conditioning unit is an inverter which changes a direct-current input to an alternating-current output.

Power Conditioning Unit Output Circuit: Conductors between the power conditioning unit and the connection to the service equipment or another electric power production source such as a utility. See Diagram 690-1.

Solar Cell: The basic photovoltaic device which generates electricity when exposed to light.

Solar Photovoltaic System: The total components and subsystems which in combination convert solar energy into electrical energy suitable for connection to a utilization load.

Stand-Alone System: A solar photovoltaic system that supplies power independently but which may receive control power from another electric power production source.

Diagram 690-1 Solar Photovoltaic Circuits

690-3. Other Articles. Wherever the requirements of other articles of this Code and Article 690 differ, the requirements of Article 690 shall apply.

690-4. Installation.

(a) Photovoltaic System. A solar photovoltaic system shall be permitted to supply a building or other structure in addition to any service(s) of another electricity supply system(s).

(b) Conductors of Different Systems. Photovoltaic source circuits and photovoltaic output circuits shall not be contained in the same raceway, cable tray, cable, outlet box, junction box or similar fitting as feeders or branch circuits of other systems.

Exception: Where the conductors of the different systems are separated by a partition or are connected together.

Array

Panel

Module

Cell

Figure 690-2. Array components.

As an example, subsection (b) requires the conductors of a yard light located near a roof-mounted photovoltaic (PV) array to be in a separate raceway or cable from the conductors of PV source circuits or PV output circuit.

(c) Module Connection Arrangement. The connections to a module or panel shall be so arranged that removal of a module or panel from a photovoltaic source circuit does not interrupt a grounded conductor to another photovoltaic source circuit.

In general, subsection (c) requires installation of a jumper between a module terminal or lead and the connection point to the grounded PV source circuit conductor so that a module can be removed without interrupting the grounded conductor to other PV source circuits. If interrupted, such conductors, although identified as grounded conductors, would be at the system potential with respect to ground, and a shock hazard could result.

B. Circuit Requirements

690-7. Maximum Voltage.

(a) Voltage Rating. In a photovoltaic power source and its direct-current circuits, the voltage considered shall be the rated open-circuit voltage.

A photovoltaic source is not a constant voltage source, and the difference between the rated open-circuit voltage and operating voltage is significant. Consequently, there is a need to use the rated open-circuit voltage to select circuit components with proper voltage ratings.

(b) Direct-Current Utilization Circuits. The voltage of direct-current utilization circuits shall conform with Section 210-6.

This covers installations where the photovoltaic output is connected to direct-current utilization circuits.

(c) Photovoltaic Source and Output Circuits. Photovoltaic source circuits and photovoltaic output circuits which do not include lampholders, fixtures or standard receptacles shall be permitted up to 600 volts.

Photovoltaic direct-current circuits in buildings are permanently connected using *Code*-recognized wiring systems, and requirements for protecting unqualified persons from contact with these circuits are included in (b) and (d) of this article. Unqualified persons are not likely to service equipment in these circuits due to their complexity. There is a significant difference between the rated open-circuit voltage and the operating voltage in photovoltaic direct-current circuits. In order for the photovoltaic system to perform its intended function, rated direct-current open-circuit voltages of up to 600 volts may be present.

(d) Circuits Over 150 Volts to Ground. In one- and two-family dwellings, live parts in photovoltaic source circuits and photovoltaic output circuits over 150 volts to ground shall not be accessible while energized to other than qualified persons.

(FPN): See Section 110-17 for guarding of live parts, and Section 210-6 for voltage to ground and between conductors.

Where direct-current circuitry over 150 volts to ground is present in one- and two-family dwellings, additional protection for unqualified persons is needed. This may take the form of a locked cabinet or an enclosure that requires tools to open and in which entry is necessary only for servicing purposes.

690-8. Circuit Sizing and Current.

(a) Ampacity and Overcurrent Devices. The ampacity of the conductors and the rating or setting of overcurrent devices in a circuit of a solar photovoltaic system shall not be less than 125 percent of the current computed in accordance with (b) below. The rating or setting of overcurrent devices shall be permitted in accordance with Section 240-3, Exception No. 1.

Exception: Circuits containing an assembly together with its overcurrent device(s) that is listed for continuous operation at 100 percent of its rating.

Sizing of the circuits for 125 percent of the rating is necessary because of continuous (3-hour or more) loads.

The exception permits use at the full rating of assemblies, such as panelboards, incorporating overcurrent devices which are listed for continuous operation at 100 percent of the rating.

(b) Computation of Circuit Current. The current for the individual type of circuit shall be computed as follows:

(1) Photovoltaic Source Circuits. The sum of parallel module operating current ratings.

(2) Photovoltaic Output Circuit. The photovoltaic power source current rating.

(3) Power Conditioning Unit Output Circuit. The power conditioning unit output current rating.

Exception: The current rating of a circuit without an overcurrent device, as permitted by the Exception to Section 690-9(a), shall be the short-circuit current, and it shall not exceed the ampacity of the circuit conductors.

Because photovoltaic arrays have a limited capacity, the power conditioning unit supplies to the load (or the utility system) whatever power is available from the arrays. Due to this characteristic, the sizing of photovoltaic circuits has to be based on the source rather than the load.

The exception specifies the use of the short-circuit current rating rather than the operating current rating to determine the current rating of a PV source circuit, PV output circuit, or the power conditioning unit output circuit, if these circuits do not incorporate an overcurrent device. The short-circuit current rating is then used to determine the needed ampacity for the conductors in these circuits.

690-9. Overcurrent Protection.

(a) Circuits and Equipment. Photovoltaic source circuit, photovoltaic output circuit, power conditioning unit output circuit, and storage battery circuit conductors and equipment shall be protected in accordance with the requirements of Article 240. Circuits connected to more than one electrical source shall have overcurrent devices so located as to provide overcurrent protection from all sources.

Exception: A conductor in a photovoltaic source circuit, photovoltaic output circuit, or power conditioning unit output circuit having an ampacity not less than the maximum available current under short-circuit or ground-fault conditions with the condition of a shorted blocking diode shall be permitted without an overcurrent device.

(FPN): Possible backfeed of current from any source of supply, including a supply through a power conditioning unit into the photovoltaic output circuit and photovoltaic source circuits, must be considered in determining whether adequate overcurrent protection from all sources is provided for conductors and modules.

In the circuit illustrated in Figure 690-3, the PV source circuit overcurrent devices are required to be rated so that the source circuit conductors are protected in accordance with Article 240, and the overcurrent device ratings do not exceed the maximum overcurrent device rating marked on the modules. Possible backfeed from the other PV source circuits, from other supply sources through the power conditioning unit, and from storage battery circuits, if any, has to be considered.

Figure 690-3. Application of blocking diodes and source circuit overcurrent devices.

Because the diodes may lose their blocking ability (due to over-temperature conditions or internal breakdown), overcurrent protection has to be considered with a condition of shorted blocking diodes, if used in the circuit.

If the rated short-circuit current of the PV power source does not exceed the ampacity of the PV output circuit conductors, overcurrent protective devices at the connections to the PV power source are not necessary. At the power conditioning unit end of the PV output circuit, the need for overcurrent protection has to be considered with respect to the maximum backfeed fault current available from the power conditioning unit.

(b) Power Transformers. Overcurrent protection for a transformer with a source(s) on each side shall be provided in accordance with Section 450-3 by considering first one side of the transformer, then the other side of the transformer as the primary.

Exception: A power transformer with a current rating on the side connected toward the photovoltaic power source not less than the short-circuit output current rating of the power conditioning unit shall be permitted without overcurrent protection from that source.

(c) Photovoltaic Source Circuits. Branch-circuit or supplementary type overcurrent devices shall be permitted to provide overcurrent protection in photovoltaic source circuits. The overcurrent devices shall be accessible, but shall not be required to be readily accessible.

By considering the overcurrent protection of photovoltaic source circuits as supplementary overcurrent protection, use of overcurrent device types and ratings, other than those suitable for branch-circuit protection, can be permitted. Use of such devices permits module protection closer to the specified ratings. It is anticipated that replacement or resetting of overcurrent devices in photovoltaic source circuits will be accomplished by qualified service personnel. Consequently, ready access (such as by the user) need not be provided.

C. Disconnecting Means

690-13. All Conductors. Means shall be provided to disconnect all current-carrying conductors of a photovoltaic power source from all other conductors in a building or other structure.

690-14. Additional Provisions. The provisions of Article 230, Part F shall apply to the photovoltaic power source disconnecting means.

Exception No. 1: The disconnecting means shall not be required to be suitable as service equipment and shall be rated in accordance with Section 690-17.

Exception No. 1 permits use of disconnecting means rated in accordance with Section 690-17, but which need not be marked as suitable for use as service equipment.

Exception No. 2: Equipment such as photovoltaic source circuit isolating switches, overcurrent devices, and blocking diodes shall be permitted on the photovoltaic power source side of the photovoltaic power source disconnecting means.

In general, there is a need to disconnect equipment from sources of supply for servicing, etc. However, in a solar photovoltaic system, some equipment, as indicated in Exception No. 2, is permitted to be located on the photovoltaic power source side of the disconnecting means. See Figure 690-4. In order to service the exempted equipment, the array or portions of the array may have to be disabled as explained under Section 690-18.

690-15. Disconnection of Photovoltaic Equipment. Means shall be provided to disconnect equipment, such as a power conditioning unit, filter assembly and the like from all ungrounded conductors of all sources. If the equipment is energized (live) from more than one source, the disconnecting means shall be grouped and identified.

690-16. Fuses. Disconnecting means shall be provided to disconnect a fuse from all sources of supply if the fuse is energized from both directions and is accessible to other than qualified

A—Disconnecting means required by Section 690-13
B—Equipment permitted to be on the photovoltaic power source
side of the photovoltaic power source disconnecting means,
per Section 690-14, Exception 2

Figure 690-4. Equipment permitted on the photovoltaic power source side of the photovoltaic power source disconnecting means.

persons. Such a fuse in a photovoltaic source circuit shall be capable of being disconnected independently of fuses in other photovoltaic source circuits.

Switches, pullouts, or similar devices having suitable ratings may serve as means to disconnect fuses from all sources of supply.

690-17. Switch or Circuit Breaker. The disconnecting means for ungrounded conductors shall consist of a manually operable switch(es) or circuit breaker(s): (1) located where readily accessible, (2) externally operable without exposing the operator to contact with live parts, (3) plainly indicating whether in the open or closed position, and (4) having ratings not less than the load to be carried. Where disconnect equipment may be energized from both sides, the disconnect equipment shall be provided with a marking to indicate that all contacts of the disconnect equipment may be live.

Exception: A disconnecting means located on the direct-current side shall be permitted to have an interrupting rating less than the current-carrying rating when the system is designed so that the direct-current switch cannot be opened under load.

690-18. Disablement of an Array. Means shall be provided to disable an array or portions of an array.

(FPN): Photovoltaic modules are energized while exposed to light. Installation, replacement, or servicing of array components while a module(s) is irradiated may expose persons to electric shock.

There are a number of methods which may accomplish disablement of an array or portions of an array for installation, servicing, or other functions during which persons may come in contact with energized parts.

One method is to cover all or portions of an array with an opaque material. Care has to be taken so that all of the area to be covered is shielded from light.

Another method is to have provisions whereby the array may be segmented to nonhazardous portions. This may be accomplished by switches or connectors. Also see Section 690-33.

Short-circuiting all or portions of an array by means of switches or plug-in connectors in conjunction with by-pass diodes may also provide the necessary disablement. (By-pass diodes are incorporated in PV power sources for performance purposes.)

D. Wiring Methods

690-31. Methods Permitted.

(a) Wiring Systems. All raceway and cable wiring methods included in this Code and other wiring systems and fittings specifically intended and identified for use on photovoltaic arrays shall be permitted. Where wiring devices with integral enclosures are used, sufficient length of cable shall be provided to facilitate replacement.

(b) Single Conductor Cable. Type UF single conductor cable shall be permitted in photovoltaic source circuits where installed in the same manner as a Type UF multiconductor cable in accordance with Article 339. Where exposed to direct rays of the sun, cable identified as sunlight-resistant shall be used.

Some photovoltaic modules are designed for a direct series connection by having terminations at both ends. To accommodate such a direct series connection without the waste of one or more conductors in a multi-conductor cable, use of a single-conductor, Type UF cable, is permitted in photovoltaic source circuits. The reference to installation as a multiconductor cable permits the single-conductor cable to be routed separately, not necessarily with the other conductors of a circuit. Since photovoltaic source circuits are direct-current circuits, increased impedance due to separated circuit conductors is not a problem.

690-32. Component Interconnections. Fittings and connectors which are intended to be concealed at the time of on-site assembly, when listed for such use, shall be permitted for on-site interconnection of modules or other array components. Such fittings and connectors shall be equal to the wiring method employed in insulation, temperature rise and fault-current withstand, and shall be capable of resisting the effects of the environment in which they are used.

690-33. Connectors. The connectors permitted by Section 690-32 shall comply with (a) through (e) below.

(a) Configuration. The connectors shall be polarized and shall have a configuration that is noninterchangeable with receptacles in other electrical systems on the premises.

(b) Guarding. The connectors shall be constructed and installed so as to guard against inadvertent contact with live parts by persons.

(c) Type. The connectors shall be of the latching or locking type.

(d) Grounding Member. The grounding member shall be the first to make and the last to break contact with the mating connector.

(e) Interruption of Circuit. The connectors shall be capable of interrupting the circuit current without hazard to the operator.

690-34. Access to Boxes. Junction, pull and outlet boxes located behind modules or panels shall be installed so that the wiring contained in them can be rendered accessible directly or by displacement of a module(s) or panel(s) secured by removable fasteners and connected by a flexible wiring system.

E. Grounding

690-41. System Grounding. For a photovoltaic power source, one conductor of a 2-wire system rated over 50 volts and a neutral conductor of a 3-wire system shall be solidly grounded.

Exception: Other methods which accomplish equivalent system protection and which utilize equipment listed and identified for the use shall be permitted.

(FPN): See the first Fine Print Note under Section 250-1.

With respect to the exception, other methods, using available equipment, may be used to achieve objectives contained in the first fine print note to Section 250-1, thereby providing protection equivalent to solid grounding for the photovoltaic power source circuits.

690-42. Point of System Grounding Connection. The direct-current circuit grounding connection shall be made at any single point on the photovoltaic output circuit.

(FPN): Locating the grounding connection point as close as practicable to the photovoltaic source will better protect the system from voltage surges due to lightning.

If other-than-solid grounding is utilized as permitted by Section 690-41, Exception, the connections should be made in accordance with the markings on the equipment or its installation instructions.

690-43. Size of Equipment Grounding Conductor. The equipment grounding conductor shall be no smaller than the required size of the circuit conductors in systems: (1) where the available photovoltaic power source short-circuit current is less than twice the current rating of the overcurrent device, or (2) where overcurrent devices are not employed as permitted in the Exception to Section 690-9(a). In other systems, the equipment grounding conductor shall be sized in accordance with Section 250-95.

690-44. Common Grounding Electrode. Exposed noncurrent-carrying metal parts of equipment and conductor enclosures of a photovoltaic system shall be grounded to the grounding electrode that is used to ground the direct-current system. Two or more electrodes that are effectively bonded together shall be considered as a single electrode in this sense.

This requirement ensures that direct-current circuits from the photovoltaic system do not enter enclosures that are grounded only by a grounding electrode of an alternating-current system without the grounding electrodes of both systems being effectively bonded together. For example, if the electrodes are not bonded together, it is possible that a small current flow through the alternating-current electrode, through the earth and back through the direct-current electrode, could result in raising the voltage on the array frame almost to line voltage.

F. Marking

690-51. Modules. Modules shall be marked with identification of terminals or leads as to polarity, maximum overcurrent device rating for module protection and with rated: (1) open-circuit voltage, (2) operating voltage, (3) maximum permissible system voltage, (4) operating current, (5) short-circuit current, and (6) maximum power.

690-52. Photovoltaic Power Source. A marking, specifying the photovoltaic power source rated: (1) operating current, (2) operating voltage, (3) open-circuit voltage, and (4) short-circuit current, shall be provided at an accessible location at the disconnecting means for the photovoltaic power source.

(FPN): Reflecting systems used for irradiance enhancement may result in increased levels of output current and power.

After installation of photovoltaic arrays, it may be difficult to determine the system's rated voltage and current. These ratings, along with the open-circuit voltage and short-circuit current, are necessary to size the remainder of the system components as specified elsewhere in Article 690.

Generally, this marking is required to be provided by the installer. The rated values for the PV power source can be calculated by adding voltage ratings of series-connected modules and adding current ratings of parallel-connected modules or PV source circuits.

With respect to the fine print note, deliberate increase in the level or irradiance by reflectors or the like can cause the power source to operate at levels above those recommended by the manufacturer. See Section 110-3.

G. Connection to Other Sources

690-61. Loss of System Voltage. The power output from a power conditioning unit in a solar photovoltaic system that is interactive with another electric system(s) shall be automatically disconnected from all ungrounded conductors in such other electric system(s) upon loss of voltage in that electric system(s) and shall not reconnect to that electric system(s) until its voltage is restored.

(FPN): For other interconnected electric power production sources, see Article 705.

An interactive system shall be permitted to operate as a stand-alone system to supply premises wiring.

This requirement prevents energizing of otherwise deenergized system conductors or output conductors of other on-site sources and is intended to prevent electric shock. This feature is normally provided as part of the power conditioning unit.

690-62. Ampacity of Neutral Conductor. If a single-phase, 2-wire power conditioning unit output is connected to the neutral and one ungrounded conductor (only) of a 3-wire system or of a 3-phase, 4-wire wye-connected system, the maximum load connected between the neutral and any one ungrounded conductor plus the power conditioning unit output rating shall not exceed the ampacity of the neutral conductor.

690-63. Unbalanced Interconnections.

(a) Single-Phase. The output of a single-phase power conditioning unit shall not be connected to a 3-phase, 3- or 4-wire electrical service derived directly from a delta-connected transformer.

(b) Three-Phase. A 3-phase power conditioning unit shall be automatically disconnected from all ungrounded conductors of the interconnected system when one of the phases opens in either source.

Exception for (a) and (b): Where the interconnected system is designed so that significant unbalanced voltages will not result.

With respect to connections to other sources, the point of interconnection has not been specified. Section 230-82, Exception No. 6 permits connection of interconnected electric power production sources to the supply side of service disconnecting means of a premises. This could be a point of interconnection.

If the interconnections are made on the load side of the service disconnecting means, such as at a distribution panelboard, possible overloading of panelboard buses, suitability of equipment such as circuit breakers for backfeeding, and a need for cautionary markings due to the presence of two sources need to be considered.

690-64. Point of Connection. The output of a power production source shall be connected as specified in (a) or (b) below.

Also see Section 705-12 for additional limitations on the location of the point of interconnection. If the aggregate of all non-utility sources of electricity on the premises does not exceed 100 KW, the interconnection point has to be at the premises service disconnecting means. Other conditions also apply to interconnections remote from the premises service disconnecting means.

(FPN): For the purposes of this section a power production source is considered to be the output of a power conditioning unit when connected to an alternating current electric source, the photovoltaic output circuit when interactive with a direct current electric source.

(a) Supply Side. To the supply side of the service disconnecting means as permitted in Section 230-82, Exception No. 6.

(b) Load Side. To the load side of the service disconnecting means of the other source(s), if all of the following conditions are met:

(1) Each source interconnection shall be made at a dedicated circuit breaker or fusible disconnecting means.

(2) The sum of the ampere ratings of overcurrent devices in circuits supplying power to a busbar or conductor shall not exceed the rating of the busbar or conductor.

Exception: For a dwelling unit the sum of the ampere ratings of the overcurrent devices shall not exceed 120 percent of the rating of the busbar or conductor.

(3) The interconnection point shall be on the line side of all ground-fault protection equipment.

Exception: Connection shall be permitted to be made to the load side of ground-fault protection provided that there is ground-fault protection for equipment from all ground-fault current sources.

(4) Equipment containing overcurrent devices in circuits supplying power to a busbar or conductor shall be marked to indicate the presence of all sources.

Exception: Equipment with power supplied from a single point of connection.

(5) Equipment such as circuit breakers, if back-fed, shall be suitable for such operation.

H. Storage Batteries

690-71. Installation.

(a) General. Storage batteries in a solar photovoltaic system shall be installed in accordance with the provisions of Article 480.

Exception: As provided in Section 690-73.

(b) Dwellings.

(1) Storage batteries for dwellings shall have the cells connected so as to operate at less than 50 volts.

Exception: Where live parts are not accessible during routine battery maintenance, a battery system voltage in accordance with Section 690-7 shall be permitted.

(2) Live parts of battery systems for dwellings shall be insulated to guard against accidental contact, regardless of voltage.

(FPN): Batteries in solar photovoltaic systems are subject to extensive charge-discharge cycles and typically require frequent maintenance, such as checking electrolyte and cleaning connections.

690-72. State of Charge. Equipment shall be provided to control the state of charge of the battery. All adjusting means for control of the state of charge shall be accessible only to qualified persons.

Exception: Where the design of the photovoltaic power source is matched to the voltage rating and charge current requirements for the interconnected battery cells.

690-73. Grounding. The interconnected battery cells shall be considered grounded where the photovoltaic power source is installed in accordance with Section 690-41, Exception.

7 Special Conditions

ARTICLE 700 — EMERGENCY SYSTEMS

Contents

A. General

700-1. Scope. The provisions of this article apply to the electrical safety of the design, installation, operation, and maintenance of emergency systems consisting of circuits and equipment intended to supply, distribute, and control electricity for illumination and/or power to required facilities when the normal electrical supply or system is interrupted.

The provisions of this article apply to the installation of emergency systems where such systems are legally required by municipal, state, federal, or other codes or a governmental agency having jurisdiction.

983

ARTICLE 700—EMERGENCY SYSTEMS

This article of the *Code* does not determine whether emergency systems are required or the location of emergency or exit lights. This function is covered in NFPA 101-1985, *Life Safety Code*.

Emergency systems are those systems legally required and classed as emergency by municipal, state, federal, or other codes, or by any governmental agency having jurisdiction. These systems are intended to automatically supply illumination and/or power to designated areas and equipment in the event of failure of the normal supply or in the event of accident to elements of a system intended to supply, distribute, and control power and illumination essential for safety to human life.

(FPN): For further information regarding wiring and installation of emergency systems in health care facilities, see Article 517.

(FPN): For further information regarding performance and maintenance of emergency systems in health care facilities, see Health Care Facilities, NFPA 99-1984 (ANSI).

(FPN): Emergency systems are generally installed in places of assembly where artificial illumination is required for safe exiting and for panic control in buildings subject to occupancy by large numbers of persons, such as hotels, theaters, sports arenas, health care facilities, and similar institutions. Emergency systems may also provide power for such functions as ventilation when essential to maintain life, fire detection and alarm systems, elevators, fire pumps, public safety communication systems, industrial processes where current interruption would produce serious life safety or health hazards, and similar functions.

(FPN): For specification of locations where emergency lighting is considered essential to life safety, see Life Safety Code, NFPA 101-1985 (ANSI).

(FPN): For further information regarding performance of emergency and standby power systems, see Emergency and Standby Power Systems, NFPA 110-1985 (ANSI).

Emergency systems are designed to maintain a specific degree of illumination or provide power for essential equipment, such as fire pumps, operating room and life support equipment in hospitals, etc., in the event of failure of the normal power supply.

Where authorities determine that emergency lighting, including the proper placement of exit signs, is required for safe egress from various classes of buildings, or parts of buildings, sufficient illumination is required to be provided for corridors, passageways, stairways, lobbies, etc.

700-2. Application of Other Articles. Except as modified by this article, all applicable articles of this Code shall apply.

700-3. Equipment Approval. All equipment shall be approved for use on emergency systems.

700-4. Tests and Maintenance.

(a) Conduct or Witness Test. The authority having jurisdiction shall conduct or witness a test on the complete system upon installation and periodically afterward.

(b) Tested Periodically. Systems shall be tested periodically on a schedule acceptable to the authority having jurisdiction to assure their maintenance in proper operating condition.

(c) Battery Systems Maintenance. Where battery systems or unit equipments are involved, including batteries used for starting or ignition in auxiliary engines, the authority having jurisdiction shall require periodic maintenance.

(d) Written Record. A written record shall be kept of such tests and maintenance.

(e) Testing Under Load. Means for testing all emergency lighting and power systems during maximum anticipated load conditions shall be provided.

700-5. Capacity.

(a) **Capacity and Rating.** An emergency system shall have adequate capacity and rating for all loads to be operated simultaneously.

It is essential that the emergency system be designed with adequate capacity and rating to carry safely the entire load connected to the emergency system at one time. The emergency system is required to be capable of restarting emergency loads, such as motors, that may have stopped.

(b) **Selective Load Pickup, Load Shedding, and Peak Load Shaving.** The alternate power source shall be permitted to supply emergency, legally required standby, and optional standby system loads where automatic selective load pickup and load shedding is provided as needed to assure adequate power to (1) the emergency circuits; (2) the legally required standby circuits; and (3) the optional standby circuits, in that order of priority. The alternate power source shall be permitted to be used for peak load shaving providing the above conditions are met.

(FPN): Peak load shaving operation may be acceptable for satisfying the test requirements of Section 700-4(b) when all conditions of Section 700-4 are met.

This permits a generator to serve more than one level of emergency, standby, or other loads. It also permits the use of a generator for peak load shaving, supplying backup power, and other uses. However, it is required that there be assurance that priority loads will be properly and reliably served. Such systems are required to be maintained and tested periodically to provide the necessary assurance.

A portable or temporary alternate source shall be available whenever the emergency generator is out of service for major maintenance or repair.

The added use that may result from serving other loads may necessitate major maintenance of emergency generator sets. On the otherhand, use of the emergency generator for nonemergency loads on a regular basis provides assurance that the emergency generator will work when called upon to supply emergency power. The requirement for a portable or temporary alternate source is to provide emergency power when the generator set is out of service for a prolonged period of time. A major maintenance or repair procedure is one that keeps the generator set out of service for more than a few hours.

700-6. Transfer Equipment. Transfer equipment shall be automatic and identified for emergency use or approved by the authority having jurisdiction. Transfer equipment shall be designed and installed to prevent the inadvertent interconnection of normal and emergency sources of supply in any operation of the transfer equipment. See Section 230-83.
Means shall be permitted to isolate the transfer switch equipment. Where isolation switches are used, inadvertent parallel operation shall be avoided.

700-7. Signals. Audible and visual signal devices shall be provided, where practicable, for the following purposes:

(a) **Derangement.** To indicate derangement of the emergency source.

(b) **Carrying Load.** To indicate that the battery is carrying load.

(c) **Not Functioning.** To indicate that the battery charger is not functioning.

(d) **Ground Fault.** To indicate a ground fault in solidly grounded wye emergency systems of more than 150 volts to ground and circuit protective devices rated 1000 amperes or more. The sensor for the ground-fault signal devices shall be located at, or ahead of, the main system disconnecting means for the emergency source, and the maximum setting of the signal devices shall be for a ground-fault current of 1200 amperes. Instructions on the course of action to be taken in event of indicated ground fault shall be located at or near the sensor location.

(FPN): For signals for generator sets, see Emergency and Standby Power Systems, NFPA 110-1985 (ANSI).

Improper testing or lack of testing, inadequate maintenance, and negligence by attendants to observe visual signals indicating a malfunction of battery-charging equipment are the major causes of emergency equipment failures.

Signal devices should be located in an area where they will be readily visible to or heard by attendants or other personnel familiar with the operation of the emergency equipment.

In locations such as theaters or assembly halls, audible signal bells or horns should be located where they will not cause panic.

Battery-operated unit equipment generally has test switches to simulate a failure of the normal system and an indicating light that glows bright while charging and dim when ready. Transparent plastic cases are required to be provided for lead-acid batteries for easy viewing of electrolyte levels.

A storage battery system is normally capable of delivering 12 V, 24 V, 32 V, or 120 V and consists of monitoring and distribution cabinets and console with battery and charger. It generally includes audio, visual, and remote signal devices, a test switch, and may provide a trouble bell and silence switch.

Although Section 700-26 indicates that ground-fault protection of equipment is not required on the alternate source for emergency systems, ground-faults can occur on such systems, and they can result in equipment burn-down. Because of the emergency nature of such systems, automatic disconnect in the event of a ground fault is not appropriate. However, detection of such a fault is desirable.

700-8. Signs.   A sign shall be placed at the service entrance equipment indicating type and location of on-site emergency power sources.

B. Circuit Wiring

700-9. Wiring, Emergency System.

(a) Identification.   All boxes and enclosures for emergency circuits shall be marked so they will be readily identified as a component of an emergency circuit.

The marking may be a color code or the marking "Emergency System" or any other type of identification that will differentiate the box or enclosure as a component of the emergency system.

(b) Wiring.   Wiring from emergency source or emergency source distribution overcurrent protection to emergency loads shall be kept entirely independent of all other wiring and equipment and shall not enter the same raceway, cable, box, or cabinet with other wiring.

Exception No. 1: In transfer equipment enclosures.

Exception No. 2: In exit or emergency lighting fixtures supplied from two sources.

Exception No. 3: In a common junction box attached to exit or emergency lighting fixtures supplied from two sources.

Exception No. 4: Wiring of two or more emergency circuits supplied from the same source shall be permitted in the same raceway.

Exception No. 5: In a common junction box attached to a unit equipment, and which contains only the branch circuit supplying the unit equipment and the emergency circuit supplied by the unit equipment.

Emergency circuit wiring is not permitted to enter the same raceway, cable, box, or cabinet with the regular or normal wiring of the building concerned. Wiring for the emergency circuits is required to be completely independent of all other wiring and equipment, thus ensuring that any fault on the normal wiring circuits will not affect the performance of the emergency wiring or equipment.

To effect an immediate throw-over from one system to the other, it is necessary for both the normal source and the emergency source to be present within a transfer switch enclosure as per Exception No. 1.

Exceptions No. 2 and 3 permit the use of two-lamp exit or two-lamp emergency fixtures where one lamp is connected to the normal supply and one lamp is connected to the alternate supply. It should be understood that both lamps may be illuminated as part of the regular lighting operation.

Wiring on the load side of a transfer switch serves as both the emergency circuit wiring and normal circuit wiring. It is not intended that two sets of wiring supply emergency loads from the transfer switch to the emergency load distribution panel shown in Figures 700-3, 700-4, and 700-5, or from these emergency distribution panels to the emergency loads.

C. Sources of Power

700-12. General Requirements. Current supply shall be such that in the event of failure of the normal supply to, or within, the building or group of buildings concerned, emergency lighting, emergency power, or both will be available within the time required for the application but not to exceed 10 seconds. The supply system for emergency purposes, in addition to the normal services to the building and meeting the general requirements of this section, shall be permitted to comprise one or more of the types of systems described in (a) through (e) below. Unit equipments in accordance with Section 700-12(f) shall satisfy the applicable requirements of this article.

In selecting an emergency source of power, consideration shall be given to the occupancy and the type of service to be rendered, whether of minimum duration, as for evacuation of a theater, or longer duration, as for supplying emergency power and lighting due to an indefinite period of current failure from trouble either inside or outside the building.

Consideration shall be given to the location and/or design of all equipment to minimize the hazards that might cause complete failure due to floods, fires, icing, and vandalism.

(FPN): Assignment of degree of reliability of the recognized emergency supply system depends upon the careful evaluation of the variables at each particular installation.

(a) Storage Battery. Storage batteries used as source of power for emergency systems shall be of suitable rating and capacity to supply and maintain the total load for a period of 1½ hours minimum, without the voltage applied to the load falling below 87½ percent of normal.

Batteries, whether of the acid or alkali type, shall be designed and constructed to meet the requirements of emergency service and shall be compatible with the charger for that particular installation.

For a sealed battery, the container shall not be required to be transparent. However, for the lead acid battery which requires water additions, transparent or translucent jars shall be furnished. Automotive-type batteries shall not be used.

An automatic battery charging means shall be provided.

(b) Generator Set.

(1) A generator set driven by a prime mover acceptable to the authority having jurisdiction and sized in accordance with Section 700-5. Means shall be provided for automatically starting the prime mover on failure of the normal service and for automatic transfer and operation of all required electrical circuits. A time delay feature permitting a 15-minute setting shall be provided to avoid retransfer in case of short-time reestablishment of the normal source.

(2) Where internal combustion engines are used as the prime mover, an on-site fuel supply shall be provided with an on-premise fuel supply sufficient for not less than 2 hours full-demand operation of the system.

(3) Prime movers shall not be solely dependent upon a public utility gas system for their fuel supply or municipal water supply for their cooling systems. Means shall be provided for automatically transferring from one fuel supply to another where dual fuel supplies are used.

Exception: Where acceptable to the authority having jurisdiction, the use of other than on-site fuels shall be permitted when there is a low probability of a simultaneous failure of both the off-site fuel delivery system and power from the outside electrical utility company.

(4) Where a storage battery is used for control or signal power, or as the means of starting the prime mover, it shall be suitable for the purpose and shall be equipped with an automatic charging means independent of the generator set.

(5) Generator sets which require more than 10 seconds to develop power are acceptable providing an auxiliary power supply will energize the emergency system until the generator can pick up the load.

(c) Uninterruptible Power Supplies. Uninterruptible power supplies used to provide power for emergency systems shall comply with the applicable provision of Section 700-12(a) and (b).

(d) Separate Service. Where acceptable to the authority having jurisdiction, a second service shall be permitted. This service shall be in accordance with Article 230, with separate service drop or lateral, widely separated electrically and physically from the normal service to minimize the possibility of simultaneous interruption of supply.

(e) Connection Ahead of Service Disconnecting Means. Where acceptable to the authority having jurisdiction, connections ahead of, but not within, the main service disconnecting means shall be permitted. The emergency service shall be sufficiently separated from the normal main service disconnecting means to prevent simultaneous interruption of supply through an occurrence within the building or groups of buildings served.

When designing emergency systems, whether for lighting, power, or both, it is required that consideration be given to the type of service rendered.

Supply systems for emergency systems can be one or more of the following:

1. One, or a group of storage batteries, provided with an automatic battery-charging means. See also Article 480 and paragraph (a) of this section.

2. A generator set driven by a prime mover, acceptable to the authority having jurisdiction, and with adequate capacity to carry the maximum load connected at one time. Prime movers may be internal-combustion engines, steam or gas turbines, or other approved types. A storage battery used to start the prime mover is required to be provided with an automatic battery-charging means. An on-site fuel supply sufficient to operate internal-combustion engines at full load for 2 hours is required to be available.

Off-site fuel supplies may be used where experience has demonstrated their reliability. Off-site fuel supplies may also be used where they will provide greater reliability than gasoline or diesel engines or in isolated areas where maintenance or refueling could be a problem.

Some types of drivers, particularly large ones, may take longer than 10 seconds to accelerate and develop generator voltage. Gas and steam turbines and large internal-combustion engines may have prolonged starting times. Depending on the specific loads, short-time supply could be provided by an uninterruptible power supply; a generator shared with other loads; or a generator with limited emergency supply, such as an expander, steam turbine, or waste heat system.

3. Two services, overhead or underground, widely separated electrically and physically, and preferred by some authorities to be completely independent of each other, that is, separate service locations, separate transformers, and supplied from separate utility substations where practical.

4. Uninterruptible power supplies (UPS) generally include a rectifier, storage battery, and inverter to ac. These may be very complex systems with redundant components and high-speed solid-state switching. It is common practice to include an automatic bypass for UPS malfunction to permit maintenance.

5. The use of a separate service or connection ahead of the service disconnect requires a judgment by the authority having jurisdiction. Such judgment should be based on the nature of the emergency loads and the expected reliability of the other available sources.

(FPN): See Section 230-82 for equipment permitted on the supply side of a service disconnecting means.

(f) Unit Equipment. Individual unit equipment for emergency illumination shall consist of: (1) a rechargeable battery; (2) a battery charging means; (3) provisions for one or more lamps mounted on the equipment and/or shall be permitted to have terminals for remote lamps; and (4) a relaying device arranged to energize the lamps automatically upon failure of the supply to the unit equipment. The batteries shall be of suitable rating and capacity to supply and maintain at not less than 87½ percent of the nominal battery voltage for the total lamp load associated with the unit for a period of at least 1½ hours, or the unit equipment shall supply and maintain not less than 60 percent of the initial emergency illumination for a period of at least 1½ hours. Storage batteries, whether of the acid or alkali type, shall be designed and constructed to meet the requirements of emergency service.

Unit equipment shall be permanently fixed in place (i.e., not portable) and shall have all wiring to each unit installed in accordance with the requirements of any of the wiring methods in Chapter 3. Flexible cord- and plug-connection shall be permitted provided that the cord does not exceed 3 feet (914 mm) in length. The branch circuit feeding the unit equipment shall be the same branch circuit as that serving the normal lighting in the area and connected ahead of any local switches. Emergency illumination fixtures that obtain power from a unit equipment and are not part of the unit equipment shall be wired to the unit equipment as required by Section 700-9 and by one of the wiring methods of Chapter 3.

Exception: In a separate and uninterrupted area supplied by a minimum of 3 normal lighting circuits, a separate branch circuit for unit equipment shall be permitted if it originates from the same panelboard as that of the normal lighting circuits and is provided with a lock-on feature.

Unit equipment may be wired with a flexible cord (not exceeding 3 ft) and attachment plug cap. This equipment must be permanently fixed in place, usually by mounting screws accessible only from within the unit. One or more lamps may be mounted on, or remote from, the unit. The unit should be located where it can be readily checked or tested for proper performance.

Unit equipment is intended to provide illumination for the area where it is installed. For instance, if a unit is located in a corridor, it is required to be connected to the branch circuit supplying the normal corridor lights (on the line side of any switching arrangements) and, in the event of loss of normal power, the unit would automatically energize the unit lamps, restoring illumination to the corridor. A separate circuit is not permitted for unit equipment (except as noted in the Exception) because, if applied to the above case, failure of the normal corridor circuit would not affect the unit equipment, and the corridor would remain in darkness.

Notes on General Requirements for Emergency Lighting Systems

TYPICAL PACKAGE
GENERATOR SET INSTALLATION

Figure 700-1. A typical generator installation supplying standby power in ratings from 55 kW to 930 kW, 60 Hz. (*Caterpillar*)

At least two sources of power are required to be provided, that is, one normal supply and one or more types of emergency systems described in Section 700-12. The sources may be (1) two services, one normal supply and one emergency supply (preferably from separate utility stations); (2) one normal service and a storage battery (or unit equipment) system; (3) one normal service and a generator set; or (4) one normal service and one emergency service connected to the line side of the normal service (usually outside the building). See Figures 700-3, 700-4, and 700-5.

A transfer means (or throw-over switch) is required to be provided to energize the emergency equipment from the alternate supply when the normal source of supply is interrupted.

Where two services are used, both may operate normally, but equipment for emergency lighting and power is required to be arranged to be energized from either service.

Where the alternate or emergency source of supply is a storage battery or a generator set, the single emergency system would usually be operated on the normal service, and the battery (or batteries) or generator would operate only if the normal service failed. See Figure 700-5. However, a generator may be used for peak load shaving, etc., in accordance with Section 700-5(b).

Two or more separate and complete systems may be used to provide current for emergency lighting, but means are required to be provided for energizing either system upon the failure of the other.

It should be noted that provisions for disconnecting means and overcurrent protection (see Figures 700-3, 700-4, and 700-5) are to be provided for emergency systems as required by Article 230. See also Section 230-83.

Figure 700-2. Self-contained fully automatic unit equipment to operate emergency lighting located on the unit or for remotely located exit signs or lighting heads. (*Dual-Lite Inc.*)

D. Emergency System Circuits for Lighting and Power

700-15. Loads on Emergency Branch Circuits. No appliances and no lamps, other than those specified as required for emergency use, shall be supplied by emergency lighting circuits.

ARTICLE 700—EMERGENCY SYSTEMS

700-16. Emergency Illumination. Emergency illumination shall include all required means of egress lighting, illuminated exit signs, and all other lights specified as necessary to provide required illumination.

Emergency lighting systems shall be so designed and installed that the failure of any individual lighting element, such as the burning out of a light bulb, cannot leave in total darkness any space which requires emergency illumination.

Where high-intensity discharge lighting such as high- and low-pressure sodium, mercury vapor, and metal halide is used as the sole source of normal illumination, the emergency lighting system shall be required to operate until normal illumination has been restored.

Exception: Where alternative means have been taken to ensure that the emergency lighting illumination level is maintained.

High-intensity discharge (HID) fixtures take some time to start once they are energized, so if they are the sole source of normal illumination in an area, the *Code* requires that the emergency lighting system operate until the normal system not only is returned to service, but also until the HID fixtures provide illumination. This may require a timing circuit, a photoelectric monitoring system, or equal.

700-17. Circuits for Emergency Lighting. Branch circuits which supply emergency lighting shall be installed to provide service from a source complying with Section 700-12 when the normal supply for lighting is interrupted. Such installations shall provide either one of the following: (1) an emergency lighting supply, independent of the general lighting supply, with provisions for automatically transferring the emergency lights upon the event of failure of the general lighting system supply, or (2) two or more separate and complete systems with independent power supply, each system providing sufficient current for emergency lighting purposes. Unless both systems are used for regular lighting purposes and are both kept lighted, means shall be provided for automatically energizing either system upon failure of the other. Either or both systems shall be permitted to be a part of the general lighting system of the protected occupancy if circuits supplying lights for emergency illumination are installed in accordance with other sections of this article.

1. General Considerations for Transfer Switches

Automatic transfer switches of double-throw construction are used primarily for emergency and standby power generation systems rated 600 V or less. These transfer switches do not normally incorporate overcurrent protection and are designed and applied in accordance with the *Code*, particularly Articles 700 and 701. They are available in ratings from 30 to 3,000 A. For reliability, most automatic transfer switches rated above 100 A are mechanically held and electrically operated from the power source to which the load is to be transferred.

An automatic transfer switch is usually located in the main or secondary distribution bus that feeds the branch circuits. Because of its location in the system, the abilities which must be designed into the transfer switch are unique and extensive as compared with the design requirements for other branch-circuit and feeder devices. For example, special consideration should be given to the following characteristics of an automatic transfer: (1) its ability to close against high in-rush currents, (2) its ability to carry full-rated current continuously from normal and emergency sources, (3) its ability to withstand fault currents, and (4) its ability to interrupt six times the full-load currents. In addition to considering each of the above characteristics individually, it is also necessary to consider the effect each has upon the other.

In arrangements that provide protection against failure of the utility service, consideration should also be given to (1) an open circuit within the building area on the load side of the incoming service, (2) overload or fault condition, and (3) electrical or mechanical failure of the electric power distribution system within the building. It is therefore desirable to locate transfer switches close to the load and have the operation of the transfer switches independent of overcurrent protection. It is often desirable to use multiple transfer switches of lower current located near the load rating rather than one large transfer switch at the point of incoming service.

Figure 700-3. Emergency load arranged to be supplied from two widely separated services [Section 700-12(d)]. Upon failure of one service, the emergency load will be transferred to the other service.

2. Location of Overcurrent Devices

The location of overcurrent devices for both normal and emergency power is covered by Section 240-21 and is not affected by the installation of an automatic transfer switch. Transfer switches should be rated for continuous duty and have low contact temperature rise.

3. Solid Neutral on AC and DC Systems

Solid neutrals can be used with the grounding connections made as required in Section 250-23 where automatic ac to ac transfer switches are used. Where multiple grounding creates objectionable ground current, corrective action specified in Section 250-21(b) is required to be made.

Section 230-95 requires ground-fault protection of equipment. Because the normal source and emergency source are typically grounded at their locations, the multiple neutral-to-ground connections usually require some additional means or devices to assure proper ground-fault sensing by the ground-fault protection device. Additional means or devices are generally required because the normal alterations to stop objectionable current per Section 250-21(b) do not apply when the objectionable current is a ground-fault current. See Section 250-21(c). Rather, solutions such as an overlapping neutral transfer pole or conventional fourth pole are often added to the transfer switch. Other solutions are isolation transformers and special ground-fault circuits, or using the service ground to also ground the generator neutral with 3-pole transfer switches.

Utility service

Service disconnecting means and overcurrent protection

Main distribution panel

Emergency supply (normal)

Transfer switch

Non-emergency loads

Emergency load distribution panel

Figure 700-4. Emergency service arranged to be supplied by the tap ahead of the main [Section 700-12(e)].

On ac to dc automatic transfer switches, a solid neutral tie between the ac and dc neutrals is not permitted where both sources of supply are exterior distribution systems. Section 250-22, regarding location of grounds for dc exterior systems, clearly specifies that the dc system can be grounded only at the supply station.

Where the dc system is an interior isolated system, such as a storage battery, solid neutral connection between the ac system neutral and the dc source is acceptable.

On an ac to dc automatic transfer switch where the neutral must be switched, the size of the neutral switching pole must be considered. A 4-pole, double-throw switch must be used where a 3-phase, 4-wire normal source and a 2-wire dc emergency source are transferred. Due to the neutral being switched, a 4-pole, double-throw transfer switch is required. In this instance, one pole of the dc emergency source would carry three times the current of the other poles.

4. Close Differential Voltage Supervision of Normal Source

Most often the normal source is an electric utility company whose power is transmitted many miles to the point of utilization. The automatic transfer switch control panel continuously monitors the voltage of all phases. (Because utility frequency is, for all practical purposes, constant, only the voltage need be monitored.) For single-phase power systems, the line-to-line voltage is monitored. For 3-phase power systems, all three line-to-line voltages should be monitored to provide full phase protection.

In addition, monitoring protects against operation at reduced voltage, such as brownouts, which can damage loads such as motors. Since the voltage sensitivity

Utility supply

Service disconnecting means and overcurrent protection

G

Main distribution panel

Emergency supply (normal)

Transfer switch

Non-emergency loads

Emergency load distribution panel

Figure 700-5. Emergency load arranged to be supplied from a generator [Section 700-12(b)] or storage battery [Section 700-12(a)].

of loads vary, the pickup (acceptable) voltage setting, and dropout (unacceptable) voltage setting of the monitors should be adjustable. Typical range of adjustment for the pickup is 85 percent to 100 percent of nominal, while the dropout setting, which is a function of the pickup setting, is 75 percent to 98 percent of the pickup selected. Usual settings for most loads are 95 percent of nominal for pickup and 85 percent of nominal for dropout (90 percent of pickup).

Consideration must be given to voltage supervision at closer differential for many installations where the load circuits are critical to voltage.

Starter-type fluorescent lighting is extremely voltage sensitive, and, at voltages below 105 V, it becomes uncertain as to whether the fluorescent lamp will operate. Therefore, a closer differential of transfer and retransfer is required for this type of lighting.

Electronic equipment load is frequently voltage critical. These installations include patient care equipment in health care facilities, X-ray equipment, television stations, cable TV centers, microwave communications, telephone communications, computers, computer-operated equipment, computer centers, and similar applications.

Polyphase motors operating at low load have a tendency to single phase, despite the loss of voltage in one phase, leading to burnout of the motor. A close differential of voltage supervision should be applied to automatic transfer switches for motor installations of the polyphase type. Differential voltage relays with a close adjustment of 2 percent for transfer and retransfer values will aid in the detection of phase outages and provide protection from single phasing.

Figure 700-6. Automatic emergency transfer switch and control panel. (*Automatic Switch Co.*)

5. Automatic Transfer Switches with Emergency Source on Automatically Started Power Plant

In these installations, the normal source is usually a utility power line, and the emergency source is an automatically started engine generator set which starts upon failure of the normal source. To ensure maximum reliability, a minimum installation should be arranged to:

1. Initiate engine starting of the power plant from a contact on the automatic transfer switch control panel (see Figure 700-7),

2. Sustain connection of load circuits to the normal source during the starting period to provide utilization of any existing service on the normal source,

3. Measure output voltage and frequency of emergency source through the use of voltage-frequency-sensitive monitor (see Figure 700-7) and effect transfer of the load circuits to the power plant only when both voltage and frequency of the power plant are approximately normal. Sensing of the emergency source need only be single phase since most applications involve an on-site engine generator with a relatively short line run to the automatic transfer switch. In addition to monitoring voltage, the emergency source's frequency should also be monitored. Unlike the utility power, the engine generator frequency can vary during startup. Frequency monitoring will avoid overloading the engine generator while it is starting and can thus avoid stalling the engine. Combined frequency and voltage monitoring will protect against transferring loads to an engine generator set with an unacceptable output, and

4. Provide visual signal and auxiliary contact for remote indication when power plant is feeding the load.

6. Time-Delay Devices on Automatic Transfer Switches

Time delays are provided to program operation of the automatic transfer switch. To avoid unnecessary starting and transfer to the alternate supply, a nominal 1-second time delay, adjustable up to 6 seconds, can override momentary interruptions and reductions in normal source voltage but allow starting and transfer if the reduction or outage is sustained. See Figure 700-7. The advantages of this feature are realized in all types of automatic transfer installations. In standby plant installations, the reduced number of false starts is especially important to minimize wear on the starting gear, battery, and associated equipment. This delay is generally set at 1 second, but may be set higher if reclosers on the high lines take longer to operate or if momentary power dips exceed 1 second. If longer delay settings are used, care must be taken to ensure that sufficient time remains to meet 10-second power restoration requirements.

Once the load is transferred to the alternate source, another timer delays retransfer to the normal source until that source has time to stabilize. See commentary following Section 700-16. This timer is required by Section 700-

996

Figure 700-7. Diagram of connections of the automatic transfer switch shown in Figure 700-6. TD, Time Delay; TO, Transfer; TC, Transfer Controls; V/FM, Voltage-Frequency-Sensitive Monitor; VM, Voltage Monitor. (*Automatic Switch Co.*)

12(b)(1) and is controlled by the preferred source voltage monitors. The timer is adjustable from 0 to 30 minutes and is normally set at 30 minutes. Another important function of this retransfer timer is to allow an engine generator to operate under load for a preselected minimum time to ensure continued good performance of the set and its starting system. This delay should be automatically nullified if the alternate source fails and the normal source is available as determined by the voltage monitors.

Engine generator manufacturers often recommend a cool-down period for their sets which allows them to run unloaded after the load is retransferred to the normal source. A third time delay, usually 5 minutes, is provided for this purpose. Running an unloaded engine for more than 5 minutes is neither necessary nor recommended since it can cause deterioration in engine performance.

It is sometimes prescribed to purposely sequence transfer of the loads to the alternate source where more than one automatic transfer switch is connected to the same engine generator. Utilization of such a sequencing scheme can reduce starting kVA capacity requirements of the generator. A fourth timer, adjustable from 0 to 5 minutes, will delay transfer to the emergency supply source for this and other similar requirements.

700-18. Circuits for Emergency Power.   For branch circuits that supply equipment classed as emergency, there shall be an emergency supply source to which the load will be transferred automatically upon the failure of the normal supply.

E. Control — Emergency Lighting Circuits

700-20. Switch Requirements.   The switch or switches installed in emergency lighting circuits shall be so arranged that only authorized persons will have control of emergency lighting.

Exception No. 1: Where two or more single-throw switches are connected in parallel to control a single circuit, at least one of these switches shall be accessible only to authorized persons.

Exception No. 2: Additional switches that act only to put emergency lights into operation but not disconnect them are permissible.

Switches connected in series or 3- and 4-way switches shall not be used.

700-21. Switch Location.   All manual switches for controlling emergency circuits shall be in locations convenient to authorized persons responsible for their actuation. In places of assembly, such as theaters, a switch for controlling emergency lighting systems shall be located in the lobby or at a place conveniently accessible thereto.

In no case shall a control switch for emergency lighting in a theater, or motion-picture theater or place of assembly be placed in a motion-picture projection booth or on a stage or platform.

Exception: Where multiple switches are provided, one such switch shall be permitted in such locations where so arranged that it can energize the circuit only, but it cannot de-energize the circuit.

700-22. Exterior Lights. Those lights on the exterior of a building that are not required for illumination when there is sufficient daylight shall be permitted to be controlled by an automatic light-actuated device.

F. Overcurrent Protection

700-25. Accessibility. The branch-circuit overcurrent devices in emergency circuits shall be accessible to authorized persons only.

(FPN): Fuses and circuit breakers for emergency circuit overcurrent protection, where coordinated to ensure selective clearing of fault currents, increase overall reliability of the system.

700-26. Ground-Fault Protection of Equipment. The alternate source for emergency systems shall not be required to have ground-fault protection of equipment.

This is an exception to the general ground-fault protection requirement of Section 230-95. It permits the designer to exercise judgment in risking equipment damage in order to keep emergency circuits in operation as long as they will continue to function.

ARTICLE 701 — LEGALLY REQUIRED STANDBY SYSTEMS

Contents

D. Overcurrent Protection
701-15. Accessibility.

701-17. Ground-Fault Protection of Equipment.

A. General

701-1. Scope. The provisions of this article apply to the electrical safety of the design, installation, operation, and maintenance of legally required standby systems consisting of circuits and equipment intended to supply, distribute, and control electricity to required facilities for illumination and/or power when the normal electrical supply or system is interrupted.

The systems covered by this article consist only of those that are permanently installed in their entirety, including the power source.

(FPN): For additional information, see Health Care Facilities, NFPA 99-1984 (ANSI).

(FPN): For further information regarding performance of emergency and standby power systems, see Emergency and Standby Power Systems, NFPA 110-1985 (ANSI).

In earlier editions of the *Code*, these requirements were included with the requirements for optional standby systems in Article 750. This tended to obscure an important level of standby systems.

Legally required standby systems are intended to provide electric power to aid in fire fighting, rescue operations, control of health hazards, and similar operations. In comparison, emergency systems (Article 700) are those which are essential for safety to human life. Optional standby systems are those whose failure could cause such effects as physical discomfort, serious interruption of an industrial process, damage to process equipment, or disruption of business.

Legally required standby systems have much the same needs as emergency systems; however, there are some differences in requirements. Upon loss of normal power, legally required systems are required to be able to supply standby power in 60 seconds or less instead of the 10 seconds or less required of emergency systems. Wiring for legally required standby systems may occupy the same raceways, cables, boxes, and cabinets as other general wiring. Wiring for emergency systems is required to be kept entirely independent of other wiring. Legally required standby systems take second order priority to emergency systems where they are involved in sharing an alternate supply and/or load shedding or peak shaving schemes.

701-2. Legally Required Standby Systems. Legally required standby systems are those systems required and so classed as legally required standby by municipal, state, federal, or other codes or by any governmental agency having jurisdiction. These systems are intended to automatically supply power to selected loads (other than those classed as emergency systems) in the event of failure of the normal source.

(FPN): Legally required standby systems are typically installed to serve loads, such as heating and refrigeration systems, communication systems, ventilation and smoke removal systems, sewerage disposal, lighting systems and industrial processes, that, when stopped during any interruption of the normal electrical supply, could create hazards or hamper rescue or fire fighting operations.

701-3. Application of Other Articles. Except as modified by this article, all applicable articles of this Code shall apply.

701-4. Equipment Approval. All equipment shall be approved for the intended use.

701-5. Tests and Maintenance for Legally Required Standby Systems.

(a) Conduct or Witness Test. The authority having jurisdiction shall conduct or witness a test on the complete system upon installation.

(b) Tested Periodically. Systems shall be tested periodically on a schedule and in a manner acceptable to the authority having jurisdiction to assure their maintenance in proper operating condition.

ARTICLE 701—LEGALLY REQUIRED STANDBY SYSTEMS

(c) Battery Systems Maintenance. Where batteries are used for starting or ignition of prime movers the authority having jurisdiction shall require periodic maintenance.

(d) Written Record. A written record shall be kept on such tests and maintenance.

(e) Testing under Load. Means for testing legally required standby systems under load shall be provided.

701-6. Capacity and Rating. A legally required standby system shall have adequate capacity and rating for the supply of all equipment intended to be operated at one time.

The alternate power source shall be permitted to supply legally required standby and optional standby system loads when automatic selective load pickup and load shedding is provided as needed to assure adequate power to the legally required standby circuits.

701-7. Transfer Equipment. Transfer equipment shall be automatic and identified for standby use or approved by the authority having jurisdiction. Transfer equipment shall be designed and installed to prevent the inadvertent interconnection of normal and alternate sources of supply in any operation of the transfer equipment.

Means to isolate the transfer switch equipment shall be permitted. Where isolation switches are used, inadvertent parallel operation shall be avoided.

701-8. Signals. Audible and visual signal devices shall be provided, where practicable, for the following purposes:

(a) Derangement. To indicate derangement of the standby source.

(b) Carrying Load. To indicate that the standby source is carrying load.

(c) Not Functioning. To indicate that the battery charger is not functioning.

(FPN): For signals for generator sets, see Emergency and Standby Power Systems, NFPA 110 (ANSI).

701-9. Signs. A sign shall be placed at the service entrance indicating type and location of on-site legally required standby power sources.

B. Circuit Wiring

701-10. Wiring Legally Required Standby Systems. The legally required standby system wiring shall be permitted to occupy the same raceways, cables, boxes and cabinets with other general wiring.

C. Sources of Power

701-11. Legally Required Standby Systems. Current supply shall be such that in event of failure of the normal supply to, or within, the building or group of buildings concerned, legally required standby power will be available within the time required for the application but not to exceed 60 seconds. The supply system for legally required standby purposes, in addition to the normal services to the building, shall be permitted to comprise one or more of the types of systems described in (a) through (e) below. Unit equipment in accordance with Section 701-11(f) shall satisfy the applicable requirements of this article.

In selecting a legally required standby source of power, consideration shall be given to the type of service to be rendered whether of short-time duration or long duration.

Consideration shall be given to the location and/or design of all equipment to minimize the hazards that might cause complete failure due to floods, fires, icing, and vandalism.

(FPN): Assignment of degree of reliability of the recognized legally required standby supply system depends upon the careful evaluation of the variables at each particular installation.

(a) Storage Battery. A storage battery of suitable rating and capacity to supply and maintain at not less than 87½ percent of system voltage the total load of the circuits supplying legally required standby power for a period of at least 1½ hours.

Batteries, whether of the acid or alkali type, shall be designed and constructed to meet the service requirements of emergency service and shall be compatible with the charger for that particular installation.

For a sealed battery, the container shall not be required to be transparent. However, for the lead acid battery which requires water additions, transparent or translucent jars shall be furnished. Automotive-type batteries shall not be used.

An automatic battery charging means shall be provided.

(b) Generator Set.

(1) A generator set driven by a prime mover acceptable to the authority having jurisdiction and sized in accordance with Section 701-6. Means shall be provided for automatically starting the prime mover on failure of the normal service and for automatic transfer and operation of all required electrical circuits. A time delay feature permitting a 15-minute setting shall be provided to avoid retransfer in case of short-time reestablishment of the normal source.

(2) Where internal combustion engines are used as the prime mover, an on-site fuel supply shall be provided with an on-premise fuel supply sufficient for not less than 2 hours full-demand operation of the system.

(3) Prime movers shall not be solely dependent upon a public utility gas system for their fuel supply or municipal water supply for their cooling systems. Means shall be provided for automatically transferring one fuel supply to another where dual fuel supplies are used.

Exception: Where acceptable to the authority having jurisdiction, the use of other than on-site fuels shall be permitted when there is a low probability of a simultaneous failure of both the off-site fuel delivery system and power from the outside electrical utility company.

(4) Where a storage battery is used for control or signal power, or as the means of starting the prime mover, it shall be suitable for the purpose and shall be equipped with an automatic charging means independent of the generator set.

(c) Uninterruptible Power Supplies. Uninterruptible power supplies used to provide power for legally required standby systems shall comply with the applicable provision of Section 701-11(a) and (b).

(d) Separate Service. Where acceptable to the authority having jurisdiction, a second service shall be permitted. This service shall be in accordance with Article 230 with separate service drop or lateral widely separated electrically and physically from the normal service to minimize the possibility of simultaneous interruption of supply.

(e) Connection Ahead of Service Disconnecting Means. Where acceptable to the authority having jurisdiction, connections ahead of, but not within, the main service disconnecting means shall be permitted. The legally required standby service shall be sufficiently separated from the normal main service disconnecting means to prevent simultaneous interruption of supply through an occurrence within the building or groups of buildings served.

(FPN): See Section 230-82 for equipment permitted on the supply side of a service disconnecting means.

(f) Unit Equipment. Individual unit equipment for legally required standby illumination shall consist of (1) a rechargeable battery; (2) a battery charging means; (3) provisions for one or more lamps mounted on the equipment and/or shall be permitted to have terminals for remote lamps; and (4) a relaying device arranged to energize the lamps automatically upon failure of the supply to the unit equipment. The batteries shall be of suitable rating and capacity to supply and maintain at not less than 87½ percent of the nominal battery voltage for the total lamp load associated with the unit for a period of at least 1½ hours, or the unit equipment shall supply and maintain not less than 60 percent of the initial legally required standby illumination for a period of at least 1½ hours. Storage batteries, whether of the acid or alkali type, shall be designed and constructed to meet the requirements of emergency service.

Unit equipment shall be permanently fixed in place (i.e., not portable) and shall have all wiring to each unit installed in accordance with the requirements of any of the wiring methods in Chapter 3. Flexible cord-and plug-connection shall be permitted provided that the cord does not exceed 3 feet (914 mm) in length. The branch circuit feeding the unit equipment shall be the same branch circuit as that serving the normal lighting in the area and connected ahead of any local switches. Legally required standby illumination fixtures that obtain power from a unit equipment and are not part of the unit equipment shall be wired to the unit equipment by one of the wiring methods of Chapter 3.

D. Overcurrent Protection

701-15. Accessibility. The branch-circuit overcurrent devices in legally required standby circuits shall be accessible to authorized persons only.

701-17. Ground-Fault Protection of Equipment. The alternate source for legally required standby systems shall not be required to have ground-fault protection of equipment.

ARTICLE 702 — OPTIONAL STANDBY SYSTEMS

Contents

A. General

702-1. Scope. The provisions of this article apply to the installation and operation of optional standby systems.

The systems covered by this article consist only of those that are permanently installed in their entirety, including prime movers.

702-2. Optional Standby Systems. Optional standby systems are intended to protect private business or property where life safety does not depend on the performance of the system. Optional standby systems are intended to supply on-site generated power to selected loads either automatically or manually.

(FPN): Optional standby systems are typically installed to provide an alternate source of electric power for such facilities as industrial and commercial buildings, farms, and residences, and to serve loads such as heating and refrigeration systems, data processing and communications systems, and industrial processes that, when stopped during any power outage, could cause discomfort, serious interruption of the process, damage to the product or process, or the like.

702-3. Application of Other Articles. Except as modified by this article all applicable articles of this Code shall apply.

702-4. Equipment Approval. All equipment shall be approved for the intended use.

702-5. Capacity. An optional standby system shall have adequate capacity and rating for the supply of all equipment intended to be operated at one time.

(FPN): The optional standby system rating need only be sufficient to carry loads selected by the user.

702-6. Transfer Equipment. Transfer equipment shall be suitable for the intended use and so designed and installed as to prevent the inadvertent interconnection of normal and alternate sources of supply in any operation of the transfer equipment.

702-7. Signals. Audible and visual signal devices shall be provided, where practicable, for the following purposes:

(a) Derangement. To indicate derangement of the optional standby source.

(b) Carrying Load. To indicate that the optional standby source is carrying load.

702-8. Signs. A sign shall be placed at the service-entrance equipment indicating type and location of on-site optional standby power sources.

B. Circuit Wiring

702-9. Wiring Optional Standby Systems. The optional standby system wiring shall be permitted to occupy the same raceways, cables, boxes and cabinets with other general wiring.

ARTICLE 705 — INTERCONNECTED ELECTRIC POWER PRODUCTION SOURCES

Contents

705-1. Scope. This article covers installation of one or more electric power production sources operating in parallel with a primary source(s) of electricity.

(FPN): The primary source may be a utility supply, on-site electric power source(s), or other sources.

This article sets forth basic safety requirements for the installation of generators and other types of power production sources that are interconnected and operate in parallel. Power sources are any system that produces electric power. They include not only electric utility sources, but also on-premises sources ranging from rotating generators (see Article 445) to solar photovoltaic systems (see Article 690) to fuel cells.

ARTICLE 705—ELECTRIC POWER PRODUCTION SOURCES

The purpose of this article is to address the basic safety requirements, specifically related to parallel operation, for the generators and other power sources, the power system that interconnects the power sources, and equipment that is connected to these systems. Proper application of these systems requires a thorough review of the entire power system.

705-2. Definitions. For purposes of this article, the following definition applies:

Interactive System: An electric power production system which is operating in parallel with and capable of delivering energy to an electric primary source supply system.

705-3. Other Articles. Interconnected electric power production sources shall comply with this article and also the applicable requirements of the following articles:

	Article
Generators	445
Solar Photovoltaic Systems	690
Emergency Systems	700
Legally Required Standby Systems	701
Optional Standby Systems	702

705-10. Directory. A permanent plaque or directory shall be installed at each service equipment location and at locations of all electric power production sources capable of being interconnected denoting all electrical power sources on or in the premises.

Exception: Installations with large numbers of power production sources shall be permitted to be designated by groups.

705-12. Point of Connection. The outputs of electric power production systems shall be interconnected at the premises service disconnecting means. See Section 230-82, Exception No. 6.

Exception No. 1: The outputs shall be permitted to be interconnected at a point or points elsewhere on the premises where the system qualifies as an integrated electric system and incorporates protective equipment in accordance with all applicable sections of Article 685.

Exception No. 2: The outputs shall be permitted to be interconnected at a point or points elsewhere on the premises where all of the following conditions are met:

a. The aggregate of nonutility sources of electricity has a capacity in excess of 100 kW or the service is above 1000 volts;

b. The conditions of maintenance and supervision assure that qualified persons will service and operate the system; and

c. Safeguards and protective equipment are established and maintained.

The point of interconnection is required to be *at* the premises service disconnecting means. This may be difficult for systems 100 kW or smaller. It is intended to avoid the indiscriminant interconnection of small generators or other sources of power, without proper protection against fire and electric shock. See Figure 705-1. It is important to utilize disconnect devices (switches, etc.) that are suitable for the purpose.

The requirement "at the premises service disconnecting means" permits connection ahead of the disconnect, or on the load side. This is to accommodate the safe work practices of many utilities to have a readily accessible disconnect for

Figure 705-1. The point of connection is required to be at the premises service disconnecting means.

dispersed generation. It is a contract matter between the utility and the customer, does not adversely affect the safety of the premises wiring, and therefore is not within the scope of the *Code*.

There are two exceptions that recognize that generators and other power sources can be safely connected elsewhere on the premises system:

- Where the premises has an integrated electrical system as set forth in Article 685; or
- Where the total generator capacity on premises is greater than 100 kW; or
- Where the service is greater than 1000 V.

Experience indicates that the larger systems usually have more knowledgeable design input and responsible installers than is common for small systems (100 kW or less, 600 V or less services).

705-14. Output Characteristics. The output of a generator or other electric power production source operating in parallel with an electric supply system shall be compatible with the voltage, wave shape, and frequency of the system to which it is connected.

(FPN): It may not be feasible to match the primary source wave shape.

The magnitude of output voltage and frequency must be controlled to cause real power and reactive power to flow in the intended amount and proper direction. Control of the driver speed causes real power (kW) to flow from a rotating generator. Control of voltage causes reactive power (kVAR) to flow to or from a synchronous generator. The parallel operation of generators is a complex balance of several variables. These are design parameters and beyond the scope of the *Code*. There is a considerable amount of data available for equipment application and design.

ARTICLE 705—ELECTRIC POWER PRODUCTION SOURCES

The output characteristics of a rotating generator are significantly different from those of a solid-state power source. Their compatibility with other sources, and with different types of loads, will be limited in different ways.

Where either the power source or the loads have solid-state equipment, such as inverters, uninterruptible power supply (UPS), or solid-state variable speed drives, there will be harmonic currents that flow in the system. See Figures 705-2, 705-3, and 705-4. These multiples of the basic supply frequency (usually 60 Hz) cause additional heating which may require derating of generators, transformers, cables, and motors. Special generator voltage control systems are required to avoid erratic operation or destruction of control devices. Circuit breakers may require derating when the higher harmonics become significant.

Significant magnitudes of harmonics may be inadvertantly matched to system resonance and result in opening capacitor fuses, overheating of circuits, and erratic operation of controls. The usual solution is to detune the system by rearrangement or installation of reactors, or both.

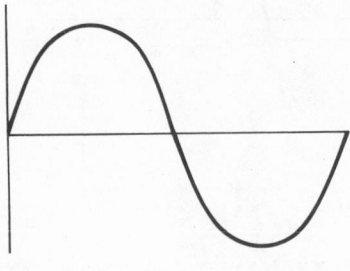

Figure 705-2. Typical output waveshape of rotating generator and system waveshape normally encountered with motor, lighting, and heating loads.

Figure 705-3. Typical output waveshape with inverter source. Motors, transformers, etc. will be driven by harmonic-rich voltage and may require derating.

Figure 705-4. Waveshape typical of system with variable speed drive, rectifier, elevator, and uninterruptible power supply loads. Source generator may require derating and special voltage control may be needed.

705-20. Disconnecting Means, Sources. Means shall be provided to disconnect all ungrounded conductors of an electric power production source(s) from all other conductors. See Article 230.

705-21. Disconnecting Means, Equipment. Means shall be provided to disconnect equipment, such as inverters or transformers, associated with a power production source, from all ungrounded conductors of all sources of supply.

Exception: Equipment intended to be operated and maintained as an integral part of a power production source exceeding 1000 volts.

An example of equipment covered under the exception is a generator designed for 4,160 V and connected to a 13,800-V system through a transformer. The transformer and generator are to be operated as a unit. It is not required that there be a disconnecting means between the generator and transformer. However, a disconnecting means is required between the transformer and the point of connection to the power system.

705-22. Disconnect Device. The disconnecting means for ungrounded conductors shall consist of a manually or power-operable switch(es) or circuit breaker(s):

(1) Located where accessible;

(2) Externally operable without exposing the operator to contact with live parts, and if power operable, of a type that can be opened by hand in the event of a power supply failure;

(3) Plainly indicating whether in the open or closed position; and

(4) Having ratings not less than the load to be carried and the fault current to be interrupted.

For disconnect equipment energized from both sides, a marking shall be provided to indicate that all contacts of the disconnect equipment may be energized.

(FPN): In parallel generation systems, some equipment, including knife blade switches and fuses, may be energized from both directions. See Section 240-40.

(FPN): Interconnection to off-premises primary source may require a visibly verifiable disconnecting device.

The requirements of Section 705-22 for disconnects are probably the most significant and important requirements in Article 705. A disconnecting means is to serve each generating source. This device or another will be the service-entrance disconnect. Still another may be applied to separate the generating systems.

The basic requirement in Section 705-22 recognizes the successful experience of applying switches as well as molded-case circuit breakers in this service. Most safe work practices on the premises utilize these disconnect devices.

The disconnect at the service entrance is required for disconnecting the premises wiring system from the utility. The utility safe work practices may also utilize this disconnect device. Utility work practices may require a visibly verifiable disconnect device. For this reason, some utility contracts require that a visible break be provided. The second fine print note is intended to bring attention to this common utility requirement.

705-30. Overcurrent Protection. Conductors shall be protected in accordance with Article 240. Equipment overcurrent protection shall be in accordance with the articles referenced in Article 240. Equipment and conductors connected to more than one electrical source shall have a sufficient number of overcurrent devices so located as to provide protection from all sources.

(1) Generators shall be protected in accordance with Section 445-4.

(2) Solar photovoltaic systems shall be protected in accordance with Article 690.

(3) Overcurrent protection for a transformer with a source(s) on each side shall be provided in accordance with Section 450-3 by considering first one side of the transformer, then the other side of the transformer, as the primary.

705-32. Ground-Fault Protection. Where ground-fault protection is used, the output of an interactive system shall be connected to the supply side of the ground-fault protection.

Exception: Connection shall be permitted to be made to the load side of ground-fault protection provided that there is ground-fault protection for equipment from all ground-fault current sources.

The protective systems that have developed for interconnected generation originated in the late 1800's. The larger systems have become very sophisticated and involve many special relays. The more usual relays are under- and over-voltage, under- and over-frequency, voltage-restrained overcurrent, anti-motoring, loss-of-field, over-temperature, and shutdowns for derangement of the mechanical driver. Small-generator installations cannot justify the cost of these switchgear-type relays. Small-generator protection comprises more common devices with fewer features. Application guides are available in technical literature and manufacturer's data.

It is important to note that the requirements in Article 705 are only for protection against conditions that may occur because generating sources are being operated in parallel. It is essential that the installation also meet the requirements of the referenced articles to provide the basic protection and safeguards for all equipment, whether or not it is involved with more than one source.

705-40. Loss of Primary Source. Upon loss of primary source, an electric power production source shall be automatically disconnected from all ungrounded conductors of the primary source, and shall not be reconnected until the primary source is restored.

(FPN): Risks to personnel and equipment associated with the primary source may occur if an interactive electric power production source can operate as an island. Special detection methods may be required to determine that a primary source supply system outage has occurred, and whether there should be automatic disconnection. When the primary source supply system is restored, special detection methods may be required to limit exposure of power production sources to out-of-phase reconnection.

(FPN): Induction generating equipment on systems with significant capacitance may become self-excited upon loss of primary source and experience severe over-voltage as a result.

When two interconnected power systems separate, they will drift out of synchronism. When the utility separates, the customer risks damage if restoration of the utility occurs out of phase. If the reconnection is at random, there will be violent electro-mechanical stresses. These can destroy mechanical components such as gears, couplings, and shafts, and can displace coils. It is essential to disconnect the premises or generator from the primary source. There are many technical guides from which to select appropriate protective systems and equipment for large systems. There is still a limited choice of low-cost devices available for application to small systems.

Induction generators are commonly used today. They have quite different characteristics from synchronous machines. They are more rugged because of the construction of the rotor. They are less expensive because of their basic design, availability, and type of starting and control equipment. Theoretically, an induction machine can continue to run on an isolated system, if there is a large capacitor bank to provide excitation. In reality, an induction machine will lose stability and be shut down quickly by one of the protective devices.

705-42. Unbalanced Interconnections. A three-phase electric power production source shall be automatically disconnected from all ungrounded conductors of the interconnected systems when one of the phases of that source opens.

Exception: An electric power production source providing power for an emergency or legally required standby system.

705-43. Synchronous Generators. Synchronous generators in a parallel system shall be provided with the necessary equipment to establish and maintain a synchronous condition.

705-50. Grounding. Interconnected electric power production sources shall be grounded in accordance with Article 250, Parts B and C, which include Sections 250-3 through 250-26.

Exception: For direct-current systems connected through an inverter directly to a grounded service, other methods which accomplish equivalent system protection and which utilize equipment listed and identified for the use shall be permitted.

ARTICLE 710 — OVER 600 VOLTS, NOMINAL
GENERAL

Contents

A. General

710-1. Scope. This article covers the general requirements for all circuits and equipment operated at more than 600 volts, nominal.

710-2. Other Articles. Provisions applicable to specific types of installations are included in Article 225, Outside Branch Circuits and Feeders; Article 230, Services; Article 240, Overcurrent Protection; Article 250, Grounding; Article 300, Wiring Methods; Article 318, Cable Trays; Article 326, Medium Voltage Cable; Article 345, Intermediate Metal Conduit; Article 346, Rigid Metal Conduit; Article 347, Rigid Nonmetallic Conduit; Article 364, Busways; Article 365, Cablebus; Article 370, Outlet, Device, Pull and Junction Boxes, Conduit Bodies and Fittings; Article 410, Lighting Fixtures, Lampholders, Lamps, Receptacles, and Rosettes; Article 427, Fixed Electric Heating Equipment for Pipelines and Vessels; Article 430, Motors, Motor Circuits, and Controllers; Article 450, Transformers and Transformer Vaults; Article 460, Capacitors; Article 600, Electric Signs and Outline Lighting; Article 660, X-Ray Equipment; Article 665, Induction and Dielectric Heating Equipment; and for construction and ampacities of high-voltage conductors, see Article 310.

710-3. Wiring Methods.

(a) Aboveground Conductors. Aboveground conductors shall be installed in rigid metal conduit, in intermediate metal conduit, in rigid nonmetallic conduit, in cable trays, as busways, as cablebus, in other suitable raceways, or as open runs of metal-clad cable suitable for the use and purpose.

In locations accessible to qualified persons only, open runs of nonmetallic-sheathed cable, bare conductors and bare busbars shall also be permitted.

(b) Underground Conductors. Underground conductors shall be suitable for the voltage and conditions under which they are installed.

Direct burial cables shall comply with the provisions of Section 310-7.

Underground cables shall be permitted to be direct buried or installed in raceways identified for the use and shall meet the depth requirements of Table 710-3(b).

Nonshielded cables shall be installed in rigid metal conduit, in intermediate metal conduit, or in rigid nonmetallic conduit encased in not less than 3 inches (76 mm) of concrete.

Exception No. 1: Type MC cable with nonshielded conductor where the metallic sheath is grounded through an effective grounding path meeting the requirements of Section 250-51.

Exception No. 2: Lead sheath cable with nonshielded conductor where the lead sheath is grounded through an effective grounding path meeting the requirements of Section 250-51.

Table 710-3(b)

Minimum Cover Requirements (Cover Means the Distance in Inches Between the Top Surface of Cable or Raceway and the Grade)

Circuit Voltage	Direct Buried Cables	Rigid Nonmetallic Conduit Approved for Direct Burial*	Rigid Metal Conduit and Intermediate Metal Conduit
Over 600–22kV	30	18	6
Over 22kV–40kV	36	24	6
Over 40kV	42	30	6

For SI units: one inch = 25.4 millimeters.

* Listed by a qualified testing agency as suitable for direct burial without encasement. All other nonmetallic systems shall require 2 inches (50.8mm) of concrete or equivalent above conduit in addition to above depth.

Exception No. 1: The above cover requirements shall be permitted to be reduced 6 inches (152 mm) for each 2 inches (50.8 mm) of concrete or equivalent above the conductors.

Exception No. 2: Areas subject to heavy vehicular traffic, such as thoroughfares or commercial parking areas, shall have a minimum cover of 24 inches (610 mm).

Exception No. 3: Lesser depths are permitted where cables and conductors rise for terminations or splices or where access is otherwise required.

Exception No. 4: In airport runways, including adjacent defined areas where trespass is prohibited, cable shall be permitted to be buried not less than 18 inches (457 mm) deep and without raceways, concrete enclosement, or equivalent.

Exception No. 5: Raceways installed in solid rock shall be permitted to be buried at lesser depth when covered by 2 inches (50.8 mm) of concrete which shall be permitted to extend to the rock surface.

(1) Protection from Damage. Conductors emerging from the ground shall be enclosed in approved raceway. Raceways installed on poles shall be of rigid metal conduit, intermediate metal conduit, PVC Schedule 80 or equivalent extending from the ground line up to a point 8 feet (2.44 m) above finished grade. Conductors entering a building shall be protected by an approved enclosure from the ground line to the point of entrance. Metallic enclosures shall be grounded.

(2) Splices. Direct burial cables shall be permitted to be spliced or tapped without the use of splice boxes provided they are installed using materials suitable for the application. The taps and splices shall be watertight and protected from mechanical damage. Where cables are shielded, the shielding shall be continuous across the splice or tap.

(3) Backfill. Backfill containing large rock, paving materials, cinders, large or sharply angular substance, or corrosive materials shall not be placed in an excavation where materials can damage raceways, cables, or other substructures or prevent adequate compaction of fill or contribute to corrosion of raceways, cables, or other substructures.

Protection shall be provided to prevent physical damage to the raceway or cable in the forms of granular or selected material or suitable sleeves.

(4) Raceway Seal. Where a raceway enters from an underground system the end within the building shall be sealed with suitable compound so as to prevent the entrance of moisture or gases, or it shall be so arranged to prevent moisture from contacting live parts.

In switch rooms, transformer vaults, and similar areas that are restricted to qualified personnel, any suitable wiring method may be used. Open wiring using bare or insulated conductors on insulators is commonly employed, as is rigid metal conduit and rigid nonmetallic conduit.

(c) Busbars. Busbars shall be permitted to be either copper or aluminum.

710-4. Braid-Covered Insulated Conductors — Open Installation. Open runs of braid-covered insulated conductors shall have a flame-retardant braid. If the conductors used do not have this protection, a flame-retardant saturant shall be applied to the braid covering after installation. This treated braid covering shall be stripped back a safe distance at conductor terminals, according to the operating voltage. This distance shall not be less than 1 inch (25.4 mm) for each kilovolt of the conductor-to-ground voltage of the circuit, where practicable.

710-6. Insulation Shielding. Metallic and semiconducting insulation shielding components of shielded cables shall be removed for a distance dependent on the circuit voltage and insulation. Stress reduction means shall be provided at all terminations of factory applied shielding.
   Metallic shielding components such as tapes, wires or braids, or combinations thereof and their associated conducting or semiconducting components shall be grounded.

Special kits are available from several manufacturers that permit a quick and easy means of providing the required stress reductions when terminating solid dielectric cables.

710-7. Grounding. Wiring and equipment installations shall be grounded in accordance with the applicable provisions of Article 250.

710-8. Moisture or Mechanical Protection for Metal-Sheathed Cables. Where cable conductors emerge from a metal sheath and where protection against moisture or physical damage is necessary, the insulation of the conductors shall be protected by a cable termination.

710-9. Protection of Service Equipment, Metal-Enclosed Power Switchgear, and Industrial Control Assemblies. Pipes or ducts foreign to the electrical installation which require periodic maintenance or whose malfunction would endanger the operation of the electrical system shall not be located in the vicinity of the service equipment, metal-enclosed power switchgear, or industrial control assemblies. Protection shall be provided where necessary to avoid damage from condensation leaks and breaks in such foreign systems. Piping and other facilities shall not be considered foreign if provided for fire protection of the electrical installation.

B. Equipment — General Provisions

710-11. Indoor Installations. See Section 110-31(a).

710-12. Outdoor Installations. See Section 110-31(b).

710-13. Metal-Enclosed Equipment. See Section 110-31(c).

710-14. Oil-Filled Equipment. Installation of electrical equipment, other than transformers, covered in Article 450, containing more than 10 gallons (37.85 L) of flammable oil per unit shall meet the requirements of Parts B and C of Article 450.

C. Equipment — Specific Provisions

(FPN): See also references to specific types of installations in Section 710-2.

710-20. Overcurrent Protection. Overcurrent protection shall be provided for each ungrounded conductor by one of the following:

(a) Overcurrent Relays and Current Transformers. Circuit breakers used for overcurrent protection of ac 3-phase circuits shall have a minimum of three overcurrent relays operated from three current transformers.

Exception No. 1: On 3-phase, 3-wire circuits, an overcurrent relay in the residual circuit of the current transformers shall be permitted to replace one of the phase relays.

Exception No. 2: An overcurrent relay, operated from a current transformer which links all phases of a 3-phase, 3-wire circuit, shall be permitted to replace the residual relay and one of the phase conductor current transformers.

(b) Fuses. A fuse shall be connected in series with each ungrounded conductor.

710-21. Circuit-Interrupting Devices.

(a) Circuit Breakers.

(1) Indoor installations shall consist of metal-enclosed units or fire-resistant cell-mounted units.

Exception: Open mounting of circuit breakers shall be permitted in locations accessible to qualified persons only.

(2) Circuit breakers used to control oil-filled transformers shall be either located outside the transformer vault or be capable of operation from outside the vault.

(3) Oil circuit breakers shall be so arranged or located that adjacent readily combustible structures or materials are safeguarded in an approved manner.

(4) Circuit breakers shall have the following equipment or operating characteristics:

a. An accessible mechanical or other approved means for manual tripping, independent of control power.

b. Be release free (trip free).

c. If capable of being opened or closed manually while energized, the main contacts shall operate independently of the speed of the manual operation.

d. A mechanical position indicator at the circuit breaker to show the open or closed position of the main contacts.

e. A means of indicating the open and closed position of the breaker at the point(s) from which they may be operated.

f. A permanent and legible nameplate showing manufacturer's name or trademark, manufacturer's type or identification number, continuous current rating, interrupting rating in mVA or amperes, and maximum voltage rating. Modification of a circuit breaker affecting its rating(s) shall be accompanied by an appropriate change of nameplate information.

For the control and protection of feeders leaving a substation, Figure 710-1 shows a typical example of modern, metal-enclosed switchgear. This industrial unit substation includes a high-voltage disconnect switch, transformer, and low-voltage switchgear with a full functioning ground-fault relay protection system.

Indicating instruments, such as voltmeters, ammeters, wattmeters, and protective relays, may be mounted on the panel doors as desired. This switchgear affords a high degree of safety because all live parts are metal enclosed, and interlocks are provided for safe operation. It is also available with air circuit breakers which eliminate the fire hazard associated with oil breakers.

Figure 710-1. An assembly of metal-enclosed switchgear. (*Federal Pacific Electric Co.*)

(5) The continuous current rating of a circuit breaker shall be not less than the maximum continuous current through the circuit breaker.

(6) The interrupting rating of a circuit breaker shall not be less than the maximum fault current the circuit breaker will be required to interrupt, including contributions from all connected sources of energy.

(7) The closing rating of a circuit breaker shall not be less than the maximum asymmetrical fault current into which the circuit breaker can be closed.

(8) The momentary rating of a circuit breaker shall not be less than the maximum asymmetrical fault current at the point of installation.

(9) The rated maximum voltage of a circuit breaker shall not be less than the maximum circuit voltage.

(b) Power Fuses and Fuseholders.

(1) Use. Where fuses are used to protect conductors and equipment a fuse shall be placed in each ungrounded conductor. Two power fuses shall be permitted to be used in parallel to protect the same load, if both fuses have identical ratings, and both fuses are installed in an identified common mounting with electrical connections that will divide the current equally. Power fuses of the vented type shall not be used indoors, underground or in metal enclosures unless identified for the use.

(2) Interrupting Rating. The interrupting rating of power fuses shall not be less than the maximum fault current the fuse will be required to interrupt, including contributions from all connected sources of energy.

(3) Voltage Rating. The maximum voltage rating of power fuses shall not be less than the maximum circuit voltage. Fuses having a minimum recommended operating voltage shall not be applied below this voltage.

(4) Identification of Fuse Mountings and Fuse Units. Fuse mountings and fuse units shall have permanent and legible nameplates showing the manufacturer's type or designation, continuous current rating, interrupting current rating, and maximum voltage rating.

(5) Fuses. Fuses that expel flame in opening the circuit shall be so designed or arranged that they will function properly without hazard to persons or property.

(6) Fuseholders. Fuseholders shall be designed or installed so that they will be de-energized while replacing a fuse.

Exception: Fuse and fuseholder designed to permit fuse replacement by qualified persons using equipment designed for the purpose without de-energizing the fuseholder.

(7) High-Voltage Fuses. Metal-enclosed switchgear and substations that utilize high-voltage fuses shall be provided with a gang-operated disconnecting switch. Isolation of the fuses from the circuit shall be provided by either connecting a switch between the source and the fuses or providing roll-out switch and fuse type of construction. The switch shall be of the load-interrupter type, unless mechanically or electrically interlocked with a load-interrupting device arranged to reduce the load to the interrupting capability of the switch.

Exception: More than one switch shall be permitted as the disconnecting means for one set of fuses where the switches are installed to provide connection to more than one set of supply conductors. The switches shall be mechanically or electrically interlocked to permit access to the fuses only when all switches are open. A conspicuous sign shall be placed at the fuses reading: "WARNING - FUSES MAY BE ENERGIZED FROM MORE THAN ONE SOURCE."

(c) Distribution Cutouts and Fuse Links — Expulsion Type.

(1) Installation. Cutouts shall be so located that they may be readily and safely operated and re-fused, and so that the exhaust of the fuses will not endanger persons. Distribution cutouts shall not be used indoors, underground, or in metal enclosures.

(2) Operation. Where fused cutouts are not suitable to interrupt the circuit manually while carrying full load, an approved means shall be installed to interrupt the entire load. Unless the fused cutouts are interlocked with the switch to prevent opening of the cutouts under load, a conspicuous sign shall be placed at such cutouts reading, "WARNING — DO NOT OPEN UNDER LOAD."

(3) Interrupting Rating. The interrupting rating of distribution cutouts shall not be less than the maximum fault current the cutout will be required to interrupt, including contributions from all connected sources of energy.

(4) Voltage Rating. The maximum voltage rating of cutouts shall not be less than the maximum circuit voltage.

(5) Identification. Distribution cutouts shall have on their body, door, or fuse tube a permanent and legible nameplate or identification showing the manufacturer's type or designation, continuous current rating, maximum voltage rating, and interrupting rating.

(6) Fuse Links. Fuse links shall have a permanent and legible identification showing continuous current rating and type.

(7) Structure Mounted Outdoors. The height of cutouts mounted outdoors on structures shall provide safe clearance between lowest energized parts (open or closed position) and standing surfaces, in accordance with Section 110-34(e).

(d) Oil-Filled Cutouts.

(1) Continuous Current Rating. The continuous current rating of oil-filled cutouts shall not be less than the maximum continuous current through the cutout.

(2) Interrupting Rating. The interrupting rating of oil-filled cutouts shall not be less than the maximum fault current the oil-filled cutout will be required to interrupt, including contributions from all connected sources of energy.

(3) Voltage Rating. The maximum voltage rating of oil-filled cutouts shall not be less than the maximum circuit voltage.

(4) Fault Closing Rating. Oil-filled cutouts shall have a fault closing rating not less than the maximum asymmetrical fault current that can occur at the cutout location, unless suitable interlocks or operating procedures preclude the possibility of closing into a fault.

(5) Identification. Oil-filled cutouts shall have a permanent and legible nameplate showing the rated continuous current, rated maximum voltage, and rated interrupting current.

(6) Fuse Links. Fuse links shall have a permanent and legible identification showing the rated continuous current.

(7) Location. Cutouts shall be so located that they will be readily and safely accessible for re-fusing, with the top of the cutout not over 5 feet (1.52 m) above the floor or platform.

(8) Enclosure. Suitable barriers or enclosures shall be provided to prevent contact with nonshielded cables or energized parts of oil-filled cutouts.

(e) Load Interrupters. Load-interrupter switches shall be permitted if suitable fuses or circuit breakers are used in conjunction with these devices to interrupt fault currents. Where these devices are used in combination, they shall be so coordinated electrically that they will safely withstand the effects of closing, carrying, or interrupting all possible currents up to the assigned maximum short-circuit rating.

Where more than one switch is installed with interconnected load terminals to provide for alternate connection to different supply conductors, each switch shall be provided with a conspicuous sign reading: "WARNING — SWITCH MAY BE ENERGIZED BY BACKFEED."

(1) Continuous Current Rating. The continous current rating of interrupter switches shall equal or exceed the maximum continuous current at the point of installation.

(2) Voltage Rating. The maximum voltage rating of interrupter switches shall equal or exceed the maximum circuit voltage.

(3) Identification. Interrupter switches shall have a permanent and legible nameplate including the following information: manufacturer's type or designation, continuous current rating, interrupting current rating, fault closing rating, maximum voltage rating.

(4) Switching of Conductors. The switching mechanism shall be arranged to be operated from a location where the operator is not exposed to energized parts and shall be arranged to open all ungrounded conductors of the circuit simultaneously with one operation. Switches shall be arranged to be locked in the open position. Metal-enclosed switches shall be operable from outside the enclosure.

(5) Stored Energy for Opening. The stored energy operator shall be permitted to be left in the uncharged position after the switch has been closed if a single movement of the operating handle charges the operator and opens the switch.

(6) Supply Terminals. Fused interrupter switches shall be so installed that all supply terminals shall be at the top of the switch enclosure.

Exception: Supply terminals are not required to be at the top of the switch enclosure if barriers are installed to prevent persons from accidentally contacting energized parts or dropping tools or fuses into energized parts.

710-22. Isolating Means. Means shall be provided to completely isolate an item of equipment. The use of isolating switches shall not be required where there are other ways of de-energizing the equipment for inspection and repairs, such as drawout-type metal-enclosed switchgear units and removable truck panels.

Isolating switches not interlocked with an approved circuit-interrupting device shall be provided with a sign warning against opening them under load.

A fuseholder and fuse, designed for the purpose, shall be permitted as an isolating switch.

710-23. Voltage Regulators. Proper switching sequence for regulators shall be assured by use of one of the following: (1) mechanically sequenced regulator bypass switch(es); (2) mechanical interlocks; or (3) switching procedure prominently displayed at the switching location.

710-24. Metal-Enclosed Power Switchgear and Industrial Control Assemblies.

(a) Scope. This section covers assemblies of metal-enclosed power switchgear and industrial control, including but not limited to switches, interrupting devices and their control, metering, protection and regulating equipment, where an integral part of the assembly, with associated interconnections and supporting structures. This section also includes metal-enclosed power switchgear assemblies that form a part of unit substations, power centers, or similar equipment.

(b) Arrangement of Devices in Assemblies. Arrangement of devices in assemblies shall be such that individual components can safely perform their intended function without adversely affecting the safe operation of other components in the assembly.

(c) Guarding of High-Voltage Energized Parts Within a Compartment. When access for other than visual inspection is required to a compartment that contains energized high-voltage parts, barriers shall be provided as follows:

(1) To prevent accidental contact with energized parts.

Exception No. 1: Fuse and fuseholder designed to permit fuse replacement by qualified persons using equipment designed for the purpose without de-energizing the fuseholder.

Exception No. 2: Exposed live parts shall be permitted within the compartment where accessible to qualified persons only.

Figure 710-2. A 300-kVa, 15-kV pad-mounted transformer integral unit containing a primary hook-stick-operated switch with a limited number of secondary breakers or switches. (*Square D Co.*)

(2) To prevent tools or other equipment from being dropped on energized parts.

(d) Guarding of Low-Voltage Energized Parts Within a Compartment. Energized bare parts mounted on doors shall be guarded where the door must be opened for maintenance of equipment or removal of drawout equipment.

(e) Clearance for Cable Conductors Entering Enclosure. The unobstructed space opposite terminals or opposite conduits or other raceways entering a switchgear or control assembly shall be adequate for the type of conductor and method of termination.

(f) Accessibility of Energized Parts.

(1) Doors which would provide nonqualified persons access to high-voltage energized parts shall be locked.

(2) Low-voltage control equipment, relays, motors, and the like shall not be installed in compartments with exposed high-voltage energized parts or high-voltage wiring unless the access door or cover is interlocked with the high-voltage switch or disconnecting means to prevent door or cover from being opened or removed unless the switch or disconnecting means is in its isolating position.

Exception No. 1: Instrument or control transformers connected to high voltage.

Exception No. 2: Space heaters.

(g) Grounding. Frames of switchgear and control assemblies shall be grounded.

(h) Grounding of Devices. Devices with metal cases and/or frames, such as instruments, relays, meters, and instrument and control transformers, located in or on switchgear or control, shall have the frame or case grounded.

Figure 710-3. A 1,500-kVa, 15-kV unit substation transformer or power center type which is adaptable to a line-up of a high-voltage switch, transformer, and low-voltage secondary. (*Square D Co.*)

(i) Door Stops and Cover Plates. External hinged doors or covers shall be provided with stops to hold them in the open position. Cover plates intended to be removed for inspection of energized parts or wiring shall be equipped with lifting handles and shall not exceed 12 square feet (1.11 sq m) in area or 60 pounds (27.22 kg) in weight, unless they are hinged and bolted or locked.

(j) Gas Discharge from Interrupting Devices. Gas discharged during operating of interrupting devices shall be so directed as not to endanger personnel.

(k) Inspection Windows. Windows intended for inspection of disconnecting switches or other devices shall be of suitable transparent material.

(l) Location of Devices. Control and instrument transfer switch handles or pushbuttons shall be in a readily accessible location at an elevation not over 78 inches (1.98 m).

Exception No. 1: Operating handles requiring more than 50 pounds (22.68 kg) of force shall not be higher than 66 inches (1.68 m) in either the open or closed position.

Exception No. 2: Operating handles for infrequently operated devices, such as drawout fuses, fused potential or control transformers and their primary disconnects, and bus transfer switches, shall not be required to be readily accessible, where they are otherwise safely operable and serviceable from a portable platform.

(m) Interlocks — Interrupter Switches. Interrupter switches equipped with stored energy mechanisms shall have mechanical interlocks to prevent access to the switch compartment unless the stored energy mechanism is in the discharged or blocked position.

1019

(n) Stored Energy for Opening. The stored energy operator shall be permitted to be left in the uncharged position after the switch has been closed if a single movement of the operating handle charges the operator and opens the switch.

Figure 710-4 (left). Group-operated interrupter-switch and power-fuse combination rated at 13.8 kV, 600 A continuous and interrupting, 40,000 A momentary, 40,000 A fault closing. Figure 710-5 (right). Components of the indoor solid-material (SM) power fuseholder (boric-acid arc-extinguishing type) with a 14.4 kV, 400 E A max, 40,000 A RMS asym. interrupting rating. Shown here are the spring and cable assembly, refill unit, holder, and snuffler. (*S & C Electric Co.*)

(o) Fused Interrupter Switches.

(1) Fused interrupter switches shall be so installed that all supply terminals shall be at the top of the switch enclosure.

Exception: Supply terminals shall not be required to be at the top of the switch enclosure if barriers are installed to prevent persons from accidentally contacting energized parts or dropping tools or fuses into energized parts.

(2) Where fuses can be energized by backfeed, a sign shall be placed on the enclosure door reading, "WARNING — FUSES MAY BE ENERGIZED BY BACKFEED."

(p) Interlocks — Circuit Breakers.

(1) Circuit breakers equipped with stored energy mechanisms shall be designed to prevent the release of the stored energy unless the mechanism has been fully charged.

(2) Mechanical interlocks shall be provided in the housing to prevent the complete withdrawal of the circuit breaker from the housing when the stored energy mechanism is in the fully charged position.

Exception: Where a suitable device is provided that prevents the complete withdrawal of the circuit breaker unless the closing function is blocked.

D. Installations Accessible to Qualified Persons Only

710-31. Enclosure for Electrical Installations. See Section 110-31.

710-32. Circuit Conductors. Circuit conductors shall be permitted to be installed in raceways, in cable trays, as metal-clad cable, as bare wire, cable, and busbars, or as nonmetallic-sheathed cables, or conductors as provided in Sections 710-3 through 710-6. Bare live conductors shall conform with Sections 710-33 and 710-34.

Insulators, together with their mounting and conductor attachments, where used as supports for wires, single-conductor cables, or busbars, shall be capable of safely withstanding the maximum magnetic forces that would prevail when two or more conductors of a circuit were subjected to short-circuit current.

Open runs of insulated wires and cables having a bare lead sheath or a braided outer covering shall be supported in a manner designed to prevent physical damage to the braid or sheath. Supports for lead-covered cables shall be designed to prevent electrolysis of the sheath.

710-33. Minimum Space Separation. In field-fabricated installations, the minimum air separation between bare live conductors and between such conductors and adjacent grounded surfaces shall not be less than the values given in Table 710-33. These values shall not apply to interior portions or exterior terminals of equipment designed, manufactured, and tested in accordance with accepted national standards.

710-34. Work Space and Guarding. See Section 110-34.

E. Mobile and Portable Equipment

710-41. General.

(a) Covered. The provisions of this part shall apply to installations and use of high-voltage power distribution and utilization equipment that is portable and/or mobile, such as substations and switch houses mounted on skids, trailers, or cars, mobile shovels, draglines, cranes, hoists, drills, dredges, compressors, pumps, conveyors, underground excavators, and the like.

(b) Other Requirements. The requirements of this part shall be additional to, or amendatory of, those prescribed in Articles 100 through 725 of this Code. Special attention shall be paid to Article 250.

(c) Protection. Adequate enclosures and/or guarding shall be provided to protect portable and mobile equipment from physical damage.

(d) Disconnecting Means. Disconnecting means shall be installed for mobile and portable high-voltage equipment according to the requirements of Part H of Article 230 and shall disconnect all ungrounded conductors.

710-42. Overcurrent Protection. Motors driving single or multiple dc generators supplying a system operating on a cyclic load basis do not require running overcurrent protection, provided that the thermal rating of the ac drive motor cannot be exceeded under any operating condition. The branch-circuit protective device(s) shall provide short-circuit and locked-rotor protection, and shall be permitted to be external to the equipment.

710-43. Enclosures. All energized switching and control parts shall be enclosed in effectively grounded metal cabinets or enclosures. These cabinets or enclosures shall be marked

Table 710-33.   Minimum Clearance of Live Parts*

Nominal Voltage Rating, kV	Impulse Withstand, B.I.L. kV		Minimum Clearance of Live Parts, in Inches			
			Phase-to-Phase		Phase-to-Ground	
	Indoors	Outdoors	Indoors	Outdoors	Indoors	Outdoors
2.4–4.16	60	95	4.5	7	3.0	6
7.2	75	95	5.5	7	4.0	6
13.8	95	110	7.5	12	5.0	7
14.4	110	110	9.0	12	6.5	7
23	125	150	10.5	15	7.5	10
34.5	150	150	12.5	15	9.5	10
	200	200	18.0	18	13.0	13
46		200		18		13
		250		21		17
69		250		21		17
		350		31		25
115		550		53		42
138		550		53		42
		650		63		50
161		650		63		50
		750		72		58
230		750		72		58
		900		89		71
		1050		105		83

For SI units: one inch = 25.4 millimeters.

* The values given are the minimum clearance for rigid parts and bare conductors under favorable service conditions. They shall be increased for conductor movement or under unfavorable service conditions, or wherever space limitations permit. The selection of the associated impulse withstand voltage for a particular system voltage is determined by the characteristics of the surge protective equipment.

"WARNING — HIGH VOLTAGE" and shall be locked so that only authorized and qualified persons can enter. Circuit breakers and protective equipment shall have the operating means projecting through the metal cabinet or enclosure so these units can be reset without opening locked doors. With doors closed, reasonable safe access for normal operation of these units shall be provided.

710-44. Collector Rings.   The collector ring assemblies on revolving-type machines (shovels, draglines, etc.) shall be guarded to prevent accidental contact with energized parts by personnel on or off the machine.

710-45. Power Cable Connections to Mobile Machines.   A metallic enclosure shall be provided on the mobile machine for enclosing the terminals of the power cable. The enclosure shall include provisions for a solid connection for the ground wire(s) terminal to effectively ground the machine frame. Ungrounded conductors shall be attached to insulators or terminated in approved high-voltage cable couplers (which include ground wire connectors) of proper voltage and ampere rating. The method of cable termination used shall prevent any strain or pull on the cable from stressing the electrical connections. The enclosure shall have provision for locking so only authorized and qualified persons may open, and shall be marked "WARNING — HIGH VOLTAGE."

710-46. High-Voltage Portable Cable for Main Power Supply.   Flexible high-voltage cable supplying power to portable or mobile equipment shall comply with Article 250 and Article 400, Part C.

710-47. Grounding.   Mobile equipment shall be grounded in accordance with Article 250.

F. Tunnel Installations

710-51. General.

(a) Covered. The provisions of this part shall apply to installation and use of high-voltage power distribution and utilization equipment which is portable and/or mobile, such as substations, trailers, or cars, mobile shovels, draglines, hoists, drills, dredges, compressors, pumps, conveyors, underground excavators, and the like.

(b) Other Articles. The requirements of this part shall be additional to, or amendatory of, those prescribed in Articles 100 through 710 of this Code. Special attention shall be paid to Article 250.

(c) Protection Against Physical Damage. Conductors and cables in tunnels shall be located above the tunnel floor and so placed or guarded to protect them from physical damage.

710-52. Overcurrent Protection. Motor-operated equipment shall be protected from overcurrent in accordance with Article 430. Transformers shall be protected from overcurrent in accordance with Article 450.

710-53. Conductors. High-voltage conductors in tunnels shall be installed in (1) metal conduit or other metal raceway; (2) Type MC cable; or (3) other approved multiconductor cable. Multiconductor portable cable shall be permitted to supply mobile equipment.

710-54. Bonding and Equipment Grounding Conductor.

(a) Grounded and Bonded. All nonenergized metal parts of electric equipment and all metal raceways and cable sheaths shall be effectively grounded and bonded to all metal pipes and rails at the portal and at intervals not exceeding 1000 feet (305 m) throughout the tunnel.

(b) Equipment Grounding Conductor. An equipment grounding conductor shall be run with circuit conductors inside the metal raceway or inside the multiconductor cable jacket. The equipment grounding conductor shall be permitted to be insulated or bare.

710-55. Transformers, Switches, and Electric Equipment. All transformers, switches, motor controllers, motors, rectifiers, and other equipment installed below ground shall be protected from physical damage by location or guarding.

710-56. Energized Parts. Bare terminals of transformers, switches, motor controllers, and other equipment shall be enclosed to prevent accidental contact with energized parts.

710-57. Ventilation System Controls. Electrical controls for the ventilation system shall be so arranged that the air flow can be reversed.

710-58. Disconnecting Means. A switching device meeting the requirements of Article 430 or 450 shall be installed at each transformer or motor location for disconnecting the transformer or motor. The switching device shall open all ungrounded conductors of a circuit simultaneously.

710-59. Enclosures. Enclosures for use in tunnels shall be dripproof, weatherproof, or submersible as required by the environmental conditions. Switch or contactor enclosures shall not be used as junction boxes or raceways for conductors feeding through or tapping off to other switches, unless special designs are used to provide adequate space for this purpose.

710-60. Grounding. Tunnel equipment shall be grounded in accordance with Article 250.

G. Electrode-type Boilers

710-70. General. The provisions of this part shall apply to boilers operating over 600 volts, nominal, in which heat is generated by the passage of current between electrodes through the liquid being heated.

710-71. Electric Supply System. Electrode-type boilers shall be supplied only from a 3-phase, 4-wire solidly grounded wye system, or from isolating transformers arranged to provide such a system. Control circuit voltages shall not exceed 150 volts, shall be supplied from a grounded system, and shall have the controls in the ungrounded conductor.

710-72. Branch Circuit Requirements.

(a) Rating. Each boiler shall be supplied from an individual branch circuit rated not less than 100 percent of the total load.

(b) Common-Trip Fault Interrupting Device. The circuit shall be protected by a 3-phase common-trip fault interrupting device, which shall be permitted to automatically reclose the circuit upon removal of an overload condition but shall not reclose after a fault condition.

(c) Phase Fault Protection. Phase fault protection shall be provided in each phase, consisting of a separate phase overcurrent relay connected to a separate current transformer in the phase.

(d) Ground Current Detection. Means shall be provided for detection of the sum of the neutral and ground currents and shall trip the circuit interrupting device if the sum of those currents exceeds the greater of 5 amperes or 7½ percent of the boiler full-load current for 10 seconds or exceeds an instantaneous value of 25 percent of the boiler full-load current.

(e) Grounded Neutral Conductor. The grounded neutral conductor shall:

(1) Be connected to the pressure vessel containing the electrodes.

(2) Be insulated for not less than 600 volts.

(3) Have not less than the ampacity of the largest ungrounded branch-circuit conductor.

(4) Be installed in the same raceway or cable tray with the ungrounded conductors.

(5) Not be used for any other circuit.

710-73. Pressure and Temperature Limit Control. Each boiler shall be equipped with a means to limit the maximum temperature and/or pressure by directly or indirectly interrupting all current flow through the electrodes. Such means shall be in addition to the temperature and/or pressure regulating systems and pressure relief or safety valves.

710-74. Grounding. All exposed noncurrent-carrying metal parts of the boiler and associated exposed grounded structures or equipment shall be bonded to the pressure vessel or to the neutral conductor to which the vessel is connected, in accordance with Section 250-79, except the ampacity of the bonding jumper shall be not less than the ampacity of the neutral conductor.

ARTICLE 720 — CIRCUITS AND EQUIPMENT OPERATING AT LESS THAN 50 VOLTS

Contents

720-6. Receptacle Rating.
720-7. Receptacles Required.
720-8. Overcurrent Protection.

720-9. Batteries.
720-10. Grounding.

720-1. Scope. This article covers installations operating at less than 50 volts, direct current or alternating current.

Exception: As covered in Articles 650, 725, and 760.

720-2. Hazardous (Classified) Locations. Installations coming within the scope of this article and installed in hazardous (classified) locations shall also comply with the appropriate provisions of Articles 500 through 517.

It should be understood that low voltage alone does not make a circuit incapable of igniting flammable atmospheres. Under some conditions, even ordinary flashlights using two 1½-V "D" cells can be a source of ignition in hazardous (classified) locations.

720-4. Conductors. Conductors shall not be smaller than No. 12 copper or equivalent. Conductors for appliance branch circuits supplying more than one appliance or appliance receptacle shall not be smaller than No. 10 copper or equivalent.

720-5. Lampholders. Standard lampholders having a rating of not less than 660 watts shall be used.

720-6. Receptacle Rating. Receptacles shall have a rating of not less than 15 amperes.

720-7. Receptacles Required. Receptacles of not less than 20-ampere rating shall be provided in kitchens, laundries, and other locations where portable appliances are likely to be used.

720-8. Overcurrent Protection. Overcurrent protection shall comply with Article 240.

720-9. Batteries. Installations of storage batteries shall comply with Article 480.

720-10. Grounding. Grounding shall comply with Sections 250-5(a) and 250-45.

ARTICLE 725 — CLASS 1, CLASS 2, AND CLASS 3 REMOTE-CONTROL, SIGNALING, AND POWER-LIMITED CIRCUITS

Contents

ARTICLE 725—REMOTE-CONTROL, SIGNALING CIRCUITS

B. Class 1 Circuits

725-11. Power Limitations for Class 1 Circuits.
  (a) Class 1 Power-Limited Circuits.
  (b) Class 1 Remote-Control and Signaling Circuits.
725-12. Overcurrent Protection.
725-13. Location of Overcurrent Devices.
725-14. Wiring Method.
725-15. Conductors of Different Circuits in Same Enclosure, Cable, or Raceway.
725-16. Conductors.
  (a) Sizes and Use.
  (b) Insulation.
725-17. Number of Conductors in Raceways, Cable Trays, and Cables, and Derating.
  (a) Class 1 Circuits.
  (b) Power-Supply Conductors and Class 1 Circuit Conductors.
  (c) Class 1 Circuit Conductors in Cable Trays.
725-18. Physical Protection.
725-19. Circuits Extending Beyond One Building.
725-20. Grounding.

C. Class 2 and Class 3 Circuits

725-31. Power Limitations of Class 2 and Class 3 Circuits.
725-32. Interconnection of Power Supplies.
725-34. Marking.
725-35. Overcurrent Protection.
725-36. Location of Overcurrent Devices.
725-37. Wiring Methods on Supply Side.
725-38. Wiring Methods and Materials on Load Side.
  (a) Separation from Light, Power, and Class 1 Conductors.
  (b) Fire Resistance of Cables.
725-39. Conductors of Different Circuits in Same Cable, Enclosure, or Raceway.
  (a) Two or More Class 2 Circuits.
  (b) Two or More Class 3 Circuits.
  (c) Class 2 Circuits with Class 3 Circuits.
  (d) Class 2 or Class 3 Circuits with Other Circuits.
725-40. Conductors.
  (a) Class 2 Circuits.
  (b) Class 3 Circuits.
725-41. Cable Marking.
725-42. Circuits Extending Beyond One Building.
725-43. Grounding.

A. Scope and General

725-1. Scope. This article covers remote-control, signaling, and power-limited circuits that are not an integral part of a device or appliance.

(FPN): The circuits described herein are characterized by usage and electrical power limitations which differentiate them from electric light and power circuits and, therefore, alternative requirements to those of Chapters 1 through 4 are given with regard to minimum wire sizes, derating factors, overcurrent protection, insulation requirements, and wiring methods and materials.

Included within the scope of Article 725 are such systems as burglar alarm circuits (a signaling system) and the coaxial cable wiring often associated with interconnection of electronic data processing (EDP) and computer equipment not within a data processing room as covered in Article 645. See Article 760 for fire protective signaling systems, Article 800 for communication circuits, Article 810 for radio and television equipment other than cable TV, and Article 820 for cable TV systems.

725-2. Locations and Other Articles. Circuits and equipment shall comply with (a), (b), (c), (d), and (e) below.

(a) Spread of Fire or Products of Combustion. Section 300-21.

(b) Ducts, Plenums, and Other Air-Handling Spaces. Section 300-22 where installed in ducts or plenums or other space used for environmental air.

Exception to (b): As permitted in Section 725-38(b)(3).

See commentary following Sections 300-22(b), 300-22(c), 725-38(b)(1) FPN, and 725-38(b)(3) FPN.

(c) Hazardous (Classified) Locations. Articles 500 through 516, and Article 517, Part G where installed in hazardous (classified) locations.

(d) Cable Trays. Article 318 where installed in cable tray.

(e) Motor Control Circuits. Article 430, Part F where tapped from the load side of the motor branch-circuit protective device(s) as specified in Section 430-72(a).

725-3. Classifications. A remote-control, signaling, or power-limited circuit is the portion of the wiring system between the load side of the overcurrent device or the power-limited supply and all connected equipment, and shall be Class 1, Class 2, or Class 3 as defined in (a) and (b) below.

(a) Class 1 Circuits. Circuits that comply with Part B of this article and in which the voltage and power limitations are in accordance with Section 725-11.

(b) Class 2 and Class 3 Circuits. Circuits that comply with Part C of this article and in which the voltage and power limitations are in accordance with Section 725-31.

(FPN): Due to their power limitations, both Class 2 and 3 circuits consider safety from a fire initiation standpoint. In addition, Class 2 circuits provide acceptable protection from electric shock. However, since Class 3 circuits permit higher allowable levels of voltage and current, additional safeguards are specified to provide protection against the electric shock hazard that could be encountered.

725-4. Safety-Control Equipment. Remote-control circuits to safety-control equipment shall be Class 1 if the failure of the equipment to operate introduces a direct fire or life hazard. Room thermostats, water temperature regulating devices, and similar controls used in conjunction with electrically controlled household heating and air conditioning shall not be considered safety-control equipment.

725-5. Communication Cables. Class 1 circuits shall not be run in the same cable with communication circuits. Class 2 and Class 3 circuit conductors shall be permitted in the same cable with communication circuits, in which case the Class 2 and Class 3 circuits shall be classified as communication circuits and shall meet the requirements of Article 800.

B. Class 1 Circuits

725-11. Power Limitations for Class 1 Circuits.

(a) Class 1 Power-Limited Circuits. These circuits shall be supplied from a source having a rated output of not more than 30 volts and 1000 volt-amperes. Power sources other than transformers shall be protected by overcurrent devices rated at not more than 167 percent of the volt-ampere rating of the source divided by the rated voltage. The overcurrent devices shall not be interchangeable with overcurrent devices of higher ratings. The overcurrent device shall be permitted to be an integral part of the power supply.

(1) Transformers. Transformers used to supply power-limited Class 1 circuits shall comply with Article 450.

(2) Other Power Sources. To comply with the 1000 volt-ampere limitation of Section 725-11(a), the maximum output of power sources other than transformers shall be limited to 2500 volt-amperes and the product of the maximum current and maximum voltage shall not exceed 10,000 volt-amperes. These ratings shall be determined with any overcurrent protective device bypassed.

(FPN): For definitions of V_{max}, I_{max}, VA_{max}, see Note 1, Tables 725-31(a) and (b).

(b) Class 1 Remote-Control and Signaling Circuits. Class 1 remote-control and signaling circuits shall not exceed 600 volts; however, the power output of the source shall not be required to be limited.

725-12. Overcurrent Protection. Conductors No. 14 and larger shall be protected against overcurrent in accordance with the values specified in Tables 310-16 through 310-31. Derating factors shall not be applied. Overcurrent protection shall not exceed 7 amperes for No. 18 conductors and 10 amperes for No. 16.

Exception No. 1: Where other articles of this Code permit or require other overcurrent protection.

(FPN): For example, see Section 430-72 for motors, Section 610-53 for cranes and hoists, and Section 660-9 for X-ray equipment.

See Section 240-4, Exception No. 2 for another example.

Exception No. 2: Transformer Secondary Conductors. Class 1 circuit conductors supplied by the secondary of a single-phase transformer having only a 2-wire (single-voltage) secondary shall be permitted to be protected by overcurrent protection provided on the primary (supply) side of the transformer, provided this protection is in accordance with Section 450-3 and does not exceed the value determined by multiplying the secondary conductor ampacity by the secondary-to-primary transformer voltage ratio. Transformer secondary conductors other than 2-wire shall not be considered to be protected by the primary overcurrent protection.

Exception No. 2 correlates with Section 240-3, Exception No. 5 and Section 430-72(b), Exception No. 3.

Exception No. 3: Class 1 circuit conductors No. 14 and larger which are tapped from the load side of the overcurrent protective device(s) of the controlled light and power circuit shall require only short-circuit and ground-fault protection and shall be permitted to be protected by the branch-circuit overcurrent protective device(s) where the rating of the protective device(s) is not more than 300 percent of the ampacity of the Class 1 circuit conductor.

Exception No. 3 correlates with Section 240-3, Exception No. 4.

725-13. Location of Overcurrent Devices. Overcurrent devices shall be located at the point where the conductor to be protected receives its supply.

Exception No. 1: Where the overcurrent device protecting the larger conductor also protects the smaller conductor.

Exception No. 2: Where overcurrent protection is provided in accordance with Section 725-12, Exception No. 2.

725-14. Wiring Method. Installations of Class 1 circuits shall be in accordance with the appropriate articles in Chapter 3.

Exception No. 1: As provided in Sections 725-15 through 725-17.

Exception No. 2: Where other articles of this Code permit or require other methods.

725-15. Conductors of Different Circuits in Same Enclosure, Cable, or Raceway. Class 1 circuits shall be permitted to occupy the same enclosure, cable, or raceway without regard to whether the individual circuits are alternating current or direct current, provided all conductors are insulated for the maximum voltage of any conductor in the enclosure, cable, or raceway. Power supply and Class 1 circuit conductors shall be permitted in the same enclosure, cable, or raceway only where the equipment powered is functionally associated.

Exception No. 1: When installed in factory- or field-assembled control centers.

Exception No. 2: Underground conductors in a manhole where one of the following conditions is met:

a. The power supply or Class 1 circuit conductors are in a metal-enclosed cable, or Type UF cable;

b. The conductors are permanently separated from the power supply conductors by a continuous firmly fixed nonconductor such as flexible tubing, in addition to the insulation on the wire;

c. The conductors are permanently and effectively separated from the power supply conductors and securely fastened to racks, insulators, or other approved supports.

This section permits the installation of Class 1 power-limited circuit conductors in manholes with wiring of non-power-limited systems where suitable separation provides the same degree of protection as is required for Class 2 and 3 power-limited circuits in Section 725-38(a), for communication circuits in Section 800-3(a), for radio/television antennas and lead-in conductors in Section 810-18(b), and for CATV conductors in Section 820-13(a).

725-16. Conductors.

(a) Sizes and Use. Conductors of Nos. 18 and 16 shall be permitted to be used provided they supply loads that do not exceed the ampacities given in Section 402-5 and are installed in a raceway, an approved enclosure, or a listed cable. Conductors larger than No. 16 shall not supply loads greater than the ampacities given in Tables 310-16 through 310-31, as applicable. Flexible cords shall comply with Article 400.

(b) Insulation. Insulation on conductors shall be suitable for 600 volts. Conductors larger than No. 16 shall comply with Article 310. Conductors in sizes No. 18 and 16 shall be Type RFH-2, RFHH-2, RFHH-3, FFH-2, TF, TFF, TFN, TFFN, PF, PFF, PGF, PGFF, PTF, PTFF, SF-2, SFF-2, PAF, PAFF, ZF, ZFF, KF-2, or KFF-2. Conductors with other types and thicknesses of insulation shall be permitted if listed for Class 1 circuit use.

725-17. Number of Conductors in Raceways, Cable Trays, and Cables, and Derating.

(a) Class 1 Circuits. Where only Class 1 circuits are in a raceway, the number of conductors shall be determined in accordance with Section 300-17. The derating factors given in Note 8 to Tables 310-16 through 310-31 shall apply only if such conductors carry continuous loads.

(b) Power-Supply Conductors and Class 1 Circuit Conductors. Where power-supply conductors and Class 1 circuit conductors are permitted in a raceway in accordance with Section 725-15, the number of conductors shall be determined in accordance with Section 300-17. The derating factors given in Note 8 to Tables 310-16 through 310-31 shall apply as follows:

(1) To all conductors when the Class 1 circuit conductors carry continuous loads and where the total number of conductors is more than three.

(2) To the power-supply conductors only, when the Class 1 circuit conductors do not carry continuous loads and where the number of power-supply conductors is more than three.

(c) Class 1 Circuit Conductors in Cable Trays. Where Class 1 circuit conductors are installed in cable trays they shall comply with the provisions of Sections 318-9 through 318-11.

725-18. Physical Protection. Where damage to remote-control circuits of safety control equipment would introduce a hazard, as covered in Section 725-4, all conductors of such remote-control circuits shall be installed in rigid metal conduit, intermediate metal conduit, rigid nonmetallic conduit, electrical metallic tubing, Type MI cable, Type MC cable, or be otherwise suitably protected from physical damage.

725-19. Circuits Extending Beyond One Building. Class 1 circuits that extend aerially beyond one building shall also meet the requirements of Article 225.

725-20. Grounding. Class 1 circuits and equipment shall be grounded in accordance with Article 250.

C. Class 2 and Class 3 Circuits

725-31. Power Limitations of Class 2 and Class 3 Circuits. As specified in Table 725-31(a) for ac circuits and Table 725-31(b) for dc circuits, the power for Class 2 and Class 3 circuits shall be either inherently limited requiring no overcurrent protection or limited by a combination of a power source and overcurrent protection.

725-32. Interconnection of Power Supplies. Class 2 or Class 3 power supplies shall not be paralleled or otherwise interconnected unless listed for such interconnection.

725-34. Marking. A Class 2 or Class 3 power supply unit shall be durably marked where plainly visible to indicate the class of supply and its electrical rating.

725-35. Overcurrent Protection. Where overcurrent protection is required, the overcurrent protective devices shall not be interchangeable with devices of higher ratings. The overcurrent device shall be permitted as an integral part of the power supply.

725-36. Location of Overcurrent Devices. Overcurrent devices, where required, shall be located at the point where the conductor to be protected receives its supply.

725-37. Wiring Methods on Supply Side. Conductors and equipment on the supply side of overcurrent protection, transformers, or current-limiting devices shall be installed in accordance with the appropriate requirements of Chapter 3. Transformers or other devices supplied from electric light or power circuits shall be protected by an overcurrent device rated not over 20 amperes.

Exception: The input leads of a transformer or other power source supplying Class 2 and Class 3 circuits shall be permitted to be smaller than No. 14, but not smaller than No. 18 if they are not over 12 inches (305 mm) long and if they have insulation that complies with Section 725-16(b).

725-38. Wiring Methods and Materials on Load Side. Conductors on the load side of overcurrent protection, transformers, and current-limiting devices shall be insulated at not less than the requirements of Section 725-40 and shall comply with (a) and (b) below.

(a) Separation from Electric Light, Power, and Class 1 Conductors.

(1) Open Conductors. Conductors of Class 2 and Class 3 circuits shall be separated at least 2 inches (50.8 mm) from conductors of any electric light, power, or Class 1 circuits.

Exception No. 1: Where either: (1) all of the electric light, power, and Class 1 circuit conductors, or (2) all of the Class 2 and Class 3 circuit conductors are in raceways or in metal-sheathed, metal-clad, nonmetallic-sheathed, or Type UF cables.

Exception No. 2: Where the conductors are permanently separated from the conductors of the other circuits by a continuous and firmly fixed nonconductor, such as porcelain tubes or flexible tubing in addition to the insulation on the wire.

Table 725-31(a). Power Limitations for Alternating Current (Class 2 and Class 3 Circuits)

Circuit	Inherently Limited Power Source (Overcurrent protection not required)				Not Inherently Limited Power Source (Overcurrent protection required)			
	Class 2			Class 3	Class 2			Class 3
Circuit Voltage V_{max} (Note 1)	0–20†	Over 20–30†	Over 30–150	Over 30–100	0–20†	Over 20–30†	Over 30–100	Over 100–150
Power Limitation $(VA)_{max}$ (Note 1) (Volt-Amperes)	—	—	—	—	250 (see Note 3)	250	250	N.A.
Current Limitation I_{max} (Note 1) (Amps)	8.0	8.0	0.005	$150/V_{max}$	$1000/V_{max}$	$1000/V_{max}$	$1000/V_{max}$	1.0
Maximum Overcurrent Protection (Amps)	—	—	—	—	5.0	$100/V_{max}$	$100/V_{max}$	1.0
Power Source Maximum Name-plate Ratings — VA (Volt-Amps)	$5.0 \times V_{max}$	100	$0.005 \times V_{max}$	100	$5.0 \times V_{max}$	100	100	100
Power Source Maximum Name-plate Ratings — Current (Amps)	5.0	$100/V_{max}$	0.005	$100/V_{max}$	5.0	$100/V_{max}$	$100/V_{max}$	$100/V_{max}$
Supply Conductors and Cables	See Section 725-37							
Circuit Conductors and Cables	See Section 725-40							

† Voltage ranges shown are for sinusoidal ac in indoor locations or where wet contact is not likely to occur. For nonsinusoidal or wet contact conditions, see Note 2.

Table 725-31(b). Power Limitations for Direct Current (Class 2 and Class 3 Circuits)

Circuit	Inherently Limited Power Source (Note 4) (Overcurrent protection not required)					Not Inherently Limited Power Source (Overcurrent protection required)			
	Class 2			Class 3		Class 2			Class 3
Circuit Voltage V_{max} (Note 1)	0–20††	Over 20–30††	Over 30–60††	Over 60–100	Over 60–150	0–20††	Over 20–60††	Over 60–100	Over 100–150
Power Limitation $(VA)_{max}$ (Note 1) (Volt-Amps)	—	—	—	—	—	250 (see Note 3)	250	250	N.A.
Current Limitation I_{max} (Note 1) (Amps)	8.0	8.0	150/V_{max}	150/V_{max}	0.005	1000/V_{max}	1000/V_{max}	1000/V_{max}	1.0
Maximum Overcurrent Protection (Amps)	—	—	—	—	—	5.0	100/V_{max}	100/V_{max}	1.0
Power Source Maximum Nameplate Ratings — VA (Volt-Amps)	5.0 × V_{max}	100	100	100	0.005 × V_{max}	5.0 × V_{max}	100	100	100
Current (Amps)	5.0	100/V_{max}	100/V_{max}	100/V_{max}	0.005	5.0	100/V_{max}	100/V_{max}	100/V_{max}
Supply Conductors and Cables	See Section 725-37								
Circuit Conductors and Cables	See Section 725-40								

†† Voltage ranges shown are for continuous dc in indoor locations or where wet contact is not likely to occur. For interrupted dc or wet contact conditions, see Note 5.

Notes for Tables 725-31(a) and (b)

Note 1. V_{max}: Maximum output voltage regardless of load with rated input applied. I_{max}: Maximum output current under any noncapacitive load, including short circuit, and with overcurrent protection bypassed if used. $(VA)_{max}$: Maximum volt-ampere output regardless of load and overcurrent protection bypassed if used. Note 2. For nonsinusoidal ac, V_{max} shall be not greater than 42.4 volts peak. Where wet contact (immersion not included) is likely to occur, Class 3 wiring methods shall be used or V_{max} shall be not greater than: 15 volts for sinusoidal ac; 21.2 volts peak for nonsinusoidal ac. Note 3. If the power source is a transformer, $(VA)_{max}$ is 350 or less when V_{max} is 15 or less. Note 4. A dry cell battery shall be considered an inherently limited power source provided the voltage is 30 volts or less and the capacity is equal to or less than that available from series connected No. 6 carbon zinc cells. Note 5. For dc interrupted at a rate of 10 to 200 Hz, V_{max} shall not be greater than 24.8 volts. Where wet contact (immersion not included) is likely to occur, Class 3 wiring methods shall be used or V_{max} shall not be greater than: 30 volts for continuous dc; 12.4 volts for dc that is interrupted at a rate of 10 to 200 Hz.

(2) In Enclosures, Raceways, Cable Trays, and Cables. Conductors of Class 2 and Class 3 circuits shall not be placed in any enclosure, raceway, cable tray, cable, compartment, outlet box, or similar fitting with conductors of electric light, power, and Class 1 circuits.

Exception No. 1: Where the conductors of the different circuits are separated by a partition.

Exception No. 2: Conductors in outlet boxes, junction boxes, or similar fittings, or compartments where power-supply conductors are introduced solely for supplying power to the equipment connected to Class 2 or Class 3 circuits to which the other conductors in the enclosure are connected.

An example is power circuit and Class 2 circuit conductors in the same motor-starter enclosure where the Class 2 circuit source is the secondary of a control transformer in the same motor-starter enclosure. In such an installation, the Class 2 conductor insulation is not required to have the same voltage rating as the insulation on the power conductors in the same enclosure.

Exception No. 3: Underground conductors in a manhole where one of the following conditions is met:

a. The electric light or power and Class 1 circuit conductors are in a metal-enclosed cable or Type UF cable;

b. The conductors are permanently separated from the conductors of the other circuits by a continuous and firmly fixed nonconductor such as flexible tubing, in addition to the insulation or covering on the wire;

c. The conductors are permanently and effectively separated from conductors of the other circuits and securely fastened to racks, insulators, or other approved supports.

This section permits the installation of Class 2 and 3 power-limited circuit conductors in manholes with wiring of non-power-limited systems where suitable separation provides the same degree of protection as is required in Section 725-38(a). See commentary following Section 725-15, Exception No. 2.

(3) In Hoistways. Class 2 or Class 3 conductors shall be installed in rigid metal conduit, intermediate metal conduit, or electrical metallic tubing in hoistways.

Exception: As provided for in Section 620-21, Exceptions No. 1 and 2 for elevators and similar equipment.

(b) Fire Resistance of Cables.

(1) Wiring Within Buildings. Single- and multiconductor cables of Class 2 and Class 3 circuits installed as wiring within buildings shall be Type CL2, CL3, or PLTC, listed as being resistant to the spread of fire. This listing requirement for Types CL2 and CL3 cables shall become effective July 1, 1988. In addition, where the cables are in a vertical run in a shaft, Section 725-38(b)(2) shall apply, and where the cables are installed in ducts, plenums, and other air-handling spaces, Section 725-38(b)(3) shall apply. Types CL2R and CL3R cables listed for use in vertical runs in accordance with Section 725-38(b)(2) and Types CL2P and CL3P cables listed for use in ducts, plenums, and other air-handling spaces in accordance with Section 725-38(b)(3) shall be permitted to be used to meet the requirements of this section.

(FPN): One method of defining resistant to the spread of fire is that the cables do not spread fire to the top of the tray in the Vertical Tray Flame Test in UL 1581.

Exception No. 1: Where the cables are enclosed in raceway or noncombustible tubing.

Exception No. 2: In nonconcealed spaces where the exposed length of cable does not exceed 10 feet (3.05 m).

ARTICLE 725—REMOTE-CONTROL, SIGNALING CIRCUITS

Exception No. 3: Listed Type CL2X Class 2 cables less than 0.25 inch (6.4 mm) in diameter and listed Type CL3X Class 3 cables less than 0.25 inch (6.4 mm) in diameter and installed in one- or two-family or multifamily dwellings.

(FPN): One method of determining the fire resistance of CL2X and CL3X cables is by testing the cables to the VW-1 requirements in UL 1581.

UL 1581, Reference Standard for Electrical Wires, Cables, and Flexible Cords, contains basic details of conductors, of the insulation, of the jackets and other coverings, and of the methods of sample preparation of specimen selection and conditioning, and of measurements and calculations that are required in the standards for Rubber-Insulated Wires and Cables (UL 44), Thermoplastic-Insulated Wires and Cables (UL 83), and Flexible Cord and Fixture Wire (UL 62). The flame test methods of these standards include the Vertical Wire Flame Test (VW-1) and the Vertical Tray Flame Test.

Figure 725-1. UL Vertical Wire Flame Test.

The method in the VW-1 Test is a small-scale test of the flammability of insulating material. It is conducted with a single specimen secured in a vertical position in a 3-sided metal enclosure which has a layer of untreated surgical cotton on the bottom. For thermoplastic or rubber-insulated wire and cable, the specimen used is an 18-in. insulated No. 14 AWG copper or No. 12 AWG aluminum conductor. A small Kraft-paper indicating flag is attached to the sample near the top. A flame is impinged 10 in. (254 mm) below the bottom of the flag for a period of 15 seconds. It is then removed for 15 seconds and reapplied for 15 seconds. This

1034

Figure 725-2. UL Vertical Tray Flame Test.

procedure is repeated until there have been five 15-second flame applications. The sample is considered to be capable of propagating fire if:

1. More than 25 percent of the indicator flag is burned away or charred, or

2. Flaming or glowing particles are emitted which ignite the surgical cotton, or

3. The specimen continues to flame longer than 60 seconds after removal of the burner.

A sample which has passed this testing may be listed as CL2X or CL3X suitable for use as a limited-use power-limited cable. This cable may be used in one- two- and multifamily dwellings.

The Vertical Tray Flame Test is a test to determine whether cables installed in a ladder-type cable tray will propagate fire from a given exposure. The test flame is supplied by a strip or ribbon-type propane gas burner.

The cables are installed in a steel ladder-type cable tray that is 12 in. wide (300 mm), 3 in. deep (76 mm), and 96 in. long (2400 mm). Cables are installed in the tray ½ diameter apart filling 75 percent of the tray width. A burner supplying 70,000 Btu/hour [738,500 (20.32) Kw/hour] is positioned 18 in. above the bottom of the tray midway between two rungs. The burner is applied to the samples for a period of 20 minutes. The samples are considered to have passed the testing if flame has not propagated to the top of the cable tray at the conclusion of the test.

A cable which has passed this testing may be listed as a CL2 or CL3 cable.

Class 2 (CL2) and Class 3 (CL3) cables may be installed in buildings. Class 2 riser cables (CL2R) and Class 3 riser cables (CL3R) may be installed in vertical runs in shafts. A Class 2 riser cable may be installed anywhere type CL2 or CL2X can be installed but may not be used in ducts, plenums, or other air-handling spaces.

(2) In Vertical Runs. Single- and multiconductor cables of Class 2 and Class 3 circuits in a vertical run in a shaft shall be Type CL2R or CL3R listed as having fire-resistant characteristics capable of preventing the carrying of fire from floor to floor. Cables listed for use in ducts, plenums, and other air-handling spaces in accordance with Section 725-38(b)(3) shall be permitted to be used to meet the requirements of this section.

Exception: Where the cables are encased in noncombustible tubing or are located in a fireproof shaft having firestops at each floor.

(3) In Ducts, Plenums, and Other Air-Handling Spaces. Single- and multiconductor cables of Class 2 and Class 3 circuits and equipment installed in ducts or plenums or other spaces used for environmental air shall also comply with Section 300-22 as to installation methods.

Exception: Types CL2P and CL3P single- and multiconductor cables of Class 2 and Class 3 circuits listed as having adequate fire-resistant and low-smoke-producing characteristics shall be permitted for ducts and plenums as described in Section 300-22(b) and other space used for environmental air as described in Section 300-22(c).

(FPN): One method of defining low-smoke-producing cables is by establishing an acceptable value of the smoke produced per the NFPA 262-1985 test to a maximum peak optical density of 0.5 and a maximum average optical density of 0.15. Similarly, fire-resistant cables may be defined as having a maximum allowable flame travel distance of 5 feet (1.52 m) in the NFPA 262-1985 test.

NFPA 262, *Standard Method of Test for Fire and Smoke Characteristics of Wires and Cables*, is a test method for electrical wires and cables which are to be installed without raceways in plenums and other spaces used for environmental air. It was originally developed as UL 910 which is an adaptation of the Steiner Tunnel Test (NFPA 255/ASTM E84/UL723).

The test is conducted in a 25-ft long horizontal duct lined with insulating masonry faced with a row of refractory fire brick. One side of the duct is provided with a row of double-paned observation windows which permit monitoring of the progress of the test. One end of the chamber, designated as the "fire end," is provided with two gas burners which deliver flames upward to engulf the test specimen. The burners are positioned transversely to each side of the centerline of the furnace so that flame is evenly distributed across the sample. Test specimens are installed in a cable tray which is 23.9 ft long.

Smoke output is measured in a metal vent pipe at the vent end of the furnace, which is opposite the fire end. When smoke passes through the vent pipe, it passes between a light source and a photocell. The output signal of the photocell is directly proportional to the amount of light received.

The cable specimens are exposed to a fire source with an output of 300,000 Btu/hour for a period of 20 minutes. A graph of the flame distance beyond $4\frac{1}{2}$ ft (the end of the flame from the burners) versus time for the duration of the test is plotted. This graph is plotted against a representative flame spread curve for a red oak specimen. A graph is also plotted for the optical density versus time for the sample.

Optical Density $= \text{Log}_{10}\ T_o/T$

where $T_o =$ Initial Light Transmission

$T =$ Light Transmission During Test.

NFPA 262 does not list pass/fail criteria. The criteria for acceptance of a given application are given in the appropriate sections of the *Code*. See fine print note above and Sections 760-28(c)(3)(FPN), 770-6(c)(FPN), 800-3(b)(3)(FPN), and 820-15(c)(FPN).

A Class 2 or Class 3 cable which has passed the requirements of this test may be used in ducts, plenums, or other air-handling spaces. In addition, it may be used anywhere in a building that a cable of the appropriate class is permitted.

725-39. Conductors of Different Circuits in Same Cable, Enclosure, or Raceway.

(a) Two or More Class 2 Circuits. Conductors of two or more Class 2 circuits shall be permitted within the same cable, enclosure, or raceway provided all conductors in the cable, enclosure, or raceway are insulated for the maximum voltage of any conductor.

(b) Two or More Class 3 Circuits. Conductors of two or more Class 3 circuits shall be permitted within the same cable, enclosure, or raceway.

(c) Class 2 Circuits with Class 3 Circuits. Conductors of one or more Class 2 circuits shall be permitted within the same cable, enclosure, or raceway with conductors of Class 3 circuits provided that the insulation of the Class 2 circuit conductors in the cable, enclosure, or raceway is at least that required for Class 3 circuits.

(d) Class 2 or Class 3 Circuits with Other Circuits. Jacketed cables of Class 2 or Class 3 circuits shall be permitted in the same enclosure or raceway with jacketed cables of any of the following:

(1) Power-limited fire-protective signaling systems in compliance with Article 760.

(2) Nonconductive and conductive optical fiber cables in compliance with Article 770.

(3) Communication circuits in compliance with Article 800.

(4) Community antenna television and radio distribution systems in compliance with Article 820.

725-40. Conductors.

(a) Class 2 Circuits. The conductor material size and insulation shall be suitable for the particular application, and shall meet the requirements of Section 725-38(b).

Exception: Where the conductors are installed in (1) cable tray, (2) in hazardous (classified) locations except as permitted by Section 501-4(b), Exception, or (3) both, the conductors shall comply with (b)(3) below except conductors used for thermocouple circuits shall be permitted to be any of the materials used for thermocouple extension wire.

Figure 725-3. Steiner Tunnel Test chamber used in NFPA 262/UL910.

(b) Class 3 Circuits. Conductors shall comply with (1), (2), or (3) below.

Exception: Where installed in cable tray or in hazardous (classified) locations, or both, conductors shall comply with (3) below.

(1) Single conductors shall not be smaller than No. 18 and shall be insulated in accordance with Section 725-16(b).

(2) Cables shall be listed as being suitable for Class 3, power-limited fire-protective signaling or communication circuits.

(3) Type PLTC nonmetallic-sheathed, power-limited tray cable shall be a factory assembly of two or more insulated conductors under a nonmetallic jacket. The insulated conductors shall be a No. 22 through 12. The conductor material shall be copper (solid or stranded). Insulation on conductors shall be suitable for 300 volts. The cable core shall be either (1) two or more parallel conductors; (2) one or more group assemblies of twisted or parallel conductors; or (3) a combination thereof. A metallic shield or a metallized foil shield with drain wire(s) shall be permitted to be applied either over the cable core, over groups of conductors, or both. The outer jacket shall be a flame-retardant, sunlight- and moisture-resistant nonmetallic material. The cable shall be marked in accordance with Sections 310-11 and 725-41. Where the use of PLTC cable is permitted in Section 501-4(b), the cable shall be installed in cable trays, in raceways, supported by messenger wires, or directly buried where the cable is listed for this use.

Exception: Where a smooth metallic sheath, welded and corrugated metallic sheath, or interlocking tape armor is applied over the nonmetallic jacket, an overall nonmetallic jacket shall not be required. On metallic-sheathed cable without an overall nonmetallic jacket, the information required in Section 310-11 shall be located on the nonmetallic jacket under the sheath.

General Discussion of Remote-Control, Signaling, and Power-Limited Circuits.

The wiring methods required by Chapters 1 through 4 of the *Code* apply to remote-control, signaling, and power-limited circuits, except as amended by Article 725 for the particular conditions.

A remote-control, signaling, or power-limited circuit is the portion of the wiring system between the load side of the overcurrent device or the power-limited supply and all connected equipment, and is separated into Class 1, Class 2, or Class 3 circuits.

Class 1 circuits are not permitted to exceed 600 V. A remote-control circuit to safety-control equipment is a Class 1 circuit if the failure of the safety control introduces a hazard to life or property. Room thermostats and water-temperature regulating devices used in conjunction with household heating and air-conditioning systems are not considered safety-control equipment. In many cases, Class 1 circuits are extensions of power systems and are subject to the requirements of the power systems, except for the following: (1) conductors sized Nos. 16 and 18 AWG may be used if properly protected against overcurrent (see Section 725-12); (2) where damage to the circuit would introduce a hazard, the circuit is required to be mechanically protected by a suitable means (see Section 725-18); (3) the derating factors of Note 8(a) to Tables 310-16 through 310-31 are to apply only if such conductors carry a continuous load (see Section 725-17).

Class 1 remote-control circuits are commonly used to operate motor-controllers in conjunction with moving equipment or mechanical processes, elevators, conveyors, and such equipment where it is necessary to control the equipment from one or more locations to prevent a hazard to life. Class 1 wiring is required in this case, even though a low-voltage, low-energy system is used. See Section 725-4.

Another example of such a Class 1 circuit is a hospital nurses' call system where it is intended that the system be used for issuing instructions during emergency conditions.

Class 1 signaling circuits often operate at 120 V, though not limited to this value, and are often used for alarm and security systems.

Conductors and equipment on the supply side of overcurrent protection, a transformer, or current-limiting devices of Class 2 and Class 3 circuits are required to be installed according to the applicable requirements of Chapter 3. Load-side conductors and equipment are required to comply with Article 725. They are required to be separated from, and not occupy, the same raceways, cable trays, cables, or enclosures as electric light, power, and Class 1 conductors (exceptions are noted in Section 725-38).

Primary batteries are satisfactory with respect to current limitations provided the voltage is 30 or less and the capacity is equal to or less than that available from series-connected No. 6 carbon-zinc cells.

Where dry cells are used, the requirements of Note 4 to Tables 725-31(a) and 725-31(b) are applicable for inherent power limitation.

Figure 725-4 illustrates a simplified diagram of an automatic domestic oil burner unit. A thermostat is supplied by a current-limiting transformer at 24 V, and the opening and closing of the thermostat contacts controls a relay that operates the oil burner ignition and pump motor. Failure of the thermostat would not introduce a hazard. Assume that the thermostat failed in the closed-contact position, thereby energizing the ignition and motor. The Class 1 circuit, in this case an extension of the power circuit, would operate and open the circuit, that is, the high-limit control (forced warm air) or pressure switch control (circulating hot water or steam). Therefore, the safety controls and ignition circuit would be considered a Class 1 circuit, and the thermostat circuit would be considered a Class 2 circuit.

Figure 725-4. Typical installation of an automatic oil burner unit.

725-41. Cable Marking. Listed Class 2 and Class 3 cables shall be marked in accordance with Table 725-41:

Table 725-41. Cable Markings

Cable Marking	Type	Reference
CL2	Class 2 Cable	725-38(b)(1)
CL2P	Class 2 Plenum Cable	725-38(b)(3)
CL2R	Class 2 Riser Cable	725-38(b)(2)
CL2X	Class 2 Cable, Limited Use	725-38(b)(1) Exceptions No. 1, 2 and 3
CL3	Class 3 Cable	725-38(b)(1)
CL3P	Class 3 Plenum Cable	725-38(b)(3)
CL3R	Class 3 Riser Cable	725-38(b)(2)
CL3X	Class 3 Cable, Limited Use	725-38(b)(1) Exceptions No. 1, 2 and 3
PLTC	Power-Limited Tray Cable	725-40(b)(3) and 725-38(b)(1)

(FPN): See the referenced sections for permitted uses.

725-42. Circuits Extending Beyond One Building. Class 2 or Class 3 circuits that extend beyond one building and are so run as to be subject to accidental contact with electric light or power conductors operating at over 300 volts to ground shall also meet the requirements of Sections 800-2, 800-11, and 800-12 for communication circuits.

725-43. Grounding. Class 2 and Class 3 circuits and equipment shall be grounded in accordance with Article 250.

ARTICLE 760 — FIRE PROTECTIVE SIGNALING SYSTEMS

Contents

760-32. Current-Carrying Continuous   (b) Insulation.
       Line-type Fire Detectors.   (c) Installation.
   (a) Application.

A. Scope and General

760-1. Scope. This article covers the installation of wiring and equipment of fire protective signaling systems operating at 600 volts, nominal, or less.

(FPN): For further information for fire alarm, guard tour, sprinkler waterflow, and sprinkler supervisory systems, refer to the following:
NFPA 71-1982 — Central Station Signaling Systems.
NFPA 72A-1985 — Local Protective Signaling Systems.
NFPA 72B-1986 — Auxiliary Protective Signaling Systems.
NFPA 72C-1986 — Remote Station Protective Signaling Systems.
NFPA 72D-1986 — Proprietary Protective Signaling Systems.
NFPA 72E-1984 — Automatic Fire Detectors.
NFPA 74-1984 — Household Fire Warning Equipment.

(FPN): Class 1, 2 and 3 circuits are defined in Article 725.

NFPA 71, *Central Station Signaling Systems*, covers the installation, maintenance, and use of central station signaling systems. These systems include the central station physical plant, exterior communication channels, satellite stations, and the signaling facilities located at the protected premises.

This standard is intended to apply primarily to supervisory and alarm service furnished by operators constantly in attendance at a central station, manually or automatically controlled, with the required maintenance, inspection, and testing force and runner service readily available. Central station companies customarily follow this standard for maintenance, testing, and inspection, with respect to other classes of contract service that they furnish.

Such systems are controlled and operated by a person, firm, or corporation whose principal business is the furnishing and maintaining of supervised signaling service.

NFPA 72A, *Local Protective Signaling Systems*, covers systems which provide fire alarm or supervisory signals within the protected premises. These systems primarily protect life by indicating the necessity for building evacuation and secondarily by protecting property.

NFPA 72B, *Auxiliary Protective Signaling Systems*, covers systems which provide protection to an individual occupancy or building or to a group of buildings of a single occupancy and utilize municipal fire alarm facilities in order to transmit an alarm to the fire department.

Alarms from an auxiliary system are received at municipal fire alarm headquarters on the same equipment and by the same methods as alarms transmitted from municipal fire alarm boxes located on streets.

An auxiliary alarm system is maintained and supervised by a responsible person or corporation. The auxiliary alarm system deals with equipment and circuits in the protected property which, of themselves, are insufficient for notifying the fire department in the event of fire, but which, in combination with a suitable municipal fire alarm system, are arranged to summon fire department response when operated.

NFPA 72C, *Remote Station Protective Signaling Systems*, covers signaling systems which serve properties under various ownership from a remote station where trained, competent personnel are in constant attendance. It covers the minimum requirements for operating personnel, the remote station, installation, maintenance, testing, power supplies, signal initiation, signal notification, and recording of signals.

NFPA 72D, *Proprietary Protective Signaling Systems*, covers the installation, maintenance, testing, and use of a signaling system which serves contiguous or noncontiguous properties under one ownership from a central supervising station at the protected property, where trained, competent personnel are in constant attendance. It covers the minimum requirements for operating personnel, the central supervising station, power supplies, signal initiation, signal notification, and automatic permanent visual recording of signals.

NFPA 72E, *Automatic Fire Detectors*, provides basic minimum requirements for performance of automatic fire detectors to ensure timely warning for the purposes of life safety and property protection.

This standard is intended for use by persons knowledgeable in fire protection. It covers minimum performance, location, mounting, testing, and maintenance requirements of automatic fire detectors for the protection of the occupant, building, space, structure, area, or object in accordance with the stated purpose.

This standard is intended to be used with other NFPA standards that deal specifically with fire alarms, extinguishment, or control. Automatic fire detectors add to fire protection by initiating emergency action but only when used in conjunction with other equipment.

NFPA 74, *Household Fire Warning Equipment*, is primarily concerned with life protection, not with the protection of property. It contemplates that the family has an exit plan and covers the requirements for the proper selection, installation, operation, and maintenance of fire warning equipment for use within family living units.

A control and associated equipment, single or multiple station alarm device(s), or any combination thereof, may be used to form a household fire warning system.

Detection and alarm systems covered by this standard are solely for the use of the protected household. If the alarm is extended to any other location, such as the fire department, the system is then considered to be one of the aforementioned systems (as applicable), except that the requirements of detector location and spacing, as they apply to home warning systems, would continue to be followed.

NFPA 1221, *Public Fire Service Communication Systems*, covers the installation, maintenance, and use of all public fire service communication facilities. These facilities include public reporting, dispatching, telephone, and both two-way and microwave radio systems, all of which fulfill two principal functions: that of receiving fire alarms or other emergency calls from the public and that of retransmitting these alarms and emergency calls to fire companies and other interested agencies.

760-2. Location and Other Articles. Circuits and equipment shall comply with (a), (b), (c), and (d) below.

(a) Spread of Fire or Products of Combustion. Section 300-21.

(b) Ducts, Plenums and Other Air-Handling Spaces. Section 300-22 where installed in ducts or plenums or other space used for environmental air.

Exception to (b): As permitted in Section 760-28(c)(3).

See commentary following Sections 300-22(b) and 300-22(c).

(c) Hazardous (Classified) Locations. Articles 500 through 516 and Article 517, Part G where installed in hazardous (classified) locations.

(d) Corrosive, Damp, or Wet Locations. Sections 110-11, 300-6 and 310-9 where installed in corrosive, damp, or wet locations.

760-3. Classifications. Fire protective signaling circuits shall be classified as nonpower limited or power limited. All fire protective signaling circuits shall comply with Part A and, in addition, nonpower-limited circuits shall comply with Part B and power-limited circuits shall comply with Part C. Circuits which do not comply with all of the requirements of Part C are classified as nonpower-limited circuits and shall comply with all of the requirements of Part B. Circuits not marked according to Section 760-23 shall comply with Part B.

760-4. Identification. Fire protective signaling circuits shall be identified at terminal and junction locations, in a manner which will prevent unintentional interference with the signaling circuit during testing and servicing.

760-5. Signaling Line Circuits Extending Beyond One Building. Fire protective signaling line circuits that extend aerially beyond one building shall either meet the requirements of Article 800 and be classified as communications circuits, or shall meet the requirements of Article 225.

760-6. Grounding. Fire protective signaling circuits and equipment shall be grounded in accordance with Article 250.

Exception: DC power-limited fire protective signaling circuits having a maximum current of 0.030 amperes.

760-7. Supervision. The circuit shall be electrically supervised so that a trouble signal shall indicate the occurrence of a single open or a single ground fault on any installation wiring circuit that would prevent proper alarm operation.

Exception: Interconnecting circuits of household fire warning equipment wholly within a dwelling unit.

(FPN): For additional information, see NFPA 74-1984, Household Fire Warning Equipment.

(FPN): See articles on electrical supervision in NFPA 71, 72A, 72B, 72C, and 72D for more information about electrical supervision.

B. Nonpower-Limited Fire Protective Signaling Circuits

760-11. Power Limitations. The power supply of nonpower-limited fire protective signaling circuits shall comply with Chapters 1 through 4 and the output voltage shall not be more than 600 volts, nominal.

760-12. Overcurrent Protection. Conductors No. 14 and larger shall be protected against overcurrent in accordance with the values specified in Tables 310-16 through 310-31, as applicable. Derating factors shall not be applied. Overcurrent protection shall not exceed 7 amperes for No. 18 conductors and 10 amperes for No. 16.

Exception: Where other articles of this Code require other overcurrent protection.

See Section 240-4, Exception No. 2 for example.

760-13. Location of Overcurrent Devices. Overcurrent devices shall be located at the point where the conductor to be protected receives its supply.

Exception No. 1: Where the overcurrent device protecting the larger conductor also protects the smaller conductor.

Exception No. 2: Where overcurrent protection is provided in accordance with Section 725-12, Exception No. 2.

760-14. Wiring Method. Wiring installation shall be in accordance with the appropriate articles in Chapter 3.

Exception No. 1: As provided in Sections 760-15 through 760-18.

Exception No. 2: Where other articles of this Code require other methods.

760-15. Conductors of Different Circuits in Same Enclosure, Cable, or Raceway. Class 1 and nonpower-limited fire protective signaling circuits shall be permitted to occupy the same enclosure, cable, or raceway without regard to whether the individual circuits are alternating current or direct current, provided all conductors are insulated for the maximum voltage of any conductor in the enclosure or raceway. Power supply and fire protective signaling circuit conductors shall be permitted in the same enclosure, cable, or raceway only when connected to the same equipment.

760-16. Copper Conductors.

(a) Sizes and Use. Copper conductors of Nos. 18 and 16 shall be permitted to be used provided they supply loads that do not exceed the ampacities given in Table 402-5 and are installed in a raceway or a listed cable. Copper conductors larger than No. 16 shall not supply loads greater than the ampacities given in Tables 310-16 through 310-31, as applicable.

(b) Insulation. Insulation on conductors shall be suitable for 600 volts. Conductors larger than No. 16 shall comply with Article 310. Conductors in sizes Nos. 18 and 16 shall be Type RFH-2, RFHH-2, RFHH-3, TF, TFN, PF, PGF, SF-2, ZF, or KF-2. Conductors with other type and thickness of insulation shall be permitted if listed for nonpower-limited fire protective signaling circuit use.

(FPN): For application provisions, see Table 402-3.

(c) Conductor Materials. Conductors shall be solid or bunch-tinned (bonded) stranded copper.

See commentary following Section 760-30(a).

Exception No. 1: Stranded copper with a maximum of 7 strands for sizes 16 and 18 shall be permitted.

Exception No. 2: Stranded copper with a maximum 19 strands for sizes 14 and larger shall be permitted.

Control of the stranding is required to prevent a single fine strand of wire from completing a circuit, making it appear the circuit is operational. The fine strand could remain intact under the current used for the supervisory signal, but burn open when required to carry the higher current of an alarm signal.
Exception No. 2 permits, for example, No. 14 AWG conductors which are dual rated THW/MTW.

Exception to (b) and (c): Wire Types PTF and PAF shall be permitted only for high-temperature applications between 90°C (194°F) and 250°C (482°F).

760-17. Multiconductor Cable for Circuits Operating at 150 Volts or Less. A multiconductor cable of two or more No. 16 or 18 solid or stranded (maximum of 7 strands) copper conductors listed for this use shall be permitted to be used on fire protective signaling circuits operating at 150 volts or less. The multiconductor cable shall be installed in a raceway or exposed in accordance with the requirements of Chapter 3 except that surface-mounted cable shall not be permitted within 7 feet (2.13 m) of the floor.

760-18. Number of Conductors in Raceways, Cable Trays, and Cables, and Derating.

(a) Nonpower-Limited Fire Protective Signaling Circuits and Class 1 Circuits. Where only nonpower-limited fire protective signaling circuits and Class 1 circuits are in a raceway, the number of conductors shall be determined in accordance with Section 300-17. The derating factors given in Note 8 to Tables 310-16 through 310-31 shall apply if such conductors carry continuous load.

(b) Power-Supply Conductors and Fire Protective Signaling Circuit Conductors. Where power-supply conductors and fire protective signaling circuit conductors are permitted in a raceway in accordance with Section 760-15, the number of conductors shall be determined in accordance with Section 300-17. The derating factors given in Note 8 to Tables 310-16 through 310-31 shall apply as follows:

(1) To all conductors when the fire protective signaling circuit conductors carry continuous loads and where the total number of conductors is more than three.

(2) To the power-supply conductors only, when the fire protective signaling circuit conductors do not carry continuous loads and where the number of power-supply conductors is more than three.

(c) Cable Trays. Where fire protective signaling circuit conductors are installed in cable trays, they shall comply with Sections 318-9 through 318-11.

C. Power-Limited Fire Protective Signaling Circuits

760-21. Power Limitations. As specified in Table 760-21(a) for ac circuits and Table 760-21(b) for dc circuits, the power for power-limited fire protective signaling circuits shall be either inherently limited requiring no overcurrent protection or limited by a combination of a power source and overcurrent protection.

760-22. Supervision. In addition to the requirements of Section 760-7, either a trouble or alarm signal shall indicate the occurrence of a multiple ground fault or any short-circuit fault on the fire alarm system primary (main) power supply, alarm initiating, signaling line, or required alarm indicating circuits that would prevent proper alarm operation.

Exception: Interconnecting circuits of household fire warning equipment wholly within a dwelling unit.

(FPN): For additional information see Household Fire Warning Equipment, NFPA 74-1984.

760-23. Circuit Marking. The circuit shall be durably marked where plainly visible at terminations to indicate that it is a power-limited fire protective signaling circuit.

760-25. Overcurrent Protection. Where overcurrent protection is required, the overcurrent protective devices shall not be interchangeable with devices of higher ratings. The overcurrent device shall be permitted as an integral part of the power supply.

760-26. Location of Overcurrent Device. Overcurrent devices, where required, shall be located at the point where the conductor to be protected receives its supply.

760-27. Wiring Methods on Supply Side. Conductors and equipment on the supply side of overcurrent protection, transformers, or current-limiting devices shall be installed in accordance with the appropriate requirements of Part B and Chapter 3. Transformers or other devices supplied from power-supply conductors shall be protected by an overcurrent device rated not over 20 amperes.

Exception: The input leads of a transformer or other power source supplying power-limited fire protective signaling circuits shall be permitted to be smaller than No. 14 but not smaller than No. 18, if they are not over 12 inches (305 mm) long and if they have insulation that complies with Section 760-16(b).

760-28. Wiring Methods and Materials on Load Side. Circuits on the load side of overcurrent protection, transformers, and current-limiting devices shall be permitted to use wiring methods and materials in accordance with (a) and (b) below.

Table 760-21(a). Power Limitations for Alternating-Current Fire Protective Signaling Circuits

	Inherently Limited Power Source (Overcurrent protection not required)			Not Inherently Limited Power Source (Overcurrent protection required)		
Circuit Voltage V_{max} (Note 1)	0–20	Over 20–30	Over 30–100	0–20	Over 20–100	Over 100–150
Power Limitation $(VA)_{max}$ (Note 1) (Volt-Amperes)	—	—	—	250 (see Note 2)	250	N.A.
Current Limitation I_{max} (Note 1) (Amps)	8.0	8.0	$150/V_{max}$	$1000/V_{max}$	$1000/V_{max}$	1.0
Maximum Overcurrent Protection (Amps)	—	—	—	5.0	$100/V_{max}$	1.0
Power Source Maximum Nameplate Ratings — VA (Volt-Amps)	$5.0 \times V_{max}$	100	100	$5.0 \times V_{max}$	100	100
Current (Amps)	5.0	$100/V_{max}$	$100/V_{max}$	5.0	$100/V_{max}$	$100/V_{max}$
Supply Conductors and Cables	See Section 760-27					
Circuit Conductors and Cables	See Section 760-30					

1047

Table 760-21(b). Power Limitations for Direct-Current Fire Protective Signaling Circuits

	Inherently Limited Power Source (Overcurrent protection not required)				Not Inherently Limited Power Source (Overcurrent protection required)		
	0–20	Over 20–30	Over 30–100	Over 100–250	0–20	Over 20–100	Over 100–150
Circuit Voltage V_{max} (Note 1)							
Power Limitation $(VA)_{max}$ (Note 1) (Volt-Amps)	—	—	—	—	250 (see Note 2)	250	N.A.
Current Limitation I_{max} (Note 1) (Amps)	8.0	8.0	$150/V_{max}$	0.030	$1000/V_{max}$	$1000/V_{max}$	1.0
Maximum Overcurrent Protection (Amps)	—	—	—	—	5.0	$100/V_{max}$	1.0
Power Source Maximum Name-plate Ratings — VA (Volt-Amps)	$5.0 \times V_{max}$	100	100	$0.030 \times V_{max}$	$5.0 \times V_{max}$	100	100
Power Source Maximum Name-plate Ratings — Current (Amps)	5.0	$100/V_{max}$	$100/V_{max}$	0.030	5.0	$100/V_{max}$	$100/V_{max}$
Supply Conductors and Cables	See Section 760-27						
Circuit Conductors and Cables	See Section 760-30						

Notes for Tables 760-21(a) and (b)

Note 1. V_{max}: Maximum output voltage regardless of load with rated input applied. I_{max}: Maximum output current after one minute of operation under any noncapacitive load, including short circuit, and with overcurrent protection bypassed if used. VA_{max}: Maximum volt-ampere output regardless of load and overcurrent protection bypassed if used.

Note 2. If the power source is a transformer, $(VA)_{max}$ is 350 or less when V_{max} is 15 or less.

FIRE PROTECTIVE SIGNALING SYSTEMS—ARTICLE 760

(a) Nonpower-Limited Wiring Methods and Materials. The appropriate articles of Chapter 3 including Section 300-17 shall apply, and, in addition, conductors shall be copper, solid, bunch-tinned, or stranded with a maximum of 19 strands.

Exception No. 1: Conductors and multiconductor cables described in and installed in accordance with Sections 760-16 and 760-17 shall be permitted.

Section 760-28(a) and Exception No. 1 permit the same wiring methods for power-limited circuits as are permitted for electric power and light circuit wiring in Chapter 3, or for nonpower-limited circuits in Sections 760-16 and 760-17. The special wiring covered by Section 760-28(b) is not the only acceptable method for wiring power-limited fire protective signaling systems. However, Section 760-29 is still applicable. Even if a Chapter 3 wiring method is used for a power-limited circuit, the conductors are required to be separated as required by Section 760-29.

Exception No. 2: The derating factors given in Note 8 to Tables 310-16 through 310-31 shall not apply.

(FPN): Power-limited circuits can be reclassified and installed as nonpower-limited circuits if the markings required by Section 760-23 are eliminated (see Section 760-3) and the entire circuit is installed using the wiring methods and materials in accordance with Part B, Nonpower-Limited Fire-Protective Signaling Circuits.

(b) Power-Limited Wiring Methods and Materials. Power-limited circuit conductors and cables described in Section 760-30 shall be installed as follows:

(1) In raceway or exposed on surface of ceiling and sidewalls or "fished" in concealed spaces. Where installed exposed, cable shall be adequately supported and terminated in approved fittings and installed in such a way that maximum protection against physical damage is afforded by building construction such as baseboards, door frames, ledges, etc. Where located within 7 feet (2.13 m) of the floor, cable shall be securely fastened in an approved manner at intervals of not more than 18 inches (457 mm).

(2) In metal raceway or rigid nonmetallic conduit when passing through a floor or wall to a height of 7 feet (2.13 m) above the floor unless adequate protection can be afforded by building construction such as detailed in (1) above, or unless an equivalent solid guard is provided.

(3) In rigid metal conduit, intermediate metal conduit or electrical metallic tubing when installed in hoistways.

Exception: As provided for in Section 620-21, Exceptions No. 1 and 2 for elevators and similar equipment.

(c) Fire Resistance of Cables.

(1) Wiring Within Buildings. Single- and multiconductor power-limited fire-protective signaling circuit cables installed as wiring within buildings shall be Type FPL listed as being resistant to the spread of fire. This listing requirement for Type FPL cable shall become effective on July 1, 1988. In addition, where the cables are in a vertical run in a shaft, Section 760-28(c)(2) shall apply, and where the cables are installed in ducts, plenums, and other air-handling spaces, Section 760-28(c)(3) shall apply. Type FPLR cables in vertical runs in accordance with Section 760-28(c)(2) or Type FPLP for use in ducts, plenums, and other air-handling spaces in accordance with Section 760-28(c)(3) shall be permitted to be used to meet the requirements of this section.

(FPN): One method of defining resistant to the spread of fire is that the cables do not spread fire to the top of the tray in the Vertical Tray Flame Test in UL 1581.

See commentary following Section 725-38(b)(1), second FPN.

1049

Exception No. 1: Where the cables are enclosed in raceway or noncombustible tubing.

Exception No. 2: In nonconcealed spaces where the exposed length of cable does not exceed 10 feet (3.05 m).

(2) In Vertical Runs. Single- and multiconductor power-limited fire-protective signaling circuit cables in a vertical run in a shaft shall be Type FPLR listed as having fire-resistant characteristics capable of preventing the carrying of fire from floor to floor. Type FPLP cables listed for use in ducts, plenums, and other air-handling spaces in accordance with Section 760-28(c)(3) shall be permitted to be used to meet the requirements of this section.

Exception: Where the cables are encased in noncombustible tubing or are located in a fireproof shaft having firestops at each floor.

(3) In Ducts, Plenums, and Other Air-Handling Spaces. Single- and multiconductor power-limited fire-protective signaling circuit cables and equipment installed in ducts or plenums or other spaces used for environmental air shall also comply with Section 300-22 as to installation methods.

Exception: Type FPLP single- and multiconductor cables covered under Part C for power-limited fire-protective signaling circuits and listed as having adequate fire-resistant and low-smoke-producing characteristics shall be permitted for ducts and plenums as described in Section 300-22(b) and other space used for environmental air as described in Section 300-22(c).

(FPN): One method of defining low-smoke-producing cables is by establishing an acceptable value of the smoke produced per the NFPA 262-1985 test to a maximum peak optical density of 0.5 and a maximum average optical density of 0.15. Similarly, fire-resistant cables may be defined as having a maximum allowable flame travel distance of 5 feet (1.52 m) in the NFPA 262-1985 test.

See commentary following Section 725-38(b)(3) FPN.

760-29. Separation of Conductors. Conductors and cables on the load side of overcurrent protection, transformers, and current-limiting devices shall comply with (a) and (b) below.

(a) Separation from Electric Light, Power, Class 1 and Nonpower-Limited Fire Protective Signaling Circuits.

(1) Power-limited circuits shall be separated at least 2 inches (50.8 mm) from conductors of any electric light, power, Class 1, or nonpower-limited fire protective signaling circuits.

Exception No. 1: Where the electric light, power, Class 1, or nonpower-limited fire protective signaling circuit conductors are in raceway or in metal-sheathed, metal-clad, nonmetallic-sheathed, or Type UF cables.

Exception No. 2: Where the power-limited circuit conductors are permanently separated from the conductors of the other circuits by a continuous and firmly fixed nonconductor, such as porcelain tubes or flexible tubing in addition to the insulation on the wire.

(2) Power-limited circuits shall not be placed in any enclosure, raceway, cable, compartment, outlet box, or similar fitting containing conductors of electric light, power, Class 1, or nonpower-limited fire protective signaling circuits.

Exception No. 1: Where the conductors of the different systems are separated by a partition.

Exception No. 2: Conductors in outlet boxes, junction boxes, or similar fittings or compartments where power-supply conductors are introduced solely for supplying power to the power-limited fire protective signaling system to which the other conductors in the enclosure are connected.

(3) Power-limited circuits shall be separated by not less than 2 inches (50.8 mm) from electric light, power, Class 1, or nonpower-limited fire protective signaling circuit conductors run in the same shaft.

Exception No. 1: Where the conductors of either the electric light, power, Class 1, the nonpower-limited fire protective signaling circuits, or the power-limited fire protective signaling circuits are encased in noncombustible tubing.

Exception No. 2: Where the electric light, power, Class 1, or the nonpower-limited fire protective signaling circuit conductors are in a raceway or are in metal-sheathed, metal-clad, nonmetallic-sheathed, or Type UF cables.

The requirements for separation from electric light, power, Class 1, and nonpower-limited fire protective signaling circuits as noted in Section 760-29(a) apply even if the power-limited circuits are wired using nonpower-limited circuit wiring methods. See commentary following Section 760-28(a), Exception No. 1.

(b) Conductors of Different Power-Limited Fire Protective Signaling Circuits and Class 2 and Class 3 Circuits in Same Cable, Enclosure, or Raceway.

(1) Cables and conductors of two or more power-limited fire protective signaling circuits or Class 3 circuits shall be permitted in the same cable, enclosure, or raceway.

(2) Conductors of one or more Class 2 circuits shall be permitted within the same cable, enclosure, or raceway with conductors of power-limited fire protective signaling circuits provided that the insulation of the Class 2 circuit conductors in the cable, enclosure, or raceway is at least that required by the power-limited fire protective signaling circuits.

760-30. Conductors and Cables. Conductors and cables for use with power-limited fire protective signaling circuits installed in accordance with Section 760-28(b) shall be listed for this use and shall meet or exceed the requirements of (a) through (e) or where coaxial cable is used, the requirements of (f) below.

(a) Conductor Materials. Conductors shall be solid copper or bunch-tinned (bonded) stranded copper.

Bunch-tinned strands are strands which have been extruded through a solder bath such that the strands are bonded together by the solder.

Exception No. 1: Stranded copper with a maximum of 7 strands for sizes 16 and 18 shall be permitted.

Exception No. 2: Stranded copper with a maximum of 19 strands for sizes 14 and larger shall be permitted.

(b) Sizes. Conductors shall not be smaller than No. 16 for single conductor, No. 19 for two or three conductor, No. 22 for four or five conductor, and No. 24 for 6 or more conductor multiconductor cables.

(c) Insulation. Cables shall be listed as being suitable for Class 3, power-limited fire-protective signaling, or communication circuits.

(d) Ratings. The cable shall have a voltage rating of not less than 300 volts and the jacket compound shall have a high degree of abrasion resistance.

(e) Coaxial Cables. Coaxial cables shall have a minimum No. 22 AWG copper or 30 percent minimum conductivity copper covered steel center conductor, an overall insulation rated at 300 volts, an overall metallic shield covered by a flame retardant nonmetallic jacket having a minimum thickness not less than 35 mils nominal (30 mils minimum), and they shall have a high degree of abrasion resistance.

(f) Optical Fiber Cables. Listed nonconductive and conductive optical fiber cables shall be permitted to be used.

760-31. Cable Marking. Listed power-limited fire-protective signaling cables shall be marked in accordance with Table 760-31.

Table 760-31. Cable Markings

Cable Marking	Type	Reference
FPL	Power-limited fire alarm cable	760-28(c)(1)
FPLP	Power-limited fire alarm plenum cable	760-28(c)(3)
FPLR	Power-limited fire alarm riser cable	760-28(c)(2)

(FPN): See the referenced sections for permitted uses.

760-32. Current-Carrying Continuous Line-type Fire Detectors.

(a) Application. Listed continuous line-type fire detectors, including insulated copper tubing of pneumatically operated detectors, employed for both detection and carrying signaling currents shall be permitted to be used in circuits having power-limiting characteristics in accordance with Section 760-21.

(b) Insulation. Insulated continuous line-type fire detectors shall be listed as being resistant to the spread of fire in accordance with the requirements of Section 760-28(c), have a voltage rating of not less than 300 volts, and the jacket compound shall have a high degree of abrasion resistance.

(c) Installation. Continuous line-type fire detectors shall be installed in accordance with Sections 760-22 through 760-29.

ARTICLE 770 — OPTICAL FIBER CABLES

Contents

770-1. Scope. The provisions of this article apply to the installation of optical fiber cables along with electrical conductors. This article does not cover the construction of optical fiber cables. It also does not cover the installation of optical fiber cables in circumstances other than those covered in this article.

Article 770 is included to permit the orderly development and usage of optical fiber technology when used in conjunction with electrical conductors for communication, signaling, and control circuits in lieu of metallic conductors.

Article 770 is not applicable to optical fiber cables except when they are installed along with electrical conductors.

Optical fiber cables may be desirable in some circumstances where electrical noise is a problem, as such systems are not affected by electrical noise.

770-2. Other Articles. Circuits and equipment shall comply with (a) and (b) below.

(a) Spread of Fire or Products of Combustion. See Section 300-21.

(b) Ducts, Plenums, and Other Air-Handling Spaces. Section 300-22 where installed in ducts or plenums or other space used for environmental air.

Exception to (b): As permitted in Section 770-6(c).

770-3. Optical Fiber Cables. Optical fiber cables transmit light for control, signaling and communications through an optical fiber.

770-4. Types. Optical fiber cables can be grouped into three types.

(a) Nonconductive. These cables contain no metallic members and no other electrically conductive materials.

(b) Conductive. These cables contain noncurrent-carrying conductive members such as metallic strength members and metallic vapor barriers.

(c) Hybrid. These cables contain optical fibers and current-carrying electrical conductors and shall be classified as electrical cables in accordance with the type of electrical conductors.

770-5. Optical Fibers and Electrical Conductors.

(a) With Conductors for Electric Light, Power, or Class 1 Circuits. Optical fibers shall be permitted within the same hybrid cable for electric light, power, or Class 1 circuits operating at 600 volts or less only where the functions of the optical fibers and the electrical conductors are associated. Nonconductive optical fiber cables shall be permitted to occupy the same raceway or cable tray with conductors for electric light, power or Class 1 circuits operating at 600 volts or less. Conductive and hybrid optical fiber cables shall not be permitted to occupy the same raceway or cable tray with conductors for electric light, power, or Class 1 circuits.

Nonconductive optical fiber cables shall not be permitted to occupy the same cabinet, panel, outlet box or similar enclosure housing the electrical terminations of an electric light, power or Class 1 circuit.

Exception No. 1: Occupancy of the same cabinet, panel, outlet box, or similar enclosure shall be permitted where nonconductive optical fiber cable is functionally associated with the electric light, power, or Class 1 circuit.

Exception No. 2: Occupancy of the same cabinet, panel, outlet box, or similar enclosure shall be permitted where nonconductive optical fiber cables are installed in factory- or field-assembled control centers.

Exception No. 3: In industrial establishments only, where conditions of maintenance and supervision assure that only qualified persons will service the installation, nonconductive optical fiber cables shall be permitted with circuits exceeding 600 volts.

Installations in raceway shall comply with Section 300-17.

(b) With Other Conductors. Optical fibers shall be permitted in the same cable, and conductive and nonconductive optical fiber cables shall be permitted in the same raceway, cable tray or enclosure with conductors of any of the following:

(1) Class 2 and Class 3 remote-control, signaling and power-limited circuits in compliance with Article 725.

(2) Power-limited fire protective signaling systems in compliance with Article 760.

(3) Communications circuits in compliance with Article 800.

(4) Community antenna television and radio distribution systems in compliance with Article 820.

(c) Grounding. Noncurrent-carrying conductive members of optical fiber cables shall be grounded in accordance with Article 250.

770-6. Fire Resistance of Cables.

(a) Wiring Within Buildings. Optical fiber cables installed as wiring within buildings shall be Type OFC or OFN listed as being resistant to the spread of fire. This listing requirement for Types OFC and OFN cables shall become effective July 1, 1988. In addition, where the cables are in a vertical run in a shaft, Section 770-6(b) shall apply and where the cables are installed in ducts, plenums, and other air-handling spaces, Section 770-6(c) shall apply. Types OFCR and OFNR cables listed for use in vertical runs in accordance with Section 770-6(b) and Types OFCP and OFNP cables listed for use in ducts, plenums, and other air-handling spaces in accordance with Section 770-6(c) shall be permitted to be used to meet the requirements of this section.

(FPN): One method of defining resistant to the spread of fire is that the cables do not spread fire to the top of the tray in the Vertical Tray Flame Test in UL 1581.

See commentary following Section 725-38(b)(1), second FPN.

Exception No. 1: Where the optical fiber cables are enclosed in raceway or noncombustible tubing.

Exception No. 2: In nonconcealed spaces where the exposed length of cable does not exceed 10 feet (3.05 m).

(b) In Vertical Runs. Optical fiber cables in a vertical run in a shaft shall be Type OFCR or OFNR listed as having fire-resistant characteristics capable of preventing the carrying of fire from floor to floor. Types OFCP and OFNP cables listed for use in ducts, plenums, and other air-handling spaces in accordance with Section 770-6(c) shall be permitted to be used to meet the requirements of this section.

Exception: Where the optical fiber cables are encased in noncombustible tubing or are located in a fireproof shaft having firestops at each floor.

(c) In Ducts, Plenums, and Other Air-Handling Spaces. Optical fiber cables and equipment installed in ducts or plenums or other spaces used for environmental air shall also comply with Section 300-22 as to installation methods.

See commentary following Sections 300-22(b) and 300-22(c).

Exception: Types OFCP and OFNP optical fiber cables listed as having adequate fire-resistant and low-smoke-producing characteristics shall be permitted for ducts and plenums as described in Section 300-22(b) and other space used for environmental air as described in Section 300-22(c).

(FPN): One method of defining low-smoke-producing cables is by establishing an acceptable value of the smoke produced per the NFPA 262-1985 test to a maximum peak optical density of 0.5 and a maximum average optical density of 0.15. Similarly, fire-resistant cables may be defined as having a maximum allowable flame travel distance of 5 feet (1.52 m) in the NFPA 262-1985 test.

See commentary following Section 725-38(b)(3) FPN.

770-7. Grounding of Entrance Cables. Where exposed to contact with electric light or power conductors, the noncurrent-carrying metallic members of optical fiber cables entering buildings shall be grounded as close to the point of entrance as practicable or shall be interrupted as close to the point of entrance as practicable by an insulating joint or equivalent device.

For purposes of this section, the point of entrance shall be considered to be at the point of emergence through an exterior wall, a concrete floor slab, or from a rigid metal conduit or an intermediate metal conduit grounded in accordance with Article 250.

770-8. Cable Marking. Listed optical fiber cables shall be marked in accordance with Table 770-8.

Table 770-8. Cable Markings

Cable Marking	Type	Reference
OFC	Conductive optical fiber cable	770-6(a)
OFCP	Conductive optical fiber plenum cable	770-6(c)
OFCR	Conductive optical fiber riser cable	770-6(b)
OFN	Nonconductive optical fiber cable	770-6(a)
OFNP	Nonconductive optical fiber plenum cable	770-6(c)
OFNR	Nonconductive optical fiber riser cable	770-6(b)

(FPN): See the referenced sections for permitted uses.

ARTICLE 780 — CLOSED-LOOP AND PROGRAMMED POWER DISTRIBUTION

Contents

780-1. Scope. The provisions of this article apply to premise power distribution systems jointly controlled by a signaling between the energy controlling equipment and utilization equipment.

This article provides requirements for the "smart house and the intelligent building." The "smart house" concept involves a central distribution center for power and communications which has feeders supplying individual branch circuit controllers located at convenient locations throughout the building. See Figure 780-1.

In a building wired in the conventional manner, branch circuits and outlets are energized up to the receptacles, and utilization equipment is energized at full potential up to the operating control switch. In the closed loop configuration, the branch-circuit wiring and the outlets are not energized until a piece of utilization equipment is connected to the circuit, and the control switch is energized. A transducer located within the appliance serves to signal the branch-circuit controller that a certain appliance is connected to the system and that it requires a specific amount of current at a given voltage. When the parameters are exceeded, the transducer sends a signal back to the controller to deenergize the system.

Buildings wired by standard wiring methods require separate sets of conductors for different systems. For example, separate circuits are required for 120- or 240-volt systems, telephone and interior communication systems, small-appliance, general lighting, and fire signaling systems, to mention some of the most common types.

In the "smart house" concept, the different systems will be integrated so that a multiple-conductor-type assembly will serve a multi-purpose receptacle outlet, capable of supplying different types of energy to specific appliances or equipment.

Figure 780-1 illustrates a typical "smart house" installation.

780-2. General.

(a) Other Articles. Except as modified by the requirements of this article, all other applicable articles of this Code shall apply.

(b) Component Parts. All equipment and conductors shall be listed and identified.

780-3. Control.
The control equipment and all power switching devices operated by the control equipment shall be listed and identified. The system shall operate such that:

(a) Characteristic Electrical Identification Required. Outlets shall not be energized unless the utilization equipment first exhibits a characteristic electrical identification.

The controller must positively identify the utilization device before supplying power to the utilization.

(b) Conditions for Deenergization. Outlets shall be deenergized when any of the following conditions occur:

(1) A nominal-operation acknowledgement signal is not being received from the utilization equipment connected to that circuit.

(2) A ground-fault condition exists.

(3) The grounded conductor is not properly grounded.

(4) Any ungrounded conductor is not at nominal voltage.

(5) An overcurrent condition exists.

(c) Controller Malfunction. In the event of a controller malfunction, all output signal and power conductors shall be deenergized.

780-5. Power Limitation in the Communication Circuits.
Power in a communication circuit shall not exceed 10 milliwatts at not more than 24 volts.

Figure 780-1. Diagram of a typical "smart house" installation.

780-6. Communication Cables and Electric Power Conductors.

(a) Hybrid Power and Communication Cabling. Listed hybrid power and communication cabling shall be permitted within separate jackets provided that the jacket insulation voltage rating is not less than the maximum nominal circuit voltage rating of any conductor in the jacket. The individual conductors of a hybrid cable shall conform to the Code provisions applicable to their current, voltage, and insulation ratings.

(b) Communication Cables and Power Conductors in Same Cabinet, Panel, or Box. Communication cables and power conductors are permitted to occupy the same cabinet, panel, or outlet box (or similar enclosure housing the electrical termination of electric light or power circuits) only if connectors specifically listed for hybrid cabling are employed.

780-7. Noninterchangeability. Receptacles, cord connectors, and attachment plugs used on closed-loop power distribution systems shall be constructed so that they are not interchangeable with other receptacles, cord connectors, and attachment plugs.

8 Communication Systems

ARTICLE 800 — COMMUNICATION CIRCUITS

Contents

A. General

800-1. Scope. This article covers telephone, telegraph (except radio), district messenger, outside wiring for fire alarm and burglar alarms, and similar central station systems; and telephone systems not connected to a central station system but using similar types of equipment, methods of installation, and maintenance.

(FPN): For classification of Class 2 and 3 circuits as communication circuits, see Section 725-5.

(FPN): For further information for fire alarm, sprinkler, supervisory, or watchman systems, see Article 760.

(FPN): For installation requirements of optical fiber cables, see Article 770.

Section 90-3, Code Arrangement, states that Chapter 8, which includes Articles 800, 810, and 820, covers communication systems and is independent of the other chapters except where they are specifically referenced therein. For instance, Section 800-2(b) references Article 500, Section 800-3(b)(3) references Section 300-22, Section 800-11(a)(3) references Section 225-14(d), etc.

ARTICLE 800—COMMUNICATION CIRCUITS

Although electronic data processing (EDP) systems are often used for or with communications systems, Article 800 does not cover EDP system wiring. It is covered by Article 725 (Article 760 if for a fire protective signaling system). In some cases, the telephone system wiring is also used for data transmission, and this use is covered by Article 800.

B. Protection

800-2. Protective Devices. A listed protector shall be provided on each circuit run partly or entirely in aerial wire or aerial cable not confined within a block. Also, a listed protector shall be provided on each circuit, aerial or underground, so located within the block containing the building served as to be exposed to accidental contact with electric light or power conductors operating at over 300 volts to ground.

(FPN): The word "block" as used in this article means a square or portion of a city, town, or village enclosed by streets and including the alleys so enclosed but not any street.

(FPN): The word "exposed" as used in this article means that the circuit is in such a position that, in case of failure of supports or insulation, contact with another circuit may result.

(FPN): On a circuit not exposed to accidental contact with power conductors, providing a listed protector in accordance with this article will help protect against other hazards such as lightning and above-normal voltages induced by fault currents on power circuits in proximity to the communication circuit. When protecting a circuit run within the block between two buildings on the same premises, providing a listed protector on each end of the circuit affords protection for both buildings.

(a) Location. The protector shall be located in, on, or immediately adjacent to the structure or building served and as close as practicable to the point at which the exposed conductors enter or attach.

For purposes of this section, the point at which the exposed conductors enter shall be considered to be the point of emergence through an exterior wall, a concrete floor slab, or from a rigid metal conduit or an intermediate metal conduit grounded to an electrode in accordance with Section 800-31(b)(5).

(FPN): Selecting a protector location to achieve the shortest practicable protector grounding conductor will help limit potential differences between communication circuits and other metallic systems.

(b) Hazardous (Classified) Locations. The protector shall not be located in any hazardous (classified) location as defined in Article 500, nor in the vicinity of easily ignitible material.

Exception: As permitted in Sections 501-14, 502-14 and 503-12.

(c) Protector Requirements. The protector shall consist of an arrester connected between each line conductor and ground in an appropriate mounting. Protector terminals shall be marked to indicate line and ground as applicable.

(1) Fuseless-type protectors shall be permitted under any of the following conditions:

a. Where circuits enter a building through metallic-sheathed cable or through a nonmetallic-sheathed cable having a metallic grounding shield between the sheath and the conductor assembly, if the metallic sheath or shield of the cable is effectively grounded, and if the conductors in the cable safely fuse on all currents greater than the current-carrying capacity of the protector and of the protector grounding conductor.

b. Where insulated conductors in accordance with Section 800-11(c)(1) are used to extend circuits to a building from a metallic-sheathed cable or from a nonmetallic-sheathed cable having a metallic grounding shield between the sheath and the conductor assembly, if the metallic sheath or shield is effectively grounded and if the conductors in the cable or cable stub, or the connections between the insulated conductors and the exposed plant safely fuse on all currents greater than the current-carrying capacity of the protector, or the associated insulated conductors and of the protector grounding conductor.

c. Where insulated conductors in accordance with Section 800-11(c)(1) or (c)(2) are used to extend circuits to a building from other than a grounded metallic-sheathed or shielded cable, if (1) the protector is listed for this purpose, and (2) the connections of the insulated conductors to the exposed plant or the conductors of the exposed plant safely fuse on all currents greater than the current-carrying capacity of the protector, or the associated insulated conductors and of the protector grounding conductor.

d. Where insulated conductors in accordance with Section 800-11(c)(1) or (c)(2) are used to extend circuits aerially to a building from an unexposed buried or underground circuit.

(FPN): Effectively grounded means intentionally connected to earth through a ground connection or connections of sufficiently low impedance and having sufficient current-carrying capacity to prevent the buildup of voltages which may result in undue hazard to connected equipment or to persons.

e. Where insulated conductors in accordance with Section 800-11(c)(1) or (c)(2) are used to extend circuits to a building from an effectively grounded metallic-sheathed or shielded cable, and if (1) the combination of the protector and insulated conductors is listed for this purpose, and (2) the insulated conductors safely fuse on all currents greater than the current-carrying capacity of the protector and of the protector grounding conductor.

(2) Where the requirements listed under (c)(1)a, (1)b, (1)c, or (1)d above are not met, fused-type protectors shall be used. Fused-type protectors shall consist of an arrester connected between each line conductor and ground, a fuse in series with each line conductor, and an appropriate mounting arrangement. Protector terminals shall be marked to indicate line, instrument, and ground, as applicable.

(d) Secondary Protector Requirements. When a secondary protector is installed in series with the indoor communication wire and cable between the protector and the equipment, it shall be listed for the purpose. The secondary protector shall include overcurrent protection which will safely fuse at currents less than the current-carrying capacity of listed indoor communication wire and cable, listed telephone set line cords, and listed communication terminal equipment having ports for external wire line communication circuits. Any overvoltage protection, arresters, or grounding connection shall be connected on the equipment terminals side of the secondary protector overcurrent protection.

800-3. Installation of Conductors. Conductors from the protector to the equipment or, where no protector is required, conductors attached to the outside or inside of the building shall comply with (a) through (e) below.

(a) Separation from Other Conductors.

(1) Open Conductors. Conductors shall be separated at least 2 inches (50.8 mm) from conductors of any electric light or power circuits or Class 1 circuits.

Exception No. 1: Where the electric light or power or Class 1 or communication circuit conductors are in a raceway or in metal-sheathed, metal-clad, nonmetallic-sheathed, Type AC, or Type UF cables.

Exception No. 2: Where the conductors are permanently separated from the conductors of the other circuit by a continuous and firmly fixed nonconductor, such as porcelain tubes or flexible tubing, in addition to the insulation on the wire.

(2) In Raceways and Boxes. Communication conductors shall not be placed in any raceway, compartment, outlet box, junction box, or similar fitting with conductors of electric light or power circuits or Class 1 circuits.

Exception No. 1: Where the conductors of the different systems are separated by a partition.

Exception No. 2: Conductors in outlet boxes, junction boxes, or similar fittings or compartments where such conductors are introduced solely for power supply to communication equipment or for connection to remote-control equipment.

(3) In Shafts. Conductors run in the same shaft with conductors of electric light or power shall be separated from light or power conductors by not less than 2 inches (50.8 mm).

Exception No. 1: Where the conductors of either system are encased in noncombustible tubing.

Exception No. 2: Where the electric light or power conductors are in a metal raceway, or in metal-sheathed, metal-clad, nonmetallic-sheathed, or Type UF cables.

(b) Fire Resistance of Wires and Cables.

(1) Wiring Within Buildings. Communication wires and cables installed as wiring within buildings shall be Type CM listed as being resistant to the spread of fire. In addition, where wires and cables are in a vertical run in a shaft, Section 800-3(b)(2) shall apply and where wires and cables are installed in ducts, plenums, and other air-handling spaces, Section 800-3(b)(3) shall apply. Type CMR wires and cables listed for use in vertical runs in accordance with Section 800-3(b)(2) and Type CMP wires and cables listed for use in ducts, plenums, and other air-handling spaces in accordance with Section 800-3(b)(3) shall be permitted to be used to meet the requirements of this section.

(FPN): One method of defining resistant to the spread of fire is that the wires and cables do not spread fire to the top of the tray in the Vertical Tray Flame Test in UL 1581.

Exception No. 1: Where the wires and cables are enclosed in raceway or noncombustible tubing.

Exception No. 2: In nonconcealed spaces where the exposed length of wires or cable does not exceed 10 feet (3.05 m).

Exception No. 3: Listed Type CMX communication wires and cables that are less than 0.25 inch (6.35 mm) in diameter and installed in one- or two-family or multifamily dwellings.

(FPN): One method of determining the fire resistance of Type CMX wires and cable is testing the cable to the VW-1 requirements in UL 1581.

(2) In Vertical Runs. Communication wires and cables in a vertical run in a shaft shall be Type CMR listed as having fire-resistant characteristics capable of preventing the carrying of fire from floor to floor. Type CMP wires and cables listed for use in ducts, plenums, or other air-handling spaces in accordance with Section 800-3(b)(3) shall be permitted to be used to meet the requirements of this section.

Exception: Where the wires and cables are encased in noncombustible tubing or are located in a fireproof shaft having firestops at each floor.

(3) In Ducts, Plenums, and Other Air-Handling Spaces. Communications wires and cables and equipment installed in ducts or plenums or other spaces used for environmental air shall also comply with Section 300-22 as to installation methods.

Exception: Type CMP communications wires and cables listed as having adequate fire-resistant and low-smoke-producing characteristics shall be permitted for ducts and plenums as described in Section 300-22(b) and other space used for environmental air as described in Section 300-22(c).

(FPN): One method of defining low-smoke-producing wires and cables is by establishing an acceptable value of the smoke produced per the NFPA 262-1985 test to a maximum peak optical density of 0.5 and a maximum average optical density of 0.15. Similarly, fire-resistant wires and cables may be defined as having a maximum allowable flame travel distance of 5 feet (1.52 m) in the NFPA 262-1985 test.

(c) Spread of Fire or Products of Combustion. Installations in hollow spaces, vertical shafts, and ventilation or air-handling ducts shall be so made that the possible spread of fire or products of combustion will not be substantially increased. Openings around penetrations through fire resistance rated walls, partitions, floors, or ceilings shall be firestopped using approved methods.

(d) With Conductors of Other Circuits. Jacketed communication wires and cables shall be permitted in the same raceway or enclosure with jacketed cables of any of the following:

(1) Class 2 and Class 3 remote-control, signaling and power-limited circuits in compliance with Article 725.

(2) Power-limited fire-protective signaling systems in compliance with Article 760.

(3) Nonconductive and conductive optical fiber cables in compliance with Article 770.

(4) Community antenna television and radio distribution systems in compliance with Article 820.

(e) Undercarpet Wiring. Communication wires and cables listed as being suitable for the purpose shall be permitted under carpets.

800-4. Listing of Communication Wires and Cables. Communications wires and cables in a building shall be listed as being suitable for the purpose.

See commentary following Sections 300-22(b) and 300-22(c).

Exception No. 1: Where the length of cable within the building does not exceed 50 feet (15.2 m) and the cable enters the building from the outside and is terminated in an enclosure or on a listed protector.

(FPN): Splice cases or terminal boxes, both metallic and plastic types, are typically used as enclosures for splicing or terminating telephone cables.

Exception No. 2: Where the cable enters the building from the outside and is run in rigid metal conduit or intermediate metal conduit and such conduits are grounded to an electrode in accordance with Section 800-31(b)(5).

800-5. Cable Marking. Listed communications cables shall be marked in accordance with Table 800-5.

See commentary following Section 725-2(b), Exception.

C. Outside Conductors

800-11. Overhead Conductors. Overhead conductors entering buildings shall comply with (a) through (c) below.

(a) On Poles and In-Span. Where communication conductors and electric light or power conductors are supported by the same pole or run in parallel in-span, the following conditions shall be met:

(1) Relative Location. Where practicable, the communications conductors shall be located below the electric light or power conductors.

(2) Attachment to Crossarms. Conductors shall not be attached to a crossarm that carries electric light or power conductors.

Table 800-5.   Cable Markings

Cable Marking	Type	Reference
CM	Communications cable	800-3(b)(1)
CMP	Communications plenum cable	800-3(b)(3)
CMR	Communications riser cable	800-3(b)(2)
CMX	Communications cable, limited use	800-3(b)(1) Exceptions No. 1, 2 and 3

(FPN): See the referenced sections for permitted uses.

(3) Climbing Space. The climbing space through communication conductors shall comply with the requirements of Section 225-14(d).

(4) Clearance. Supply service drops of 0-750 volts running above and parallel to communication service drops shall be permitted to have a minimum separation of 12 inches (30.48 cm) at any point in the span including the point of and at their attachment to the building provided the nongrounded conductors are insulated and that a clearance of 40 inches (1.02 m) is maintained between the two services at the pole.

(b) On Roofs.   Conductors passing over buildings shall be kept at least 8 feet (2.44 m) above any roof that may be readily walked upon.

Exception No. 1: Auxiliary buildings, such as garages and the like.

Exception No. 2: A reduction in clearance above only the overhanging portion of the roof to not less than 18 inches (457 mm) shall be permitted if (1) not more than 4 feet (1.22 mm) of communication service-drop conductors pass above the roof overhang, and (2) they are terminated at a through-the-roof raceway or support.

(c) Circuits Requiring Protectors.   Circuits that require protectors as provided in Section 800-2 shall comply with the following:

(1) Insulation, Wires, and Cables. Wires and cables without a metallic shield, running from the last outdoor support to the protector, shall be listed as being suitable for the purpose and having current-carrying capacity as specified in Sections 800-2(c)(1) b. or c.

(2) On Buildings. Open conductors shall be separated at least 4 inches (102 mm) from electric light or power conductors not in a raceway or cable, or be permanently separated from conductors of the other system by a continuous and firmly fixed nonconductor in addition to the insulation on the wires, such as porcelain tubes or flexible tubing. Open conductors exposed to accidental contact with electric light and power conductors operating at over 300 volts to ground and attached to buildings shall be separated from woodwork by being supported on glass, porcelain, or other insulating material.

Exception: Separation from woodwork shall not be required where fuses are omitted as provided for in Section 800-2(c)(1), or where conductors are used to extend circuits to a building from a cable having a grounded metal sheath.

(3) Entering Buildings. Where a protector is installed inside the building, the conductors shall enter the building either through a noncombustible, nonabsorbent insulating bushing, or through a metal raceway. The insulating bushing shall not be required where the entering conductors (1) are in metal-sheathed cable; (2) pass through masonry; (3) meet the requirements of (c)(1) above and fuses are omitted as provided in Section 800-2(c)(1); or (4) meet the

1064

requirements of (c)(1) above and are used to extend circuits to a building from a cable having a grounded metal sheath. Raceways or bushings shall slope upward from the outside or, where this cannot be done, drip loops shall be formed in the conductors immediately before they enter the building. Raceways shall be equipped with an approved service head. More than one conductor shall be permitted to enter through a single raceway or bushing. Conduits or other metal raceways located ahead of the protector shall be grounded.

800-12. Lightning Conductors. Where practicable, a separation of at least 6 feet (1.83 m) shall be maintained between open conductors of communication systems on buildings and lightning conductors.

D. Underground Circuits

800-21. Underground Circuits Entering Buildings. Underground conductors of communication circuits entering buildings shall comply with (a) and (b) below.

(a) With Electric Light or Power Conductors. Underground conductors in a raceway, handhole, or manhole containing electric light or power conductors shall be in a section separated from such conductors by means of brick, concrete, or tile partitions.

(b) Underground Block Distribution. Where the entire street circuit is run underground and the circuit within the block is so placed as to be free from likelihood of accidental contact with electric light or power circuits of over 300 volts to ground, the insulation requirements of Section 800-11(c)(1) and (c)(3) shall not apply, insulating supports shall not be required for the conductors, and bushings shall not be required where the conductors enter the building.

E. Grounding

800-31. Grounding. Equipment shall be grounded as specified in (a) and (b) below.

(a) Cable Sheath. Where exposed to contact with electric light or power conductors, the metal sheath of cables entering buildings shall be grounded as close as practicable to the point of entrance or shall be interrupted as close to the point of entrance as practicable by an insulating joint or equivalent device.

For purposes of this section, the point of entrance shall be considered to be at the point of emergence through an exterior wall, a concrete floor slab, or from a rigid metal conduit or an intermediate metal conduit grounded to an electrode in accordance with (b)(5) of this section.

(b) Protector Ground. The protector ground shall comply with the following:

(1) Insulation. The grounding conductor shall have a 30-mil rubber insulation and shall be covered by a substantial fibrous covering. Conductors listed for this use having less than 30-mil rubber insulation or having other kinds of insulation shall be permitted.

(2) Size. The grounding conductor shall not be smaller than No. 14 AWG copper or equivalent.

(3) Run in Straight Line. The grounding conductor shall be run to the grounding electrode in as straight a line as practicable.

(4) Physical Damage. Where necessary, the grounding conductor shall be guarded from physical damage. When the grounding conductor is run in a metal raceway, both ends of the raceway shall be bonded to the grounding conductor or the same terminal or electrode to which the grounding conductor is connected.

(5) Electrode. The grounding conductor shall be connected as follows:

a. To the nearest accessible location on (1) the building or structure grounding electrode system as covered in Section 250-81, (2) the grounded interior metal water piping system as covered in Section 250-80(a), (3) the power service accessible means external to enclosures as covered in Section 250-71(b), (4) the metallic power service raceway, (5) the service equipment enclosure, (6) the grounding electrode conductor or the grounding electrode conductor metal enclosure, or (7) to the grounding conductor or the grounding electrode of a building or structure disconnecting means which is grounded to an electrode as covered in Section 250-24; or

b. If the building or structure served has no grounding means as described in (5)a, to any one of the individual electrodes described in Section 250-81; or

c. If the building or structure served has no grounding means as described in (5)a or (5)b, to: (1) an effectively grounded metal structure, or (2) a continuous and extensive underground metal gas piping system where acceptable to both the gas supplier and to the authority having jurisdiction, or (3) to a ground rod or pipe driven into permanently damp earth and separated from lightning conductors as covered in Section 800-12 and at least 6 feet (1.83 m) from electrodes of other systems. Steam or hot water pipes or lightning-rod conductors shall not be employed as electrodes for protectors.

(6) Electrode Connection. Connections to grounding electrodes shall comply with Section 250-115. Where a metal gas pipe electrode is used, connection shall be made between the gas meter and the street main. Connectors, clamps, fittings, or lugs used to attach grounding conductors and bonding jumpers to grounding electrodes or to each other which are to be concrete-encased or buried in the earth shall be suitable for its application.

(7) Bonding of Electrodes. A bonding jumper not smaller than No. 6 copper or equivalent shall be connected between the communication and the power grounding electrodes where the requirements of (5) above result in the use of separate electrodes. Bonding together of all separate electrodes shall be permitted.

(FPN): See Section 250-86 for use of lightning rods.

(FPN): Bonding together of all separate electrodes will limit potential differences between them and between their associated wiring systems.

ARTICLE 810 — RADIO AND TELEVISION EQUIPMENT

Contents

A. General

810-1. Scope. This article covers radio and television receiving equipment and amateur radio transmitting and receiving equipment, but not equipment and antennas used for coupling carrier current to power line conductors.

810-2. Other Articles. Wiring from the source of power to and between devices connected to the interior wiring system shall comply with Chapters 1 through 4 other than as modified by Sections 640-3, 640-4, and 640-5. Wiring for radio-frequency and audio-frequency equipment and loud speakers shall comply with Article 640. Where optical fiber is used Article 770 shall apply.

810-3. Community Television Antenna. The antenna shall comply with this article. The distribution system shall comply with Article 820.

810-4. Radio Noise Suppressors. Radio interference eliminators, interference capacitors, or noise suppressors connected to power-supply leads shall be of a listed type. They shall not be exposed to physical damage.

B. Receiving Equipment — Antenna Systems

810-11. Material. Antennas and lead-in conductors shall be of hard-drawn copper, bronze, aluminum alloy, copper-clad steel or other high-strength, corrosion-resistant material.

Exception: Soft-drawn or medium-drawn copper shall be permitted for lead-in conductors where the maximum span between points of support is less than 35 feet (10.67 m).

810-12. Supports. Outdoor antennas and lead-in conductors shall be securely supported. The antennas shall not be attached to the electric service mast. They shall not be attached to poles or similar structures carrying open electric light or power wires or trolley wires of over 250 volts between conductors. Insulators supporting the antenna conductors shall have sufficient mechanical strength to safely support the conductors. Lead-in conductors shall be securely attached to the antennas.

810-13. Avoidance of Contacts with Conductors of Other Systems. Outdoor antennas and lead-in conductors from an antenna to a building shall not cross over open conductors of electric light or power circuits and shall be kept well away from all such circuits so as to avoid the possibility of accidental contact. Where proximity to open electric light or power service conductors of less than 250 volts between conductors cannot be avoided, the installation shall be such as to provide a clearance of at least 2 feet (610 mm).

Where practicable, antenna conductors shall be so installed as not to cross under open electric light or power conductors.

One of the leading causes of electrical shock and electrocution, according to statistical reports, is the accidental contact of radio and television receiving antennas and equipment, and amateur radio transmitting and receiving antennas and equipment, with light or power conductors. Extreme caution should therefore be exercised during this type of installation, and periodic visual inspections should be conducted thereafter.

810-14. Splices. Splices and joints in antenna spans shall be made mechanically secure with approved splicing devices or by such other means as will not appreciably weaken the conductors.

Conductor spans from antennas should be of sufficient size and strength to maintain clearances and avoid possible contact with light or power conductors. Splices and joints should be made with approved connectors or other means providing sufficient mechanical strength so as not to weaken appreciably the conductors.

810-15. Grounding. Masts and metal structures supporting antennas shall be grounded in accordance with Section 810-21.

810-16. Size of Wire-Strung Antenna — Receiving Station.

(a) Size of Antenna Conductors. Outdoor antenna conductors for receiving stations shall be of a size not less than given in Table 810-16(a).

Table 810-16(a)
Size of Receiving-Station Outdoor Antenna Conductors

	Minimum Size of Conductors		
	When Maximum Open Span Length is		
Material	Less than 35 feet	35 feet to 150 feet	Over 150 feet
Aluminum alloy, hard-drawn copper	19	14	12
Copper-clad steel, bronze, or other high-strength material	20	17	14

For SI units: one foot = 0.3048 meter.

(b) Self-Supporting Antennas. Outdoor antennas, such as vertical rods or dipole structures, shall be of corrosion-resistant materials and of strength suitable to withstand ice and wind loading conditions, and shall be located well away from overhead conductors of electric light and power circuits of over 150 volts to ground, so as to avoid the possibility of the antenna or structure falling into or making accidental contact with such circuits.

810-17. Size of Lead-in — Receiving Station. Lead-in conductors from outside antennas for receiving stations shall, for various maximum open span lengths, be of such size as to have a tensile strength at least as great as that of the conductors for antennas as specified in Section 810-16. Where the lead-in consists of two or more conductors that are twisted together, are enclosed in the same covering, or are concentric, the conductor size shall, for various maximum open span lengths, be such that the tensile strength of the combination will be at least as great as that of the conductors for antennas as specified in Section 810-16.

810-18. Clearances — Receiving Stations.

(a) On Outside of Buildings. Lead-in conductors attached to buildings shall be so installed that they cannot swing closer than 2 feet (610 mm) to the conductors of circuits of 250 volts or less between conductors, or 10 feet (3.05 m) to the conductors of circuits of over 250 volts between conductors, except that in the case of circuits not over 150 volts between conductors, where all conductors involved are supported so as to ensure permanent separation, the clearance shall be permitted to be reduced but shall not be less than 4 inches (102 mm). The clearance between lead-in conductors and any conductor forming a part of a lightning rod system shall not be less than 6 feet (1.83 m) unless the bonding referred to in Section 250-86 is accomplished.

(b) Antennas and Lead-ins — Indoors. Indoor antennas and indoor lead-ins shall not be run nearer than 2 inches (50.8 mm) to conductors of other wiring systems in the premises.

Exception No. 1: Where such other conductors are in metal raceways or cable armor.

Exception No. 2: Where permanently separated from such other conductors by a continuous and firmly fixed nonconductor, such as porcelain tubes or flexible tubing.

(c) In Boxes or Other Enclosures. Indoor antennas and indoor lead-ins shall be permitted to occupy the same box or enclosure with conductors of other wiring systems where separated from such other conductors by an effective permanently installed barrier.

810-19. Electric Supply Circuits Used in Lieu of Antenna — Receiving Stations. Where an electric supply circuit is used in lieu of an antenna, the device by which the radio receiving set is connected to the supply circuit shall be listed.

The approved device is usually a small fixed condenser connected between the antenna terminal of the receiving set and one wire of the lighting circuit. As is the case with most receiving sets, the condenser should be designed for operation at not less than 300 V, and mica should be used as the dielectric. This ensures a high degree of safety and minimizes the possibility of a breakdown in the condenser thereby avoiding a short circuit to ground through the antenna coil of the set.

810-20. Antenna Discharge Units — Receiving Stations.

(a) Where Required. Each conductor of a lead-in from an outdoor antenna shall be provided with a listed antenna discharge unit.

Exception: Where the lead-in conductors are enclosed in a continuous metallic shield that is either permanently and effectively grounded, or is protected by an antenna discharge unit.

(b) Location. Antenna discharge units shall be located outside the building or inside the building between the point of entrance of the lead-in and the radio set or transformers, and as near as practicable to the entrance of the conductors to the building. The antenna discharge unit shall not be located near combustible material nor in a hazardous (classified) location as defined in Article 500.

A lightning arrester is not required where the lead-in conductors are enclosed in a continuous metal shield, such as rigid or intermediate metal conduit, or electrical metallic tubing, or any metal raceway or metal-shielded cable that is effectively grounded. A lightning discharge will take the path of lower impedance and jump from the lead-in conductors to the metal raceway or shield rather than take the path through the antenna coil of the receiving set.

(c) Grounding. The antenna discharge unit shall be grounded in accordance with Section 810-21.

810-21. Grounding Conductors — Receiving Stations. Grounding conductors shall comply with (a) through (j) below.

(a) Material. The grounding conductor shall be of copper, aluminum, copper-clad steel, bronze, or similar corrosion-resistant material.

(b) Insulation. Insulation on grounding conductors shall not be required.

(c) Supports. The grounding conductors shall be securely fastened in place and shall be permitted to be directly attached to the surface wired over without the use of insulating supports.

Exception: Where proper support cannot be provided, the size of the grounding conductors shall be increased proportionately.

(d) Mechanical Protection. The grounding conductor shall be protected where exposed to physical damage, or the size of the grounding conductors shall be increased proportionately to compensate for the lack of protection.

(e) Run in Straight Line. The grounding conductor for an antenna mast or antenna discharge unit shall be run in as straight a line as practicable from the mast or discharge unit to the grounding electrode.

(f) Electrode. The grounding conductor shall be connected as follows:

(1) To the nearest accessible location on (1) the building or structure grounding electrode system as covered in Section 250-81, (2) the grounded interior metal water piping system as covered in Section 250-80(a), (3) the power service accessible means external to enclosures as covered in Section 250-71(b), (4) the metallic power service raceway, (5) the service equipment enclosure, or (6) the grounding electrode conductor or the grounding electrode conductor metal enclosures; or

(2) If the building or structure served has no grounding means as described in (f)(1), to any one of the individual electrodes described in Section 250-81; or

(3) If the building or structure served has no grounding means as described in (f)(1) or (f)(2), to: (1) an effectively grounded metal structure, or (2) to any of the individual electrodes described in Section 250-83.

(g) Inside or Outside Building. The grounding conductor shall be permitted to be run either inside or outside the building.

(h) Size. The grounding conductor shall not be smaller than No. 10 copper or No. 8 aluminum or No. 17 copper-clad steel or bronze.

(i) Common Ground. A single grounding conductor shall be permitted for both protective and operating purposes.

The requirements for grounding are in accordance with the provisions of Article 250. Antenna masts are required to be grounded to the same grounding electrode used for the electrical system of the building. This is necessary to assure that all exposed dead metal parts are at the same potential. In many cases, masts are (incorrectly) connected to conveniently located vent pipes, metal gutters, and downspouts. This could create potential differences between various metal parts located in or on buildings and lead-in conductors, resulting in potential shock and fire hazards. Underground gas piping systems are not permitted to be used as the required grounding electrode.

(j) Bonding of Electrodes. A bonding jumper not smaller than No. 6 copper or equivalent shall be connected between the radio and television equipment ground and the power grounding electrodes where the requirements of (f) above result in the use of separate electrodes. Bonding together of all separate electrodes shall be permitted.

C. Amateur Transmitting and Receiving Stations — Antenna Systems

810-51. Other Sections. In addition to complying with Part C, antenna systems for amateur transmitting and receiving stations shall also comply with Sections 810-11 through 810-15.

810-52. Size of Antenna. Antenna conductors for transmitting and receiving stations shall be of a size not less than given in Table 810-52.

Table 810-52. Size of Amateur Station Outdoor Antenna Conductors

| | Minimum Size of Conductors | |
| | Where Maximum Open Span Length is | |
Material	Less Than 150 feet	Over 150 feet
Hard-drawn copper...	14	10
Copper-clad steel, bronze or other high-strength material	14	12

For SI units: one foot = 0.3048 meter.

810-53. Size of Lead-in Conductors. Lead-in conductors for transmitting stations shall, for various maximum span lengths, be of a size at least as great as that of conductors for antennas as specified in Section 810-52.

810-54. Clearance on Building. Antenna conductors for transmitting stations, attached to buildings, shall be firmly mounted at least 3 inches (76 mm) clear of the surface of the building on nonabsorbent insulating supports, such as treated pins or brackets equipped with insulators having not less than 3-inch (76-mm) creepage and airgap distances. Lead-in conductors attached to buildings shall also comply with these requirements.

Exception: Where the lead-in conductors are enclosed in a continuous metallic shield that is permanently and effectively grounded, they shall not be required to comply with these requirements. Where grounded, the metallic shield shall also be permitted to be used as a conductor.

The creepage distance is measured from the conductor, across the face of the supporting insulator, to the building surface. The airgap distance is measured from the conductor (at its closest point), across the air space (not necessarily in a straight line), to the surface of the building. The exception covers coaxial cable with the shield permanently and effectively grounded.

810-55. Entrance to Building. Except where protected with a continuous metallic shield that is permanently and effectively grounded, lead-in conductors for transmitting stations shall enter buildings by one of the following methods: (1) through a rigid, noncombustible, nonabsorbent insulating tube or bushing; (2) through an opening provided for the purpose in which the entrance conductors are firmly secured so as to provide a clearance of at least 2 inches (50.8 mm); or (3) through a drilled window pane.

810-56. Protection Against Accidental Contact. Lead-in conductors to radio transmitters shall be so located or installed as to make accidental contact with them difficult.

810-57. Antenna Discharge Units — Transmitting Stations. Each conductor of a lead-in for outdoor antennas shall be provided with an antenna discharge unit or other suitable means that will drain static charges from the antenna system.

Exception No. 1: Where protected by a continuous metallic shield that is permanently and effectively grounded.

Exception No. 2: Where the antenna is permanently and effectively grounded.

Where a lightning arrester is not installed at a transmitting station, protection against lightning may be provided by a switch that connects the lead-in to ground during the time the station is not in operation.

810-58. Grounding Conductors — Amateur Transmitting and Receiving Stations. Grounding conductors shall comply with (a) through (c) below.

(a) Other Sections. All grounding conductors for amateur transmitting and receiving stations shall comply with Section 810-21(a) through (g).

(b) Size of Protective Grounding Conductor. The protective grounding conductor for transmitting stations shall be as large as the lead-in, but not smaller than No. 10 copper, bronze, or copper-clad steel.

(c) Size of Operating Grounding Conductor. The operating grounding conductor for transmitting stations shall not be less than No. 14 copper or its equivalent.

D. Interior Installation — Transmitting Stations

810-70. Clearance from Other Conductors. All conductors inside the building shall be separated at least 4 inches (102 mm) from the conductors of any electric light, power, or signaling circuit.

Exception No. 1: As provided in Article 640.

Exception No. 2: Where separated from other conductors by raceway or some firmly fixed nonconductor, such as porcelain tubes or flexible tubing.

810-71. General. Transmitters shall comply with (a) through (c) below.

(a) Enclosing. The transmitter shall be enclosed in a metal frame or grille, or separated from the operating space by a barrier or other equivalent means, all metallic parts of which are effectively connected to ground.

(b) Grounding of Controls. All external metal handles and controls accessible to the operating personnel shall be effectively grounded.

(c) Interlocks on Doors. All access doors shall be provided with interlocks that will disconnect all voltages of over 350 volts between conductors when any access door is opened.

ARTICLE 820 — COMMUNITY ANTENNA TELEVISION AND RADIO DISTRIBUTION SYSTEMS

Contents

A. General

820-1. Scope. This article covers coaxial cable distribution of radio frequency signals typically employed in community antenna television (CATV) systems.

(FPN): Where the installation is other than coaxial, see Articles 770 and 800 as applicable.

820-2. Energy Limitations. The coaxial cable shall be permitted to deliver low-energy power to equipment directly associated with the radio frequency distribution system if the voltage is not over 60 volts and if the current supply is from a transformer or other device having energy-limiting characteristics.

820-3. Material. Coaxial cable used for radio frequency distribution systems shall be suitable for the application.

820-4. Cable Marking. Listed community antenna television and radio distribution cables shall be marked in accordance with Table 820-4.

B. Protection

820-7. Grounding of Outer Conductive Shield of a Coaxial Cable. Where coaxial cable is exposed to lightning or to accidental contact with lightning arrester conductors or power conductors operating at a voltage of over 300 volts to ground, the outer conductive shield of the coaxial cable shall be grounded at the building premises as close to the point of cable entry as practicable. For purposes of this section, the point at which the exposed cable enters shall be

1073

ARTICLE 820—COMMUNITY ANTENNA TELEVISION SYSTEMS

Table 820-4. Cable Markings

Cable Marking	Type	Reference
CATV	CATV cable	820-15(a)
CATVD	CATV drop cable	820-11(b)
CATVP	CATV plenum cable	820-15(c)
CATVR	CATV riser cable	820-15(b)
CATVX	CATV cable, limited use	820-15(a) Exceptions No. 1, 2 and 3

(FPN): See the referenced sections for permitted uses.

considered to be the point of emergence through an exterior wall, a concrete floor slab or from a rigid or intermediate metal conduit grounded to an electrode in accordance with Section 820-22(f).

(FPN): Selecting a grounding location to achieve the shortest practicable grounding conductor will help limit potential differences between CATV and other metallic systems.

(a) Shield Grounding.   Where the outer conductive shield of a coaxial cable is grounded, no other protective devices shall be required.

(b) Shield Protective Devices.   Grounding of a coaxial drop cable shield by means of a protective device that does not interrupt the grounding system within the premises shall be permitted.

This section permits the use of a shield protective device which does not interrupt the grounding system within the premises. This permits protection against overheating for the CATV service-drop cable. Overheating can occur due to neutral fault currents in the power and lighting system. Such a protective device would have to maintain the integrity of the coaxial system to prevent RF leakage. An ordinary fuse, for example, would not be suitable.

C. Installation of Cable

820-11. Outside Conductors.   Coaxial cables, prior to the point of grounding, as defined in Section 820-7, shall comply with (a) through (e) below.

(a) On Poles.   Where practicable, conductors on poles shall be located below the electric light or power conductors and shall not be attached to a cross-arm that carries electric light or power conductors.

(b) Lead-in Clearance.   Lead-in or aerial-drop cables from a pole or other support, including the point of initial attachment to a building or structure, shall be kept away from electric light or power circuits so as to avoid the possibility of accidental contact.

Exception: Where proximity to electric light or power service conductors cannot be avoided, the installation shall be such as to provide clearances of not less than 12 inches (305 mm) from light or power service drops.

(c) Over Roofs.   Cables passing over buildings shall be at least 8 feet (2.44 m) above any roof that may be readily walked upon.

Exception No. 1: Auxillary buildings such as garages and the like.

Exception No. 2: A reduction in clearance above only the overhanging portion of the roof to not less than 18 inches (457 mm) shall be permitted if (1) not more than 4 feet (1.22 m) of communication service drop conductors pass above the roof overhang, and (2) they are terminated at a through-the-roof raceway or support.

(d) Between Buildings. Cables extending between buildings and also the supports or attachment fixtures shall be acceptable for the purpose and shall have sufficient strength to withstand the loads to which they may be subjected.

Exception: Where a cable does not have sufficient strength to be self-supporting, it shall be attached to a supporting messenger cable that, together with the attachment fixtures or supports, shall be acceptable for the purpose and shall have sufficient strength to withstand the loads to which they may be subjected.

(e) On Buildings. Where attached to buildings, cables shall be securely fastened in such a manner that they will be separated from other conductors as follows:

(1) Electric Light or Power. The coaxial cable shall have a separation of at least 4 inches (102 mm) from electric light or power conductors not in raceway or cable, or be permanently separated from conductors of the other system by a continuous and firmly fixed nonconductor in addition to the insulation on the wires.

(2) Other Communication Systems. Coaxial cable shall be installed so that there will be no unnecessary interference in the maintenance of the separate systems. In no case shall the conductors, cables, messenger strand, or equipment of one system cause abrasion to the conductors, cable, messenger strand, or equipment of any other system.

(3) Lightning Conductors. Where practicable, a separation of at least 6 feet (1.83 m) shall be maintained between any coaxial cable and lightning conductors.

820-13. Conductors Inside Buildings. Beyond the point of grounding, as defined in Section 820-7, the cable installation shall comply with (a) through (c) below.

(a) Electric Light or Power. Coaxial cable shall be separated at least 2 inches (50.8 mm) from conductors of any electric light or power circuits or Class 1 circuits.

Exception No. 1: Where the electric light or power or Class 1 or coaxial cable circuit conductors are in a raceway, or in metal-sheathed, metal-clad, nonmetallic-sheathed, or Type UF cables.

Exception No. 2: Where the conductors are permanently separated from the conductors of the other circuit by a continuous and firmly fixed nonconductor, such as porcelain tubes or flexible tubing, in addition to the insulation on the wire.

Exception No. 3: Coaxial cable shall be permitted to occupy the same box or enclosure with conductors of other wiring systems where separated from such other conductors by an effective permanently installed barrier.

(b) In Raceways and Boxes. Coaxial cable shall not be placed in any raceway, compartment, outlet box, junction box, or other enclosures with conductors of electric light or power circuits or Class 1 circuits.

Exception No. 1: Where the conductors of the different systems are separated by a permanent partition.

Exception No. 2: Conductors in outlet boxes, junction boxes, or similar fittings or compartments where such conductors are introduced solely for power supply to the coaxial cable system distribution equipment or for power connection to remote-control equipment.

(c) With Conductors of Other Circuits. Coaxial cables shall be permitted in the same raceway or enclosure with jacketed cables of any of the following:

(1) Class 2 and Class 3 remote-control, signaling, and power-limited circuits in compliance with Article 725.

(2) Power-limited fire-protective signaling systems in compliance with Article 760.

(3) Communications circuits in compliance with Article 800.

(4) Optical fiber cables in compliance with Article 770.

820-14. Spread of Fire or Products of Combustion. Installations in hollow spaces, vertical shafts, and ventilation or air-handling ducts shall be so made that the possible spread of fire or products of combustion will not be substantially increased. Openings around penetrations through fire resistance rated walls, partitions, floors, or ceilings shall be firestopped using approved methods.

820-15. Fire Resistance of Coaxial Cables.

(a) Wiring Within Buildings. Coaxial cables installed as wiring within buildings shall be Type CATV listed as being resistant to the spread of fire. This listing requirement for Type CATV cables shall become effective July 1, 1988. In addition, where coaxial cables are in a vertical run in a shaft, Section 820-15(b) shall apply and where coaxial cables are installed in ducts, plenums, and other air-handling spaces, Section 820-15(c) shall apply. Type CATVR coaxial cables listed for use in vertical runs in accordance with Section 820-15(b) and Type CATVP cables listed for use in ducts, plenums, and other air-handling spaces in accordance with Section 820-15(c) shall be permitted to be used to meet the requirements of this section.

See commentary following Sections 300-22(b), FPN and 300-22(c), FPN.

(FPN): One method of defining resistant to the spread of fire is that the cables do not spread fire to the top of the tray in the Vertical Tray Flame Test in UL 1581.

See commentary following Section 725-38(b)(1), second FPN.

Exception No. 1: Where the coaxial cables are enclosed in raceway or noncombustible tubing.

Exception No. 2: In nonconcealed spaces where the exposed length of coaxial cable does not exceed 10 feet (3.05 m).

Exception No. 3: Listed Type CATVX coaxial cables that are less than 0.375 inch (9.52 mm) in diameter and installed in one- or two-family or multifamily dwellings.

(FPN): One method of determing the fire resistance of Type CATVX cable is by testing the cable to the VW-1 requirements in UL-1581.

(b) In Vertical Runs. Coaxial cables in a vertical run in a shaft shall be Type CATVR listed as having fire-resistant characteristics capable of preventing the carrying of fire from floor to floor. Type CATVP coaxial cables listed for use in ducts, plenums, or other air-handling spaces in accordance with Section 820-15(c) shall be permitted to be used to meet the requirements of this section.

Exception: Where the coaxial cables are encased in noncombustible tubing or are located in a fireproof shaft having firestops at each floor.

(c) In Ducts, Plenums, and Other Air-Handling Spaces. Coaxial cables and equipment installed in ducts or plenums or other spaces used for environmental air shall also comply with Section 300-22 as to installation methods.

Exception to (c): Type CATVP coaxial cables listed as having adequate fire-resistant and low-smoke-producing characteristics shall be permitted for ducts and plenums as described in Section 300-22(b) and other space used for environmental air as described in Section 300-22(c).

(FPN): One method of defining low-smoke-producing materials is by establishing an acceptable value of the smoke produced per the NFPA 262-1985 test to a maximum peak optical density of 0.5 and a maximum average optical density of 0.15. Similarly, fire-resistant cables may be defined as having a maximum allowable flame travel distance of 5 feet (1.52 m) in the NFPA 262-1985 test.

D. Underground Circuits

820-18. Entering Buildings. Underground coaxial cables in a duct, pedestal, handhole, or manhole containing electric light or power conductors shall be in a section permanently separated from such conductors by means of a suitable barrier.

E. Grounding

820-22. Cable Grounding. Coaxial cable shall be grounded as specified in (a) through (h) below.

(a) Insulation. The grounding conductor shall have a rubber or other suitable kind of insulation.

(b) Material. The grounding conductor shall be copper or other corrosion-resistant conductive material, stranded or solid.

(c) Size. The grounding conductor shall not be smaller than No. 14; it shall have a current-carrying capacity approximately equal to that of the outer conductor of the coaxial cable.

(d) Run in Straight Line. The grounding conductor shall be run to the grounding electrode in as straight a line as practicable.

(e) Physical Protection. Where necessary, the grounding conductor shall be guarded from physical damage.

(f) Electrode. The grounding conductor shall be connected as follows:

(1) To the nearest accessible location on (1) the building or structure grounding electrode system as covered in Section 250-81, (2) the grounded interior metal water piping system as covered in Section 250-80(a), (3) the power service accessible means external to enclosures as covered in Section 250-71(b), (4) the metallic power service raceway, (5) the service equipment enclosure, (6) the grounding electrode conductor or the grounding electrode conductor metal enclosure, or (7) to the grounding conductor or to the grounding electrode of a building or structure disconnecting means which is grounded to an electrode as covered in Section 250-24; or

(2) If the building or structure served has no grounding means as described in (f)(1), to any one of the individual electrodes described in Section 250-81; or

(3) If the building or structure served has no grounding means as described in (f)(1) or (f)(2), to: (1) an effectively grounded metal structure, or (2) to any one of the individual electrodes described in Section 250-83.

(g) Electrode Connection. Connections to grounding electrodes shall comply with Section 250-115. Where a metal gas pipe electrode is used, connection shall be made between the gas meter and the street main.

(h) Bonding of Electrodes. A bonding jumper not smaller than No. 6 copper or equivalent shall be connected between the antenna systems and the power grounding electrodes where the requirements of (f) above result in the use of separate electrodes. Bonding together of all separate grounding electrodes shall be permitted.

(FPN): See Section 250-86 for use of lightning rods.

The most common error made in grounding CATV systems is to connect the coaxial cable sheath to a ground rod, driven by the CATV installer at a convenient location near the point of cable entry to the building. This is permitted by the *Code* only if the building or structure has none of the grounding means described in Sections 820-22(f)(1) or (f)(2), which is extremely unlikely. The *Code* does not require that these grounding means be readily available; if they exist, they are required to be used.

Proper bonding of the CATV system coaxial cable sheath to the electrical power ground is needed to prevent potential fire and shock hazards. The earth cannot be used as an equipment grounding conductor or bonding conductor as it will not have the low-impedance path needed. See Section 250-91(c).

Both CATV systems and power systems are subject to current surges as a result, for example, of induced voltages from lightning in the vicinity of the usually extensive outside distribution systems. Surges also result from switching operations on power systems. If the grounded conductors and parts of the two systems are not bonded by a low-impedance path, such line surges can raise the potential difference between the two systems to many thousands of volts. This can result in arcing between the two systems, for example, wherever the coaxial cable jacket contacts a grounded part inside the building, such as a metal water pipe or metal structural member.

If a person is the interface between the two systems, and the bonding has not been done in accordance with the *Code*, the high-voltage surge could result in electric shock. More common, however, is burnout of the TV tuner, as this part is almost always an interface between the two systems. The tuner is connected to the power system ground through the grounded neutral of the power supply, even if the TV set itself is not provided with an equipment grounding conductor.

Also see commentary following Sections 250-71(b)(3) and 820-7(b).

820-23. Equipment Grounding. Unpowered equipment and enclosures or equipment powered by the coaxial cable shall be considered grounded where connected to the metallic cable shield.

9 Tables and Examples

Contents

A. Tables
Notes to Tables

1. Tables 3A, 3B and 3C apply only to complete conduit or tubing systems and are not intended to apply to sections of conduit or tubing used to protect exposed wiring from physical damage.

2. Equipment grounding or bonding conductors, when installed, shall be included when calculating conduit or tubing fill. The actual dimensions of the equipment grounding or bonding conductor (insulated or bare) shall be used in the calculation.

3. When conduit or tubing nipples having a maximum length not to exceed 24 inches (610 mm) are installed between boxes, cabinets, and similar enclosures, the nipple shall be permitted to be filled to 60

percent of its total cross-sectional area, and Note 8(a) of Tables 310-16 through 310-31 does not apply to this condition.

4. For conductors not included in Chapter 9, such as compact or multiconductor cables, the actual dimensions shall be used.

5. See Table 1 for allowable percentage of conduit or tubing fill.

(FPN): Table 1 is based on common conditions of proper cabling and alignment of conductors where the length of the pull and the number of bends are within reasonable limits. It should be recognized that for certain conditions a larger size conduit or a lesser conduit fill should be considered.

Tables 3A, 3B, and 3C provide for the maximum allowable number of conductors that may be enclosed in complete systems of conduit or tubing, based on the percentage fill of Table 1, and do not apply to short sections of conduit or tubing used for the physical protection of conductors and cables. Cables are commonly protected from physical damage by conduit or tubing sleeves sized to enable the cable to be passed through with relative ease without injuring or abrading the protective jacket of the cable.

Conduit nipples, not exceeding 24 in. in length, may be filled to 60 percent of their capacity, and the derating factors of Note 8(a) to Tables 310-16 through 310-31 need not be applied.

All conductors occupy space in a raceway, and they must therefore all be counted, including equipment grounding or bonding conductors (insulated, bare or covered) and neutral or grounded conductors (insulated, bare or covered). The only exception to this rule is the addition of an uninsulated grounding conductor permitted within ⅜-in. flexible metal conduit (see footnote to Table 350-3). The dimensions of bare conductors are given in Table 8.

For conductors not included in Chapter 9, such as high-voltage types, the cross-sectional area may be calculated in the following manner, using the actual dimensions of each conductor:

D = outside diameter of a conductor (including insulation)

CM = circular mils

1 in. = 1,000 mils (1 mil = 0.001 in.)

CM = [π(3.1416) ÷ 4] = 0.7854 of a square mil

Diameter in mils squared × 0.7854 = cross-sectional area

Table 1. Percent of Cross Section of Conduit and Tubing for Conductors
(See Table 2 for Fixture Wires)

Number of Conductors	1	2	3	4	Over 4
All conductor types except lead-covered	53	31	40	40	40
Lead-covered conductors	55	30	40	38	35

Note 1. See Tables 3A, 3B, and 3C for number of conductors all of the same size in trade sizes of conduit or tubing ½ inch through 6 inch.

Note 2. For conductors larger than 750 MCM or for combinations of conductors of different sizes, use Tables 4 through 8, Chapter 9, for dimensions of conductors, conduit and tubing.

Note 3. Where the calculated number of conductors, all of the same size, includes a decimal fraction, the next higher whole number shall be used where this decimal is 0.8 or larger.

Note 4. When bare conductors are permitted by other sections of this Code, the dimensions for bare conductors in Table 8 of Chapter 9 shall be permitted.

Note 5. A multiconductor cable of two or more conductors shall be treated as a single conductor cable for calculating percentage conduit fill area. For cables that have elliptical cross section, the cross-sectional area calculation shall be based on using the major diameter of the ellipse as a circle diameter.

Example: Three 15-kV single conductors are to be installed in conduit. The outside diameter of each conductor measures 1⅝ in. (1⅝ in. = 1.62 in.).

$$1.62 \times 1.62 \times .7854 \times 3 = 6.18 \text{ sq in.}$$

Table 1 allows 40 percent conduit fill for three or more conductors. Table 4 indicates that 40 percent of a 5-in. conduit is 8.00 sq in., thus accommodating three 15-kV single conductors.

The percentage fills of Table 1 for conduit and tubing are to be used where any conflict occurs in Tables 3A, 3B, or 3C and also when various conductor sizes are to be installed in the same conduit.

An example of computing the conduit size for various conductor sizes follows:

Number	Wire size and type	Table 5 cross-sectional area (ea.)	Subtotal cross-sectional area
4	12 THWN	0.0117	0.0468
3	8 TW	0.0471	0.1413
3	6 THW	0.0819	0.2457
		Total cross-sectional area	0.4338

The 40 percent column (three or more conductors) of Table 4 indicates that 40 percent of a 1¼-in. conduit is 0.60 sq in., the required conduit size for these ten conductors.

An example based on Note 3 (decimal fractions) is to determine how many No. 12 THWN conductors are permitted in a ¾-in. conduit. Table 1 permits a 40 percent fill (three or more conductors); hence, from Table 4, 40 percent of a ¾-in. conduit is 0.21 sq in., and, from Table 5, the cross-sectional area of a No. 12 THWN conductor is 0.0117 sq in.

$$0.21 \div 0.0117 = 17.9$$

Eighteen such conductors are permitted in a ¾-in. conduit. [Since the decimal (0.9) is more than 0.8, it is increased to the next higher whole number. If the decimal had been less than 0.8, the decimal would have been dropped.]

Table 2. Maximum Number of Fixture Wires in Trade Sizes of Conduit or Tubing
(40 Percent Fill Based on Individual Diameters)

Conduit Trade Size (Inches)	½					¾					1					1¼					1½					2				
Wire Types	18	16	14	12	10	18	16	14	12	10	18	16	14	12	10	18	16	14	12	10	18	16	14	12	10	18	16	14	12	10
PTF, PTFF, PGFF, PGF, PFF, PF, PAF, PAFF, ZF, ZFF	23	18	14			40	31	24			65	50	39			115	90	70			157	122	95			257	200	156		
TFFN, TFN	19	15				34	26				55	43				97	76				132	104				216	169			
SF-1	16					29					47					83					114					186				
SFF-1	15					26					43					76					104					169				
TF	11	10				20	18				32	30				57	53				79	72				129	118			
RFH-1	11					20					32					57					79					129				
TFF	11	10				20	17				32	27				56	49				77	66				126	109			
AF	11	9	7	4	3	19	16	12	7	5	31	26	20	11	8	55	46	36	19	15	75	63	49	27	20	123	104	81	44	34
SFF-2	9	7	6			16	12	10			27	20	17			47	36	30			65	49	42			106	81	68		
SF-2	9	8	6			16	14	11			27	23	18			47	40	32			65	55	43			106	90	71		
FFH-2	9	7				15	12				25	19				44	34				60	46				99	75			
RFH-2	7	5				12	10				20	16				36	28				49	38				80	62			
KF-1, KFF-1, KF-2, KFF-2	36	32	22	14	9	64	55	39	25	17	103	89	63	41	28	182	158	111	73	49	248	216	152	100	67	406	353	248	163	110

Table 3A. Maximum Number of Conductors in Trade Sizes of Conduit or Tubing

(Based on Table 1, Chapter 9)

Type Letters	Conductor Size AWG, MCM	½	¾	1	1¼	1½	2	2½	3	3½	4	5	6
TW, XHHW (14 thru 8)	14	9	15	25	44	60	99	142					
	12	7	12	19	35	47	78	111	171				
	10	5	9	15	26	36	60	85	131	176			
	8	2	4	7	12	17	28	40	62	84	108	133	
RHW and RHH (without outer covering), THW	14	6	10	16	29	40	65	93	143	192			
	12	4	8	13	24	32	53	76	117	157			
	10	4	6	11	19	26	43	61	95	127	163		
	8	1	3	5	10	13	22	32	49	66	85		
TW, THW	6	1	2	4	7	10	16	23	36	48	62	97	141
	4	1	1	3	5	7	12	17	27	36	47	73	106
	3	1	1	2	4	6	10	15	23	31	40	63	91
	2		1	2	4	5	9	13	20	27	34	54	78
	1		1	1	3	4	6	9	14	19	25	39	57
FEPB (6 thru 2), RHW and RHH (without outer covering)	1/0		1	1	2	3	5	8	12	16	21	33	49
	2/0		1	1	1	3	5	7	10	14	18	29	41
	3/0			1	1	2	4	6	9	12	15	24	35
	4/0				1	1	3	5	7	10	13	20	29
	250			1	1	1	2	4	6	8	10	16	23
	300			1	1	1	2	3	5	7	9	14	20
	350				1	1	1	3	4	6	8	12	18
	400				1	1	1	2	4	5	7	11	16
	500				1	1	1	1	3	4	6	9	14
	600					1	1	1	3	4	5	7	11
	700					1	1	1	2	3	4	7	10
	750					1	1	1	2	3	4	6	9

Note: This table is for concentric stranded conductors only. For cables with compact conductors, the dimensions in Table 5A shall be used.

Table 3B. Maximum Number of Conductors in Trade Sizes of Conduit or Tubing
(Based on Table 1, Chapter 9)

Type Letters	Conductor Size AWG, MCM	1/2	3/4	1	1¼	1½	2	2½	3	3½	4	5	6
THWN,	14	13	24	39	69	94	154	164	160	106	136		
	12	10	18	29	51	70	114	104	79				
	10	6	11	18	32	44	73	51					
	8	3	5	9	16	22	36						
THHN, FEP (14 thru 2), FEPB (14 thru 8), PFA (14 thru 4/0), PFAH (14 thru 4/0) Z (14 thru 4/0) XHHW (4 thru 500MCM)	6	1	4	6	11	15	26	37	57	76	98	154	
	4	1	2	4	7	9	16	22	35	47	60	94	137
	3	1	1	3	6	8	13	19	29	39	51	80	116
	2	1	1	3	5	7	11	16	25	33	43	67	97
	1		1	1	3	5	8	12	18	25	32	50	72
	1/0		1	1	3	4	7	10	15	21	27	42	61
	2/0		1	1	2	3	6	8	13	17	22	35	51
	3/0		1	1	1	3	5	7	11	14	18	29	42
	4/0		1	1	1	2	4	6	9	12	15	24	35
	250			1	1	1	3	4	7	10	12	20	28
	300			1	1	1	3	4	6	8	11	17	24
	350				1	1	2	3	5	7	9	15	21
	400				1	1	1	3	5	6	8	13	19
	500				1	1	1	2	4	5	7	11	16
	600				1	1	1	1	3	4	5	9	13
	700					1	1	1	3	4	5	8	11
	750					1	1	1	2	3	4	7	11
XHHW	6	1	3	5	9	13	21	30	47	63	81	128	185
	600				1	1	1	1	3	4	5	9	13
	700					1	1	1	3	4	5	7	11
	750					1	1	1	2	3	4	7	10

Note: This table is for concentric stranded conductors only. For cables with compact conductors, the dimensions in Table 5A shall be used.

Table 3C. Maximum Number of Conductors in Trade Sizes of Conduit or Tubing
(Based on Table 1, Chapter 9)

Type Letters	Conductor Size AWG, MCM	1/2	3/4	1	1 1/4	1 1/2	2	2 1/2	3	3 1/2	4	5	6
RHW,	14	3	6	10	18	25	41	58	90	121	155		
	12	3	5	9	15	21	35	50	77	103	132		
	10	2	4	7	13	18	29	41	64	86	110		
	8	1	2	4	7	9	16	22	35	47	60	94	137
RHH	6	1	1	2	5	6	11	15	24	32	41	64	93
	4	1	1	1	3	5	8	12	18	24	31	50	72
	3	1	1	1	3	4	7	10	16	22	28	44	63
	2		1	1	3	4	6	9	14	19	24	38	56
	1				1	3	5	7	11	14	18	29	42
(with outer covering)	1/0		1	1	1	2	4	6	9	12	16	25	37
	2/0			1	1	1	3	5	8	11	14	22	32
	3/0			1	1	1	3	4	7	9	12	19	28
	4/0			1	1	1	2	4	6	8	10	16	24
	250				1	1	1	3	5	6	8	13	19
	300				1	1	1	3	4	5	7	11	17
	350				1	1	1	2	4	5	6	10	15
	400				1	1	1	1	3	4	6	9	14
	500				1	1	1	1	3	4	5	8	11
	600					1	1	1	2	3	4	6	9
	700					1	1	1	1	3	3	6	8
	750						1	1	1	3	3	5	8

Note: This table is for concentric stranded conductors only. For cables with compact conductors, the dimensions in Table 5A shall be used.

Tables 4 through 8, Chapter 9. Tables 4 through 8 give the nominal size of conductors and conduit or tubing for use in computing size of conduit or tubing for various combinations of conductors. The dimensions represent average conditions only, and variations will be found in dimensions of conductors and conduits of different manufacture.

Table 4. Dimensions and Percent Area of Conduit and of Tubing

Areas of Conduit or Tubing for the Combinations of Wires Permitted in Table 1, Chapter 9

Trade Size	Internal Diameter Inches	Total 100%	Not Lead Covered				Lead Covered			
			2 Cond. 31%	Over 2 Cond. 40%	1 Cond. 53%	1 Cond. 55%	2 Cond. 30%	3 Cond. 40%	4 Cond. 38%	Over 4 Cond. 35%
½	.622	.30	.09	.12	.16	.17	.09	.12	.11	.11
¾	.824	.53	.16	.21	.28	.29	.16	.21	.20	.19
1	1.049	.86	.27	.34	.46	.47	.26	.34	.33	.30
1¼	1.380	1.50	.47	.60	.80	.83	.45	.60	.57	.53
1½	1.610	2.04	.63	.82	1.08	1.12	.61	.82	.78	.71
2	2.067	3.36	1.04	1.34	1.78	1.85	1.01	1.34	1.28	1.18
2½	2.469	4.79	1.48	1.92	2.54	2.63	1.44	1.92	1.82	1.68
3	3.068	7.38	2.29	2.95	3.91	4.06	2.21	2.95	2.80	2.58
3½	3.548	9.90	3.07	3.96	5.25	5.44	2.97	3.96	3.76	3.47
4	4.026	12.72	3.94	5.09	6.74	7.00	3.82	5.09	4.83	4.45
5	5.047	20.00	6.20	8.00	10.60	11.00	6.00	8.00	7.60	7.00
6	6.065	28.89	8.96	11.56	15.31	15.89	8.67	11.56	10.98	10.11

Area—Square Inches

Table 5. Dimensions of Rubber-Covered and Thermoplastic-Covered Conductors

Size AWG MCM	Types RFH-2, RH, RHH,*** RHW,*** SF-2		Types TF, THW,† TW		Types TFN, THHN, THWN		Types**** FEP, FEPB, FEPW, TFE, PF, PFA, PFAH, PGF, PTF, Z, ZF, ZFF		Types XHHW, ZW††		Types KF-1, KF-2, KFF-1, KFF-2	
	Approx. Diam. Inches	Approx. Area Sq. In.	Approx. Diam. Inches	Approx. Area Sq. In.	Approx. Diam. Inches	Approx. Area Sq. In.	Approx. Diam. Inches	Approx. Area Sq. Inches	Approx. Diam. Inches	Approx. Area Sq. In.	Approx. Diam. Inches	Approx. Area Sq. In.
Col. 1	Col. 2	Col. 3	Col. 4	Col. 5	Col. 6	Col. 7	Col. 8	Col. 9	Col. 10	Col. 11	Col. 12	Col. 13
18	.146	.0167	.106	.0088	.089	.0062	.081	.0052	....	....	.065	.0033
16	.158	.0196	.118	.0109	.100	.0079	.092	.0066	....	....	.070	.0038
14	30 mils .171	.0230	.131	.0135	.105	.0087	.105 .105	.0087 .0087	....	....	.083	.0054
14	45 mils .204*	.0327*	.162†	.0206†	....	....	....	....	.129	.0131	....	....
12	30 mils .188	.0278	.148	.0172	.122	.0117	.121 .121	.0115 .0115	....	....	.102	.0082
12	45 mils .221*	.0384*	.179†	.0252†	....	....	....	....	.146	.0167	....	....
10	.242	.0460	.168	.0222	.153	.0184	.142 .142	.0158 .0158	.166	.0216	.124	.0121
10	....	....	.199†	.0311†	....	....	....	....	....	....	....	....
8	.328	.0845	.245	.0471	.218	.0373	.206 .186	.0333 .0272	.241	.0456	....	....
8	....	....	.276†	.0598†	....	....	....	....	....	....	....	....
6	.397	.1238	.323	.0819	.257	.0519	.244	.0468	.282	.0625	....	....
4	.452	.1605	.372	.1087	.328	.0845	.292	.0670	.328	.0845	....	....
3	.481	.1817	.401	.1263	.356	.0995	.320	.0804	.356	.0995	....	....
2	.513	.2067	.433	.1473	.388	.1182	.352	.0973	.388	.1182	....	....
1	.588	.2715	.508	.2027	.450	.1590	.420	.1385	.450	.1590	....	....
1/0	.629	.3107	.549	.2367	.491	.1893	.462	.1676	.491	.1893	....	....
2/0	.675	.3578	.595	.2781	.537	.2265	.498	.1948	.537	.2265	....	....
3/0	.727	.4151	.647	.3288	.588	.2715	.560	.2463	.588	.2715	....	....
4/0	.785	.4840	.705	.3904	.646	.3278	.618	.3000	.646	.3278	....	....

Table 5 (Continued)

Size AWG MCM	Types RFH-2, RH, RHH,*** RHW,*** SF-2		Types TF, THW,† TW		Types TFN, THHN, THWN		Types**** FEP, FEPB, FEPW, TFE, PF, PFA, PFAH, PGF, PTF, Z, ZF, ZFF		Types XHHW, ZW††	
	Approx. Diam. Inches	Approx. Area Sq. In.	Approx. Diam. Inches	Approx. Area Sq. In.	Approx. Diam. Inches	Approx. Area Sq. In.	Approx. Diam. Inches	Approx. Area Sq. Inches	Approx. Diam. Inches	Approx. Area Sq. In.
Col. 1	Col. 2	Col. 3	Col. 4	Col. 5	Col. 6	Col. 7	Col. 8	Col. 9	Col. 10	Col. 11
250	.868	.5917	.788	.4877	.716	.4026	....	....	.716	.4026
300	.933	.6837	.843	.5581	.771	.4669	....	....	.771	.4669
350	.985	.7620	.895	.6291	.822	.5307	....	....	.822	.5307
400	1.032	.8365	.942	.6969	.869	.5931	....	....	.869	.5931
500	1.119	.9834	1.029	.8316	.955	.7163	....	....	.955	.7163
600	1.233	1.1940	1.143	1.0261	1.058	.8791	....	....	1.073	.9043
700	1.304	1.3355	1.214	1.1575	1.129	1.0011	....	....	1.145	1.0297
750	1.339	1.4082	1.249	1.2252	1.163	1.0623	....	....	1.180	1.0936
800	1.372	1.4784	1.282	1.2908	1.196	1.1234	....	....	1.210	1.1499
900	1.435	1.6173	1.345	1.4208	1.259	1.2449	....	....	1.270	1.2668
1000	1.494	1.7530	1.404	1.5482	1.317	1.3623	....	....	1.330	1.3893
1250	1.676	2.2062	1.577	1.9532	....	....	....	....	1.500	1.7671
1500	1.801	2.5475	1.702	2.2751	....	....	....	....	1.620	2.0612
1750	1.916	2.8832	1.817	2.5930	....	....	....	....	1.740	2.3779
2000	2.021	3.2079	1.922	2.9013	....	....	....	....	1.840	2.6590

* The dimensions of Types RHH and RHW.

† Dimensions of THW in sizes No. 14 through No. 8. No. 6 THW and larger is the same dimension as TW.

*** Dimensions of RHH and RHW without outer covering are the same as THW No. 10, solid; No. 8 and larger, stranded.

**** In Columns 8 and 9 the values shown for sizes No. 1 through 4/0 are for TFE and Z only. The right-hand values in Columns 8 and 9 are for FEPB, Z, ZF, and ZFF only.

†† No. 14 through No. 2.

Table 5A. Aluminum Building Wire Nominal Dimensions* and Areas

Size AWG or MCM	Bare Conductor**		Type THW		Type THHN		Type XHHW		Size AWG or MCM
	Number of Strands	Diam. Inches	Approx. Diam. Inches	Approx. Area Sq. In.	Approx. Diam. Inches	Approx. Area Sq. In.	Approx. Diam. Inches	Approx. Area Sq. In.	
8	7	.134	.255	.0510	—	—	.224	.0394	8
6	7	.169	.290	.0660	.240	.0452	.260	.0530	6
4	7	.213	.335	.0881	.305	.0730	.305	.0730	4
2	7	.268	.390	.1194	.360	.1017	.360	.1017	2
1	19	.299	.465	.1698	.415	.1352	.415	.1352	1
1/0	19	.336	.500	.1963	.450	.1590	.450	.1590	1/0
2/0	19	.376	.545	.2332	.495	.1924	.490	.1885	2/0
3/0	19	.423	.590	.2733	.540	.2290	.540	.2290	3/0
4/0	19	.475	.645	.3267	.595	.2780	.590	.2733	4/0
250	37	.520	.725	.4128	.670	.3525	.660	.3421	250
300	37	.570	.775	.4717	.720	.4071	.715	.4015	300
350	37	.616	.820	.5281	.770	.4656	.760	.4536	350
400	37	.659	.865	.5876	.815	.5216	.800	.5026	400
500	37	.736	.940	.6939	.885	.6151	.880	.6082	500
600	61	.813	1.050	.8659	.985	.7620	.980	.7542	600
700	61	.877	1.110	.9676	1.050	.8659	1.050	.8659	700
750	61	.908	1.150	1.0386	1.075	.9076	1.090	.9331	750
1000	61	1.060	1.285	1.2968	1.255	1.2370	1.230	1.1882	1000

* Dimensions are from industry sources
** Compact conductor per ASTM B 400

Most aluminum building wire in types THW, THWN/THHN, and XHHW is compact stranded. New Table 5A provides appropriate dimensions for these types of wire.

TABLES AND EXAMPLES

Table 6. Dimensions of Lead-Covered Conductors
Types RL and RHL

Size AWG-MCM	Single Conductor		Two Conductor		Three Conductor	
	Diam. Inches	Area Sq. In.	Diam. Inches	Area Sq. In.	Diam. Inches	Area Sq. In.
14	.28	.062	.28 × .47	.115	.59	.273
12	.29	.066	.31 × .54	.146	.62	.301
10	.35	.096	.35 × .59	.180	.68	.363
8 sol.	.41	.132	.41 × .71	.255	.82	.528
8 str.	.43	.145	.43 × .75	.282	.86	.581
6	.49	.188	.49 × .86	.369	.97	.738
4	.55	.237	.54 × .96	.457	1.08	.916
2	.60	.283	.61 × 1.08	.578	1.21	1.146
1	.67	.352	.70 × 1.23	.756	1.38	1.49
1/0	.71	.396	.74 × 1.32	.859	1.47	1.70
2/0	.76	.454	.79 × 1.41	.980	1.57	1.94
3/0	.81	.515	.84 × 1.52	1.123	1.69	2.24
4/0	.87	.593	.90 × 1.64	1.302	1.85	2.68
250	.98	.754	. . . .	. . . .	2.02	3.20
300	1.04	.85	. . . .	. . . .	2.15	3.62
350	1.10	.95	. . . .	. . . .	2.26	4.02
400	1.14	1.02	. . . .	. . . .	2.40	4.52
500	1.23	1.18	. . . .	. . . .	2.59	5.28

The above cables are limited to straight runs or with nominal offsets equivalent to not more than two quarter bends.

Note: No. 14 through No. 10, solid conductors; No. 8, solid or stranded conductors; No. 6 and larger, stranded conductors.

Table 7. Dimensions of Asbestos-Varnished-Cambric Insulated Conductors
Types AVA, AVB, and AVL

Size AWG, MCM	Type AVA		Type AVB		Type AVL	
	Approx. Diam. Inches	Approx. Area Sq. In.	Approx. Diam. Inches	Approx. Area Sq. In.	Approx. Diam. Inches	Approx. Area Sq. In.
14	.245	.047	.205	.033	.320	.080
12	.265	.055	.225	.040	.340	.091
10	.285	.064	.245	.047	.360	.102
8 sol.	.310	.075	.270	.057	.390	.119
8 str.	.325	.083	.285	.064	.390	.119
6	.395	.122	.345	.094	.430	.145
4	.445	.155	.395	.123	.480	.181
2	.505	.200	.460	.166	.570	.255
1	.585	.268	.540	.229	.620	.300
1/0	.625	.307	.580	.264	.660	.341
2/0	.670	.353	.625	.307	.705	.390
3/0	.720	.406	.675	.358	.755	.447
4/0	.780	.478	.735	.425	.815	.521
250	.885	.616	.855	.572	.955	.715
300	.940	.692	.910	.649	1.010	.800
350	.995	.778	.965	.731	1.060	.885
400	1.040	.850	1.010	.800	1.105	.960
500	1.125	.995	1.095	.945	1.190	1.118
550	1.165	1.065	1.135	1.01	1.265	1.26
600	1.205	1.140	1.175	1.09	1.305	1.34
650	1.240	1.21	1.210	1.15	1.340	1.41
700	1.275	1.28	1.245	1.22	1.375	1.49
750	1.310	1.35	1.280	1.29	1.410	1.57
800	1.345	1.42	1.315	1.36	1.440	1.63
850	1.375	1.49	1.345	1.43	1.470	1.70
900	1.405	1.55	1.375	1.49	1.505	1.78
950	1.435	1.62	1.405	1.55	1.535	1.85
1000	1.465	1.69	1.435	1.62	1.565	1.93

Note: No. 14 through No. 10, solid: No. 8, solid or stranded; No. 6 and larger, stranded; except AVL where all sizes are stranded.

Varnished-Cambric Insulated Conductors
Type V

The insulation thickness for varnished-cambric conductors, Type V, is the same as for rubber-covered conductors, Type RHH, except for No. 8 which has 45-mil insulation for varnished-cambric, and 60-mil insulation for rubber-covered conductors. See Table 310-13. Therefore, Table 3C shall be permitted to be used for the number of varnished-cambric insulated conductors in a conduit or tubing.

TABLES AND EXAMPLES

Table 8. Conductor Properties

Size AWG/ MCM	Area Cir. Mils	Stranding Quantity	Stranding Diam. In.	Overall Diam. In.	Overall Area In.²	Copper Uncoated ohm/MFT	Copper Coated ohm/MFT	Aluminum ohm/ MFT
18	1620	1	—	0.040	0.001	7.77	8.08	12.8
18	1620	7	0.015	0.046	0.002	7.95	8.45	13.1
16	2580	1	—	0.051	0.002	4.89	5.08	8.05
16	2580	7	0.019	0.058	0.003	4.99	5.29	8.21
14	4110	1	—	0.064	0.003	3.07	3.19	5.06
14	4110	7	0.024	0.073	0.004	3.14	3.26	5.17
12	6530	1	—	0.081	0.005	1.93	2.01	3.18
12	6530	7	0.030	0.092	0.006	1.98	2.05	3.25
10	10380	1	—	0.102	0.008	1.21	1.26	2.00
10	10380	7	0.038	0.116	0.011	1.24	1.29	2.04
8	16510	1	—	0.128	0.013	0.764	0.786	1.26
8	16510	7	0.049	0.146	0.017	0.778	0.809	1.28
6	26240	7	0.061	0.184	0.027	0.491	0.510	0.808
4	41740	7	0.077	0.232	0.042	0.308	0.321	0.508
3	52620	7	0.087	0.260	0.053	0.245	0.254	0.403
2	66360	7	0.097	0.292	0.067	0.194	0.201	0.319
1	83690	19	0.066	0.332	0.087	0.154	0.160	0.253
1/0	105600	19	0.074	0.373	0.109	0.122	0.127	0.201
2/0	133100	19	0.084	0.419	0.138	0.0967	0.101	0.159
3/0	167800	19	0.094	0.470	0.173	0.0766	0.0797	0.126
4/0	211600	19	0.106	0.528	0.219	0.0608	0.0626	0.100
250	—	37	0.082	0.575	0.260	0.0515	0.0535	0.0847
300	—	37	0.090	0.630	0.312	0.0429	0.0446	0.0707
350	—	37	0.097	0.681	0.364	0.0367	0.0382	0.0605
400	—	37	0.104	0.728	0.416	0.0321	0.0331	0.0529
500	—	37	0.116	0.813	0.519	0.0258	0.0265	0.0424
600	—	61	0.099	0.893	0.626	0.0214	0.0223	0.0353
700	—	61	0.107	0.964	0.730	0.0184	0.0189	0.0303
750	—	61	0.111	0.998	0.782	0.0171	0.0176	0.0282
800	—	61	0.114	1.03	0.834	0.0161	0.0166	0.0265
900	—	61	0.122	1.09	0.940	0.0143	0.0147	0.0235
1000	—	61	0.128	1.15	1.04	0.0129	0.0132	0.0212
1250	—	91	0.117	1.29	1.30	0.0103	0.0106	0.0169
1500	—	91	0.128	1.41	1.57	0.00858	0.00883	0.0141
1750	—	127	0.117	1.52	1.83	0.00735	0.00756	0.0121
2000	—	127	0.126	1.63	2.09	0.00643	0.00662	0.0106

These resistance values are valid ONLY for the parameters as given. Using conductors having coated strands, different stranding type, and especially, other temperatures, change the resistance.

Formula for temperature change: $R_2 = R_1 [1 + \alpha(T_2 - 75)]$ where: $\alpha_{cu} = 0.00323$, $\alpha_{AL} = 0.00330$.

Conductors with compact and compressed stranding have about 9 percent and 3 percent, respectively, smaller bare conductor diameters than those shown. See Table 5A for actual compact cable dimensions.

The IACS conductivities used: bare copper = 100%, aluminum = 61%.

Class B stranding is listed as well as solid for some sizes. Its overall diameter and area is that of its circumscribing circle.

(FPN): The construction information is per NEMA WC8-1976 (Rev 5-1980). The resistance is calculated per National Bureau of Standards Handbook 100, dated 1966, and Handbook 109, dated 1972.

Table 9. AC Resistance and Reactance for 600 V cables, 3 phase 60, Hz, 75°C (167°F)—Three Single Conductors in Conduit

Ohms to neutral per 1000 feet

Size AWG/MCM	X (Inductance) for All Wires		AC Resistance for Uncoated Copper Wires			AC Resistance for Aluminum Wires			Effective Z at .85 PF for Uncoated Copper Wires			Effective Z at .85 PF for Aluminum Wires			Size AWG/MCM
	PVC, Al. Conduits	Steel Conduit	PVC Conduit	Al. Conduit	Steel Conduit	PVC Conduit	Al. Conduit	Steel Conduit	PVC Conduit	Al. Conduit	Steel Conduit	PVC Conduit	Al. Conduit	Steel Conduit	
14	.058	.073	3.1	3.1	3.1	—	—	—	2.7	2.7	2.7	—	—	—	14
12	.054	.068	2.0	2.0	2.0	3.2	3.2	3.2	1.7	1.7	1.7	2.8	2.8	2.8	12
10	.050	.063	1.2	1.2	1.2	2.0	2.0	2.0	1.1	1.1	1.1	1.8	1.8	1.8	10
8	.052	.065	0.78	0.78	0.78	1.3	1.3	1.3	0.69	0.69	0.70	1.1	1.1	1.1	8
6	.051	.064	0.49	0.49	0.49	0.81	0.81	0.81	0.44	0.45	0.45	0.71	0.72	0.72	6
4	.048	.060	0.31	0.31	0.31	0.51	0.51	0.51	0.29	0.29	0.30	0.46	0.46	0.46	4
3	.047	.059	0.25	0.25	0.25	0.40	0.41	0.40	0.23	0.24	0.24	0.37	0.37	0.37	3
2	.045	.057	0.19	0.20	0.20	0.32	0.32	0.32	0.19	0.19	0.20	0.30	0.30	0.30	2
1	.046	.057	0.15	0.16	0.16	0.25	0.26	0.25	0.16	0.16	0.16	0.24	0.24	0.25	1
1/0	.044	.055	0.12	0.13	0.12	0.20	0.21	0.20	0.13	0.13	0.13	0.19	0.20	0.20	1/0
2/0	.043	.054	0.10	0.10	0.10	0.16	0.16	0.16	0.11	0.11	0.11	0.16	0.16	0.16	2/0
3/0	.042	.052	0.077	0.082	0.079	0.13	0.13	0.13	0.088	0.092	0.094	0.13	0.13	0.14	3/0
4/0	.041	.051	0.062	0.067	0.063	0.10	0.11	0.10	0.074	0.078	0.080	0.11	0.11	0.11	4/0
250	.041	.052	0.052	0.057	0.054	0.085	0.090	0.086	0.056	0.070	0.073	0.094	0.098	0.10	250
300	.041	.051	0.044	0.049	0.045	0.071	0.076	0.072	0.059	0.063	0.065	0.082	0.086	0.088	300
350	.040	.050	0.038	0.043	0.039	0.061	0.066	0.063	0.053	0.058	0.060	0.073	0.077	0.080	350
400	.040	.049	0.033	0.038	0.035	0.054	0.059	0.055	0.049	0.053	0.056	0.066	0.071	0.073	400
500	.039	.048	0.027	0.032	0.029	0.043	0.048	0.045	0.043	0.048	0.050	0.057	0.061	0.064	500
600	.039	.048	0.023	0.028	0.025	0.036	0.041	0.038	0.040	0.044	0.047	0.051	0.055	0.058	600
750	.038	.048	0.019	0.024	0.021	0.029	0.034	0.031	0.036	0.040	0.043	0.045	0.049	0.052	750
1000	.037	.046	0.015	0.019	0.018	0.023	0.027	0.025	0.032	0.036	0.040	0.039	0.042	0.046	1000

Notes:

1. These values are based on the following constants: UL-type RHH wires with Class B stranding, in cradled configuration. Wire conductivities are 100% IACS copper, and 61% IACS aluminum, and aluminum conduit is 45% IACS. Capacitive reactance is ignored since it is negligible at these voltages. These resistance values are valid only at 75°C (167°F) and for the parameters as given, but are representative for 600-volt wire types operating at 60 Hz.

2. "Effective Z" is defined as $R \cos(\text{theta}) + X \sin(\text{theta})$, where "theta" is the power factor angle of the circuit. Multiplying current by effective impedance gives a good approximation for line to neutral voltage drop. Effective impedance values shown in this table are valid only at .85 power factor. For another circuit power factor (PF), effective impedance (Ze) can be calculated from R and X values given in this table as follows:

$$Z_e = R \times PF + X \sin[\arccos(PF)]$$

TABLES AND EXAMPLES

B. Examples

Selection of Conductors. In the following examples, the results are generally expressed in amperes. To select conductor sizes, refer to Tables 310-16 through 310-31 and the Notes that pertain to such tables.

Voltage. For uniform application of Articles 210, 215 and 220, a nominal voltage of 120, 120/240, 240 and 208Y/120 volts shall be used in computing the ampere load on the conductor.

Fractions of an Ampere. Except where the computations result in a major fraction of an ampere (0.5 or larger), such fractions may be dropped.

Ranges. For the computation of the range loads in these examples, Column A of Table 220-19 has been used. For optional methods, see Columns B and C of Table 220-19.

SI Units: For SI units: one square foot = 0.093 square meter; one foot = 0.3048 meter.

In the following examples, loads are assumed to be properly balanced on the system. Where loads are not properly balanced, additional feeder capacity may be required.

Example No. 1(a). One-Family Dwelling

The dwelling has a floor area of 1500 sq. ft. exclusive of unoccupied cellar, unfinished attic, and open porches. Appliances are a 12-kW range and a 5.5-kW, 240-volt dryer. Assume range and dryer kW ratings equivalent to kVA ratings in accordance with Sections 220-18 and 220-19.

Computed Load [see Section 220-10(a)]:
General Lighting Load:
1500 sq. ft. at 3 volt-amperes per sq. ft. = 4500 volt-amperes.

Minimum Number of Branch Circuits Required [see Section 220-3(b)]:
General Lighting Load:
4500 volt-amperes ÷ 120 volts = 37.5 A: This requires three 15 A 2-wire or two 20 A 2-wire circuits.
Small Appliance Load: Two 2-wire 20 A circuits [see Section 220-4(b)].
Laundry Load: One 2-wire 20 A circuit [see Section 220-4(c)].

Minimum Size Feeder Required [see Section 220-10(a)]:

General Lighting	4500 volt-amperes
Small Appliance Load	3000 volt-amperes
Laundry	1500 volt-amperes
Total General Light & Small Appliance	9000 volt-amperes
3000 volt-amperes at 100%	3000 volt-amperes
9000–3000 = 6000 volt-amperes at 35%	2100 volt-amperes
Net General Lighting & Small Appliance Load	5100 volt-amperes
Range Load (see Table 220-19)	8000 volt-amperes
Dryer Load (see Table 220-18)	5500 volt-amperes
Total Load	18,600 volt-amperes

For 120/240-volt 3-wire single-phase service or feeder, 18,600 volt-amperes ÷ 240 volts = 77.5 A.

Net computed load exceeds 10 kVA. Service conductors shall be 100 amperes [see Section 230-42(b)(2)].

Neutral for Feeder and Service

Lighting and Small Appliance Load	5100 volt-amperes
Range Load 8000 volt-amperes at 70%	5600 volt-amperes
Dryer Load 5500 volt-amperes at 70%	3850 volt-amperes
Total	14,500 volt-amperes

14,500 VA ÷ 240 V = 60.6 amperes

The general lighting and general-use receptacle load is computed from the outside dimensions of the building, apartment, or other area involved. For a dwelling unit(s), the computed floor area is not to include open porches, garages, or unused or unfinished spaces unadaptable for future use. See Section 220-3(b).

Example: A two-story dwelling measures 30 ft × 30 ft for the first floor and 30 ft × 20 ft for the second floor.

$$30 \text{ ft} \times 30 \text{ ft} = 900 \text{ sq ft (first floor)}$$
$$30 \text{ ft} \times 20 \text{ ft} = 600 \text{ sq ft (second floor)}$$
$$\text{Total area} = 1{,}500 \text{ sq ft}$$

Example No. 1(b). One-Family Dwelling

Same conditions as Example No. 1(a), plus addition of one 6-ampere 230-volt room air-conditioning unit and one 12-ampere 115-volt room air-conditioning unit*, one 8-ampere 115-volt rated disposal and one 10-ampere 120-volt rated dishwasher*. See Article 430 for general motors and Article 440, Part G for air-conditioning equipment. Motors have nameplate ratings of 115 V and 230 V for use on 120 V and 240 V nominal voltage systems.

From previous Example No. 1(a), feeder current is 78 amperes (3-wire 240 volts).

	Line A	Neutral	Line B
Amperes from Example No. 1(a)	78	61	78
One 230-V air conditioner	6	—	6
One 115-V air conditioner and 120-V dishwasher	12	12	10
One 115-V disposal	—	8	8
25% of largest motor (Section 430-24)	3	3	2
Amperes per line	99	84	104

*For feeder neutral, use largest of the two appliances for unbalance.

Example No. 2(a). Optional Calculation for One-Family Dwelling
Heating Larger than Air-Conditioning
(See Section 220-30.)

Dwelling has a floor area of 1500 sq. ft. exclusive of unoccupied cellar, unfinished attic, and open porches. It has a 12-kW range, a 2.5-kW water heater, a 1.2-kW dishwasher, 9 kW of electric space heating installed in five rooms, a 5-kW clothes dryer, and a 6-ampere 230-volt room air-conditioning unit. Assume range, water heater, dishwasher, space heating, and clothes dryer kW ratings equivalent to kVA.

Air conditioner kVA is $6 \times 230 \div 1000 = 1.38$ kVA

1.38 kVA is less than the connected load of 9 kVA of space heating; therefore, the air conditioner load need not be included in the service calculation (see Section 220-21).

1500 sq. ft. at 3 volt-amperes	4.5 kVA
Two 20-ampere appliance outlet circuits at 1500 volt-amperes each	3.0 kVA
Laundry circuit	1.5 kVA
Range (at nameplate rating)	12.0 kVA
Water heater	2.5 kVA
Dishwasher	1.2 kVA
Clothes dryer	5.0 kVA
	29.7 kVA

First 10 kVA of other load at 100%   = 10.0 kVA
Remainder of other load at 40% (19.7 kVA × .4) = 7.9 kVA
                    Total of other load = 17.9 kVA
9 kVA of heat at 40% (9 × .4)   = 3.6 kVA
                         Total load = 21.5 kVA

Calculated load for service size
21.5 kVA = 21,500 volt-amperes
21,500 VA ÷ 240 volts = 90 amperes

Therefore, this dwelling may be served by a 100-ampere service.

Feeder Neutral Load, per Section 220-22:

1500 sq. ft. at 3 volt-amperes	4500 volt-amperes
Three 20-amp. circuits at 1500 volt-amperes	4500 volt-amperes
Total	9000 volt-amperes
3000 volt-amperes at 100%	3000 volt-amperes
9000 VA − 3000 VA = 6000 volt-amperes at 35%	2100 volt-amperes
	5100 volt-amperes
Range—8 kVA at 70%	5600 volt-amperes
Clothes dryer—5 kVA at 70%	3500 volt-amperes
Dishwasher	1200 volt-amperes
Total	15,400 volt-amperes

15,400 VA ÷ 240 volts = 64.2 amperes

1095

TABLES AND EXAMPLES

Example No. 2(b).   Optional Calculation for One-Family Dwelling
Air Conditioning Larger than Heating

(See Section 220-30.)

Dwelling has a floor area of 1500 sq. ft. exclusive of unoccupied cellar, unfinished attic, and open porches. It has two 20-ampere small appliance circuits, one 20-ampere laundry circuit, two 4-kW wall-mounted ovens, one 5.1-kW counter-mounted cooking unit, a 4.5-kW water heater, a 1.2-kW dishwasher, a 5-kW combination clothes washer and dryer, six 7-ampere 230-volt room air-conditioning units, and a 1.5-kW permanently installed bathroom space heater. Assume wall-mounted ovens, counter-mounted cooking unit, water heater, dishwasher and combination clothes washer and dryer kW ratings equivalent to kVA.

Air Conditioning kVA Calculation:

Total amperes $6 \times 7 = 42.00$ amperes

$42 \times 240 \div 1000 = 10.08$ kVA of air-conditioned load. Assume P.F. = 1.0

The air-conditioning load is counted at 100 percent, and this load is calculated separately in order to comply with the requirements of Section 220-30 and Table 220-30.

Load Included at 100%:

Air conditioning (See below)

Space heater (omit; see Section 220-21)

Other Load:	kVA
1500 sq. ft. at 3 volt-amperes	4.5
Two 20-amp. small appliance circuits	
at 1500 volt-amperes	3.0
Laundry circuit	1.5
Two ovens	8.0
One cooking unit	5.1
Water heater	4.5
Dishwasher	1.2
Washer/dryer	5.0
Total other load	32.8
1st 10 kVA at 100%	10.0 kVA
Remainder at 40% (22.8 kVA $\times$ .4)	9.12 kVA
Total other load	19.12 kVA

Other load .... 19.12 kVA
Air conditioning .... 10.08 kVA
29.2 kVA = 29,200 volt-amperes

29,200 VA $\div$ 240 V = 122 amperes (service rating)

Feeder Neutral Load, per Section 220-22:

(It is assumed that the two 4-kVA wall-mounted ovens are supplied by one branch circuit, the 5.1-kVA counter-mounted cooking unit by a separate circuit.)

1500 sq. ft. at 3 volt-amperes	4500 volt-amperes
Three 20-amp. circuits at 1500 volt-amperes	4500 volt-amperes
Total	9000 volt-amperes
3000 volt-amperes at 100%	3000 volt-amperes
9000 VA $-$ 3000 VA = 6000 volt-amperes at 35%	2100 volt-amperes
	5100 volt-amperes

Two 4-kVA ovens plus one 5.1-kVA cooking unit totals 13.1 kVA
Table 220-19 permits 55% demand factor
13.1 kVA $\times$ .55 = 7.2 kVA feeder capacity

7200 VA $\times$ 70% for neutral load	5040 volt-amperes
Clothes washer/dryer—5 kVA $\times$ 70% for neutral load	3500 volt-amperes
Dishwasher	1200 volt-amperes
Total	14,840 volt-amperes

14,840 VA $\div$ 240 V = 61.83 (use 62 amperes)

1096

Example No. 3. Store Building

A store 50 ft. by 60 ft., or 3000 sq. ft., has 30 ft. of show window. There are a total of 80 duplex receptacles. The service is 120/240-volt, single-phase (3-wire service). Actual connected lighting load, 8500 volt-amperes.

Computed Load (Section 220-10):

*General Lighting Load:	
3000 sq. ft. at 3 volt-amperes per sq. ft. × 1.25..	11,250 volt-amperes
Show Window Lighting Load:	
30 ft. at 200 volt-amperes per foot...	6000 volt-amperes
Receptacle Load (Section 220-13):	
80 receptacles at 180 VA = 14,400 VA	
10,000 VA at 100%..	10,000 volt-amperes
(14,400—10,000) VA at 50%..	2200 volt-amperes
Outside sign circuit 1200 volt-amperes [Section 600-6(c)]...............................	1200 volt-amperes
Total	30,650 volt-amperes

Minimum Number of Branch Circuits Required:

General Lighting Load:
   11,250 volt-amperes ÷ 240 volts = 47 amperes for 3-wire, 120/240.
The lighting load may be served by 2-wire or 3-wire 15- or 20-ampere circuits with combined capacity equal to 47 amperes or greater for 3-wire circuits or 94 amperes or greater for 2-wire circuits.

Show Window:

   6000 volt-amperes ÷ 240 volts = 25 amperes for 3-wire, 120/240.
The show window lighting may be served by 2-wire or 3-wire circuits with a capacity equal to 25 amperes or greater for 3-wire circuits or 50 amperes or greater for 2-wire circuits.
Receptacles required by Section 210-62 are assumed to be included in the receptacle load above if these receptacles do not supply the show window lighting load.
Receptacle Load: 14,400 volt-amperes ÷ 240 volts = 60 amperes for 3-wire, 120/240.
The receptacle load may be served by 2-wire or 3-wire circuits with a capacity equal to 60 amperes or greater for 3-wire circuits or 120 amperes or greater for 2-wire circuits.

Minimum Size Feeders (or Service Conductors) Required (Section 215-3):

For 120/240-volt, 3-wire system:
   30,650 volt-amperes ÷ 240 volts = 128 amperes

*The above examples assume that the entire lighting load is continuous. The general lighting load is increased 125 percent in accordance with Section 220-10(b).
In the example, 125 percent of the actual connected lighting load (8500 VA × 1.25 = 10,625 VA) is less than 125 percent of the load from Table 220-3(b), so the minimum lighting load from Table 220-3(b) is used in the calculation. Had the actual lighting load been greater than the value computed from Table 220-3(b), 125 percent of the actual connected lighting load would have been used.

Example No. 4(a). Multifamily Dwelling

Multifamily dwelling having 40 dwelling units.

Meters in two banks of 20 each and individual subfeeders to each dwelling unit.

One-half of the dwelling units are equipped with electric ranges not exceeding 12 kW each. Assume range kW rating equivalent to kVA rating in accordance with Section 220-19. Other half of ranges are gas ranges.

Area of each dwelling unit is 840 sq. ft.

Laundry facilities on premises available to all tenants. Add no circuit to individual dwelling unit. Add 1500 volt-amperes for each laundry circuit to house load and add to the example as a "house load."

Computed Load for Each Dwelling Unit (Article 220):

General Lighting Load:	
840 sq. ft. at 3 volt-amperes per sq. ft.	2520 volt-amperes
Special Appliance Load:	
Electric Range (Section 220-19)...	8000 volt-amperes

TABLES AND EXAMPLES

Example No. 4(a) (Continued)

Minimum Number of Branch Circuits Required for Each Dwelling Unit (Section 220-4):

General Lighting Load: 2520 volt-amperes ÷ 120 volts = 21 amperes or two 15-ampere, 2-wire circuits; or two 20-ampere, 2-wire circuits.

Small Appliance Load: Two 2-wire circuits of No. 12 wire. [See Section 220-4(b).]

Range Circuit: 8000 volt-amperes ÷ 240 = 33 amperes or a circuit of two No. 8 and one No. 10 as permitted by Section 220-22. (See Section 210-19.)

Minimum Size Subfeeder Required for Each Dwelling Unit (Section 215-2):

Computed Load (Article 220):

General Lighting Load	2520 volt-amperes
Small Appliance Load, two 20-ampere circuits	3000 volt-amperes
Total Computed Load (without ranges)	5520 volt-amperes

Application of Demand Factor:

3000 volt-amperes at 100%	3000 volt-amperes
2520 volt-amperes at 35%	882 volt-amperes
Net Computed Load (without ranges)	3882 volt-amperes
Range Load	8000 volt-amperes
Net Computed Load (with ranges)	11,882 volt-amperes

Size of Each Subfeeder (see Section 215-3).
For 120/240-volt, 3-wire system (without ranges):
Net Computed Load, 3882 volt-amperes ÷ 240 volts = 16.2 amperes.
For 120/240-volt, 3-wire system (with ranges):
Net Computed Load, 11,882 volt-amperes ÷ 240 volts = 49.5 amperes.

Subfeeder Neutral:

Lighting and Small Appliance Load	3882 volt-amperes
Range Load, 8000 volt-amperes at 70% (see Section 220-22)	5600 volt-amperes

(Not included for apartments without electric range)

Net Computed Load (neutral)	9482 volt-amperes

9482 volt-amperes ÷ 240 volts = 39.5 amperes

Minimum Size Feeders Required from Service Equipment to Meter Bank (For 20 Dwelling Units—10 with Ranges):

Total Computed Load:

Lighting and Small Appliance Load, 20 × 5520 volt-amperes	110,400 volt-amperes

Application of Demand Factor:

3000 volt-amperes at 100%	3000 volt-amperes
107,400 volt-amperes at 35%	37,590 volt-amperes
Net Computed Lighting and Small Appliance Load	40,590 volt-amperes
Range Load, 10 ranges (less than 12 kVA, Col. A, Table 220-19)	25,000 volt-amperes
Net Computed Load (with ranges)	65,590 volt-amperes

For 120/240-volt, 3-wire system:
Net Computed Load, 65,590 volt-amperes ÷ 240 volts = 273 amperes.

Feeder Neutral:

Lighting and Small Appliance Load	40,590 volt-amperes
Range Load: 25,000 volt-amperes at 70% (see Section 220-22)	17,500 volt-amperes
Computed Load (neutral)	58,090 volt-amperes

58,090 volt-amperes ÷ 240 volts = 242 amperes.

Further Demand Factor (Section 220-22):

200 amperes at 100%	200 amperes
42 amperes at 70%	29 amperes
Net Computed Load (neutral)	229 amperes

Minimum Size Main Feeder (or Service Conductors) Required (less house load) (For 40 Dwelling Units—20 with Ranges):

Total Computed Load:

Lighting and Small Appliance Load, 40 × 5520 volt-amperes	220,800 volt-amperes

Example No. 4(a) (Continued)

Application of Demand Factor:

3000 volt-amperes at 100%	3000 volt-amperes
117,000 volt-amperes at 35%	40,950 volt-amperes
100,800 volt-amperes at 25%	25,200 volt-amperes
Net Computed Lighting and Small Appliance Load	69,150 volt-amperes
Range Load, 20 ranges (less than 12 kVA, Col. A, Table 220-19)..	35,000 volt-amperes
Net Computed Load..	104,150 volt-amperes

For 120/240-volt, 3-wire system:
Net Computed Load, 104,150 volt-amperes ÷ 240 volts = 434 amperes.

Feeder Neutral:

Lighting and Small Appliance Load	69,150 volt-amperes
Range Load, 35,000 volt-amperes at 70% (see Section 220-22).................	24,500 volt-amperes
Computed Load (neutral)...	93,650 volt-amperes

93,650 volt-amperes ÷ 240 volts = 390 amperes.

Further Demand Factor (see Section 220-22):

200 amperes at 100%...	200 amperes
190 amperes at 70%...	133 amperes
Net Computed Load (neutral)	333 amperes

See Tables 310-16 through 310-31, Notes 8 and 10.

Example No. 4(b). Optional Calculation for Multifamily Dwelling

Multifamily dwelling equipped with electric cooking and space heating or air conditioning and having 40 dwelling units.

Meters in two banks of 20 each plus house metering and individual subfeeders to each dwelling unit.

Each dwelling unit is equipped with an electric range of 8-kW nameplate rating, four 1.5-kW separately controlled 240-volt electric space heaters, and a 2.5-kW 240-volt electric water heater. Assume range, space heater, and water heater kW ratings equivalent to kVA.

A common laundry facility is available to all tenants [Section 210-52(e), Exception No. 1].

Area of each dwelling unit is 840 square feet.

Computed Load for Each Dwelling Unit (Article 220):

General Lighting Load:

840 sq. ft. at 3 volt-amperes per sq. ft.	2520 volt-amperes
Electric Range	8000 volt-amperes
Electric Heat 6 kVA	6000 volt-amperes
(or air conditioning if larger)	
Electric Water Heater	2500 volt-amperes

Minimum Number of Branch Circuits Required for Each Dwelling Unit:

General Lighting Load 2520 volt-amperes ÷ 120 volts = 21 amperes or two 15-amperes 2-wire circuits or two 20-ampere 2-wire circuits.

Small Appliance Loads: Two 2-wire circuits of No. 12 [see Section 220-4(b)].

Range circuit 8000 volt-amperes × 80% ÷ 240 volts = 27 amperes on a circuit of three No. 10 AWG as permitted in Column C of Table 220-19.

Space Heating 6000 volt-amperes ÷ 240 volts = 25 amperes.

No. of circuits (see Section 220-4).

Minimum Size Subfeeder Required for Each Dwelling Unit (Section 215-2):

Computed Load (Article 220):

General Lighting Load	2520 volt-amperes
Small Appliance Load, two 20-ampere circuits	3000 volt-amperes
Total Computed Load	5520 volt-amperes
(without range and space heating)	

Example No. 4(b) (Continued)

Application of Demand Factor:

3000 volt-amperes at 100%	3000 volt-amperes
2520 volt-amperes at 35%	882 volt-amperes
Net Computed Load	3882 volt-amperes
(without range and space heating)	
Range Load	6400 volt-amperes
Space Heating (Section 220-15)	6000 volt-amperes
Water Heater	2500 volt-amperes
Net Computed Load for individual dwelling unit	18,782 volt-amperes

For 120/240-volt 3-wire system
Net Computed Load 18,782 volt-amperes ÷ 240 volts = 78 amperes

Subfeeder Neutral (Section 220-22):

Lighting and Small Appliance Load	3882 volt-amperes
Range Load, 6400 volt-amperes at 70% (see Section 220-22)	4480 volt-amperes
Space and Water Heating (no neutral), 240 volt	0 volt-amperes
Net Computed Load (neutral)	8362 volt-amperes

8362 volt-amperes ÷ 240 volts = 35 amperes

Minimum Size Feeder Required from Service Equipment to Meter Bank for 20 Dwelling Units:

Total Computed Load:

Lighting and Small Appliance Load 20 × 5520	110,400 volt-amperes
Water and Space Heating Load 20 × 8500	170,000 volt-amperes
Range Load 20 × 8000 volt-amperes	160,000 volt-amperes
Net Computed Load (20 dwelling units)	440,400 volt-amperes

Net Computed Load Using Optional Calculation (Table 220-32)

440,400 volt-amperes × .38	167,352 volt-amperes

167,352 volt-amperes ÷ 240 volts = 697 amperes

Minimum Size Main Feeder Required (less house load) for 40 Dwelling Units

Total Computed Load:

Lighting and Small Appliance Load 40 × 5520	220,800 volt-amperes
Water and Space Heating 40 × 8500	340,000 volt-amperes
Range Load 40 × 8000 volt-amperes	320,000 volt-amperes
Net Computed Load (40 dwelling units)	880,800 volt-amperes
Net Computed Load Using Optional Calculation (Table 220-32)	
880,800 volt-amperes × .28	246,624 volt-amperes

246,624 volt-amperes ÷ 240 volts = 1028 amperes

Feeder Neutral Load for Feeder from Service Equipment to Meter Bank for 20 Dwelling Units:

Lighting and Small Appliance Load:

20 × 5520 volt-amperes	110,400 volt-amperes
First 3000 volt-amperes at 100%	3000 volt-amperes
107,400 volt-amperes at 35%	37,590 volt-amperes
Subtotal	40,590 volt-amperes
20 Ranges = 35,000 volt-amperes at 70%	24,500 volt-amperes
(See Table 220-19 and Section 220-22.)	
Total	65,090 volt-amperes

65,090 volt-amperes ÷ 240 volts = 271 amperes

Further Demand Factor (Section 220-22):

First 200 amperes at 100%	200 amperes
Balance: 71 amperes at 70%	50 amperes
Total	250 amperes

Feeder Neutral Load of Main Feeder (less house load) for 40 Dwelling Units:

Lighting and Small Appliance Load:

40 × 5520 volt-amperes	220,800 volt-amperes
First 3000 volt-amperes at 100%	3000 volt-amperes
120,000 volt-amperes − 3000 volt-amperes =	
117,000 volt-amperes at 35%	40,950 volt-amperes
220,800 volt-amperes − 120,000 volt-amperes =	
100,800 volt-amperes at 25%	25,200 volt-amperes

Example No. 4(b) (Continued)

Net Computed Lighting and Small Appliance Load	69,150 volt-amperes
40 Ranges = 55,000 volt-amperes at 70%...	38,500 volt-amperes
(See Table 220-19 and Section 220-22.)	
Total..	107,650 volt-amperes

107,650 volt-amperes ÷ 240 volts = 449 amperes

Further Demand Factor (Section 220-22):

First 200 amperes at 100%	200 amperes
Balance: 249 amperes at 70%	174 amperes
Total	374 amperes

Example No. 5(a).   Multifamily Dwelling Served at 208Y/120 Volts, Three Phase

All conditions and calculations the same as for Multifamily Dwelling [Example No. 4(a)] served at 120/240 volts, single phase except as follows:

Service to each dwelling unit shall be two phase legs and neutral.

Minimum Number of Branch Circuits Required for Each Dwelling Unit (Section 220-4):

Range Circuit: 8000 volt-amperes ÷ 208 volts = 38 amperes or a circuit of two No. 8 and one No. 10 as permitted by Section 220-22.

Minimum Size Subfeeder Required for Each Dwelling Unit (Section 215-2):

For 120/208-volt, 3-wire system (without ranges)
  Net Computed Load: 3882 volt-amperes ÷ 208 volts = 18.7 amperes
For 120/208-volt, 3-wire system (with ranges)
  Net Computed Load: 11,882 volt-amperes ÷ 208 volts = 57.1 amperes
  Subfeeder Neutral: 9482 volt-amperes ÷ 208 volts = 45.6 amperes

Minimum Size Feeders Required from Service Equipment to Meter Bank (For 20 Dwelling Units—10 with Ranges):

For 208Y/120-volt, 3-phase, 4-wire system
  Ranges: Maximum number between any two phase legs = 4
  Twice 4 = 8. Table 220-19 Demand = 23,000 volt-amperes.
  Per phase demand: 23,000 volt-amperes ÷ 2 = 11,500 volt-amperes
  Equivalent 3-phase load = 34,500 volt-amperes
  Net Computed Load (total): 40,590 volt-amperes + 34,500 volt-amperes = 75,090 volt-amperes
    75,090 volt-amperes ÷ (208)(1.732) = 208.4 amperes

Feeder Neutral Size:
  40,590 volt-amperes + 34,500 volt-amperes at 70% = 64,700 volt-amperes
Net Computed Neutral Load:
    64,700 volt-amperes ÷ (208)(1.732) = 179.6 amperes

Minimum Size Main Feeder (less house load) (For 40 Dwelling Units—20 with Ranges):

For 208Y/120-volt, 3-phase, 4-wire system
  Ranges: Maximum number between any two phase legs = 7
  Twice 7 = 14. Table 220-19 Demand = 29,000 volt-amperes.
  Per phase demand: 29,000 ÷ 2 = 14,500 volt-amperes
  Equivalent 3-phase load = 43,500 volt-amperes
  Net Computed Load (total): 69,150 volt-amperes + 43,500 volt-amperes = 112,650 volt-amperes
    112,650 volt-amperes ÷ (208)(1.732) = 312.7 amperes

Main Feeder Neutral Size:
  69,150 volt-amperes + 43,500 volt-amperes at 70% = 99,600 volt-amperes
    99,600 volt-amperes ÷ (208)(1.732) = 276.5 amperes

Further Demand Factor (Section 220-22):

200 amperes at 100%..	200.0 amperes
76.5 amperes at 70%...	53.6 amperes
Net Computed Load..	253.6 amperes

TABLES AND EXAMPLES

Example No. 5(b). Optional Calculation for Multifamily Dwelling Served at 208Y/120 Volts, Three Phase

All conditions and calculations the same as for Optional Calculation for Multifamily Dwelling [Example No. 4(b)] served at 120/240 volts, single phase except as follows:

Service to each dwelling unit shall be two phase legs and neutral.

Minimum Number of Branch Circuits Required for Each Dwelling Unit (Section 220-4):

Range Circuit: 8000 volt-amperes at 80% ÷ 208 volts = 30.7 amperes or a circuit of two No. 8 and one No. 10 as permitted by Section 220-22.

Space Heating: 6000 volt-amperes ÷ 208 volts = 28.8 amperes. Two 20-ampere, 2-pole circuits required, No. 12.

Minimum Size Subfeeder Required for Each Dwelling Unit:

Computed Load (120/208-volt, 3-wire circuit)
Net Computed Load: 18,782 volt-amperes ÷ 208 volts = 90.3 amperes
Net Computed Load (neutral):
$$[(3882 \text{ volt-amperes} \div 2) \div (120 \text{ volts})] +$$
$$[(6400 \text{ volt-amperes} \times 0.7) \div (208 \text{ volts})] = 37.7 \text{ amperes}$$

Minimum Size Feeder Required for Service Equipment to Meter Bank (For 20 dwelling units):

Net Computed Load: 167,352 volt-amperes ÷ (208)(1.732) = 464.9 amperes

Feeder Neutral Load: 65,090 volt-amperes ÷ (208)(1.732) = 180.67 amperes

Minimum Size Main Feeder Required (less house load) (for 40 dwelling units):

Net Computed Load: 246,624 volt-amperes ÷ (208)(1.732) = 685.1 amperes

Main Feeder Neutral Load:
107,650 volt-amperes ÷ (208)(1.732) = 298.8 amperes

Further Demand Factor (Section 220-22):
200 amperes at 100%...200.0 amperes
98.8 amperes at 70%... 69.2 amperes
Net Computed Load..269.2 amperes

Example No. 6. Maximum Demand for Range Loads

Table 220-19, Column A applies to ranges not over 12 kW. The application of Note 1 to ranges over 12 kW (and not over 27 kW) is illustrated in the following examples:

A. Ranges all the same rating.

Assume 24 ranges each rated 16 kW.

From Column A the maximum demand for 24 ranges of 12 kW rating is 39 kW.
16 kW exceeds 12 kW by 4.
5% × 4 = 20% (5% increase for each kW in excess of 12).
39 kW × 20% = 7.8 kW increase.
39 + 7.8 = 46.8 kW: value to be used in selection of feeders.

B. Ranges of unequal rating.

Assume 5 ranges each rated 11 kW.
2 ranges each rated 12 kW.
20 ranges each rated 13.5 kW.
3 ranges each rated 18 kW.

5 × 12	=	60 Use 12 kW for range rated less than 12.
2 × 12	=	24
20 × 13.5	=	270
3 × 18	=	54
30		408 kW

408 ÷ 30 = 13.6 kW (average to be used for computation)

From Column A the demand for 30 ranges of 12 kW rating is 15 + 30 = 45 kW.
13.6 exceeds 12 by 1.6 (use 2).
5% × 2 = 10% (5% increase for each kW in excess of 12).
45 kW × 10% = 4.5 kW increase.
45 + 4.5 = 49.5 kW: value to be used in selection of feeders.

Example No. 8.   Motors, Conductors, Overload, and Short-Circuit and Ground-Fault Protection

(See Sections 430-6, 430-7, 430-22, 430-24, 430-32, 430-34, 430-52, 430-62, and Tables 430-150 and 430-152.)

Determine the conductor size, the motor overload protection, the branch-circuit short-circuit and ground-fault protection, and the feeder protection, for one 25-horsepower squirrel-cage induction motor (full-voltage starting, service factor 1.15, Code letter F), and two 30-horsepower wound-rotor induction motors (40°C rise), on a 460-volt, 3-phase, 60-Hertz supply.

Conductor Loads

The full-load current of the 25-horsepower motor is 34 amperes (Table 430-150). A full-load current of 34 amperes × 1.25 = 42.5 amperes (Section 430-22). The full-load current of the 30-horsepower motor is 40 amperes (Table 430-150). A full-load current of 40 amperes × 1.25 = 50 amperes (Section 430-22).

The feeder ampacity will be 125 percent of 40 plus 40 plus 34, or 124 amperes (Section 430-24).

Overload and Short-Circuit and Ground-Fault Protection

Overload. Where protected by a separate overload device, the 25-horsepower motor, with full-load current of 34 amperes, must have overload protection of not over 42.5 amperes [Sections 430-6(a) and 430-32(a)(1)]. Where protected by a separate overload device, the 30-horsepower motor, with full-load current of 40 amperes, must have overload protection of not over 50 amperes [Sections 430-6(a) and 430-32(a)(1)]. If the overload protection is not sufficient to start the motor or to carry the load, it may be increased according to Section 430-34. For a motor marked "thermally protected," overload protection is provided by the thermal protector [see Sections 430-7(a)(12) and 430-32(a)(2)].

Branch-Circuit Short-Circuit and Ground-Fault. The branch circuit of the 25-horsepower motor must have branch-circuit short-circuit and ground-fault protection of not over 300 percent for a nontime-delay fuse (Table 430-152) or 3.00 × 34 = 102 amperes. The next smaller standard size fuse is 100 amperes. The fuse size may be increased to 110 or 125 amperes (Section 430-52, Exception No. 1) if the 100-ampere fuse is not sufficient for the starting current of the motor.

For the 30-horsepower motor, the branch-circuit short-circuit and ground-fault protection is 150 percent (Table 430-152) or 1.50 × 40 = 60 amperes. Where the maximum value of branch-circuit short-circuit and ground-fault protection is not sufficient to start the motor, the value for a nontime-delay fuse may be increased to 400 percent [Section 430-52, Exception No. 2(a)].

Feeder Circuit. The maximum rating of the feeder short-circuit and ground-fault protection device is based on the sum of the largest branch-circuit protective device (110-ampere fuse) plus the sum of the full-load currents of the other motors or 110 plus 40 plus 40 = 190 amperes. The nearest standard fuse which does not exceed this value is 175 amperes [Section 430-62(a)].

The basic requirement of Section 430-52 is to place a top limit on the rating of the branch-circuit short-circuit and ground-fault protective device for the value calculated. This does not prevent use of a lower value. In the example, the calculated value for the branch-circuit short-circuit and ground-fault protection is 102 amperes. Although Exception No. 1 would permit going to the next higher value (110 amperes), use of a 100-ampere device (the next smaller standard size) is also acceptable. Also, it provides better protection and permits use of smaller, and usually less expensive, fuses and fuse-holding equipment.

Appendix A

Extracts

This appendix identifies those *NEC* figures, tables, or actions (first column) that are identified in the *NEC* by a superscript letter "x" (e.g., $515\text{-}2^x$ = A-515-2), and the NFPA document (second column) and section or equal (third column) from which the material in the *NEC* was extracted.

Requests for interpretations or proposed revisions of the extracted text will be referred to the NFPA Committee having responsibility for the document from which the text was extracted.

(See Section 90-3, Paragraph 4)

A-514-2	Automotive and Marine Service Station Code, NFPA 30A-1984	Section 6-3
A-Table 514-2	Automotive and Marine Service Station Code, NFPA 30A-1984	Table 6
A-515-2	Flammable and Combustible Liquids Code, NFPA 30-1984	Paragraph 5-7.3
A-Table 515-2	Flammable and Combustible Liquids Code, NFPA 30-1984	Table 5-7.3
A-516-2(a)(1)	Standard for Spray Application Using Flammable and Combustible Materials, NFPA 33-1985	Section 1-2 Spray Area
A-516-2(a)(2)	Standard for Spray Application Using Flammable and Combustible Materials, NFPA 33-1985	Section 1-2 Spray Area
A-516-2(a)(3)	Standard for Spray Application Using Flammable and Combustible Materials, NFPA 33-1985	Section 1-2 Spray Area
A-516-2(a)(4)	Standard for Dipping and Coating Processes Using Flammable or Combustible Liquids, NFPA 34-1982	Section 1-2, Vapor Source, and Paragraph 6-2.2
A-516-2(a)(5)	Standard for Dipping and Coating Processes Using Flammable or Combustible Liquids, NFPA 34-1982	Paragraph 6-2.1
A-516-2(b)(1)	Standard for Spray Application Using Flammable and Combustible Materials, NFPA 33-1985	Paragraph 4-7.1
A-516, Fig. 1	Standard for Spray Application Using Flammable and Combustible Materials, NFPA 33-1985	Figure 1
A-516-2(b)(2)	Standard for Spray Application Using Flammable and Combustible Materials, NFPA 33-1985	Paragraph 4-7.2
A-516, Fig. 2	Standard for Spray Application Using Flammable and Combustible Materials, NFPA 33-1982	Figure 2
A-516, Fig. 3	Standard for Spray Application Using Flammable and Combustible Materials, NFPA 33-1985	Figure 3

A-516-2(b)(3)	Standard for Spray Application Using Flammable and Combustible Materials, NFPA 33-1985	Paragraph 4-7.3
A-516-2(b)(4)	Standard for Spray Application Using Flammable and Combustible Materials, NFPA 33-1985	Paragraph 4-7.4
A-516-2(b)(5)	Standard for Dipping and Coating Processes Using Flammable or Combustible Liquids, NFPA 34-1982	Paragraphs 6-2.3 and 6-2.4
A-516, Fig. 4	Standard for Dipping and Coating Processes Using Flammable or Combustible Liquids, NFPA 34-1982	Figure 6-1
A-516-3(b)	Standard for Spray Application Using Flammable and Combustible Materials, NFPA 33-1985	Section 4-5
A-516-3(d)	Standard for Spray Application Using Flammable and Combustible Materials, NFPA 33-1985	Section 4-9
A-516-4	Standard for Spray Application Using Flammable and Combustible Materials, NFPA 33-1982	Chapter 9
A-516-5	Standard for Spray Application Using Flammable and Combustible Materials, NFPA 33-1985	Chapter 10
A-516-6	Standard for Spray Application Using Flammable and Combustible Materials, NFPA 33-1985	Chapter 13
A-517-32	Standard for Health Care Facilities, NFPA 99-1984	8-5
A-517-40	" " "	8-4.1,Exception
A-517-44(a)	" " "	8-4.2
A-517-44(b)	" " "	8-4.2
A-517-45	" " "	8-4.3
A-517-46	" " "	8-4.4
A-517-47(b)	" " "	8-2.1.1.2
A-517-60(a)(1)	" " "	8-2.1.1.1
A-517-60(a)(2)	" " "	8-3.1
A-517-60(a)(3)	" " "	8-3.1
A-517-60(a)(4)	" " "	8-3.1
A-517-61	" " "	8-3.2.1
A-517-62	" " "	8-3.2.2
A-517-63	" " "	8-3.2.3
A-517-64	" " "	8-3.3
A-517-65(a)	" " "	8-2.1.1.1
A-517-65(b)	" " "	8-2.1.1.2
A-517-80(b)	" " "	9-1.5
A-517-100(a)(1)	" " "	2-2
A-517-101(a)(1)	" " "	3-2.5.2.1(a)
A-517-103	" " "	3-3.5.1.6(a)
A-517-104(a)(1)	" " "	3-3.3.1.1 3-3.3.2.3
A-517-104(b)	" " "	3-3.3.4
A-517-105	" " "	3-2.5.2

Appendix

The following rules on Tentative Interim Amendments and Formal Interpretations are excerpted from the NFPA Regulations Governing Committee Projects as adopted by the Board of Directors on December 3, 1977, with amendments through December 6, 1985.

Section 15. Tentative Interim Amendments

15-1. Authorization. A Tentative Interim Amendment to any existing Document may be processed if the Tentative Interim Amendment is of an emergency nature requiring prompt action and has the endorsement of a Member of the involved Technical Committee.

15-2. Determination of Compliance. A proposed Tentative Interim Amendment shall be submitted to the Council Secretary who, after consultation with the appropriate Committee Chairman, shall determine compliance with 15-1.

15-3. Processing. If such compliance is determined, the proposed Tentative Interim Amendment shall be processed in the following manner:

(a) The text of a proposed Tentative Interim Amendment may be processed as submitted or may be changed, but only with the approval of the submitter.

(b) A proposed Tentative Interim Amendment which meets the provisions of 15-1 shall be published by the Association in appropriate media with a notice that the proposed Tentative Interim Amendment has been forwarded to the responsible Technical Committee for processing and that anyone interested may comment on the proposed Tentative Interim Amendment within the time period established and published.

(c) The proposed Tentative Interim Amendment shall be submitted for letter ballot and comment of the Technical Committee in accordance with Section 12. Such balloting shall be completed concurrently with the public review period. Any public comments inconsistent with the vote of any Committee Member shall be circulated to the Committee for supplemental letter ballot. A recommendation for approval shall be established if three-fourths of the voting Members calculated in accordance with Section 12 have voted in favor of the Tentative Interim Amendment.

(d) The proposed Tentative Interim Amendment shall be submitted for letter ballot and comment of the Correlating Committee, if any, which shall make a recommendation to the Council with respect to the disposition of the Tentative Interim Amendment.

(e) All public comments, Technical Committee and Correlating Committee ballots and comments on the proposed Tentative Interim Amendment shall be summarized in a staff report and forwarded to the Council for action in accordance with 15-4.

15-4. Action of the Council. The Council shall review the material submitted in accordance with 15-3(e) and shall take one of the following actions:

1107

Appendix

(a) issue the proposed Tentative Interim Amendment,

(b) issue the proposed Tentative Interim Amendment as amended by the Council,

(c) reject the proposed Tentative Interim Amendment,

(d) return the proposed Tentative Interim Amendment to the Technical Committee with appropriate instruction,

(e) direct a different action.

15-5. Publication of Tentative Interim Amendment. The Association shall publish in one of its publications sent to all members notice of the issuance of each Tentative Interim Amendment, shall issue a news release to applicable and interested technical journals, and shall also include in any subsequent distribution of the Document to which the Tentative Interim Amendment applies the text of the Tentative Interim Amendment in a manner judged most feasible to accomplish the desired objectives. The tentative character of the Tentative Interim Amendment shall be clearly indicated in the publication and release.

15-6. Subsequent Processing of Tentative Interim Amendments. The Technical Committee concerned shall process the subject matter of any Tentative Interim Amendment through normal Technical Committee procedures (see Sections 10, 11, and 12) at the next meeting of the Association to which the Technical Committee reports.

15-7. Exception. When the Board of Directors authorizes other procedures for the processing and/or issuance of Tentative Interim Amendments, the provisions of this Section shall not apply.

Section 16. Formal Interpretations Procedure

16-1. General. The following Formal Interpretation procedure is for the purpose of providing formal explanations of the meaning or intent of any specific provision or provisions of any Document.

A statement, written or oral, that is not processed in accordance with Section 16 of these Regulations shall not be considered the official position of NFPA or any of its Committees and shall not be considered to be, nor be relied upon as, a Formal Interpretation.

NOTE: This Formal Interpretation procedure does not prevent any Committee Chairman, Member of any Committee, or the Staff Liaison from expressing an opinion on the meaning or intent of any provision of any such Document, provided that:

(a) the person rendering the opinion orally or in writing clearly states that "the opinion is personal and does not represent the position of the Committee or the Association and may not be considered to be or relied upon as such"; and

(b) written opinions are rendered only in response to written requests and a copy of the request and the response is sent to the Staff Liaison.

16-2. Nature of Formal Interpretations. Two general forms of Formal Interpretations are recognized:

(a) those making an Interpretation of the literal text, and

(b) those making an Interpretation of the intent of the Technical Committee when the particular text was issued.

16-3. Editions to Be Interpreted. Interpretations shall be rendered on the text of the latest edition of the Document and shall apply to any text of earlier editions which is identical to the text in the latest edition. Interpretations may be rendered to the requester on text of an outdated Document where such has been revised in or deleted from later editions. If possible, the requester should be informed why the text was revised or deleted.

16-4. Method of Requesting Formal Interpretations. A request for a Formal Interpretation shall be directed to the Council Secretary. The request shall include a statement in which shall appear specific references to a single problem and identifying the portion (article, section, paragraph, etc.) of the Document and edition of the Document on which an Interpretation is requested. Such a request shall be in writing and shall indicate the business interest of the requester. A request involving an actual field situation shall so state and all parties involved shall be named and notified.

16-5. Qualifications for Processing. A request for an Interpretation may be processed if it:

(a) complies with 16-2 and 16-4,

(b) does not involve a determination of compliance of a design, installation, or product or equivalency of protection,

(c) does not involve a review of plans or specifications, or require judgement or knowledge that can only be acquired as a result of on-site inspection,

(d) does not involve text that clearly and decisively provides the requested information.

16-6. Determination of Qualification. The Council Secretary, after consultation with the appropriate Staff Liaison, shall determine the qualification in accordance with 16-5.

16-7. Editing of Interpretation Request. A request for an Interpretation may be rephrased. The rephrased version and any pertinent background information shall be sent to the requester and all parties named in the request for agreement. A deadline for receipt of agreement shall be established.

16-8. Establishment of Interpretations Subcommittee. If accepted for consideration, each request shall then be submitted to letter ballot of an Interpretations Subcommittee made up of five or more Members of the Technical Committee(s) or Subcommittee having primary jurisdiction of the Document or portion thereof covering the subject under consideration. The Members shall be selected by the Committee Chairmen or the Council Secretary, if the Chairmen are not available. No Member shall be eligible for appointment to an Interpretations Subcommittee if he is directly involved in the particular case prompting the request for the Interpretation. The Interpretations Subcommittee should include Committee Members representing the same interest categories as the requester and the other parties involved, as well as representatives of other parties. The personnel of Interpretations Subcommittees may be varied for each request.

16-9. Voting on Interpretations. In any case where more than twenty percent of the Subcommittee Members disagree on the Interpretation, the request for Interpretation shall be referred to the entire Technical Committee(s). Under these conditions, a Formal Interpretation requires a two-thirds majority agreement of the Technical Committee(s) as tallied in accordance with 12-7. Where the necessary agreement is not received, the item shall be placed on the docket for regular processing by the Technical Committee(s) for subsequent possible action.

16-10. Publication of Interpretation. If the required agreement is secured from the Interpretations Subcommittee(s) or from the Technical Committee, the requester and all named parties shall be informed by the Staff Liaison and the Interpretation shall be published by the Association in one of its publications sent to all members and announced in an Association news release to other media.

Appendix

Interpretations of text of an outdated Document which has been revised in or deleted from later editions shall not be published by the Association but shall be sent to the requester and all parties named in the request.

16-11. Action Following Issuance of Formal Interpretations. Any Technical Committee(s) whose Document has been the subject of a Formal Interpretation shall review the item on which the Interpretation has been issued to determine whether any change may be desired to the text of the Document on which the Interpretation has been rendered. If such a change is indicated, the Technical Committee(s) shall process such change in conformance with procedures set forth in Sections 10, 11, and 12 and the Interpretation shall no longer be published.

16-12. Applicability of Formal Interpretations. Any Formal Interpretation issued shall apply to the edition of the Document for which the Interpretation is made and to any other edition of the Document if the text is identical to the text of the edition of which the Formal Interpretation was rendered. (See 16-3.)

Section 18. Operating Procedures

18-1. Authorization. A Committee may adopt internal operating procedures, provided that such procedures are consistent with the Bylaws of the Association and with these Regulations. Such procedures and amendments thereto shall be promptly transmitted to the Council Secretary who shall submit them to the Council for approval. Amendments to the Bylaws of the Association or to these Regulations shall automatically supersede any such procedures which may be in conflict therewith.

The following procedures on Tentative Interim Amendments and Formal and Informal Interpretations are excerpted from the "Operating Procedures for the National Electrical Code Committee" as adopted by the NFPA Standards Council on July 8, 1981 and amended October 7, 1982, and November 10, 1984.

PART B—TENTATIVE INTERIM AMENDMENTS TO THE *NATIONAL ELECTRICAL CODE*

Section 110. Procedures for Processing Tentative Interim Amendments

111. A Proposal for a Tentative Interim Amendment shall include a specific statement of what new text or amendment of the existing text of the *National Electrical Code* is recommended, and a full explanation of the Proposal supported by all relevant data. The Proposal shall also include justification for qualification as being of an emergency nature requiring processing before the next scheduled edition of the *National Electrical Code*.

112. In order to determine compliance with Section 15-1 of the Regulations, the results of a ballot of a Special Subcommittee appointed by the Chairman of the Correlating Committee shall be submitted to the Standards Council Secretary. The Subcommittee shall consist of, in addition to the Correlating Committee Chairman, no less than two Members of the Correlating Committee and the Chairman or Chairmen of the Code-Making Panel(s) concerned with the proposed Tentative Interim Amendment. A majority vote by the Members of the Subcommittee to support the Proposal results in an affirmative recommendation.

PART C—FORMAL AND INFORMAL INTERPRETATIONS OF THE *NATIONAL ELECTRICAL CODE*

Section 200. General

201. Certain questions arise in the application of the requirements of the *National Electrical Code* which are not subject to Formal Interpretation under the established procedures. In addition to those outlined in the Regulations, these questions include the degree and extent of a hazardous (classified) location, interpretation of suitability of isolation or guarding, and interpretation of equivalent protection. However, such questions are suitable for "Informal" Interpretations and are covered in Section 220 of these Procedures.

Section 210. Procedures for Processing Formal Interpretations

211. The Secretary of the National Electrical Code Committee, after consultation with the Chairman of the Correlating Committee and any others as appropriate, shall advise the Standards Council Secretary of any request the Committee Secretary believes should be processed as a Formal Interpretation.

212. The National Electrical Code Committee Secretary with the assistance of the Correlating Committee Chairman shall, if necessary, rephrase the request so that it is suitable for balloting by an Interpretation Subcommittee. Any rewording shall be transmitted to the requester for concurrence.

213. The Interpretation Subcommittee shall consist of the following taking into account Section 16-8 of the Regulations:

(a) The Chairman of the Correlating Committee, who shall be the Chairman of the Interpretation Subcommittee and a voting Member.

(b) The Chairman of that Code-Making Panel which is responsible for the affected Article of the Code for which an Interpretation is requested, and

(c) At least three other Members or Alternates of the National Electrical Code Committee selected by the Chairman of the Correlating Committee depending upon the availability, experience, knowledge, and interest of the Members or Alternates.

214. The appropriate Code-Making Panel shall review the text of any Section of the *National Electrical Code* for which a Formal Interpretation has been issued to the end that a suitable revision of the text may be recommended to eliminate the difficulty which prompted the request for a Formal Interpretation.

Section 220. Procedures for Processing Informal Interpretations

221. All requests for written Informal Interpretations shall be either answered by the Committee Member to which it is addressed or referred to the Secretary of the National Electrical Code Committee for reply.

As stated in Section 16-1 of the Regulations, a Committee Chairman, a Member of any Committee, or the Secretary of the National Electrical Code Committee may express an opinion on the meaning or intent of any provision of the *National Electrical Code*, provided that the opinion is clearly identified as not being a Formal Interpretation of the National Electrical Code Committee or of the Association and shall not be relied upon as such.

A copy of the request, any necessary accompanying material, and the response shall be sent, as appropriate, to

Appendix

a. The Chairman of the Correlating Committee

b. The Chairman of the appropriate Code-Making Panel(s)

c. The Secretary of the National Electrical Code Committee.

Time Schedule for the 1990 *National Electrical Code*

Nov. 6, 1987 (5:00 PM E.S.T.)	Final date for receipt of proposals from the public for revision of the 1987 *National Electrical Code* preparatory to the issuance of the 1990 edition. Proposals should be forwarded to the Secretary of the Standards Council, National Fire Protection Association, Batterymarch Park, Quincy, MA 02269.
Jan. 4–23, 1988	Code-Making Panels Preliminary Meeting to consider proposals for *Code* changes.
May 9–13, 1988	Correlating Committee reviews the Preliminary Report submitted by the Code-Making Panels. Establishes that no conflicts exist, that satisfactory correlation is achieved among the recommendations of the Code-Making Panels, and that the Committee's activities have been conducted in accordance with the Regulations Governing Committee Projects and the NEC Operating Procedures.
June 17, 1988	*National Electrical Code Technical Committee Report* (NEC-TCR or "Preprint") for the 1990 *National Electrical Code* published for distribution to the National Electrical Code Committee and other interested parties.
June 17–Oct. 21, 1988	Period of study by interested parties and submittal of recommendations for modifying report to the Secretary of the Standards Council, NFPA.
Oct. 21, 1988 (5:00 PM E.S.T.)	Closing date for comments.
Nov. 28–Dec. 9, 1988	Code-Making Panels meet to act on public comments.
March 6–10, 1989	Correlating Committee meeting to review the Code-Making Panel action on comments.
April 7, 1989	NFPA prints and distributes the *National Electrical Code Technical Committee Documentation* (NEC-TCD) and the Advanced Printing of the Proposed 1990 *National Electrical Code* to members of the National Electrical Code Committee and other interested parties.
May 15–18, 1989	Action by NFPA Annual Meeting (Washington, DC).
July, 1989	Action by NFPA Standards Council.
September, 1989	Publication of the 1990 *National Electrical Code.*

NFPA Publications

The NFPA Electrical Codes and Standards that relate to electrical requirements are frequently revised. Booklet editions of those Codes and Standards available at the time of publication are listed below. Contact the NFPA Customer Service Department, Batterymarch Park, Quincy, MA 02269 for current prices.

Pub. No.   *Title*

NFPA 20   Centrifugal Fire Pumps, 1983.

NFPA 70   *National Electrical Code*, 1987.

NFPA 70A*   Electrical Code for One- and Two-Family Dwellings, 1987.

NFPA 70B   Electrical Equipment Maintenance, 1983.

NFPA 70E   Electrical Safety Requirements for Employee Workplaces, 1983.

NFPA 71   Central Station Signaling Systems, 1985.

NFPA 72A   Local Protective Signaling Systems, 1985.

NFPA 72B   Auxiliary Protective Signaling Systems, 1986.

NFPA 72C   Remote Station Protective Signaling Systems, 1986.

NFPA 72D   Proprietary Protective Signaling Systems, 1986.

NFPA 72E   Automatic Fire Detectors, 1984.

NFPA 72F   Emergency Voice/Alarm Communication Systems.

NFPA 74   Household Fire Warning Equipment, 1984.

NFPA 75   Protection of Electronic Computer/Data Processing Equipment, 1981.

NFPA 77   Recommended Practice on Static Electricity, 1983.

NFPA 78   Lightning Protection Code, 1986.

NFPA 79   Electrical Standard for Industrial Machinery, 1985.

NFPA *101*®   *Life Safety Code*®, 1985

NFPA 493   Intrinsically Safe Apparatus and Associated Apparatus for Use in Class I, II, and III, Division 1 Hazardous Locations, 1978.

NFPA 496   Purged and Pressurized Enclosures for Electrical Equipment in Hazardous (Classified) Locations, 1982.

NFPA 497A   Classification of Class I Hazardous (Classified) Locations for Electrical Installations in Chemical Process Areas, 1986.

NFPA 497M   Classification of Gases, Vapors and Dusts for Electrical Equipment in Hazardous (Classified) Locations, 1986.

NFPA 907M   Manual on the Investigation of Fires of Electrical Origin, 1983.

NFPA 1221   Public Fire Service Communication Systems, 1984.

*Available February, 1987.

Index

INDEX

INDEX

Lampholders *(Continued)*
Infrared lamps, 422-15
Mogul base, see Mogul base lampholders
Outdoor, 225-25
Pendant
  Bathrooms, 410-4(d)
  Not in clothes closets, 410-8
  Not in theater dressing rooms, 520-71
Screw-shell types for lamps only, 410-47
Signs and outline lighting, 600-22
Unswitched over combustible material, 410-6

Lamps, Art. 410, see also Lighting, Lighting
  fixtures, and Hazardous (classified) locations
Arc, see Arc lamps
Clothes closets, in, 410-8
Electric discharge, 410-Q, 410-R
Electric discharge, enclosure, 410-54
Fluorescent, see Fluorescent lighting fixture
Guards, see Guarding and guards
Headlamps, see Handlamps
Incandescent, see Incandescent lamps
Infrared, see Infrared lamp heating appliances
Motion picture projectors, 540-14, 540-20
Motion picture studios
  Film storage vaults, 530-51
  Stages, 530-16, 530-17
  Viewing, cutting tables, 530-41
Outdoor, location, 225-25
Portable
  Flexible cords for, 400-7
  Motion picture studios, in, 530-16, 530-17
  Show windows, show cases, 400-11
Theaters
  Border and proscenium, 520-44
  Dressing rooms, 520-72
  Festoons, 520-65
  Footlights, 520-43
  Scene docks in, 520-47
  Stage, arc, 520-61
  Switchboards, pilot lights, 520-53(g)
Wattage marking, flush and recessed fixtures,
  410-70

Laundry, outlets, dwellings, 210-50(c), 210-
52(e), 220-4(c)

Legally required standby systems, Art.
  701
Capacity and rating, 701-6
Circuit wiring, 701-B
Overcurrent protection, 701-D
Signals, 701-8
Signs, 701-9
Tests and maintenance, 701-5
Transfer equipment, 701-7

Lengths
Busways used as branch circuits, 364-14
Free conductors at outlets and switches, 300-14,
  424-43, 426-23, 550-10(h), 551-17
Intermediate metal conduit, 345-16(a)
Nonmetallic flexible tubing with open wiring,
  320-10
Nonmetallic rigid metal conduit, 347-17
Pull and junction boxes, 370-18(a), 370-51
Rigid metal conduit, 346-15(a)
Space heating cable, nonheating leads, 424-34
Taps, 210-19, 240-21
  10-ft. rule, 240-21 Ex. 2

Lengths *(Continued)*
25-ft. rule, 240-21 Ex. 3
25-ft. rule, transformers, 240-21 Ex. 8
100-ft. rule, 240-21 Ex. 10
Motor feeders, 430-28, 430-53(d)

Lighting
Branch circuits, calculation of load, 220-3(b)
Cove, see Cove lighting
Electric discharge, see Electric discharge lighting
Emergency, Art. 700
Feeders, calculation of load, 220-10(a), 220-30
Festoon, see Festoon lighting
Fixtures, see Lighting fixtures
Outlets, see Outlets, Lighting
Outline, see Outline lighting
Track, 410-S

Lighting fixtures, Art. 410, see also Hazardous
  (classified) locations
Autotransformers
  Ballasts supplying fluorescent fixtures, 410-78
  Supply circuits, 210-9
Auxiliary equipment, 410-77
Boxes, canopies, pans, 410-C
Branch circuits
  Computation of, 220-3(a), (b), and (c)
  Sizes, 210-22, 210-23
  Voltages, 210-6, 410-73
Clothes closets, 410-8
Combustible material, near, 410-5, 410-76
Connection, fluorescent, 410-14, 410-30
Construction, 410-N thru 410-P
Corrosive, 410-4(b)
Damp, wet, or corrosive locations, 410-4,
  410-49
Ducts or hoods, in, 410-4(c)
Electric discharge, see Electric discharge lighting
Fluorescent, see Fluorescent lighting fixtures
Flush, 410-N, 410-P
Grounding, 410-E
Live parts, 410-3
Location, 410-B
Motion picture studios, Art. 530
Outdoors, 410-4(a)
Outlets required, 210-70
Overcurrent protection, wires and cords, 240-4
Polarization, 410-23
Raceways, 410-31
Recessed, see Recessed lighting fixtures
Recreational vehicles, 551-22
Show windows, 410-7
Supports, 410-D
Swimming pools, 680-20
Theaters, Art. 520
Wet, 410-4
Wiring, 410-F

Lighting outlets, see Outlets, Lighting

Lightning rods
As a ground, 250-86
Irrigation machines, 675-15
Spacing from, 250-46

Lightning (surge) arresters, Art. 280
Antenna discharge units, 810-20
Connections at services, 230-82 Ex. 4
Grounding, 250-46, 250-86, 280-25

INDEX

Multispeed motors *(Continued)*
Marking, 430-7
Overload protection, 430-32(a) and (c)

Multiwire branch circuit, see Branch circuits, Multiwire

Nameplates, see articles on wiring and equipment involved

Neat and workmanlike installation, 110-12

Neutral, see also Conductors, Grounded
Bare, 230-22 Ex., 230-30 Ex., 230-41 Ex.
Bonding to service equipment, 250-72(a)
Common, see Common neutral
Conductor, Notes 3 and 10 to Tables 310-16 thru 310-31
Continuity of, 300-13
Definition, Art. 100
Equipment, grounding to, 250-61
Feeder load, 220-22
Grounding of
AC systems, 250-5, 250-25, 250-26
DC systems, 250-3, 250-22
Identification, Art. 200
Ranges and dryers, grounding, 250-60
Uninsulated, where permitted, 230-22 Ex., 230-30 Ex., 230-41 Ex., 250-60(c), 338-3(b)

Nightclubs, Art. 518

Nipples, conduit, see Conduit nipples

Nonautomatic
Definition, Art. 100

Nonelectrical equipment, grounding, 250-44

Nongrounding-type receptacles, replacements, see Receptacles, Nongrounding type

Nonmetallic boxes, see Boxes, Nonmetallic

Nonmetallic extensions, Art. 342
Definition, 342-1
Fittings, 342-6
Installation
As aerial cable, 342-7(b)
As surface extensions, 342-7(a)
Marking, 342-8
Splices and taps, 342-5
Uses not permitted, 342-4
Uses permitted, 342-3

Nonmetallic rigid conduit, see Rigid nonmetallic conduit

Nonmetallic-sheathed cable, Art. 336
Accessible attics, 336-13
Bends, 336-14
Conductors, 336-26
Construction, 336-C
Definition, 336-1
Devices with integral enclosures, 336-18
Installation, 336-B
Exposed work, 336-10

Nonmetallic-sheathed cable *(Continued)*
Insulating devices, 336-16
Marking, 336-27
Nonmetallic outlet boxes, 336-17
Supports, 336-15
Three floor limitation, 336-4(a)(1)
Through studs, joists, rafters, 300-4, 336-11
Unfinished basements, 336-12
Uses not permitted, 336-4
Uses permitted, 336-3

Nontamperable
Circuit breakers, 240-82
Type S fuses, 240-54(d), 550-4

Number of services, 230-2

Occupancy, lighting loads, Table 220-3(b), 220-3(c)

Office furnishings, Art. 605
General, 605-2
Lighting, 605-5
Partitions
Interconnections, 605-4
Fixed-type, 605-6
Freestanding type, 605-7, 605-8
Wireways, 605-3

Official interpretations, see Formal interpretations

Oil (filled) cutout
Definition, 100-B

Open wiring on insulators, Art. 320
Accessible attics, 320-15
Ampacity, 320-5(b)
Conductors, types permitted, 320-5(a)
Definition, 320-1
Drip loops, 320-13
Flexible nonmetallic tubing, 320-10
Passing through walls and floors, 320-11
Separation from metal work and piping, 320-12
Supports, 320-6, 320-7
Switches, 320-16
Tie wires, 320-8
Use permitted, 320-3

Openings in equipment to be closed, 110-12, 370-8, 373-4

Operable, externally
Definition, Art. 100

Operating rooms, hospital, 517-G
Emergency lighting system, Art. 700

Optical fiber cables, Art. 770
Cables
Fire resistance, 770-6
Marking, 770-8
Definition, 770-3
Ducts, plenums, etc., 770-2(b)
Grounding of entrance cables, 770-7
Optical fibers and electrical conductors, 770-5
Spread of fire or products of combustion, 770-2(a)
Types, 770-4

1142

INDEX

INDEX

Taps *(Continued)*
Busways, 364-12 Ex. 1
Feeders, see Feeders, Taps
Overcurrent protection, 240-21
Service-entrance conductors, 230-46

Telegraph systems, see Communication circuits

Telephone exchanges, circuit load, 220-3(c) Ex. 4

Telephone systems, see Communication circuits

Television and radio distribution systems, community antenna, see Community antenna television and radio distribution systems

Television equipment, see Radio and television equipment

Television studios, Art. 520, Art. 530

Temperature limitations
Conductors, 310-10
In outlet boxes for fixtures, 410-11
Nonmetallic raceways and tubing, see Raceway of tubing type

Service-entrance cable, 338-3(c)

Temporary wiring, Art. 305
Branch circuits, 305-4(c)
Disconnecting means, 305-4(e)
Feeders, 305-4(b)
Grounding, 305-5
Guarding over 600 volts, 305-7
Lamp protection, 305-4(f)
Receptacles, 305-4(d), 305-6
Services, 305-4(a)
Time constraints, 305-3

Terminal housing, grounding through motor, 430-145(a)

Terminals
Connections to, 110-14, 250-112, 250-113
Electric discharge tubing, signs, etc., 600-34
Flat conductor cable, 363-20
Identification
Fire protective signaling system, 760-3
Motors, controllers, 430-9
Polarity, 200-9 thru 200-11

Tests
Emergency systems, 700-4
Ground-fault protection, 230-95(c)
Insulation resistance, space heating cables, 424-45
Legally required standby systems, 701-5
Lighting fixtures, 410-45
Mobile homes, 550-12
Recreational vehicles, 551-27

Theaters, Art. 520
Arc lamps, 410-55
Dressing room, 520-F

Theaters *(Continued)*
Emergency lighting systems, Art. 700
Grounding, 520-G
Fixed electric equipment, 250-43(f)
Stage equipment
Fixed, 520-C
Portable, 520-E
Switchboard
Fixed, 520-B
Portable, 520-D

Therapeutic pools and tubs, 517-90(c), 680-F

Thermal cutouts
Definition, Art. 100
Disconnecting means, 240-40

Thermal devices
Motors, 430-40
Overcurrent protection, 240-9

Thermal protector
Definition, Art. 100

Thermally protected (thermal protection)
Definition, Art. 100
Fixtures, recessed, 410-65(c)
Fluorescent lamp ballasts in fixtures, 410-73(e)

Marking on motors, 430-7(a) and (b)

Three overload units, motors, Table 430-37

Tools
Double insulated, 250-45 Ex. 2
Metal working machine, see Industrial machinery
Motor-operated, hand-held, grounding, 250-45

Transformers, Art. 450, see also Hazardous (classified) locations
Arc welders, 630-B
Autotransformers, 450-4, 450-5
Capacitors, 460-2
Installation, Art. 450
X-ray equipment, 517-148, 660-C
Definitions, 450-2
Dry-type, 450-21, 450-22
Electric discharge lighting systems
1000 volts or less, 410-Q
More than 1000 volts, 410-R
Instrument, grounding, 250-L
Connections at services, 230-82 Ex. 4
Isolating, in anesthetizing
locations, and patient care areas, 517-84(e), 517-90(c), 517-104(a)
Less-flammable liquid-insulated, 450-23
Location, 450-13
Modification of, 450-28
Overcurrent protection, 450-3
Power and signaling circuits, remote control, 725-11, 725-31
Remote control circuits for, 430-74(b), 725-11, 725-31
Research and development, 450-1 Ex. 8
Signs and outline lighting, 600-32
Two-winding, underwater lighting, 680-5(a)
Vaults, 450-C

1152

INDEX

Tentative Interim Amendment 70-87-1

to the

National Electrical Code

NFPA 70-1987

Pursuant to Section 15 of the NFPA Regulations Governing Committee Projects, the National Fire Protection Association has issued the following Tentative Interim Amendment to NFPA 70, *National Electrical Code*, 1987 edition. The TIA was issued by the Board of Directors on September 26, 1986, as a result of an appeal on Article 331.

A Tentative Interim Amendment is tentative because it has not been processed through the entire standards-making procedures. It is interim because it is effective only between editions of the standard. A TIA automatically becomes a Proposal of the proponent for the next edition of the standard; as such, it then is subject to all the procedures of the standards-making process.

1.   Add a fine print note to Section 331-1 as follows:

(FPN):   It is intended that the material used has ignitability, flammability, smoke generation, and toxicity characteristics which do not exceed those of rigid (nonplasticized) polyvinyl chloride.

TENTATIVE INTERIM AMENDMENT

Tentative Interim Amendment 70-87-2 to

NFPA 70

National Electrical Code®

1987 Edition

Pursuant to Section 15 of the Regulations Governing Committee Projects, the National Fire Protection Association has issued the following Tentative Interim Amendment to NFPA 70, *National Electrical Code*, 1987 edition. The TIA was issued by the Standards Council on January 22, 1987, as a result of a complaint on Section 225-26.

A Tentative Interim Amendment is tentative because it has not been processed through the entire standards-making procedures. It is interim because it is effective only between editions of the standard. A TIA automatically becomes a Proposal of the proponent for the next edition of the standard; as such, it then is subject to all the procedures of the standards-making process.

1. Add Exception to Section 225-26 to read as follows:

Exception No. 2: Outdoor lighting fixtures and associated equipment installed on trees where supplied by an underground wiring system with the branch-circuit conductors extended up the trees by an approved wiring method.

Tentative Interim Amendment 70-87-3 to

NFPA 70

National Electrical Code®

1987 Edition

Pursuant to Section 15 of the NFPA Regulations Governing Committee Projects, the National Fire Protection Association has issued the following Tentative Interim Amendment to NFPA 70, *National Electrical Code*. The TIA was processed by the National Electrical Code Committee and was issued by the Standards Council on July 16, 1987.

A Tentative Interim Amendment is tentative because it has not been processed through the entire standards making procedures. It is interim because it it effective only between editions of the standard. A TIA automatically becomes a Proposal of the proponent for the next edition of the standard; as such, it then is subject to all the procedures of the standards making process.

1. Reinstate "surface metal raceway" *in Section 300-22(c) by modifying the second paragraph to read as follows:*

"Other type cables and conductors shall be installed in electrical metallic tubing, flexible metallic tubing, intermediate metal conduit, rigid metal conduit, flexible metal conduit, or where accessible, surface metal raceway or wireway with metal covers or solid bottom metal cable tray with solid metal covers."